Handbook
of Multiphase
Systems

Handbook of Multiphase Systems

Editor-in-Chief
Gad Hetsroni

Department of Mechanical Engineering
Technion-Israel Institute of Technology

● *HEMISPHERE PUBLISHING CORPORATION*

Washington   New York   London

McGRAW-HILL BOOK COMPANY

New York   St. Louis   San Francisco   Auckland   Bogotá
Hamburg   Johannesburg   London   Madrid   Mexico
Montreal   New Delhi   Panama   Paris   São Paulo
Singapore   Sydney   Tokyo   Toronto

HANDBOOK OF MULTIPHASE SYSTEMS

1 2 3 4 5 6 7 8 9 0   B R B R   8 9 8 7 6 5 4 3 2 1

This book was set in Press Roman by Hemisphere Publishing Corporation. The editors were Judith B. Gandy, Mary Dorfman, and Edward Millman; the production supervisor was Miriam Gonzalez; and the typesetter was Shirley J. McNett.
Braun-Brumfield, Inc., was printer and binder.

Library of Congress Cataloging in Publication Data

Main entry under title:

Handbook of multiphase systems.

   Bibliography: p.
   Includes index.
   1. Multiphase flow—Handbooks, manuals, etc.
I. Hetsroni, G.
TA357.H29   532'.05   81-6790
ISBN 0-07-028460-1   AACR2

To my family
Ruth, Anath, Orli, and Yael Hetsroni

Contents

8 FLUIDIZATION

Subject coordinator: *John R. Grace*

Contributors

J. M. BEECKMANS, Department of Chemical Engineering, University of Western Ontario, London, Ontario, Canada N6A 5Bg

M. A. BERGOUGNOU, Department of Chemical Engineering, University of Western Ontario, London, Ontario, Canada N6A 5Bg

J. A. BOURE, STT, Centre d'Etudes Nucléaires de Grenoble, 38041 Grenoble Cedex, France

D. BUTTERWORTH, AERE, Harwell, Oxfordshire OX11 0RA, England

B. T. CHAO, Department of Mechanical Engineering, University of Illinois, Urbana, Illinois 61801 USA

J. G. COLLIER, AERE, Harwell, Oxfordshire OX11 0RA, England

DOUGLAS W. COOPER, Department of Environmental Health Science, Harvard School of Public Health, Boston, Massachusetts 02115 USA

J. M. DELHAYE, STT, Centre d'Etudes Nucléaires de Grenoble, 38041 Grenoble Cedex, France

HEINZ L. ENGELBRECHT, Air Pollution Division, Wheelabrator-Frye, Inc., Pittsburgh, Pennsylvania 15219 USA

N. EPSTEIN, Department of Chemical Engineering, University of British Columbia, Vancouver, Canada V6T 1W5

STANISLAV FABIC, U.S. Nuclear Regulatory Commission, Washington, D.C. 20555 USA

A. G. FANE, School of Chemical Engineering, University of New South Wales, Kensington, New South Wales, Australia

RAYMOND W. FLUMERFELT, Department of Chemical Engineering, University of Houston, Houston, Texas 77004 USA

MARK P. FREEMAN, Thermal Process Technology, Dorr-Oliver, Inc., Stamford, Connecticut 06904 USA

M. GIOT, Faculte des Sciences Appliquées, Université Catholique de Louvain, B-1348 Louvain-la-Neuve, Belgium

J. C. GODFREY, School of Chemical Engineering, University of Bradford, West Yorkshire BD7 1DP, England

JOHN R. GRACE, Department of Chemical Engineering, University of British Columbia, Vancouver, Canada V6T 1W5

J. J. GRAHAM, Badger America, Inc., Cambridge, Massachusetts 02142 USA

PETER GRIFFITH, Department of Mechanical Engineering, Massachusetts Institute of Technology, Cambridge, Massachusetts 02139 USA

C. GUTFINGER, Department of Mechanical Engineering, Technion, Haifa, Israel

C. HANSON, School of Chemical Engineering, University of Bradford, West Yorkshire BD7 1DP, England

G. F. HEWITT, AERE, Harwell, Oxfordshire, OX11 0RA, England

S. HOVMAND, Miro Atomizer, Inc., Columbia, Maryland 21045 USA

Y. Y. HSU, U.S. Nuclear Regulatory Commission, Washington, D.C. 20555 USA

M. ISHII, Argonne National Laboratory, Argonne, Illinois 60439 USA

RAJAN A. JAISINGHANI, Nelson Industries, Stoughton, Wisconsin 53589 USA

W. W. JUKKOLA, Thermal Process Technology, Dorr-Oliver, Inc., Stamford, Connecticut 06904 USA

DAVID LEITH, Department of Environmental Health Sciences, Harvard School of Public Health, Boston, Massachusetts 02115 USA

A. LIEBERMAN, Royco, Menlo Park, California 94025 USA

K. B. MATHUR, University of British Columbia, Vancouver, Canada V6T 1W5

J. M. MATSEN, Exxon Research and Engineering Co., Florham Park, New Jersey 07932 USA

M. E. O'NEILL, Department of Mathematics, University College, London WCIE GBT, England

RICHARD L. PESKIN, Department of Mechanical, Industrial, and Aerospace Engineering, Rutgers University, New Brunswick, New Jersey 08903 USA

K. B. RANGER, Department of Mathematics, University of Toronto, Toronto, Canada M5S 1A1

WARREN M. ROHSENOW, Department of Mechanical Engineering, Massachusetts Institute of Technology, Cambridge, Massachusetts 02139 USA

JOHN C. SLATTERY, Department of Chemical Engineering, Northwestern University, Evanston, Illinois 60201 USA

S. L. SOO, Department of Mechanical Engineering, University of Illinois, Urbana, Illinois 61801 USA

ARTHUR M. SQUIRES, Department of Chemical Engineering, Virginia Polytechnic Institute, Blacksburg, Virginia 24061 USA

JAMES H. TURNER, U.S. Environmental Protection Agency, Research Triangle Park, North Carolina 27711 USA

M. E. WEBER, Department of Chemical Engineering, McGill University, Montreal, Canada H3A 2A7

C. Y. WEN, Department of Chemical Engineering, West Virginia University, Morgantown, West Virginia 26506 USA

STEPHEN WHITAKER, Department of Chemical Engineering, University of California, Davis, California, 95616 USA

J. YERUSHALMI, Electric Power Research Institute, Palo Alto, California 94303 USA

Preface

Two-phase flow is the most common flow of fluids in nature. The flow of blood, the drift of clouds in the atmosphere, the fluidized beds, the pneumatic conveyance of granular solids, boiling liquids, and, of course, the free flow of champagne are only a few examples of two-phase (or multiphase) systems.

This handbook is the first attempt to unify the approaches to multiphase systems developed in various traditional disciplines such as chemical, mechanical, and nuclear engineering, and atmospheric and aerosol sciences. This volume thus proceeds from basics, where mathematical rigor and finesse prevail, to applications and design of equipment, where empirical formulas are extensively invoked.

This handbook will be of particular value to

The *manufacturing, process, instrumentation,* and *control engineer* for design and operation of equipment and processes such as chemical reactors, heat exchangers (including boilers and condensers), and fluidized beds.

The *nuclear engineer* for designing nuclear power plants and for studying scheduled and unscheduled transients and events.

The *engineering student* who may not plan to specialize in multiphase systems, but who realizes that knowledge of the fundamentals of such systems is essential.

The *educator* in technical schools and universities, who can base one or more complete courses on the concise and systematic format of this handbook.

The *self-starting* and *experienced scientist* who wants to broaden his or her knowledge and augment it from the fundamentals to detailed knowledge in a particular area.

In a compendium of this size and with so many authors, one must expect variations in style as well as in the degree of rigor and detail. I would appreciate receiving suggestions from readers as to how the handbook's usefulness might be improved in future editions.

Finally, I wish to extend special and warm appreciation to the authors for their hard work in the preparation of their contributions, and to all individuals and organizations who have helped. In particular, thanks are due to the Electric Power Research Institute in Palo Alto, California, where I spent my sabbatical year and where the handbook began to take form in substance and cohesion.

תושלב"ע

Gad Hetsroni

Handbook
of Multiphase
Systems

1 BASIC PRINCIPLES

1.1 Laws of Continuum Physics for Single-Phase, Single-Component Systems

Stephen Whitaker

In this section we will present the laws of continuum physics for single-phase, single-component systems. Because of the absence of electrostatic and electromagnetic effects in the subjects treated in this handbook, we will confine our attention to the laws associated with mass, linear and angular momentum, energy, and entropy; thus, Maxwell's laws will not be discussed. In subsequent sections, the axioms explored here will be broadened to include multicomponent fluids and the analysis will be extended to include multiphase systems.

1.1.1 CONSERVATION OF MASS

The laws of physics take their simplest form when stated in terms of the behavior of bodies, and the principle of conservation of mass can be stated for a body as

The mass of a body is independent of time.

If we designate the mass of a body by M, we can restate the principle of conservation of mass in its rate form as

$$\frac{DM}{Dt} = 0 \qquad [1.1.1]$$

where the symbol D/Dt represents the time rate of change determined by an observer moving with the body. We normally think of bodies as being distinguished by a phase interface that separates them from their surroundings. However, it is consistent with the continuum point of view to invoke the *Euler cut principle* (Truesdell 1968a, p. 193), which states that the laws of continuum physics apply not only to distinct bodies identified by a phase interface, but also to any imaginary body that we may wish to *cut out of* a distinct body. The mass of a body cut from a distinct body is assumed to be a continuous function of the volume; thus a density function exists and the mass can be expressed as

$$M = \int_{V_m(t)} \rho \, dV \qquad [1.1.2]$$

Here the volume of the body $V_m(t)$ may be a function of time since the material under consideration may be deforming, thus changing in shape and position. Use of [1.1.2] in [1.1.1] leads to the mathematical statement of the principle of conservation of mass for a continuous medium:

$$\frac{D}{Dt} \int_{V_m(t)} \rho \, dV = 0 \qquad [1.1.3]$$

To obtain a useful form of [1.1.3], we need two results from the kinematics of continuous media. The first of these concerns the material derivative of any *point function* ψ and is expressed as

$$\frac{D\psi}{Dt} = \frac{\partial \psi}{\partial t} + \mathbf{U} \cdot \nabla \psi \qquad [1.1.4]$$

Here we think of D/Dt as representing the time derivative determined by an observer moving with a vanishingly small body (i.e., a particle) and $\partial/\partial t$ as representing the time derivative determined by an observer fixed in space. We refer to D/Dt as the *material derivative* and $\partial/\partial t$ as the *partial derivative*. In [1.1.4] the symbol $\mathbf{U}$ refers to the velocity of the medium and is given explicitly by

$$\frac{D\mathbf{r}}{Dt} = \mathbf{U} \qquad [1.1.5]$$

where $\mathbf{r}$ is the position vector locating the particle under consideration. The derivation of [1.1.4] represents a straightforward application of the chain rule of differentiation, and details are given elsewhere (Whitaker 1977, p. 194).

The second result that we need from the kinematics of continuous media is known as the *Reynolds transport theorem*. For any point function ψ this theorem takes the form

$$\frac{D}{Dt} \int_{V_m(t)} \psi \, dV = \int_{V_m(t)} \left[\frac{\partial \psi}{\partial t} + \nabla \cdot (\psi \mathbf{U}) \right] dV \qquad [1.1.6]$$

A graphic derivation of this result is given by Whitaker (1977, p. 194), and a more elegant derivation is given by Aris (1962, p. 84). One can think of [1.1.6] as an application of the Leibniz rule, and a derivation illustrating this point of view is available from Slattery & Gaggioli (1962). Use of [1.1.6] and [1.1.3] yields

$$\frac{D}{Dt} \int_{V_m(t)} \rho \, dV = \int_{V_m(t)} \left[\frac{\partial \rho}{\partial t} + \nabla \cdot (\rho \mathbf{U}) \right] dV = 0 \qquad [1.1.7]$$

Since $V_m(t)$ is arbitrary and ρ and $\mathbf{U}$ are assumed to be continuous functions of time and space, the integrand must be zero, and from [1.1.7] we extract the *continuity equation*:

$$\frac{\partial \rho}{\partial t} + \nabla \cdot (\rho \mathbf{U}) = 0 \qquad [1.1.8]$$

When the density undergoes small variations in the region of interest, the flow is called incompressible. Under these circumstances it is a satisfactory approximation to take ρ to be a constant, and [1.1.8] simplifies to

$$\nabla \cdot \mathbf{U} = 0 \qquad \text{for incompressible flow} \qquad [1.1.9]$$

Throughout this section we have used the vector operator ∇, which takes the following form in rectangular Cartesian coordinates:

$$\nabla = \mathbf{i} \frac{\partial}{\partial x} + \mathbf{j} \frac{\partial}{\partial y} + \mathbf{k} \frac{\partial}{\partial z} \qquad [1.1.10]$$

In performing the operation indicated in [1.1.9] we obtain

$$\nabla \cdot \mathbf{U} = \left(\mathbf{i} \frac{\partial}{\partial x} + \mathbf{j} \frac{\partial}{\partial y} + \mathbf{k} \frac{\partial}{\partial z} \right) \cdot (\mathbf{i}u + \mathbf{j}v + \mathbf{k}w) = \frac{\partial u}{\partial x} + \frac{\partial v}{\partial y} + \frac{\partial w}{\partial z} \qquad [1.1.11]$$

where u, v, and w represent the three scalar components of the velocity vector $\mathbf{U}$. An alternative representation of $\nabla \cdot \mathbf{U}$ can be obtained by using e_1, e_2, and e_3 for the base vectors $\mathbf{i}$, $\mathbf{j}$, and $\mathbf{k}$; using x_1, x_2, and x_3 for the spatial coordinates x, y, and z; and using U_1, U_2, and U_3 for the three scalar components of the velocity vector. Under these circumstances [1.1.11] takes the form

$$\nabla \cdot \mathbf{U} = \left(e_1 \frac{\partial}{\partial x_1} + e_2 \frac{\partial}{\partial x_2} + e_3 \frac{\partial}{\partial x_3} \right) \cdot (e_1 U_1 + e_2 U_2 + e_3 U_3)$$

$$= \frac{\partial U_1}{\partial x_1} + \frac{\partial U_2}{\partial x_2} + \frac{\partial U_3}{\partial x_3} = \sum_{i=1}^{i=3} \frac{\partial U_i}{\partial x_i} \qquad [1.1.12]$$

To further simplify this representation we invoke the *summation convention*, which requires that repeated indices are summed from 1 to 3. This allows us to write [1.1.12] as

$$\nabla \cdot \mathbf{U} = \frac{\partial U_i}{\partial x_i} \qquad [1.1.13]$$

and the same convention can be used to express [1.1.8] as

$$\frac{\partial \rho}{\partial t} + \frac{\partial}{\partial x_i} (\rho U_i) = 0 \qquad [1.1.14]$$

In subsequent sections in this handbook [1.1.13] and [1.1.14] will be used repeatedly in the analysis of a variety of flow phenomena. Often these equations will appear in an integrated form, which is sometimes referred to as the *macroscopic mass balance*. When multicomponent systems are encountered, [1.1.3] will stand as the first axiom concerning mass; however, a second axiom concerning the motion and creation of individual molecular species will be required.

From the continuity equation one can obtain an interesting variation of the Reynolds transport theorem. We begin with [1.1.6] and let the function ψ be given by

$$\psi = \rho\Omega \qquad [1.1.15]$$

This leads to

$$\frac{D}{Dt}\int_{V_m(t)} \rho\Omega \, dV = \int_{V_m(t)} \left[\frac{\partial}{\partial t}(\rho\Omega) + \nabla \cdot (\rho\Omega\mathbf{U})\right] dV \qquad [1.1.16]$$

Operating on the products on the right-hand side allows us to arrange this result in the form

$$\frac{D}{Dt}\int_{V_m(t)} \rho\Omega \, dV = \int_{V_m(t)} \left[\rho\frac{\partial\Omega}{\partial t} + \rho\mathbf{U} \cdot \nabla\Omega\right] dV + \int_{V_m(t)} \Omega\left[\frac{\partial\rho}{\partial t} + \nabla \cdot (\rho\mathbf{U})\right] dV$$

$$[1.1.17]$$

The second integral on the right-hand side of [1.1.17] is zero by the continuity equation, and this result simplifies to

$$\frac{D}{Dt}\int_{V_m(t)} \rho\Omega \, dV = \int_{V_m(t)} \rho\frac{D\Omega}{Dt} \, dV \qquad [1.1.18]$$

We will refer to [1.1.18] as the *special form of the Reynolds transport theorem*.

1.1.2 LAWS OF MECHANICS

The laws of mechanics that apply to distant bodies and to arbitrary bodies cut out of a continuum can be stated as

$$\left\{\begin{array}{l}\text{The time rate of change of the}\\ \text{linear momentum of a body}\end{array}\right\} = \left\{\begin{array}{l}\text{the force acting}\\ \text{on the body}\end{array}\right\} \qquad [1.1.19]$$

$$\left\{\begin{array}{l}\text{The time rate of change of the}\\ \text{angular momentum of a body}\end{array}\right\} = \left\{\begin{array}{l}\text{the torque acting}\\ \text{on the body}\end{array}\right\} \qquad [1.1.20]$$

Here the linear momentum is measured relative to an inertial frame, and the angular momentum and torque are measured relative to the same fixed point in an inertial frame. For his calculations of the orbit of Mars around the sun, Newton chose the stars as elements of an inertial frame (Greider 1973), and for meteorological (Dutton 1976) and oceanographic (Weyl 1970) flows, we continue to use the stars to construct inertial frames. For the small-scale problems commonly encountered by engineers, a frame fixed relative to the earth is a satisfactory approximation to an inertial frame. We will make use of noninertial frames in our discussion of equilibrium states in section 1.1.4.

1.1.2.1 Stress Equations of Motion

To construct the mathematical representation of [1.1.19] and [1.1.20] we refer to the body shown in figure 1.1.1. This body is moving and deforming. The linear

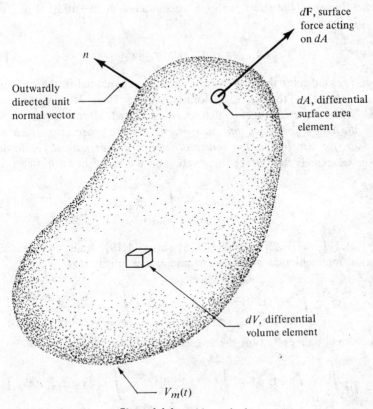

Figure 1.1.1 Arbitrary body.

momentum of the body is the sum of the momenta of all the differential elements; thus the left-hand side of [1.1.19] can be expressed as

$$\left\{ \begin{array}{l} \text{The time rate of change of the} \\ \text{linear momentum of a body} \end{array} \right\} = \frac{D}{Dt} \int_{V_m(t)} \rho \mathbf{U} \, dV \qquad [1.1.21]$$

The force acting on the body can be separated into body forces, such as gravitational and electrostatic forces, and contact forces, which act on the surface $A_m(t)$ of the body. We designate the body force vector per unit mass by $\mathbf{b}$ and express this portion of the force acting on the body as

$$\{\text{Body force}\} = \int_{V_m(t)} \rho \mathbf{b} \, dV \qquad [1.1.22]$$

In treating the surface force, we define the *stress vector* as

$$\mathbf{t}_{(\mathbf{n})} = \frac{d\mathbf{F}}{dA} \qquad [1.1.23]$$

Here the subscript $(\mathbf{n})$ is a reminder that the stress vector depends on the outwardly directed unit normal vector $\mathbf{n}$ in addition to being a function of time and space.

The simplest form of the stress vector is encountered in the study of hydrostatics, where $t_{(n)}$ is given by

$$t_{(n)} = -p\mathbf{n} \qquad \text{static fluids} \qquad [1.1.24]$$

This expression indicates that the pressure always acts normal to the surface and is opposite in direction to the unit normal vector. There is a sign convention associated with the stress vector that may be stated as: *the stress vector* $t_{(n)}$ *represents the vector force per unit area exerted by the phase into which* **n** *points on the phase for which* **n** *is the outwardly directed unit normal.* Following this convention we express the surface force acting on the body shown in figure 1.1.1 as

$$\{\text{Surface force}\} = \int_{A_m(t)} t_{(n)} \, dA \qquad [1.1.25]$$

Use of [1.1.21], [1.1.22], and [1.2.25] in [1.1.19] leads to the following mathematical representation of the linear momentum principle:

$$\frac{D}{Dt} \int_{V_m(t)} \rho \mathbf{U} \, dV = \int_{V_m(t)} \rho \mathbf{b} \, dV + \int_{A_m(t)} t_{(n)} \, dA \qquad [1.1.26]$$

This process may be repeated for the angular momentum principle to obtain

$$\frac{D}{Dt} \int_{V_m(t)} \mathbf{r} \times \rho \mathbf{U} \, dV = \int_{V_m(t)} \mathbf{r} \times \rho \mathbf{b} \, dV + \int_{V_m(t)} \mathbf{r} \times t_{(n)} \, dA \qquad [1.1.27]$$

We may refer to [1.1.26] and [1.1.27] as the linear and angular momentum principles, or Euler's two laws of mechanics (Truesdell 1968b). These two axioms of continuum mechanics contain all of Newton's three laws in addition to requiring the central force law (Marion 1970) that is tacitly assumed in the applications of Newton's third law.

Embedded in [1.1.26] and [1.1.27] are important results regarding the nature of the stress vector. These results escaped Euler, but his ideas laid the groundwork for Cauchy's clear and concise presentation of the concept of stress (Truesdell 1968a). By applying [1.1.26] to the body shown in figure 1.1.2 and allowing the thickness of that body to shrink to zero, one obtains *Cauchy's first lemma*

$$t_{(n)} = -t_{(-n)} \qquad [1.1.28]$$

This result has considerable intuitive appeal and is often considered self-evident. Cauchy's next step required that [1.1.26] again be applied to a special body—in this case the tetrahedron shown in figure 1.1.3. When the volume shrinks to zero, we are left with a balance of surface forces that yields

$$t_{(n)} = (\mathbf{n} \cdot \mathbf{i})t_{(i)} + (\mathbf{n} \cdot \mathbf{j})t_{(j)} + (\mathbf{n} \cdot \mathbf{k})t_{(k)} \qquad [1.1.29]$$

This relation is really nothing more than a result from statics; however, the use of the projected area relations listed in figure 1.1.3 may be new, along with the

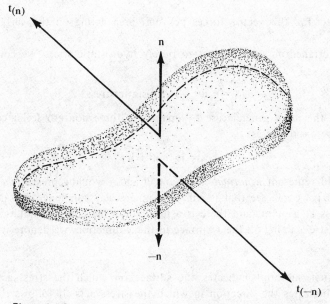

Figure 1.1.2 Body in the form of a thin slice cut from a moving, deforming medium.

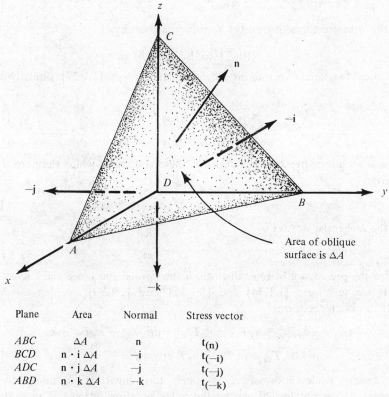

Plane	Area	Normal	Stress vector
ABC	ΔA	$\mathbf{n}$	$\mathbf{t}_{(\mathbf{n})}$
BCD	$\mathbf{n} \cdot \mathbf{i}\,\Delta A$	$-\mathbf{i}$	$\mathbf{t}_{(-\mathbf{i})}$
ADC	$\mathbf{n} \cdot \mathbf{j}\,\Delta A$	$-\mathbf{j}$	$\mathbf{t}_{(-\mathbf{j})}$
ABD	$\mathbf{n} \cdot \mathbf{k}\,\Delta A$	$-\mathbf{k}$	$\mathbf{t}_{(-\mathbf{k})}$

Figure 1.1.3 Body in the form of a tetrahedron cut from a moving, deforming medium.

notation used for the vector forces per unit area acting on the surfaces of the tetrahedron.

If the tetrahedron were subject to purely hydrostatic stress, we could express $t_{(i)}$ as

$$t_{(i)} = -ip \quad \text{hydrostatic stress} \qquad [1.1.30]$$

However, in the more general case $t_{(i)}$ may have three nonzero scalar components and should be expressed as

$$t_{(i)} = i\alpha + j\beta + k\gamma \qquad [1.1.31]$$

Here α would represent a *normal stress* and β and γ would represent *shear stresses*. From [1.1.29] we can see that it will take nine scalar components to describe the state of stress at a point, and there is a need for some compact notation. Since α represents a stress acting on the x surface in the x direction, we denote it by

$$\alpha = T_{xx} \qquad [1.1.32]$$

where the first subscript indicates the surface on which the stress acts and the second one indicates the direction in which the stress acts. It follows that β and γ are given by

$$\beta = T_{xy} \qquad \gamma = T_{xz} \qquad [1.1.33]$$

and the stress vector acting on the x surface is given by

$$t_{(i)} = iT_{xx} + jT_{xy} + kT_{xz} \qquad [1.1.34]$$

The other two stress vectors on the right-hand side of [1.1.29] similarly take the form

$$t_{(j)} = iT_{yx} + jT_{yy} + kT_{yz} \qquad [1.1.35a]$$

$$t_{(k)} = iT_{zx} + jT_{zy} + kT_{zz} \qquad [1.1.35b]$$

There is an alternative nomenclature for these stresses in which the normal stresses are given by

$$\sigma_x = T_{xx} \qquad \sigma_y = T_{yy} \qquad \sigma_z = T_{zz} \qquad [1.1.36]$$

and the tangential stresses by

$$\tau_{xy} = T_{xy} \qquad \tau_{xz} = T_{xz} \qquad \dots \qquad [1.1.37]$$

but for the present we will not distinguish the normal and tangential stresses.

If we substitute [1.1.34] and [1.1.35] into [1.1.29], we can rearrange the result to obtain the form

$$t_{(n)} = i(n_x T_{xx} + n_y T_{yx} + n_z T_{zx}) + j(n_x T_{xy} + n_y T_{yy} + n_z T_{zy})$$
$$+ k(n_x T_{xz} + n_y T_{yz} + n_z T_{zz}) \qquad [1.1.38]$$

This result, while informative, is much too unwieldy. A more streamlined representation is obtained if we use the index notation introduced in section 1.1.1 and express [1.1.38] as

$$t_{(n)} = e_1(n_1 T_{11} + n_2 T_{21} + n_3 T_{31}) + e_2(n_1 T_{12} + n_2 T_{22} + n_3 T_{32})$$
$$+ e_3(n_1 T_{13} + n_2 T_{23} + n_3 T_{33}) \qquad [1.1.39]$$

which can be written in compact form as

$$t_{(n)} = \sum_{j=1}^{j=3} \sum_{i=1}^{i=3} e_j n_i T_{ij} \qquad [1.1.40]$$

or, using the summation convention, as

$$t_{(n)} = e_j n_i T_{ij} \qquad [1.1.41]$$

It should be clear that the scalar components of the stress vector are given by

$$t_j = n_i T_{ij} \qquad [1.1.42]$$

where $t_{(n)}$ has been expressed as

$$t_{(n)} = e_1 t_1 + e_2 t_2 + e_3 t_3 \qquad [1.1.43]$$

The nine components represented by T_{ij} are the scalar components of the *stress tensor*, and T_{ij} is sometimes expressed as

$$T_{ij} = \begin{pmatrix} T_{11} & T_{21} & T_{31} \\ T_{12} & T_{22} & T_{32} \\ T_{13} & T_{23} & T_{33} \end{pmatrix} \qquad [1.1.44]$$

and referred to as the *stress matrix*.

Equation [1.1.42] provides a compact relation between the scalar components of the stress vector and the scalar components of the stress tensor. We will also need a similar relation for the vector and the tensor themselves. Returning to [1.1.29], we define the dyadic product by

$$(n \cdot i)t_{(i)} = n \cdot (it_{(i)}) \qquad [1.1.45]$$

Here we encounter a new type of vector multiplication, which is neither the dot (scalar) product nor the cross (vector) product. The new vector product $it_{(i)}$ has precisely the properties that we demand of it; i.e., when we form the dot product with n it gives us the term we want in [1.1.29]. We now rewrite [1.1.29] as

$$t_{(n)} = n \cdot [it_{(i)} + jt_{(j)} + kt_{(k)}] \qquad [1.1.46]$$

and identify the term in brackets as the stress tensor T, so that

$$t_{(n)} = n \cdot T \qquad [1.1.47]$$

By using the index notation and [1.1.34] and [1.1.35], we can show that T is given by

$$T = \sum_{i=1}^{i=3} \sum_{j=1}^{j=3} e_i e_j T_{ij} \qquad [1.1.48]$$

or, invoking the summation convention,

$$\mathbf{T} = \mathbf{e}_i\mathbf{e}_j T_{ij} \qquad [1.1.49]$$

Clearly there are two directions associated with the state of stress at a point—the direction of the stress vector and the direction of the unit normal. The doubly directed nature of stress shows up explicitly in $\mathbf{T}$. For convenience, one should think of $\mathbf{T}$ as an operator that maps the unit normal vector $\mathbf{n}$ into the stress vector $\mathbf{t}_{(\mathbf{n})}$.

Use of [1.1.47] in [1.1.26] leads to

$$\frac{D}{Dt}\int_{V_m(t)} \rho U\, dV = \int_{V_m(t)} \rho b\, dV + \int_{A_m(t)} \mathbf{n}\cdot\mathbf{T}\, dA \qquad [1.1.50]$$

Use of the special form of the Reynolds transport theorem and the divergence theorem for a tensor allows us to express [1.1.50] as

$$\int_{V_m(t)} \left[\rho\frac{DU}{Dt} - \rho b - \nabla\cdot\mathbf{T} \right] dV = 0 \qquad [1.1.51]$$

Since the limits of integration are arbitrary and the integrand is continuous, the integrand must be identically zero, and *Cauchy's first equation* results:

$$\rho\frac{DU}{Dt} = \rho b + \nabla\cdot\mathbf{T} \qquad [1.1.52]$$

This is also referred to as the stress equations of motion and we must remember that it applies to any continuous medium. Using [1.1.47] and [1.1.52], one can extract from [1.1.27] the point representation of the angular momentum principle (Aris 1962). This result is known as *Cauchy's second equation* and it simply requires that the stress tensor be symmetrical:

$$\mathbf{T} = \mathbf{T}^T \qquad [1.1.53]$$

Our analysis to this point has provided us with 10 equations (one from [1.1.8], three from [1.1.52], and six from [1.1.53]) and 13 unknowns (one in ρ, three in U, and nine in $\mathbf{T}$). Clearly a constitutive equation is required.

1.1.2.2 Constitutive Equations

In the study of the mechanics of continua one encounters two classic materials—the linear elastic solid and the linear fluid. The former obeys Hooke's law of elasticity (stress is a linear function of the strain) and the latter obeys Newton's law of viscosity (stress is a linear function of the rate of strain). Both of these constitutive equations are restricted to isotropic media.

In the construction of the constitutive equation for a linear fluid, we will represent the stress tensor in terms of an isotropic, thermodynamic stress $-p\mathbf{l}$ and the viscous stress tensor τ.

$$\mathbf{T} = -p\mathbf{I} + \tau \qquad [1.1.54]$$

Since the pressure p is defined in terms of thermodynamic quantities, we must think of [1.1.54] as defining τ. The tensor τ is sometimes referred to as the *extra stress tensor* or the *deviatoric stress tensor*; however, we will use the phrase *viscous stress tensor* because τ results from the viscous nature of the fluid. The unit tensor $\mathbf{I}$ has the property that

$$\mathbf{a} \cdot \mathbf{I} = \mathbf{I} \cdot \mathbf{a} = \mathbf{a} \qquad [1.1.55]$$

An explicit representation of the scalar components of $\mathbf{I}$ similar to that given for $\mathbf{T}$ in [1.1.44] is

$$I_{ij} = \begin{pmatrix} 1 & 0 & 0 \\ 0 & 1 & 0 \\ 0 & 0 & 1 \end{pmatrix} \qquad [1.1.56]$$

Here the scalar components of $\mathbf{I}$ are given by the Kronecker delta; thus, the representation of $\mathbf{I}$ analogous to [1.1.49] is

$$\mathbf{I} = \mathbf{e}_i \mathbf{e}_j \delta_{ij} \qquad [1.1.57]$$

One can use [1.1.57] to show that the result given by [1.1.55] is correct.
    Substitution of [1.1.54] into [1.1.52] leads to

$$\rho \frac{D\mathbf{U}}{Dt} = -\nabla p + \rho \mathbf{b} + \nabla \cdot \tau \qquad [1.1.58]$$

a result often referred to as the viscous stress equations of motion. These equations can be used to analyze the motion of any continuum, provided we obtain a representation of τ in terms of the velocity field.
    Returning to [1.1.54] and forming the scalar product of that equation with $\mathbf{n}$ yields the following expression for the stress vector:

$$\mathbf{t}_{(n)} = \mathbf{n} \cdot \mathbf{T} = -p\mathbf{n} \cdot \mathbf{I} + \mathbf{n} \cdot \tau \qquad [1.1.59]$$

In view of [1.1.55], the stress vector can be represented as

$$\mathbf{t}_{(n)} = -p\mathbf{n} + \mathbf{n} \cdot \tau \qquad [1.1.60]$$

Since the stress vector for a static fluid is given by

$$\mathbf{t}_{(n)} = -p\mathbf{n} \quad \text{static fluids} \qquad [1.1.24]$$

we require that τ be zero for static fluids.
    A linear fluid is one for which the viscous stress tensor is a linear function of the rate of strain tensor $\mathbf{D}$. An explicit representation for $\mathbf{D}$ is

$$\mathbf{D} = \tfrac{1}{2}(\nabla \mathbf{U} + \nabla \mathbf{U}^T) \qquad [1.1.61]$$

and the scalar components can be expressed as

$$D_{ij} = \begin{pmatrix} \dfrac{1}{2}\left(\dfrac{\partial u}{\partial x} + \dfrac{\partial u}{\partial x}\right) & \dfrac{1}{2}\left(\dfrac{\partial v}{\partial x} + \dfrac{\partial u}{\partial y}\right) & \dfrac{1}{2}\left(\dfrac{\partial w}{\partial x} + \dfrac{\partial u}{\partial z}\right) \\[2mm] \dfrac{1}{2}\left(\dfrac{\partial u}{\partial y} + \dfrac{\partial v}{\partial x}\right) & \dfrac{1}{2}\left(\dfrac{\partial v}{\partial y} + \dfrac{\partial v}{\partial y}\right) & \dfrac{1}{2}\left(\dfrac{\partial w}{\partial y} + \dfrac{\partial v}{\partial z}\right) \\[2mm] \dfrac{1}{2}\left(\dfrac{\partial u}{\partial z} + \dfrac{\partial w}{\partial x}\right) & \dfrac{1}{2}\left(\dfrac{\partial v}{\partial z} + \dfrac{\partial w}{\partial y}\right) & \dfrac{1}{2}\left(\dfrac{\partial w}{\partial z} + \dfrac{\partial w}{\partial z}\right) \end{pmatrix}$$ [1.1.62]

Here we see that the rate of strain tensor is composed of all the possible velocity gradients that could occur in a completely general type of flow.

In proposing a constitutive equation for a linear fluid, we require that τ be a linear function of D and that $\tau = 0$ when $D = 0$. For an isotropic fluid it can be shown (Whitaker 1981) that τ is related to D by

$$\tau = 2\mu D + [(\kappa - \tfrac{2}{3}\mu)\nabla \cdot U]I$$ [1.1.63]

This expression is known as Newton's law of viscosity, where μ is referred to as the shear coefficient of viscosity and κ as the bulk coefficient of viscosity. The appearance of $\nabla \cdot U$ in a linear representation of τ in terms of D results from the fact that the sum of the diagonal elements of [1.1.62] is equal to $\nabla \cdot U$. Thus this quantity is linearly related to D. There are many fluids for which [1.1.63] is quite satisfactory. For example, air and water are accurately described by [1.1.63] and are referred to as Newtonian fluids. Gasoline and lubricating oils are Newtonian fluids, as is honey, but slurries such as paper pulp and toothpaste are not. Common house paint is a classic example of a slurry that is designed to have nonlinear properties that provide easy application; i.e., more paint on the house and less on the painter. In other sections of this handbook, we will consider nonlinear fluids and other representations for τ.

Although all fluids are compressible, there are very few flows for which the term $[(\kappa - \tfrac{2}{3}\mu)\nabla \cdot U]I$ is important,* and an excellent approximation to τ is

$$\tau = 2\mu D = \mu(\nabla U + \nabla U^T)$$ [1.1.64]

Using this expression in the viscous stress equations of motion [1.1.58] and assuming that μ is a constant, we obtain the well-known Navier-Stokes equations

$$\rho\frac{DU}{Dt} = -\nabla p + \rho b + \mu\nabla^2 U$$ [1.1.65]

If all body forces except the gravitational force are excluded, we can express the Navier-Stokes equations as

$$\rho\left(\frac{\partial U}{\partial t} + U \cdot \nabla U\right) = -\nabla p + \rho g + \mu\nabla^2 U$$ [1.1.66]

Here we have expanded the left-hand side to clearly identify the local acceleration $\partial U/\partial t$ and the convective acceleration $U \cdot \nabla U$.

---

*In the analysis of the structure of shock waves and of acoustic phenomena the complete representation given by [1.1.63] must be used.

1.1.2.3 Dimensional Analysis

In subsequent sections of this handbook, special forms of [1.1.66] will be used. For example, in the study of the motion of small particles the convective inertial terms are generally negligible and [1.1.66] can be simplified to

$$\rho\left(\frac{\partial U}{\partial t}\right) = -\nabla p + \rho g + \mu \nabla^2 U \qquad \text{for negligible convective inertial effects} \quad [1.1.67]$$

Under these circumstances the analysis is greatly simplified, for [1.1.67] is linear and the complete Navier-Stokes equations are not.

Although many flow phenomena can be analyzed by using simplified forms of the Navier-Stokes equations, many phenomena must be studied experimentally. In those cases, it is important to use dimensional analysis to minimize the number of scaling parameters. For incompressible flows, the governing differential equations for a Newtonian fluid are given by

$$\rho\left(\frac{\partial U}{\partial t} + U \cdot \nabla U\right) = -\nabla p + \rho g + \mu \nabla^2 U \qquad [1.1.68]$$

$$\nabla \cdot U = 0 \qquad [1.1.69]$$

Here we note that the dependent variables (U and p) are functions of

1. The independent variables (x, y, z, and t)
2. The parameters that appear in the governing differential equations (ρ, μ, and g)
3. The parameters that appear in the boundary conditions

The last source of parameters is an important one, for the boundary conditions change from problem to problem but the governing differential equations do not.

Before developing the dimensionless form of [1.1.68] and [1.1.69], it is beneficial to note that the gravity vector can be expressed as the gradient of a scalar:

$$g = -\nabla \phi \qquad [1.1.70]$$

and the pressure and body force terms can be combined in the form

$$-\nabla p + \rho g = -\nabla(p + \rho\phi) \qquad [1.1.71]$$

where it is assumed that the flow is incompressible so that the density is taken inside the gradient operator. If we define a new pressure $P = p + \rho\phi$ that includes the variation of pressure due to gravity, we can express the Navier-Stokes equations as

$$\rho\left(\frac{\partial U}{\partial t} + U \cdot \nabla U\right) = -\nabla P + \mu \nabla^2 U \qquad [1.1.72]$$

We can see that for hydrostatic conditions ($U = 0$) the pressure P is constant. It would appear that we have eliminated gravity as a parameter; however, when multiphase systems are analyzed the effect of gravity shows up in the boundary conditions (Whitaker 1981, p. 164).

If we designate u_0 as a characteristic velocity and L as a characteristic length, [1.1.72] can be made dimensionless by multiplying each term by $L/\rho u_0^2$:

$$\frac{\partial \mathbf{U}^+}{\partial t^+} + \mathbf{U}^+ \cdot \nabla^+ \mathbf{U}^+ = -\nabla^+ P^+ + \left(\frac{\mu}{\rho u_0 L}\right)\nabla^+ \cdot \nabla^+ \mathbf{U}^+ \qquad [1.1.73]$$

Here we have made use of the fact that the Laplacian operator can be expressed as $\nabla^2 = \nabla \cdot \nabla$; thus, the dimensionless form is given by $\nabla^+ \cdot \nabla^+$. The continuity equation can be made dimensionless by multiplying [1.1.69] by L/u_0; thus, our dimensionless governing differential equations are

$$\frac{\partial \mathbf{U}^+}{\partial t^+} + \mathbf{U}^+ \cdot \nabla^+ \mathbf{U}^+ = -\nabla P^+ + \frac{1}{\text{Re}}\nabla^+ \cdot \nabla^+ \mathbf{U}^+ \qquad [1.1.74]$$

$$\nabla^+ \cdot \mathbf{U}^+ = 0 \qquad [1.1.75]$$

where we defined the Reynolds number as

$$\text{Re} = \frac{u_0 L}{\nu} \qquad [1.1.76]$$

The functional dependence of the two independent variables can now be expressed as

$$\mathbf{U}^+ = \mathbf{U}^+(t^+, x^+, y^+, z^+, \text{Re}, \text{BC}^{\text{I}}) \qquad [1.1.77]$$

$$P^+ = P^+(t^+, x^+, y^+, z^+, \text{Re}, \text{BC}^{\text{I}}) \qquad [1.1.78]$$

where the symbol BC^{I} represents the parameters that appear in the dimensionless form of the boundary conditions. In two-phase systems, the boundary condition for the stress vector yields two additional dimensionless parameters known as the Froude number and the Weber number.

1.1.2.4 Drag Coefficients and Friction Factors

In the experimental study of complex flows, one is generally interested in the force exerted by the fluid on some surface. This force is given in terms of the stress vector as

$$\mathbf{F} = \int_A \mathbf{t}_{(\mathbf{n})}\, dA \qquad [1.1.79]$$

where $\mathbf{n}$ is the unit normal vector pointing into the fluid. In general, there is only one component of the drag force vector that is of importance, and this scalar can be expressed as

$$F_D = \mathbf{i} \cdot \int_A \mathbf{t}_{(\mathbf{n})}\, dA \qquad [1.1.80]$$

where a coordinate system has been chosen so that the unit base vector $\mathbf{i}$ is parallel to the component of $\mathbf{F}$ represented by F_D. It is convenient to correlate experimentally determined drag forces in terms of a dimensionless drag force defined as

$$\xi = \frac{F_D}{\rho u_0^2 L^2} = \left(\frac{i}{\rho u_0^2 L^2} \right) \cdot \int_A t_{(n)} \, dA \qquad [1.1.81]$$

The quantity ξ is referred to as a drag coefficient when the fluid is exerting a force on an immersed body and as a friction factor when the fluid is exerting a force on a closed conduit.

When using drag coefficients and friction factors one must be careful to establish the definition of ξ. For example, a slightly different definition of the drag coefficient is given by

$$\xi' = \frac{F_D}{\frac{1}{2} \rho u_0^2 L^2} \qquad [1.1.82]$$

and for flow past immersed bodies one could use

$$\xi'' = \frac{F_D}{\frac{1}{2} \rho u_0^2 A_{\text{wetted}}} \qquad [1.1.83]$$

However, the preferred definition uses the projected area

$$\xi''' = \frac{F_D}{\frac{1}{2} \rho u_0^2 \, A_{\text{projected}}} \qquad [1.1.84]$$

Similar difficulties exist for closed conduit flow, and for pipes there are two widely used friction factors—the Darcy-Weisbach and the Fanning friction factors. Throughout this handbook, drag coefficients and friction factors will be defined when they are used.

The stress vector has the same functional dependence as the velocity vector; thus, the functional dependence of the dimensionless stress vector is given by

$$\frac{t_{(n)}}{\rho u_0^2} = \mathfrak{F} \left(t^+, x^+, y^+, z^+, \text{Re}, \text{BC}^I \right) \qquad [1.1.85]$$

Performing the area integral indicated in [1.1.81] removes the dependence on $x^+, y^+,$ and z^+, and the functional dependence of the drag coefficient can be expressed as

$$\xi = \xi(\text{Re}, \text{BC}^I) \qquad [1.1.86]$$

for steady flow conditions. One should keep in mind that the dependence on the dimensionless parameters represented by BC^I can be crucial. For example, the friction factor for turbulent flow in pipes depends on the wall roughness parameter ϵ/D, and this parameter enters the functional dependence through the boundary condition that the relative velocity is zero at the wall of the pipe (Whitaker 1981, p. 293).

1.1.2.5 Order of Magnitude Analysis

Because of the complexity of the complete Navier-Stokes equations, there is considerable incentive to simplify these equations for special cases. Decisions are often made regarding the relative importance of viscous and inertial effects based on the magnitude of the Reynolds number. Since the Reynolds number is the ratio of inertial to viscous effects, this seems like a reasonable thing to do; however, it is not always correct. For example, figure 1.1.4 illustrates laminar flow in a tube containing a venturi meter. If the Reynolds number is large, say Re = 1000, the inertial terms in the equations of motion will be zero in the long, straight portion of the tube, but they will not be negligible in the venturi meter.

We can develop a criterion for determining the relative importance of viscous and inertial effects by using order of magnitude analysis (Whitaker 1977) and the Navier-Stokes equations as given by [1.1.72]. To determine the importance of the various terms we need to estimate their magnitude, and this is most difficult to do with the convective inertial term. We begin by noting that the velocity can be expressed in terms of its magnitude U and a unit vector λ that is tangent to a streamline. This encourages us to write

$$\mathbf{U} \cdot \nabla \mathbf{U} = U\lambda \cdot \nabla \mathbf{U} \qquad [1.1.87]$$

The quantity $\lambda \cdot \nabla$ is known as the directional derivative (Whitaker 1981, p. 232), and when λ is equal to one of the unit base vectors, it takes the familiar special forms

$$\mathbf{i} \cdot \nabla = \frac{\partial}{\partial x} \quad \mathbf{j} \cdot \nabla = \frac{\partial}{\partial y} \quad \mathbf{k} \cdot \nabla = \frac{\partial}{\partial z} \qquad [1.1.88]$$

For an arbitrary unit vector λ we write

$$\lambda \cdot \nabla = \frac{d}{ds} \qquad [1.1.89]$$

where s is the arc length measured along a streamline for which λ is a unit tangent vector. Using [1.1.87] and [1.1.89], we can express [1.1.72] as

$$\rho \left[\frac{\partial \mathbf{U}}{\partial t} + U \left(\frac{d\mathbf{U}}{ds} \right) \right] = -\nabla P + \mu \nabla^2 \mathbf{U} \qquad [1.1.90]$$

This form of the Navier-Stokes equations is not useful for generating solutions for the velocity field, but it is convenient for estimating the magnitude of the individual terms.

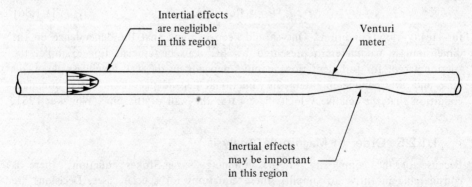

Intertial effects are negligible in this region

Venturi meter

Inertial effects may be important in this region

Figure 1.1.4 Laminar flow in a tube containing a venturi meter.

In constructing our order of magnitude estimates we first note that

$$\mathbf{U} = \mathbf{O}(\langle U \rangle) \qquad [1.1.91]$$

where $\langle U \rangle$ is the average value of the magnitude of the velocity vector in the region of interest. For the pipe flow illustrated in figure 1.1.4 the velocity vector is given explicitly as

$$\mathbf{U} = \mathbf{k}2\langle U \rangle \left[1 - \left(\frac{r}{r_0} \right)^2 \right] \qquad [1.1.92]$$

and thus the magnitude of $\mathbf{U}$ varies from zero at the wall to twice the average value at the centerline. Under these circumstances we consider [1.1.91] to be an excellent order of magnitude estimate.

If τ is the time during which significant changes in the velocity take place, then our order of magnitude estimate of the first term in [1.1.90] is

$$\frac{\partial \mathbf{U}}{\partial t} = \mathbf{O}\left(\frac{\langle U \rangle}{\tau} \right) \qquad [1.1.93]$$

If the flow is steady, $\tau = \infty$ and the local acceleration is zero. Continuing with the second term on the left-hand side of [1.1.90], we let L_ρ be the distance along a streamline over which significant variations in the velocity occur. Our order of magnitude estimate of the convective inertial terms can be expressed as

$$\mathbf{U} \cdot \nabla \mathbf{U} = U \left(\frac{d\mathbf{U}}{ds} \right) = \mathbf{O}\left(\frac{\langle U \rangle^2}{L_\rho} \right) \qquad [1.1.94]$$

To estimate the magnitude of the viscous terms we note that

$$\nabla^2 \mathbf{U} = \frac{\partial^2 \mathbf{U}}{\partial x^2} + \frac{\partial^2 \mathbf{U}}{\partial y^2} + \frac{\partial^2 \mathbf{U}}{\partial z^2} \qquad [1.1.95]$$

One of the second derivatives may be larger than the other two, and we designate the distance associated with that derivative as L_μ. The order of magnitude estimate of the viscous terms now takes the form

$$\nabla^2 \mathbf{U} = \mathbf{O}\left(\frac{\langle U \rangle}{L_\mu^2} \right) \qquad [1.1.96]$$

We refer to L_ρ as the *inertial length* and L_μ as the *viscous length*. Figure 1.1.5 shows the flow field in a venturi meter with the inertial and viscous lengths indicated. We now rewrite [1.1.90] with the appropriate order of magnitude estimate in parentheses over each term

$$\left(\rho \frac{\langle U \rangle}{\tau} \right) \left(\rho \frac{\langle U \rangle^2}{L_\rho} \right) \qquad \left(\frac{\mu \langle U \rangle}{L_\mu^2} \right)$$

$$\rho \left(\frac{\partial \mathbf{U}}{\partial t} \right) + \rho U \left(\frac{d\mathbf{U}}{ds} \right) = -\nabla P + \mu \nabla^2 \mathbf{U} \qquad [1.1.97]$$

With this result we can make some reasonable decisions regarding the nature of any flow process. For example, we can treat a flow as quasi-steady if the local acceleration term is small compared to the viscous term. Thus, if

$$\frac{\rho\langle U \rangle}{\tau} \ll \frac{\mu\langle U \rangle}{L_\mu^2}$$

or

$$\tau \gg \frac{L_\mu^2}{\nu} \qquad\qquad [1.1.98]$$

we could simplify the Navier-Stokes equations to

$$\rho(\mathbf{U} \cdot \nabla\mathbf{U}) = -\nabla p + \rho\mathbf{g} + \mu\nabla^2\mathbf{U} \qquad \text{quasi-steady flow} \qquad [1.1.99]$$

In making the simplification from [1.1.66] to [1.1.99] we have assumed that small causes produce small effects. This is usually but not always true (Birkhoff 1960), and one should remember this when invoking this assumption.

The relative importance of inertial and viscous effects in terms of our order of magnitude estimates is now expressed as the ratio

$$\frac{\text{Convective inertial effects}}{\text{Viscous effects}} = 0\left(\frac{\rho\langle U \rangle^2 / L_\rho}{\mu\langle U \rangle / L_\mu^2}\right)$$

Using the viscous length in the definition of the Reynolds number

$$\text{Re} = \frac{\langle U \rangle L_\mu}{\nu}$$

this ratio becomes

$$\frac{\text{Convective inertial effects}}{\text{Viscous effects}} = \text{Re}\left(\frac{L_\mu}{L_\rho}\right) \qquad [1.1.100]$$

In arriving at this result we think of the viscous length L_μ as a well-defined characteristic length that can be specified a priori. Since $L_\rho \geqslant L_\mu$, viscous effects will always predominate when $\text{Re} < 1$. When $\text{Re} \gg 1$, the convective inertial effects may or may not be important, depending on L_μ/L_ρ. One must be careful in applying this to turbulent flows, which are considered next.

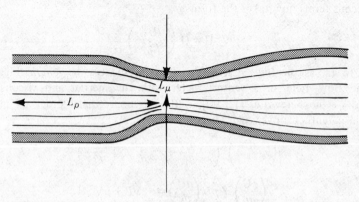

Figure 1.1.5 Viscous and inertial lengths associated with the flow in a venturi meter.

1.1.2.6 Turbulent Flow

In the analysis of turbulent flows, one generally seeks solutions for the time-averaged velocity, which is defined as

$$\bar{U} = \frac{1}{2\,\Delta t} \int_{\eta=t-\Delta t}^{\eta=t+\Delta t} U(r, \eta)\, d\eta \qquad [1.1.101]$$

Here it is assumed that the period over which the average is formed is sufficiently large that $\bar{U}$ is smoothed out into a well-behaved function. To obtain the governing differential equations for $\bar{U}$, we form the time average of the continuity equation and the Navier-Stokes equations, giving

$$\overline{\nabla \cdot U} = 0 \qquad [1.1.102]$$

$$\rho \left(\overline{\frac{\partial U}{\partial t}} \right) + \rho \overline{U \cdot \nabla U} = -\overline{\nabla p} + \rho g + \mu \overline{\nabla^2 U} \qquad [1.1.103]$$

Since time and spatial coordinates are independent, we can interchange differentiation and integration in [1.1.102] to obtain the continuity equation for the time-averaged velocity

$$\nabla \cdot \bar{U} = 0 \qquad [1.1.104]$$

The same procedure can be used with [1.1.103] to obtain

$$\rho \left(\overline{\frac{\partial U}{\partial t}} \right) + \rho \overline{U \cdot \nabla U} = -\nabla \bar{p} + \rho g + \mu \nabla^2 \bar{U} \qquad [1.1.105]$$

It is not necessarily obvious, but as shown elsewhere (Whitaker 1977) the time average of the time derivative is equal to the time derivative of the time average. This allows us to express [1.1.105] as

$$\rho \left(\frac{\partial \bar{U}}{\partial t} \right) + \rho \overline{U \cdot \nabla U} = -\nabla \bar{p} + \rho g + \mu \nabla^2 \bar{U} \qquad [1.1.106]$$

We can represent the velocity as

$$U = \bar{U} + U' \qquad [1.1.107]$$

and, provided $\bar{U}$ is essentially constant over the time $2\,\Delta t$, this leads to

$$\overline{U'} = 0 \qquad [1.1.108]$$

In view of [1.1.9] and [1.1.104], the fluctuating velocity U' must also satisfy a continuity equation

$$\nabla \cdot U' = 0 \qquad [1.1.109]$$

Using [1.1.107] through [1.1.109], we can express the convective inertial term in [1.1.106] as

$$\rho \overline{U \cdot \nabla U} = \rho \bar{U} \cdot \nabla \bar{U} + \nabla \cdot (\rho \overline{U'U'})$$

This allows us to put the time-averaged Navier-Stokes equations in the form

$$\rho\left(\frac{\partial\bar{U}}{\partial t}+\bar{U}\cdot\nabla\bar{U}\right)=-\nabla\bar{p}+\rho g+\mu\nabla^2\bar{U}-\nabla\cdot(\rho\overline{U'U'}) \qquad [1.1.110]$$

where $\rho\overline{U'U'}$ is referred to as the *turbulent stress* or the *Reynolds stress*. The key problem in the theory of turbulence is the construction of constitutive equations for this term.

In assessing the importance of the various terms in [1.1.110], we can follow the procedure outlined in section 1.1.2.5; however, in this case we must be careful to distinguish between the convective inertial terms in [1.1.110] and inertial effects. When the constraint

$$\mathrm{Re}\left(\frac{L_\mu}{L_\rho}\right)\ll 1$$

is satisfied, the time-averaged convective inertial terms in [1.1.110] will be negligible compared to the viscous terms

$$\rho\bar{U}\cdot\nabla\bar{U}\ll\mu\nabla^2\bar{U}$$

but this does not mean that inertial effects are negligible. The turbulent stress term $\nabla\cdot(\rho\overline{U'U'})$ will be important relative to the viscous term, and one needs to study the general subject of turbulence (Hinze 1975) before attempting to estimate the order of magnitude of this term. It will suffice at this point to say that the turbulent stress cannot be neglected relative to the viscous stress when the flow is turbulent.

1.1.3 THE ENERGY PRINCIPLE

For isotropic materials that obey the classic linear constitutive equations, we can state the laws of thermodynamics of single-component systems in terms of four axioms. Two of these are primarily concerned with energy, and we state them as

(I) $\left\{\begin{array}{l}\text{The time rate of change}\\ \text{of internal and kinetic}\\ \text{energy of a body}\end{array}\right\}=\left\{\begin{array}{l}\text{the rate at which}\\ \text{heat is transferred}\\ \text{to the body}\end{array}\right\}+\left\{\begin{array}{l}\text{the rate at which}\\ \text{work is done on}\\ \text{the body}\end{array}\right\}$

$$[1.1.111]$$

(II) $\left\{\begin{array}{l}\text{The internal energy is uniquely}\\ \text{specified by the entropy and}\\ \text{the density}\end{array}\right\}$ $\qquad [1.1.112]$

Applying the first of these to the body illustrated in figure 1.1.1, we obtain

$$\frac{D}{Dt}\int_{V_{m(t)}}(\rho u+\tfrac{1}{2}\rho U^2)\,dV=-\int_{A_{m(t)}}(q+q^R)\cdot n\,dA+\int_{A_{m(t)}}t_{(n)}\cdot U\,dA$$

$$+\int_{V_{m(t)}}\rho b\cdot U\,dV \qquad [1.1.113]$$

Here the heat transferred to the body is expressed in terms of the usual heat flux vector $\mathbf{q}$ and the radiant energy heat flux vector $\mathbf{q}^R$. The work done on the body is separated into the work done by surface forces $\mathbf{t}_{(n)} \cdot \mathbf{U}$ and the work done by body forces $\rho \mathbf{b} \cdot \mathbf{U}$. The second axiom is expressed as

$$u = u(s, \rho) \qquad [1.1.114]$$

where s is the specific entropy. This expression is sometimes referred to as the *caloric equation of state* and it symbolizes the fact that the internal energy is a function of the instantaneous state of the system.

These two axioms and the two that follow in section 1.1.4 are broader in scope than the axioms of thermostatics put forth by Gibbs (1928). These axioms represent thermodynamics as it is used in the analysis of practical problems, provided we restrict ourselves to isotropic materials that obey the classic linear constitutive equations (Coleman & Mizel 1964). We will refer to this approach as *continuum thermodynamics*. More general caloric equations of state have been proposed (Coleman 1964) to describe the behavior of viscoelastic fluids. For the present, we use [1.1.114] to define the temperature and pressure as

$$T = \left(\frac{\partial u}{\partial s}\right)_\rho \qquad [1.1.115]$$

$$p = \rho^2 \left(\frac{\partial u}{\partial \rho}\right)_s \qquad [1.1.116]$$

To derive the differential equation associated with the first axiom, we make use of the special form of the Reynolds transport theorem [1.1.18], the stress vector-stress tensor relation [1.1.47], and the divergence theorem to put [1.1.113] in the form

$$\int_{V_m(t)} \rho \frac{D}{Dt}\left(u + \frac{1}{2}U^2\right) dV = -\int_{V_m(t)} (\nabla \cdot \mathbf{q} + \nabla \cdot \mathbf{q}^R)\, dV + \int_{V_m(t)} \nabla \cdot (\mathbf{T} \cdot \mathbf{U})\, dV$$

$$+ \int_{V_m(t)} \rho \mathbf{b} \cdot \mathbf{U}\, dV \qquad [1.1.117]$$

Here we have expressed the stress vector in terms of the stress tensor so that the rate of surface work could be written as

$$\int_{A_m(t)} \mathbf{t}_{(n)} \cdot \mathbf{U}\, dA = \int_{A_m(t)} \mathbf{n} \cdot \mathbf{T} \cdot \mathbf{U}\, dA = \int_{V_m(t)} \nabla \cdot (\mathbf{T} \cdot \mathbf{U})\, dV \qquad [1.1.118]$$

The differential equation resulting from [1.1.117] is often expressed as

$$\rho \frac{D}{Dt}\left(u + \frac{1}{2}U^2\right) = -\nabla \cdot \mathbf{q} + \nabla \cdot (\mathbf{T} \cdot \mathbf{U}) + \rho \mathbf{b} \cdot \mathbf{U} + \Phi \qquad [1.1.119]$$

where $\Phi = -\nabla \cdot \mathbf{q}^R$ represents the source or sink of electromagnetic energy (Whitaker 1977, p. 383). It is convenient to remove the mechanical energy terms from [1.1.119], and this can be accomplished by forming the scalar product of the stress equations of motion [1.1.52] with the velocity vector **U** to obtain

$$\rho \frac{D}{Dt}\left(\frac{1}{2}U^2\right) = \mathbf{\nabla} \cdot (\mathbf{T} \cdot \mathbf{U}) - \mathbf{\nabla U} : \mathbf{T} + \rho \mathbf{b} \cdot \mathbf{U} \qquad [1.1.120]$$

Subtracting this mechanical energy equation from [1.1.119] leads to what is referred to as the thermal energy equation

$$\rho \frac{Du}{Dt} = - \mathbf{\nabla} \cdot \mathbf{q} + \mathbf{\nabla U} : \mathbf{T} + \Phi \qquad [1.1.121]$$

Using [1.1.54] to represent the stress tensor in terms of the pressure and the viscous stress tensor allows us to express the thermal energy equation as

$$\rho \frac{Du}{Dt} = -\mathbf{\nabla} \cdot \mathbf{q} - p\mathbf{\nabla} \cdot \mathbf{U} + \mathbf{\nabla U} : \tau + \Phi \qquad [1.1.122]$$

Here $\mathbf{\nabla U} : \tau$ is referred to as the viscous dissipation.

To apply this result we want an expression containing either the enthalpy or the temperature. Defining the specific enthalpy as

$$h = u + \frac{p}{\rho} \qquad [1.1.123]$$

allows us to express [1.1.122] as

$$\rho \frac{Dh}{Dt} = - \mathbf{\nabla} \cdot \mathbf{q} + \frac{Dp}{Dt} + \mathbf{\nabla U} : \tau + \Phi \qquad [1.1.124]$$

Since the enthalpy is a function of pressure and temperature we can write

$$\frac{Dh}{Dt} = \left(\frac{\partial h}{\partial T}\right)_p \frac{DT}{Dt} + \left(\frac{\partial h}{\partial p}\right)_T \frac{Dp}{Dt} \qquad [1.1.125]$$

and a modest amount of manipulation with [1.1.124] (Whitaker 1977, p. 215) leads to

$$\rho c_p \frac{DT}{Dt} = - \mathbf{\nabla} \cdot \mathbf{q} + T\beta \frac{Dp}{Dt} + \mathbf{\nabla U} : \tau + \Phi \qquad [1.1.126]$$

where β is the coefficient of thermal expansion

$$\beta = - \frac{1}{\rho}\left(\frac{\partial \rho}{\partial T}\right)_p$$

At this point we use the constitutive equation, Fourier's law, to express the heat flux vector as

$$\mathbf{q} = -\lambda \mathbf{\nabla} T \qquad [1.1.127]$$

Use of this relation in [1.1.126] leads to the final form of the thermal energy equation

$$\rho c_p \left(\frac{\partial T}{\partial t} + \mathbf{U} \cdot \mathbf{\nabla} T\right) = \mathbf{\nabla} \cdot (\lambda \mathbf{\nabla} T) + T\beta \frac{Dp}{Dt} + \mathbf{\nabla U} : \tau + \Phi \qquad [1.1.128]$$

In other sections of this handbook special forms of this result are utilized in the analysis of a variety of multiphase systems.

1.1.3.1 Dimensional Analysis

When [1.1.128] cannot be solved by analytic or numerical techniques, experimental methods must be employed. Under these circumstances, dimensional analysis must be used as a guide in constructing experiments and interpreting the results. In our study of [1.1.128] we assume that the thermal conductivity is constant and the flow is incompressible. This allows us to use [1.1.64] for the viscous stress tensor and write [1.1.128] as

$$\frac{\partial T}{\partial t} + \mathbf{U} \cdot \nabla T = \kappa \nabla^2 T + \left(\frac{\mu}{\rho c_p}\right) \nabla \mathbf{U} : (\nabla \mathbf{U} + \nabla \mathbf{U}^T) + \left(\frac{\Phi}{\rho c_p}\right) \qquad [1.1.129]$$

We will follow the development given in section 1.1.2.3 and assume the existence of a characteristic length L and a characteristic velocity u_0. In addition, we will assume that there are two reference temperatures T_1 and T_0 associated with every process. In general, we should think of T_1 and T_0 as being the maximum and minimum temperatures for the particular process under consideration. Since T_0 is independent of space and time, [1.1.129] can be rewritten in the form

$$\frac{\partial(T - T_0)}{\partial t} + \mathbf{U} \cdot \nabla(T - T_0) = \kappa \nabla^2 (T - T_0) + \left(\frac{\mu}{\rho c_p}\right) \nabla \mathbf{U} : (\nabla \mathbf{U} + \nabla \mathbf{U}^T) + \left(\frac{\Phi}{\rho c_p}\right)$$

$$[1.1.130]$$

If we now multiply this equation by $L/u_0 \, (T_1 - T_0)$ we obtain

$$\frac{\partial T^+}{\partial t^+} + \mathbf{U}^+ \cdot \nabla^+ T^+ = \left(\frac{\kappa}{u_0 L}\right) \nabla^+ \cdot \nabla^+ T^+ + \left(\frac{\mu u_0}{\rho c_p (T_1 - T_0) L}\right) \nabla^+ \mathbf{U}^+ : [\nabla^+ \mathbf{U}^+ + (\nabla^+ \mathbf{U}^+)^T]$$

$$+ \left(\frac{\Phi L}{\rho c_p (T_1 - T_0) u_0}\right) \qquad [1.1.131]$$

The dimensionless radiant energy source or sink is given by

$$\Phi^+ = \frac{\Phi L}{\rho c_p (T_1 - T_0) u_0} \qquad [1.1.132]$$

and the other two dimensionless groups in [1.1.131] can be arranged as

$$\frac{\kappa}{u_0 L} = \frac{1}{(u_0 L/\nu)(\nu/\kappa)} = \frac{1}{\text{Re Pr}} \qquad [1.1.133]$$

$$\frac{\mu u_0}{\rho c_p (T_1 - T_0) L} = 2 \left[\frac{\frac{1}{2} \rho u_0^2}{\rho c_p (T_1 - T_0)}\right] \frac{1}{\rho u_0 L/\mu} = 2 \left(\frac{\text{Ec}}{\text{Re}}\right) \qquad [1.1.134]$$

Here we see that the Prandtl number is the ratio of the kinematic viscosity to the thermal diffusivity, while the Eckert number is the ratio of a characteristic kinetic energy per unit volume to a characteristic thermal energy per unit volume. Using [1.1.132] through [1.1.134], we can express [1.1.131] as

$$\frac{\partial T^+}{\partial t^+} + \mathbf{U}^+ \cdot \mathbf{\nabla}^+ T^+ = \frac{1}{\text{Re Pr}} \mathbf{\nabla}^+ \cdot \mathbf{\nabla}^+ T^+ + 2\left(\frac{\text{Ec}}{\text{Re}}\right) \mathbf{\nabla}^+ \mathbf{U}^+ : [\mathbf{\nabla}^+ \mathbf{U}^+ + (\mathbf{\nabla}^+ \mathbf{U}^+)^T] + \Phi^+$$

[1.1.135]

From this result we conclude that the functional dependence of the dimensionless temperature is given by

$$T^+ = T^+\left(t^+, x^+, y^+, z^+, \text{Re Pr}, \frac{\text{Ec}}{\text{Re}}, \Phi^+, \mathbf{U}^+, \text{BC}^{II}\right)$$

[1.1.136]

From section 1.1.2.3 we know the functional dependence of $\mathbf{U}^+$, and it can be removed from [1.1.136], leading to

$$T^+ = T^+\left(T^+, x^+, y^+, z^+, \text{Re Pr}, \frac{\text{Ec}}{\text{Re}}, \Phi^+, \text{Re}, \text{BC}^{I}, \text{BC}^{II}\right)$$

[1.1.137]

It is important to note that the dimensionless parameters appearing in the boundary conditions for the velocity field can affect the temperature field. Because the Reynolds number appears as a result of the functional dependence on $\mathbf{U}^+$ in addition to appearing directly in [1.1.135] in conjunction with the Prandtl and Eckert numbers, it is best to represent the functional dependence of T^+ as

$$T^+ = T^+(t^+, x^+, y^+, z^+, \text{Re}, \text{Pr}, \text{Ec}, \Phi^+, \text{BC}^{I}, \text{BC}^{II})$$

[1.1.138]

1.1.3.2 Heat Transfer Coefficients

Experimental studies of heat transfer processes are generally conducted to determine the total rate of heat transfer over a surface of area A. This is given by

$$\dot{Q} = -\int_A \mathbf{q} \cdot \mathbf{n} \, dA$$

[1.1.139]

a result that one might think of as a scalar analogy of the drag force given by [1.1.79]. Here, too, we find it convenient to form dimensionless quantities to correlate experimental data. We again represent the characteristic length for the system as L, and we designate the characteristic temperature difference as ΔT. Multiplying [1.1.139] by $L/\lambda A \, \Delta T$ leads to the dimensionless relation

$$\frac{\dot{Q}L}{\lambda A \, \Delta T} = -\frac{L}{\lambda A \, \Delta T} \int_A \mathbf{q} \cdot \mathbf{n} \, dA = \text{Nu}$$

[1.1.140]

Here the dimensionless overall heat transfer rate is defined as the Nusselt number Nu, and ΔT and $\mathbf{n}$ are always chosen so that Nu is positive. The Nusselt number is analogous to the drag coefficient discussed in section 1.1.2.4. When using an experimentally determined Nusselt number to calculate $\dot{Q}$ from

$$\dot{Q} = \frac{\text{Nu} \, \lambda A \, \Delta T}{L}$$

[1.1.141]

one must be extremely careful to determine the length that was used in the definition of Nu. Also, A and ΔT must be clearly established. Furthermore, one must know precisely how the thermal conductivity was evaluated in order to use the experimental correlation in the manner in which it was constructed.

The Nusselt number has the same function dependence as the dimensionless temperature T^+, except that it does not depend on x^+, y^+, or z^+, or on t^+ if the process is steady:

$$\text{Nu} = \text{Nu}(\text{Re}, \text{Pr}, \text{Ec}, \Phi^+, \text{BC}^\text{I}, \text{BC}^\text{II}) \qquad [1.1.142]$$

Often viscous dissipation and radiation effects are negligible and the functional dependence of the Nusselt number can be expressed as

$$\text{Nu} = \text{Nu}(\text{Re}, \text{Pr}, \text{BC}^\text{I}, \text{BC}^\text{II}) \qquad [1.1.143]$$

It is tradiational and convenient to extract another defined quantity from the variables in [1.1.140]. This is known as the film heat transfer coefficient α, and it is defined as

$$\alpha = \frac{\dot{Q}}{A \, \Delta T} \qquad [1.1.144]$$

Like the Nusselt number, the experimentally determined film heat transfer coefficient can be used to calculate the total rate of heat transfer

$$\dot{Q} = \alpha A \, \Delta T \qquad [1.1.145]$$

and again, one must know precisely how α was defined to use this parameter with success. In terms of the film heat transfer coefficient, the Nusselt number is expressed as

$$\text{Nu} = \frac{\alpha L}{\lambda} \qquad [1.1.146]$$

1.1.3.3 Order of Magnitude Analysis

The thermal energy equation, as given by [1.1.128], is a challenging partial differential equation. The method of order of magnitude analysis discussed in section 1.1.2.5 can be used to extract simplified versions of [1.1.128]. To illustrate, assuming that the source terms are negligible and the thermal conductivity is constant, we can write [1.1.128] as

$$\frac{\partial T^+}{\partial t} + \mathbf{U} \cdot \nabla T^+ = \kappa \nabla^2 T^+ \qquad [1.1.147]$$

where T^+ is the dimensionless temperature defined as

$$T^+ = \frac{T - T_0}{T_1 - T_0} \qquad [1.1.148]$$

We have in mind here that T_1 and T_0 are the maximum and minimum temperatures so that the order of magnitude of T^+ is given by

$$T^+ = \mathbf{O}(1) \qquad\qquad [1.1.149]$$

Following [1.1.93] and [1.1.94], we express the order of magnitude of the transient term and the convective term as

$$\frac{\partial T^+}{\partial t} = \mathbf{O}\left(\frac{1}{\tau}\right) \qquad\qquad [1.1.150]$$

$$\mathbf{U} \cdot \nabla T^+ = U\left(\frac{dT^+}{ds}\right) = \mathbf{O}\left(\frac{\langle U \rangle}{L_{\rho c_p}}\right) \qquad\qquad [1.1.151]$$

Here we use $L_{\rho c_p}$ to represent the distance along a streamline over which significant variations in the temperature occur. Often this *convective length* will be comparable to the inertial length discussed in section 1.1.2.5, but this need not be the case.

In analyzing the right-hand side of [1.1.147], we are not so much interested in knowing when conductive transport can be neglected relative to convective transport as in knowing which parts of conductive transport can be neglected. Because of this, we expand the right-hand side of [1.1.147] and indicate the order of magnitude estimate in parentheses over each term

$$\left(\frac{1}{\tau}\right) \quad \left(\frac{\langle U \rangle}{L_{\rho c_p}}\right) \qquad\quad \left(\frac{\kappa}{L_x^2}\right) \ \left(\frac{\kappa}{L_y^2}\right) \ \left(\frac{\kappa}{L_z^2}\right)$$
$$\frac{\partial T^+}{\partial t} + \mathbf{U} \cdot \nabla T^+ = \kappa\left(\frac{\partial^2 T^+}{\partial x^2} + \frac{\partial^2 T^+}{\partial y^2} + \frac{\partial^2 T^+}{\partial z^2}\right) \qquad [1.1.152]$$

Usually one of the conductive lengths is smaller than the other two and the order of magnitude estimates are compared with this conductive term. For example, we assume that L_y is small compared to L_x and L_z and note that:

1. The processes are quasi-steady if $\tau^{-1} \ll \kappa/L_y^2$. This can be expressed as

$$\mathrm{Fo} \gg 1$$

where the Fourier number is defined as

$$\mathrm{Fo} = \frac{\tau\kappa}{L_y^2}$$

2. Conductive transport in the z direction is negligible compared to convective transport if $\kappa/L_z^2 \ll \langle U \rangle/L_{\rho c_p}$. This can be expressed as

$$\mathrm{Pe}\left(\frac{L_z}{L_y}\right)\left(\frac{L_z}{L_{\rho c_p}}\right) \gg 1$$

where the Peclet number is defined by $\mathrm{Pe} = \langle U \rangle L_y/\kappa$. The use of order of magnitude analysis to simplify the thermal energy equation and the associated boundary conditions have been treated extensively elsewhere (Whitaker 1977).*

*See especially sections 2.6, 2.9, 2.10, 4.2, 5.5, 5.7, 5.11, 7.4, and 7.5 there.

1.1.3.4 Turbulent Flow

In the study of turbulent flows, we proceed as in section 1.1.2.6 in order to develop the governing equation for the time-averaged temperature. We will restrict our discussion here to incompressible flows, constant physical properties, and negligible viscous dissipation and radiant energy exchange. Under these circumstances the thermal energy equation simplifies to

$$\rho c_p \left(\frac{\partial T}{\partial t} + \mathbf{U} \cdot \nabla T \right) = \lambda \nabla^2 T \qquad [1.1.153]$$

Following our discussion of time averaging in section 1.1.2.6, we form the time average of [1.1.153] to obtain

$$\rho c_p \left(\frac{\partial \bar{T}}{\partial t} + \overline{\mathbf{U} \cdot \nabla T} \right) = \lambda \nabla^2 \bar{T} \qquad [1.1.154]$$

Representing the velocity and temperature as before allows us to express [1.1.154] in the form

$$\rho c_p \left(\frac{\partial \bar{T}}{\partial t} + \bar{\mathbf{U}} \cdot \nabla \bar{T} \right) = \lambda \nabla^2 T - \nabla \cdot (\rho c_p \overline{\mathbf{U}'T'}) \qquad [1.1.155]$$

where $\rho c_p \overline{\mathbf{U}'T'}$ is referred to as the turbulent heat flux. The key problem in the study of turbulent heat transfer is the construction of constitutive equations for this term.

1.1.4 THE ENTROPY PRINCIPLE

Up to this point we have put forth two axioms concerning thermodynamics. The second of these, given by [1.1.114], involved the specific entropy s. Except in defining thermodynamic pressure and temperature, we have made no use of the entropy. Now it is time to explore the remaining two axioms of the thermodynamics of single-component systems and see where entropy fits into our theoretical framework.

We begin by taking the material derivative of the caloric equation of state given by [1.1.114]:

$$\frac{Du}{Dt} = \left(\frac{\partial u}{\partial s} \right)_\rho \frac{Ds}{Dt} + \left(\frac{\partial u}{\partial \rho} \right)_s \frac{D\rho}{Dt} \qquad [1.1.156]$$

and using the definitions of temperature and pressure given by [1.1.115] and [1.1.116] to obtain

$$\frac{Du}{Dt} = T \frac{Ds}{Dt} + \frac{p}{\rho^2} \frac{D\rho}{Dt} \qquad [1.1.157]$$

Substitution of this result into the thermal energy equation given by [1.1.122] yields an entropy transport equation of the form

$$\rho \frac{Ds}{Dt} = -\frac{1}{T} \nabla \cdot \mathbf{q} + \frac{1}{T} \nabla \mathbf{U} : \tau + \frac{\Phi}{T} \qquad [1.1.158]$$

Here we have made use of the fact that

$$\frac{1}{\rho} \frac{D\rho}{Dt} = -\nabla \cdot \mathbf{U} \qquad [1.1.159]$$

To obtain an interesting result we use the relation

$$\frac{1}{T} \nabla \cdot \mathbf{q} = \nabla \cdot \left(\frac{\mathbf{q}}{T}\right) + \frac{1}{T^2} \mathbf{q} \cdot \nabla T \qquad [1.1.160]$$

so that we can express the entropy transport equation in the form

$$\rho \frac{Ds}{Dt} = -\nabla \cdot \left(\frac{\mathbf{q}}{T}\right) - \frac{1}{T^2} \mathbf{q} \cdot \nabla T + \frac{1}{T} \nabla \mathbf{U} : \tau + \frac{\Phi}{T} \qquad [1.1.161]$$

Integrating this result over $V_m(t)$ and using the special form of the Reynolds transport theorem with $s = \Omega$ in [1.1.18] yields

$$\frac{D}{Dt} \int_{V_m(t)} \rho s \, dV = - \int_{A_m(t)} \left(\frac{\mathbf{q}}{T}\right) \cdot \mathbf{n} \, dA$$

$$+ \int_{V_m(t)} \frac{1}{T} \left[-\left(\frac{\mathbf{q}}{T}\right) \cdot \nabla T + \nabla \mathbf{U} : \tau + \Phi \right] dV \qquad [1.1.162]$$

Here we see that the time rate of change of the entropy of a body depends on the flux of entropy at the surface of the body in addition to the rate of production of entropy due to temperature gradients, velocity gradients, and the absorption or emission of radiant energy.

The final two axioms of thermodynamics may now be stated in terms of the following inequalities:

$$-\mathbf{q} \cdot \nabla T \geqslant 0 \qquad [1.1.163]$$

$$\nabla \mathbf{U} : \tau \geqslant 0 \qquad [1.1.164]$$

The first of these simply states that the conductive heat flux gives rise to a transport of energy from a high-temperature region to a low-temperature region. The second indicates that viscous dissipation is always positive. Truesdell (1969) refers to the first as Fourier's postulate and the second as Planck's postulate. There appears to have been no effort to test these postulates in the form given by [1.1.163] and [1.1.164]; instead, these inequalities are inferred from macroscopic observations and solutions of the thermal energy equation.

If we accept these final two axioms, we can express [1.1.162] as

$$\frac{D}{Dt} \int_{V_m(t)} \rho s \, dV + \int_{A_m(t)} \left(\frac{\mathbf{q}}{T}\right) \cdot \mathbf{n} \, dA - \int_{V_m(t)} \left(\frac{\Phi}{T}\right) dV \geqslant 0 \quad [1.1.165]$$

which is often referred to as the Clausius-Duhem inequality. An isolated system is one that cannot communicate with its surroundings either by transport across the bounding surface or by absorption or emission of radiant energy. Thus, for an isolated system, the time rate of change of the entropy is always greater than or equal to zero

$$\frac{D}{Dt} \int_{V_m(t)} \rho s \, dV \geq 0 \qquad \text{for an isolated system} \qquad [1.1.166]$$

This result is often referred to as the second law of thermodynamics; however, it is more appealing to view [1.1.163] and [1.1.164] as laws of nature and consider the inequality [1.1.166] as a derived result.

The entropy inequality [1.1.166] is valuable because of the constraint it imposes on the Gibbs free energy under equilibrium conditions. Defining the equilibrium state as the state in which the entropy inequality becomes an equality, we write

$$\frac{D}{Dt} \int_{V_m(t)} \rho s \, dV = 0 \qquad \text{at equilibrium} \qquad [1.1.167]$$

An alternative point of view would be to define the equilibrium state as the state in which the following constraints are satisfied:

$$\Phi = 0 \qquad -\mathbf{q} \cdot \nabla T = 0 \qquad \nabla \mathbf{U} : \tau = 0 \qquad \text{at equilibrium} \qquad [1.1.168]$$

If one views this as the definition of the equilibrium state, [1.1.167] is a derived result. Restricting ourselves to the constitutive equations for τ and $\mathbf{q}$ given by [1.1.63] and [1.1.127] means that the equilibrium condition is described by

$$\Phi = 0 \qquad \nabla T = 0 \qquad \mathbf{D} = 0 \qquad \text{at equilibrium} \qquad [1.1.169]$$

Note that the vanishing of the viscous dissipation does not require that the velocity be zero or that the gradient of the velocity $\nabla \mathbf{U}$ be zero. It simply requires that the motion be rigid body motion.

At this point we are interested in knowing what results can be obtained from [1.1.169] that are consistent with the principles of mass, momentum, and energy. To do this we write the appropriate transport equations for a general, noninertial frame. Since the continuity equation and the thermal energy equation are assumed to be frame-indifferent (Slattery 1972), their form remains unchanged:

$$\frac{\partial \rho}{\partial t} + \nabla \cdot (\rho \mathbf{U}) = 0 \qquad [1.1.170]$$

$$\rho \frac{Du}{Dt} = -\nabla \cdot \mathbf{q} - p \nabla \cdot \mathbf{U} + \nabla \mathbf{U} : \tau + \Phi \qquad [1.1.171]$$

For a noninertial frame the viscous stress equations of motion take the form

$$\rho \frac{D\mathbf{U}}{Dt} + \rho \mathbf{a} + 2\rho \omega \times \mathbf{U} + \rho \dot{\omega} \times \mathbf{r} + \rho \omega \times (\omega \times \mathbf{r}) = -\nabla p + \rho \mathbf{g} + \nabla \cdot \tau$$

$$[1.1.172]$$

Here $\mathbf{a}$ is the acceleration and ω is the angular velocity relative to an inertial frame. We are interested in choosing a noninertial frame that reduces the velocity of our rigid body to zero. Choosing this frame and imposing the constraints indicated in [1.1.169] leads to

$$\frac{\partial \rho}{\partial t} = 0 \qquad [1.1.173]$$

$$\frac{\partial u}{\partial t} = 0 \qquad [1.1.174]$$

$$0 = -\nabla p + \rho [\mathbf{g} - \mathbf{a} - \dot{\omega} \times \mathbf{r} - \omega \times (\omega \times \mathbf{r})] \qquad [1.1.175]$$

On the basis of [1.1.173], [1.1.174], and the caloric equation of state [1.1.114], we require that all thermodynamic functions be independent of time in our noninertial frame; thus [1.1.175] simplifies to

$$0 = -\nabla p + \rho [\mathbf{g} - \mathbf{a} - \omega \times (\omega \times \mathbf{r})] \qquad [1.1.176]$$

where the motion is restricted to the case where $\mathbf{a}$ and ω are constants. Note that in maintaining this degree of generality we are able to include in our discussion the case of equilibrium in a centrifuge. Representing the gravitational body force and the apparent body forces as gradients of scalars

$$\mathbf{g} = -\nabla \phi \qquad [1.1.177a]$$

$$\mathbf{a} + \omega \times (\omega \times \mathbf{r}) = \nabla \phi' \qquad [1.1.177b]$$

allows us to express the equations of motion as

$$\frac{1}{\rho} \nabla p = -\nabla(\phi + \phi') \qquad [1.1.178]$$

We should keep in mind that the equations of motion listed here are restricted by [1.1.169], the continuity equation, the thermal energy equation, and the caloric equation of state given earlier as

$$u = u(s, \rho) \qquad [1.1.114]$$

Taking the gradient of this equation leads to the completely general result

$$\nabla u = T \nabla s + \frac{p}{\rho^2} \nabla \rho \qquad [1.1.179]$$

We now make use of the definition of the specific Gibbs free energy

$$g = u + \frac{p}{\rho} - Ts \qquad [1.1.180]$$

and take the gradient to obtain

$$\nabla g = \nabla u + \frac{\nabla p}{\rho} - \frac{p}{\rho^2} \nabla \rho - T \nabla s - s \nabla T \qquad [1.1.181]$$

Making use of the generally valid result given by [1.1.179] and imposing the restriction $\nabla T = 0$ leads to

$$\nabla g = \frac{\nabla p}{\rho}$$ [1.1.182]

If we now impose the restricted form of the equations of motion given by [1.1.178], we can express [1.1.182] in the form

$$\nabla(g + \phi + \phi') = 0$$ [1.1.183]

Recall that equilibrium was defined as the state in which the constraints given by [1.1.168] were satisfied. Using those constraints, the transport equations for mass, momentum, and thermal energy, and the caloric equation of state, we were able to prove that

In a noninertial frame that reduces the velocity to zero, all thermodynamic functions are independent of time.

This result along with $\nabla T = 0$ requires that at equilibrium

$$T = \text{constant} \qquad \text{at equilibrium}$$ [1.1.184]

Remembering that our rigid body motion is constrained so that ϕ and ϕ' are independent of time, we can use [1.1.183] to conclude that

$$g + \phi + \phi' = \text{constant} \qquad \text{at equilibrium}$$ [1.1.185]

If the body is at rest relative to an inertial frame, ϕ' is zero and [1.1.185] simplifies to

$$g + \phi = \text{constant} \qquad \text{at equilibrium in an inertial frame}$$ [1.1.186]

Often gravitational effects are negligible, and one simply states that the specific Gibbs free energy is a constant under equilibrium conditions.

In subsequent sections of this handbook the Gibbs free energy will play an important role in the analysis of multiphase, multicomponent systems. In multicomponent systems the specific Gibbs free energy is a function of composition and will be represented in terms of the chemical potentials of the individual species.

In our discussion of the equilibrium state for single-component, single-phase systems, we have said nothing about the stability of the equilibrium state. For the simple systems examined in this section, the question of stability appears to be unimportant. However, for multicomponent, multiphase systems this is not the case, and the reader is referred to Modell & Reid (1974) and Slattery (1977) for discussions of this subject.

1.2 General Equations and Two-Phase Flow Modeling

J. A. Bouré and J. M. Delhaye

1.2.1 LOCAL INSTANTANEOUS EQUATIONS

In single-phase flow, local balance laws at point **r** are expressed in terms of partial differential equations if point **r** does not belong to a surface of discontinuity. If point **r** belongs to a surface of discontinuity, the local balance laws are formulated in terms of jump conditions that relate the values of the flow parameters on both sides of the surface of discontinuity (Truesdell & Toupin 1960; Slattery 1972).

In two-phase flow, interfaces can be considered as surfaces of discontinuity. Consequently, the balance laws for each phase are expressed in terms of partial differential equations, whereas on the interface they are formulated in terms of jump conditions.

Local instantaneous equations constitute the rational basis for almost all two-phase flow modeling procedures. They are used directly, as in the study of bubble dynamics or film flows, or in an averaged form, as in the study of pipe flows.

Jump conditions constitute a characteristic feature of two-phase flow analysis and provide relations between the phase interaction terms that appear in the averaged equations (Delhaye 1974; Ishii 1975). Two kinds of jump conditions—primary and secondary—can be derived. *Primary jump conditions* are derived directly from the integral laws written for mass, linear momentum, angular momentum, total energy, and entropy. *Secondary jump conditions* are established by combining the primary ones and are written for mechanical energy, internal energy, enthalpy, and entropy.

The interfacial entropy source, obtained from the entropy jump conditions, leads to the interfacial boundary conditions. If the interface transfers are assumed reversible, it can thus be demonstrated that there is neither slip nor a temperature jump across the interface and that a certain relation exists between the free enthalpies of the individual phases.

The derivation of the local instantaneous equations starts with the integral balance laws written for a fixed control volume containing both phases. These integral laws are then transformed by means of the Leibniz rule and the Gauss theorems to obtain a sum of two volume integrals and a surface integral. The volume integrals lead to the local instantaneous partial differential equations valid in each phase, whereas the surface integral furnishes the local instantaneous jump conditions valid on the interface only.

1.2.1.1 Mathematical Tools

Speed of Displacement of a Geometric Surface

Consider a set of geometric surfaces defined by

$$\mathbf{r} = \mathbf{r}(u,\, v,\, t) \tag{1.2.1}$$

where u and v are the coordinates of a point on this surface and t is time. The velocity of the surface point $(u,\, v)$ is defined by

$$\mathbf{U}_I \triangleq \left(\frac{\partial \mathbf{r}}{\partial t}\right)_{u,\,v\,\text{const}} \tag{1.2.2}$$

The surface equation may also be expressed by

$$f(x,\, y,\, z,\, t) = 0 \tag{1.2.3}$$

The unit normal vector $\mathbf{n}$ is related to the surface equation by

$$\mathbf{n} = \frac{\nabla f}{|\nabla f|} \tag{1.2.4}$$

The speed of displacement of the surface (Truesdell & Toupin 1960) is defined as the scalar product of $\mathbf{U}_I$ by $\mathbf{n}$:

$$\mathbf{U}_I \cdot \mathbf{n} = \frac{-\,\partial f/\partial t}{|\nabla f|} \tag{1.2.5}$$

This equation shows that the projection of $\mathbf{U}_I$ on the normal vector depends only on the surface equation expressed by [1.2.3]. Equation [1.2.5] is unique, whereas [1.2.2] depends on the choice of u and v.

Leibniz Rule

Consider a geometric volume $V(t)$ that is moving in space (figure 1.2.1) and is bounded by a closed surface $A(t)$. At a given point on this surface $\mathbf{n}$ is the unit

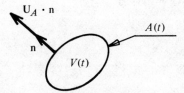

Figure 1.2.1   Geometric volume moving in space.

normal vector outwardly directed. The speed of displacement of the surface at that point is denoted $\mathbf{U}_A \cdot \mathbf{n}$. The Leibniz rule (Truesdell & Toupin 1960; Whitaker 1968; Slattery 1972; Germain 1973) enables the time rate of change of a volume integral to be transformed into the sum of a volume integral and a surface integral:

$$\frac{d}{dt} \int_{V(t)} f(x, y, z, t) \, dV = \int_{V(t)} \frac{\partial f}{\partial t} \, dV + \oint_{A(T)} f \mathbf{U}_A \cdot \mathbf{n} \, dA \qquad [1.2.6]$$

Note that $V(t)$ is a geometric volume, not necessarily a material one. If $V(t)$ is a material volume the Leibniz rule reduces to the Reynolds transport theorem [1.1.7].

Gauss Theorems

Consider the geometric volume in figure 1.2.2. This volume, bounded by surface A, is material or not, moving of not. At a given point on A, the unit normal vector $\mathbf{n}$ is outwardly directed. Let $\mathbf{B}$ and $\mathbf{M}$ be vector and tensor fields. The Gauss theorems enable a surface integral to be transformed into a volume integral according to the relations:

$$\oint_A \mathbf{n} \cdot \mathbf{B} \, dA = \int_V \nabla \cdot \mathbf{B} \, dV \qquad [1.2.7]$$

$$\oint_A \mathbf{n} \cdot \mathbf{M} \, dA = \int_V \nabla \cdot \mathbf{M} \, dV \qquad [1.2.8]$$

1.2.1.2 Integral Balances

Consider a fixed control volume V cut by an interface $A_I(t)$. This interface divides the control volume V into subvolumes $V_1(t)$ and $V_2(t)$, respectively, bounded by surfaces $A_1(t)$ and $A_I(t)$, $A_2(t)$ and $A_I(t)$ (figure 1.2.3). We postulate the following balance laws for the control volume V. For the sake of simplicity we do not introduce surface tension here.

Mass

The time rate of change of mass contained in the control volume V is equal to the net influx of mass into V through the boundary surface A:

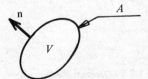

Figure 1.2.2 Geometric volume.

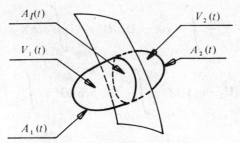

Figure 1.2.3 Fixed volume cut by an interface.

$$\frac{d}{dt} \int_{V_1(t)} \rho_1 \, dV + \frac{d}{dt} \int_{V_2(t)} \rho_2 \, dV = - \int_{A_1(t)} \rho_1 U_1 \cdot n_1 \, dA$$

$$- \int_{A_2(t)} \rho_2 U_2 \cdot n_2 \, dA \qquad\qquad [1.2.9]$$

where ρ_k and U_k are the density and the velocity vector of phase $k(k = 1, 2)$.

Linear Momentum

The time rate of change of linear momentum in the control volume V is equal to the sum of (1) the net influx of momentum into V through the boundary surface A and (2) the resultant of the external forces acting on V and A. These forces are composed of volume forces (i.e., gravity forces) and surface forces (i.e., stress tensor):

$$\frac{d}{dt} \int_{V_1(t)} \rho_1 U_1 \, dV + \frac{d}{dt} \int_{V_2(t)} \rho_2 U_2 \, dV = - \int_{A_1(t)} \rho_1 U_1 (U_1 \cdot n_1) \, dA$$

$$- \int_{A_2(t)} \rho_2 U_2 (U_2 \cdot n_2) \, dA + \int_{V_1(t)} \rho_1 b \, dV + \int_{V_2(t)} \rho_2 b \, dV$$

$$+ \int_{A_1(t)} n_1 \cdot T_1 \, dA + \int_{A_2(t)} n_2 \cdot T_2 \, dA \qquad\qquad [1.2.10]$$

where b is the external force per unit mass and T the stress tensor.

Angular Momentum

The time rate of change of angular momentum in the control volume V is equal to the sum of (1) the net influx of angular momentum into V through the boundary surface A and (2) the resultant of the external torques acting on V and A:

$$\frac{d}{dt} \int_{V_1(t)} \mathbf{r} \times \rho_1 \mathbf{U}_1 \, dV + \frac{d}{dt} \int_{V_2(t)} \mathbf{r} \times \rho_2 \mathbf{U}_2 \, dV = - \int_{A_1(t)} \mathbf{r} \times \rho_1 \mathbf{U}_1 (\mathbf{U}_1 \cdot \mathbf{n}_1) \, dA$$

$$- \int_{A_2(t)} \mathbf{r} \times \rho_2 \mathbf{U}_2 (\mathbf{U}_2 \cdot \mathbf{n}_2) \, dA + \int_{V_1(t)} \mathbf{r} \times \rho_1 \mathbf{b} \, dV + \int_{V_2(t)} \mathbf{r} \times \rho_2 \mathbf{b} \, dV$$

$$+ \int_{A_1(t)} \mathbf{r} \times (\mathbf{n}_1 \cdot \mathbf{T}_1) \, dA + \int_{A_2(t)} \mathbf{r} \times (\mathbf{n}_2 \cdot \mathbf{T}_2) \, dA \qquad [1.2.11]$$

where $\mathbf{r}$ is the position vector.

Total Energy

The time rate of change of total energy (kinetic energy and internal energy) in the control volume V is equal to the sum of (1) the net influx of total energy into V through the boundary surface A, (2) the power of the external forces acting on V and A, and (3) the heat flux entering V through A:

$$\frac{d}{dt} \int_{V_1(t)} \rho_1 \left(\frac{1}{2} \mathbf{U}_1^2 + u_1 \right) dV + \frac{d}{dt} \int_{V_2(t)} \rho_2 \left(\frac{1}{2} \mathbf{U}_2^2 + u_2 \right) dV$$

$$= - \int_{A_1(t)} \rho_1 \left(\frac{1}{2} \mathbf{U}_1^2 + u_1 \right) \mathbf{U}_1 \cdot \mathbf{n}_1 \, dA - \int_{A_2(t)} \rho_2 \left(\frac{1}{2} \mathbf{U}_2^2 + u_2 \right) \mathbf{U}_2 \cdot \mathbf{n}_2 \, dA$$

$$+ \int_{V_1(t)} \rho_1 \mathbf{b} \cdot \mathbf{U}_1 \, dV + \int_{V_2(t)} \rho_2 \mathbf{b} \cdot \mathbf{U}_2 \, dV$$

$$+ \int_{A_1(t)} (\mathbf{n}_1 \cdot \mathbf{T}_1) \cdot \mathbf{U}_1 \, dA + \int_{A_2(t)} (\mathbf{n}_2 \cdot \mathbf{T}_2) \cdot \mathbf{U}_2 \, dA$$

$$- \int_{A_1(t)} \mathbf{q}_1 \cdot \mathbf{n}_1 \, dA - \int_{A_2(t)} \mathbf{q}_2 \cdot \mathbf{n}_2 \, dA \qquad [1.2.12]$$

where u is the internal energy per unit mass and $\mathbf{q}$ is the heat flux.

Entropy

The time rate of change of entropy in the control volume V is equal to the sum of (1) the net influx of entropy into V through the boundary surface A due to the mass flow, (2) the net influx of entropy into V due to conduction through A, and (3) the entropy source within V:

$$\frac{d}{dt} \int_{V_1(t)} \rho_1 s_1 \, dV + \frac{d}{dt} \int_{V_2(t)} \rho_2 s_2 \, dV$$

$$+ \int_{A_1(t)} \rho_1 s_1 \mathbf{U}_1 \cdot \mathbf{n}_1 \, dA + \int_{A_2(t)} \rho_2 s_2 \mathbf{U}_2 \cdot \mathbf{n}_2 \, dA$$

$$+ \int_{A_1(t)} \frac{1}{T_1} \mathbf{q}_1 \cdot \mathbf{n}_1 \, dA + \int_{A_2(t)} \frac{1}{T_2} \mathbf{q}_2 \cdot \mathbf{n}_2 \, dA$$

$$= \int_{V_1(t)} \Delta_1 \, dV + \int_{V_2(t)} \Delta_2 \, dV + \int_{A_I} \Delta_I \, dA \geqslant 0 \qquad [1.2.13]$$

where equality occurs when the evolution is reversible. In [1.2.13] s_k is the entropy per unit mass, T_k is the absolute temperature, and Δ_k is the local entropy source per unit volume and per unit of time within each phase and Δ_I is the local entropy source per unit of area and per unit of time.

As [1.2.13] is verified whatever $V_1(t)$, $V_2(t)$ and A_I are, then

$$\Delta_k \geqslant 0 \qquad (k = 1, 2) \qquad \Delta_I \geqslant 0 \qquad [1.2.14]$$

Generalized Integral Balance

Integral balances [1.2.9]-1.2.13] can be rewritten in the following condensed form:

$$\sum_{k=1,2} \frac{d}{dt} \int_{V_k(t)} \rho_k \psi_k \, dV = - \sum_{k=1,2} \int_{A_k(t)} \rho_k \psi_k (\mathbf{U}_k \cdot \mathbf{n}_k) \, dA$$

$$+ \sum_{k=1,2} \int_{V_k(t)} \rho_k \phi_k \, dV - \sum_{k=1,2} \int_{A_k(t)} \mathbf{n}_k \cdot \mathbf{J}_k \, dA + \int_{A_I(t)} \phi_I \, dA \qquad [1.2.15]$$

For each balance law, the values of specific quantity ψ_k, flux term $\mathbf{J}_k$, source term ϕ_k, and ϕ_I are given in table 1.2.1. where $\mathbf{R}$ is the antisymmetric tensor corresponding to vector $\mathbf{r}$ (Aris 1962).

1.2.1.3   Transformation of the Integral Balance

The integral balance law [1.2.15] is transformed by means of the Leibniz rule [1.2.6] and the Gauss theorems [1.2.7] and [1.2.8] into the form

Table 1.2.1 Values of ψ_k, $\mathbf{J}_k$, ϕ_k, and ϕ_I for Integral Balances

Balance	ψ_k	$\mathbf{J}_k$	ϕ_k	ϕ_I
Mass	1	0	0	0
Linear momentum	$\mathbf{U}_k$	$-\mathbf{T}_k$	$\mathbf{b}$	0
Angular momentum	$\mathbf{r} \times \mathbf{U}_k$	$-\mathbf{T}_k \cdot \mathbf{R}$	$\mathbf{r} \times \mathbf{b}$	0
Total energy	$u_k + \frac{1}{2}\mathbf{U}_k^2$	$\mathbf{q}_k - \mathbf{T}_k \cdot \mathbf{U}_k$	$\mathbf{b} \cdot \mathbf{U}_k$	0
Entropy	s_k	$\dfrac{1}{T_k}\mathbf{q}_k$	$\dfrac{1}{\rho_k}\Delta_k$	Δ_I

$$\sum_{k=1,2} \int_{V_k(t)} \left[\frac{\partial}{\partial t}\rho_k\psi_k + \nabla \cdot (\rho_k\psi_k\mathbf{U}_k) + \nabla \cdot \mathbf{J}_k - \rho_k\phi_k \right] dV$$

$$+ \int_{A_I(k)} \left(\sum_{k=1,2} \dot{m}_k\psi_k + \mathbf{n}_k \cdot \mathbf{J}_k + \phi_I \right) dA = 0 \qquad [1.2.16]$$

with
$$\dot{m}_k \triangleq \rho_k(\mathbf{U}_k - \mathbf{U}_I) \cdot \mathbf{n}_k \qquad [1.2.17]$$

where $\dot{m}_k$ is the mass transfer per unit area of interface and per unit time. Equation [1.2.16] has to be satisfied for any $V_k(t)$ and $A_I(t)$. Thus, the local instantaneous phase equation is

$$\frac{\partial}{\partial t}\rho_k\psi_k + \nabla \cdot (\rho_k\psi_k\mathbf{U}_k) + \nabla \cdot \mathbf{J}_k - \rho_k\phi_k = 0 \qquad [1.2.18]$$

and the local instantaneous jump condition is

$$\sum_{k=1,2} \dot{m}_k\psi_k + \mathbf{n}_k \cdot \mathbf{J}_k + \phi_I = 0 \qquad [1.2.19]$$

For each local instantaneous balance law, the values of ψ_k, $\mathbf{J}_k$, ϕ_k, and ϕ_I are given in table 1.2.1.

1.2.1.4 Phase Equations

Primary Equations

Mass

$$\frac{\partial\rho_k}{\partial t} + \nabla \cdot (\rho_k\mathbf{U}_k) = 0 \qquad [1.2.20]$$

Linear momentum

$$\frac{\partial\rho_k\mathbf{U}_k}{\partial t} + \nabla \cdot (\rho_k\mathbf{U}_k\mathbf{U}_k) - \rho_k\mathbf{b} - \nabla \cdot \mathbf{T}_k = 0 \qquad [1.2.21]$$

Angular momentum This balance law does not supply any new local instantaneous equation. It simplifies to the relation

$$\mathbf{T}_k = \mathbf{T}_k^t \tag{1.2.22}$$

where $\mathbf{T}_k^t$ is the transposed form of tensor $\mathbf{T}_k$. The stress tensor is thus symmetrical.

Total energy

$$\frac{\partial}{\partial t}\left[\rho_k\left(\frac{1}{2}\mathbf{U}_k^2 + u_k\right)\right] + \nabla \cdot \left[\rho_k\left(\frac{1}{2}\mathbf{U}_k^2 + u_k\right)\mathbf{U}_k\right]$$

$$- \rho_k\mathbf{b} \cdot \mathbf{U}_k - \nabla \cdot (\mathbf{T}_k \cdot \mathbf{U}_k) + \nabla \cdot \mathbf{q}_k = 0 \tag{1.2.23}$$

Entropy inequality

$$\frac{\partial}{\partial t}(\rho_k s_k) + \nabla \cdot (\rho_k s_k \mathbf{U}_k) + \nabla \cdot \left(\frac{1}{T_k}\mathbf{q}_k\right) = \Delta_k \geqslant 0 \tag{1.2.24}$$

Secondary Equations

Mechanical energy equation Multiplying the momentum equation [1.2.21] by $\mathbf{U}_k$, we get

$$\frac{\partial}{\partial t}\left(\frac{1}{2}\rho_k\mathbf{U}_k^2\right) + \nabla \cdot \left(\frac{1}{2}\rho_k\mathbf{U}_k^2\mathbf{U}_k\right) - \rho_k\mathbf{b} \cdot \mathbf{U}_k$$

$$- \nabla \cdot (\mathbf{T}_k \cdot \mathbf{U}_k) + \mathbf{T}_k : \nabla\mathbf{U}_k = 0 \tag{1.2.25}$$

Internal energy Subtracting the mechanical energy equation [1.2.25] from the total energy equation [1.2.23], we obtain

$$\frac{\partial}{\partial t}(\rho_k u_k) + \nabla \cdot (\rho_k u_k \mathbf{U}_k) + \nabla \cdot \mathbf{q}_k - \mathbf{T}_k : \nabla\mathbf{U}_k = 0 \tag{1.2.26}$$

Enthalpy Introducing the specific enthalpy h_k and the viscous stress tensor τ_k:

$$u_k = h_k - \frac{p_k}{\rho_k} \tag{1.2.27}$$

$$\mathbf{T}_k = -p_k\,\mathbf{U} + \tau_k \tag{1.2.28}$$

where p_k is the pressure within phase k and $\mathbf{U}$ is the unit tensor. Equation [1.2.26] then reads

$$\frac{\partial}{\partial t}(\rho_k h_k - p_k) + \nabla \cdot (\rho_k h_k \mathbf{U}_k) - \mathbf{U}_k \cdot \nabla p_k$$

$$+ \nabla \cdot \mathbf{q}_k - \tau_k : \nabla\mathbf{U}_k = 0 \tag{1.2.29}$$

Entropy Recall the fundamental thermodynamic equation (Callen 1960):

$$u_k = u_k(s_k, \rho_k) \tag{1.2.30}$$

and the definitions of pressure and temperature:

$$p_k \stackrel{\Delta}{=} \rho_k^2 \left(\frac{\partial u_k}{\partial \rho_k}\right)_{s_k} \tag{1.2.31}$$

$$T_k \stackrel{\Delta}{=} \left(\frac{\partial u_k}{\partial s_k}\right)_{\rho_k} \tag{1.2.32}$$

Equations [1.2.30]–[1.2.32] lead directly to the Gibbs equation:

$$\frac{du_k}{dt} = T_k \frac{ds_k}{dt} - p_k \frac{d}{dt}\left(\frac{1}{\rho_k}\right) \tag{1.2.33}$$

This equation is used to transform the internal energy equation [1.2.26] into an entropy equation. By taking into account the mass balance [1.2.20] and the definition of the Lagrangian derivative:

$$\frac{d}{dt} \stackrel{\Delta}{=} \frac{\partial}{\partial t} + \mathbf{U}_k \cdot \mathbf{V} \tag{1.2.36}$$

[1.2.26] is transformed into

$$\rho_k \frac{du_k}{dt} + \mathbf{V} \cdot \mathbf{q}_k - \mathbf{T}_k : \mathbf{V}\, \mathbf{U}_k = 0$$

or, with [1.2.28],

$$\rho_k \frac{du_k}{dt} + \mathbf{V} \cdot \mathbf{q}_k + p_k \mathbf{V} \cdot \mathbf{U}_k - \tau_k : \mathbf{V}\mathbf{U}_k = 0 \tag{1.2.35}$$

On the other hand, the Gibbs equation can be rewritten by means of [1.2.20] and [1.2.34]:

$$\frac{du_k}{dt} = T_k \frac{ds_k}{dt} - \frac{p_k}{\rho_k} \mathbf{V} \cdot \mathbf{U}_k \tag{1.2.36}$$

Combining [1.2.35] and [1.2.36]:

$$\rho_k \frac{ds_k}{dt} + \mathbf{V} \cdot \left(\frac{1}{T_k} \mathbf{q}_k\right) - \mathbf{q}_k \cdot \mathbf{V} \frac{1}{T_k} - \frac{1}{T_k} \tau_k : \mathbf{V}\mathbf{U}_k = 0 \tag{1.2.37}$$

Entropy Source

By means of the mass balance [1.2.20] and the definition of the Lagrangian derivative [1.2.34], the entropy inequality [1.2.24] becomes

$$\rho_k \frac{ds_k}{dt} + \mathbf{V} \cdot \left(\frac{1}{T_k} \mathbf{q}_k\right) = \Delta_k \geqslant 0 \tag{1.2.38}$$

Equating [1.2.37] and [1.2.38], we have the expression for the entropy source;

$$\Delta_k = q_k \cdot \nabla \frac{1}{T_k} + \frac{1}{T_k} \tau_k : \nabla U_k \geqslant 0 \qquad [1.2.39]$$

1.2.1.5 Primary Jump Conditions

Mass

$$\rho_1(U_1 - U_I) \cdot n_1 + \rho_2(U_2 - U_I) \cdot n_2 = 0 \qquad [1.2.40]$$

or
$$\dot{m}_1 + \dot{m}_2 = 0 \qquad [1.2.41]$$

with
$$\dot{m}_k \overset{\Delta}{=} \rho_k(U_k - U_I) \cdot n_k \qquad [1.2.42]$$

If there is no mass transfer we have

$$\dot{m}_1 \equiv \dot{m}_2 \equiv 0 \qquad [1.2.43]$$

and consequently
$$(U_1 - U_I) \cdot n_1 = 0 \qquad [1.2.44]$$

$$(U_2 - U_I) \cdot n_2 = 0 \qquad [1.2.45]$$

Eliminating the interface displacement velocity:

$$(U_1 - U_2) \cdot n_1 = 0 \qquad [1.2.46]$$

Resolving U_1 and U_2 into their normal and tangential components:

$$U_1 = (U_1 \cdot n_1)n_1 + U_1^t \qquad [1.2.47]$$

$$U_2 = (U_2 \cdot n_2)n_2 + U_2^t \qquad [1.2.48]$$

If there is no relative tangential velocity between the phases at the interface (section 1.2.1.8), for a justification of this hypothesis then

$$U_1^t \equiv U_2^t \qquad [1.2.49]$$

which, taking [1.2.46]–[1.2.49] into account, gives

$$U_1 \equiv U_2 \qquad [1.2.50]$$

Linear Momentum

In the absence of surface tension we thus have

$$\dot{m}_1 U_1 + \dot{m}_2 U_2 - n_1 \cdot T_1 - n_2 \cdot T_2 = 0 \qquad [1.2.51]$$

or, taking into account the mass balance [1.2.43],

$$\dot{m}_1(U_1 - U_2) - n_1 \cdot T_1 - n_2 \cdot T_2 = 0 \qquad [1.2.52]$$

Inviscid phases The stress tensor simplifies to the pressure term only. Therefore [1.2.52] becomes

$$\dot{m}_1(\mathbf{U}_1 - \mathbf{U}_2) + (p_1 - p_2)\mathbf{n}_1 = 0 \qquad [1.2.53]$$

Separating the normal and tangential components of $\mathbf{U}_k$ we have

$$\dot{m}_1(\mathbf{U}_1^n - \mathbf{U}_2^n) + \dot{m}_1(\mathbf{U}_1^t - \mathbf{U}_2^t) + (p_1 - p_2)\mathbf{n}_1 = 0 \qquad [1.2.54]$$

with $$\qquad\qquad\qquad \mathbf{U}_k = \mathbf{U}_k^n + \mathbf{U}_k^t \qquad [1.2.55]$$

Resolving [1.2.54] into normal and tangential components gives

$$\dot{m}_1(\mathbf{U}_1^n - \mathbf{U}_2^n) + (p_1 - p_2)\mathbf{n}_1 = 0 \qquad [1.2.56]$$

$$\mathbf{U}_1^t = \mathbf{U}_2^t \qquad [1.2.57]$$

Therefore, if there is mass transfer between two inviscid fluids there is no relative tangential velocity at the interface.

Viscous phases Consider a one-dimensional flow in which the interface is perpendicular to the flow direction (figure 1.2.4). The momentum jump condition [1.2.52] reads

$$\dot{m}_1(\mathbf{U}_1 - \mathbf{U}_2) + (p_1 - p_2)\mathbf{n}_1 + (\tau_2 - \tau_1) \cdot \mathbf{n}_1 = 0 \qquad [1.2.58]$$

Doing scalar multiplication by $\mathbf{n}_1$ gives

$$\dot{m}_1(\mathbf{U}_1 - \mathbf{U}_2) \cdot \mathbf{n}_1 + (p_1 - p_2) + [(\tau_2 - \tau_1) \cdot \mathbf{n}_1] \cdot \mathbf{n}_1 = 0 \qquad [1.2.59]$$

Since the flow is assumed to be one-dimensional, the mass balance in phase k, which is assumed to be incompressible, is simplified to

$$\frac{dU_{kx}}{dx} \equiv 0 \qquad [1.2.60]$$

where U_{kx} is the x component of $\mathbf{U}_k$. Consequently,

$$\tau_k \equiv 0 \qquad [1.2.61]$$

The momentum jump condition [1.2.59] is therefore simplified to

$$\dot{m}_1(\mathbf{U}_1 - \mathbf{U}_2) \cdot \mathbf{n}_1 + p_1 - p_2 = 0 \qquad [1.2.62]$$

But since from [1.2.42]

$$\left(\frac{1}{\rho_1} - \frac{1}{\rho_2}\right)\dot{m}_1 = (\mathbf{U}_1 - \mathbf{U}_2) \cdot \mathbf{n}_1 \qquad [1.2.63]$$

[1.2.62] leads to

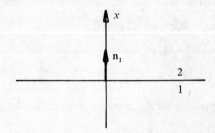

Figure 1.2.4 One-dimensional flow.

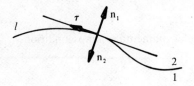

Figure 1.2.5 Two-dimensional flow.

$$p_1 - p_2 = \frac{\rho_1 - \rho_2}{\rho_1 \rho_2} \dot{m}_1^2 \qquad [1.2.64]$$

The pressure is therefore higher in the denser fluid, whatever the transfer sense ($\dot{m}_1 \lesseqgtr 0$). This conclusion is sometimes forgotten in the study of hydrodynamics of liquid films with interfacial phase change. This point was discussed by Spindler et al. (1979).

Two-dimensional case with surface tension If surface tension σ is taken into account, the integral balances for momentum and energy must include surface tension effects. The general three-dimensional derivation of the corresponding jump conditions and a comparison of the results obtained with prior works can be found in Delhaye (1974) and in section 1.4. The two-dimensional momentum jump condition can be derived directly by considering the momentum balance on a portion of interface. It reads

$$\dot{m}_1 \mathbf{U}_1 + \dot{m}_2 \mathbf{U}_2 - \mathbf{n}_1 \cdot \mathbf{T}_1 - \mathbf{n}_2 \cdot \mathbf{T}_2 + \frac{d\sigma}{dl} \tau - \frac{\sigma}{R} \mathbf{n}_1 = 0 \qquad [1.2.65]$$

where R is the radius of curvature, τ the unit tangential vector and l the curvilinear abscissa along the interface (figure 1.2.5).

The fifth term in [1.2.65] expresses the mechanical effects due to surface tension gradients and is responsible for the Marangoni effect (Sterling & Scriven 1959; Kenning 1968; Levich & Krylov 1969). If there is no mass transfer and the phases are inviscid, [1.2.65] becomes

$$(p_1 - p_2)\mathbf{n}_1 + \frac{d\sigma}{dl} \tau - \frac{\sigma}{R} \mathbf{n}_1 = 0 \qquad [1.2.66]$$

This relation implies

$$\frac{d\sigma}{dl} = 0 \qquad [1.2.67]$$

which is not the general case. Consequently, in the absence of phase change, the hypothesis of inviscid phases is not consistent with the presence of surface tension gradients. If the phases are viscous, the surface tension gradients necessarily induce fluid motions. If the surface tension is constant, the momentum jump condition [1.2.66] simplifies to

$$p_1 - p_2 = \frac{\sigma}{R} \qquad [1.2.68]$$

which is the well-known Laplace law.

Angular Momentum

No new information is afforded by the angular momentum jump condition.

Total Energy

$$\dot{m}_1(u_1 + \tfrac{1}{2} \mathbf{U}_1^2) + \dot{m}_2(u_2 + \tfrac{1}{2} \mathbf{U}_2^2) + \mathbf{q}_1 \cdot \mathbf{n}_1 + \mathbf{q}_2 \cdot \mathbf{n}_2$$
$$- (\mathbf{n}_1 \cdot \mathbf{T}_1) \cdot \mathbf{U}_1 - (\mathbf{n}_2 \cdot \mathbf{T}_2) \cdot \mathbf{U}_2 = 0 \qquad [1.2.69]$$

Entropy Inequality

$$\Delta_I = - \dot{m}_1 s_1 - \dot{m}_2 s_2 - \frac{1}{T_1} \mathbf{q}_1 \cdot \mathbf{n}_1 - \frac{1}{T_2} \mathbf{q}_2 \cdot \mathbf{n}_2 \geqslant 0 \qquad [1.2.70]$$

1.2.1.6 Secondary Jump Conditions

Mechanical Energy

A mechanical energy jump condition can be derived by multiplying the momentum jump condition [1.2.51] by the velocity $\mathbf{U}_p$ of the interfacial fluid particles, whose normal component is the speed of displacement of the interface:

$$\mathbf{U}_p = (\mathbf{U}_I \cdot \mathbf{n}_k) \, \mathbf{n}_k - \mathbf{U}^t \qquad [1.2.71]$$

where $\mathbf{U}^t$ is the tangential component of $\mathbf{U}_p$. Equation [1.2.51] becomes

$$\dot{m}_1 \mathbf{U}_1 \cdot \mathbf{U}_p + \dot{m}_2 \mathbf{U}_2 \cdot \mathbf{U}_p - (\mathbf{n}_1 \cdot \mathbf{T}_1) \cdot \mathbf{U}_p - (\mathbf{n}_2 \cdot \mathbf{T}_2) \cdot \mathbf{U}_p = 0 \qquad [1.2.72]$$

Internal Energy

Subtracting the mechanical energy jump condition [1.2.72] from the total energy jump condition [1.2.69] gives

$$\dot{m}_1 [u_1 + \tfrac{1}{2} (\mathbf{U}_1 - \mathbf{U}_p)^2] + \dot{m}_2 [u_2 + \tfrac{1}{2} (\mathbf{U}_2 - \mathbf{U}_p)^2] + \mathbf{q}_1 \cdot \mathbf{n}_1 + \mathbf{q}_2 \cdot \mathbf{n}_2$$
$$- (\mathbf{n}_1 \cdot \mathbf{T}_1) \cdot (\mathbf{U}_1 - \mathbf{U}_p) - (\mathbf{n}_2 \cdot \mathbf{T}_2) \cdot (\mathbf{U}_2 - \mathbf{U}_p) = 0 \qquad [1.2.73]$$

In contrast to the phase equation derivation, the kinetic energy of each phase is not eliminated here. In fact, the method used here enables the interface kinetic energy to be eliminated when the interfacial thermodynamic properties are taken into account (Delhaye 1974).

Enthalpy

From the definition [1.2.42] of $\dot{m}_k$ we derive the identity

$$\mathbf{U}_k - \mathbf{U}_p = \frac{\dot{m}_k}{\rho_k} \mathbf{n}_k + \mathbf{U}_k^t - \mathbf{U}^t \qquad [1.2.74]$$

where $\mathbf{U}_k^t$ is the tangential component of $\mathbf{U}_k$. Taking into account the definitions of the enthalpy [1.2.27] and the stress tensor [1.2.28], [1.2.73] combined with [1.2.74] can be transformed into

$$\dot{m}_1 \left[h_1 + \frac{1}{2}(U_1 - U_p)^2 - \frac{1}{\rho_1}(\tau_1 \cdot n_1) \cdot n_1 \right]$$

$$+ \dot{m}_2 \left[h_2 + \frac{1}{2}(U_2 - U_p)^2 - \frac{1}{\rho_2}(\tau_2 \cdot n_2) \cdot n_2 \right] + q_1 \cdot n_1 + q_2 \cdot n_2$$

$$- (\tau_1 \cdot n_1) \cdot (U_1^t - U^t) - (\tau_2 \cdot n_2) \cdot (U_2^t - U^t) = 0 \qquad [1.2.75]$$

Entropy

To transform the enthalpy jump condition [1.2.75] into an entropy jump condition, we introduce the free enthalpy g_k of each phase:

$$g_k \overset{\Delta}{=} h_k - T_k s_k \qquad [1.2.76]$$

Equation [1.2.75] then becomes

$$\dot{m}_1 \left[T_1 s_1 + g_1 + \frac{1}{2}(U_1 - U_p)^2 - \frac{1}{\rho_1}(\tau_1 \cdot n_1) \cdot n_1 \right]$$

$$+ \dot{m}_2 \left[T_2 s_2 + g_2 + \frac{1}{2}(U_2 - U_p)^2 - \frac{1}{\rho_2}(\tau_2 \cdot n_2) \cdot n_2 \right] + q_1 \cdot n_1 + q_2 \cdot n_2$$

$$- (\tau_1 \cdot n_1) \cdot (U_1^t - U^t) - (\tau_2 \cdot n_2) \cdot (U_2^t - U^t) = 0 \qquad [1.2.77]$$

1.2.1.7 Interfacial Entropy Source

To combine the entropy inequality [1.2.70] with the entropy equation [1.2.77] we introduce an arbitrary temperature T_I, which appears to be the interface temperature when the interface thermodynamic properties are taken into account (Delhaye 1974; Ishii 1974). This leads to the following expression for the entropy source:

$$\Delta_I = \sum_{k=1,2} \left\{ \frac{\dot{m}_k}{T_I} \left[g_k + \frac{1}{2}(U_k - U_p)^2 - \frac{1}{\rho_k}(\tau_k \cdot n_k) \cdot n_k \right] \right.$$

$$\left. + (q_k \cdot n_k + \dot{m}_k s_k T_k)\left(\frac{1}{T_I} - \frac{1}{T_k}\right) - \frac{1}{T_I}(\tau_k \cdot n_k) \cdot (U_k^t - U^t) \right\} \qquad [1.2.78]$$

1.2.1.8 Interfacial Boundary Conditions

Assume that the interface transfers are reversible. The entropy source Δ_I must be equal to zero whatever the mass flux, viscous stress tensors, and heat fluxes are. We then deduce the following interfacial boundary conditions.

Thermal Boundary Condition

$$T_1 \stackrel{\cdot}{=} T_2 \equiv T_I \qquad\qquad [1.2.79]$$

Mechanical Boundary Condition

$$\mathbf{U}_1^t \stackrel{\cdot}{=} \mathbf{U}_2^t \equiv \mathbf{U}^t \qquad\qquad [1.2.80]$$

Phase Change Boundary Condition

$$g_1 - g_2 = \frac{1}{2}(\mathbf{U}_2 - \mathbf{U}_p)^2 - \frac{1}{2}(\mathbf{U}_1 - \mathbf{U}_p)^2$$

$$- \left[\frac{1}{\rho_2}(\tau_2 \cdot \mathbf{n}_2) \cdot \mathbf{n}_2 - \frac{1}{\rho_1}(\tau_1 \cdot \mathbf{n}_1) \cdot \mathbf{n}_1 \right] \qquad [1.2.81]$$

which can be written by use of [1.2.74] and [1.2.80]:

$$g_1 - g_2 = \frac{1}{2}\dot{m}_k\left(\frac{1}{\rho_2^2} - \frac{1}{\rho_1^2}\right) - \left[\frac{1}{\rho_2}(\tau_2 \cdot \mathbf{n}_2) \cdot \mathbf{n}_2 - \frac{1}{\rho_1}(\tau_1 \cdot \mathbf{n}_1) \cdot \mathbf{n}_1 \right] \qquad [1.2.82]$$

1.2.2   INSTANTANEOUS, SPACE–AVERAGED EQUATIONS

Space-averaged equations for two-phase flow were derived by Delhaye (1968) and Vernier & Delhaye (1968), following an article by Birkhoff (1964) on the errors to be avoided when setting up such equations for single-phase flow. The most thorough study of these equations and their application to a problem of liquid film hydrodynamics, within the frame of a two-fluid model, is in Kocamustafaogullari's thesis (1971).

1.2.2.1   Mathematical Tools

Limiting Forms of the Leibniz and Gauss Theorems for a Volume

Consider a fixed tube with axis Oz (unit vector $\mathbf{n}_z$) in which a volume V_k^* is cut by two cross-sectional planes located a distance Z apart over area A_{k1} and A_{k2} (figure 1.2.6). Let V_k be the volume limited by A_{k1}, A_{k2}, and the portions A_I and A_{kW} of interface and wall enclosed between the two cross-sectional planes. The unit vector normal to the interface and directed away from phase k is denoted by $\mathbf{n}_k$. The cross-sectional planes limiting the volume V_k are not necessarily fixed and their speeds of displacement are denoted by $-\mathbf{U}_{Ak1} \cdot \mathbf{n}_z$ and $\mathbf{U}_{Ak2} \cdot \mathbf{n}_z$.

Leibniz rule   The Leibniz rule applied to volume V_k leads to

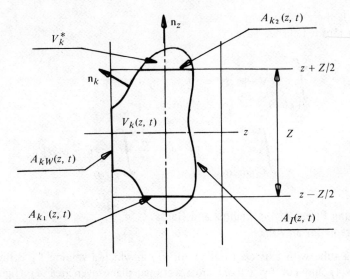

Figure 1.2.6   Volume cut by two cross-sectional planes.

$$\frac{\partial}{\partial t} \int_{V_k(z,t)} f(x, y, z, t)\, dV = \int_{V_k(z,t)} \frac{\partial f}{\partial t}\, dV + \int_{A_I(z,t)} f\mathbf{U}_I \cdot \mathbf{n}_k\, dA$$

$$- \int_{A_{k_1}(z,t)} f\mathbf{U}_{Ak_1} \cdot \mathbf{n}_z\, dA + \int_{A_{k_2}(z,t)} f\mathbf{U}_{Ak_2} \cdot \mathbf{n}_z\, dA \qquad [1.2.83]$$

where $\mathbf{U}_I \cdot \mathbf{n}_k$ is the speed of displacement of the interface A_I.

Gauss theorems   The Gauss theorems applied to volume V_k leads to

$$\int_{V_k(z,t)} \nabla \cdot \mathbf{B}\, dV = \int_{A_I(z,t)} \mathbf{n}_k \cdot \mathbf{B}\, dA + \int_{A_{kW}(z,t)} \mathbf{n}_k \cdot \mathbf{B}\, dA$$

$$- \int_{A_{k_1}(z,t)} \mathbf{n}_z \cdot \mathbf{B}\, dA + \int_{A_{k_2}(z,t)} \mathbf{n}_z \cdot \mathbf{B}\, dA \qquad [1.2.84]$$

which yields

$$\int_{V_k(z,t)} \nabla \cdot \mathbf{B}\, dV = \int_{A_I(z,t)} \mathbf{n}_k \cdot \mathbf{B}\, dA + \int_{A_{kW}(z,t)} \mathbf{n}_k \cdot \mathbf{B}\, dA + \frac{\partial}{\partial z} \int_{V_k(z,t)} B_z\, dV$$

$$[1.2.85]$$

where B_z is the z component of $\mathbf{B}$.

For a tensor field we have

$$\int_{V_k(z,t)} \nabla \cdot \mathbf{M} \, dV = \int_{A_I(z,t)} \mathbf{n}_k \cdot \mathbf{M} \, dA$$

$$+ \int_{A_{kW}(z,t)} \mathbf{n}_k \cdot \mathbf{M} \, dA + \frac{\partial}{\partial z} \int_{V_k(z,t)} \mathbf{n}_z \cdot \mathbf{M} \, dV \qquad [1.2.86]$$

Limiting Forms of the Leibniz and Gauss Theorems for an Area

Consider a tube with axis Oz (unit vector $\mathbf{n}_z$) in which a volume V_k is limited by a boundary A_I and cut by a fixed cross-sectional plane over area A_k (figure 1.2.7). The unit vector normal to the interface and directed away from phase k is denoted by $\mathbf{n}_k$. The intersection of interface A_I with the cross-sectional plane is denoted by C. The unit vector normal to C, located in the cross-sectional plane and directed away from phase k, is denoted by $\mathbf{n}_{kC}$.

Leibniz rule

$$\frac{\partial}{\partial t} \int_{A_k(z,t)} f(x, y, z, t) \, dA = \int_{A_k(z,t)} \frac{\partial f}{\partial t} \, dA + \int_{C(z,t)} f \mathbf{U}_I \cdot \mathbf{n}_k \, \frac{dC}{\mathbf{n}_k \cdot \mathbf{n}_{kC}}$$

$$[1.2.87]$$

Gauss theorems   For vector fields we have

$$\int_{A_k(z,t)} \nabla \cdot \mathbf{B} \, dA = \frac{\partial}{\partial z} \int_{A_k(z,t)} B_z \, dA + \int_{C(z,t)} \mathbf{n}_k \cdot \mathbf{B} \, \frac{dC}{\mathbf{n}_k \cdot \mathbf{n}_{kC}} \qquad [1.2.88]$$

If we take $\mathbf{B} = \mathbf{n}_z$ we obtain

$$\frac{\partial A_k(z,t)}{\partial z} = - \int_{C(z,t)} \mathbf{n}_k \cdot \mathbf{n}_z \, \frac{dC}{\mathbf{n}_k \cdot \mathbf{n}_{kC}} \qquad [1.2.89]$$

For tensor fields,

$$\int_{A_k(z,t)} \nabla \cdot \mathbf{M} \, dA = \frac{\partial}{\partial z} \int_{A_k(z,t)} \mathbf{n}_z \cdot \mathbf{M} \, dA + \int_{C(z,t)} \mathbf{n}_k \cdot \mathbf{M} \, \frac{dC}{\mathbf{n}_k \cdot \mathbf{n}_{kC}} \qquad [1.2.90]$$

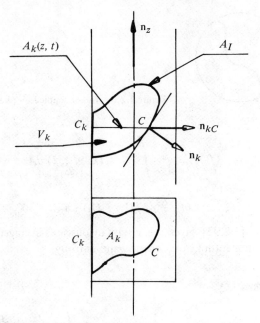

Figure 1.2.7 Volume cut by one cross-sectional plane.

1.2.2.2 Instantaneous Area-averaged Equations

Average the local intantaneous balance equation for phase k over the cross-sectional area occupied by phase k (figure 1.2.8). The local, instantaneous balance equation is integrated over the area $A_k(z,t)$ limited by the boundaries $C(z,t)$ with the other phase and $C_k(z, t)$ with the pipe wall:

$$\int_{A_k(z,t)} \frac{\partial}{\partial t} \rho_k \psi_k \, dA + \int_{A_k(z,t)} \nabla \cdot (\rho_k \psi_k \mathbf{U}_k) \, dA$$

$$+ \int_{A_k(z,t)} \nabla \cdot \mathbf{J}_k \, dA - \int_{A_k(z,t)} \rho_k \phi_k \, dA = 0 \qquad [1.2.91]$$

Applying the limiting forms of the Leibniz rule [1.2.87] and of the Gauss theorems [1.2.88] and [1.2.90], we obtain, since the pipe wall is fixed and impermeable,

$$\frac{\partial}{\partial t} A_k \langle \rho_k \psi_k \rangle_2 + \frac{\partial}{\partial z} A_k \langle \mathbf{n}_z \cdot (\rho_k \psi_k \mathbf{U}_k) \rangle_2 + \frac{\partial}{\partial z} A_k \langle \mathbf{n}_z \cdot \mathbf{J}_k \rangle_2 - A_k \langle \rho_k \phi_k \rangle_2$$

$$= - \int_{C(z,t)} (\dot{m}_k \psi_k + \mathbf{n}_k \cdot \mathbf{J}_k) \frac{dC}{\mathbf{n}_k \cdot \mathbf{n}_{kC}} - \int_{C_k(z,t)} \mathbf{n}_k \cdot \mathbf{J}_k \frac{dC}{\mathbf{n}_k \cdot \mathbf{n}_{kC}} \qquad [1.2.92]$$

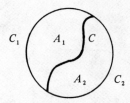

Figure 1.2.8 Areas occupied by phases 1 and 2.

where

$$\langle f_k \rangle_2 \triangleq \frac{1}{A_k} \int_{A_k(z,t)} f_k(x, y, z, t)\, dA \qquad [1.2.93]$$

$$\dot{m}_k \triangleq \rho_k (\mathbf{U}_k - \mathbf{U}_I) \cdot \mathbf{n}_k \qquad [1.2.94]$$

From table 1.2.1, [1.2.92] gives the instantaneous area-averaged equations for the balance of mass, momentum, total energy, and entropy.

Balance of Mass

$$\frac{\partial}{\partial t} A_k \langle \rho_k \rangle_2 + \frac{\partial}{\partial z} A_k \langle \rho_k U_{kz} \rangle_2 = -\int_{C(z,t)} \dot{m}_k \frac{dC}{\mathbf{n}_k \cdot \mathbf{n}_{kC}} \qquad [1.2.95]$$

Balance of Momentum

Splitting the stress tensor $\mathbf{T}_k$ into the pressure term and the viscous stress tensor, we have

$$\frac{\partial}{\partial t} A_k \langle \rho_k \mathbf{U}_k \rangle_2 + \frac{\partial}{\partial z} A_k \langle \rho_k U_{kz} \mathbf{U}_k \rangle_2 - A_k \langle \rho_k \mathbf{b} \rangle_2 + \frac{\partial}{\partial z} A_k \langle p_k \mathbf{n}_z \rangle_2 - \frac{\partial}{\partial z} A_k \langle \mathbf{n}_z \cdot \tau_k \rangle_2$$

$$= -\int_{C(z,t)} (\dot{m}_k \mathbf{U}_k - \mathbf{n}_k \cdot \mathbf{T}_k) \frac{dC}{\mathbf{n}_k \cdot \mathbf{n}_{kC}} + \int_{C_k(z,t)} \mathbf{n}_k \cdot \mathbf{T}_k \frac{dC}{\mathbf{n}_k \cdot \mathbf{n}_{kC}} \qquad [1.2.96]$$

Projecting along the tube axis, we have

$$\frac{\partial}{\partial t} A_k \langle \rho_k U_{kz} \rangle_2 + \frac{\partial}{\partial z} A_k \langle \rho_k U_{kz}^2 \rangle_2 - A_k \langle \rho_k b_z \rangle_2 + \frac{\partial}{\partial z} A_k \langle p_k \rangle_2 - \frac{\partial}{\partial z} A_k \langle (\mathbf{n}_z \cdot \tau_k) \cdot \mathbf{n}_z \rangle_2$$

$$= -\int_{C(z,t)} \mathbf{n}_z \cdot (\dot{m}_k \mathbf{U}_k - \mathbf{n}_k \cdot \mathbf{T}_k) \frac{dC}{\mathbf{n}_k \cdot \mathbf{n}_{kC}} + \int_{C_k(z,t)} \mathbf{n}_z \cdot (\mathbf{n}_k \cdot \mathbf{T}_k) \frac{dC}{\mathbf{n}_k \cdot \mathbf{n}_{kC}}$$

$$[1.2.97]$$

where U_{kz} is the z component of the velocity vector $\mathbf{U}_k$. Assume that the pressure p_k is constant along C and C_k and equal to the averaged pressure $\langle p_k \rangle_2$ over A_k. Then by using [1.2.89], [1.2.97] can be written

$$\frac{\partial}{\partial t} A_k \langle \rho_k U_{kz} \rangle_2 + \frac{\partial}{\partial z} A_k \langle \rho_k U_{kz} \rangle_2 - A_k \langle \rho_k b_z \rangle_2 + A_k \frac{\partial p_k}{\partial z} - \frac{\partial}{\partial z} A_k \langle (\mathbf{n}_z \cdot \tau_k) \cdot \mathbf{n}_z \rangle_2$$

$$= - \int_{C(z,t)} \mathbf{n}_z \cdot (\dot{m}_k U_k - \mathbf{n}_k \cdot \tau_k) \frac{dC}{\mathbf{n}_k \cdot \mathbf{n}_{kC}} + \int_{C_k(z,t)} \mathbf{n}_z \cdot (\mathbf{n}_k \cdot \tau_k) \frac{dC}{\mathbf{n}_k \cdot \mathbf{n}_{kC}}$$

$$[1.2.98]$$

Balance of Total Energy

Introduce the enthalpy h_k per unit of mass:

$$\frac{\partial}{\partial t} A_k \langle \rho_k \left(\frac{1}{2} \mathbf{U}_k^2 + u_k \right) \rangle_2 + \frac{\partial}{\partial z} A_k \langle \rho_k \left(\frac{1}{2} \mathbf{U}_k^2 + h_k \right) U_{kz} \rangle_2 - A_k \langle \rho_k \mathbf{b} \cdot \mathbf{U}_k \rangle_2$$

$$- \frac{\partial}{\partial z} A_k \langle (\tau_k \cdot \mathbf{U}_k) \cdot \mathbf{n}_z \rangle_2 + \frac{\partial}{\partial z} A_k \langle \mathbf{q}_k \cdot \mathbf{n}_z \rangle_2$$

$$= - \int_{C(z,t)} \left[\dot{m}_k \left(\frac{1}{2} \mathbf{U}_k^2 + u_k \right) - (\mathbf{T}_k \cdot \mathbf{U}_k) \cdot \mathbf{n}_k + \mathbf{q}_k \cdot \mathbf{n}_k \right] \frac{dC}{\mathbf{n}_k \cdot \mathbf{n}_{kC}}$$

$$+ \int_{C_k(z,t)} \mathbf{q}_k \cdot \mathbf{n}_k \frac{dC}{\mathbf{n}_k \cdot \mathbf{n}_{kC}}$$

$$[1.2.99]$$

Entropy Inequality

$$\frac{\partial}{\partial t} A_k \langle \rho_k s_k \rangle_2 + \frac{\partial}{\partial z} A_k \langle \rho_k s_k U_{kz} \rangle_2 + \frac{\partial}{\partial z} A_k \langle \frac{1}{T_k} \mathbf{q}_k \cdot \mathbf{n}_z \rangle_2$$

$$+ \int_{C(z,t)} \left(\dot{m}_k s_k + \frac{1}{T_k} \mathbf{q}_k \cdot \mathbf{n}_k \right) \frac{dC}{\mathbf{n}_k \cdot \mathbf{n}_{kC}}$$

$$+ \int_{C_k(z,t)} \frac{1}{T_k} \mathbf{q}_k \cdot \mathbf{n}_k \frac{dC}{\mathbf{n}_k \cdot \mathbf{n}_{kC}} = A_k \langle \Delta_k \rangle_2 \geqslant 0 \qquad [1.2.100]$$

1.2.2.3 Instantaneous Volume-averaged Equations

Transient two-phase flow modeling sometimes requires the solution of a set of partial differential equations written in terms of instantaneous area averages. This set of partial differential equations is usually solved by one of the following techniques:

1. A finite-difference method involving discretization of the partial differential equations over finite-sized meshes and leading to a *distributed* parameter model.
2. A profile method involving integration over a finite length and leading to a *lumped* parameter model.

In essence, both resolution techniques deal with volume-averaged quantities. This section gives the instantaneous volume-averaged equations with which the equations of both models must finally be reconciled.

Assume no mass flow through the wall. The integral balance over $V_k(z, t)$ reads

$$\frac{\partial}{\partial t} \int_{V_k(z,t)} \rho_k \psi_k \, dV = - \int_{A_I(z,t)} \rho_k \psi_k \, (\mathbf{U}_k - \mathbf{U}_I) \cdot \mathbf{n}_k \, dA$$

$$+ \int_{A_{k_1}(z,t)} \rho_k \psi_k \, (\mathbf{U}_k - \mathbf{U}_{Ak1}) \cdot \mathbf{n}_z \, dA - \int_{A_{k_2}(z,t)} \rho_k \psi_k \, (\mathbf{U}_k - \mathbf{U}_{Ak2}) \cdot \mathbf{n}_z \, dA$$

$$- \int_{A_I(z,t)} \mathbf{n}_k \cdot \mathbf{J}_k \, dA - \int_{A_{kW}(z,t)} \mathbf{n}_k \cdot \mathbf{J}_k \, dA$$

$$+ \int_{A_{k_1}(z,t)} \mathbf{n}_z \cdot \mathbf{J}_k \, dA - \int_{A_{k_2}(z,t)} \mathbf{n}_z \cdot \mathbf{J}_k \, dA + \int_{V_k(z,t)} \rho_k \phi_k \, dV \qquad [1.2.101]$$

By taking account of the following definitions:

$$\langle f_k \rangle_3 \triangleq \frac{1}{V_k} \int_{V_k(z,t)} f_k \, dV \qquad [1.2.102]$$

$$\dot{m}_k \triangleq \rho_k \, (\mathbf{U}_k - \mathbf{U}_I) \cdot \mathbf{n}_k \qquad [1.2.103]$$

the integral balance [1.2.101] can be written as

$$\frac{\partial}{\partial t} \underbrace{V_k \langle \rho_k \psi_k \rangle_3}_{①} \quad \underbrace{- V_k \langle \rho_k \phi_k \rangle_3}_{②}$$

$$\left. \begin{array}{l} = \displaystyle\int_{A_{k_1}(z,t)} \mathbf{n}_z \cdot [\rho_k \psi_k \, (\mathbf{U}_k - \mathbf{U}_{Ak1}) + \mathbf{J}_k] \, dA \\[2em] - \displaystyle\int_{A_{k_2}(z,t)} \mathbf{n}_z \cdot [\rho_k \psi_k \, (\mathbf{U}_k - \mathbf{U}_{Ak2}) + \mathbf{J}_k] \, dA \end{array} \right\} ③$$

$$[1.2.104]$$

$$- \int_{A_I(z,t)} (\dot{m}_k \psi_k^* + \mathbf{n}_k \cdot \mathbf{J}_k)\, dA - \int_{A_{kW}(z,t)} \mathbf{n}_k \cdot \mathbf{J}_k\, dA \qquad [1.2.104]$$

$$\underbrace{\hspace{4cm}}_{④} \qquad \underbrace{\hspace{3cm}}_{⑤}$$

The physical significance of [1.2.104] is straightforward: term 1 is the storage of quantity ψ_k inside volume V_k, term 2 is the source of ψ_k inside volume V_k, and terms 3 are the fluxes of ψ_k across the cross-sectional planes. Terms 4 and 5 are the fluxes of ψ_k across the interface and the wall; they are of a particular importance since they are directly connected to the flow pattern through the interfacial area $A_I(z, t)$ and the wall area $A_{kW}(z, t)$ in contact with phase k.

An equivalent form of [1.2.104] is

$$\frac{\partial}{\partial t} V_k \langle \rho_k \psi_k \rangle_3 + \frac{\partial}{\partial z} V_k \langle \rho_k \psi_k U_{kz} + \mathbf{n}_z \cdot \mathbf{J}_k \rangle_3 - V_k \langle \rho_k \phi_k \rangle_3$$

$$= \int_{A_{k2}(z,t)} \rho_k \psi_k \mathbf{U}_{Ak1} \cdot \mathbf{n}_z\, dA - \int_{A_{k1}(z,t)} \rho_k \psi_k \mathbf{U}_{Ak2} \cdot \mathbf{n}_z\, dA$$

$$- \int_{A_I(z,t)} (\dot{m}_k \psi_k + \mathbf{n}_k \cdot \mathbf{J}_k)\, dA - \int_{A_{kW}(z,t)} \mathbf{n}_k \cdot \mathbf{J}\, dA \qquad [1.2.105]$$

where the integrals over A_{k1} and A_{k2} vanish if the cross-sectional planes are fixed. By use of table 1.2.1, [1.2.104] and [1.2.105] give the instantaneous volume-averaged equations for the balances of mass, momentum, total energy, and entropy.

1.2.3 LOCAL, TIME–AVERAGED EQUATIONS

Use of time-averaged local variables in two-phase flows was proposed by Teletov (1958) and reconsidered by Vernier & Delhaye (1968). Ishii (1975) traces the history of the subject in detail and compares the different types of averages used.

For solving two-dimensional or three-dimensional transient problems, the local instantaneous equations can be time-averaged over a time interval $[t - T/2; t + T/2]$. As for single-phase turbulent flow, this time interval $[T]$ must be carefully chosen, large enough compared to the turbulence fluctuations, and small enough compared to the overall flow fluctuations. This is not always possible; a thorough discussion of this complex problem is given by Delhaye & Achard (1977, 1978).

After recalling a few theorems on the derivatives of piecewise continuous functions, we will define a time-averaging operator and obtain the local time-averaged equations.

1.2.3.1 Mathematical Tools

Consider a point in a two-phase flow. Phase k passes this point intermittently, and a function f_k associated with phase k is shown in figure 1.2.9. It is a piecewise continuous function.

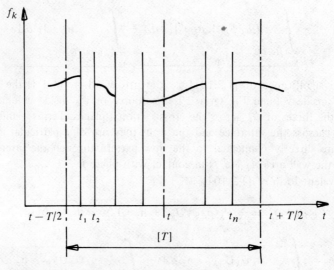

Figure 1.2.9   Function f_k over the time interval $t - T/2$ to $t + T/2$.

Consider the time interval $[t - T/2; \; t + T/2]$. Let $[T_k]$ be the subset of residence time intervals of phase k belonging to the interval $[T]$ and $[T_k]$ the cumulated residence time of phase k in the interval $[T]$.

Limiting Form of the Leibniz Theorem

$$\int_{[T_k]} \frac{\partial f_k}{\partial t} \, dt = \frac{\partial}{\partial t} \int_{[T_k]} f_k \, dt - \sum_{\substack{\text{disc} \\ \in [T]}} \frac{1}{|\mathbf{U}_I \cdot \mathbf{n}_k|} f_k \mathbf{U}_I \cdot \mathbf{n}_k \qquad [1.2.106]$$

If $f_k \equiv 1$, [1.2.106] reads

$$\frac{\partial \alpha_k}{\partial t} = \frac{1}{T} \sum_{\substack{\text{disc} \\ \in [T]}} \frac{\mathbf{U}_I \cdot \mathbf{n}_k}{|\mathbf{U}_I \cdot \mathbf{n}_k|} \qquad [1.2.107]$$

where α_k is the residence time fraction of phase k, defined by

$$\alpha_k \overset{\Delta}{=} \frac{T_k}{T} \qquad [1.2.108]$$

Limiting Forms of the Gauss Theorems

$$\int_{[T_k(\mathbf{r})]} \nabla \cdot \mathbf{B}_k(\mathbf{r}, t) \, dt = \nabla \cdot \int_{[T_k(\mathbf{r})]} \mathbf{B}_k(\mathbf{r}, t) \, dt + \sum_{\substack{\text{disc} \\ \in [T]}} \frac{1}{|\mathbf{U}_I \cdot \mathbf{n}_k|} \mathbf{n}_k \cdot \mathbf{B}_k(\mathbf{r}, t)$$

$$[1.2.109]$$

The vector $\mathbf{B}_k$ can be replaced by a tensor $\mathbf{M}_k$. A relation identical to [1.2.109] is obtained. In particular, if

$$\mathbf{M}_k = \mathbf{U} \qquad [1.2.110]$$

we have

$$\nabla \alpha_k = -\frac{1}{T} \sum_{\substack{\text{disc} \\ \in [T]}} \frac{1}{|\mathbf{U}_I \cdot \mathbf{n}_k|} \qquad [1.2.111]$$

1.2.3.2 Single Time-averaged Equations

The local instantaneous balance law is integrated over $[T_k]$:

$$\int_{|T_k|} \frac{\partial}{\partial t} \rho_k \psi_k \, dt + \int_{|T_k|} \nabla \cdot (\rho_k \psi_k \mathbf{U}_k) \, dt + \int_{|T_k|} \nabla \cdot \mathbf{J}_k \, dt - \int_{|T_k|} \rho_k \phi_k \, dt = 0$$

$$[1.2.112]$$

By taking into account the limiting forms of the Leibniz and Gauss theorems [1.2.106] and [1.2.109], [1.2.112] becomes

$$\frac{\partial}{\partial t} \alpha_k \overline{\rho_k \psi_k}^X + \nabla \cdot \alpha_k \overline{\rho_k \psi_k \mathbf{U}_k}^X + \nabla \cdot \alpha_k \overline{\mathbf{J}_k}^X - \alpha_k \overline{\rho_k \phi_k}^X$$

$$= -\sum_j l_j^{-1} (\dot{m}_k \psi_k + \mathbf{J}_k \cdot \mathbf{n}_k)_j \qquad [1.2.113]$$

where

$$\overline{f_k}^X \triangleq \frac{1}{T_k} \int_{|T_k|} f_k \, dt \qquad [1.2.114]$$

$$l_j \triangleq T |\mathbf{U}_I \cdot \mathbf{n}_k|_j \qquad [1.2.115]$$

j denoting the $j$the interface passing through $\mathbf{r}$ during the time interval $[T]$.

Remarks on the Definition of $\overline{f_k}^X$

A phase density function $X_k(\mathbf{r}, t)$ is defined by

$$X_k(\mathbf{r}, t) \triangleq \begin{cases} 1 & \text{if point } \mathbf{r} \text{ pertains to phase } k \\ 0 & \text{if point } \mathbf{r} \text{ does not pertain to phase } k \end{cases} \qquad [1.2.116]$$

The time fraction α_k, defined by [1.2.108], is then

$$\alpha_k(\mathbf{r}, t) \triangleq \frac{T_k}{T} = \frac{1}{T} \int_{|T|} X_k(\mathbf{r}, t) \, dt \triangleq \overline{X_k}(\mathbf{r}, t) \qquad [1.2.117]$$

On the other hand, $\overline{f_k}^X$, defined by [1.2.114] is

$$\overline{f_k}^X = \frac{(1/T)\int_{|T|} X_k f_k \, dt}{(1/T)\int_{|T|} X_k \, dt} \triangleq \frac{\overline{X_k f_k}}{\overline{X_k}} \tag{1.2.118}$$

Hence, we can see that the time average of f_k over $[T_k]$ is the X_k-weighted average of f_k over $[T]$. This justifies the notation $\overline{f_k}^X$.

Primary Balance Equations

By use of table 1.2.1, [1.2.113] gives the local time-averaged equations for the balances of mass, momentum, total energy, and entropy.

Mass

$$\frac{\partial}{\partial t} \alpha_k \overline{\rho_k}^X + \nabla \cdot \alpha_k \overline{\rho_k \mathbf{U}_k}^X = -\sum_j l_j \dot{m}_{kj} \tag{1.2.119}$$

Momentum

$$\frac{\partial}{\partial t} \alpha_k \overline{\rho_k \mathbf{U}_k}^X + \nabla \cdot \alpha_k \overline{\rho_k \mathbf{U}_k \mathbf{U}_k}^X - \nabla \cdot \alpha_k \overline{\mathbf{T}_k}^X - \alpha_k \overline{\rho_k \mathbf{b}}^X$$

$$= -\sum_j l_j^{-1} (\dot{m}_k \mathbf{U}_k - \mathbf{T}_k \cdot \mathbf{n}_k)_j \tag{1.2.120}$$

Total energy

$$\frac{\partial}{\partial t} \alpha_k \overline{\rho_k \left(u_k + \frac{1}{2} \mathbf{U}_k^2 \right)}^X + \nabla \cdot \alpha_k \overline{\rho_k \left(u_k + \frac{1}{2} \mathbf{U}_k^2 \right) \mathbf{U}_k}^X$$

$$+ \nabla \cdot \alpha_k \overline{\mathbf{T}_k \cdot \mathbf{U}_k}^X + \nabla \cdot \alpha_k \overline{\mathbf{q}_k}^X - \alpha_k \overline{\rho_k \mathbf{b} \cdot \mathbf{U}_k}^X$$

$$= -\sum_j l_j^{-1} \left[\dot{m}_k \left(u_k + \frac{1}{2} \mathbf{U}_k^2 \right) - (\mathbf{T}_k \cdot \mathbf{U}_k) \cdot \mathbf{n}_k + \mathbf{q}_k \cdot \mathbf{n}_k \right]_j \tag{1.2.121}$$

Entropy

$$\frac{\partial}{\partial t} \alpha_k \overline{\rho_k s_k}^X + \nabla \cdot \alpha_k \overline{\rho_k s_k \mathbf{U}_k}^X + \nabla \cdot \alpha_k \overline{\frac{1}{T_k} \mathbf{q}_k}^X$$

$$+ \sum_j l_j^{-1} \left(\dot{m}_k s_k + \frac{1}{T_k} \mathbf{q}_k \cdot \mathbf{n}_k \right) = \overline{\alpha_k \Delta_k}^X \geqslant 0 \tag{1.2.122}$$

1.2.3.3 Comments on the Single Time-averaging Operators

In [1.2.117] and [1.2.118] the single time-averaging operator was used as defined by

$$\bar{g}\,(\mathbf{r},\,t) \triangleq \frac{1}{T} \int_{[T]} g\,(\mathbf{r},\,z)\,dz \qquad [1.2.123]$$

In two-phase flow, the g function is of the type

$$g\,(\mathbf{r},\,t) = X_k f_k \qquad [1.2.124]$$

and can be expanded in a Fourier series. The *message* $g\,(\mathbf{r},\,t)$ can be split into two parts: (1) the *signal* $g_s\,(\mathbf{r},\,t)$, which is, in our case, the sum of the expansion terms whose angular frequencies are lower than an arbitrary cutoff frequency, and (2) the *noise* $g_n\,(\mathbf{r},\,t)$, which is the sum of the remaining terms. Hence,

$$g\,(\mathbf{r},\,t) = g_s(\mathbf{r},\,t) + g_n\,(\mathbf{r},\,t) \qquad [1.2.125]$$

The time-averaging operator [1.2.123] is expected to low-pass filter the message $g\,(\mathbf{r},\,t)$ on which it is acting:

$$\bar{g}\,(\mathbf{r},\,t) \cong g_s\,(\mathbf{r},\,t) \qquad [1.2.126]$$

As the first time derivatives of the time-averaged variables appear in the single time-averaged balance equation [1.2.113], it is worthwhile to have also:

$$\frac{\partial}{\partial t}\,\bar{g}\,(\mathbf{r},\,t) \cong \frac{\partial}{\partial t}\,g_s\,(\mathbf{r},\,t) \qquad [1.2.127]$$

Delhaye & Achard (1977, 1978) showed that the single time-averaging operator [1.2.123] does not always fulfill conditions [1.2.126] and [1.2.127]. Furthermore, the first time derivative of $\bar{g}$ is discontinuous. For these reasons, Delhaye & Achard (1977, 1978) introduced a double time-averaging operator.

1.2.4 COMPOSITE–AVERAGED EQUATIONS

The importance of composite-averaged (i.e., space/time- or time/space-averaged) equations is considerable, since all practical problems of two-phase flow in channels are now dealt with using these equations.

Composite-averaged equations can be obtained in two ways: (1) by averaging the time-averaged local equations over a channel cross-sectional area or over a slice, or (2) by averaging over a time interval the instantaneous equations averaged over the cross-sectional areas or slices occupied by each phase.

To verify the equivalence of the results obtained with these methods, we first establish or recall theorems concerning the commutativity of averaging operators. Also, local and integral specific areas are introduced, since these quantities are important in mass, momentum, and energy interface transfers. We conclude by demonstrating the identity of the space/time- and time/space-averaging operators.

1.2.4.1 Commutativity of the Averaging Operators

Consider any scalar, vector, or tensor function associated with phase k. The aim of the calculation is to find the group or variables on which a permutation of the time- and space-averaging operators can be carried out.

By means of the averaging operator definitions:

$$\ll \alpha_k \overline{f_k}^X \gg_2 = \ll \overline{X_k f_k} \gg_2 \triangleq \frac{1}{A} \int_A \frac{1}{T} \int_{[T]} X_k f_k \, dt \; dA \qquad [1.2.128]$$

Reversing the order of integration yields

$$\ll \alpha_k \overline{f_k}^X \gg_2 = \frac{1}{T} \int_{[T]} \frac{1}{A} \int_A X_k f_k \, dA \; dt \qquad [1.2.129]$$

$$\ll \alpha_k \overline{f_k}^X \gg_2 = \frac{1}{T} \int_{[T]} \frac{1}{A} \int_{A_k} f_k \, dA \; dt \qquad [1.2.130]$$

As a consequence we obtain the fundamental relation (Vernier & Delhaye 1968)

$$\ll \alpha_k \overline{f_k}^X \gg_2 \equiv \overline{R_{k2} \langle f_k \rangle_2} \qquad [1.2.131]$$

where R_{k2} is the area fraction of phase k in the cross section, defined by

$$R_{k2} \triangleq \frac{A_k}{A} \qquad [1.2.132]$$

Equation [1.2.131] plays an essential part in two-phase flow modeling. In effect, it is more or less convenient to formulate hypotheses on local time-averaged quantities (such as α_k or $\overline{f_k}^X$) than on instantaneous area-averaged quantities (such as R_{k2} or $\langle f_k \rangle_2$), depending on the flow pattern (e.g., bubbly flow or slug flow). A particular case for [1.2.131] is obtained by taking

$$f_k \equiv 1$$

which leads to
$$\ll \alpha_k \gg_2 \equiv \overline{R_{k2}} \qquad [1.2.133]$$

It is obvious that [1.2.131] and [1.2.133] established for areas are also valid for segments and volumes. More generally,

$$\ll \alpha_k \overline{f_k}^X \gg_n \equiv \overline{R_{kn} \langle f_k \rangle_n} \qquad [1.2.134]$$

where $n = 1$, for segments; $n = 2$, for areas; and $n = 3$, for volumes.

By writing [1.2.134] for segments ($n = 1$), probe measurements of local void fraction can be tallied with radiation attenuation measurements of segment void fractions (see chapter 12).

1.2.4.2 Local and Integral Specific Areas

Fundamental Identity

Consider a pipe and a fixed control volume V limited by the pipe wall and the cross sections A' and A'' located a distance Z apart (figure 1.2.10). The area of the *moving* interfaces contained in volume V is denoted by $A_I(t)$.

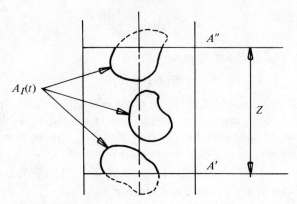

Figure 1.2.10   Areas of moving interfaces in a fixed control volume.

For any arbitrary continuous vector field $\mathbf{B}(\mathbf{r}, t)$, the following identity is satisfied (Delhaye 1976; Delhaye & Achard 1978):

$$\int_V \sum_j l_j^{-1}\,(\mathbf{B}_k \cdot \mathbf{n}_k)_j \;\; dV \equiv \overline{\int_{A_I(t)} \mathbf{B}_k \cdot \mathbf{n}_k \; dA} \qquad [1.2.135]$$

with
$$l_j = T|\mathbf{U}_I \cdot \mathbf{n}_k|_j \qquad [1.2.136]$$

where T is the integration period and $\mathbf{U}_I \cdot \mathbf{n}_k$ the speed of displacement of $A_I(t)$. Subscript j denotes the jth interface passing through $\mathbf{r}$ during the time interval $[T]$.

If $\mathbf{B}_k$ is chosen in such a way that on the interfaces

$$\mathbf{B}_k \equiv \mathbf{n}_k \qquad [1.2.137]$$

identity [1.2.135] leads to a relation that connects the interfacial area to the speed of displacement of the interfaces:

$$\int_V \left(\sum_j l_j^{-1} \right) dV \equiv \overline{A_I(t)} \qquad [1.2.138]$$

Specific Areas

The following definitions can then be set:

1. The *local specific area* $\daleth(\mathbf{r}, t)$ is a local quantity defined over the time interval $[T]$ by

$$\daleth(\mathbf{r}) \triangleq \sum_j l_j^{-1} \qquad [1.2.139]$$

2. The *integral specific area* $\daleth_3(t)$ is an instantaneous quantity defined on the volume V by

$$\daleth_3(t) \triangleq \frac{A_I(t)}{V} \qquad [1.2.140]$$

Identity [1.2.138] can then be written

$$\langle\!\langle \daleth(\mathbf{r})\rangle\!\rangle_3 \equiv \overline{\daleth_3(t)} \qquad [1.2.141]$$

Identities [1.2.138] and [1.2.141] are fundamental as far as interfacial area measurements are concerned. They provide the link between the integral specific area, which can be measured by chemical methods, and the local specific area, which can be determined by probe techniques (Veteau 1979).

Limiting Form of the Fundamental Identity

If $Z \rightarrow 0$, [1.2.135] becomes

$$\langle\!\langle \sum_j l_j^{-1} (\mathbf{B}_k \cdot \mathbf{n}_k)_j \rangle\!\rangle_2 \equiv \frac{1}{A} \int_C \overline{\mathbf{B}_k \cdot \mathbf{n}_k \frac{dC}{\mathbf{n}_k \cdot \mathbf{n}_{kC}}} \qquad [1.2.142]$$

which will appear as the link between the interaction terms occurring in the space/time- or time/space-averaged equations. In [1.2.142], $\mathbf{n}_{kC}$ denotes the unit vector normal to C, located in the cross-sectional plane and directed away from phase k. Curve C is the intersection of interface A_I with the cross-sectional plane.

1.2.4.3 Space/Time- or Time/Space-averaged Equations

Time-average over $[T]$ the instantaneous area-averaged balance equation:

$$\frac{\partial}{\partial t} \overline{A_k \langle \rho_k \psi_k \rangle_2} + \frac{\partial}{\partial z} \overline{A_k \langle \mathbf{n}_z \cdot (\rho_k \psi_k \mathbf{U}_k) \rangle_2} + \frac{\partial}{\partial z} \overline{A_k \langle \mathbf{n}_z \cdot \mathbf{J}_k \rangle_2} - \overline{A_k \langle \rho_k \phi_k \rangle_2}$$

$$= - \int_{C(z,t)} \overline{(\dot{m}_k \psi_k + \mathbf{n}_k \cdot \mathbf{J}_k) \frac{dC}{\mathbf{n}_k \cdot \mathbf{n}_{kC}}} - \int_{C_k(z,t)} \overline{\mathbf{n}_k \cdot \mathbf{J}_k \frac{dC}{\mathbf{n}_k \cdot \mathbf{n}_{kC}}}$$

$$[1.2.143]$$

Area-average the local time-averaged balance equation over the total cross-sectional area:

$$\frac{\partial}{\partial t} A \langle\!\langle \alpha_k \overline{\rho_k \psi_k}^X \rangle\!\rangle_2 + \frac{\partial}{\partial z} A \langle\!\langle \alpha_k \overline{\mathbf{n}_z \cdot (\rho_k \psi_k \mathbf{U}_k)}^X \rangle\!\rangle_2 + \frac{\partial}{\partial z} A \langle\!\langle \alpha_k \mathbf{n}_z \cdot \overline{\mathbf{J}_k}^X \rangle\!\rangle_2$$

$$- A \langle\!\langle \alpha_k \overline{\rho_k \phi_k}^X \rangle\!\rangle_2 = - A \langle\!\langle \sum_j l_j^{-1} (\overline{\dot{m}_k \psi_k + \mathbf{J}_k \cdot \mathbf{n}_k})_j \rangle\!\rangle_2$$

$$- \int_{C_1 + C_2} \alpha_k \mathbf{n}_k \cdot \overline{\mathbf{J}_k}^X \frac{dC}{\mathbf{n}_k \cdot \mathbf{n}_{kC}} \qquad [1.2.144]$$

Because of [1.2.131] and [1.2.142], [1.2.143] and [1.2.144] are identical. Similar equations can be written for volume-averaged quantities.

1.2.5 MULTIPHASE FLOW MODELING

1.2.5.1 Statement of the Problem

A mathematical model is a set of equations (including the relevant boundary and initial conditions) that is assumed to represent the behavior of a physical system under certain specific conditions.

The physical system of interest here consists of the multiphase mixture occupying some flow field, physical conditions being imposed at the flow field boundaries by some other physical systems (vessel or pipe walls, pumps, etc.). The relevant physical properties of the phases and the relevant initial conditions are supposed to be known. Therefore, mathematical modeling involves the mass, momentum, and energy balances, the relevant constitutive laws of the phases, and the boundary and initial conditions.

If local instantaneous equations are used, the corresponding set of equations is closed. The model consists, for instance, of [1.2.20], [1.2.21], [1.2.23], [1.2.40], [1.2.51], and [1.2.69] (or any equivalent set), plus constitutive laws for ρ_k, $\mathbf{T}_k$, $\mathbf{q}_k$, and the boundary and initial conditions.

In most cases, however, practicability requires some sort of averaging. Averaging entails loss of information about the flow structure, including that at the boundaries, and closure of the set of equations requires that some of this information be restored in the model by specific equations.

Finally, multiphase flow mathematical modeling is based on

1. The so-called conservation principles, which lead to balances of mass, linear momentum, and total energy (as recalled in section 1.2.1, balance of angular momentum implies only symmetry of the stress tensor). These balances apply to each phase and to the interfaces as well (jump conditions).
2. Some idealization of the flow structure, taking into account the available experimental data (flow patterns, distributions of the flow variables within the control volume, etc.). Just as the conservation principles lead to balance equations, the foregoing idealization leads to what may be called *topological laws*.
3. Some idealization of the relevant physical properties of the phases and of the interfaces, taking into account the available experimental data and subject to some universal axioms (Truesdell & Toupin 1960) such as the principle of material indifference and the second law of thermodynamics. This idealization leads to *constitutive laws* stricto sensu.
4. Some idealization of the transfers occurring at the phase boundaries, taking into account the available experimental data. This idealization leads to *transfer laws*.
5. Some theoretical and practical constraints (necessity of a closed set of equations, tractability of the equations, etc.).

Topological laws, constitutive laws, and transfer laws have different physical significances. Considered together, their practical role is to provide a closure to the set of balance equations. This is why, through an unfortunate and misleading extension of meaning, they are often aggregated under the name of constitutive laws.

1.2.5.2 Topological, Constitutive, and Transfer Laws

In the averaged balanced equations (e.g., [1.2.143] and [1.2.144], the case of [1.2.92], [1.2.104], or [1.2.113] being similar) the *field terms* contain composite quantities such as $\blacktriangleleft \alpha_k \rho_k \overline{\psi_k}^X \blacktriangleright$. These terms always involve some information:

1. On the flow structure, through the occurrence of *averages of products*
2. On the flow structure again, through the appearance of *global quantities* such as R_k (space fraction) or α_k (time fraction), which are not present in the local instantaneous equations
3. On the phase *physical properties*, through the occurrence of ρ_k or $\mathbf{J}_k$

Averages of products are expressed in terms of the relevant dependent variables by means of topological laws. Very little has been done about this problem and it is not discussed further here, which does not mean that it may be considered unimportant, especially in the momentum equations. In current practice, the averaging symbols are simply ignored and $\blacktriangleleft \alpha_k \overline{\rho_k \psi_k}^X \blacktriangleright$, for instance, is written $\alpha_k \rho_k \psi_k$, which means something different, like $\blacktriangleleft \alpha_k \blacktriangleright \blacktriangleleft \overline{\rho_k}^X \blacktriangleright \blacktriangleleft \overline{\psi_k}^X \blacktriangleright$. Whenever fluctuations and/or transverse distributions are present, this practice is obviously questionable.

Present global quantities (in practice, with composite-averaged two-phase flow equations, the classical void fraction $\overline{R}_G = \blacktriangleleft \alpha_G \blacktriangleright$, written α_G below, and its complement to 1, α_L) are also provided by specific topological laws. The *void fraction topological law* plays an essential part in the modeling process. Since $\blacktriangleleft \overline{p}_G^X \blacktriangleright$ is not, in practice, very different from $\blacktriangleleft \overline{p}_L^X \blacktriangleright$ (except for surface tension effects), it has become customary to assume

$$\blacktriangleleft \overline{p}_G^X \blacktriangleright = \blacktriangleleft \overline{p}_L^X \blacktriangleright$$

which enables elimination of one dependent variable and serves therefore as a substitute for the unknown void fraction topological law.

The trouble is that $\blacktriangleleft \overline{p}_G^X \blacktriangleright \cong \blacktriangleleft \overline{p}_L^X \blacktriangleright$ does not entail the same property for their partial derivatives. The assumption $\blacktriangleleft \overline{p}_G^X \blacktriangleright = \blacktriangleleft \overline{p}_L^X \blacktriangleright$ is therefore very restrictive when derivatives are involved. It requires that pressure disturbances have the same averaged effect on the two phases and, in particular, that they propagate at the same velocity within the two phases. The assumption $\blacktriangleleft \overline{p}_G^X \blacktriangleright = \blacktriangleleft \overline{p}_L^X \blacktriangleright$ has proved useful in many cases, but it is definitely too restrictive when propagation phenomena are important. Developing a better void fraction topological law is crucial to get rid of this questionable assumption and to achieve a satisfactory description of propagation phenomena.

Physical properties are provided by constitutive laws. The universal practice is again to ignore the averaging symbols and to use classical constitutive laws, which also implies that local thermodynamic equilibrium is achieved within each phase; for example, the equation of state

$$\rho_k = \rho_k(p_k, h_k)$$

is used to calculate $\langle \bar{\rho}_k^X \rangle$ as a function of $\langle \bar{p}_k^X \rangle$ and $\langle \bar{h}_k^X \rangle$.

The averaged balance equations also contain *boundary terms:* transfer terms, including those at the interfaces, in the field equations, and interfacial transfer terms plus storage terms (surface tension terms) in the jump conditions.

The same procedure, used above for the field terms, may be applied to express the boundary terms. In particular, by ignoring as above the averaging operators, each boundary term may be considered as the product of a global quantity (the appropriate boundary area in the common case of volume-averaged equations) and a flux density. Again, the global quantity is provided by a topological law (for instance, a topological law for the specific area $\bar{7}_3$), whereas the flux density is provided by a constitutive law.

However, since neither of these two laws is known, boundary terms are still often considered unsplit: storage terms are generally neglected, and transfer terms are provided by transfer laws.

1.2.5.3 Practical Modeling: Two-Fluid Models for Two-Phase Pipe Flows

As the first step of the modeling procedure, the flow field may be divided into several domains, while taking the flow structure into account. For instance, this can be convenient when the flow pattern is known and the phases fairly well separated (annular, stratified, or slug flows). In each domain, the fluid is either a single-phase or a multiphase mixture.

In some cases, a multiphase mixture may be considered as a single, fictitious fluid: this leads to *one-fluid models,* in which the balance equations are formally identical to the single-phase equations, the crucial problem being to determine the physical properties of the fictitious fluid. With the noticeable exception of the homogeneous model (compare section 1.2.9.3), one-fluid models are not as widespread as they should be. For instance, useful one-fluid models may involve a fictitious fluid whose density is time dependent. With ρ, p, U, and h being respectively the density, pressure, velocity, and enthalpy of the fictitious fluid, and its "equilibrium" density being $\rho^* = \rho^*(p, h)$, the equation of state of the fictitious fluid is written

$$\frac{\partial \rho}{\partial t} + U \frac{\partial \rho}{\partial z} - \frac{1}{C^2}\left(\frac{\partial p}{\partial t} + U \frac{\partial p}{\partial z}\right) + \frac{\rho - \rho^*}{\theta} = 0$$

C^2, which characterizes the propagation velocity of small pressure disturbances, and ϕ, which characterizes the relaxation toward equilibrium, may be determined from experimental data. At least one existing computer program is based on the foregoing one-fluid model. Unfortunately, this computer program, NATREX, is proprietary.

However, true multiphase flow modeling involves the consideration of each phase as a distinct fluid, which leads to *multifluid models.* Of particular interest is the case of two-phase pipe flow. When the flow pattern is not known (or may change), such flows are generally represented by one-domain, two-fluid models, which are discussed in some detail in the following sections. As should be clear from the preceding discussion, the form of the balance equations is insensitive to the flow pattern, which, however, affects the topological and transfer laws. Knowledge of the topological and transfer laws, including their mathematical form, which plays an essential role in the response of the model to disturbances, is still deficient. Discussions can be found in Bouré (1978a, 1978c).

1.2.6 TOWARD PRACTICAL PIPE–FLOW EQUATIONS: PHASE EQUATIONS, PRIMARY FORMS

1.2.6.1 Introduction

Practical equations of two-phase flows in pipes are based on composite-averaged equations (section 1.2.4). It is implicitly assumed that the velocity field remains roughly parallel to some direction taken as the Oz axis. Space averaging is performed over a volume V comprised between two fixed cross sections located Δz apart. The equations are divided by Δz, which is then taken as vanishingly small. Time averaging may be replaced by statistical averaging, which does not affect the form of the balance equations (Delhaye & Achard 1977). In accordance with the choice of the Oz axis, the projections of the momentum equations perpendicularly to this axis are often ignored, which results in one-dimensional modeling. No mass transfer is assumed to take place between the flow and the pipe walls, but such transfer could be easily included. The equations are written within a Galilean frame of reference.

Practical equations are often written in terms of the dependent variables α_k (with $\alpha_G + \alpha_L = 1$), ρ_k, p_k, $\mathbf{U}_k$ (and its projection w_k along Oz), and h_k; ρ_k (or sometimes h_k) is ultimately eliminated, using the equation of state of phase k. (Because of the order of magnitude of the partial derivative of ρ_k with respect to p_k, enthalpy being kept constant, determination of p_k from the equation of state, starting with an approximate value of ρ_k, may result in very large errors, at least for water at pressures not very close to the critical pressure. Therefore, elimination of p_k must be avoided as it would be damaging to numerical accuracy.)

The equations can be made dimensionless, using for instance characteristic values l_0 (or t_0), ρ_0, w_0, Δh_0 as units for lengths (or times), densities, velocities, and enthalpies. The only difference between the dimensional and the dimensionless balance equations lies in the appearance of the ratio

$$\eta = \frac{w_0^2}{\Delta h_0}$$

in the energy equations. The interest in dimensionless equations rests primarily on the choice of physically significant characteristic values as units. Such characteristic values cannot be specified here, since they depend on the physical phenomena in the particular system to be modeled. In many situations, η is very small and the terms that contain it may be regarded as corrective or discarded. Other advantages of dimensionless equations may appear when the topological and transfer laws are written. The equations given here and in the following sections are dimensionless. However, since there is no ambiguity, the dimensionless symbol + is omitted for clarity.

1.2.6.2 Balances of Mass

Field Equation

$$\frac{\partial}{\partial t}(A\alpha_k\rho_k) + \frac{\partial}{\partial z}(A\alpha_k\rho_k w_k) - AM_{kI} = 0 \qquad [1.2.145]$$

with
$$AM_{kI} \stackrel{\Delta}{=} \lim_{\Delta z \to 0}\left[-\frac{1}{\Delta z}\int_{A_I}\rho_k(\mathbf{U}_k - \mathbf{U}_I)\cdot\mathbf{n}_k\,dA \right]$$

A_I being the instantaneous interfacial area present in volume V and M_{kI} the mass transfer flux toward phase k, per unit of volume.

Jump Condition

$$\sum_k (AM_{kI}) = 0 \qquad [1.2.146]$$

1.2.6.3 Balances of Momentum

Field Equation

$$\frac{\partial}{\partial t}(A\alpha_k\rho_k\mathbf{U}_k) + \frac{\partial}{\partial z}(A\alpha_k\rho_k w_k\mathbf{U}_k) + \frac{\partial}{\partial z}(A\alpha_k p_k\mathbf{n}_z)$$

$$-\frac{\partial}{\partial z}(A\alpha_k\tau_k\cdot\mathbf{n}_z) - A(MV)_{kI} - A(FF)_{kI} - A(FP)_{kI}$$

$$- A(FF)_{kW} - A(FP)_{kW} - A\alpha_k\rho_k\mathbf{b} = 0 \qquad [1.2.147]$$

with

$$A(MV)_{kI} \stackrel{\Delta}{=} \lim_{\Delta z \to 0}\left\{ -\frac{1}{\Delta z}\int_{A_I}[\rho_k(\mathbf{U}_k - \mathbf{U}_I)\cdot\mathbf{n}_k]\,\mathbf{U}_k\,dA \right\}$$

$$A(FF)_{kI} \stackrel{\Delta}{=} \lim_{\Delta z \to 0}\left(\frac{1}{\Delta z}\int_{A_I}\tau_k\cdot\mathbf{n}_k\,dA \right) \qquad A(FF)_{kW} \stackrel{\Delta}{=} \lim_{\Delta z \to 0}\left(\frac{1}{\Delta z}\int_{A_{kW}}\tau_k\cdot\mathbf{n}_k\,dA \right)$$

$$A(\mathbf{FP})_{kI} \triangleq \lim_{\Delta z \to 0} \left(-\frac{1}{\Delta z} \int_{A_I} \overline{p_k \mathbf{n}_k} \, dA \right) \quad A(\mathbf{FP})_{kW} \triangleq \lim_{\Delta z \to 0} \left(-\frac{1}{\Delta z} \int_{A_{kW}} \overline{p_k \mathbf{n}_k} \, dA \right)$$

Alternative Form of the Field Equation

Using the Gauss theorem [1.2.86], with $\mathbf{M} = p_k \mathbf{U}$, yields

$$\frac{\partial}{\partial z} (A\alpha_k p_k \mathbf{n}_z) - A(\mathbf{FP})_{kI} - A(\mathbf{FP})_{kW} = A\alpha_k \, \nabla p_k \qquad [1.2.148]$$

so that [1.2.147] may also be written

$$\frac{\partial}{\partial t} (A\alpha_k \rho_k \mathbf{U}_k) + \frac{\partial}{\partial z} (A\alpha_k \rho_k w_k \mathbf{U}_k) + A\alpha_k \, \nabla p_k$$

$$- \frac{\partial}{\partial z} (A\alpha_k \tau_k \cdot \mathbf{n}_z) - A(\mathbf{MV})_{kI} - A(\mathbf{FF})_{kI} - A(\mathbf{FF})_{kW} - A\alpha_k \rho_k \mathbf{b} = 0 \qquad [1.2.149]$$

It may be worthwhile to recall that, in [1.2.149], $\alpha_k \, \nabla p_k$ stands for $\overline{R_k \langle \nabla p_k \rangle}$ or $\langle\!\langle \alpha_k \, \overline{\nabla p_k}^X \rangle\!\rangle$.

Jump Condition

$$\sum_k [A(\mathbf{MV})_{kI} + A(\mathbf{FF})_{kI} + A(\mathbf{FP})_{kI}] - A(\mathbf{I}\sigma)_I = 0 \qquad [1.2.150]$$

with
$$A(\mathbf{I}\sigma)_I \triangleq \lim_{\Delta z \to 0} \left\{ \frac{1}{\Delta z} \int_{A_I} \overline{[\nabla_s \sigma - \sigma(\nabla_s \cdot \mathbf{n}_G)\mathbf{n}_G]} \, dA \right\}$$

Equations [1.2.147] and [1.2.149] are strictly equivalent, but additional assumptions may later impair this equivalence, as discussed below (section 1.2.6.5). All things considered, use of [1.2.147] may be recommended when p_G is allowed to differ from p_L (see the discussion in section 1.2.5.2), whereas use of [1.2.149], which is more compact, may be preferred in other cases.

1.2.6.4 Balances of Energy

Field Equation

$$\frac{\partial}{\partial t} \left[A\alpha_k \rho_k \left(h_k + \frac{\eta}{2} \mathbf{U}_k^2 \right) \right] + \frac{\partial}{\partial z} \left[A\alpha_k \rho_k w_k \left(h_k + \frac{\eta}{2} \mathbf{U}_k^2 \right) \right]$$

$$- \eta \frac{\partial}{\partial t} (A\alpha_k p_k) - \eta \frac{\partial}{\partial z} [A\alpha_k (\tau_k \cdot \mathbf{n}_z) \cdot \mathbf{U}_k] + \frac{\partial}{\partial z} (A\alpha_k \mathbf{q}_k \cdot \mathbf{n}_z)$$

$$- A(MH)_{kI} - \eta A(MC)_{kI} - \eta A(EF)_{kI} - \eta A(EP)_{kI} - A(EQ)_{kI}$$
$$- \eta A(EF)_{kW} - \eta A(EP)_{kW} - A(EQ)_{kW} - \eta A\alpha_k\rho_k\mathbf{U}_k \cdot \mathbf{b} = 0 \qquad [1.2.151]$$

with
$$A(MH)_{kI} \overset{\triangle}{=} \lim_{\Delta z \to 0} \left\{ \overline{-\frac{1}{\Delta z} \int_{A_I} [\rho_k(\mathbf{U}_k - \mathbf{U}_I) \cdot \mathbf{n}_k] \, h_k \, dA} \right\}$$

$$A(MC)_{kI} \overset{\triangle}{=} \lim_{\Delta z \to 0} \left\{ \overline{-\frac{1}{\Delta z} \int_{A_I} \frac{1}{2} [\rho_k(\mathbf{U}_k - \mathbf{U}_I) \cdot \mathbf{n}_k] \, \mathbf{U}_k^2 \, dA} \right\}$$

$$A(EF)_{kI} \overset{\triangle}{=} \lim_{\Delta z \to 0} \left[\overline{\frac{1}{\Delta z} \int_{A_I} (\tau_k \cdot \mathbf{n}_k) \cdot \mathbf{U}_k \, dA} \right]$$

$$A(EF)_{kW} \overset{\triangle}{=} \lim_{\Delta z \to 0} \left[\overline{\frac{1}{\Delta z} \int_{A_{kW}} (\tau_k \cdot \mathbf{n}_k) \cdot \mathbf{U}_W \, dA} \right]$$

$$A(EP)_{kI} \overset{\triangle}{=} \lim_{\Delta z \to 0} \left(\overline{-\frac{1}{\Delta z} \int_{A_I} p_k\mathbf{U}_I \cdot \mathbf{n}_k \, dA} \right)$$

$$A(EP)_{kW} \overset{\triangle}{=} \lim_{\Delta z \to 0} \left(\overline{-\frac{1}{\Delta z} \int_{A_{kW}} \rho_k\mathbf{U}_W \cdot \mathbf{n}_k \, dA} \right)$$

$$A(EQ)_{kI} \overset{\triangle}{=} \lim_{\Delta z \to 0} \left(\overline{-\frac{1}{\Delta z} \int_{A_I} \mathbf{q}_k \cdot \mathbf{n}_k \, dA} \right)$$

$$A(EQ)_{kW} \overset{\triangle}{=} \lim_{\Delta z \to 0} \left(\overline{-\frac{1}{\Delta z} \int_{A_{kW}} \mathbf{q}_k \cdot \mathbf{n}_k \, dA} \right)$$

$\mathbf{U}_W$ being the wall velocity (often zero, in practice).

Alternative Form of the Field Equation

Using the Leibniz rule, [1.2.83] (rewritten for the case of a wall moving at velocity $\mathbf{U}_W$) with $f = p_k$, yields

$$\frac{\partial}{\partial t}(A\alpha_k p_k) + A(EP)_{kI} + A(EP)_{kW} = A\alpha_k \frac{\partial p_k}{\partial t} \qquad [1.2.152]$$

so that [1.2.151] may also be written

$$\frac{\partial}{\partial t}\left[A\alpha_k \rho_k \left(h_k + \frac{\eta}{2}\mathbf{U}_k^2\right)\right] + \frac{\partial}{\partial z}\left[A\alpha_k \rho_k w_k \left(h_k + \frac{\eta}{2}\mathbf{U}_k^2\right)\right]$$

$$-\eta A\alpha_k \frac{\partial p_k}{\partial t} - \eta \frac{\partial}{\partial z}[A\alpha_k(\tau_k \cdot \mathbf{n}_z) \cdot \mathbf{U}_k] + \frac{\partial}{\partial z}(A\alpha_k q_k \cdot \mathbf{n}_z)$$

$$- A(MH)_{kI} - \eta A(MC)_{kI} - \eta A(EF)_{kI} - A(EQ)_{kI}$$

$$- \eta A(EF)_{kW} - A(EQ)_{kW} - \eta A\alpha_k \rho_k \mathbf{U}_k \cdot \mathbf{b} = 0 \qquad [1.2.153]$$

It may be worthwhile to recall that in [1.2.152] and [1.2.153] $\alpha_k \partial p_k / \partial t$ stands for $\overline{R_k \langle \partial p_k / \partial t \rangle}$ or $\ll \alpha_k \partial p_k / \partial t^X \gg$.

Jump Condition

$$\sum_k [A(MH)_{kI} + \eta A(MC)_{kI} + \eta A(EF)_{kI} + \eta A(EP)_{kI} + A(EQ)_{kI}] - \eta A(E\sigma)_I = 0$$

$$[1.2.154]$$

with

$$A(E\sigma)_I \triangleq \lim_{\Delta z \to 0}\left[\frac{1}{\Delta z}\int_{A_I} \overline{\nabla_s \cdot (\sigma \mathbf{U}^t)}\, dA\right]$$

Equations [1.2.151] and [1.2.153] are strictly equivalent. The discussion is similar to that concerning the momentum balance. Use of [1.2.151] is recommended when p_G is allowed to differ from p_L.

1.2.6.5 The Closure Problem

From the balance equations [1.2.145]–[1.2.147] or [1.2.149]–[1.2.151] or [1.2.153] and [1.2.154], the closure problem can be summarized by table 1.2.2. The set of equations is closed when all the laws enumerated in table 1.2.2 and the relevant boundary and initial conditions are specified. Closure is a critical step in the development of a model, the information available about topological, transfer, and storage laws being very scarce. The physical significance of the closure laws must not be forgotten, especially since numerous, more or less arbitrary assumptions are unavoidable.

Restrictions on the form of the closure laws result from the fact that the set of

Table 1.2.2 Summary of Closure Problem

Dependent variables appearing in balance equations	Number	Corresponding equations
ρ_k, U_k, h_k, p_k	8	6 field balance equations 2 equations of state (1 per phase)
τ_k, q_k	4	4 constitutive laws (2 per phase)
α_k	2	1 void fraction topological law 1 relationship, $\alpha_G + \alpha_L = 1$
M_{kI}	2	1 interfacial balance (jump condition) 1 interfacial mass transfer law
$(MV)_{kI}, (FF)_{kI}, (FP)_{kI}$	6	1 interfacial balance (jump condition) 5 interfacial momentum transfer laws[a]
$(I\sigma)_I$	1	1 interfacial momentum storage law
$(MH)_{kI}, (MC)_{kI}, (EF)_{kI}, (EP)_{kI}, (EQ)_{kI}$	10	1 interfacial balance (jump condition) 9 interfacial energy transfer laws[a]
$(E\sigma)_I$	1	1 interfacial energy storage law
$(FF)_{kW}, (FP)_{kW}$	4	4 wall momentum transfer laws[a]
$(EF)_{kW}, (EP)_{kW}, (EQ)_{kW}$	6	6 wall energy transfer laws[a]

[a]It is stressed here that the laws written for $(FP)_{kI}$ and $(FP)_{kW}$ on the one hand, and for $(EP)_{kI}$ and $(EP)_{kW}$ on the other hand, must be compatible, respectively, with the Gauss theorem and the Leibniz rule, [1.2.148] and [1.2.152].

equations must be left formally unchanged by any Galilean change of frame and by any change of the origin of enthalpies (Bouré 1978a). These restrictions are

$$(MV)_{kI} = \sum_j (M_{kI}^j U_{Mk}^j) \quad \text{with} \sum_j M_{kI}^j = M_{kI} \qquad [1.2.155]$$

$$(MH)_{kI} = \sum_j (M_{kI}^j h_{Tk}^j) \quad \text{with} \sum_j M_{kI}^j = M_{kI} \qquad [1.2.156]$$

$$(MC)_{kI} = \sum_j \{M_{kI}^j [U_{Mk}^j \cdot U_{Ck}^j - \tfrac{1}{2}(U_{Ck}^j)^2]\} \quad \text{with} \sum_j M_{kI}^j = M_{kI}$$
$$[1.2.157]$$

$$(EF)_{kI} = \sum_j [(FF)_{kI}^k \cdot U_{Dk}^j] \quad \text{with} \sum_j (FF)_{kI}^j = (FF)_{kI} \qquad [1.2.158]$$

$$(EP)_{kI} = \sum_j [(FP)_{kI}^j \cdot U_{Pk}^j] \quad \text{with} \sum_j (FP)_{kI}^j = (FP)_{kI} \qquad [1.2.159]$$

$$(E\sigma)_I = \sum_j [(I\sigma)_I^j \cdot U_{\sigma I}] \quad \text{with} \sum_j (I\sigma)_I^j = (I\sigma)_I \qquad [1.2.160]$$

$$(EF)_{kW} = \sum_j [(\mathbf{FF})^j_{kW} \cdot \mathbf{U}_{DkW}] \quad \text{with} \quad \sum_j (\mathbf{FF})^j_{kW} = (\mathbf{FF})_{kW} \quad [1.2.161]$$

$$(EP)_{kW} = \sum_j [(\mathbf{FP})^j_{kW} \cdot \mathbf{U}_{PkW}] \quad \text{with} \quad \sum_j (\mathbf{FP})^j_{kW} = (\mathbf{FP})_{kW} \quad [1.2.162]$$

In these expressions, $\mathbf{U}^j_{Mk}$, h^j_{Tk}, $\mathbf{U}^j_{Ck}$, $\mathbf{U}^j_{Dk}$, $\mathbf{U}^j_{Pk}$, $\mathbf{U}^j_{\sigma I}$, $\mathbf{U}^j_{DkW}$, and $\mathbf{U}^j_{PkW}$ are arbitrary velocities or enthalpies. All the other closure laws must be left formally unchanged by the foregoing changes. In particular, they must involve neither velocities (only velocity differences) nor enthalpies (only enthalpy differences) nor $\partial/\partial t$ operators.

The field viscous and conduction terms:

$$\frac{\partial}{\partial z}(A\alpha_k \tau_k \cdot \mathbf{n}_z) \quad \frac{\partial}{\partial z}[A\alpha_k(\tau_k \cdot \mathbf{n}_z) \cdot \mathbf{U}_k] \quad \frac{\partial}{\partial z}(A\alpha_k \mathbf{q}_k \cdot \mathbf{n}_g)$$

are generally small compared to the other terms of the momentum and energy balances. (This must not be considered as granted in all cases. In liquid metals, for instance, the conduction term may become sizable.) Moreover, their presence, using classical constitutive laws for τ_k and $\mathbf{q}_k$, results in the occurrence of second-order partial derivatives in the balance equations. In practice, these terms are always neglected, which removes four constitutive laws from table 1.2.2.

The surface tension terms:

$$(\mathbf{I}\sigma)_I \text{ and } (E\sigma)_I$$

are also generally small and neglected, at least in nuclear engineering applications, which removes the two storage laws from table 1.2.2.

When forms [1.2.149] and [1.2.153] are used instead of, respectively, forms [1.2.147] and [1.2.151] for the momentum and energy balances, it is no longer necessary to specify $(\mathbf{FP})_{kI}$ and $(\mathbf{FP})_{kW}$, $(EP)_{kI}$, and $(EP)_{kW}$ (eight laws, which must be compatible with the Gauss theorem [1.2.148] and the Leibniz rule [1.2.152]), but only $\Sigma_k(\mathbf{FP})_{kI}$ and $\Sigma_k(EP)_{kI}$ (two laws). However, the problem is not as simple as it appears, since widespread assumptions (namely p_k uniform and not fluctuating over the control volume, and algebraic transfer terms) lead to a hyperbolic set of first-order partial differential equations when forms [1.2.149] and [1.2.151] are used, and to a nonhyperbolic set when forms [1.2.149] and [1.2.153] are used. In fact, because of the assumption on p_k, [1.2.148] and [1.2.152] may be reduced to

$$A(\mathbf{FP})_{kI} + A(\mathbf{FP})_{kW} = p_k \frac{\partial(A\alpha_k)}{\partial z}\mathbf{n}_z \quad [1.2.163]$$

$$A(EP)_{kI} + A(EP)_{kW} = -p_k \frac{\partial(A\alpha_k)}{\partial t} \quad [1.2.164]$$

which shows that the foregoing assumptions may be incompatible, at least when [1.2.147] and [1.2.151] are used. The mathematical nature of the set of equations cannot be ascertained as long as the topological and transfer laws are not specified.

This mathematical nature [a set of first-order partial differential equations is hyperbolic when all its characteristic directions (Courant & Hilbert 1961) are real, strictly hyperbolic when moreover these characteristic directions are distinct and finite, and nonhyperbolic when some characteristic directions are complex] has been a subject of controversy, as illustrated by the papers by Lyczkowski et al. (1978) and Bouré & Latrobe (1976–1977). It must be reemphasized that the primary problem is that of closure, the problem of the mathematical nature of the set being secondary from the physical point of view.

However, the mathematical nature of the set has numerical as well as physical implications of major practical importance, and some discussion may be useful. The numerical methods used in two-phase flow calculations are adapted from single-phase flow methods. Single-phase flow models are hyperbolic and single-phase flow problems are posed as initial-value or boundary-value problems. It turns out that for nonhyperbolic sets of equations, the *linear* initial- or boundary-value problem is not correctly set and leads to instabilities, a property on which everybody agrees.

From this point on, three lines of reasoning are possible, and the present state of knowledge does not enable a clear choice to be made:

1. The nature of the two-phase flow sets of equations is not a priori determined, but when the set is nonhyperbolic, the initial- or boundary-value problem is not the right problem to pose. This line of reasoning was explored by Bouré & Latrobe (1976–1977).
2. The nature of the two-phase flow sets of equations is not a priori determined, but when the set is nonhyperbolic, the linearized problem is actually unstable, the possible stability of the physical system resulting from nonlinear effects.
3. The linear initial- or boundary-value problem is actually representative of the two-phase flow behavior, and the two-phase flow set of equations must be hyperbolic.

These three approaches are not completely mutually exclusive. The last two lines of reasoning lead naturally to the consideration of flow pattern transitions as instability phenomena. The controversy arose from the fact that most authors restrict themselves to the third possibility.

When the frame of reference is fixed with respect to the pipe (a very common case), the wall transfer terms $(EF)_{kW}$ and $(EP)_{kW}$ vanish, which removes four transfer laws from table 1.2.2. It is not possible in this chapter to make more specific recommendations on practical closure laws. The corresponding knowledge is missing, especially when transients are involved. Ad hoc closure laws have been proposed by many authors of models. Some are given in the following chapters.

1.2.6.6 Discussion

The balance equations [1.2.145]–[1.2.147] or [1.2.149]–[1.2.151] or [1.2.153] and [1.2.154] are written as they result directly from the conservation principles. Hence the term *primary*. The term *conservative* is also used for the field balance equations [1.2.145], [1.2.147], and [1.2.151] because no coefficient appears before the partial derivatives.

Practical use of the primary balance equations is hampered by their complexity. Moreover, the resulting set of partial differential equations is generally singular for $\alpha_G = 0$ or 1 (and numerically ill-conditioned for small and large values of α_G), since many coefficients vanish in the equations of the corresponding phase. However, precisely because they do not involve further algebra, primary balance equations are often of interest in theoretical studies.

The primary balance equations are at the basis of all models, but they are generally transformed before use. Customary transformations involve expansion of the partial derivatives and linear combinations between the various balance equations. A large number of the resulting sets, which are all mathematically equivalent to the set of equations [1.2.145]–[1.2.147], [1.2.150], [1.2.151], and [1.2.154], may be found in the literature. Only the most important are given in the following sections. Customary transformations also involve further assumptions, restrictions, and simplifications.

1.2.7 TOWARD PRACTICAL PIPE-FLOW EQUATIONS: PHASE EQUATIONS, SECONDARY FORMS

As just recalled, numerous equivalent forms may be proposed for the set of field balance equations. *Secondary* phase equations result from linear combinations of the three *primary* phase equations [1.2.145], [1.2.147] or [1.2.149], [1.2.151] or [1.2.153]. Each secondary equation combines at least two of the mass, momentum, and energy balances, but usually retains the essence of one of these balances only. It is customary to name each secondary phase equation after the corresponding primary balance.

When the equations are written in terms of the dependent variables α_k, p_k, $\mathbf{U}_k$, h_k, and when the classical assumptions (see section 1.2.6.5) are made that p_k is uniform and not fluctuating over the control volume and field viscous and conduction terms are negligible, the simplest set of secondary phase equations is the one given below. Other equivalent sets would involve more field terms.

1.2.7.1 Mass

Eliminating the enthalpy derivatives from the expanded mass balance of phase k is possible through the combination

$$\frac{1}{A}\,[1.2.145] \;-\; \frac{1}{A\rho_k}\left(\frac{\partial \rho_k}{\partial h_k}\right)_p \left\{ [1.2.153] \;-\; \eta\mathbf{U}_k\;[1.2.149] \;-\left(h_k - \frac{\eta}{2}\,\mathbf{U}_k^2\right)[1.2.145]\right\}$$

Taking into account the thermodynamic relationship

$$\left(\frac{\partial \rho_k}{\partial p_k}\right)_h + \frac{\eta}{\rho_k}\left(\frac{\partial \rho_k}{\partial h_k}\right)_p = \left(\frac{\partial \rho_k}{\partial p_k}\right)_s$$

the partial derivatives of the density that appear when ρ_k is eliminated by means of the equation of state of phase k are $(\partial\rho_k/\partial p_k)_s$ and $(\partial\rho_k/\partial h_k)_p$. They are denoted, respectively, ρ'_{kPs} and ρ'_{kHP}. Similarly, $\partial A/\partial t$ and $\partial A/\partial z$ are denoted, respectively, A'_t and A'_z.

The secondary mass equation is

$$\rho_k \left(\frac{\partial \alpha_k}{\partial t} + w_k \frac{\partial \alpha_k}{\partial z} \right) + \alpha_k \rho'_{kPs} \left(\frac{\partial p_k}{\partial t} + w_k \frac{\partial p_k}{\partial z} \right) + \alpha_k \rho_k \frac{\partial w_k}{\partial z} + \alpha_k \rho_k \left(\frac{A'_t}{A} + w_k \frac{A'_z}{A} \right)$$

$$- M_{kI} + \frac{\rho'_{kHp}}{\rho_k} \left[(MH)_{kI} - M_{kI} h_k + (EQ)_{kI} + (EQ)_{kW} \right]$$

$$+ \eta \frac{\rho'_{kHp}}{\rho_k} \left[(MC)_{kI} - (MV)_{kI} \cdot \mathbf{U}_k + \frac{1}{2} M_{kI} \mathbf{U}_k^2 + (EF)_{kI} - (FF)_{kI} \cdot \mathbf{U}_k \right.$$

$$\left. + (EF)_{kW} - (FF)_{kW} \cdot \mathbf{U}_k \right] = 0 \qquad [1.2.165]$$

It is interesting to compare the form of the transfer terms in [1.2.165] to [1.2.155]–[1.2.158] and [1.2.161].

1.2.7.2 Momentum

Simplifying the momentum balance of phase k is possible through the combination

$$\frac{1}{A \alpha_k \rho_k} ([1.2.149] - \mathbf{U}_k [1.2.145])$$

The secondary momentum equation is

$$\frac{1}{\rho_k} \frac{\partial p_k}{\partial z} \mathbf{n}_z + \frac{\partial \mathbf{U}_k}{\partial t} + w_k \frac{\partial \mathbf{U}_k}{\partial z} - \frac{(MV)_{kI} - M_{kI} \mathbf{U}_k}{\alpha_k \rho_k} - \frac{(FF)_{kI}}{\alpha_k \rho_k}$$

$$- \frac{(FF)_{kW}}{\alpha_k \rho_k} - \mathbf{b} = 0 \qquad [1.2.166]$$

Since the transfer terms must tend toward zero when α_k tends toward zero (Bouré 1978c), the division by α_k is allowed and the transfer laws must be chosen accordingly.

1.2.7.3 Energy

The secondary energy equation is the combination

$$\frac{1}{A \alpha_k \rho_k} \left\{ [1.2.153] - \eta \mathbf{U}_k \cdot [1.2.149] - \left(h_k - \frac{\eta}{2} \mathbf{U}_k^2 \right) [1.2.145] \right\}$$

already used to simplify the mass balance.

The secondary energy equation is

$$\left(\frac{\partial h_k}{\partial t} - \frac{\eta}{\rho_k} \frac{\partial p_k}{\partial t} \right) + w_k \left(\frac{\partial h_k}{\partial z} - \frac{\eta}{\rho_k} \frac{\partial p_k}{\partial z} \right) - \frac{(MH)_{kI} - M_{kI} h_k}{\alpha_k \rho_k} - \frac{(EQ)_{kI}}{\alpha_k \rho_k} - \frac{(EQ)_{kW}}{\alpha_k \rho_k}$$

$$- \eta \, \frac{(MC)_{kI} - (\mathbf{MV})_{kI} \cdot \mathbf{U}_k + \frac{1}{2} \, M_{kI} \mathbf{U}_k^2}{\alpha_k \rho_k} - \eta \, \frac{(EF)_{kI} - (\mathbf{FF})_{kI} \cdot \mathbf{U}_k}{\alpha_k \rho_k}$$

$$- \eta \, \frac{(EF)_{kW} - (\mathbf{FF})_{kW} \cdot \mathbf{U}_k}{\alpha_k \rho_k} = 0 \qquad\qquad [1.2.167]$$

Since $T_k ds_k = dh_k - (\eta/\rho_k) \, dp_k$, [1.2.167] is essentially the entropy balance equation of phase k. It may be observed that [1.2.167] is under the *characteristic* form. It expresses the fact that, because of the assumptions made, entropy variations are transported along Oz at velocity w.

1.2.7.4 Discussion

Use of the set of secondary balance equations [1.2.165]-[1.2.167] may be recommended within the framework of *complete* two-fluid models (i.e., when all conservation laws are actually written for both phases). However, in practical models, one or several balance laws are often replaced by assumptions [e.g., $h_k = h_{k\,\text{sat}}\,(p_k)$]. Since each secondary equation involves two or three balance laws, replacing one of the above secondary equations by an assumption has no plain physical significance and must be avoided.

Contrary to the set of primary conservation equations, and thanks to the divisions by α_k performed above, the set [1.2.165]-[1.2.167] is neither singular for $\alpha_G = 0$ or 1 nor ill-conditioned for small and large values of α_G.

1.2.8 TOWARD PRACTICAL PIPE-FLOW EQUATIONS: EQUATION SETS INVOLVING THE MIXTURE BALANCE EQUATIONS

The balance equations written in sections 1.2.6 and 1.2.7 are phase equations and interface equations. Their complete set (nine equations) is equivalent to a set consisting of three overall (mixture) balances, complemented, for instance, by three phase balances and three interface balances. The mixture balances express the conservation of mass, momentum, and energy for the two-phase mixture considered as a whole and are obtained on summing up the corresponding phase and interface balances in their primary forms. The mixture balances do not contain any interfacial transfer terms, since these terms cancel out in the addition. The wall transfer terms contained in the mixture balances are the sums of individual transfers between the wall and each phase. They are better known experimentally than these individual transfers.

Many practical models are simplified two-fluid models in which some individual phase balances are replaced by assumptions, the corresponding interface balances being ignored. However, the three mixture balances are implicit in all models. Therefore, explicit consideration of the mixture balances is of particular interest whenever simplified models are involved.

1.2.8.1 Mixture Mass Balance

It results from the addition of the three equations $[1.2.145\ G\ \text{and}\ L]$, $[1.2.146]$:

$$\frac{\partial}{\partial t}\left[A(\alpha_G\rho_G + \alpha_L\rho_L)\right] + \frac{\partial}{\partial z}\left[A(\alpha_G\rho_G w_G + \alpha_L\rho_L w_L)\right] = 0 \quad [1.2.168]$$

It may be observed that $\alpha_G\rho_G + \alpha_L\rho_L$ is the average mixture density within the control volume, and that $\alpha_G\rho_G w_G + \alpha_L\rho_L w_L$ is the mixture mass flux per unit cross section.

1.2.8.2 Mixture Momentum Balance

It results from the addition of the three equations $[1.2.147\ G\ \text{and}\ L]$, $[1.2.150]$, neglecting the field viscous terms:

$$\frac{\partial}{\partial t}\left[A(\alpha_G\rho_G \mathbf{U}_G + \alpha_L\rho_L \mathbf{U}_L)\right] + \frac{\partial}{\partial z}\left[A(\alpha_G\rho_G w_G \mathbf{U}_G + \alpha_L\rho_L w_L \mathbf{U}_L)\right]$$

$$+ \frac{\partial}{\partial z}\left[A(\alpha_G p_G + \alpha_L p_L)\right]\mathbf{n}_z - A(\mathbf{I}\sigma)_I - A\left[(\mathbf{FF})_{GW} + (\mathbf{FF})_{LW}\right]$$

$$- A\left[(\mathbf{FP})_{GW} + (\mathbf{FP})_{LW}\right] - A(\alpha_G\rho_G + \alpha_L\rho_L)\mathbf{b} = 0 \quad [1.2.169]$$

1.2.8.3 Mixture Energy Balance

It results from the addition of the three equations $[1.2.151\ G\ \text{and}\ L]$, $[1.2.154]$, neglecting the field viscous and conduction terms:

$$\frac{\partial}{\partial t}\left\{A\left[\alpha_G\rho_G\left(h_G + \frac{\eta}{2}\mathbf{U}_G^2\right) + \alpha_L\rho_L\left(h_L + \frac{\eta}{2}\mathbf{U}_L^2\right)\right]\right\} - \eta\frac{\partial}{\partial t}\left[A(\alpha_G p_G + \alpha_L p_L)\right]$$

$$+ \frac{\partial}{\partial z}\left\{A\left[\alpha_G\rho_G w_G\left(h_G + \frac{\eta}{2}\mathbf{U}_G^2\right) + \alpha_L\rho_L w_L\left(h_L + \frac{\eta}{2}\mathbf{U}_L^2\right)\right]\right\} - \eta A(E\sigma)_I$$

$$- \eta A\left[(EF)_{GW} + (EF)_{LW}\right] - \eta A\left[(EP)_{GW} + (EP)_{LW}\right] - A\left[(EQ)_{GW} + (EQ)_{LW}\right]$$

$$- \eta A(\alpha_G\rho_G\mathbf{U}_G + \alpha_L\rho_L\mathbf{U}_L)\cdot\mathbf{b} = 0 \quad [1.2.170]$$

1.2.8.4 Other Forms of the Mixture Balance Equations

There is, of course, some analogy between the mixture balance equations $[1.2.168]$–$[1.2.170]$ and the corresponding single-phase balance equations. As a matter of fact, examination of $[1.2.168]$–$[1.2.170]$ shows that the similarity would be complete if the two velocities $\mathbf{U}_G$ and $\mathbf{U}_L$ were equal. In such a case, defining $\mathbf{U}$, ρ, p, and h by

$$\mathbf{U} \triangleq \mathbf{U}_G = \mathbf{U}_L$$

$$\left.\begin{array}{l} \rho \stackrel{\triangle}{=} \alpha_G \rho_G + \alpha_L \rho_L \\[2mm] p \stackrel{\triangle}{=} \alpha_G p_G + \alpha_L p_L \\[2mm] h \stackrel{\triangle}{=} \dfrac{\alpha_G \rho_G h_G + \alpha_L \rho_L h_L}{\alpha_G \rho_G + \alpha_L \rho_L} \end{array}\right\} \qquad [1.2.171]$$

and introducing the overall wall transfer terms

$$(\mathbf{FF})_W \stackrel{\triangle}{=} (\mathbf{FF})_{GW} + (\mathbf{FF})_{LW} \qquad (\mathbf{FP})_W \stackrel{\triangle}{=} (\mathbf{FP})_{GW} + (\mathbf{FP})_{LW}$$

$$(EF)_W \stackrel{\triangle}{=} (EF)_{GW} + (EF)_{LW} \qquad (EP)_W \stackrel{\triangle}{=} (EP)_{GW} + (EP)_{LW}$$

$$(EQ)_W \stackrel{\triangle}{=} (EQ)_{GW} + (EQ)_{LW}$$

result in equations that are formally identical to the single-phase balance equations except for the surface tension terms. Unfortunately, this similarity is blurred by the existence of the two velocities $\mathbf{U}_G$ and $\mathbf{U}_L$.

As in the cases of the single-phase flow equations and of the phase equations (section 1.2.7), secondary forms may be obtained through combinations between the three mixture balance equations. However, again because of the presence of $\mathbf{U}_G$ and $\mathbf{U}_L$, the secondary mixture equations are not significantly simpler than the primary ones. Clearly, the existence of two velocities is the major reason for the complexity of the two-phase flow equations.

Since [1.2.168]–[1.2.170] pertain to the mixture, it may be of interest to let *mixture variables* appear explicitly in these equations. Several sets of mixture variables may be used. They must yield the proper single-phase limits when α_G tends toward 0 or 1. Obvious possibilities for the mixture density, the mixture pressure, and the mixture enthalpy are provided by [1.2.171]. However, because the equations of state of the phases are involved, it would not be pertinent to eliminate completely ρ_k, p_k, h_k from the balance equations; the mixture variables ρ, p, h must be regarded as convenient supplementary variables.

Two simple mixture velocities may be considered. The velocity of the center of mass

$$\mathbf{U}_M \stackrel{\triangle}{=} \frac{\alpha_G \rho_G \mathbf{U}_G + \alpha_L \rho_L \mathbf{U}_L}{\alpha_G \rho_G + \alpha_L \rho_L}$$

leads to

$$\mathbf{U}_G = \mathbf{U}_M + \frac{\alpha_L \rho_L}{\rho} \Delta\mathbf{U} \qquad \mathbf{U}_L = \mathbf{U}_M - \frac{\alpha_G \rho_G}{\rho} \Delta\mathbf{U} \qquad [1.2.172]$$

where

$$\Delta\mathbf{U} \stackrel{\triangle}{=} \mathbf{U}_G - \mathbf{U}_L \qquad [1.2.173]$$

is the velocity difference. The velocity of the center of volume

$$\mathbf{U} \stackrel{\triangle}{=} \alpha_G \mathbf{U}_G + \alpha_L \mathbf{U}_L$$

leads to

$$\mathbf{U}_G = \mathbf{U} + \alpha_L \Delta\mathbf{U} \qquad \mathbf{U}_L = \mathbf{U} - \alpha_G \Delta\mathbf{U} \qquad [1.2.174]$$

Using the center of mass velocity may appear more logical but, because of the presence of denominators in [1.2.172], it results in a good deal of complication. Using the center of volume velocity turns out to be more convenient. $\mathbf{U}_M$ and $\mathbf{U}$ are related through

$$\mathbf{U}_M = \mathbf{U} + \alpha_G \alpha_L \frac{\Delta\rho}{\rho} \Delta\mathbf{U} \qquad [1.2.175]$$

where $\Delta\rho \triangleq \rho_G - \rho_L$.

Finally, the mixture mass balance [1.2.168] reads

$$\frac{\partial}{\partial t}(A\rho) + \frac{\partial}{\partial z}[A(\rho w + \alpha_G \alpha_L \Delta\rho \Delta w)] = 0 \qquad [1.2.176]$$

The mixture momentum balance [1.2.169] reads

$$\frac{\partial}{\partial t}[A(\rho\mathbf{U} + \alpha_G \alpha_L \Delta\rho\Delta\mathbf{U})]$$

$$+ \frac{\partial}{\partial z}\{A[\rho w\mathbf{U} + \alpha_G \alpha_L \Delta\rho(w\Delta\mathbf{U} + \mathbf{U}\Delta w) + \alpha_G \alpha_L(\alpha_L \rho_G + \alpha_G \rho_L)\Delta w\Delta\mathbf{U}]\}$$

$$+ \frac{\partial}{\partial z}(Ap)\mathbf{n}_z - A(\mathbf{I}\sigma)_r - A(\mathbf{FF})_W - A(\mathbf{FP})_W - A\rho\mathbf{b} = 0 \qquad [1.2.177]$$

The combination $(1/A\rho)\,([1.2.177] - \mathbf{U}\,[1.2.176])$ is a secondary mixture momentum equation:

$$\frac{\partial\mathbf{U}}{\partial t} + \frac{1}{A\rho}\frac{\partial}{\partial t}(A\alpha_G \alpha_L \Delta\rho\Delta\mathbf{U}) + \left(w + \alpha_G \alpha_L \frac{\Delta\rho}{\rho}\Delta w\right)\frac{\partial\mathbf{U}}{\partial z}$$

$$+ \frac{1}{A\rho}\frac{\partial}{\partial z}\{A\alpha_G \alpha_L[(\Delta\rho)w\Delta\mathbf{U} + (\alpha_L \rho_G + \alpha_G \rho_L)\Delta w\Delta\mathbf{U}]\} + \frac{1}{A\rho}\frac{\partial}{\partial z}(Ap)\mathbf{n}_z$$

$$- \frac{1}{\rho}(\mathbf{I}\sigma)_I - \frac{1}{\rho}(\mathbf{FF})_W - \frac{1}{\rho}(\mathbf{FP})_W - \mathbf{b} = 0 \qquad [1.2.178]$$

The mixture energy balance [1.2.170] reads

$$\frac{\partial}{\partial t}\left\{A\rho h + \frac{\eta}{2}A\left[\rho\mathbf{U}^2 + 2\alpha_G \alpha_L(\Delta\rho)\mathbf{U}\cdot\Delta\mathbf{U} + \alpha_G \alpha_L(\alpha_L \rho_G + \alpha_G \rho_L)(\Delta\mathbf{U})^2\right]\right\}$$

$$- \eta\frac{\partial(Ap)}{\partial t} + \frac{\partial}{\partial z}\{A[\rho wh + \alpha_G \alpha_L \Delta w(\rho_G h_G - \rho_L h_L)]\}$$

$$+ \frac{\eta}{2}\frac{\partial}{\partial z}(A\{\rho w\mathbf{U}^2 + \alpha_G \alpha_L \Delta\rho(\mathbf{U}^2\Delta w + 2w\mathbf{U}\cdot\Delta\mathbf{U})$$

$$+ \alpha_G \alpha_L(\alpha_L \rho_G + \alpha_G \rho_L)[2\Delta w\mathbf{U}\cdot\Delta\mathbf{U} + w(\Delta\mathbf{U})^2]$$

$$+ \alpha_G \alpha_L(\alpha_L^2 \rho_G - \alpha_G^2 \rho_L)\Delta w(\Delta\mathbf{U})^2\})$$

$$- \eta A(E\sigma)_I - \eta A(EF)_W - \eta A(EP)_W - A(EQ)_W - \eta A(\rho\mathbf{U} + \alpha_G \alpha_L \Delta\rho\Delta\mathbf{U})\cdot\mathbf{b} = 0$$

$$[1.2.179]$$

The combination

$$\frac{1}{A\rho} \; [1.2.179] - \eta\mathbf{U} \cdot [1.2.177] - \left(h - \frac{\eta}{2}\mathbf{U}^2\right) [1.2.176]$$

is a secondary mixture energy equation. It contains the terms

$$\frac{\partial h}{\partial t} - \frac{\eta}{\rho}\frac{\partial p}{\partial t} + w\left(\frac{\partial h}{\partial z} - \frac{\eta}{\rho}\frac{\partial p}{\partial z}\right)$$

but also many partial derivative terms involving Δw and $\Delta\mathbf{U}$, which reduces its practical interest.

1.2.8.5 Discussion

For practical use, the foregoing mixture balance equations must be expanded, the various partial derivative terms being expressed in terms of the partial derivatives of the main dependent variables. With [1.2.168]–[1.2.170] as the starting point, the main dependent variables are often α_G, p_k, $\mathbf{U}_k$, h_k as in section 1.2.7. With [1.2.176], [1.2.177], or [1.2.178] and [1.2.179] as the starting point a convenient set of main dependent variables is α_G, p_k, $\mathbf{U}$, $\Delta\mathbf{U}$, h_k.

To complete the set of balance equations, the mixture balance equations must be complemented by three independent interfacial equations ([1.2.146], [1.2.150], and [1.2.154] or combinations of these) and three independent field equations. The simplest way to introduce the field equations is to use secondary phase equations (section 1.2.7).

The secondary "energy" equations [1.2.167 G and L] are simple. They are under the characteristic form. Each of them involves both the energy and the mass balances of the corresponding phase and is linearly independent of the mixture balances (in particular the mixture energy balance). Therefore, they can be used as two of the complementary field equations. Incidentally, this raises a vocabulary problem, since the set now contains three equations that are termed energy. Hence the necessity to distinguish carefully the energy balance equations (e.g., [1.2.151], [1.2.153], [1.2.170], and [1.2.179]) from the so-called energy equations that are *not* energy balances. Equation [1.2.167] can be regarded as controlling primarily the enthalpy h_k. Accordingly, it is often called the *thermal nonequilibrium equation of phase k*. Then the mixture energy balance equation [1.2.170] or [1.2.179] is often regarded as controlling primarily the void fraction α_G or the quality x, defined as

$$x \triangleq \frac{\alpha_G\rho_G w_G}{\alpha_G\rho_G w_G + \alpha_L\rho_L w_L}$$

The secondary momentum equations [1.2.166 G and L] are also simple. Any of them can be used as the last field equation. However, the difference between [1.2.166 G] and [1.2.166 L] is also of interest, because it introduces explicitly the velocity difference $\mathbf{U}_G - \mathbf{U}_L$ and preserves the symmetry of the roles of the phase variables. This equation, which may be called the *slip equation*, is

$$\left(\frac{1}{\rho_G} \frac{\partial p_G}{\partial z} - \frac{1}{\rho_L} \frac{\partial p_L}{\partial z} \right) \mathbf{n}_z + \frac{\partial}{\partial t} (\mathbf{U}_G - \mathbf{U}_L) + w_G \frac{\partial \mathbf{U}_G}{\partial z} - w_L \frac{\partial \mathbf{U}_L}{\partial z}$$

$$- \left[\frac{(\mathbf{MV})_{GI} - M_{GI}\mathbf{U}_G}{\alpha_G \rho_G} - \frac{(\mathbf{MV})_{LI} - M_{LI}\mathbf{U}_L}{\alpha_L \rho_L} \right] - \left[\frac{(\mathbf{FF})_{GI}}{\alpha_G \rho_G} - \frac{(\mathbf{FF})_{LI}}{\alpha_L \rho_L} \right]$$

$$- \left[\frac{(\mathbf{FF})_{GW}}{\alpha_G \rho_G} - \frac{(\mathbf{FF})_{LW}}{\alpha_L \rho_L} \right] = 0 \qquad\qquad [1.2.180]$$

or, introducing $\mathbf{U}$ and $\Delta\mathbf{U}$, w and Δw:

$$- \Delta w \Delta \mathbf{U} \frac{\partial \alpha_G}{\partial z} + \left(\frac{1}{\rho_G} \frac{\partial p_G}{\partial z} - \frac{1}{\rho_L} \frac{\partial p_L}{\partial z} \right) \mathbf{n}_z + \Delta w \frac{\partial \mathbf{U}}{\partial z} + \frac{\partial}{\partial t} (\Delta\mathbf{U})$$

$$+ [w - (\alpha_G - \alpha_L) \Delta w] \frac{\partial}{\partial z} (\Delta\mathbf{U}) - \left[\frac{(\mathbf{MV})_{GI} - M_{GI}\mathbf{U}_G}{\alpha_G \rho_G} - \frac{(\mathbf{MV})_{LI} - M_{LI}\mathbf{U}_L}{\alpha_L \rho_L} \right]$$

$$- \left[\frac{(\mathbf{FF})_{GI}}{\alpha_G \rho_G} - \frac{(\mathbf{FF})_{LI}}{\alpha_L \rho_L} \right] - \left[\frac{(\mathbf{FF})_{GW}}{\alpha_G \rho_G} - \frac{(\mathbf{FF})_{LW}}{\alpha_L \rho_L} \right] = 0 \qquad\qquad [1.2.181]$$

Finally, the set of balance equations involving explicitly the mixture balance equations consists of:

1. The mixture mass and energy balance equations, [1.2.168] or [1.2.176] and [1.2.170] or [1.2.179], the associated main dependent variables being α_G, p_G, p_L.
2. The mixture momentum equation and the slip equation, [1.2.169] or [1.2.177] or [1.2.178] and [1.2.180] or [1.2.181], the associated main dependent variables being $\mathbf{U}_G$ and $\mathbf{U}_L$ or $\mathbf{U}$ and $\Delta\mathbf{U}$.
3. The thermal nonequilibrium equations [1.2.167 G and L], the associated main dependent variables being h_G and h_L.
4. The interfacial balance equations [1.2.146], [1.2.150], [1.2.154].

With reference to table 1.2.2, it can be noted that only $\Sigma_k (\mathbf{FP})_{kW}$ and $\Sigma_k (EP)_{kW}$ appear in the foregoing set (in the mixture momentum and energy equations, respectively), instead of the individual terms $(\mathbf{FP})_{kW}$ and $(EP)_{kW}$.

It can also be noted that only $\Sigma_k (\mathbf{FP})_{kI}$ and $\Sigma_k (EP)_{kI}$ appear in the foregoing set, instead of the individual terms $(\mathbf{FP})_{kI}$ and $(EP)_{kI}$. Moreover, these terms appear only in the interfacial balances (momentum and energy, respectively). However, $\Sigma_k (\mathbf{FP})_{kI}$ and $\Sigma_k (EP)_{kI}$ are related to $\Sigma_k (\mathbf{FP})_{kW}$ and $\Sigma_k (EP)_{kW}$, respectively, as consequences of [1.2.163] and [1.2.164]—i.e., of the Gauss theorem and Leibniz rule, taking the assumptions on pressure into account. It is therefore necessary to write explicitly the momentum and energy interfacial balances.

Eliminating $\Sigma_k (\mathbf{FP})_{kI}$ and $\Sigma_k (EP)_{kI}$ or $\Sigma_k (\mathbf{FP})_{kW}$ and $\Sigma_k (EP)_{kW}$ from the set is possible, using [1.2.163] and [1.2.164]. Since $(EP)_{kW}$ is often zero in practice (i.e., when the frame of reference is fixed with respect to the pipe; section 1.2.6.4), it is advisable to eliminate $\Sigma_k (FP)_{kI}$ and $\Sigma_k (EP)_{kI}$ and to replace, in the interfacial energy balance equation [1.2.154]:

$$\eta A \sum_k (EP)_{kI} \quad \text{by} -\eta A \sum_k (EP)_{kW} - \eta \left(p_G \frac{\partial A\alpha_G}{\partial t} + p_L \frac{\partial A\alpha_L}{\partial t} \right)$$

and in the interfacial momentum balance equation [1.2.150]:

$$A \sum_k (FP)_{kI} \quad \text{by} -A \sum_k (FP)_{kW} + \left(p_G \frac{\partial A\alpha_G}{\partial z} + p_L \frac{\partial A\alpha_L}{\partial z} \right) n_z$$

This elimination being made, the matrices A_t and A_z of the foregoing set, written

$$A_t \frac{\partial X}{\partial t} + A_z \frac{\partial X}{\partial z} + B = 0 \qquad [1.2.182]$$

are given in tables 1.2.3 and 1.2.4. X is the vector of the main dependent variables:

$$X^t = [\alpha_G, p_G, p_L, U, \Delta U, h_G, h_L]$$

B is the vector containing the terms due to changes of the cross-sectional area, the surface tension terms, the remaining interfacial and wall transfer terms, and the gravity terms. The form [1.2.182] does not imply anything about the mathematical form of B, in particular about the presence or absence in B of partial derivatives of the main dependent variables. Again, it is recalled that for a given set of values for the dependent variables X, and depending on the mathematical forms of B and of the topological law, the resulting closed set of equations may be hyperbolic or nonhyperbolic (section 1.2.6.5).

A_t and A_z are *rectangular matrices* (nine rows, seven columns). In tables 1.2.3 and 1.2.4, the rows correspond, in order, to [1.2.168, 170, 169]/A, [1.2.181], [1.2.167 G and L], and [1.2.146, 154, 150]. The following conventions are used:

$$\rho'_{kPH} \stackrel{\Delta}{=} \left(\frac{\partial \rho_k}{\partial p_k} \right)_{h_k} \qquad \rho'_{kHP} \stackrel{\Delta}{=} \left(\frac{\partial \rho_k}{\partial h_k} \right)_{p_k} \qquad h_k^* \stackrel{\Delta}{=} h_k + \frac{\eta}{2} U_k^2$$

and, f_k being any arbitrary quantity pertaining to phase k,

$$\Sigma f \stackrel{\Delta}{=} f_G + f_L \qquad \Delta f \stackrel{\Delta}{=} f_G - f_L$$

A dot following a vector in some elements of the matrices indicates that the scalar product is to be taken between this vector and the corresponding partial derivative (which is, of course, also a vector).

Table 1.2.3 Matrix A_t

	$\dfrac{\partial \alpha_G}{\partial t}$	$\dfrac{\partial p_G}{\partial t}$	$\dfrac{\partial p_L}{\partial t}$	$\dfrac{\partial U}{\partial t}$	$\dfrac{\partial \Delta U}{\partial t}$	$\dfrac{\partial h_G}{\partial t}$	$\dfrac{\partial h_L}{\partial t}$
Mixture mass $\dfrac{}{A}$	$\Delta \rho$	$\alpha_G \rho'_{GPH}$	$\alpha_L \rho'_{LPH}$	0	0	$\alpha_G \rho'_{GHP}$	$\alpha_L \rho'_{LHP}$
Mixture energy $\dfrac{}{A}$	$\begin{aligned}&\Delta(\rho h^*)\\&-\eta\Sigma(\alpha\rho U)\cdot\Delta U\\&-\eta\Delta p\end{aligned}$	$\begin{aligned}&\alpha_G \rho'_{GPH} h^*_G\\&-\eta\alpha_G\end{aligned}$	$\begin{aligned}&\alpha_L \rho'_{LPH} h^*_L\\&-\eta\alpha_L\end{aligned}$	$\eta\Sigma(\alpha\rho U)\cdot$	$\eta\alpha_G\alpha_L\Delta(\rho U)\cdot$	$\alpha_G \rho_G\left(1+\dfrac{\rho'_{GHP}}{\rho_G}h^*_G\right)$	$\alpha_L \rho_L\left(1+\dfrac{\rho'_{LHP}}{\rho_L}h^*_L\right)$
Mixture momentum $\dfrac{}{A}$	$\Delta\rho(U-\Delta\alpha\Delta U)$	$\alpha_G \rho'_{GPH} U_G$	$\alpha_L \rho'_{LPH} U_L$	$\Sigma(\alpha\rho)$	$\alpha_G\alpha_L\Delta\rho$	$\alpha_G \rho'_{GHP} U_G$	$\alpha_L \rho'_{LHP} U_L$
Slip	0	0	0	0	1	0	0
Thermal nonequilibrium phase G	0	$-\dfrac{\eta}{\rho_G}$	0	0	0	1	0
Thermal nonequilibrium phase L	0	0	$-\dfrac{\eta}{\rho_L}$	0	0	0	1
Interfacial mass	0	0	0	0	0	0	0
Interfacial energy	$-\eta\Delta p$	0	0	0	0	0	0
Interfacial momentum	0	0	0	0	0	0	0

Table 1.2.4 Matrix A_z

	$\dfrac{\partial \alpha_G}{\partial z}$	$\dfrac{\partial p_G}{\partial z}$	$\dfrac{\partial p_L}{\partial z}$	$\dfrac{\partial U}{\partial z}$	$\dfrac{\partial \Delta U}{\partial z}$	$\dfrac{\partial h_G}{\partial z}$	$\dfrac{\partial h_L}{\partial z}$
Mixture mass A	$\Delta\rho(w - \Delta\alpha\Delta w)$	$\alpha_G\rho'_{GPH}w_G$	$\alpha_L\rho'_{LPH}w_L$	$\Sigma(\alpha\rho)\mathbf{n}_z\cdot$	$\alpha_G\alpha_L\Delta\rho\,\mathbf{n}_z\cdot$	$\alpha_G\rho'_{GHP}w_G$	$\alpha_L\rho'_{LHP}w_L$
Mixture energy A	$\Delta(\rho h^*)(w - \Delta\alpha\Delta w)$ $-\eta\Sigma(\alpha\rho w\mathbf{U})\cdot\Delta\mathbf{U}$	$\alpha_G\rho'_{GPH}w_G h^*_G$	$\alpha_L\rho'_{LPH}w_L h^*_L$	$\Sigma(\alpha\rho h^*)\mathbf{n}_z\cdot$ $+\eta\Sigma(\alpha\rho w\mathbf{U})\cdot$	$\alpha_G\alpha_L\Delta(\rho h^*)\mathbf{n}_z\cdot$ $+\eta\alpha_G\alpha_L\Delta(\rho w\mathbf{U})\cdot$	$\alpha_G\rho'_{G}w_G\left(1 + \dfrac{\rho'_{GHP}}{\rho_G}h^*_G\right)$	$\alpha_L\rho'_{L}w_L\left(1 + \dfrac{\rho'_{LHP}}{\rho_L}h^*_L\right)$
Mixture momentum A	$\Delta(\rho w)(\mathbf{U} - \Delta\alpha\Delta\mathbf{U})$ $-\Sigma(\alpha\rho\mathbf{U})\Delta w$ $+\Delta p\mathbf{n}_z$	$\alpha_G\rho'_{GPH}w_G\mathbf{U}_G$ $+\alpha_G\mathbf{n}_z$	$\alpha_L\rho'_{LPH}w_L\mathbf{U}_L$ $+\alpha_L\mathbf{n}_z$	$\Sigma(\alpha\rho w)$ $+\Sigma(\alpha\rho\mathbf{U})\mathbf{n}_z\cdot$	$\alpha_G\alpha_L\Delta(\rho w)$ $+\alpha_G\alpha_L\Delta(\rho\mathbf{U})\mathbf{n}_z\cdot$	$\alpha_G\rho'_{GHP}w_G\mathbf{U}_G$	$\alpha_L\rho'_{LHP}w_L\mathbf{U}_L$
Slip	$-\Delta w\Delta\mathbf{U}$	$\dfrac{1}{\rho_G}\mathbf{n}_z$	$-\dfrac{1}{\rho_L}\mathbf{n}_z$	Δw	$w - \Delta\alpha\Delta w$	0	0
Thermal nonequilibrium phase G	0	$-\dfrac{\eta}{\rho_G}w_G$	0	0	0	w_G	0
Thermal nonequilibrium phase L	0	0	$-\dfrac{\eta}{\rho_L}w_L$	0	0	0	w_L
Interfacial mass	0	0	0	0	0	0	0
Interfacial energy	0	0	0	0	0	0	0
Interfacial momentum	$\Delta p\mathbf{n}_z$	0	0	0	0	0	0

1.2.9   TOWARD PRACTICAL PIPE–FLOW EQUATIONS: SIMPLIFIED MODELS

1.2.9.1   Introduction: Bases of Simplified Models

As discussed in section 1.2.6.5, closing the set of equations of the complete two-fluid model is not easy in the present state of knowledge. Accordingly, numerous models are based on incomplete two-fluid models, in which the closure problem is simplified by the use of *restrictions*. These restrictions may be expressed either by equations or inequalities.

Restrictions expressed by equations, such as the classical restrictions $p_G = p_L$, $\mathbf{U}_G = \mathbf{U}_L$, $h_G = h_{G\,\mathrm{sat}}(p_G)$, $h_L = h_{L\,\mathrm{sat}}(p_G)$, involve the course of evolution of dependent variables, since they entail restrictions on the derivatives of the corresponding variables (e.g., $p_G = p_L$ entails $\partial p_G/\partial t = \partial p_L/\partial t$, $\partial p_G/\partial z = \partial p_L/\partial z$). Accordingly, such restrictions may be called *evolution restrictions*.

Restrictions expressed by inequalities are, for instance,

$$\frac{p_G - p_L}{\Delta p_0} \ll 1 \qquad \frac{\mathbf{U}_G - \mathbf{U}_L}{\Delta \mathbf{U}_0} \ll 1 \qquad \frac{h_G - h_{G\,\mathrm{sat}}(p_G)}{\Delta h_0} \ll 1 \qquad \frac{h_L - h_{L\,\mathrm{sat}}(p_G)}{\Delta h_0} \ll 1$$

Δp_0, $\Delta \mathbf{U}_0$, Δh_0 being characteristic values. The inequalities state that the differences between some dependent variables and corresponding reference values remain small when compared to characteristic values of these differences. Such restrictions may be called *approximations* and written $p_G \cong p_L$, $\mathbf{U}_G \cong \mathbf{U}_L$, $h_G \cong h_{G\,\mathrm{sat}}(p_G)$, $h_L \cong h_{L\,\mathrm{sat}}(p_G)$.

Obviously, evolution restrictions are stronger than approximations. They are also more difficult to appraise because of their implications for derivatives, and may be questionable, as when propagation phenomena are involved (as discussed in section 1.2.5.2). However, evolution restrictions are the classical way to introduce simplified models. By making, for instance, a physical assumption about the evolution of one of the main dependent variables, it is mathematically possible to ignore the void fraction topological law (section 1.2.5.2). By making physical assumptions about the evolutions of several dependent variables, it is possible to ignore, besides the void fraction topological law, one or several balance equations and the transfer terms that do not appear in the other equations. This is the origin of must current simplified models.

The only rigorous way to establish a simplified model based on evolution assumptions is to satisfy the conditions for the assumed evolution(s) to belong to the solution of the complete model. As expected, it is easy to show, by the theory of linear algebraic sets of equations, that the above conditions involve the void fraction topological law and the transfer laws (Bouré 1975). When these conditions are fulfilled, the complete set of equations, which contains more equations than unknown quantities, may be reduced, some equations being linear combinations of the remaining equations. The calculations are easy, but tedious, involving large determinants.

In current practice, when a simplified model is based on evolution assumptions, the ignored balance equations are chosen according to physical intuition, without further justification. If, for instance, $h_k = h_{k\,\text{sat}}(p_k)$ is assumed, the energy balance equation of phase k is ignored. As pointed out in section 1.2.7.4, use, in the simplified model, of secondary equations involving the ignored balances must be avoided.

Using approximations is a better way to introduce simplified models. As shown above, approximation involves consideration of *reference flow conditions* and of *differences* between the actual flow conditions and the reference flow conditions. The reference conditions should be as close as possible to the actual flow conditions. They often correspond to some idea of what might be called equilibrium conditions and are accordingly loosely called equilibrium conditions. A set of dependent variables is used to describe the reference conditions. Another set of dependent variables—the difference variables or, loosely, the nonequilibrium variables—is used to describe the differences between the actual and reference flow conditions.

The set of dependent variables describing the reference conditions is often associated with the mixture balance equations, as well as with some complementary algebraic equations. Based on the relative importance of the various terms in the secondary "balance" equations and in the void fraction topological law, each difference variable is explicitly associated with one of these equations (see example below).

Simplified models are obtained by ignoring some difference variable(s) and the associated equation(s). In this approach, a simplified model is then based (1) on the assumption that the order of magnitude of the ignored difference variable(s) is small, and (2) when the ignored difference variable(s) appear in the equations associated with the reference conditions, on the assumption that the corresponding term(s) may be neglected.

It is possible (Bouré 1978b) to get rid of the second assumption through an appropriate choice of the reference conditions. These reference conditions are described by seven dependent variables (e.g., $\mathbf{X}_0^t = [\alpha_{G0},\ p_{G0},\ p_{L0},\ U_{G0},\ U_{L0},\ h_{G0},\ h_{L0}]$). The associated equations involve the mixture balance equations, written with a particular set of topological and transfer laws, and consist, in fact, of three differential equations and four algebraic equations. The difference variables $\delta\mathbf{X} = \mathbf{X} - \mathbf{X}_0$ are also seven in number. However this sophisticated treatment is recent and is not considered further here.

In the rest of this section the reference conditions are, by analogy with the single-phase flow description, described by three variables (e.g., α_G, p_G, $\mathbf{U}$) and the actual flow conditions are characterized by these variables and four complementary variables (e.g., $\Delta p \triangleq p_G - p_L$, $\Delta \mathbf{U}$, h_G, h_L). The choice of p_G as a reference stems from the fact that, local thermodynamic equilibrium being assumed, the enthalpies of the phases at the interface are close to $h_{k\,\text{sat}}(p_G)$ (Ishii 1975). The actual enthalpies h_G and h_L may then be compared to $h_{G\,\text{sat}}(p_G)$ and $h_{L\,\text{sat}}(p_G)$ and the differences $\Delta h_G \triangleq h_G - h_{G\,\text{sat}}(p_G)$, $\Delta h_L \triangleq h_L - h_{L\,\text{sat}}(p_G)$ may be regarded as characterizing thermal nonequilibriums.

Since any consistent model should involve at least the three mixture balance equations, the three reference condition variables are associated with the mixture balance equations and the set used is the set given in section 1.2.8.5. Concerning the difference variables, Δp is associated with the void fraction topological law, ΔU with the slip equation [1.2.180] or [1.2.181], and h_G and h_L with the thermal nonequilibrium equations [1.2.167 G and L]. This is only a convenience for Δp but it is fairly reasonable for ΔU, h_G, h_L, in agreement with the interpretation in section 1.2.8.5.

1.2.9.2 Restrictions Used in Simplified Models

Except for the surface tension effect, the possibility of a pressure difference between the phases is taken into account only in refined models, and these models always involve two velocities and two enthalpies, which may differ from the saturation enthalpies. Therefore, the first restriction always concerns Δp, the unknown void fraction topological law being replaced by $\Delta p = 2\sigma/R$ (often neglected in practice), where R is the averaged interfacial radius of curvature, positive for bubbles and negative for droplets. The corresponding limitations have been discussed in section 1.2.5.2. It was concluded that restrictions on Δp impair the ability of the models to deal with pressure propagation phenomena.

The other restrictions are used in any number (0 to 3) and any combination. Often, when a restriction on the velocities is used, either it is $\Delta U = 0$ (no relative velocity) or it consists in an algebraic relationship between U_G and U_L. Since the inertias of the two phases may be very different, such restrictions are difficult to justify, except for steady state in which an algebraic law for a relationship between U_G and U_L can be empirically adjusted. However, restrictions on the velocities have been used extensively, for instance through correlations for the so-called velocity ratio U_G/U_L. More elaborate restrictions have also been proposed, for instance in so-called diffusion models (Ishii 1977).

When a restriction on the velocities is used, the slip equation [1.2.180] or [1.2.181] is not written, and it is implicitly assumed that it is always satisfied. Therefore, a restriction on the velocities implies a necessary condition on the momentum transfer laws (including interfacial and wall friction laws) through the expression

$$\left[\frac{(MV)_{GI} - M_{GI}U_G}{\alpha_G \rho_G} - \frac{(MV)_{LI} - M_{LI}U_L}{\alpha_L \rho_L} \right] + \left[\frac{(FF)_{GI}}{\alpha_G \rho_G} - \frac{(FF)_{LI}}{\alpha_L \rho_L} \right]$$

$$+ \left[\frac{(FF)_{GW}}{\alpha_G \rho_G} - \frac{(FF)_{LW}}{\alpha_L \rho_L} \right]$$

This condition involves partial derivatives in general (e.g., $\partial p_G/\partial z$ and $\partial p_L/\partial z$ when the relative velocity is zero). Its fulfillment does not ensure that the velocities will obey the restriction (i.e., the condition is not sufficient).

When a restriction on the enthalpy h_k is used, it is in general: $h_k = h_{k\,sat}(p_G)$. It is justified when thermal nonequilibrium effects within phase k are not important and it has been used extensively. When such a restriction is used, the corresponding thermal nonequilibrium equation [1.2.167 k] is not written, and it is implicitly assumed that it is always satisfied. Therefore a restriction on an enthalpy implies a necessary condition on the transfer laws (essentially, a condition on the energy transfer laws) through the expression

$$\frac{(MH)_{kI} - M_{kI}h_k}{\alpha_k \rho_k} + \frac{(EQ)_{kI}}{\alpha_k \rho_k} + \frac{(EQ)_{kW}}{\alpha_k \rho_k}$$

$$+ \eta \left[\frac{(MC)_{kI} - (\mathbf{MV})_{kI} \cdot \mathbf{U}_k + \frac{1}{2} M_{kI}\mathbf{U}_k^2}{\alpha_k \rho_k} + \frac{(EF)_{kI} - (\mathbf{FF})_{kI} \cdot \mathbf{U}_k}{\alpha_k \rho_k} \right.$$

$$\left. + \frac{(EF)_{kW} - (\mathbf{FF})_{kW} \cdot \mathbf{U}_k}{\alpha_k \rho_k} \right]$$

Fulfillment of this condition does not ensure that the enthalpy will obey the restriction.

1.2.9.3 Simplified Models

The characteristics of the existing simplified models are summarized in table 1.2.5, which includes the complete model for comparison. The mixture balance equations being present in all models, they are not listed in table 1.2.5, nor are the transfer and storage terms that appear in the mixture balances. These terms (there are seven of them, only three being essential) must be specified in any model. They are:

$(\mathbf{I}\sigma)_r$ and $(E\sigma)_I$, respectively, interfacial momentum and energy storage terms
$\Sigma_k(\mathbf{FF})_{kW}$ overall wall friction term
$\Sigma_k(\mathbf{FP})_{kW}$, overall wall pressure term,
$\Sigma_k(EF)_{kW}$, power associated with wall friction, often zero in practice (section 1.2.6.4)
$\Sigma_k(EP)_{kW}$, power associated with wall pressure, often zero in practice (section 1.2.6.4)
$\Sigma_k(EQ)_{kW}$, overall wall heat transfer

The other equations (complementary equations) and the other necessary transfer laws (complementary transfer laws) are listed in table 1.2.5. When some interfacial transfer terms may be ignored, the same is true for the interfacial balance(s) that contain them. When some transfer terms—and the associated interfacial balance equation—are present only through terms involving η, they do not play an essential part and they are listed in brackets.

Table 1.2.5 is based on a rational approach toward simplified models, as discussed in section 1.2.9.1. However, as already noted, the complementary equations are often chosen according to physical intuition, and the sets found in the literature are not always strictly equivalent to the sets given in table 1.2.5. In particular, the thermal nonequilibrium equation of phase k is often replaced, either by the mass balance of the same phase or by the so-called *thermal energy equation* of phase k, which is in fact a secondary energy equation:

Table 1.2.5 Two-Phase Pipe-Flow Models

Restrictions (on flow variables)		Dependent variables (besides α_G, p_G, U)	Equations complementing mixture balance equations	Complementary transfer laws needed	
Number	Nature			Total number	Number per nature
0	—	$p_L, \Delta U, h_G, h_L$	Void fraction topological law Slip equation Thermal nonequilibrium equation, phase G Thermal nonequilibrium equation, phase L 3 interfacial balances	9 (+5)	Interface $\begin{cases}1 \text{ mass}\\3 \text{ momentum}\\3(+4)\text{ energy}\end{cases}$ Wall $\begin{cases}1 \text{ friction one phase}\\1(+1)\text{ energy one phase}\end{cases}$
1	Δp (e.g., equal pressure)	$\Delta U, h_G, h_L$	Slip equation Thermal nonequilibrium equation, phase G Thermal nonequilibrium equation, phase L 3 interfacial balances	9 (+5)	Interface $\Big\}$ same as Wall $\Big\}$ above
2	$\Delta p, h_G$ or h_L	$\Delta U, h_L$ or h_G	Slip equation Thermal nonequilibrium, phase L or G 2 interfacial balances $\begin{cases}\text{mass}\\\text{momentum}\end{cases}$	8 (+3)	Interface $\begin{cases}1 \text{ mass}\\3 \text{ momentum}\\2(+2)\text{ energy}\end{cases}$ Wall $\begin{cases}1 \text{ friction one phase}\\1(+1)\text{ energy one phase}\end{cases}$

Table 1.2.5 Two-Phase Pipe-Flow Models (*Cont.*)

Restrictions (on flow variables)		Dependent variables (besides α_G, p_G, U)	Equations complementing mixture balance equations	Complementary transfer laws needed	
Number	Nature			Total number	Number per nature
2	Δp, Δu	h_G, h_L	Thermal nonequilibrium, phase G Thermal nonequilibrium, phase L 2 interfacial balances [mass, energy] (+ momentum interfacial balance)	5 (+9)	Interface $\begin{cases}1\text{ mass}\\(3\text{ momentum})\\3(+4)\text{ energy}\end{cases}$ Wall $\begin{cases}1\text{ friction one phase}\\1(+1)\text{ energy one phase}\end{cases}$
3	Δp, h_G, h_L (e.g., thermal equilibrium)	ΔU	Slip equation 2 interfacial balances $\begin{cases}\text{mass}\\\text{momentum}\end{cases}$	5 (+10)	Interface $\begin{cases}1\text{ mass}\\3\text{ momentum}\end{cases}$ Wall: 1 friction one phase
3	Δp, ΔU, h_G or h_L	h_L or h_G	Thermal nonequilibrium, phase L or G No interfacial balance	4 (+6)	Interface $\begin{cases}1\text{ mass}\\2(+2)\text{ energy}\\2\text{ momentum}\end{cases}$ Wall $\begin{cases}1\text{ friction one phase}\\1(+1)\text{ energy one phase}\end{cases}$
4	Δp, ΔU, h_G, $\dot{u}_L$ (e.g., homogeneous model)	No	No	0	—

$$\frac{1}{A}\left([1.2.153] - \eta \mathbf{U}_k \cdot [1.2.149] + \frac{\eta}{2}\mathbf{U}_k^2\,[1.2.145]\right) = \alpha_k \rho_k\,[1.2.167]$$

$$+ \frac{h_k}{A}\,[1.2.145]$$

This equation is

$$\frac{\partial}{\partial t}\left(\alpha_k \rho_k h_k\right) + \frac{\partial}{\partial z}\left(\alpha_k \rho_k w_k h_k\right) - \eta \alpha_k \left(\frac{\partial p_k}{\partial t} + w_k\,\frac{\partial p_k}{\partial z}\right) + \alpha_k \rho_k h_k \left(\frac{A'_t}{A} + w_k\,\frac{A'_z}{A}\right)$$

$$- (MH)_{kI} - (EQ)_{kI} - (EQ)_{kW} - \eta \left\{\left[(MC)_{kI} - (MV)_{kI} \cdot \mathbf{U}_k + \frac{1}{2}M_{kI}\mathbf{U}_k^2\right]\right.$$

$$+ \left[(EF)_{kI} - (FF)_{kI} \cdot \mathbf{U}_k\right] + \left[(EF)_{kW} - (FF)_{kW} \cdot \mathbf{U}_k\right]\Big\} \qquad [1.2.183]$$

Complete Model

The complementary equations are those listed in section 1.2.8.5 plus the void fraction topological law. The number of complementary transfer laws is 14, in agreement with table 1.2.2, taking into account the presence in the equations of $\Sigma_k(\mathbf{FP})_{kW}$ and $\Sigma_k(EP)_{kW}$ instead of the individual terms $(\mathbf{FP})_{kW}$ and $(EP)_{kW}$, and the elimination of $(\mathbf{FP})_{kI}$ and $(EP)_{kI}$. Of these 14 laws, 9 play an essential part. The nonessential laws being written between brackets, the 14 laws are

1 interfacial mass transfer law for 2 terms, M_{kI}, related through the interfacial mass balance

3 interfacial momentum transfer laws for 4 terms, $(\mathbf{MV})_{kI}$, $(\mathbf{FF})_{kI}$, related through the interfacial momentum balance

3 interfacial energy transfer laws for 4 terms, $(MH)_{kI}$, $(EQ)_{kI}$, related through the interfacial energy balance

[+ 4 interfacial energy transfer laws for 4 terms, $(MC)_{kI}$, $(EF)_{kI}$]

1 wall friction law for 2 terms, $(\mathbf{FF})_{kW}$, related through the overall wall friction

1 wall heat transfer for 2 terms, $(EQ)_{kW}$, related through the overall wall heat transfer

[+ 1 wall energy transfer law for 2 terms, $(EF)_{kW}$, related through the overall term $\Sigma_k(EF)_{kW}$]

Models Involving Only One Restriction, on the Pressure Difference

Except for the void fraction topological law, the complementary equations and the complementary transfer laws are the same as above. These models are often referred to as six-equation models since they involve six partial differential balance equations (Solbrig et al. 1975; Andersen et al. 1978; Houdayer et al. 1978).

Models Involving Two Restrictions, on the Pressure Difference and on One Enthalpy

If the enthalpy restriction is, say, on h_G, the thermal nonequilibrium equation of the gas phase is ignored. Four interfacial energy transfer terms, namely $(MH)_{GI}$, $(MC)_{GI}$, $(EF)_{GI}$, $(EQ)_{GI}$, no longer appear in the set, except for the interfacial energy balance, which may therefore be ignored. The wall energy transfer terms $(EF)_{GW}$ and $(EQ)_{GW}$ do not disappear, since they are the differences between $\Sigma_k(EF)_{kW}$ and $\Sigma_k(EQ)_{kW}$, present in the mixture energy balance, and, respectively, $(EF)_{LW}$ and $(EQ)_{LW}$. It follows that the number of complementary transfer laws is reduced to 11. Of these, eight play an essential part, since there are two essential interfacial energy transfer laws, $(MH)_{LI}$ and $(EQ)_{LI}$, instead of three for the complete model.

These models are often of interest, as when, because of the small specific heat of the gas phase, a deviation from thermal equilibrium in this phase has only minor consequences.

Models Involving Two Restrictions, on the Pressure Difference and on the Velocities

The restriction of the velocities replaces the slip equation, which is ignored. All the complementary momentum transfer terms remain present in the set, through the thermal nonequilibrium equations, but they no longer play an essential part. Accordingly, the number of complementary transfer laws remains 14, but the number of such laws playing an essential part is reduced to 5 (i.e., no interfacial momentum transfer laws and no wall friction law, compared to 3 and 1, respectively, for the complete model).

These models may be of interest, for instance when the momentum transfer between the two phases is so large that only a small velocity difference is possible. In general, they yield hyperbolic sets of partial differential equations (Hancox et al. 1975).

Models Involving Three Restrictions, on the Pressure Difference and on Both Enthalpies

The restrictions on the enthalpies replace the thermal nonequilibrium equations, which are ignored. All the phasic energy transfer terms (interface, wall) disappear from the set, except for the interfacial energy balance, which may therefore be ignored. It follows that the number of complementary transfer laws is reduced to five, all playing an essential part. Their list is the same as in the complete model, with deletion of the energy and heat transfer laws.

These models, and especially the *thermal equilibrium model,* are often of interest, for instance for two-component two-phase flows, or when thermal non-equilibrium phenomena may be expected to have only minor consequences.

Models Involving Three Restrictions, on the Pressure Difference, on the Velocities, and on One Enthalpy

The restriction on the velocities replaces the slip equation, which is ignored. The restriction on one enthalpy, say h_G, replaces a thermal nonequilibrium equation, which is ignored. All the interfacial transfer terms pertaining to the phase subjected to the enthalpy restriction (here the gas phase) disappear from the set, except for the three interfacial balances, which may therefore be ignored. The number of complementary transfer laws is the number of transfer terms present in the remaining thermal nonequilibrium equation—that is, 10—but only 4 of them play an essential part, namely the mass transfer law, two interfacial energy transfer laws [here $(MH)_{LI}$ and $(EQ)_{LI}$], and a wall heat transfer law [here $(EQ)_{LW}$].

These models have been used extensively, especially in nuclear engineering. They include the *diffusion models* (Ishii 1977) characterized by an equation for the *drift velocity* $\mathbf{U}_{GJ} \triangleq \mathbf{U}_G - \mathbf{U} = (1 - \alpha_G) \, \Delta\mathbf{U}$ and by the replacement of the remaining thermal nonequilibrium equation by the mass balance equation of the gas phase. They also include many one-dimensional models in which the velocity ratio w_G/w_L is imposed on the basis of some steady-state empirical correlation (not adapted to the study of transients) and in which the remaining thermal non-equilibrium equation is often replaced by the thermal energy equation [1.2.183].

The interest of the diffusion models rests on the adequacy of the drift velocity equation (a substitute for the slip equation [1.2.180]). The other models are often used because they minimize the number of complementary transfer laws.

Models Involving Four Restrictions

In these models, only the mixture balance equations are written. Because of this, they are akin to one-fluid models (section 1.2.5.3). They include the well-known homogeneous model, characterized by the restrictions

$$\Delta p \cong \frac{2\sigma}{R} \qquad \Delta\mathbf{U} \cong 0 \qquad h_G \cong h_{G\,\mathrm{sat}}(p_G) \qquad h_L \cong h_{L\,\mathrm{sat},}(p_G)$$

Incidentally, the homogeneous model is also a one-fluid model, in which the fluid equation of state is $\rho = \alpha_G \rho_{G\,\mathrm{sat}}(p_G) + \alpha_L \rho_{L\,\mathrm{sat}}(p_G)$. As in the case of three-restriction models, four-restriction models also include many models involving a velocity ratio correlation.

The interest of four-restriction models rests on their simplicity. They are extensively used, in particular in preliminary or unrefined studies.

1.3 Particle-Fluid Interaction

M. E. O'Neill and K. B. Ranger

1.3.1 INTRODUCTION AND BASIC EQUATIONS

The theory of laminar flows caused by the motion of particles in viscous fluids at small Reynolds numbers began with the celebrated work of Stokes (1851), in which he derived his famous law for the drag force acting on a rigid sphere translating through a quiescent fluid with uniform velocity. This initial work led, during the past century and a quarter, to a variety of developments and extensions that take into account the effects of particle rotation, nonspherical geometry, inertial effects, wall effects, liquid droplets and gas bubbles, particle-particle interactions in multi-particle systems, particle-interface interactions in multiphase flows involving immiscible fluids, deformable particles, nonhomogeneous particles such as dipolar particles in ferrofluids, non-Newtonian fluids, and electric or magnetic forces acting on the particles and/or the fluid. Furthermore, knowledge of the detailed velocity field around the particles has revealed a complexity in the flow structure, not hitherto expected in low-Reynolds-number flows, with wakes and eddies forming in many flow situations.

These developments may be broadly classified as pertaining to uniform stream-ing flows past the particle or particles insofar as relative motions of particle and fluid are concerned. In general, such flows are realized by the action of an external force on the particle, such as gravity in the case of a particle sedimenting in a quiescent fluid, or some restraining force in the case of a fluid streaming past a stationary particle. In nonuniform flows, much attention has been directed to the behavior of neutrally buoyant particles in externally driven flows, where it is assumed that the densities of the particle and fluid are identical, so that no differential motion of the particle relative to the surrounding fluid occurs through the action of gravity or of any other external force on the particle. Motion of the particle is induced solely by the shearing motion of the fluid in which it is suspended. This shearing motion creates stresses at the particle surface, and these surface forces impart motion to the particle. Such shearing motion may arise from the movement of boundaries, as in the simple shear flow between two parallel flat plates that are in relative translational motion, or from the action of an external pressure gradient, as in Poiseuille flow through a circular pipe. Other simple and important examples of externally driven flows are elongational flow, generated by the extension of a thread of viscous fluid as in polymer drawing processes, and stagnation flow such as arises during the impaction of particles on a collector.

Applications involving laminar motion of effectively neutrally buoyant particles in nonuniform flows are widespread. Examples are suspension and polymer rheology, continuum mechanics and diffusional transport processes in suspensions of Brownian particles, red cell motion in capillary blood flow, distortions of flows in tubes and ducts caused by boundary irregularities, novel separation techniques based on nonuniform particle distributions over the cross section of a circular tube, separation of macromolecules according to size by gel-permeation chromatography, flow of fiber suspensions in papermaking processes and of latex particles in emulsion-based paints, diffusion of large molecules and colloidal particles through membranes, ferrofluid rheology, anisotropic transport processes in liquid crystals subject to shear, streaming birefringence, shear-gradient coagulation in hydrosols, and emulsification in colloid mills. Another possible application is in the formation of certain igneous rocks by the motion of suspended rock crystals in molten rocks. In applications involving flow of polymer solutions, the term particle is employed in a generalized sense to denote a dissolved solute macromolecule. As pointed out by Einstein (1956), this is generally valid when the overall dimensions of the solute macromolecule are large compared with the average distance between solvent molecules, so that the macromolecule may be regarded as a macroscopic particle, albeit flexible, that is suspended in a fluid continuum composed of the solvent. In such circumstances, however, in addition to the purely hydrodynamic aspect of the problem, one must also include the random translational and rotary Brownian movements of the particle.

Reviews that highlight various aspects of particle motion in nonuniform flows are given by Brenner (1966, 1972a, 1972b), Cox (1970), Brenner & Bungay (1971), Goldsmith & Mason (1967), Cox & Mason (1971), and Batchelor (1972). In this article we consider certain fundamental studies in the theory of laminar flows of viscous fluids at low Reynolds numbers during the last 20 yr.

1.3.1.1   Equations of Stokes Flows

The equations governing the motion of an incompressible Newtonian fluid are the equation of continuity [1.1.8] and the Navier-Stokes equations [1.1.66]. From the Navier-Stokes equations there emerges a significant dimensionless number known as the Reynolds number. As illustrated in section 1.1 the technique used to expose this number is to render the Navier-Stokes equations dimensionless. This puts the physical principle underlying the equations in its clearest form since the equations are now free of arbitrary choices of scales and units. Suppose that a flow is characterized by a certain linear dimension L, a velocity U, and the (constant) density ρ. For example, in considering the steady streaming flow past a body such as a sphere, L could be the radius or diameter of the sphere and U the magnitude of the velocity far from the sphere where the effect of its presence is negligible. We can then nondimensionalize the physical quantities appearing in the Navier-Stokes equations. The velocity is rendered dimensionless with reference to U, the space coordinates (x, y, z) are made dimensionless with reference to L, the pressure is made dimensionless with reference to $\pi\rho U^2$, and time is made dimensionless with reference to L/U. In this way, in the absence of a body force, the Navier-Stokes equations take the form

$$\text{Re}\left[\frac{\partial \mathbf{U}}{\partial \tau} + (\mathbf{U} \cdot \nabla)\mathbf{U}\right] = -\nabla p + \nabla^2 \mathbf{U} \qquad [1.3.1]$$

where $\mathbf{U}$ and p are, respectively, the dimensionless velocity and pressure and τ is a dimensionless time variable. The quantity Re is the Reynolds number defined by

$$\text{Re} = \frac{UL}{\nu} \qquad [1.3.2]$$

where ν is the kinematic viscosity of the fluid. In flow situations where $\text{Re} \ll 1$, the fluid motion is governed by the linearized Navier-Stokes equations

$$\nabla p = \nabla^2 \mathbf{U} \qquad [1.3.3]$$

It is often more convenient to revert to the equations written in terms of dimensional variables. Thus [1.3.3] is equivalent to

$$\nabla p = \mu \nabla^2 \mathbf{U} \qquad [1.3.4]$$

where the physical quantities and variables are now dimensional. Equation [1.3.4] and the equation of continuity

$$\nabla \cdot \mathbf{U} = 0 \qquad [1.3.5]$$

together constitute the Stokes or creeping flow equations. In the case of non-uniform flows the Reynolds number is conveniently defined by

$$\text{Re} = \frac{L^2 S}{\nu}$$

where S is some characteristic macroscopic shear rate. In the event that the motion of the fluid is unsteady when viewed from an inertial frame, neglecting the local acceleration term $\rho \partial \mathbf{U}/\partial t$ is equivalent to assuming that the flow is essentially or quasi-steady. Such an assumption, of course, hinges on U/L being the correct time scale for the flow. This can in general be justified, and the time-varying term would be nonnegligible only in, say, rapidly oscillating flows. Thus a flow at low Reynolds number, either steady or unsteady, can in general be described by the Stokes equations provided the Reynolds number is sufficiently small.

Additional particle Reynolds number criteria for neglecting fluid inertial effects may be formulated, based, for example, on the choice of the translational or angular velocity of the particle as the characteristic velocity. In nonuniform flows, however, these do not constitute independent criteria, since the translational and angular velocities of the freely suspended particle are linearly dependent on the shear rate S. For a neutrally buoyant particle suspended in a Poiseuille flow in a tube, other Reynolds numbers, such as the tube Reynolds number

$$\text{Re} = \frac{R_0 \bar{U}}{\nu}$$

where R_0 is the tube radius and $\bar{U}$ is the mean velocity across the tube cross section, arise in considering the validity of [1.3.4]. This Reynolds number need not be small compared with unity for [1.3.4] to be valid in the neighborhood of the particle, but it must be small enough for the global flow to be laminar rather than turbulent.

Under ordinary conditions the assumption is made that the same particles of fluid remain in contact with a rigid boundary. This is the no-slip condition. Thus if the boundary is moving with a known velocity, the fluid velocity at this boundary is specified, and consequently at a stationary boundary $U = 0$. In many problems the stress may be specified on a known or an unknown boundary. The latter case is a free boundary problem whose solution requires finding the form of the boundary.

There cannot be more than one solution for the velocity field in a given finite region with prescribed boundary conditions, if the flow is Stokesian. An interesting related result is that Stokes flow has a smaller rate of dissipation of energy than any other incompressible flow in the same region with the same value of the velocity on the boundary or boundaries of that region. Both of these results were established by Helmholtz, and proofs can be found in Batchelor (1967). There is a proof of uniqueness for the Stokes streaming flow of an unbounded fluid past a finite body (e.g., Finn & Noll 1957; Ladyzhenskaya 1963). Finn & Noll also showed that in two-dimensional Stokes flow past an obstacle that consists of a finite number of piecewise smooth nonintersecting simple closed curves, the fluid velocity at an infinite distance from the obstacle must be infinite. This gives rise to Stokes' paradox, or the inability to solve the Stokes equations for two-dimensional streaming flow past a cylindrical body when a uniform stream condition is imposed at infinity. Proofs of the uniqueness of Stokes flows involving multifluid systems are sparse. A proof has been given, for instance, by Davis et al. (1975) of the uniqueness of the solution of the Stokes equations appropriate to axisymmetric flow caused by a rotating body or finite system of bodies in a quiescent system of unbounded invisible fluids. They also showed that if only one of the fluids is unbounded, the velocity decays to zero as the inverse square of the distance from the bodies.

1.3.2 SINGLE PARTICLE IN A BOUNDED MEDIUM

After the publication in 1851 of Stokes' law, there was considerable activity in finding solutions of the Stokes equations for flows past isolated bodies. Kirchhoff (1876) gave the solution for a sphere slowly rotating about a diameter. The solution for a neutrally buoyant rigid sphere suspended in a homogeneous shearing flow that extends to infinity was probably first obtained by Einstein (1956) in his theory of suspension viscosity. This was extended to nonspherical particles, where a new feature arises due to the orientation of the particle relative to the principal axes of shear, by Jeffery's (1922) classic analysis of the periodic rotation of an ellipsoid of revolution suspended in a simple shearing motion of viscous fluid. This solution finds wide application in such areas as suspension and polymer rheology, anisotropic transport properties in suspensions and in liquid crystals, and streaming birefringence. The status of knowledge in the field is summarized and theory and experiment are compared in Goldsmith & Mason (1967).

In the real world, a particle does not exist in isolation in an infinite fluid. Boundaries such as walls or other particles are present that interact with the particle. If these boundaries are sufficiently remote, the interactions are very small and the classical solutions for particles in isolation suffice. However, when the particle comes close to the wall, the interaction is significant. Up to the mid-1960s a great deal of work was done in obtaining first- and higher-order wall corrections for particles in flows that are bounded by plane or cylindrical walls (see Happel & Brenner 1965). The methods used, such as the method of reflections, require that the distance of a particle from a wall be very much larger than its representative dimension, and it was not until the work of Dean & O'Neill (1963) that the force and torque acting on a spherical particle, moving at an arbitrary distance from a plane wall, could be accurately determined. The limiting behavior when the sphere almost makes contact with the wall was examined rigorously by O'Neill & Stewartson (1967) and Goldman et al. (1967). In this section we examine in some detail this exact mathematical analysis.

Consider a rigid sphere of radius a that translates steadily without rotation parallel to, and at a distance d from, a rigid plane wall. Let the plane be given by $z = 0$ in a system of Cartesian coordinates such that the components of the velocity of the sphere are $(U, 0, 0)$. From the solution for this case, it is clear that the solution for the problem when the sphere has velocity $(0, U, 0)$ can be easily deduced. The boundary conditions require that the velocity $\mathbf{U}$ vanish at all points of the plane $z = 0$ and that at any point of the sphere with cylindrical polar coordinates (r, θ, z), the cylindrical polar components (u, v, w) of $\mathbf{U}$ must satisfy the conditions

$$u = U \cos \theta \qquad v = - U \sin \theta \qquad w = 0 \qquad [1.3.6]$$

By assuming constant fluid density ρ and viscosity μ, [1.3.4] and [1.3.5], which govern the motion of the fluid, are satisfied by writing the pressure p and u, v, w in the forms

$$cp = \mu U Q_1 \cos \theta \qquad cu = \tfrac{1}{2} U[r Q_1 + c(U_2 + U_0)] \cos \theta \qquad [1.3.7]$$

$$cv = \tfrac{1}{2} Uc(U_2 - U_0) \sin \theta \qquad cw = \tfrac{1}{2} U(2Q_1 + 2cw_1) \cos \theta \qquad [1.3.8]$$

where c is a constant with dimensions of length that are defined later and Q_1, U_0, U_2, and w_1 are functions of r and z only, satisfying

$$L_0^2 U_0 = L_2^2 U_2 = L_1^2 Q_1 = L_1^2 w_1 = 0 \qquad [1.3.9]$$

the operators being defined by

$$L_m^2 = \frac{\partial^2}{\partial r^2} + \frac{1}{r} \frac{\partial}{\partial r} - \frac{m^2}{r^2} + \frac{\partial^2}{\partial z^2} \qquad (m = 0, 1, 2)$$

with the representation [1.3.7] and [1.3.8], the equation of continuity is satisfied if

$$\left(3 + r\frac{\partial}{\partial r} + z\frac{\partial}{\partial z}\right)Q_1 + c\left[\frac{\partial U_0}{\partial r} + \left(\frac{\partial}{\partial r} + \frac{2}{r}\right)U_2 + 2\frac{\partial w_1}{\partial z}\right] = 0 \quad [1.3.10]$$

O'Neill (1964) showed that the problem of determining the functions U_0, U_2, Q_1, and w_1 can be conveniently solved by introducing bispherical coordinates (ξ, θ, η), which are related to the cylindrical coordinates (r, θ, z) by

$$r = \frac{c\sin\eta}{\cosh\xi - \cos\eta} \qquad z = \frac{c\sinh\xi}{\cosh\xi - \cos\eta} \qquad (0 \leqslant \eta \leqslant \pi)$$

The plane is defined by $\xi = 0$ and the sphere by $\xi = \alpha > 0$ if $a = c$ cosech α and $d = c$ coth α, so that for a given choice of a and d, both α and the constant c appearing in [1.3.7] and [1.3.8] are uniquely determined. Equations [1.3.7]-[1.3.9] are satisfied when

$$w_1 = (\cosh\xi - \sigma)^{1/2}\sum_{n=1}^{\infty} A_n \sinh (n + \tfrac{1}{2})\xi P_n^1(\sigma) \qquad [1.3.11]$$

$$Q_1 = (\cosh\xi - \sigma)^{1/2}\sum_{n=1}^{\infty}[B_n \cosh (n + \tfrac{1}{2})\xi + C_n \sinh (n + \tfrac{1}{2})\xi]P_n^1(\sigma)$$

$$[1.3.12]$$

$$U_0 = (\cosh\xi - \sigma)^{1/2}\sum_{n=0}^{\infty}[D_n \cosh (n + \tfrac{1}{2})\xi + E_n \sinh (n + \tfrac{1}{2})\xi]P_n(\sigma)$$

$$[1.3.13]$$

$$U_2 = (\cosh\xi - \sigma)^{1/2}\sum_{n=2}^{\infty}[F_n \cosh (n + \tfrac{1}{2})\xi + G_n \sinh (n + \tfrac{1}{2})\xi]P_n^2(\sigma)$$

$$[1.3.14]$$

where $\sigma = \cos\eta$, $P_n(\sigma)$ is the Legendre polynomial of order n, and $P_n^m(\sigma) = (1 - \sigma^2)^{m/2} d^m[P_n(\sigma)]/d\sigma^m$ with $m = 1$, 2. The assumption that solutions of type [1.3.11]-[1.3.14] exist implies that each of the series is necessarily convergent for $0 \leqslant \xi \leqslant \alpha$ and $|\sigma| \leqslant 1$. It is therefore evident that

$$w_1 = U_0 = U_2 = rQ_1 = 0 \qquad [1.3.15]$$

where $\xi = \eta = 0$, which corresponds to infinity in the physical space, and this implies that the kinematic condition of quiescence at infinity is satisfied.

The boundary conditions on the plane and the sphere, when expressed in terms of the bispherical coordinates, give

$$U_0 = U_2 = -\frac{Q_1 \sin \eta}{2(1 - \cos \eta)} \quad (\xi = 0) \qquad [1.3.16]$$

$$w_1 = 0 \quad (\xi = 0) \qquad [1.3.17]$$

$$U_0 - 2U = U_2 = \frac{Q_1 \sin \eta}{2(\cosh \alpha - \cos \eta)} \quad (\xi = \alpha) \qquad [1.3.18]$$

Equation [1.3.17] is automatically satisfied by w_1 given by [1.3.11], but an additional condition is obtained from the equation of continuity requiring that $\partial w / \partial z = 0$ on $\xi = 0$. Hence

$$Q_1 = -2c \left(\frac{\partial w_1}{\partial z} \right)_{\xi=0} = -2c \lim_{\xi \to 0} \frac{w_1}{z} \qquad [1.3.19]$$

Equations [1.3.15] and [1.3.17]-[1.3.19] allow the coefficient sequences B_n, $C_n, \ldots, G_n$ to be expressed in terms of A_n only. Satisfaction of the equation of continuity leads to two relations between the coefficient sequences, one of which is satisfied identically because use has already been made of the equation of continuity on the plane. The second relation leads to the second-order difference equation for A_n

$$[(2n - 1)k_{n-1} - (2n - 3)k_n] \left[\frac{(n - 1)A_{n-1}}{2n - 1} - \frac{nA_n}{2n + 1} \right]$$

$$- [(2n + 5)k_n - (2n + 3)k_{n+1}] \left[\frac{(n + 1)A_n}{2n + 1} - \frac{(n + 2)A_{n+1}}{2n + 3} \right]$$

$$= \sqrt{2} \left[2 \coth \left(n + \frac{1}{2} \right) \alpha - \coth \left(n - \frac{1}{2} \right) \alpha - \coth \left(n + \frac{3}{2} \right) \alpha \right] \quad (n \geq 1)$$

$$[1.3.20]$$

where $k_n = (n + \frac{1}{2}) \coth (n + \frac{1}{2})\alpha - \coth \alpha \ (n \geq 0)$. Although it has not been possible to solve [1.3.20] in closed form, the significant solution, which necessarily decays to zero exponentially as $n \to \infty$, can easily be found by a numerical method because of the compact tridiagonal structure of the matrix of coefficients of A_n $(n = 1, 2, \ldots)$.

The components (F_x, F_y, F_z) of the force exerted by the fluid on the sphere are

$$F_x = \pi \mu U c \int_{-1}^{1} \left(\frac{Q_1}{2c} \frac{\partial r}{\partial \xi} - \frac{r}{2c} \frac{\partial Q_1}{\partial \xi} - \frac{\partial U_0}{\partial \xi} \right) d\sigma \qquad [1.3.21]$$

$$F_y = F_z = 0 \qquad [1.3.22]$$

and the components (G_x, G_y, G_z) of the couple exerted by the fluid on the sphere are

$$G_x = G_z = 0 \qquad\qquad [1.3.23]$$

$$G_y = -\pi\mu U \, \text{cosech } \alpha \int_{-1}^{1} \left[\frac{\partial r}{\partial \xi} \frac{\partial}{\partial \xi} \left(\frac{1}{2} zQ_1 + cw_1 \right) - \frac{\partial z}{\partial \xi} \frac{\partial}{\partial \xi} \left(\frac{1}{2} rQ_1 + cU_0 \right) \right] d\sigma$$

$$[1.3.24]$$

where the integrands in [1.3.21] and [1.3.24] are evaluated at $\xi = \alpha$. After defining dimensionless force and couple coefficients F^* and G^* by

$$F^* = -\frac{F_x}{6\pi\mu U a} \qquad G^* = \frac{G_y}{8\pi\mu U a^2}$$

and evaluating the integrals in [1.3.21] and [1.3.24], O'Neill (1967) showed that

$$F^* = \frac{1}{6} \sqrt{2} \, \text{sinh } \alpha \sum_{n=0}^{\infty} [E_n + n(n+1)C_n] \qquad [1.3.25]$$

$$G^* = -\frac{1}{8} \sqrt{2} \, \text{sinh}^2 \, \alpha \sum_{n=0}^{\infty} \{4n(n+1)A_n - [E_n + n(n+1)C_n] \, \text{coth } \alpha\}$$

$$[1.3.26]$$

The force and couple exerted on the rigid plane can be shown to be equal and opposite to those exerted on the sphere.

Dean & O'Neill (1963) considered the corresponding problem where the sphere rotates without translation about a diameter parallel to the plane. By combining their solution with that of O'Neill (1964), it is possible to compute the total force and couple acting on a sphere that translates along and rotates about any directions parallel to the plane, because of the linearity of the equations governing the flow. The values of the force and couple coefficients F, G computed by Dean & O'Neill were in error because of a misplaced factor of 2 that appeared in the solution for the coefficient sequence A_n. Recomputed values of F, G were published by Goldman et al. (1967) and by Cooley & O'Neill (1968). Values of F^*, G^*, F, and G have been calculated over a wide range of values of α down to 0.02, which corresponds to $d/a = 1.0002$, so that the sphere is very close to the plane. Even at this small gap it is found that $F^* = 5.4973$ and $G^* = 0.65912$, compared with the values 1 and 0, respectively, when the sphere is infinitely far from the plane. However, a crude approximation, in which the sphere is replaced by a plane in the neighborhood of the closest points between sphere and plane, shows that these quantities become infinite as contact between the boundaries is approached.

To determine the nature of the singularities in F^* and G^*, one must take into account the curvature of the sphere as in the analyses of Goldman et al. (1967) and O'Neill & Stewartson (1967). These studies and the companion study by Cooley & O'Neill (1968) are of interest in another connection. Although the theory of lubrication is extremely important for engineering design and has been applied to a large number of separate flow problems, little effort has been put into establishing its validity experimentally or theoretically. In their discussion of experiments on bearings, Pinkus & Sternlicht (1961) pointed out that although there is an abundance of test data, significant experiments on bearings are rare. One reason is the difficulty of constructing and maintaining bearings with minute clearances of the necessary accuracy. Another and more important reason concerns the lubricant viscosity. To quote Pinkus & Sternlicht, "It is almost impossible to vary a parameter during testing without simultaneously varying the viscosity field of the lubricant. The only possible escape from this difficulty would be to use a fluid whose viscosity is not affected by temperature, pressure or rate of shear. Such a lubricant, however, does not exist." The experiments they report do, nevertheless, show an encouraging agreement with theory, in that part of the flow region where it may be expected to hold, provided neither large subatmospheric loops in the pressure nor cavitation occurs.

From the standpoint of embedding lubrication theory in a theory of fluid mechanics based on the Navier-Stokes equations and assessing the errors made in applying the theory to specific problems, little has been achieved. Hence it is believed that the theoretical work that has been done in considering the motion of a sphere very close to a plane is of some use for assessing the merits of lubrication theory, for it has one of the few exact solutions of the Stokes equations in which the flow region contains a region to which lubrication theory can be applied.

The method of solution adopted is to divide the flow into two parts. There is first an inner region, which is in the neighborhood of 0, the closest point of the plane to the sphere, and where the velocity gradients and pressure are large. In this region the leading term in the asymptotic expansion of the solution of the Stokes equations satisfies the equations of lubrication theory, and successive terms may be obtained in a straightforward manner. Second, there is an outer region of flow consisting of the remainder of the fluid. In this region the velocity gradients are moderate and it is possible to assume that ϵa, the minimum clearance between the sphere and the plane, is 0. (ϵ is a small nondimensional parameter $0 < \epsilon \ll 1$.) Tangent sphere coordinates are employed to solve for the flow in the outer region. These coordinates have the effect of reducing the outer flow problem to that of flow between two parallel planes with singularities at infinity, i.e., at the inner edge of the outer region near 0. These singularities lead to a perfect match with the structure of the inner region solution on leaving the neighborhood of 0. In this way, a completely consistent solution is obtained when $\epsilon \ll 1$, which may be made the first term in an asymptotic solution of the Stokes equations. O'Neill & Stewartson (1967) obtained the first three terms in the asymptotic expansions of F^* and G^* when $\epsilon \ll 1$:

$$F^* = \left(\frac{8}{15} + \frac{64}{375}\epsilon\right)\log\left(\frac{2}{\epsilon}\right) + 0.58461 + O(\epsilon) \qquad [1.3.27]$$

$$G^* = \left(\frac{1}{10} + \frac{43}{250}\epsilon\right)\log\left(\frac{2}{\epsilon}\right) - 0.26227 + O(\epsilon) \qquad [1.3.28]$$

The values of F^* and G^* given by [1.3.27] and [1.3.28], ignoring terms $O(\epsilon)$ and smaller, are shown in table 1.3.1 under the headings f^* and g^*, respectively. These

Table 1.3.1   Exact Values F^* and G^* Compared with Values f^* and g^* Obtained by Use of the Asymptotic Theory

ϵ	f^*	F^*	g^*	G^*
0.00020	5.4971	5.4973	0.65908	0.65912
0.00045	5.0649	5.0651	0.57831	0.57834
0.00080	4.7584	4.7587	0.52120	0.52120
0.00125	4.5208	4.5123	0.47707	0.47706
0.00180	4.3269	4.3275	0.44118	0.44116
0.00245	4.1631	4.1639	0.41100	0.41096
0.00320	4.0213	4.0223	0.38500	0.38496
0.00405	3.8964	3.8976	0.36220	0.36214
0.00500	3.7847	3.7863	0.34195	0.34187

can be compared with the exact values of F^* and G^* calculated by O'Neill (1964). Notice the close agreement between the results of the asymptotic theory and the values predicted by O'Neill's exact solution.

In the analysis by Goldman et al. (1967), the singular terms in [1.3.27] and [1.3.28] are correctly given. These terms are predicted solely from the leading (lubrication theory) term in the inner region expansion of the solution. We can therefore say that in the neighborhood of 0, lubrication theory gives a description of the local flow properties accurate to $O(\epsilon)$, as would be expected. The theory is, however, of more limited validity when used to compute the overall forces and couples, because it is then only on equal footing with the theory of weakly sheared flow past the rest of the sphere. For instance, according to lubrication theory, the force and couple acting on the sphere are of the form $A \log \epsilon + B$, where A and B are independent of ϵ if terms of $O(\epsilon)$ are neglected. The value of A is correctly given, but the value of B is uncertain since it depends on the limits assigned to the lubrication zone. The actual force and couple are $A \log \epsilon + C + O$ ($\epsilon \log c$), where C has been calculated explicitly by the method of matched asymptotic expansions and depends significantly on the flow past the rest of the sphere. Thus, while lubrication theory describes local flow properties, it does not provide a reliable estimate of quantities that depend on overall flow properties, such as forces and couples, if the flow region includes a substantial region of weakly sheared flow. Nevertheless, its predictions of the force and couple in the present problem are formally correct in the limit $\epsilon \to 0$.

The corresponding problem, where the sphere is close to the plane and rotating about a diameter parallel to the plane, has been analyzed by Cooley & O'Neill (1968). Their work complements that of Dean & O'Neill (1963) for arbitrary clearance between the sphere and the plane. They find that the sphere experiences a force with Cartesian components $(- 6\pi\mu\Omega a^2 F,\ 0,\ 0)$ and a couple with Cartesian components $(0,\ - 8\pi\mu\Omega a^3 G,\ 0)$ if $(0,\ \Omega,\ 0)$ is the steady angular velocity of the sphere. Again, the force and couple acting on the plane are equal and opposite to those acting on the sphere. The asymptotic expansions of F and G, when the minimum clearance ϵa is very small, are given by

$$F = (- \tfrac{2}{15} + \tfrac{86}{375} \epsilon) \log \epsilon - 0.25725 + O(\epsilon) \qquad [1.3.29]$$

$$G = (-\tfrac{2}{5} + \tfrac{66}{125}\,\epsilon)\log\epsilon + 0.37085 + O(\epsilon) \qquad [1.3.30]$$

The close agreement between the values of F and G computed from [1.3.29] and [1.3.30] when terms of $O(\epsilon)$ are ignored and the exact values calculated from Dean & O'Neill's theory is illustrated in table 1.3.2, where the values given by the first three terms of [1.3.29] and [1.3.30] are denoted f and g.

By combining the results of Cooley & O'Neill (1968) with those of O'Neill & Stewartson (1967) for a sphere with a translational velocity $(a\Omega, 0, 0)$ and an angular velocity $(0, \Omega, 0)$, in Cartesian components, and letting $\epsilon \to 0$, one has the apparently well-posed mathematical problem of a rigid sphere rolling on a plane wall. However, when [1.3.27] and [1.3.28] are combined with [1.3.29] and [1.3.30], it is seen that the sphere experiences a dimensionless drag force of magnitude

$$-\tfrac{2}{5}\log\epsilon + O(1) \qquad [1.3.31]$$

together with a dimensionless couple resisting the motion of magnitude

$$-\tfrac{3}{10}\log\epsilon + O(1) \qquad [1.3.32]$$

when ϵ is very small. Consequently, Stokes flow theory, including the no-slip boundary condition at the point of contact, predicts that an infinite force and couple must be applied to maintain the motion when the sphere rolls on the plane. Examination of the flow structure near the point of contact shows that the pressure is $\sim 1/r^3$ for small cylindrical polar coordinate r, while the velocity of the fluid remains bounded and essentially parabolic in the limit $\epsilon \to 0$.

To complete the description of the flow caused by the motion of a rigid sphere in the presence of a rigid plane, one must add to the contributions from the asymmetric part of the flow, described above, the contributions due to the axisymmetric part of the flow. The solution for a rigid sphere of radius a rotating with steady angular velocity $(0, 0, \Omega)$ was given by Jeffery (1915). The sphere experiences a couple of magnitude $8\pi\mu\Omega a^3\,\tau$ resisting its motion, where τ is given by

$$\tau = \sinh^3\alpha \sum_{m=1}^{\infty} \operatorname{cosech}^3 m\alpha \qquad [1.3.33a]$$

Table 1.3.2 Comparison of Exact Values F and G with Values f and g Computed from Asymptotic Expansions

ϵ	f	F	g	G
0.00045	0.76946	0.77107	3.4515	3.4553
0.00080	0.69221	0.69491	3.2201	3.2265
0.00125	0.63209	0.63606	3.0402	3.0495
0.00180	0.58276	0.58820	2.8927	2.9054
0.00245	0.54088	0.54794	2.7676	2.7840
0.00320	0.50441	0.51326	2.6588	2.6793
0.00405	0.47208	0.48285	2.5624	2.5874
0.00500	0.44300	0.45582	2.4758	2.5056

where α is the bispherical coordinate for the sphere as defined earlier. In the limit $\alpha \to 0$, the sphere makes contact with the plane and we have

$$\tau \to \sum_{m=1}^{\infty} m^{-3} = \zeta(3) = 1.20206 \qquad [1.3.33b]$$

No exact solution has been found to the problem where the sphere translates toward or away from the plane. The difficulty is that the location of the sphere relative to the plane is a function of time so that the fluid motion is unsteady. However, there are many practical situations, as in the sedimentation of solid particles and the motion of suspensions, where the time scale for changes in the fluid velocity is sufficiently large that the flow may be regarded as essentially steady, in the sense that the time-dependent term in the Navier-Stokes equations as well as the convective term is negligible if the Reynolds number is very small. When the time-dependent term is negligible, the flow is said to be quasi-steady. Applicable in such flow regimes is the solution derived by Brenner (1961) for the approach of a rigid sphere toward a planar surface, which may be either rigid or free but is impermeable. Brenner gave explicit expressions in the form of infinite series for the force acting on the sphere in the two cases. Again, an exact solution of the (quasi-steady) Stokes equations is obtained in terms of bispherical coordinates, and for the case of a sphere approaching a rigid plane boundary with (constant) speed U, the force acting on the sphere is $6\pi\mu U a f$ in the direction opposing the motion of the sphere. Brenner showed that

$$f = \frac{4}{3} \sinh \alpha \sum_{n=1}^{\infty} \left[\frac{n(n+1)}{(2n-1)(2n+3)} \frac{2 \sinh (2n+1)\alpha + (2n+1) \sinh 2\alpha}{4 \sinh^2 (n+\frac{1}{2})\alpha - (2n+1)^2 \sinh^2 \alpha} \right]$$

$$[1.3.34]$$

where α is as defined earlier and is related to the minimum clearance between the sphere and the plane by $\cosh \alpha = 1 + \epsilon$. In [1.3.34] the value of α may be arbitrarily chosen, but the series converges more slowly for smaller α and diverges when $\alpha \to 0$ and the sphere touches the plane. Cox & Brenner (1968) and Cooley & O'Neill (1969) examined the limiting behavior of the drag force as a function of ϵ as $\epsilon \to 0$ and found it to be of the form $A\epsilon^{-1} + B \log \epsilon + C + O(\epsilon \log \epsilon)$. The values of A and B can be found completely from knowledge of the two leading terms in the asymptotic expansion of the stream function in the inner region forming the neighborhood where the sphere is closest to the plane. These are given by Cox & Brenner and Cooley & O'Neill. To determine C completely requires knowledge of the leading term in the outer region solution in the singular perturbation procedure. Cooley & O'Neill determined this constant exactly. Thus the asymptotic expansion for f when $\epsilon \ll 1$ is

$$f = \frac{1}{\epsilon} - \frac{1}{5} \log \epsilon + 0.971280 + O(\epsilon \log \epsilon) \qquad [1.3.35]$$

Both of the papers referred to above show that Brenner's series [1.3.34] has the three leading terms given by [1.3.35] when $\alpha \to 0$.

Experimental work by MacKay & Mason (1961) on the sedimentation of a solid sphere (nylon) through a viscous fluid (silicone oil) toward a horizontal rigid plane surface showed close agreement between the experimental values of the ratio $(-ad\epsilon/dt)/V_s$, where V_s is the Stokes velocity of the sphere in unbounded fluid, and the theoretical values calculated from

$$\frac{-ad\epsilon/dt}{V_s} = \frac{1}{f} \qquad [1.3.36]$$

with f determined from [1.3.34]. This sedimentation problem is an excellent example in which to examine the validity of the condition of essential steadiness of the flow. At any instant, the time scale for the problem is $\epsilon a/U$, so the unsteady terms in the Navier-Stokes equations are negligible in comparison with the viscous terms provided $UL^2\rho/\epsilon\mu a \ll 1$, where L is the length scale on which the viscous terms change and we are assuming that the magnitude of the fluid velocity is $O(U)$. Clearly, when $\epsilon = O(1)$, $L = a$, in which case the flow is quasi-steady when $\mathrm{Re} = Ua\rho/\mu \ll 1$. When $\epsilon \ll 1$, $L = \epsilon a$ in the neighborhood of the points of the sphere and plane closest to each other, so that the flow in this region will be quasi-steady when $\mathrm{Re} \ll \epsilon^{-1}$, but in the rest of the fluid $L = a$, and thus essential steadiness of the flow in the whole of the fluid requires that $\mathrm{Re} \ll \epsilon$. This condition can be realized without difficulty, however, and in the context of the sedimentation problem

$$U = -a\frac{d\epsilon}{dt} = \frac{a^2(\rho_1 - \rho)g}{6\pi\mu f(\epsilon)} \qquad [1.3.37]$$

where ρ_1 is the density of the sphere and $f(\epsilon)$ is given by [1.3.35]. The requirement $\mathrm{Re} \ll \epsilon$ is thus satisfied when

$$a^3\left(\frac{\rho_1}{\rho} - 1\right)g \ll 6\pi\nu^2 \ \epsilon f(\epsilon)$$

where $\nu = \mu/\rho$ denotes the kinematic viscosity of the fluid. This is equivalent to

$$1 < \frac{\rho_1}{\rho} \ll 1 + \frac{6\pi\nu^2}{a^3 g}\ \epsilon f(\epsilon) \sim 1 + \frac{6\pi\nu^2}{a^3 g}$$

In the experiments of MacKay & Mason, $\rho_1 = 1.18 \ \mathrm{g/cm^3}$, $\rho = 1.065 \ \mathrm{g/cm^3}$, $\mu = 30$ P, and the radii of the spheres were of order 0.2 cm. Thus

$$\frac{\rho_1}{\rho} \approx 1.1 \qquad \frac{6\pi\nu^2}{a^3 g} \approx 1906.5$$

and the condition $\mathrm{Re} \ll \epsilon$ is easily satisfied.

Singular perturbation theory was initially employed to analyze particle-fluid behavior close to a rigid boundary in the papers cited above for the motion of a sphere in a fluid of semi-infinite extent, bounded by a plane rigid wall. The results were incorporated by Bungay & Brenner (1973a) into an analysis of flow within a circular cylinder in which a relatively small sphere moves in close proximity parallel to the tube wall. Singular perturbation analyses complement regular perturbation analyses of hydrodynamic interaction phenomena—e.g., the method of reflections.

Cox & Brenner (1967) developed a general theory for the effect of rigid walls on the hydrodynamic resistance of a particle that translates and rotates. Their theory rests on regular expansions that are valid in the limit where the particle's dimension is small compared with its distance from the boundaries of the fluid. The same restriction applies to the method of reflection results pertaining to a small sphere moving in a circular tube, such as those of Brenner & Happel (1958), Brenner (1966, 1970), and Greenstein & Happel (1968).

When the flow is axisymmetric, the range of validity of such regular expansions can be extended to relatively large ratios of the particle and wall diameters. Generation of such higher-order terms by the method of reflections is typified by the treatment of Bohlin (1960) for flow past a sphere whose center lies on the axis of a circular tube. Haberman & Sayre (1958) considered the same axisymmetric configuration and arrived at more accurate expansions, which were convergent for sphere-to-tube radius ratios between 0 and 0.8. Wang & Skalak (1969) extended these single-sphere results to an infinite train of identical, equally spaced spheres, all of whose centers lie along the axis of the tube. Convergence of the resulting expressions for the drag and pressure drop was obtained up to a radius ratio of 0.9, but the values near this upper limit are probably accurate to only two significant figures. The effect of particle spacing on hydrodynamic resistance was weak in this train of spheres model. Each sphere behaved as an essentially isolated body for particle spacings exceeding approximately one tube diameter. The large-sphere results indicate that particle-particle interactions are weak for all spacing distances. Chen & Skalak (1970) replaced the spheres by identical spheroids whose axes of symmetry lie along the axis of the tube. The flow remained axisymmetric in this model, so that the influence of particle shape could be partially investigated to a similar order of accuracy.

In each of the theoretical studies cited above it was assumed that the fluid inertial effects are small. A scheme for incorporating to some extent the additional effects arising from inertia was developed by Cox & Brenner (1968), and discussed in detail by Brenner (1966), for spheres that satisfy the method of reflections requirement of having a small radius compared with their distance from the nearest wall. No comparable technique has yet been formulated for a closely fitting sphere in a tube, but Bungay & Brenner (1973b) suggested a scheme whereby the Reynolds number dependence can be incorporated into the singular perturbation scheme. They used singular perturbation techniques to investigate the slow axisymmetric flow around a sphere positioned eccentrically within a long circular cylindrical tube filled with viscous fluid. The results apply to situations in which the sphere spans virtually the entire cross section of the tube, so that the clearance between the sphere and the tube wall is everywhere small compared with the sphere and tube radii. The technique provides an improvement over conventional lubrication theory analyses. The results find application in capillary blood flow, pipeline transport of encapsulated materials, and falling-ball viscometers.

1.3.3 TWO–PARTICLE INTERACTION

Consider the behavior of two rigid particles moving slowly through a viscous fluid under the influence of external forces, typically gravity, applied to maintain the motion of the bodies. It is assumed that the particles are sufficiently close that they interact hydrodynamically with each other, but sufficiently remote from boundary walls or other particles to be considered suspended in an unbounded fluid. Attention will be directed predominantly to situations where the fluid at infinity is at rest. The magnitude of the interaction between particles is, in general, governed by (1) the shapes and sizes of the particles, (2) the distances between them, (3) their orientations relative to each other, (4) their individual orientations relative to the direction of an applied force, and (5) their translational and angular velocities relative to the fluid at infinity.

For prescribed translational and angular particle velocities, the macroscopic parameters of primary physical interest are the hydrodynamic forces and torques exerted by the fluid on the particles. Once these parameters are known for a pair of particles, one can solve the inverse problem of determining the motion of the particles from the known gravitational body forces and torques acting on them.

Assume that the equations governing the flow about the particles are the quasi-steady Stokes equations and the equation of continuity of an incompressible homogeneous fluid of constant density ρ and dynamic viscosity μ. The equations of motion of the fluid are

$$\nabla p = \mu \nabla^2 \mathbf{U} \qquad [1.3.38]$$

$$\nabla \cdot \mathbf{U} = 0 \qquad [1.3.39]$$

where $\mathbf{U}$ and p are, respectively, the velocity and pressure of the fluid. The most general motion that rigid particles may undergo is a combination of translation and rotation. Because of the linearity of [1.3.38] and [1.3.39] and the appropriate boundary conditions, the two modes of motion of the particles may be studied separately and the results superposed. First consider the case where the particles translate, without rotation, as they move through a quiescent fluid.

Identify the particles by their surfaces s_1 and s_2 and suppose that they are translating through the fluid with arbitrary velocities $\mathbf{U}_1$ and $\mathbf{U}_2$, respectively. The boundary conditions that $\mathbf{U}$ must satisfy are

$$\mathbf{U} = \mathbf{U}_i \quad \text{on } s_i \quad (i = 1, 2) \qquad [1.3.40]$$

$$\mathbf{U} \to 0 \quad \text{as } r \to \infty \qquad [1.3.41]$$

where r denotes distance from some suitably chosen origin of coordinates.

The only exact solution of a two-particle problem of this class is that of the motion of two spheres. This has proved to be possible primarily because of the existence of bispherical coordinates, which have a pair of nonintersecting spheres as members of one of the sets of level surfaces and therefore permit simultaneous satisfaction of the boundary conditions on the two particles. For larger collections of spheres, or for a pair of nonspherical particles, it is not possible to find a coordinate system that permits simultaneous satisfaction of all boundary conditions on the particles. Accordingly, an approximate solution to the problem is sought by a scheme of successive iterations, whereby the boundary-value problem may in principle be solved to any degree of accuracy by considering boundary conditions associated with one particle at a time. Such a scheme is provided by the method of reflections. This technique was first applied by Smoluchowski (1911); it is described and a number of applications are given in Happel & Brenner (1965). No rigorous proof exists that the iteration scheme converges to the desired solution, but a limited ad hoc proof is afforded by the satisfactory agreement between the results of the approximate theory and those of the exact theory for two spheres, and by the measure of agreement with results obtained experimentally in a limited number of other situations.

Axisymmetric motion of two external spheres situated an arbitrary distance apart, rotating about their line of centers, was first considered by Jeffery (1915), who pioneered the application of bispherical coordinates to such problems. Stimson & Jeffery (1976) solved the more difficult problem of two spheres translating along their line of centers with the same velocity. Their solution is based on determining the Stokes stream function ψ for the motion of the fluid. Once ψ is known, the forces necessary to maintain the steady motion of the spheres can be found.

The equation that must be satisfied by ψ is

$$L_{-1}^2 \, \psi = 0 \qquad [1.3.42]$$

where
$$L_{-1} = \frac{\partial^2}{\partial r^2} - \frac{1}{r}\frac{\partial}{\partial r} + \frac{\partial^2}{\partial z^2} \qquad [1.3.43]$$

with (r, θ, z) denoting cylindrical polar coordinates in which the z axis coincides with the axis of symmetry of the motion, i.e., the line of centers of the spheres. Happel & Brenner (1965) showed that the components (F_x, F_y, F_z) of the force acting on an axisymmetric body translating in a viscous fluid are given by

$$F_x = F_y = 0 \qquad F_z = \mu\pi \int r^3 \frac{\partial}{\partial n}\left(\frac{L_{-1}\,\psi}{r^2}\right) ds \qquad [1.3.44]$$

where the integral is taken around a meridional section of either sphere in a direction that makes a positive right angle with $\mathbf{n}$, the normal out of the sphere into the fluid.

Stimson & Jeffery (1926) cast the problem in bispherical coordinates (ζ, θ, η), whose relation to cylindrical coordinates (r, θ, z) was given in the previous section. The boundary conditions [1.3.40] are equivalent to

$$\psi + \tfrac{1}{2}\,Ur^2 = 0 \qquad \frac{\partial}{\partial n}\left(\psi + \tfrac{1}{2}\,Ur^2\right) = 0 \qquad [1.3.45]$$

where U denotes the (common) velocity of the spheres.

A solution of [1.3.42] in bispherical coordinates was given by Stimson & Jeffery (1926) as

$$\psi = (\cosh \zeta - \sigma)^{-3/2} \sum_{n=0}^{\infty} U_n(\zeta)v_n(\sigma) \qquad [1.3.46]$$

where
$$U_n(\zeta) = A_n \cosh (n - \tfrac{1}{2})\zeta + B_n \sinh (n - \tfrac{1}{2})\zeta$$
$$+ C_n \cosh (n + \tfrac{3}{2})\zeta + D_n \sinh (n + \tfrac{3}{2})\zeta \qquad [1.3.47]$$

$$v_n(\sigma) = P_{n-1}(\sigma) - P_{n+1}(\sigma) \tag{1.3.48}$$

and σ is such that $\sigma = \cos \eta$. Note that $v_n(\sigma)$ is related to the Gegenbauer polynomial $C_{n+1}^{-1/2}(\sigma)$ of order $n + 1$ and degree $-\frac{1}{2}$ by

$$C_{n+1}^{-1/2}(\sigma) = \frac{P_{n-1}(\sigma) - P_{n+1}(\sigma)}{2n + 1}$$

The constants $A_n, \ldots, D_n$ are determined from the boundary conditions on the spheres, which may be written as

$$\psi = -\frac{1}{2} Uc^2 \frac{1 - \sigma^2}{(\cosh \zeta - \sigma)^2} \qquad \frac{\partial \psi}{\partial \zeta} = \frac{1}{2} Uc^2(1 - \sigma^2) \frac{\partial}{\partial \zeta} (\cosh \zeta - \sigma)^{-2}$$

$$\tag{1.3.49}$$

when $\zeta = \alpha$ or β, the parameters defining the two spheres. It is assumed that $\alpha > 0 > \beta$, so that the radii of the spheres, say a and b, and the distances d_1 and d_2 from their centers to the origin are given by

$$a = c \operatorname{cosech} \alpha \qquad b = -c \operatorname{cosech} \beta$$

$$d_1 = c \coth \alpha \qquad d_2 = -c \coth \beta$$

With a, b, d_1, and d_2 prescribed, α, β, and c are uniquely determined. The boundary condition [1.3.41] at infinity is automatically satisfied once [1.3.49] are satisfied. Satisfaction of these equations leads to four simultaneous linear equations for A_n, B_n, C_n, and D_n, whose values were given explicitly by Stimson & Jeffery (1926). The forces that must be applied to maintain the motion of the spheres are $(0, 0, F_z)$, where

$$F_z = \frac{2\pi\mu\sqrt{2}}{c} \sum_{n=1}^{\infty} (2n + 1)(A_n \pm B_n + C_n \pm D_n) \tag{1.3.50}$$

where the upper signs apply to the sphere $\zeta = \alpha$ and the lower signs to the sphere $\zeta = \beta$.

For equal-sized spheres, B_n and D_n vanish, so the force acting on each sphere is given by

$$F_z = \sigma\pi\mu Ua f \tag{1.3.51}$$

where

$$f = \frac{4}{3} \sinh \alpha \sum_{n=1}^{\infty} \frac{n(n + 1)}{(2n - 1)(2n + 3)} \left[1 - \frac{4 \sinh^2 (n + \frac{1}{2})\alpha - (2n + 1)^2 \sinh^2 \alpha}{2 \sinh (2n + 1)\alpha + (2n + 1) \sinh 2\alpha} \right]$$

$$\tag{1.3.52}$$

As pointed out by Happel & Brenner (1965), there is a typographic error in the original Stimson & Jeffery paper, where the constant coefficient that precedes the summation sign in [1.3.52] is given as $\frac{2}{3}$ instead of $\frac{4}{3}$. Stimson & Jeffery correctly tabulated values of f for a limited range of values of α in the range $0.5 \leqslant \alpha \leqslant 3.0$, but did not give any numerical results for unequal-sized spheres. A comprehensive tabulation of results for equal or nonequal spheres was given by Cooley & O'Neill (1969a). Letting the forces on the spheres be given by $\sigma\pi\mu Uaf_1$ for the sphere $\zeta = \alpha$ and $\sigma\pi\mu Uaf_2$ for the sphere $\zeta = \beta$ (again, these are the forces that must be applied to maintain steady motion and are equal and opposite to the drag forces exerted by the fluid on the spheres), Cooley & O'Neill tabulated f_1, when the centers of the spheres are a distance $(1 + k + \epsilon)a$ apart, for different values of k and ϵ. The quantity $k = b/a$ and ϵa is the minimum clearance between the spheres. Values of f_2 can be determined from those of f_1 very conveniently from

$$f_1(k^{-1}, k^{-1}\,\epsilon) = k^{-1}\,f_2(k, \epsilon) \qquad\qquad [1.3.53]$$

$$f_2(k^{-1}, k^{-1}\,\epsilon) = k^{-1}\,f_1(k, \epsilon) \qquad\qquad [1.3.54]$$

which follow from the property of reversibility of Stokes flows. Curves of f_1 plotted against ϵ are shown in figure 1.3.1 for $0.25 \leqslant k \leqslant 10.0$. An interesting feature of these results is the dissimilar behavior of the forces on the larger and smaller spheres as contact is approached. Denoting the ratio of the radius of the larger sphere to that of the smaller sphere by λ, in which case λ is either k or $1/k$ for k greater or less than unity, Cooley & O'Neill (1969a) showed that the force of the smaller sphere decreases monotonically with ϵ from its maximum value when the spheres are infinitely far apart to its minimum value at contact for all values of λ. However, the force on the larger sphere decreases monotonically with ϵ, attaining its minimum value at contact, only when $1 < \lambda < \lambda^*$, where the critical value $\lambda^* \cong 10/7$. For $\lambda > \lambda^*$, the force on the larger sphere is a minimum at a certain nonzero value of ϵ that depends on λ. The curves in figure 1.3.1 illustrate this behavior.

Although the case of touching spheres is not covered by Stimson & Jeffery's

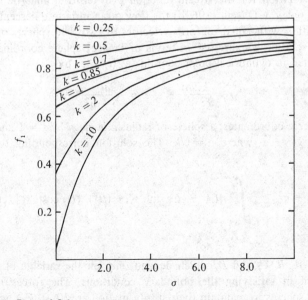

Figure 1.3.1 Curves of f_1 plotted against σ.

solution, their expressions for the forces on the spheres can be evaluated in the limit $\alpha \to 0$. For instance, Faxén (1927) noted that [1.3.52] gives f as a continuous function of α, and on evaluating the limit of this expression as $\alpha \to 0$ by means of the Euler-Maclaurin theorem, he found that for equal-sized spheres in contact, the dimensionless force coefficient f is given by

$$f = \frac{1}{3} \int_0^\infty \left(1 - \frac{2 \sinh^2 s - 2s^2}{\sinh 2s + 2s} \right) ds \qquad [1.3.55]$$

On evaluating the integral numerically, Faxén obtained the value $f = 0.645$, which agrees to three decimal places with the computed value of $f = 0.645141$ given by Cooley & O'Neill (1976a). Comparison of this value of f obtained exactly with the modified form of the solution of Dahl (1925), who carried the computation of f for equal-sized spheres to the ninth power in $a/2d$, d being the half-distance between the sphere centers, reveals, on extrapolation of the value of f obtained by this method of reflections approach to the case of contact, the value $f = 0.64658991$. This is remarkably close to the exact value. [Dahl's computation is reported fully in Happel & Brenner (1965).]

The value of the force predicted here agrees very well with corresponding experimental values. Experiments were carried out by Bart (1959) at Reynolds numbers smaller than 0.05 with a ratio of the diameter of the sphere to that of the fluid-containing cylinder of 0.0163, and by Eveson et al. (1959) at Reynolds numbers less than 0.02 and a corresponding diameter ratio of about 0.0339. Both give $f = 0.647$ when correction factors of 0.99 and 0.98, respectively, are applied to the measurements to take account of the vessel walls. Details of the derivation of the wall corrections are given in Happel & Brenner (1965).

An exact solution for the stream function ψ in terms of analytic functions was obtained by Cooley & O'Neill (1969b) for flow of an infinite quiescent fluid caused by the translation with equal uniform velocities of two rigid spheres of any radii in contact. This solution is expressed in terms of tangent sphere coordinates (ζ, θ, η), which are related to cylindrical polar coordinates (r, θ, z) by

$$r = \frac{2a\eta}{\zeta^2 + \eta^2} \qquad z = \frac{2a\zeta}{\zeta^2 + \eta^2} \qquad [1.3.56]$$

In terms of these coordinates, a sphere of radius a is given by $\zeta = 1$ and a sphere of radius ka by $\zeta = -\alpha$, where $\alpha = 1/k$. The solution corresponding to [1.3.46] is given by

$$\psi = \eta(\zeta^2 + \eta^2)^{-3/2} \int_0^\infty [(A + \zeta C) \sinh s\zeta + (B + \zeta D) \cosh s\zeta] J_1(s\eta)\, ds$$

$$[1.3.57]$$

The functions A, B, C, and D, which depend only on the variable of integration s, are determined in satisfying the boundary conditions. The forces that must be applied to the spheres to maintain their steady motion are $(0, 0, F_z)$, where

$$F_z = \pi\mu Va \int_0^\infty s(B \pm A)\, ds \qquad [1.3.58]$$

with the upper sign being taken for the sphere $\zeta = 1$ and the lower sign for the sphere $\zeta = -\alpha$. If the forces are denoted by $\sigma\pi\mu Uaf_1$ and $\sigma\pi\mu Uaf_2$, respectively, it is clear that f_1 and f_2 are functions of α and satisfy

$$f_1(\alpha) = \alpha f_2\left(\frac{1}{\alpha}\right) \qquad f_2(\alpha) = \alpha f_1\left(\frac{1}{\alpha}\right) \qquad [1.3.59]$$

or equivalently

$$f_1\left(\frac{1}{k}\right) = k^{-1}f_2(k) \qquad f_2\left(\frac{1}{k}\right) = k^{-1}f_1(k) \qquad [1.3.60]$$

These relations may be deduced from the dynamical equivalence of the flows when spheres of radii a and ka move with equal velocities along the positive z axis and spheres of radii a and a/k move with equal velocities along the negative z axis. Thus, through [1.3.60], the values of the dimensionless forces f_1 and f_2 are known for all values of k once the values of f_1 and f_2 in the range $0 < k \leqslant 1$ are known. Curves of f_1 and f_2 plotted against k are shown in figure 1.3.2. Cooley & O'Neill (1969a) calculated f_1 and f_2 over a wide range of k and their results are consistent with the limiting values attained by the corresponding results from the solutions of Stimson & Jeffery. They also evaluated the right-hand side of [1.3.58] explicitly for the case of equal-sized spheres and corroborated [1.3.55].

The solutions already referred to are, of course, solutions of the steady Stokes equations, since it is assumed that the spheres translate with identical steady velocities. No exact solution has yet been found for the problem where the spheres

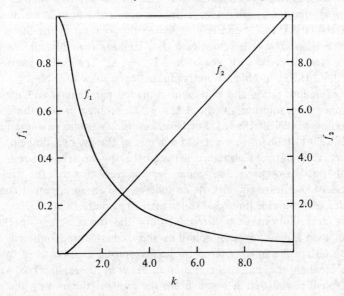

Figure 1.3.2 Curves of f_1 and f_2 plotted against k.

have different velocities and the fluid motion is consequently unsteady. However, as pointed out in section 1.3.2, there are practical situations (e.g., sedimentation of solid particles, motion of suspensions or of the gas within an inverse bubble) where the time scale on which the fluid velocity changes is so large that the fluid motion may be regarded as essentially steady, whereupon the steady Stokes equations can be used to describe the flow. Also discussed in section 1.3.2 was the restriction on Re, based on the sphere velocity and radius, under which the steady Stokes equations are value for a sphere approaching a plane rigid wall. This condition is normally Re $\ll$ 1, except where the sphere is very close to the wall. Similar arguments show that the restrictions on Re are the same when two spheres move along their line of centers with different velocities. These restrictions are dealt with by Rushton & Davies (1978).

In such essentially steady flow regimes one can apply the solution derived by Brenner (1961) and by Maude (1961), which is a modification of the Stimson-Jeffery solution to deal with the approach of a sphere to a rigid plane wall or nonpermeable free surface. The approach of a solid sphere to a nonpermeable free surface is equivalent dynamically to the approach of identical rigid spheres, as considered by Frankel & Acrivos (1967). Numerical convergence of these solutions becomes poor as the gap width between the two surfaces approaches zero, and this difficulty was overcome by Cox & Brenner (1967) by applying an asymptotic procedure based on singular perturbation theory for the quasi-steady approach of a rigid sphere to a rigid plane wall.

Cooley & O'Neill (1969a) extended the solution of Brenner (1961) and Maude (1961) to describe the motion of a viscous fluid caused by the approach of a sphere with uniform speed toward a stationary sphere when the minimum clearance between the spheres is arbitrary. The spheres may be exterior to each other or one may enclose the other, as would be the case in an inverse bubble. Cooley & O'Neill showed that the problem of a sphere approaching an unequal stationary sphere with velocity $\mathbf{U}$ may be solved by adding the solution of the Stimson-Jeffery problem for two spheres with velocities $\frac{1}{2} \mathbf{U}$, $\frac{1}{2} \mathbf{U}$ along their line of centers to the solutions for two spheres with velocities $\frac{1}{2} \mathbf{U}$, $-\frac{1}{2} \mathbf{U}$. The forces exerted on the spheres for the $\frac{1}{2} \mathbf{U}$, $\frac{1}{2} \mathbf{U}$ problem were computed by Cooley & O'Neill (1969a) for a wide range of radius ratios and minimum clearance parameters, and these authors also determined the solution of the $\frac{1}{2} \mathbf{U}$, $-\frac{1}{2} \mathbf{U}$ problem when the spheres are unequal (Cooley & O'Neill 1969b). Furthermore, using singular perturbation theory, Cooley & O'Neill (1969b) gave a detailed analysis of the asymptotic behavior of the solution when the minimum clearance between the spheres tends to zero. The flow was divided into two parts: an inner region consisting of the fluid in the neighborhood of the nearest points of the spheres, and an outer region consisting of the remainder of the fluid. Inner and outer matching solutions were found for these regions. The contributions were determined for the forces acting on the spheres arising from these inner and outer solutions and evaluated and summed, and these were used to obtain the singular terms in the asymptotic expansions of the force on either sphere when the minimum clearance between the spheres is very small. Cooley & O'Neill found that if a and b are the radii of the moving and stationary spheres, respectively, ϵa is the minimum clearance, and $|k| = a/b$ with $k < 0$ when the spheres are exterior to each other and $0 < k < 1$ when the stationary sphere encloses the translating sphere, the force exerted on the moving sphere has cylindrical polar components $(0, 0, \sigma\pi\mu uaF)$, where

$$F = \frac{1}{(1-k)^2\epsilon} - \frac{(1-7k+k^2)}{5(1-k)^2} \log \epsilon + \mathbf{O}(1) \qquad [1.3.61]$$

The force acting on the stationary sphere has components $(0, 0, -6\,\pi\mu uaF)$.

Hansford (1970) subsequently used essentially the same method as Cooley & O'Neill to calculate the force experienced by either of two identical rigid spheres that approach each other with the same speed when the gap between the spheres is very small. Cox & Brenner (1967) used singular perturbation theory to calculate the first-order effects of the convective and local acceleration inertial terms in the Navier-Stokes equations for the problem of a sphere approaching a rigid plane. The force on the particle differs according to whether it moves toward or away from the wall. Up to now, this type of analysis has not been applied to the two-sphere problem.

The possibility of separation of a flow from a boundary is a recent development in the study of Stokes flows. The current state of knowledge in this area is reviewed in sections 1.3.6 and 1.3.7 and will not be considered further in this section, which is primarily concerned with how the interaction between the spheres affects the mechanical action of the fluids on the particles. One observation, however, is that separation is a widespread phenomenon, particularly in strong interaction situations when particles are close together.

So far, only axisymmetric motions of two spheres have been considered. Although Stimson & Jeffery's classic paper appeared in 1926, it was not until some 40 yr later that the exact solution of the problem of asymmetric flow—caused, for instance, by the translation of two spheres perpendicular to their line of centers— was found. Dean & O'Neill (1963) and O'Neill (1964a) described a technique for constructing exact solutions of the problems posed when a sphere either rotates about or translates along a direction parallel to a plane wall. Bispherical coordinates were employed, and the theory offered scope for application to two-sphere problems. Subsequently, O'Neill (1964b, 1969, 1970), Goldman et al. (1966), and Wakiya (1965) solved the problems of two equal-sized spheres in translational or rotational motion along directions perpendicular to their line of centers. Comprehensive analyses of the asymmetric Stokes flows caused by translation or rotation of two spheres of arbitrary size followed (Davis 1969; O'Neill & Majumdar 1970a). The latter authors reduced the general problem to the superposition of solutions of two basic asymmetric problems: problem I, in which a sphere S_A of radius a rotates with angular velocity $(0, \Omega, 0)$ in a Cartesian frame in which the z axis joins the center of S_A to the center of a stationary sphere S_B of radius b, and problem II, in which S_A translates with velocity $(U, 0, 0)$ while S_B again remains at rest. The solutions of these problems are represented in the form of infinite series, whose coefficients are expressible in terms of two pivotal coefficient sequences that satisfy a pair of linked difference equations for problems I and II. The difference equations are solved numerically and the forces and couples exerted on the spheres can then be found.

For problem I, sphere S_A experiences a force $(-6\pi\mu\Omega a^2 f_{11}, 0, 0)$ and a couple $(0, -8\pi\mu\Omega a^3 g_{11}, 0)$ in terms of Cartesian components. The force and couple exerted on sphere S_B are $(-6\pi\mu\Omega b^2 f_{12}, 0, 0)$ and $(0, -8\pi\mu\Omega b^3 g_{12}, 0)$. The corresponding forces and couples in problem II are $(-6\pi\mu U a f_{21}, 0, 0)$ and $(0, -8\pi\mu U a^2 g_{21}, 0)$ for S_A and $(-6\pi\mu U b f_{22}, 0, 0)$ and $(0, -8\pi\mu U b^2 g_{22}, 0)$ for S_B. The nondimensional force and couple coefficients f_{ij} and g_{ij} $(i, j = 1, 2)$ may be determined for any values of the parameter $k = b/a$ and the minimum clearance ϵa. Consequently, the contribution to the complete mechanical action exerted by the fluid on either sphere that is derived from the part of the flow caused by asymmetric translation and/or rotation of the spheres may be calculated for any values of k and ϵ. For example, if S_A moves with velocity $(U_1, 0, 0)$ of translation and velocity $(0, \Omega_1, 0)$ of rotation, and S_B now moves with velocity $(U_2, 0, 0)$ of translation and velocity $(0, \Omega_2, 0)$ of rotation, it is clear that each f_{ij} and g_{ij} is a function of k and ϵ. The linearity of the governing equations and boundary conditions for the flow permits solution of this problem by superposition of the solutions of four basic problems of type I or type II. The resulting forces on S_A and S_B are $(F_A, 0, 0)$ and $(F_B, 0, 0)$, respectively, where

$$F_A = -6\pi\mu a \left[\Omega_1 a f_{11}(k, \epsilon) - \Omega_2 a f_{12}(k^{-1}, \epsilon k^{-1}) + U_1 f_{21}(k, \epsilon)\right.$$
$$\left. + U_2 f_{22}(k^{-1}, \epsilon k^{-1})\right] \tag{1.3.62}$$

$$F_B = -6\pi\mu b \left[\Omega_1 b f_{12}(k, \epsilon) - \Omega_2 b f_{11}(k^{-1}, \epsilon k^{-1}) + U_1 f_{22}(k, \epsilon)\right.$$
$$\left. + U_2 f_{21}(k^{-1}, \epsilon k^{-1})\right] \tag{1.3.63}$$

The corresponding couples are $(0, G_A, 0)$ and $(0, G_B, 0)$, respectively, with G_A and G_B given by

$$G_A = -8\pi\mu a^2 \left[\Omega_1 a g_{11}(k, \epsilon) - \Omega_2 a g_{12}(k^{-1}, \epsilon k^{-1}) + U_1 g_{21}(k, \epsilon)\right.$$
$$\left. + U_2 g_{22}(k^{-1}, \epsilon k^{-1})\right] \tag{1.3.64}$$

$$G_B = -8\pi\mu b^2 \left[-\Omega, b g_{12}(k, \epsilon) + \Omega_2 b g_{11}(k^{-1}, \epsilon k^{-1}) - U_1 g_{22}(k, \epsilon)\right.$$
$$\left. - U_2 g_{21}(k^{-1}, \epsilon k^{-1})\right] \tag{1.3.65}$$

For flows where the spheres have more general velocities of rotation and translation, it is observed that the components of the forces and couples that arise from the asymmetric velocity distributions of the spheres require the calculation of at most two expressions of type [1.3.62]–[1.3.65]. O'Neill & Majumdar (1970a) give a set of tables of f_{ij} and g_{ij} covering a wide range of k and ϵ.

Although the theory described above helps to determine to any desired degree of accuracy the solutions of the equations governing the flow for any geometric configuration of the spheres, it would be advantageous to know analytically how the coefficients f_{ij} and g_{ij} behave as contact between the spheres is approached. For the case of a finite volume of fluid bounded by slightly eccentric spheres with almost equal radii, this constitutes the spherical journal-bearing problem when the spheres rotate; analyses of this problem when the inner journal rotates have been given by Wannier (1950) and Tanner (1958) for a fixed bearing and by Gross (1962) for a bearing that may also rotate. The authors apply lubrication theory to the entire flow region, which for formal validity requires that the clearance between the journal and bearing be uniformly small in comparison with the radius of the journal. In general, and indeed always when the spheres are external to each other in an infinite fluid, this condition does not apply, and a more comprehensive analysis is required. To discuss the properties of the flow in the entire fluid in a rigorous way, it is necessary to approach problem I or problem II in a manner analogous to the treatments given by O'Neill & Stewartson (1967) and Cooley & O'Neill (1968) for determining the asymptotic structure of the Stokes flow caused by the motion of a sphere near a plane. Such an approach necessitates the construction of matching asymptotic expansions of the solution of the Stokes equations valid in the inner strongly sheared flow region and is the outer region consisting of the rest of the fluid. O'Neill & Majumdar (1970b) derived only the first term of the asymptotic expansion of the solution for the inner region, but this was shown to be sufficient to describe completely the singular nature of the forces and couples acting on the spheres as $\epsilon \to 0$ if the existence of a matching outer solution is tacitly assumed. The leading term of the outer solution was found by O'Neill (1969) for equal-sized spheres that rotate about axes through their centers and perpendicular to their line of centers with equal and opposite angular velocities. This was generalized by Cooley (1971) to include unequal-sized spheres external to each other, or one enclosing the other, that have arbitrary angular velocities about axes perpendicular to their line of centers.

The asymptotic structure for $\epsilon \ll 1$ of the force and couple coefficients appearing in [1.3.62]–[1.3.65] was found to be

$$f_{11} = \pm \frac{2}{15} \frac{1 - 4\lambda}{(1 - \lambda)^2} \log \epsilon + O(1) \qquad [1.3.66]$$

$$g_{11} = \pm \frac{2}{5} \frac{1}{1 - \lambda} \log \epsilon + O(1) \qquad [1.3.67]$$

$$f_{12} = \pm \frac{2}{15} \frac{\lambda^2(1 - 4\lambda)}{(1 - \lambda)^2} \log \epsilon + O(1) \qquad [1.3.68]$$

$$g_{12} = \pm \frac{1}{10} \frac{\lambda^2}{1 - \lambda} \log \epsilon + O(1) \qquad [1.3.69]$$

$$f_{21} = \pm \frac{4}{15} \frac{2 - \lambda + 2\lambda^2}{(1 - \lambda)^3} \log \epsilon + O(1) \qquad [1.3.70]$$

$$g_{21} = \pm \frac{1}{10} \frac{1 - 4\lambda}{(1 - \lambda)^2} \log \epsilon + O(1) \qquad [1.3.71]$$

$$f_{22} = \pm \frac{4}{15} |\lambda| \frac{2 - \lambda + 2\lambda^2}{(1 - \lambda)^3} \log \epsilon + O(1) \qquad [1.3.72]$$

$$g_{22} = \pm \frac{1}{10} \frac{|\lambda| (4 - \lambda)}{(1 - \lambda)^2} \log \epsilon + O(1) \qquad [1.3.73]$$

where $|\lambda| = 1/k$ and $\lambda < 0$ when S_B lies in the half-space $z < 0$ and $1 > \lambda > 0$ when S_B encloses S_A. The lower sign in [1.3.66]–[1.3.73] is taken when $\lambda > 1$, in which case S_A encloses S_B.

From these expressions, infer the following interesting properties of the forces and couples exerted by the fluid on the spheres. When the spheres move in an infinite fluid, the forces and couples become singular for all values of λ as contact is approached irrespective of whether the moving sphere translates or rotates. However, when the stationary sphere encloses the moving sphere–i.e., when $0 < \lambda < 1$–the force on each sphere, if the moving sphere is rotating, or the couple exerted on each sphere (when moments of the surface stresses for both spheres are taken about the center of the moving sphere), if the moving sphere is translating, remains bounded as contact between the spheres is approached when $\lambda = \frac{1}{4}$–i.e., when the radius of the outer stationary sphere is four times that of the moving sphere. Furthermore, if $0 < \lambda < \frac{1}{4}$, the singular parts of f_{11} and g_{21} are negative, but for $\frac{1}{4} < \lambda < 1$, they are positive. In addition, the calculations of O'Neill & Majumdar (1970a) indicate that when the stationary sphere encloses a moving sphere whose radius is less than one-fourth that of the stationary sphere, the forces acting on the spheres vanish at a certain nonzero value of ϵ that depends on λ in such a way that it increases as λ decreases, when the moving sphere rotates. Furthermore, the direction in which each force acts reverses as ϵ passes through this critical value. If the moving sphere translates, the couples acting on the spheres vanish at a critical nonzero value of ϵ and the direction of each couple reverses as ϵ passes through this critical value. For a given value of λ with $0 < \lambda < 1$, the critical values of ϵ for the translational and rotational problems are the same. When $\frac{1}{4} < \lambda < 1$, these types of behavior are not exhibited by the force and couple coefficients, and they decrease monotonically as ϵ increases. For $\lambda > 1$, the moving sphere encloses the stationary sphere. The forces and couples then become singular as contact is approached and are monotonic decreasing functions without changes of sign as ϵ increases.

It is also of interest to compare the results for the asymptotic forms for the forces and couples in the case where the fluid is contained between eccentric spherical boundaries with those obtained by Wannier (1950) for the spherical journal-bearing problem with inner rotating journal. Wannier's analysis leads to a prediction that the irregular parts of the force and couple coefficients f_{11} and g_{11} are $\sim -2\lambda^2 \log \epsilon / 5(1-\lambda)^2$ and $-2\lambda \log \epsilon / 5(1-\lambda)$, respectively, as $\epsilon \to 0$, when expressed in the notation of O'Neill & Majumdar. The apparent divergence between such asymptotic forms and those given in [1.3.66] and [1.3.67] is resolved by noting that the necessity for a uniformly thin journal-bearing clearance in Wannier's analysis required that

$$0 < \epsilon < \zeta < 1 \qquad \zeta = O(\epsilon)$$

where ζ denotes the maximum clearance. Thus $\lambda = 1 - O(\epsilon)$ and consequently lubrication theory predicts singularities in the force and couple such as

$$-\frac{2}{5} \frac{\log \epsilon}{(1-\lambda)^2} + O(\epsilon^{-1} \log \epsilon) \qquad [1.3.74]$$

and

$$-\frac{2}{5} \frac{\log \epsilon}{1-\lambda} + O(\log \epsilon) \qquad [1.3.75]$$

respectively. The asymptotic analysis of O'Neill & Majumdar (1970b) is based on the assumption that the region of strongly sheared flow is on a length scale of $\epsilon^{1/2}$

in the r coordinate; thus flow regimes, for which lubrication theory is applicable, cannot strictly be discussed by their analysis. However, it is interesting to note that when one sets $\lambda = 1 - \mathbf{O}(\epsilon)$ in [1.3.66] and [1.3.67], the same leading terms as in [1.3.74] and [1.3.75] appear.

A second effect of hydrodynamic interactions between particles is modification of the local particle advection velocity relative to that in the absence of such interactions. Specifically, one must calculate the hydrodynamic modification of the particle motion when the bulk fluid phase undergoes a complicated flow around a collector. In the theory of particle capture in filtration and scrubbing processes (see section 9.2.2), it is necessary to know the hydrodynamic forces on the particles suspended in the flow, and in particular the extent of the influence of collectors on these forces when the particles are moving close to the collectors. In many practical situations, the suspended particles are much smaller than the collector and it is possible to make the simplifying assumptions that (1) the flow field past the collectors is undisturbed by the particles except in their immediate vicinity, and (2) at particle-collector distances exceeding several particle diameters the particle center moves along a streamline of the undisturbed flow. However, for smaller distances between particle and collector, hydrodynamic interactions between the particle and the collector become increasingly important and the latter assumption is no longer valid.

Goren & O'Neill (1971) outlined a proper resolution of the general problem comprising a series of simpler hydrodynamic problems for the case where the collector particle is rigid and much larger than the colloidal particles that are being collected. They utilized the fact that the region of hydrodynamic interaction extends over only a few particle radii from the surface of the collector. This means that the collector surface is locally modeled as flat and the relevant undisturbed flow is obtained as a Taylor series expansion around the point of the collector nearest to the particle. In this way, the general undisturbed flow can be decomposed into an axisymmetric stagnation point flow, a linear shear flow, a quadratic shear flow, a local rotation, and a straining motion. Goren & O'Neill showed that this expansion, up to and including quadratic terms, yields an asymptotically correct description of the particle-collector hydrodynamic interactions for small values of the ratio of particle radius to collector radius. For sufficiently small values of this ratio a particle is not expected to deviate from an undisturbed streamline until its center is two or three particle radii from the surface of the collector, and thereafter its motion can be approximated accurately by that of a particle moving near a plane wall. On approaching the collector, the particle does not immediately respond to the curving of the fluid streamlines as they divide past the collector, but when the particle comes within range of the hydrodynamic repulsion of the collector, it then moves permanently to the outside of the fluid streamline that it was initially following upstream. This type of behavior was also reported by Michael (1967) for flow of a dusty gas past a solid sphere.

The interaction of a fluid sphere with a rigid plane or fluid-fluid interface is of considerable interest in connection with processes such as dispersed-phase flotation, which involves motions of small colloidal particles in a viscous fluid relative to motions of much larger collector particles such as bubbles or drops, and, at a more fundamental level, in connection with the development of proper theories for the transport and rheological properties of a fluid interface in the presence of an adsorbed surfactant species. An exact analytic solution by a procedure similar to that of Stimson & Jeffery (1926) was given by Bart (1968) for the problem of a liquid droplet approaching a plane nonpermeable interface between two immiscible fluids. Wacholder & Weihs (1972) gave results for a pair of identical fluid spheres falling along their line of centers. Rushton & Davies (1970, 1973) and Haber et al. (1974) considered the relative motion of two arbitrary droplets along their line of centers and provided explicit expressions for the corrections to the Hadamard-Rybezinski drag force. These papers and others related to axisymmetric motions involving two fluid particles are reviewed by Rushton & Davies (1978). Insofar as the asymmetric motions of two fluid particles are concerned, no exact analysis, along the lines of that of Dean & O'Neill for solid particles, has yet appeared, although in principle there is no difficulty that prevents such an analysis if it is assumed that the droplets maintain an exactly spherical shape. A solution has been obtained, subject to this assumption, by Hetsroni & Haber (1978), using the method of reflections. They considered the motion of two drops submerged in an unbounded arbitrary velocity field. As special cases, they considered the motion of two droplets in a quiescent fluid that settle under gravity and also the motion of two droplets in a simple shear flow. Approximations to the drag, to order $(a/l)^m (b/l)^n$ (when $m + n < 5$), and to the settling velocities are obtained.

1.3.4   PARTICLE–INTERFACE INTERACTION

The motion of a particle in the presence of a free fluid-fluid interface is of some importance and interest in chemical engineering. The general motion of an arbitrary particle is a problem of considerable complexity, and in this section only the simplest geometry is considered, namely the thin circular disk straddling an interface edge on.

First, consider a disk moving parallel to itself with uniform velocity (Ranger 1978). The Stokes equations in the two phases are expressed by

$$\nabla p_j = \mu_j \nabla^2 \mathbf{v}_j \quad \mathbf{v}_j = 0 \quad j = 1,2 \qquad [1.3.76]$$

where p is pressure. The region $x > 0$ has viscosity μ_1 and the region $x < 0$ viscosity μ_2. The disk is defined by $x = 0$, $0 < r < 1$, and moves in the interface $x = 0$ with velocity expressed by

$$\mathbf{v}_0 = \mathbf{r} \cos \phi - \hat{\phi} \sin \phi$$

The fluid velocity in the two phases can be represented by

$$\mathbf{v}_j = \nabla \times \nabla \times \frac{\psi_j}{r} \mathbf{i} \cos \phi + \nabla \times \left(\frac{\chi_j}{r} \mathbf{i} \sin \phi \right) \qquad [1.3.77]$$

where $\mathbf{i}$ is unit vector along the x axis and ψ is a solution of $L^2_{-1} \psi = 0$ as [1.3.78], and where ψ_j and χ_j satisfy

$$L^2_{-1} \psi_j = 0 \quad L_{-1} \chi_j = 0 \qquad [1.3.78]$$

and
$$L_{-1} = \frac{\partial^2}{\partial x^2} + \frac{\partial^2}{\partial r^2} - \frac{1}{r}\frac{\partial}{\partial r}$$

Here (x, r, ϕ) are cylindrical polar coordinates. If $\mathbf{v}_j = v_x^j \mathbf{i} + v_r^j \mathbf{r} + v_\phi^j \boldsymbol{\phi}$, then

$$v_x^j = \left(\frac{1}{r}\frac{\partial^2 \psi_j}{\partial x^2} - \frac{1}{r} L_{-1} \psi_j \right) \cos \phi$$

$$v^j = \left[\frac{\partial}{\partial r} \left(\frac{1}{r}\frac{\partial \psi_j}{\partial x} \right) + \frac{\chi_j}{r^2} \right] \cos \phi$$

$$v_\phi^j = \left[\frac{1}{r^2}\frac{\partial \psi_j}{\partial x} + \frac{\partial}{\partial r}\left(\frac{\chi_j}{r} \right) \right] \sin \phi$$

An appropriate form for ψ_j is

$$\psi_j = x V_j \qquad L_{-1} V_j = 0 \qquad\qquad [1.3.79]$$

Now on the disk $x = 0,\ 0 < r < 1$

$$v_x^j = 0 \qquad v_r^j = \cos \phi \qquad v_\phi^j = -\sin \phi$$

and in terms of V_j and χ_j these conditions are equivalent to

$$V_j = \tfrac{1}{2} r^2 \qquad \chi_j = \tfrac{1}{2} r^2 \qquad \text{at } x = 0 \qquad 0 < r < 1$$

The normal component of velocity is

$$v_x^j = 0 \qquad x = 0 \qquad r > 1$$

so that the condition of zero normal velocity on the interface is satisfied as well as on the disk. The interface conditions require continuity of the velocity as well as stress on $x = 0,\ r > 1$. It is found that the tangential components of velocity are continuous if

$$V_1 = V_2 \qquad \chi_1 = \chi_2 \qquad \text{at } x = 0 \qquad r > 1$$

It is also found that the normal component of stress is continuous at the interface if

$$P_{xx}^{(1)} = P_{xx}^{(2)}$$

and since $P_{xx}^{(j)}$, the normal stress, is identically zero, this condition is satisfied. The tangential components of stress are continuous if

$$\left. \begin{aligned} \mu_1 \frac{\partial V_1}{\partial x} &= \mu_2 \frac{\partial V_2}{\partial x} \\[2mm] \mu_1 \frac{\partial \chi_1}{\partial x} &= \mu_2 \frac{\partial \chi_2}{\partial x} \end{aligned} \right\} x = 0 \qquad r > 1$$

Thus V_j and χ_j satisfy identical mixed boundary value problems, which may be stated in the form

$$L_{-1} V_j = 0$$

subject to $V_j = \frac{1}{2} r^2$ at $x = 0, 0 \leqslant r \leqslant 1$

$$V_1 = V_2 \quad \text{at } x = 0 \quad r > 1$$

$$\mu_1 \frac{\partial V_2}{\partial x} = \mu_2 \frac{\partial V_2}{\partial x} \quad \text{at } x = 0 \quad r > 1$$

In addition, the fluid velocity vanishes at infinity and this is satisfied if $v_j \to 0$ as $x^2 + r^2 \to \infty$.

Appropriate integral representations for $v_j (x, r)$ are

$$v_1(x, r) = \int_0^r \frac{v_1(x, y)y \, dy}{(r^2 - y^2)^{1/2}} = \int_r^\infty \frac{u_1(x, y)y \, dy}{(y^2 - r^2)^{1/2}} \qquad [1.3.80]$$

for $x \geqslant 0$ and

$$V_2(x, r) = \int_0^r \frac{v_2(-x, y)y \, dy}{(r^2 - y^2)^{1/2}} = \int_r^\infty \frac{u_2(-x, y)y \, dy}{(y^2 - r^2)^{1/2}} \qquad [1.3.81]$$

for $x \leqslant 0$. Here (u_j, v_j) are conjugate two-dimensional harmonics even and odd in y and expressible in the form

$$u_j + iv_j = \int_0^\infty f_j(k)e^{-k(x+iy)} \, dk \qquad [1.3.82]$$

where $f_j(k)$, an integral transform, are real functions of k, a transform variable. On the disk

$$V_j(0, r) = \frac{1}{2} r^2 = \int_0^r \frac{v_j(0, y) \, y \, dy}{(r^2 - y^2)^{1/2}} \qquad 0 \leqslant r \leqslant 1$$

The inverse of the Abel-type integral equation is

$$v_j(0, y) = \frac{2}{\pi y} \frac{d}{dy} \int_0^y \frac{V_j(0, r)r \, dr}{(y^2 - r^2)^{1/2}} = \frac{2y}{\pi} \qquad 0 \leqslant y \leqslant 1$$

Again, on the interface

$$V_1(0, r) - V_2(0, r) = \int_0^r \frac{[v_1(0, y) - v_2(0, y)]y \, dy}{(r^2 - y^2)^{1/2}}$$

$$= \int_1^r \frac{[v_1(0, y) - v_2(0, y)]y \, dy}{(r^2 - y^2)^{1/2}} = 0$$

for $r > 1$. The latter equation implies

$$v_1(0, y) = v_2(0, y) \quad \text{for } |y| > 1$$

Also on the interface

$$\left(\mu_1 \frac{\partial V_1}{\partial x} - \mu_2 \frac{\partial V_2}{\partial x} \right)_{x=0} = \int_r^\infty \frac{(\mu_1 \partial u_1/\partial x + \mu_2 \partial u_2/\partial x)_{x=0}}{(y^2 - r^2)^{1/2}} \, y \, dy = 0$$

for $r > 1$, and this implies

$$\mu_1 \frac{\partial u_1}{\partial x} + \mu_2 \frac{\partial u_2}{\partial x} = \mu_1 \frac{\partial v_1}{\partial y} + \mu_2 \frac{\partial v_2}{\partial y} = 0 \quad \text{for } x = 0 \quad |y| > 1$$

so that

$$\mu_1 v_1(0, y) + \mu_2 v_2(0, y) = A \quad |y| > 1$$

where A is a constant. Thus

$$v_1(0, y) = v_2(0, y) = \frac{A}{\mu_1 + \mu_2} = B \quad \text{say for } |y| > 1$$

It is observed that

$$\mu_1 \frac{\partial V_1}{\partial x} = \mu_2 \frac{\partial V_2}{\partial x} = 0 \quad \text{for } x = 0 \quad r > 1$$

and a similar result is valid for χ_1 and χ_2, so that the stress vanishes over the interface. The solution for $v_j(x, y)$ can now be determined by standard Green's function methods and is given by

$$v_j(x, y) = \frac{x}{\pi} \int_{-\infty}^\infty \frac{v_j(0, s) \, ds}{x^2 + (s - y)^2} \tag{1.3.83}$$

where

$$v_j(0, s) = \frac{2}{\pi} s \quad |s| < 1$$

$$= B \quad s > 1$$

$$= -B \quad s < -1$$

and s is a parameter of integration. Substitution in the integral and evaluation gives

$$v_j(x, y) = \frac{2y}{\pi^2} \left[\tan^{-1} \left(\frac{1-y}{x} \right) - \tan^{-1} \left(\frac{-1-y}{x} \right) \right] + \frac{x}{\pi^2} \log \left[\frac{x^2 + (1-y)^2}{x^2 + (1+y)^2} \right]$$

$$+ \frac{B}{\pi} \left[\tan^{-1} \left(\frac{-1-y}{x} \right) - \tan^{-1} \left(\frac{1-y}{x} \right) \right] \tag{1.3.84}$$

To determine the constant B, consider the velocity components on $x = 0, r > 1$. It suffices to investigate v_r^j, which is given by

$$v_r^j = \left[\frac{\partial}{\partial r} \left(\frac{V_j(0, r)}{r} \right) + \frac{V_j(0, r)}{r^2} \right] \cos \phi$$

and on calculation

$$V_j(0, r) = \frac{r^2}{\pi} \sin^{-1} \frac{1}{r} + B - \frac{1}{\pi} (r^2 - 1)^{1/2}$$

Hence $v_r^j = \frac{1}{r} \frac{\partial V_j}{\partial r} (0, r) \cos \phi$

$$= \left[\frac{2}{\pi} \sin^{-1} \frac{1}{r} - \frac{1}{\pi} \frac{1}{(r^2 - 1)^{1/2}} + B - \frac{1}{\pi} \frac{1}{(r^2 - 1)^{1/2}} \right] \cos \phi$$

Since the velocity is finite as $r \to 1+$ the singularity is eliminated by choosing $B = 2/\pi$. Now $v_j(x, y)$ is given by

$$v_j(x, y) = \frac{2}{\pi^2}(y - 1) \left[\tan^{-1} \left(\frac{1 - y}{x} \right) - \tan^{-1} \left(\frac{-1 - y}{x} \right) \right]$$

$$+ \frac{2}{\pi^2} \log \left[\frac{x^2 + (1 - y)^2}{x^2 + (1 + y)^2} \right] \qquad \text{[1.3.85]}$$

$V_j(x, r)$ and $\chi_j(x, r)$ are now found from

$$V_1(x, r) = \chi_1(x, r) = \int_0^r \frac{v_1(x, y)y \, dy}{(r^2 - y^2)^{1/2}} \qquad x \geqslant 0$$

$$V_2(x, r) = \chi_2(x, r) = \int_0^r \frac{v_2(-x, y) \, dy}{(r^2 - y^2)^{1/2}} \qquad x \leqslant 0$$

It is clear that the fluid velocity field is independent of the ratio of viscosities of the two phases, so that basically the solution represents the edgewise motion of a disk through an infinite homogeneous fluid. This follows from the fact that the stress vanishes over the interface. Thus the drag on a disk of radius a moving with speed V is given by

$$D = \frac{16}{3} Va(\mu_1 + \mu_2) \qquad \text{[1.3.86]}$$

1.3.4.1 Axisymmetrical Flow: Disk Moving Perpendicular to Interface

In this flow the thin circular disk $x = 0$, $0 \leqslant r \leqslant 1$, straddles the interface $x = 0$ and is moving perpendicular to it. The fluid velocities in the two phases are given by

$$\mathbf{U}_j = \nabla \times \left(\frac{-\psi_j}{r} \hat{\phi} \right) \qquad j = 1, 2 \qquad [1.3.87]$$

An appropriate representation for ψ_j is

$$\psi_j = U_j - x \left(\frac{\partial U_j}{\partial x} - V_j \right) \qquad [1.3.88]$$

where U_j and V_j satisfy

$$L_{-1} U_j = L_{-1} V_j = 0 \qquad [1.3.89]$$

The boundary conditions on the disk require

$$\left. \begin{array}{l} U_x^j = \dfrac{1}{r} \dfrac{\partial \psi_j}{\partial r} = -1 \\[3mm] U_r^j = \dfrac{1}{r} \dfrac{\partial \psi_j}{\partial x} = 0 \end{array} \right\} \quad \text{at } x = 0 \quad 0 \leqslant r \leqslant 1$$

and these conditions are satisfied if

$$U_j = \tfrac{1}{2} r^2 \quad V_j = 0 \quad \text{at } x = 0 \quad 0 < r < 1$$

The advantages of the representation for ψ_j in terms of U_j and V_j is that the fluid velocity and stress are continuous across the interface $x = 0, r > 1$, if

$$\left. \begin{array}{ll} U_1 = U_2 \quad V_1 = V_2 \\[3mm] \mu_1 \dfrac{\partial U_1}{\partial x} = \mu_2 \dfrac{\partial U_z}{\partial x} \quad \mu_1 \dfrac{\partial V_1}{\partial x} = \mu_2 \dfrac{\partial V_2}{\partial x} \end{array} \right\} \quad \text{at } x = 0 \quad r > 1$$

It is readily shown that since $V_j \to 0$ as $x^2 + r^2 \to \infty$, then $V_j(x, r)$ is identically zero everywhere. The mixed boundary value problem for $U_j(x, r)$ is then expressed in the form

$$U_j = \tfrac{1}{2} r^2 \qquad \text{at } x = 0 \quad 0 < r < 1$$

$$U_1 = U_2 \qquad \text{at } x = 0 \quad r > 1$$

$$\mu_1 \frac{\partial U_1}{\partial x} = \mu_2 \frac{\partial U_2}{\partial x} \qquad \text{at } x = 0 \quad r > 1 \qquad [1.3.90]$$

$$U_j \to 0 \qquad \text{as } x^2 + r^2 \to \infty$$

Again employing the integral representations

$$U_1(x, r) = \int_0^r \frac{v_1(x, y) y \, dy}{(r^2 - y^2)^{1/2}} = \int_r^\infty \frac{u_1(x, y) y \, dy}{(y^2 - r^2)^{1/2}} \qquad x \geqslant 0$$

$$U_2(x, r) = \int_0^r \frac{v_2(-x, y)y \, dy}{(r^2 - y^2)^{1/2}} = \int_r^\infty \frac{u_2(-x, y)y \, dy}{(y^2 - r^2)^{1/2}} \qquad x \leqslant 0$$

the problem for $u_j + iv_j$ is the same as in the previous asymmetrical flow, and from those results we have

$$v_j(x, y) = \frac{2y}{\pi^2}\left[\tan^{-1}\left(\frac{1-y}{x}\right) - \tan^{-1}\left(\frac{-1-y}{x}\right)\right] + \frac{x}{\pi^2}\log\left[\frac{x^2 + (1-y)^2}{x^2 + (1+y)^2}\right]$$

$$+ \frac{2}{\pi^2}\left[\tan^{-1}\left(\frac{-1-y}{x}\right) - \tan^{-1}\left(\frac{1-y}{x}\right)\right] \qquad [1.3.91]$$

As in the previous flow, the fluid velocity field is independent of the ratio of viscosities and it is straightforward to calculate the drag on the disk, which for radius a and velocity V results in

$$D = 8 \, Va(\mu_1 + \mu_2) \qquad [1.3.92]$$

1.3.4.2 Rotation

Schneider et al. (1973) considered an exact solution of the Stokes equations for the motion of two immiscible viscous fluids with a plane interface, the motion being caused by slow steady rotation of a body straddling the interface of the fluids. They assumed that the body is convex with its boundary formed from two intersecting spheres or a sphere and a circular disk, and that the circle of intersection of the composite surfaces lies in the interface of the fluids. The body rotates about its axis of symmetry. By use of toroidal coordinates, they demonstrated that the general solution of the problem could be expressed concisely. Later, Majumdar et al. (1974), using toroidal coordinates, derived an exact solution for the velocity field induced in two immiscible semi-infinite viscous fluids, with a plane interface, by the slow rotation of a concave spherical lens, such that the circle of intersection of the composite spherical surface lies in the plane of the interface.

The coordinate systems are illustrated in figure 1.3.3. The relations connecting the cylindrical coordinates (R_i, ϕ, z) and the toroidal coordinates (ξ_i, ϕ, η_i) for either regime are

$$z_i = \frac{c \sin \eta_i}{\cosh \xi_i - \cos \eta_i} \qquad R_i = \frac{c \sinh \xi_i}{\cosh \xi_i - \cos \eta_i} \qquad i = 1,2 \qquad [1.3.93]$$

The spherical surface of radius a_i is given by $\eta_i = \eta_i'$, where η_i' is a constant such that $a_i = c \operatorname{cosec} \eta_i'$, and the ranges of values taken by the parameters are

$$0 \leqslant \xi_i < \infty \qquad 0 \leqslant \xi_2 < \infty \qquad 0 \leqslant \phi \leqslant 2\pi \qquad 0 \leqslant \eta_1 \leqslant \eta_1'$$

$$0 \leqslant \eta_2 \leqslant \eta_2' \qquad \text{where } \pi < \eta_1' < 2\pi \qquad \text{and } 0 < \eta_2' < \pi$$

The case where the lens degenerates into a spherical bowl is given by $\eta_1' = 2\pi - \eta_2'$.

The equations of motion are

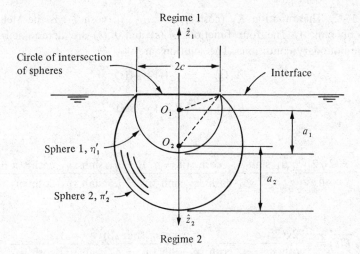

Figure 1.3.3 Geometric configuration of the problem of a general concave spherical lens.

$$\nabla P_i = \mu_i \nabla^2 \mathbf{U}_i \qquad \nabla \mathbf{U}_i = 0 \qquad i = 1, 2 \tag{1.3.94}$$

where P is pressure, and these are satisfied by

$$\mathbf{U}_1 = \hat{\phi}_1 v_1 (R_1, z_1) \qquad \mathbf{U}_2 = \hat{\phi}_2 v_2 (R_2, z_2)$$

and $P_1 = P_2 = \text{const}$, where $v_1 \equiv v_{\phi_1}$, $v_2 = v_{\phi_2}$ are the tangential components in the two fluids. The equation of continuity is now automatically satisfied and the Stokes equation reduces to

$$\frac{\partial^2 v_i}{\partial R_i^2} + \frac{1}{R_i}\frac{\partial v_i}{\partial R_i} + \frac{\partial^2 v_i}{\partial z_i^2} - \frac{v_i}{R_i^2} = 0 \qquad i = 1, 2 \tag{1.3.95}$$

The boundary conditions require that the velocity and stress vectors are continuous at the interface, the no-slip condition is satisfied on the lens, and the velocity decays to zero at infinity. These conditions yield in turn

$$v_1 = -v_2 \qquad (z_1 = z_2 = 0 \quad R > c) \tag{1.3.96}$$

$$\mu_1 \frac{\partial v_1}{\partial z_1} = \mu_2 \frac{\partial v_2}{\partial z_2} \qquad (z_1 = z_2 = 0 \quad R > c) \tag{1.3.97}$$

$$v_i = wR_1 \qquad v_2 = -wR_2 \qquad \text{on the lens surface}$$

$$v_i \to 0 \qquad \text{as } R_i^2 + z_i^2 \to \infty \qquad i = 1, 2$$

In toroidal coordinates suitable forms for the velocity fields in the two regimes are

$$v_i(\xi_i, \eta_i) = (\cosh \xi_i - \cos \eta_i)^{1/2} \int_0^{\infty} [A_i(s) \cosh s\eta_i + B_i(s) \sinh s\eta_i]$$

$$K_s'(\cosh \xi_i) \, ds \tag{1.3.98}$$

with $i = 1, 2$. The function $K'_s (\cosh \xi_i) = P'_{-1/2 + is} (\cosh \xi_i)$ is the Mehler conal function of rank 1. The four functions $A_i(s)$ and $B_i(s)$ are determined so as to satisfy the boundary conditions. The solutions are

$$A_1(s) = -A_2(s) = A(s)$$

$$B_1(s) = \frac{\mu_2}{\mu_1} B_1(s) = B(s)$$

[1.3.99]

where

$$A(s) = \frac{-2\sqrt{2}\, wc}{\cosh s\pi} \frac{\mu_1 \sinh s\eta'_2 \cosh s(\pi - \eta'_1)s + \mu_2 \sinh s\eta'_1 \cosh s(\pi - \eta'_2)s}{\mu_1 \cosh s\eta'_1 \sinh s\eta'_2 + \mu_2 \sinh s\eta'_1 \cosh s\eta'_2}$$

[1.3.100]

and

$$B(s) = \frac{-2\sqrt{2}\, wc}{\cosh s\pi} \frac{\mu_2 \sinh s\pi \sinh s(\eta'_2 - \eta'_1)}{\mu_1 \cosh s\eta'_1 \sinh s\eta'_2 + \mu_2 \sinh s\eta'_1 \cosh s\eta'_2}$$

[1.3.101]

In the degenerate case of a spherical bowl, the intersecting spherical surfaces coincide. The values of η'_1 and η'_2 may then be written

$$\eta'_1 = 2\pi - \eta_0 \qquad \eta'_2 = \eta_0$$

The torques T_{zi} that arise from the action of the fluids on the surfaces a_i are

$$T_{zi} = \sqrt{2}\, \pi \mu_i c^2 \int_0^\infty (1 + 4s^2)[A_i(s) + B_i(s) \coth s\pi]\, ds \quad [1.3.102]$$

with $i = 1, 2$, and the total torque is

$$T_z = T_{z1} + T_{z2} = \sqrt{2}\pi\, (\mu_1 + \mu_2)c^2 \int_0^\infty (1 + 4s^2)A(s)\, ds \quad [1.3.103]$$

When the fluids are identical in viscosity, $\mu_1 = \mu_2 = \mu$, this result takes a particularly simple form

$$T_z = -8\mu wc^3 \left[\frac{2}{3} + \cot \eta_0 \operatorname{cosec} \eta_0 + (\pi - \eta_0) \operatorname{cosec}^3 \eta_0 \right]$$

$$= -8\mu wc^3 \left\{ \frac{2}{3} + \frac{a}{c} \left[\left(\frac{a}{c}\right)^2 - 1 \right]^{1/2} + \left(\frac{a}{c}\right)^3 \left[\pi - \sin^{-1}\left(\frac{c}{a}\right) \right] \right\}$$

[1.3.104]

Majumdar et al. also considered the case where the interface is a free surface. Davis et al. (1975) considered some properties of multifluid Stokes flows. The solution of the Stokes equation for a rotating axisymmetric body that possesses reflection symmetry about a planar interface between two infinite immiscible quiescent viscous fluids is independent of the viscosities of the fluids and identical to the solution when the fluids have the same viscosity. The result was generalized to a rotating axisymmetric system of bodies with reflection symmetry about each interface of a plane stratified system of fluids. An analogous result for two-fluid systems with a nonplanar static interface was also derived. The effect of torque reduction produced by the presence of a second fluid layer adjacent to a rotating axisymmetric body is considered and explicit calculations are given for the case of a sphere.

A sphere of radius a rotates with angular velocity Ω in immiscible fluids with viscosities μ_1 and μ_2. The fluid with viscosity μ_1 is confined to the region $a \leqslant r \leqslant c$ and the remaining space is occupied by the fluid with viscosity μ_2. If i applies to the region occupied by the fluid with viscosity μ_i, the flows in the two fluids are given by

$$q_i = v_i(R, z)\phi \qquad P_i = 0 \qquad\qquad [1.3.105]$$

where ϕ is directed perpendicular to the azimuthal plane $\phi = \text{const}$ and in the sense of ϕ increasing, and $v_i(R, z)$ satisfies

$$\left(\frac{\partial^2}{\partial R^2} + \frac{1}{R}\frac{\partial}{\partial R} - \frac{1}{R^2} + \frac{\partial^2}{\partial z^2}\right)v_i = 0 \qquad i = 1, 2 \qquad\qquad [1.3.106]$$

The boundary conditions are

$$v_1 = \Omega R \qquad r = a \qquad \text{and } v_2 \to 0 \qquad \text{as } r \to \infty \qquad [1.3.107]$$

The interface conditions are

$$v_1 = v_2 \qquad \mu_1 \frac{\partial}{\partial R}\left(\frac{v_1}{R}\right) = \mu_2 \frac{\partial}{\partial R}\left(\frac{v_2}{R}\right) \qquad \text{at } r = c \qquad [1.3.108]$$

In spherical polar coordinates (r, θ) defined by $z = r \cos\theta$, $R = r \sin\theta$ the velocities are

$$v_1 = \Omega r\left[1 - \frac{1}{a}\left(\frac{\mu_1}{\mu_2 c^3} + \frac{1}{a^3} - \frac{1}{c^3}\right)^{-1} + \frac{1}{r^3}\left(\frac{\mu_1}{\mu_2 c^3} + \frac{1}{a^3} - \frac{1}{c^3}\right)^{-1}\right]\sin\theta \qquad a < r < c$$

$$[1.3.109]$$

$$v_2 = \frac{\mu_1 \Omega \sin\theta}{\mu_2 r^2}\left(\frac{\mu_1}{\mu_2 c^3} + \frac{1}{a^3} - \frac{1}{c^3}\right)^{-1} \qquad r > c \qquad\qquad [1.3.110]$$

The torque resisting the rotation of the sphere is

$$T_1 = 8\pi\mu_1 \Omega\lambda\left[\frac{1}{c^3} + \lambda\left(\frac{1}{a^3} - \frac{1}{c^3}\right)\right]^{-1} \qquad\qquad [1.3.111]$$

where $\lambda = \mu_2/\mu_1$. Now if the entire region $r > a$ were occupied by homogeneous fluid with viscosity μ_2, the torque acting on the sphere would be

$$T_2 = 8\pi\mu_2 \Omega a^3 \qquad\qquad [1.3.112]$$

Thus
$$T_1 = \gamma T_2$$
where
$$\gamma = [s^3 + \lambda(1 - s^3)]^{-1} \qquad [1.3.113]$$

with $s = a/c < 1$. Clearly $\gamma < 1$ when $\lambda > 1$, so the torque acting on the sphere is always reduced when there is a layer of fluid adjacent to the sphere with a viscosity lower than that of the bulk of the fluid. The torque reduction can be substantial, since if $\lambda = 10$, then $\gamma \approx 0.27$ when $s = 0.9$ and $\gamma \approx 0.11$ when $s = 0.5$. A two-dimensional analog of this flow exists when the body is a circular cylinder, in which case the Navier-Stokes equations can be solved exactly.

O'Neill & Ranger (1978) considered the problem of a sphere rotating with axial symmetry in the presence of a flat interface separating two immiscible fluids of differing viscosities. O'Neill et al. (1978) considered a similar problem in which the sphere is moving with uniform velocity perpendicular to the interface.

1.3.5 STOKES RESISTANCE OF MULTIPARTICLE SYSTEMS

The hydrodynamic interaction between members of an aggregate of small particles suspended in a viscous fluid in motion is of fundamental importance in a variety of engineering applications. For flows with small Reynolds numbers, the Stokesian resistance for a number of specific particle shapes has been determined, either theoretically or experimentally, when the particles are in isolation in an unbounded fluid or so far apart that hydrodynamic interactions can be ignored (Happel & Brenner 1965). A general theory applicable to a single particle of arbitrary shape was developed by Brenner (1963, 1964a). Brenner demonstrated that the resistance for an arbitrarily shaped particle that translates and rotates arbitrarily in an unbounded quiescent incompressible fluid, in a low-Reynolds-number flow, can be characterized by three second-rank tensors that are uniquely determined from the external geometry of the particle. By combining the matrix equivalents of these tensors into a single 6×6 matrix—the grand resistance matrix—one can express the resistance of a particle in a form that isolates the parts that depend on the translational and angular velocities of the particle from the parts that depend only on its geometric characteristics. The components of the force and torque acting on a single particle in a linear shear flow can be quantified by the shear dyadic and two triadics whose components depend solely on the geometric characteristics of the particle (Brenner 1964b).

The matrix representation of the relations between resistance and velocity fields for purely translational and rotational motions in a quiescent fluid has been generalized by Brenner (1964a) to multiparticle systems. This follows naturally because of the immediate representation of a dyadic as a 3×3 matrix. Brenner and O'Neill (1972) showed the relations between the resistance and velocity fields of a linear shear flow, first for a single arbitrary particle and then for a general multiparticle system.

The only multiparticle system for which the resistance of the particles can be exactly determined by a theoretical method is the two-sphere system. The solution for the flow caused by two spheres rotating about their line of centers was obtained by Jeffery (1915). Later, Stimson and Jeffery (1926) solved the axisymmetrical problem where two spheres translate with the same velocity along their line of centers, and carried out calculation's for equal-sized spheres. Cooley & O'Neill (1969b) recalculated the Stimson & Jeffery values and gave a more comprehensive set of values for cases where the spheres are of unequal size. These results and those of Cooley & O'Neill (1969a) for two spheres approaching each other with the same speed, assuming quasi-steady motion, enable the computation of the total forces acting on the spheres when they have different velocities along their line of centers. Davis (1969) calculated the forces on the spheres when one is in motion along the line of centers while the other is at rest; these results can also be used to calculate the forces on the spheres when they have different velocities along the line of centers. To compute the complete forces and torques acting on spheres that move with arbitrary translational and angular velocities, one must add in the contributions from the asymmetrical parts of the motion—i.e., the forces and torques that arise when the spheres translate along or rotate about axes perpendicular to their line of centers. Calculations were carried out for equal-sized spheres by Goldman et al. (1966) and for unequal spheres by Davis (1969) and O'Neill & Majumdar (1970). Thus, for fluid motions caused by translation or rotation of spheres in a quiescent fluid, the resistance is determinate and the elements of the grand resistance matrix can be found.

For fluid that is in a simple shearing motion in the absence of the spheres, the forces and torques on stationary spheres were determined by Wakiya (1967), who used a modified form of the analysis developed by Dean & O'Neill (1963) to solve the asymmetrical two-sphere or sphere-plane problem where the sphere(s) translate or rotate in a quiescent fluid. Wakiya's analysis covered only the case where the line of centers of the spheres is in the plane of the shear, but an extension of Wakiya's work for unequal spheres, with an arbitrary orientation of the line of centers relative to the plane of the shear, was carried out by Lin et al. (1970) and Curtis & Hocking (1970). The latter included an additional London-type force of attraction.

If the fluid is quiescent, natural Cartesian axes are body axes with one axis along the line of centers. If the fluid is in a shearing motion, besides the body axes there is a space frame of reference in which the shear flow can be described in the simplest form. The relation between the orientations of the body axes and the space axes is to some extent arbitrary, and in each of the three analyses referred to above a different relation is adopted. Because of the algebraic complexity of the force and torque components for this problem, comparison of the results of different authors is not easy. Here we will give the general scheme of Brenner & O'Neill (1972) for representing the forces and torques in forms that separate out purely geometric quantities, which appear in the grand resistance and shear resistance matrices, from quantities that depend on the velocity fields.

1.3.5.1 Stokes Resistance of a Single Particle of Arbitrary Shape

Consider a rigid particle suspended in an infinite incompressible viscous fluid that is sheared at a uniform rate, characterized by the velocity gradient $\mathbf{G}$. The fluid velocity and pressure are, respectively, $\mathbf{v}$ and p referred to axes fixed in space. If O

is any point of the particle, U_O is the instantaneous velocity of this point, and ω is the instantaneous angular velocity of the particle, the no-slip condition on the surface s_p of the particle requires that on s_p

$$v = U_O + \omega \times r_O \qquad [1.3.114]$$

where r_O denotes the position vector of any point of s_p relative to O. At large distances from the particle, v must tend asymptotically to the undisturbed shear velocity. Thus

$$v \rightarrow u = u_O + r_O \cdot G \qquad [1.3.115]$$

as $|r_O| \rightarrow \infty$. The dyadic $G = \nabla u$, while u_O is the approach velocity of the undisturbed flow at O. It is convenient to express G as the sum of constant symmetrical and antisymmetrical dyadics $G = S + \Lambda$, where

$$S = \tfrac{1}{2} (G + G^{\dagger}) \qquad \Lambda = \tfrac{1}{2} (G - G^{\dagger}) \qquad [1.3.116]$$

and $\dagger$ denotes the transposition operator. If the fluid spin ω_f is defined as half the vorticity of the fluid, it follows that since

$$\nabla \times u = - \ \epsilon{:}\Lambda$$

where ϵ is the unit isotropic alternating triadic, the boundary condition [1.3.115] can be restated as

$$v \rightarrow u = u_O + \omega_f \times r_O + S \cdot r_O \qquad [1.3.117]$$

as $|r_O| \rightarrow \infty$.

The total hydrodynamic force and torque (about O) exerted by the fluid on the particle are given by

$$F = \int_{s_p} ds \cdot \pi \qquad [1.3.118]$$

$$T_O = \int_{s_p} r_O \times (ds \cdot \pi) \qquad [1.3.119]$$

where ds is a directed element of surface area pointing into the fluid and π is the stress dyadic

$$\pi = - \ Ip + \mu[\nabla v + (\nabla v)^{\dagger}] \qquad [1.3.120]$$

arising from the fields (v, p). I is the unit dyadic. Brenner (1964b) showed that [1.3.118] and [1.3.119] can be written

$$F = - \mu[K \cdot (U_O - u_O) + C_O^{\dagger} \cdot (\omega - \omega_f) + \phi_O{:}S] \qquad [1.3.121]$$

$$T_O = - \mu[C_O \cdot (U_O - u_O) + \Omega_O \cdot (\omega - \omega_f) + \tau_O{:}S] \qquad [1.3.122]$$

Since the dyadics K, C_O, and Ω_O have the forms

$$K = K_{ij}i_i i_j \qquad C_O = C_{ij}i_i i_j \qquad \Omega_O = \Omega_{ij}i_i i_j$$

it follows that in the absence of shearing motion, [1.3.121] and [1.3.122] can be written compositely in the matrix form

$$\begin{bmatrix} (\mathbf{F}) \\ (\mathbf{T}_O) \end{bmatrix} = -\mu \begin{bmatrix} (K_{ij}) & (C_{ji}) \\ (C_{ij}) & (\Omega_{ij}) \end{bmatrix} \begin{bmatrix} (\mathbf{U}_O) \\ (\boldsymbol{\omega}) \end{bmatrix}$$

[1.3.123]

where the 3×1 partitioned column matrices $(\mathbf{F})$, $(\mathbf{T}_O)$, $(\mathbf{U}_O)$, and $(\boldsymbol{\omega})$ have elements that are the ordered resolutes of $\mathbf{F}, \boldsymbol{\tau}_O, \mathbf{U}_O$, and $\boldsymbol{\omega}$, respectively, along $\mathbf{i}_1$, $\mathbf{i}_2$, and $\mathbf{i}_3$. (K_{ij}) is a 3×3 matrix whose nine scalar elements are the components of the dyadic $\mathbf{K}$; similar interpretations apply for (C_{ij}) and (Ω_{ij}). The force-torque vector $(\mathbf{F})$, the velocity-spin vector $(\mathbf{U})$, and the grand resistance matrix $(\mathbf{R})$ are defined as follows:

$$(\mathbf{F}) = \begin{bmatrix} (\mathbf{F}) \\ (\mathbf{T}_O) \end{bmatrix} \qquad (\mathbf{U}) = \begin{bmatrix} (\mathbf{U}_O) \\ (\boldsymbol{\omega}) \end{bmatrix} \qquad (\mathbf{R}) = \begin{bmatrix} (K_{ij}) & (C_{ji}) \\ (C_{ij}) & (\Omega_{ij}) \end{bmatrix}$$

and [1.3.123] can be written in the equivalent form

$$(\mathbf{F}) = -\mu(\mathbf{R})(\mathbf{U})$$

[1.3.124]

For translational and rotational particle motions in a fluid at rest at infinity, the instantaneous rate of energy dissipation in a Stokes flow is

$$D = -\int_{s_p} ds \cdot \boldsymbol{\pi} \cdot \mathbf{v}$$

On using the boundary value of $\mathbf{v}$ on s_p, it can easily be verified that

$$D = \mu[\mathbf{U}_O \cdot \mathbf{K} \cdot \mathbf{U}_O + 2\boldsymbol{\omega} \cdot \mathbf{C}_O \cdot \mathbf{U}_O + \boldsymbol{\omega} \cdot \boldsymbol{\Omega}_O \cdot \boldsymbol{\omega}]$$

which is equivalent to

$$D = \mu(\mathbf{U})^\dagger (\mathbf{R})(\mathbf{U})$$

[1.3.125]

Since D is essentially positive, the right-hand side of this expression is a positive definite quadratic form and consequently $\det (\mathbf{R}) > 0$. Thus $(\mathbf{R})$ is nonsingular and possesses an inverse $(\mathbf{R})^{-1}$. It follows that if the force and torque acting on the particle are known, its translational and angular velocities can immediately be determined from [1.3.124], giving

$$(\mathbf{U}) = -\mu^{-1}(\mathbf{R})^{-1}(\mathbf{F})$$

[1.3.126]

The elements of $(\mathbf{R})$ depend only on the geometry of the particle and may therefore in principle be calculated once and for all. Equations [1.3.124] and [1.3.126] then provide a means of calculating either the mechanical action of the fluid on the particle or its translational and angular velocities in a simple and straightforward way.

Consider the case where the shear field is nonzero. The force-torque vector and the grand resistance matrix are defined as above, but the velocity-spin vector $(\mathbf{U})$ is now defined by

$$(\mathbf{U}) = \begin{bmatrix} (\mathbf{U}_O - \mathbf{u}_O) \\ (\omega - \omega_f) \end{bmatrix} \qquad [1.3.127]$$

Because the additional terms in $\mathbf{F}$ and $\mathbf{T}_O$ arising from the pure shear involve the triadics ϕ_O and τ_O, their matrix representation does not follow as naturally as that of the translational and rotational terms, which involve only dyadics. However, a convenient scheme for the matrix representation of these terms can be derived as follows.

The contributions to $\mathbf{F}$ and $\mathbf{T}_O$ arising from the shear field may be written in Cartesian tensor notation as

$$\mathbf{F}'_i = \mu \phi_{ijk} S_{kj} \qquad [1.3.128]$$

$$\mathbf{T}'_i = -\mu \tau_{ijk} S_{kj} \qquad [1.3.129]$$

These contributions do depend on the base point O of the particle, but this is suppressed to simplify the notation. Since i, j, k each ranges over 1, 2, 3, the tensors ϕ_{ijk} and τ_{ijk} contain 27 components each. However, the symmetry relation $S_{jk} = S_{kj}$ leads to

$$\phi_{ijk} = \phi_{ikj} \qquad \tau_{ijk} = \tau_{ikj}$$

Thus the triadics ϕ and τ have no more than 18 independent components. The matrix representation of these components is achieved by taking the last two indices in ϕ_{ijk} or τ_{ijk} and the two indices of S_{jk} and contracting them into a single index l. Thus

$$\underset{(jk)}{\text{Tensor}} \equiv \underset{(l)}{\text{matrix}}$$

In particular, the following ordering scheme is adopted:

Tensor indices: 11 22 33 23 32 31 13 12 21
Matrix index: 1   2   3   4   5   6

Furthermore, since $\phi_{112} = \phi_{121}$, $\tau_{112} = \tau_{121}$, etc. for quantities with two unequal final indices, introduce a factor $\frac{1}{2}$ and write

$$\tfrac{1}{2}\phi_{16} = \phi_{112} = \phi_{121} \qquad \tfrac{1}{2}\tau_{16} = \tau_{112} = \tau_{121}$$

and so on. In this way [1.3.128] and [1.3.129] can be written

$$\mathbf{F}'_i = -\mu \phi_{ijk} S_{jk} = -\mu \phi_{il} S_l \qquad [1.3.130]$$

$$\mathbf{T}'_i = -\mu \tau_{ijk} S_{jk} = -\mu \tau_{il} S_l \qquad [1.3.131]$$

where $i = 1, 2, 3$ and $l = 1, 2, \ldots 6$. Define the force-torque vector $(\mathbf{F}')$, the shear vector $(\mathbf{S})$, and the shear resistance matrix (Φ) in the following way:

$$(\mathbf{F}')^\dagger = [\mathbf{F}'_1, \mathbf{F}'_2, \mathbf{F}'_3, \mathbf{T}'_1, \mathbf{T}'_2, \mathbf{T}'_3]$$

$$(\mathbf{S})^\dagger = [\mathbf{S}_1, \mathbf{S}_2, \mathbf{S}_3, \mathbf{S}_4, \mathbf{S}_5, \mathbf{S}_6]$$

$$(\Phi) = \begin{bmatrix} \phi_{11} & \phi_{12} & \phi_{13} & \phi_{14} & \phi_{15} & \phi_{16} \\ \phi_{21} & \phi_{22} & \phi_{23} & \phi_{24} & \phi_{25} & \phi_{26} \\ \phi_{31} & \phi_{32} & \phi_{33} & \phi_{34} & \phi_{35} & \phi_{36} \\ \tau_{11} & \tau_{12} & \tau_{13} & \tau_{14} & \tau_{15} & \tau_{16} \\ \tau_{21} & \tau_{22} & \tau_{23} & \tau_{24} & \tau_{25} & \tau_{26} \\ \tau_{31} & \tau_{32} & \tau_{33} & \tau_{34} & \tau_{35} & \tau_{36} \end{bmatrix} = \begin{bmatrix} (\phi) \\ (\tau) \end{bmatrix}$$

Equations [1.3.130] and [1.3.131] can be expressed in the compact matrix form

$$(\mathbf{F}') = -\mu(\Phi)(\mathbf{S}) \qquad [1.3.132]$$

where it is observed that the matrices are conformable since $(\mathbf{\dot{F}}')$ is 6×1, (Φ) is 6×6, and $(\mathbf{S})$ is 6×1. Combine [1.3.132] with [1.3.124] using $(\mathbf{U})$ defined by [1.3.127]. This gives the following matrix representation of the general expressions for the force and torque acting on the particle given by [1.3.121] and [1.3.122]:

$$(\mathbf{F}) = -\mu[(\mathbf{R})(\mathbf{U}) + (\Phi)(\mathbf{S})] \qquad [1.3.133]$$

The matrix form of the force and torque equations has a great advantage, e.g., in discussing a neutrally buoyant particle moving freely in a linear shear field. In this case $(\mathbf{F}) = 0$, so that [1.3.133] gives immediately the expressions for the components of the translational and angular velocities of the particle:

$$(\mathbf{U}) = -(\mathbf{R})^{-1}(\Phi)(\mathbf{S}) \qquad [1.3.134]$$

The elements of $(\mathbf{R})$ and (Φ) are intrinsic properties of the particle and are invariant for all choices of $\mathbf{S}$. To construct (Φ) use was made of the symmetry of the dyadic $\mathbf{S}$, which resulted in a reduction of the independent components of ϕ or τ from 27 to 18. Without loss of generality, this number may be reduced to 15 by noticing that for the equation of continuity of an incompressible fluid to be satisfied, it is necessary that $\mathbf{I}:\mathbf{S} = 0$. This means that ϕ is determinate only to within a term of the form $a\mathbf{I}$, where a may be any vector. Brenner (1964b) demonstrated that this property makes it possible to set any one of the components of ϕ of the form ϕ_{jmm} equal to zero for each j, where $j, m = 1, 2, 3$ and the m value need not be the same for each j.

It is easy to determine the elements of $(\mathbf{R})$ and (Φ) for particles having certain degrees of symmetry, since such elements are readily determined when the structure of the polyadics $\mathbf{K}$, $\mathbf{C}_O$, $\mathbf{\Omega}_O$, ϕ_O, and τ_O is known. Brenner (1964a, 1964b) studied the structure of such polyadics for particles with a variety of symmetry properties. Consider particles that have an axis of rotational symmetry, and choose a triad of unit vectors $(\mathbf{e}_1, \mathbf{e}_2, \mathbf{e}_3)$ fixed in the particle with $\mathbf{e}_3$ along the axis of symmetry. The fundamental polyadics for such a particle have the forms

$$\mathbf{K} = a(\mathbf{I} - \mathbf{e}_3\mathbf{e}_3) + b\mathbf{e}_3\mathbf{e}_3$$

$$\mathbf{C}_O = c(\epsilon \cdot \mathbf{e}_3)$$

$$\mathbf{\Omega}_O = d(\mathbf{I} - \mathbf{e}_3\mathbf{e}_3) + e\mathbf{e}_3\mathbf{e}_3$$

$$\phi_O = f\mathbf{e}_3\mathbf{e}_3\mathbf{e}_3 + g[(\mathbf{I}\mathbf{e}_3) + (\mathbf{I}\mathbf{e}_3)^\dagger]$$

$$\tau_O = h[(\epsilon \cdot e_3 e_3) + (\epsilon \cdot e_3 e_3)^\dagger]$$

where the scalar coefficients $a, \ldots, h$ depend only on the size and external shape of the body.

Majumdar & O'Neill (1972) evaluated these coefficients for a solid dumbbell formed from two equal spheres in contact and obtained

$$a = -12\pi a_p(0.7243) \quad b = -12\pi a_p(0.6451) \quad c = 0$$

$$d = 16\pi a_p^3(1.8704) \quad e = 16\pi a_p^3(0.9015) \quad f = 0$$

$$g = 0 \quad h = 16\pi a_p^3(0.5556)$$

The grand resistance and shear resistance matrices are accordingly

$$(\mathbf{R}) = \begin{bmatrix} a & 0 & 0 & 0 & 0 & 0 \\ 0 & a & 0 & 0 & 0 & 0 \\ 0 & 0 & b & 0 & 0 & 0 \\ 0 & 0 & 0 & d & 0 & 0 \\ 0 & 0 & 0 & 0 & d & 0 \\ 0 & 0 & 0 & 0 & 0 & e \end{bmatrix} \quad (\mathbf{\Phi}) = \begin{bmatrix} 0 & 0 & 0 & 0 & 0 & 0 \\ 0 & 0 & 0 & 0 & 0 & 0 \\ 0 & 0 & 0 & 0 & 0 & 0 \\ 0 & 0 & 0 & 2h & 0 & 0 \\ 0 & 0 & 0 & 0 & -2h & 0 \\ 0 & 0 & 0 & 0 & 0 & 0 \end{bmatrix}$$

with a, b, d, e, and h given above. For a neutrally buoyant dumbbell, it is simple to determine the translational and angular velocities of the body in a shear field by using [1.3.134]:

$$U_O = u_O \quad \omega = \omega_f - 2hd^{-1}(S_{23}e_1 - S_{13}e_2)$$

Thus the dumbbell translates with the approach velocity of the fluid at O, and its angular velocity is such that the component along the axis of symmetry is the same as that of the angular velocity of the fluid. The other components of ω along body axes mutually perpendicular to the axis of symmetry are

$$\omega_1 = \tfrac{1}{2}S(2hd^{-1} - 1) \cos \alpha \sin \beta$$

$$\omega_2 = \tfrac{1}{2}S[1 - 2hd^{-1}(\cos^2 \alpha - \sin^2 \alpha)] \cos \beta$$

where the direction of the shear flow makes an angle $\pi - \alpha$ with e_3 and the plane of the shear is inclined at angle β to the plane perpendicular to the direction of e_2. Brenner & O'Neill (1972) calculated the grand resistance and shear resistance matrices for a general axisymmetrical body with or without fore-aft symmetry. The elements are listed for a general ellipsoid, and Dorrepaal (1978) calculated the elements of these matrices for a spherical cap.

The foregoing analysis is applicable to any type of linear shear field. For instance, consider a neutrally buoyant circular disk in a squeeze shear field with velocity

$$u = -\tfrac{1}{2}S(x_1 i_1 + x_2 i_2 - 2x_3 i_3)$$

where i_1, i_2, i_3 are directions along right-handed Cartesian axes fixed in space with their origin at the center of the disk. For this shear field

$$u_O = \omega_f = 0 \quad S = -\tfrac{1}{2}S(I - 3i_3 i_3)$$

The disk has no translational velocity and its angular velocity is given by

$$\omega = S_4 e_1 - S_5 e_2$$

where S_4 and S_5 are elements of the vector representation of the components of $\mathbf{S}$ relative to the body axes. If θ and ϕ are the spherical polar angles for i_3 relative to the body frame, then

$$S_4 = S_{23} = \tfrac{3}{2} S \sin \theta \cos \theta \sin \phi$$

$$S_5 = S_{13} = \tfrac{3}{2} S \sin \theta \cos \theta \cos \phi$$

1.3.5.2 Generalization to More Than One Particle

Consider n particles of arbitrary shape, identified by their surfaces s_i ($i = 1$, $2, \ldots, n$). Suppose that s_i has angular velocity ω_i and its translational velocity is such that a point O_i of it moves with translational velocity $\mathbf{U}_i$. The aggregate of particles are moving in an infinite fluid, which would move in a linear shear flow in the absence of the particles with velocity

$$\mathbf{u} = \mathbf{u}_O + \omega_f \times \mathbf{r}_O + \mathbf{S} \cdot \mathbf{r}_O \qquad [1.3.135]$$

O being any fixed origin in the fluid and $\mathbf{r}_O$ the position vector of an arbitrary point relative to O.

Since the equations governing the fluid motion are linear, the velocity field $\mathbf{v}$ and the pressure field p may be decomposed into

$$\mathbf{v} = \mathbf{u} + \sum_{i=1}^{n} \mathbf{v}_i \qquad p = \sum_{i=1}^{n} p_i \qquad [1.3.136]$$

where $\mathbf{u}$ is given by [1.3.135] and the $\mathbf{v}_i$ satisfy the boundary conditions

$$\mathbf{v}_i = \mathbf{U}_i + \omega_f \times \mathbf{r}_i - \mathbf{u}_O - \omega_f \times \mathbf{r}_O - \mathbf{S} \cdot \mathbf{r}_O \qquad \text{on } s_i \qquad [1.3.137]$$

$$\mathbf{v}_i = 0 \quad \text{on } s_j(j \neq i) \qquad \mathbf{v}_i \to 0 \quad \text{as } |\mathbf{r}_i| \to \infty \qquad [1.3.138]$$

with $\mathbf{r}_i$ denoting the position vector of an arbitrary point relative to O_i. Denote by u_i the value of u at O_i. It follows that [1.3.137] can be restated

$$\mathbf{v}_i = (\mathbf{U}_i - \mathbf{u}_i) + (\omega_i - \omega_f) \times \mathbf{r}_i - \mathbf{S} \cdot \mathbf{r}_i \qquad \text{on } s_i \qquad [1.3.139]$$

By analogy with a single particle, it is inferred that the force $\mathbf{F}_i$ and torque $\mathbf{T}_i$ (about O_i) on the ith particle have the forms

$$\mathbf{F}_i = -\mu \left\{ \sum_{j=1}^{n} [\mathbf{K}_{ij} \cdot (\mathbf{U}_j - \mathbf{u}_j) + \mathbf{C}_{ji}^{\dagger} \cdot (\omega_j - \omega_f)] + \phi_i : \mathbf{S} \right\} \qquad [1.3.140]$$

$$\mathbf{T}_i = -\left\{ \sum_{j=1}^{n} [\mathbf{C}_{ij} \cdot (\mathbf{U}_j - \mathbf{u}_j) + \Omega_{ij} \cdot (\omega_j - \omega_f)] + \tau_i : \mathbf{S} \right\} \qquad [1.3.141]$$

The dyadics K_{ij}, C_{ij}, Ω_{ij} and triadics ϕ_i, τ_i are intrinsic properties of the (instantaneous) geometric configuration of the system of particles alone. In particular, they depend only on the size of the particles, the shapes of their wetted surfaces, the relative displacements of their origins O_i, and their relative orientations. Define the partitioned $3n \times 1$ column matrices (F), (T), $(U - u)$, and $(\omega - \omega_f)$ by relations of the form

$$(F) = [(F_1), (F_2), \ldots, (F_n)]^\dagger$$

where (F_i) is itself a 3×1 column matrix whose elements are the three components of the vector force F_i acting on the particle s_i. Also define the square partitioned $3n \times 3n$ matrices (K), (Ω), (C) by expressions of the form

$$(K) = \begin{bmatrix} (K_{11}) & (K_{12}) & \cdots & (K_{1n}) \\ \cdots & \cdots & \cdots & \cdots \\ (K_{n1}) & (K_{n2}) & \cdots & (K_{nn}) \end{bmatrix}$$

where (K_{ij}) is the 3×3 matrix whose nine scalar elements are the components of the dyadic K_{ij}. Brenner (1964a) showed that K_{ij} and Ω_{ij} are symmetrical, which will imply that the matrices (K) and (Ω) are also symmetrical.

Now let (ϕ_i) and (τ_i) denote the 3×6 matrices that can be formed from the components of ϕ_i and τ_i, respectively, according to the scheme described in detail earlier. From these matrices construct the $6n \times 6$ partitioned matrix (Φ) in the following way:

$$(\Phi)^\dagger = [(\phi_1) \cdots (\phi_n)(\tau_1) \cdots (\tau_n)]$$

On defining (R) as

$$(R) = \begin{bmatrix} (K) & (C)^\dagger \\ (C) & (\Omega) \end{bmatrix} \qquad [1.3.5.142]$$

and (S), (F), and (U) as

$$(F) = \begin{bmatrix} (F) \\ (T) \end{bmatrix} \qquad (U) = \begin{bmatrix} (U - u) \\ (\omega - \omega_f) \end{bmatrix} \qquad (S) = \begin{bmatrix} S_1 \\ \cdots \\ S_6 \end{bmatrix}$$

it follows [1.3.140] and [1.3.141] can be written in the compact matrix form

$$(F) = - \mu[(R)(U) + (\Phi)(S)] \qquad [1.3.143]$$

In the case of neutrally buoyant particles, the translational and angular velocities of the particles are given by

$$(U) = - (R)^{-1}(\Phi)(S) \qquad [1.3.144]$$

The fact that (R) is nonsingular and therefore has an inverse can again be verified by considering the rate of energy dissipation for the n particles moving in a quiescent fluid. Also, (R) is symmetrical although (C) is generally not.

Expression [1.3.143] applies to any Stokesian system of particles of arbitrary shape that are individually translating and rotating in a viscous fluid that is itself in a general linear shearing motion. The elements of $(\mathbf{R})$ and (Φ) are independent of the velocity fields, depending only on the geometry of the particles and their relative displacements and relative orientations. The matrix representation [1.3.143] not only shows the structure of the forces and torques in terms of the velocity fields and the intrinsic geometric properties of system, which are embedded in $(\mathbf{R})$ and (Φ), but also is readily amenable to computational procedures.

1.3.5.3 Elements of Resistance Matrices for Two Spheres

At present, the only multiparticle system for which exact values of the elements of $(\mathbf{R})$ and (Φ) can be determined is that of two spheres. Choose e_3 to be a unit vector drawn from the center O_1 of sphere s_1 to the center O_2 of sphere s_2; the unit vectors e_1 and e_2 are chosen so that e_1, e_2, and e_3 form a right-handed set of unit vectors in the body frame. The system of two spheres is geometrically a body with rotational symmetry about the line of centers, and Brenner (1964a, 1964b) determined the structure of the fundamental polyadics for such bodies. For an origin on the line of centers, the polyadics have the general forms

$$\mathbf{K}_{ij} = A_{ij}(e_1 e_1 + e_2 e_2) + B_{ij} e_3 e_3 \qquad [1.3.145]$$

$$\mathbf{C}_{ij} = C_{ij}(\epsilon \cdot e_3) \qquad [1.3.146]$$

$$\mathbf{\Omega}_{ij} = D_{ij}(e_1 e_1 + e_2 e_2) + E_{ij} e_3 e_3 \qquad [1.3.147]$$

$$\phi_i = F_i e_3 e_3 e_3 + G_i[(\mathbf{I}e_3) + (\mathbf{I}e_3)^{\dagger}] \qquad [1.3.148]$$

$$\tau_i = H_i[(\epsilon \cdot e_3 e_3) + (\epsilon \cdot e_3 e_3)^{\dagger}] \qquad [1.3.149]$$

with $i, j = 1, 2$. The subscript i identifies the sphere for which the particular polyadic is evaluated. To be consistent with the notation for the general multibody problem, the convention is adopted that the polyadics $\mathbf{C}_{ij}$, $\mathbf{\Omega}_{ij}$, ϕ_i, τ_i, which depend on the choice of origin, are evaluated relative to O_1 for s_1 and to O_2 for s_2. If $e_1 e_1 + e_2 e_2 = \mathbf{I} - e_3 e_3$, where $\mathbf{I}$ is the dyadic idemfactor, only e_3 of the triad of body vectors enters into the relations, since $A_{ij}, \ldots, H_i$ are scalars that depend only on the radii a_1 and a_2 of the spheres and the distance $2h$ between their centers. This is to be expected because of the axial symmetry of the system. The elements of $(\mathbf{R})$ and (Φ) can quickly be determined from [1.3.145] to [1.3.149] by noting that

$$\epsilon \cdot e_3 = e_1 e_2 - e_2 e_1$$

$$(\mathbf{I}e_3) + (\mathbf{I}e_3)^{\dagger} = e_1(e_1 e_3 + e_3 e_1) + e_2(e_2 e_3 + e_3 e_2) + 2e_3 e_3 e_3$$

$$(\epsilon \cdot e_3 e_3) + (\epsilon \cdot e_3 e_3)^{\dagger} = e_1(e_2 e_3 + e_3 e_2) - e_2(e_1 e_3 + e_3 e_1)$$

Determination of these elements in $(\mathbf{R})$ from [1.3.145] to [1.3.147] is immediate. The shear resistance matrix (Φ) can be written in terms of partitioned 3×3 matrices as

$$(\Phi) = \begin{bmatrix} (\theta_1) & (\psi_1) \\ (\theta_2) & (\psi_2) \\ 0 & (\chi_1) \\ 0 & (\chi_2) \end{bmatrix} \qquad [1.3.150]$$

with
$$(\theta_i) = \begin{bmatrix} 0 & 0 & 0 \\ 0 & 0 & 0 \\ 0 & 0 & F_i + 2G_i \end{bmatrix} \qquad (\psi_i) = \begin{bmatrix} 0 & 2G_i & 0 \\ 2G_i & 0 & 0 \\ 0 & 0 & 0 \end{bmatrix}$$

$$(\chi_i) = \begin{bmatrix} 2H_i & 0 & 0 \\ 0 & -2H_i & 0 \\ 0 & 0 & 0 \end{bmatrix}$$

All the fundamental scalar coefficients can be determined from the solutions of a number of two-sphere problems in the literature. The elements of $(\mathbf{R})$ are known from the solutions for two unequal spheres translating or rotating in arbitrary directions in a quiescent fluid. Such solutions can be split into axisymmetrical and asymmetrical parts. The axisymmetrical rotation problem was solved by Jeffery (1915) and Stimson & Jeffery (1926) for equal spheres moving with equal velocities along their line of centers. Cooley & O'Neill (1969a, 1969b) gave the forces for unequal spheres moving with the same speed and treated the problem of unequal spheres moving toward each other. Combining these results permits the evaluation of the total forces and torques acting on the spheres due to the axisymmetrical part of their motion. To these forces and torques are added the contributions from the asymmetrical motion of the spheres, particularly spheres translating or rotating about directions perpendicular to their line of centers. Solutions of these problems are available in Davis (1969) and O'Neill & Majumdar (1970).

Davis (1971) also computed the forces and torques acting on stationary spheres in a simple shear flow whose velocity field in the absence of the spheres is given by

$$\mathbf{u} = gz'\mathbf{i}_1' \qquad [1.3.151]$$

where the unit vectors $\mathbf{i}_1'$, $\mathbf{i}_2'$, $\mathbf{i}_3'$ in the Cartesian space frame (x', y', z') are related to the unit vectors of the body frame in such a way that $\mathbf{e}_2$ lies in the plane $z' = 0$. If α is the angle between $\mathbf{e}_2$ and $\mathbf{i}_2'$ and χ is the angle between $\mathbf{e}_3$ and $\mathbf{i}_3'$, as shown in figure 1.3.4, it follows that [1.3.151] can be written

$$\mathbf{u} = g[-x \sin \chi + (z - h_x) \cos \chi](\cos \chi \cos \alpha \, \mathbf{e}_1 + \sin \alpha \, \mathbf{e}_2 + \cos \alpha \sin \chi \, \mathbf{e}_3)$$

$$[1.3.152]$$

where (x, y, z) are coordinates in the body frame and h_x is the distance of X, the point of intersection of $\mathbf{e}_3$ with the plane of zero velocity, from a fixed point O on the line of centers, which is the origin of the coordinates (x, y, z). Since the spheres are at rest in this problem, the forces and torques acting on them are

$$\mathbf{F}_i = \mu[\mathbf{K}_{i1} \cdot \mathbf{u}_1 + \mathbf{K}_{i2} \cdot \mathbf{u}_2 + (\mathbf{C}_{1i}^\dagger + \mathbf{C}_{2i}^\dagger) \cdot \boldsymbol{\omega}_f] - \mu\boldsymbol{\phi}_i : \mathbf{S} \qquad [1.3.153]$$

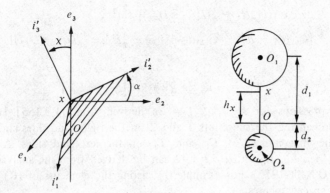

Figure 1.3.4 Definition sketch for two spheres in a shearing field.

$$T_i = \mu[C_{i1} \cdot u_1 + C_{i2} \cdot u_2 + (\Omega_{i1} + \Omega_{i2}) \cdot \omega_f] - \mu\tau_i : S \qquad [1.3.154]$$

It then follows that since

$$u_1 = g(d_1 - h_x) \cos \chi i'_1 \qquad u_2 = -g(d_2 + h_x) \cos \chi i'_1$$
$$\omega_f = \tfrac{1}{2}g i'_2 \qquad S = \tfrac{1}{2}g(i'_1 i'_3 + i'_3 i'_1)$$

with $d_1 = |\overrightarrow{OO_1}|$, $d_2 = |\overrightarrow{OO_2}|$, and

$$e_1 \cdot i'_1 = \cos \alpha \cos \chi \qquad e_2 \cdot i'_1 = \sin \alpha$$
$$e_3 \cdot i'_1 = \cos \alpha \sin \chi$$
$$e_1 \cdot i'_2 = -\sin \alpha \cos \chi \qquad e_2 \cdot i'_2 = \cos \alpha$$
$$e_3 \cdot i'_2 = -\sin \alpha \sin \chi$$
$$e_1 \cdot i'_3 = -\sin \chi \qquad e_3 \cdot i'_3 = 0 \qquad e_3 \cdot i'_3 = \cos \chi$$

these results, together with [1.3.145]–[1.3.149], yield the following expressions for the components of F_1 and T_1 along the space axes:

$$F_{11} = -\mu g \cos \alpha \{[-2G_1 + \tfrac{1}{2}(c_{11} + c_{21})] \sin^2 \chi$$
$$- [A_{11}(d_1 - h_x) - A_{12}(d_2 + h_x) - G_1 + \tfrac{1}{2}(c_{11} + c_{21})] \cos^2 \chi\}$$

$$[1.3.155]$$

$$F_{12} = \mu g \cos \chi \sin \alpha[-A_{11}(d_1 - h_x) + A_{12}(d_2 + h_x) + G_1$$
$$+ \tfrac{1}{2}(C_{11} + C_{21})]$$

$$[1.3.156]$$

$$F_{13} = -\mu g \sin \chi \cos \chi \cos \alpha[B_{12}(d_2 + h_x) - B_{11}(d_1 - h_x) + 2G_1 + F_1]$$

$$[1.3.157]$$

$$T_{11} = -\mu g \sin \alpha \cos \chi[C_{11}(d_1 - h_x) - C_{12}(d_2 + h_x) - H_1 - \tfrac{1}{2}(D_{11} + D_{12})]$$

$$[1.3.158]$$

$$T_{12} = -\mu g \cos \alpha \{[2H_1 - \tfrac{1}{2}(D_{11} + D_{12})] \sin^2 \chi$$
$$+ [C_{11}(d_1 - h_x) - C_{12}(d_2 + h_x) - \tfrac{1}{2}H_1 - \tfrac{1}{2}(D_{11} + D_{12})] \cos^2 \chi\}$$

[1.3.159]

$$T_{13} = -\mu g \sin \chi \cos \alpha \, \tfrac{1}{2}(E_{11} + E_{12})$$ [1.3.160]

The expressions for $F_{21}, \ldots, T_{23}$ are derived from [1.3.155]–[1.3.160] by simply interchanging the subscripts 1 and 2 on the right-hand sides and replacing 1 by 2 in the first indices of F_{1i} and T_{1i} on the left-hand sides. All the scalar coefficients $A_{ij}, \ldots, E_i$ with $i, j = 1, 2$ can be derived from the analytic work (see Brenner & O'Neill 1972). For example, by listing the elements of $(\mathbf{R})$ and $(\mathbf{\Phi})$ for two widely spaced spheres:

$$(\mathbf{K}_{11}) = 6\pi a_1 \begin{bmatrix} 1 + \dfrac{9}{64}\dfrac{a_1 a_2}{h^2} & 0 & 0 \\[2ex] 0 & 1 + \dfrac{9}{64}\dfrac{a_1 a_2}{h^2} & 0 \\[2ex] 0 & 0 & \dfrac{9}{16}\dfrac{a_1 a_2}{h^2} \end{bmatrix}$$

$$(\mathbf{K}_{21}) = \dfrac{-9}{4}\pi a_2 \begin{bmatrix} \dfrac{a_1}{h} & 0 & 0 \\[2ex] 0 & \dfrac{a_1}{h} & 0 \\[2ex] 0 & 0 & \dfrac{a_1}{h} \end{bmatrix}$$

$$(\mathbf{\Omega}_{11}) = 8\pi a_1^3 \begin{bmatrix} 1 + \dfrac{3}{64}\dfrac{a_2 a_1^3}{h^4} & 0 & 0 \\[2ex] 0 & 1 + \dfrac{3}{64}\dfrac{a_2 a_1^3}{h^4} & 0 \\[2ex] 0 & 0 & 1 \end{bmatrix}$$

$$(\mathbf{\Omega}_{21}) = \dfrac{\pi}{2}\dfrac{a_2^3 a_1^3}{h^3} \begin{bmatrix} 1 & 0 & 0 \\ 0 & 1 & 0 \\ 0 & 0 & -2 \end{bmatrix}$$

$$(\mathbf{C}_{11}) = -\dfrac{9}{16}\pi\dfrac{a_1^4 a_2}{h^3} \begin{bmatrix} 0 & 1 & 0 \\ -1 & 0 & 0 \\ 0 & 0 & 0 \end{bmatrix}$$

$$(\mathbf{C}_{21}) = -\dfrac{3}{2}\pi\dfrac{a_1 a_2^3}{h^2} \begin{bmatrix} 0 & 1 & 0 \\ -1 & 0 & 0 \\ 0 & 0 & 0 \end{bmatrix}$$

The remaining 10 matrices that make up $(\mathbf{R})$ can be deduced from the above by interchanging all the subscripts 1 and 2 and/or by transposing. The shear resistance matrix (Φ) is

$$(\Phi) = \begin{bmatrix} (\theta_1) & (\psi_1) \\ (\theta_2) & (\psi_2) \\ 0 & (\chi_1) \\ 0 & (\chi_2) \end{bmatrix}$$

where the 3×3 matrices into which (Φ) is partitioned are given by

$$(\theta_i) = \begin{bmatrix} 0 & 0 & 0 \\ 0 & 0 & 0 \\ 0 & 0 & F_i' \end{bmatrix} \qquad (\psi_i) = \begin{bmatrix} 0 & 2G_i & 0 \\ 2G_i & 0 & 0 \\ 0 & 0 & 0 \end{bmatrix}$$

$$(\chi_i) = \begin{bmatrix} 2H_i & 0 & 0 \\ 0 & -2H_i & 0 \\ 0 & 0 & 0 \end{bmatrix}$$

for $i = 1, 2$, where

$$F_1' = - \pi a_1 a_2 \left[\frac{15}{4} \left(\frac{a_2}{h} \right)^2 + \frac{45}{16} \left(\frac{a_1}{h} \right)^3 + \frac{3}{8} \left(\frac{a_2}{h} \right)^4 + \frac{9}{64} \left(\frac{a_1}{h} \right)^5 \right]$$

$$G_1 = - \pi a_1 a_2 \left[\frac{3}{16} \left(\frac{a_2}{h} \right)^4 + \frac{9}{128} \left(\frac{a_1}{h} \right)^5 \right]$$

$$H_1 = \pi a_2 \left[\frac{5}{16} a_2^2 \left(\frac{a_1}{h} \right)^3 + \frac{3}{64} a_1^2 \left(\frac{a_1}{h} \right)^6 \right]$$

The expressions for F_2' and G_2 are given by F_1' and G_1 with the 1 and 2 interchanged and the signs reversed; H_2 is given by H_1 with only the subscripts interchanged.

1.3.6   STRUCTURE AND PROPERTIES OF TWO-DIMENSIONAL STOKES FLOW

Two-dimensional problems in Stokes flow have provided several interesting examples of separated flow. If the flow is two-dimensional the fluid velocity $\mathbf{u}$ can be expressed in the form

$$\mathbf{u} = \nabla \times (- \psi \mathbf{k}) \qquad\qquad [1.3.161]$$

where $\psi(x, y)$ is the Earnshaw stream function and $\mathbf{k}$ is a unit vector perpendicular to the x, y plane. The equation satisfied by ψ is the biharmonic equation

$$\nabla_1^4 \psi = 0 \qquad \nabla_1^2 \equiv \frac{\partial^2}{\partial x^2} + \frac{\partial^2}{\partial y^2} \qquad [1.3.162]$$

The fluid velocity vanishes on the boundary c:

$$\psi = \frac{\partial \psi}{\partial n} = 0 \quad \text{on } c \qquad\qquad [1.3.163]$$

where $\partial/\partial n$ is differentiation along the normal to c drawn in the fluid.

Dean (1944) considered the shear flow past a projection described in parametric form by the equations

$$x = \tan \tfrac{1}{2}\theta + \beta(1 + \cos \theta) \quad y = \beta \sin \theta$$

where $\tfrac{1}{2} \leqslant |\beta| \leqslant 1$. A single eddy is attached to the boundary and in the case $\beta = 1$ the separation streamline is the straight line $y = x - 1$.

Jeffery (1922) considered the flow between rotating cylinders that are eccentric. The stream function is expressed in bipolar coordinates

$$x = \frac{c \sinh \xi}{\cosh \xi - \cos \eta} \quad y = \frac{c \sin \eta}{\cosh \xi - \cos \eta}$$

the boundaries corresponding to $\xi = \alpha$ and $\xi = \beta$, respectively. The stream function ψ is of the form $\psi = f(\xi) + g(\xi) \cos \eta$ and Jeffery was concerned mainly with the torques on the cylinders. However, Wannier (1950) investigated the special case in which the inner cylinder is rotating and the outer cylinder is at rest. For certain distances between the axes there is separation, the flow dividing into two parts. This is illustrated in figure 1.3.5. The case in which the inner cylinder is in contact with the outer boundary is illustrated in figure 1.3.6.

1.3.6.1 Dean-Moffatt Eddies

Dean & Montagnon (1949) first considered the flow in a wedge-shaped region, and Moffatt (1964) showed that eddies form in the flow region when the angle of the wedge is less than a certain value.

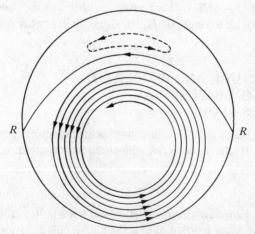

Figure 1.3.5 Streamlines for a journal bearing a diameter ratio 5:9. Eccentricity 50%. Points of flow reversal on stationary surface are designated by R.

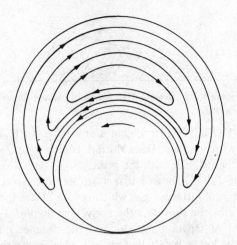

Figure 1.3.6 Streamlines for a journal bearing of diameter ratio 5:9. Full eccentricity (zero clearance).

In polar coordinates (r, θ) the velocity components are

$$u_r = -\frac{1}{r}\frac{\partial \psi}{\partial \theta} \qquad u_\theta = \frac{\partial \psi}{\partial r} \qquad [1.3.164]$$

where ψ satisfies

$$\nabla_1^4 \psi = 0 \qquad \nabla_1^2 \equiv \frac{\partial^2}{\partial r^2} + \frac{1}{r}\frac{\partial}{\partial r} + \frac{1}{r^2}\frac{\partial^2}{\partial \theta^2} \qquad [1.3.165]$$

in the region $0 \leqslant \theta \leqslant \alpha$. We seek a separable solution

$$\psi = r^k f_k(\theta) \qquad [1.3.166]$$

Substitution in [1.3.165] yields an equation for $f_k(\theta)$ and on solution

$$f_k(\theta) = A \cos k\theta + B \sin k\theta + C \cos (k-2)\theta + D \sin (k-2)\theta \qquad k = 2, 3, \ldots$$

$$[1.3.167]$$

The boundary conditions

$$\psi = \frac{\partial \psi}{\partial r} = 0 \qquad \text{at } \theta = 0, \alpha \qquad [1.3.168]$$

reduce to

$$f_k(\alpha) = f_k(0) = f_k'(0) = f_k'(\alpha) = 0 \qquad [1.3.169]$$

If $\alpha > 146.3°$ there is no separation, whereas if $\alpha < 146.3°$ the eigenvalues k are complex, corresponding to the fact that there is an infinite set of eddies nested in the channel. For a given α the angle at which the separation streamlines intersect the boundary is constant (figure 1.3.7). The axisymmetrical analog of flow in a conical region was treated by Schwiderski et al. (1966). The first global two-dimensional flow in which Dean-Moffatt eddies were observed appears to have been

Figure 1.3.7 Dean-Moffatt eddies in a wedge-shaped channel.

discussed by Schubert (1967). The problem examined is the linear shear flow past a cylinder in contact with a plane. Dean-Moffatt eddies were shown to exist in the region of contact of the cylinder with the plane.

Michael & O'Neill (1977) showed that a Stokes flow can separate from a point on a smooth body at an arbitrary angle, which can be determined only by reference to the global solution for the flow past the body. The dominant mode in the stream function near a point of separation is $O(r^3)$ in the distance r from the separation point. When the body has a protruding cusped edge, separation can occur at an arbitrary inclination to the edge, which must again be determined from the global solution. In this case the stream function is $O(r^{3/2})$ near the edge. When the flow is locally within a wedge-shaped region of angle β, where $\beta \neq \pi$ or 2π and $\beta > 146.3°$, the dominant modes near the vertex of the wedge are nonseparating modes, but the extent of the eddy region was not found.

More comprehensive studies of flows in which Dean-Moffat eddies exist as an integral part of the overall global flow structure are described in Wakiya (1975), O'Neill (1977), and Davis & O'Neill (1977b) for flow over a circular cylindrical ridge or trough in a plane. Wakiya and O'Neill showed that for a simple shear flow over such a ridge, when the angle of intersection η_0 between the ridge and the plane is less than 146.3° (figure 1.3.8), an infinite set of Dean-Moffatt eddies exists in the intersection region. The eddies are confined to a finite region bounded by a streamline that separates the eddy region from the general flow past the ridge. The extent of the eddy region grows as η_0 decreases and becomes a maximum when η_0

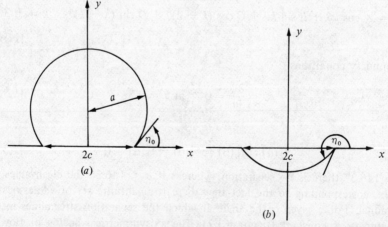

Figure 1.3.8 Geometric configuration of boundaries: (*a*) plane with a cylindrical ridge and (*b*) plane with a cylindrical trough.

approaches zero; if the radius of the ridge boundary remains constant, this corresponds to a circular cylinder in contact with a plane, which was studied by Schubert. For simple shear flow over a plane with a trough, O'Neill showed that a single eddy forms at the bottom of the trough when η_0 is about $245.15°$. For $180 < \eta_0 < 245.15°$ separation from the boundary does not occur. For $\eta_0 > 245.15°$ the eddy grows and the points of detachment and attachment move up the wall of the trough, reaching the corner edges only when $\eta_0 = 360°$. There is no evidence of multiple eddy formation in trough flow as opposed to ridge flow. The situation with regard to separation can be summarized as follows:

$0 \leqslant \eta_0 < 146.3°$	Separation from both cylindrical ridge and plane at an infinity of points. Infinite set of eddies in closed region of flow.
$146.3 < \eta_0 \leqslant 245.15°$	No separation.
$245.15 < \eta_0 < 360°$	Separation from the cylinder at only two points. A single eddy forms in closed region of flow.
$\eta_0 = 360°$	Separation from the edges.

Figure 1.3.9 shows streamlines for two values of η_0 that typify the flow structure in the two ranges of η_0 in which the flow separates. Similar results hold for other Stokes flows with this geometry. Undisturbed flow is a two-dimensional stagnation point flow, where the Dean-Moffatt eddies form for flow over a ridge if $\eta_0 < 146.3°$ and a single eddy forms in the trough if $\eta_0 > 224.46°$. The closeness of this angle to $255°$ or $5\pi/4$ is coincidental. This value of η_0 is the smallest angle at which the streamline detaches from the trough wall. As expected, the critical angle at which Dean-Moffatt eddies form for flows over ridges is independent of the flow at infinity, but this is not so for the formation of single separation eddies in troughs.

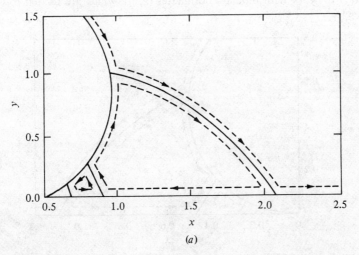

(a)

Figure 1.3.9 (*a*) Separation streamlines when a cylindrical ridge intersects a plane at $\eta_0 = 30°$.

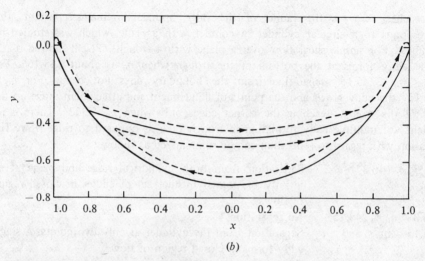

(b)

Figure 1.3.9 *(b)* Separation streamline and eddies for a cylindrical trough with $\eta_0 = 1.4\pi$.

1.3.6.2   Linear Shear Flow Past a Cylinder and Plane

Schubert (1967) showed that Dean-Moffatt eddies exist in the cusp when there is slow linear shear flow over a circular cylinder in contact with a plane, but did not give details of the structure and extent of the eddy region. A comprehensive study is given by Davis & O'Neill (1977a), and figure 1.3.10 shows the first two eddies of the infinite sequence together with the dividing streamlines.

To solve the problem when the cylinder is not in contact with the plane it is advantageous to work with bipolar coordinates (ξ, η), which are related to Cartesian coordinates by

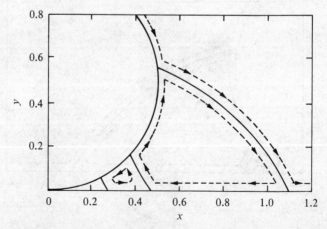

Figure 1.3.10   Separation streamlines when the cylinder touches the plane.

$$x = \frac{c \sin \eta}{\cosh \xi - \cos \eta} \qquad y = \frac{c \sinh \xi}{\cosh \xi - \cos \eta} \qquad [1.3.170]$$

with $c = \frac{1}{2} \sinh \alpha$. The plane is given by $\xi = 0$, the cylinder by $\xi = \alpha$. The distance from the center of the cylinder to the plane is $\frac{1}{2} \cosh \alpha$, and the flow region is accordingly given by $0 < \xi < \alpha$, $|\eta| \leqslant \pi$.

When the cylinder is not in contact with the plane, the value of the stream function on the cylinder is a constant M that depends on the distance of the cylinder from the plane and is an unknown. Therefore write the stream function ψ as

$$\psi = \tfrac{1}{2} y^2 - \chi + M\phi \qquad [1.3.171]$$

where χ and ϕ are plane biharmonic functions that satisfy the boundary conditions

$$\chi = \frac{\partial \chi}{\partial \xi} = \phi = \frac{\partial \phi}{\partial \xi} = 0 \qquad \xi = 0$$

$$\chi = \frac{1}{2} y^2 \qquad \frac{\partial \chi}{\partial \xi} = y \frac{\partial y}{\partial \xi} \qquad \phi = 1 \qquad \frac{\partial \phi}{\partial \xi} = 0 \qquad \xi = \alpha \qquad [1.3.172]$$

$$\chi, \phi = O(y^2) \qquad \xi^2 + \chi^2 \to 0$$

In this way the boundary-value problems for χ and ϕ are uncoupled from the unknown constant M. Seek χ and ϕ such that ψ is an even periodic function of η with period 2π, noting that $y\Phi$ and $(x^2 + y^2)\Phi$ are biharmonic functions if Φ is harmonic. It follows that suitable biharmonic functions that satisfy the boundary conditions on the plane are given by

$$\chi = \frac{1}{2} c^2 (\cosh \xi - \cos \eta)^{-1} \sum_{n=0}^{\infty} \chi_n(\xi) \cos n\eta \qquad [1.3.173]$$

$$\phi = (\cosh \xi - \cos \eta)^{-1} [\phi_0(\xi) + \phi_1(\xi) \cos \eta] \qquad [1.3.174]$$

where

$$\chi_0(\xi) = A_0 \, \xi \sinh \xi + B_0 (\xi \cosh \xi - \sinh \xi) \qquad [1.3.175]$$

$$\chi_1(\xi) = A_1 (\cosh 2\xi - 1) + B_1 (\sinh 2\xi - 2\xi) \qquad [1.3.176]$$

$$\chi_n(\xi) = A_n [\cosh (n + 1)\xi - \cosh (n - 1)\xi] + B_n [(n - 1) \sinh (n + 1)\xi$$

$$- (n + 1) \sinh (n - 1)\xi] \qquad n = 2 \qquad [1.3.177]$$

$$\phi_0(\xi) = a_0 \xi \sinh \xi + b_0 (\xi \cosh \xi - \sinh \xi) \qquad [1.3.178]$$

$$\phi_1(\xi) = a_1 (\cosh 2\xi - 1) + b_1 (\sinh 2\xi - 2\xi) \qquad [1.3.179]$$

the coefficients $a_0, b_0, \ldots, A_n$, and B_n $(n \geqslant 2)$ being independent of ξ and η. These coefficients are determined in satisfying the boundary conditions on the cylinder (Davis & O'Neill 1977a).

The constant M is determined from the condition that the pressure p is single-valued throughout the fluid. The Stokes equations imply that p and $\mu \nabla^2 \psi$ are conjugate functions. Thus for p to be single-valued we must have

$$\int_C \frac{\partial}{\partial n} (\nabla^2 \psi) \, ds = 0 \tag{1.3.180}$$

where C is any closed curve drawn in the fluid. The simplest choice of C is the x axis and a semicircle at infinity. Utilizing the boundary condition at infinity gives, after some simplification,

$$M = \frac{2\alpha^2 + \alpha \sinh 2\alpha - 4 \sinh^2 \alpha}{16\alpha} \tag{1.3.181}$$

Evidently $M > 0$ for all positive values of α, indicating that fluid flows between the cylinder and the plane, no matter how small the gap. For small gaps, $\alpha \ll 1$ and $M \sim \alpha^5/180 + O(\alpha^7)$. Thus if $\epsilon = d - a$, with d and a the distance from the center of the cylinder to the plane and the cylinder radius, respectively, it is evident that ϵ is the minimum clearance between the cylinder and the plane. Thus $\epsilon = \frac{1}{2}(\cosh \alpha - 1) \sim \frac{1}{4} \alpha^2$ and

$$M \sim \frac{4\sqrt{2}}{45} \epsilon^{5/2} + O(\epsilon^{7/2}) \tag{1.3.182}$$

for small gap widths.

The streamline $\psi = M$ consists of the cylinder and a curve in the fluid with asymptote $y = (2M)^{1/2}$. This curve is the dividing streamline, which separates the fluid that flows through the gap from the fluid that flows over and past the cylinder. In the case $\alpha \gg 1$, when the cylinder is far from the plane, $M \sim e^{2\alpha}/32 \sim d^2/2$.

When $\alpha \ll 1$ the asymptotic form of ϕ is

$$\phi \sim \frac{\xi^2}{\alpha^2} \left(3 - \frac{2\xi}{\alpha} \right) \tag{1.3.183}$$

when η is not small. The points on the cylinder that are closest to the plane have $\eta \sim \pi$ and therefore $y \sim \frac{1}{4} \alpha\xi$. Also the minimum clearance $\epsilon \sim \frac{1}{4} \alpha^2$. Thus

$$\phi \sim \frac{y^2}{\epsilon^2} \left(3 - \frac{2y}{\epsilon} \right) \tag{1.3.184}$$

so that when $\alpha \ll 1$ and $\eta \sim \pi$, ϕ approximates the stream function of a plane Poiseuille flow through the gap with unit flux. The total contribution to ψ from ϕ is $M\phi$, which is $O(\alpha^5)$ when $\alpha \ll 1$—i.e., algebraically small. The form of the series solution for χ is unsuitable for examining the behavior of χ when $\alpha \ll 1$, since all terms are then significant. To obtain a more suitable form, define the complex function $F(z)$ of the complex variable $z = x + iy$ as

$$F(z) = \frac{A(z) \sinh z\xi \sinh \xi + B(z)(z \cosh z\xi \sinh \xi - \sinh z\xi \cosh \xi)}{\sin \pi z \sec (\pi - \eta)z(\sinh^2 z\alpha - z^2 \sinh^2 \alpha)} \tag{1.3.185}$$

with $\quad A(z) = z(z - \coth \alpha) \sinh^2 \alpha + e^{-2\alpha} \sinh z\alpha \qquad B(z) = -z \sinh^2 \alpha$

The residues of $F(z)$ at the zeros of $\sin \pi z$ are $\pi^{-1}\chi_0(\xi)$ at $z = 0$ and $(2\pi)^{-1}\chi_n(\xi)$ $\cos n\eta$ at $z = n$ when $n \geqslant 1$. On integrating $F(z)$ around a contour consisting of the imaginary axis indented at the origin together with the infinite semicircle in the half-plane $\mathrm{Re}(z) > 0$, the following series expression is found for $\frac{1}{2} y^2 - \chi$:

$$
\frac{1}{2} y^2 - \chi = \frac{-c^2 \pi}{\cosh \xi - \cos \eta} \, \mathrm{Re} \sum_{n=1}^{\infty} \left\{ \frac{\cosh \left[\sigma_n(\pi - \eta)/\alpha\right]}{\sinh (\sigma_n \pi/\alpha)} \right.
$$

$$
\cdot \frac{\sinh \xi \sin \sigma_n(1 - \xi/\alpha) + \sin (\sigma_n\xi/\alpha) \sinh (\alpha - \xi)}{\alpha \cos \sigma_n + \sinh \alpha}
$$

$$
+ \frac{\cosh \left[\tau_n(\pi - \eta)/\alpha\right]}{\sinh (\tau_n \pi/\alpha)}
$$

$$
\left. \cdot \frac{\sinh \xi \sin \tau_n(1 - \xi/\alpha) - \sin (\tau_n\xi/\alpha) \sinh (\alpha - \xi)}{\alpha \cos \tau_n - \sinh \alpha} \right\}
$$

$$[1.3.186]$$

where $\qquad \alpha \sin \sigma_n + \sigma_n \sinh \alpha = 0 \qquad \alpha \sin \tau_n - \tau_n \sinh \alpha = 0$

with the ordering of σ_n and τ_n being such that the real part of either increases with n. This series representation for $\frac{1}{2} y^2 - \chi$ is most suitable for determining the asymptotic structure of the flow as $\alpha \to 0$ since the terms of the series decrease exponentially in absolute magnitude as $\alpha \to 0$. On writing $\xi = \alpha u$, $\eta = \alpha v$, and letting $\alpha \to 0$, the solution for the cylinder touching the plane can be recaptured in this limit since ϕ is bounded and $M \to 0$ as $\alpha \to 0$, so it is only $\frac{1}{2} y^2 - \chi$ that survives.

For the flow to separate on either boundary it is necessary for $\partial^2 \psi/\partial \xi^2$ to vanish either on the cylinder or on the plane. When $\alpha \ll 1$ the possibility of separation from the boundaries occurring in the region where the algebraically small $M\phi$ is the dominant part of ψ can be excluded by noting that vanishing of $\partial^2 \phi/\partial \xi^2$ on either $\xi = 0$ or $\xi = \alpha$ requires that $\cos \eta = 1 - O(\alpha^2)$, and consequently $\eta = O(\alpha)$. If $\alpha \ll 1$ and $\eta = O(\alpha)$, and writing $\eta = \alpha v$ and then substituting for M, it is clear that for

$$(15\pi)^{-1} \alpha^3 (1 - \cos \alpha v) \ll |\lambda_1 \exp (- \lambda_1 v)| \qquad [1.3.187]$$

where $\lambda_1 = \lim_{\alpha \to 0} \sigma_1 = 4.21239 + 2.25073i$, the flow separates from the cylinder and the plane and the separation points are approximately those when the cylinder touches the plane. The outermost separation point on the cylinder is the point from which the streamline emanates that divides the fluid passing over the cylinder from that flowing through the gap between the cylinder and the plane. As α is decreased, the additional separation points appear in pairs since a separation streamline must begin and end on the same boundary.

To determine the location of the separation points for general values of α and establish the distance of the cylinder from the plane needed for separation to occur, it is necessary to find the zeros of

$$\frac{\partial^2 \psi}{\partial \xi^2} = 0 \qquad [1.3.188]$$

on both the cylinder $\xi = \alpha$ and the plane $\xi = 0$. Separation first occurs at the largest double zero of this equation. The numerical work of Davis & O'Neill reveals that separation first occurs from the plane when $\alpha = 1.1123$, which corresponds to $d/a \approx 1.685$. The point on the plane where separation starts has a dimensionless x coordinate of 1.148. This differs little from 1.117, the value of x at the outermost separation point on the plane when the cylinder and plane are in contact. When d/a is decreased below this critical value a single eddy forms on the plane, the point of reattachment of its bounding streamline to the plane approaching the point with coordinate 0.433, which is the second outermost separation point on the plane when the cylinder and plane are in contact. Separation from the cylinder commences when $\alpha = 0.2448$, giving $d/a \approx 1.030$, and the point on the cylinder where separation first occurs has Cartesian coordinates $x = 0.341$, $y = 0.149$. A single eddy forms and grows from this point as α is decreased. A second eddy forms on the plane when $\alpha = 0.046$. With a further decrease in α, the second eddy forms on the cylinder, followed by a third eddy on the plane, and so on, with the eddies forming alternately on the plane and the cylinder. As the eddies grow the dividing streamlines come closer together, but since the fluid that upstream lies between the planes $y = 0$ and $y = (2M)^{1/2}$ must pass through the gap between the cylinder and the plane, it is forced to "snake" its way between the interlacing eddies that form on either side of the plane $x = 0$. Thus the infinite nest of eddies develops in the flow when the cylinder approaches contact with the plane.

Although separation from the plane occurs when the minimum gap between the cylinder and the plane is $0.685a$ or less, separation from the cylinder does not commence until the gap is reduced to 3% of the cylinder radius, and it is when this already small gap approaches zero that the infinite set of nested eddies is produced in the flow. Figure 1.3.11 shows the separation streamlines for $\alpha = 0.15$, corresponding to $d/a \approx 1.01$. At this value of α separation occurs on both the plane and the cylinder, but there is only one eddy on either boundary. The broken line indicates the general direction of the flow.

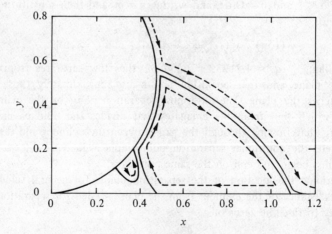

Figure 1.3.11 Dividing streamline and eddies when $\alpha = 0.15$.

1.3.6.3 Free Eddies

Finn & Noll (1957) showed that in a two-dimensional Stokes flow past an obstacle consisting of a finite number of piecewise smooth nonintersecting simple closed curves, the fluid velocity at an infinite distance must be infinite. This gives rise to Stokes' paradox, and it is therefore not possible to invoke a uniform stream condition on the fluid at infinity. Proudman & Pearson (1957) showed that the Stokes approximation is not uniformly valid far from the body, but the problem can be resolved by using matched asymptotic expansions in which the Reynolds number is the perturbation parameter. In this new scheme, the Stokes approximation gives the first term in the inner region expansion of the stream function. If the leading term in the outer region expansion is that of a uniform stream, then the matching procedure requires that the (inner) Stokes solution behave like

$$\psi \sim r \log r \sin \theta$$

as $r \to \infty$, where ψ is the inner expansion stream function and (r, θ) are polar coordinates. Thus one can speak of a uniform two-dimensional Stokes streaming flow provided the stream function in the inner region close to the body satisfies the above condition at infinity.

Uniform Stokes streaming flow past two equal cylinders, where the direction of flow is perpendicular to the line joining the centers, was considered by O'Neill & Dorrepaal (1978) for both touching and nontouching cylinders. For cylinders in contact, an infinite set of eddies is present in the flow, which is in the neighborhood of the point of contact, as expected by comparison with the problem of a cylinder in contact with a plane in a linear shear flow. Unlike that flow, however, the flow past two cylinders has a centerline symmetry that makes it difficult to predict how the eddies develop in a systematic way as nontouching cylinders are drawn closer together. O'Neill & Dorrepaal showed that there is always a flux of fluid through the gap between the cylinders, no matter how small. Two streamlines emanate from each cylinder, one on each side, and together these divide the fluid passing through the gap from the flow around and past the cylinders. There is no separation if the gap width exceeds $0.0446a$, where a denotes the cylinder radius. At this critical distance two stagnation points appear in the fluid along the centerline, one on either side of the gap, and as the gap is narrowed each stagnation point bifurcates into two and eddies develop in the fluid that are completely isolated from the cylinder boundaries. The flow therefore develops a form of intrafluid separation—a phenomenon not observed in a Stokes flow before. This type of eddy is called a free eddy. It is unlike the eddies that are detached from a body in high-Reynolds-number flows in that it is steady and fixed in space for a given gap width. The more usual type of separation eddies attached to the cylinder do not develop until the gap is reduced to $0.0022a$. For still smaller gap widths another set of free eddies appears along the centerline, and as the cylinders approach tangency, free and boundary eddies form alternately so that the fluid moving through the gap must follow a tortuous path between the vortices as in the previously discussed flow.

The above flow is a two-dimensional analog for the three-dimensional axisymmetrical streaming motion past an anchor ring torus. By computing the stream function with the complex solution of Pell & Payne (1960), O'Neill & Dorrepaal (1978) verified that free eddies exist in this flow. With decreasing hole size, the number of free eddies and boundary eddies on the torus increases indefinitely, and they interlace so that in the limit of a closed torus with zero hole, an infinite set of toroidal vortices exists in the cusp region. This flow will be considered in more detail later. Another example of free eddies in two dimensions is given by Jeffery (1978), considering flow between nonparallel planes with a line source or sink located along the line of intersection of the planes. If the flow at infinity is symmetrical about the bisector of the angle, then the flow consists of a sequence of interlacing free eddies centered on the angle bisector and boundary eddies on the planes, together with a tortuous streaming flow between the eddies toward (or away from) the line of intersection between the planes.

1.3.6.4   Flow between Rotating Cylinders

Jeffery (1922b) also discussed the flow produced by two cylinders, externally separated, rotating with arbitrary angular velocities in an infinite fluid. He found that in general it was not possible to satisfy the boundary condition of zero velocity at infinity. There was one simplifying case when the cylinders were rotating with equal and opposite angular velocities. A uniform stream was induced by the flow, and recently Ranger & O'Neill (1978) analyzed the motion. They found that the cylinders are encased by a streamline $\psi = 0$ separating the flow near the boundaries from the flow in the mainstream. This is pictured in figure 1.3.12.

1.3.6.5   Cylinder Rotating in the Presence of a Plane

Introducing bipolar coordinates defined by

$$\alpha + i\beta = \log \frac{x + i(y + a)}{x + i(y - a)} \qquad [1.3.189]$$

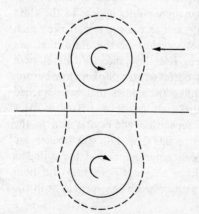

Figure 1.3.12 Streamline for cylinders rotating with equal and opposite angular velocities.

or expressing x and y in terms of α and β,

$$hx = \sinh \alpha \qquad hy = \sin \beta$$

where $ch = \cosh \alpha - \cos \beta$, the curve $\alpha = $ const corresponds to the circle

$$(x - c \coth \alpha)^2 + y^2 = c^2 \operatorname{cosech}^2 \alpha \qquad [1.3.190]$$

In particular, $\alpha = 0$ corresponds to the plane $x = 0$ and the cylinder is represented by the constant value $\alpha = \alpha_1$, say, with $\alpha_1 > 0$. The angular velocity of the cylinder is ω. The components of fluid velocity in the positive directions of α, β are u_α, u_β, respectively, where

$$u_\alpha = -h \frac{\partial \psi}{\partial \beta} = -\frac{\partial}{\partial \beta} (h\psi) + \frac{\psi}{c} \sin \beta$$

$$[1.3.191]$$

$$u_\beta = h \frac{\partial \psi}{\partial \alpha} = \frac{\partial}{\partial \alpha} (h\psi) - \frac{\psi}{c} \sinh \alpha$$

ψ is the Earnshaw stream function and is a solution of the two-dimensional biharmonic equation expressible in the form

$$\chi = h\psi = A_0 \cosh \alpha + B_0 \, \alpha \cosh \alpha + c_0 \sinh \alpha + D_0 \, \alpha \sinh \alpha$$

$$+ (A_1 \cosh 2\alpha + B_1 + C_1 \sinh 2\alpha - B_0 \, \alpha) \cos \beta \qquad [1.3.192]$$

The boundary conditions to be applied on the cylinder $\alpha = \alpha_1$ are

$$\frac{\partial \chi}{\partial \alpha} = \frac{\psi_1 \sinh \alpha_1}{c} - \frac{c\omega}{\sinh \alpha_1} \qquad [1.3.193]$$

$$\psi = \psi_1 = \text{const} \qquad [1.3.194]$$

and on the plane $\alpha = 0$

$$\psi = 0 \qquad \frac{\partial \chi}{\partial \alpha} = 0 \qquad [1.3.195]$$

ψ is then found to be

$$\chi = h\psi = \frac{c\omega \cosh \alpha_1}{\sinh^3 \alpha_1} (\sinh \alpha - \alpha \cosh \alpha)$$

$$+ \cos \beta \left[\frac{c\omega (\cosh 2\alpha - 1)}{\sinh^2 \alpha_1} \frac{c\omega \cosh \alpha_1 \sinh 2\alpha}{2 \sinh^3 \alpha_1} + \frac{c\omega \cosh \alpha_1 \, \alpha}{\sinh^3 \alpha_1} \right]$$

$$[1.3.196]$$

A general expression for the vorticity is

$$c\zeta = h \left(\frac{\partial^2 \chi}{\partial \alpha^2} + \frac{\partial^2 \chi}{\partial \beta} \right) - 2 \left(\sinh \alpha \frac{\partial \chi}{\partial \alpha} + \sin \beta \frac{\partial \chi}{\partial \beta} \right) + (\cosh \alpha + \cos \beta)\chi$$

$$[1.3.197]$$

and on the plane $\alpha = 0$

$$c\zeta = (1 - \cos \beta)(2D_0 + 4A_1 \cos \beta) = \frac{4c\,(1 - \cos \beta)\cos \beta}{\sinh^3 \alpha_1} \qquad [1.3.198]$$

The vorticity on the plane is positive for $0 \leqslant \beta \leqslant \pi/2$ and negative for $\pi/2 < \beta < \pi$. This change of sign is indicative of separation along the plane starting at $\beta = \pi/2$ and spreading to infinity. In terms of x and y, separation commences at the points $x = 0$, $y = \pm c$ on the plane $x = 0$ and continues along the plane to $y = \pm \infty$. The streamline separating the reverse flow from the remainder of the motion is given by

$$\frac{\cosh \alpha_1}{\sinh^3 \alpha_1}\left(\frac{\sinh \alpha}{\alpha} - \cosh \alpha\right)$$

$$+ \cos \beta\left(\frac{\cosh 2\alpha - 1}{\alpha \sinh^2 \alpha_1} - \frac{1}{2}\frac{\cosh \alpha_1 \sinh 2\alpha}{\sinh^3 \alpha_1\,\alpha} + \frac{\cosh \alpha_1}{\sinh^3 \alpha_1}\right) = 0 \qquad [1.3.199]$$

A rough sketch of the principal streamlines is given in figure 1.3.13.

1.3.6.6 Stokes Flow around a Cylinder without Fore-Aft Symmetry

In section 1.3.7 the streaming Stokes flow past a spherical cap will be described with particular reference to the eddy attached to the concave face of the cap. It may be expected that an eddy will form on any axisymmetrical body that presents a concave face to the fluid. However, there are considerable analytic difficulties in showing this result. To this end consider the two-dimensional analog, where there is more variety in the methods that can be used. The disadvantage of two-dimensional flows is the Stokes paradox, where it is not possible to obtain convergence to a uniform stream at infinity with zero velocity on the boundary. However, we are mainly interested in the flow close to the boundary, and we choose the solution of the Stokes equation that tends to infinity most slowly. In fact, the flow at infinity is the same as that produced by a Stokeslet at the origin.

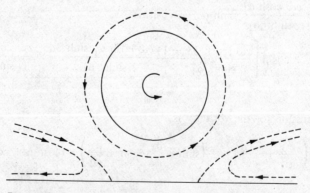

Figure 1.3.13 Principal streamlines for cylinder rotating in the presence of a plane.

The transformation

$$x_i = \frac{x-c}{R^2} \qquad y_i = \frac{y}{R^2} \qquad R_i^2 = x_i^2 + y_i^2 \qquad [1.3.200]$$

and $R^2 = (x-c)^2 + y^2$ defines geometric inversion with respect to the unit circle centered at the point $(c, 0)$ in the x, y plane. If ψ_i is the stream function in the inverse plane, it is known that

$$\psi_i = \frac{\psi}{R^2} \qquad [1.3.201]$$

where ψ_i is biharmonic in the x_i, y_i plane and ψ is biharmonic in the x, y plane. In the present situation the boundary in the x, y plane is an oblate ellipse defined by

$$z = x + iy = \varsigma + \frac{\lambda^2}{\varsigma} \qquad |\lambda| < 1 \qquad [1.3.202]$$

with $|\varsigma| = 1$ on the ellipse c. The inverse curve c_i is of fourth order, which in general possesses a region that is concave to the fluid region. The inverse transformation is

$$\varsigma = \frac{z}{2} + \frac{1}{2}(z^2 + 4\lambda^2)^{1/2} \qquad [1.3.203]$$

so the exterior of the unit circle $|\varsigma| = 1$ maps into the exterior of the ellipse. Furthermore, if $z(d) = c$, $d > 1$ the exterior of the ellipse inverts into the exterior of the closed curve c_i and vice versa. The flow at infinity in the x_i, y_i plane is equivalent to a Stokeslet at the origin and is given by

$$\psi_i \sim y_i \log R_i \qquad R_i \to \infty \qquad [1.3.204]$$

so that in the x, y plane there is a Stokeslet at $z = c$ and the local flow is expressed by

$$\psi \sim \frac{y_i}{R_i^2} \log R_i = -y \log R \qquad R \to 0 \qquad [1.3.205]$$

Using complex variable methods, it is possible to determine the complex velocity in a finite form. This is given by

$$u + iv = 2i \frac{\partial \psi}{\partial \bar{z}}$$

$$= \log\left(\frac{1 - d\bar{\varsigma}}{1 - \bar{\varsigma}/d}\right) - \frac{A}{d^2}\frac{\varsigma}{1 - \bar{\varsigma}/d} - \log\left(\frac{\varsigma - d}{\varsigma - 1/d}\right)$$

$$+ \frac{A}{d^2}\frac{1}{\varsigma - 1/d} + \frac{\varsigma - \lambda^2/\varsigma - 1/\bar{\varsigma} + \lambda^2\bar{\varsigma}}{1 + \lambda^2/\bar{\varsigma}^2}\left(\frac{1}{\bar{\varsigma} - d} - \frac{1}{\bar{\varsigma} - 1/d} + \frac{A}{d^2}\frac{1}{(\bar{\varsigma} - 1/d)^2}\right)$$

$$[1.3.206]$$

where the constant A is expressed by

$$A = \frac{(1 - d^2)(1 + \lambda^2)}{d(1 + \lambda^2/d^2)} \qquad [1.3.207]$$

The vorticity on the boundary is expressed by

$$\omega = \text{Im}\left[z'(\varsigma)g'\left(\frac{1}{\varsigma}\right) \right]$$

$$= \frac{(1 - \lambda^2)(1 - d^2)\sin\phi}{d^2 + 1 - 2d\cos\phi} + \frac{A[\sin 2\phi\,(d^2 - \lambda^2) - 2d(1 - \lambda^2)\sin\phi]}{d^2 + 1 - 2d\cos\phi)^2}$$

$$[1.3.208]$$

and changes sign at $\phi = \alpha$, where

$$(1 - \lambda^2)(1 - d^2)(d^2 + 1 - 2d\cos\alpha) + 2A[\cos\alpha(d^2 - \lambda^2) - 2d(1 - \lambda^2)] = 0$$

$$[1.3.209]$$

To show that a real value of α $(0 < \alpha < \pi)$ exists, consider the local sign of ω as $\phi \to 0$, $\phi \to \pi$. First, as $\phi \to 0$

$$\omega \sim \phi\left\{ \frac{(1 - \lambda^2)(1 - d^2)}{(d - 1)^2} + \frac{2A[\lambda^2 - d^2 - (1 - \lambda^2)d]}{(d - 1)^4} \right\} \qquad [1.3.210]$$

which is always negative. As ϕ approaches π

$$\omega \sim \frac{(\pi - \phi)(d - 1)}{(d + 1)^2(d^2 + \lambda^2)}[2d(d - \lambda^2)(1 + \lambda^2) - (1 - \lambda^2)(1 + d)(d^2 + \lambda^2)]$$

$$[1.3.211]$$

and choosing a representative value $\lambda^2 = \frac{1}{2}$

$$\omega \sim \frac{(\pi - \phi)(d - 1)}{(d + 1)^2(d^2 + \frac{1}{2})}\left[3d\left(d - \frac{1}{2}\right) - \frac{1}{2}(1 + d)\left(d^2 + \frac{1}{2}\right) \right] \qquad [1.3.212]$$

The sign of ω depends on the sign of

$$3d(2d - 1) - (1 + d)(d^2 + \tfrac{1}{2}) \qquad [1.3.213]$$

At $d = 1$ this is zero, and for values of d slightly greater than unity it is positive. For some $\beta > 1$ the quartic vanishes at $d = \beta$, then the expression is negative for larger values of d. Hence as d increases from unity it is initially negative but becomes positive, indicating a region of reverse flow. For $\lambda = 1$, which is the case of the circular arc,

$$\omega \sim \frac{(\pi - \phi)\,4d(d - 1)^2}{(d + 1)^2(d^2 + 1)} > 0 \qquad [1.3.214]$$

indicating that a vortex forms on the concave side of the arc. Dorrepaal (1978) extended this analysis and established criteria for separation to take place. In particular, he studied the case of the circular arc in some detail and found that separation from the tips of the arc takes place at exactly the same angle as in the case of a spherical cap presented later.

1.3.7 STRUCTURE AND PROPERTIES OF THREE-DIMENSIONAL STOKES FLOW

1.3.7.1 Axisymmetrical Stokes Flow

The streaming flow of a viscous fluid past a fixed obstacle is a central problem in fluid dynamics. Interest in the Stokes flow problem dates back to the last century with the classical solution for flow past a sphere. This section concerns more recent work in this area, with special reference to flow structures, which have been neglected in favor of the calculation of drag and torque coefficients.

For the most part we are concerned with axisymmetrical flows past bodies of revolution. In cylindrical polar coordinates (z, r, ϕ) the fluid velocity can be written

$$\mathbf{u} = \nabla \times \left(-\frac{\psi}{r}\, \boldsymbol{\phi} \right) \qquad [1.3.215]$$

where $\psi(z, r)$ is the Stokes stream function and $\boldsymbol{\phi}$ is the unit vector perpendicular to the azimuthal plane $\phi = $ const and in the sense of ϕ increasing. In particular, if $\mathbf{u} = u_z \mathbf{i} + u_r \mathbf{r}$, then

$$u_z = -\frac{1}{r}\frac{\partial \psi}{\partial r} \qquad u_r = \frac{1}{r}\frac{\partial \psi}{\partial z}$$

The equation satisfied by ψ is the repeated Stokes operator equation expressed by

$$L_{-1}^2(\psi) = 0 \qquad [1.3.216]$$

where
$$L_{-1} \equiv \frac{\partial^2}{\partial z^2} + \frac{\partial^2}{\partial r^2} - \frac{1}{r}\frac{\partial}{\partial r} \qquad [1.3.217]$$

The boundary conditions to be applied are

$$\psi = \text{const} \qquad \frac{\partial \psi}{\partial n} = 0$$

on the body S and at infinity

$$\psi \sim \tfrac{1}{2} U_\infty r^2 \qquad z^2 + r^2 \to \infty$$

This boundary-value problem has been the subject of many investigations and the recent work dates back to Payne & Pell (1960b). These authors employed various representation and decomposition formulas for the solution of the Stokes repeated operator equation and in this way many new shapes of the obstacle could be dealt with. For example, ψ can be written as

$$\psi = \tfrac{1}{2} U_\infty r^2 (1 - v^{(1)} - v^{(3)}) \qquad [1.3.218]$$

where $v^{(k)}$ is a solution of the axisymmetrical Laplace equation $L_k(v) = 0$ in a space of $k + 2$ dimensions:

$$L_k(v) \equiv \left(\frac{\partial^2}{\partial z^2} + \frac{\partial^2}{\partial r^2} + \frac{k}{r} \frac{\partial}{\partial r} \right) v = 0$$

Consider the case of a sphere $R = a$ where

$$z = R \cos \theta \qquad r = R \sin \theta$$

Suitable forms for $v^{(k)}$, $k = 1, 3$, are

$$v^{(1)} = \frac{3a}{2R} \qquad v^{(3)} = -\frac{1}{2} \frac{a^3}{R^3}$$

and

$$\psi = \frac{1}{2} u_\infty r^2 \left(1 - \frac{3a}{2R} + \frac{1}{2} \frac{a^3}{R^3} \right) \qquad [1.3.219]$$

It is observed that $v^{(1)}$ is a point source in three dimensions whereas $v^{(3)}$ is a point sink in five dimensions.

The decomposition formula [1.3.218] is also suitable for prolate and oblate ellipsoids of revolution. First consider the prolate ellipsoid and introduce the conformal mapping transformation

$$z + ir = c \cosh (\xi + i\eta)$$

or

$$z = c \cosh \xi \cos \eta \qquad r = c \sinh \xi \sin \eta$$

The equation $L_k(v) = 0$ transforms into

$$\frac{1}{\sinh^k \xi} \frac{\partial}{\partial \xi} \left(\sinh^k \xi \frac{\partial v}{\partial \xi} \right) + \frac{1}{\sin^k \eta} \frac{\partial}{\partial \eta} \left(\sin^k \eta \frac{\partial v}{\partial \eta} \right) = 0$$

If the boundary corresponds to $\xi = \xi_0$, suitable forms for $v^{(1)}$ and $v^{(3)}$ are

$$v^{(1)} = A \int_\xi^\infty \frac{du}{\sinh u} \qquad v^{(3)} = B \int_\xi^\infty \frac{du}{\sinh^3 u}$$

where the constants A and B are determined by the boundary conditions

$$1 - v^{(1)} - v^{(3)} = \frac{\partial}{\partial \xi} (1 - v^{(1)} - v^{(3)}) = 0 \qquad \text{on } \xi = \xi_0$$

In the case of the oblate ellipsoid the appropriate conformal mapping transformation is

$$z + ir = \sinh (\xi + i\eta)$$

and then

$$v^{(1)} = A \int_\xi^\infty \frac{du}{\cosh u} \qquad v^{(\xi)} = B \int_\xi^\infty \frac{du}{\cosh^3 u}$$

By using decomposition formulas of the type [1.3.218], it was possible to solve explicitly for ψ in the cases of a lens, two externally separated spheres, a spindle, and a torus (Payne & Pell 1960a, 1960b; Pell & Payne 1960). Collins (1963) first gave the solution using dual series equations for the spherical cap, and Ranger (1965) gave the solution for an elliptic limaçon of revolution by inverting a flow interior to a prolate ellipsoid. Bourot (1975) and Richardson (1977) considered the cardioid of revolution. In these papers interest centered mainly on the drag coefficient and little or no attention was paid to the flow structure and streamlines for the flow. It may be remarked that it is necessary to calculate the global velocity field to determine the drag. Recently some attention has been paid to the flow structure for bodies that lack fore-aft symmetry and some interesting physical features have emerged in that separation and reverse flow are possible.

The first example to be considered is that of the spherical cap that is parachute- or umbrella-shaped. In spherical polar coordinates (r, θ) the velocity components can be written

$$u_r = -\frac{1}{r^2 \sin \theta} \frac{\partial \psi}{\partial \theta} \qquad u_\theta = \frac{1}{r \sin \theta} \frac{\partial \psi}{\partial r} \qquad \text{[1.3.220]}$$

where ψ satisfies [1.3.216] and L_{-1} in (r, θ) is given by

$$L_{-1} \equiv \frac{\partial^2}{\partial r^2} + \frac{\sin \theta}{r^2} \frac{\partial}{\partial \theta} \left(\frac{1}{\sin \theta} \frac{\partial}{\partial \theta} \right)$$

The cap is defined by $r = 1, 0 \leqslant \theta \leqslant \alpha$, and the boundary conditions in nondimensional terms are

$$\psi = \frac{\partial \psi}{\partial r} = 0 \qquad r = 1 \qquad 0 \leqslant \theta \leqslant \alpha$$

$$\psi \sim \tfrac{1}{2} r^2 \sin^2 \theta \qquad r \to \infty$$

In addition, $\psi, \partial\psi/\partial r, \partial^2\psi/\partial r^2, \partial^3\psi/\partial r^3$ are continuous on the part of the sphere not occupied by the cap, i.e., $r = 1, \alpha < \theta \leqslant \pi$. A suitable decomposition formula for the stream function is

$$\psi = \frac{1}{2} r^2 \sin^2 \theta - V_1 + (r^2 - 1) \left(\frac{r}{2} \frac{\partial V_1}{\partial r} - V_2 \right) \qquad \text{[1.3.221]}$$

where $v_j, j = 1, 2$, are solutions of $L_{-1}(V_j) = 0$. Appropriate representations for the functions V_j are

$$V_j(r, \theta) = r^{1/2} \int_0^\theta \frac{v_j(r, \lambda) \sin \lambda \, d\lambda}{(\cos \lambda - \cos \theta)^{1/2}}$$

$$= -r^{1/2} \int_\theta^\pi \frac{u_j(r, \lambda) \sin \lambda \, d\lambda}{(\cos \theta - \cos \lambda)^{1/2}} \qquad r < 1$$

$$\text{[1.3.222]}$$

$$V_j(r, \theta) = r^{1/2} \int_0^\theta \frac{v_j(1/r, \lambda) \sin \lambda \, d\lambda}{(\cos \lambda - \cos \theta)^{1/2}}$$

$$= - r^{1/2} \int_0^\pi \frac{u_j(1/r, \lambda) \sin \lambda \, d\lambda}{(\cos \theta - \cos \lambda)^{1/2}} \qquad r > 1 \qquad [1.3.222]$$

u_j, v_j are conjugate harmonics in the r, λ plane expressible in the form

$$u_j + iv_j = \frac{2^{3/2}}{\pi} \sum_{n=1}^\infty A_n^j (re^{i\lambda})^{n + 1/2} \qquad\qquad [1.3.223]$$

Under the integral transformations [1.3.222] and [1.3.223], u_j, v_j map into

$$V_j(r, \theta) = \sum_{n=1}^\infty A_n^j r^{n+1} \left[P_{n-1} (\cos \theta) - P_{n+1} (\cos \theta) \right] \qquad r < 1$$

$$= \sum_{n=1}^\infty A_n^j r^{-n} \left[P_{n-1} (\cos \theta) - P_{n+1} (\cos \theta) \right] \qquad r > 1$$

where $P_n(\cos \theta)$ is the Legendre polynomial of degree n. The boundary condition on the cap requires

$$\frac{1}{2} \sin^2 \theta = \int_0^\theta \frac{v_j(1, \lambda) \sin \lambda \, d\lambda}{(\cos \lambda - \cos \theta)^{1/2}} \qquad 0 \leqslant \theta \leqslant \alpha$$

which is an Abel-type integral equation whose solution is

$$v_j(1, \lambda) = \frac{2^{3/2}}{3\pi} \sin \frac{3}{2} \lambda \qquad 0 \leqslant \lambda \leqslant \alpha$$

On the part of the sphere not occupied by the cap the velocity and stress are continuous. This is equivalent to the conditions that $\psi, \partial\psi/\partial r, \partial^2\psi/\partial r^2, \partial^3\psi/\partial r^3$ are continuous at $r = 1$, $\alpha < \theta \leqslant \pi$. The first two conditions are automatically satisfied and $\partial^2\psi/\partial r^2$ is continuous if

$$\int_\theta^\pi \left(3 \frac{\partial u_1}{\partial r} - 4 \frac{\partial u_2}{\partial r} \right) \frac{\sin \lambda \, d\lambda}{(\cos \theta - \cos \lambda)^{1/2}} = 0 \qquad r = 1 \qquad \alpha < \theta < \pi$$

or equivalently

$$3 \frac{\partial u_1}{\partial r} - 4 \frac{\partial u_2}{\partial r} = \frac{1}{r} \left(3 \frac{\partial v_1}{\partial \lambda} - 4 \frac{\partial v_2}{\partial \lambda} \right) = 0 \qquad r = 1 \qquad \alpha < \lambda \leqslant \pi$$

The condition that $\partial^3\psi/\partial r^3$ be continuous reduces to

$$2\frac{\partial^3 v_1}{\partial \lambda^3} + \frac{1}{2}\frac{\partial v_1}{\partial \lambda} + 2\frac{\partial v_2}{\partial \lambda} = 0 \qquad r = 1 \qquad \alpha < \lambda \leqslant \pi$$

The general solutions for $v_j(1, \lambda)$ are found to be

$$v_1(1, \lambda) = C + D\cos\lambda + E\sin\lambda$$

$$v_2(1, \lambda) = B + \tfrac{3}{4}D\cos\lambda + \tfrac{3}{4}E\sin\lambda$$

for $\alpha < \lambda \leqslant \pi$. For u_r to be finite as $\theta \to \pi, r = 1$, it is necessary that $\partial v_1/\partial\lambda \to 0$ as $\lambda \to \pi, r = 1$. This implies $E = 0$. Now

$$u_r(1, \theta) = -\cos\theta + \frac{1}{\sin\theta}\frac{dV_1}{d\phi}(1, \theta)$$

so that for u_r to be finite at the rim of the cap it is necessary that the singularity $dV_1(1, \theta)/d\theta$ as $\theta \to \alpha + 0$ be eliminated. In addition, there are no sources or sinks on the axis, and this condition is $V_j(1, \pi) = 0, j = 1, 2$. These conditions suffice to determine B, C, D, which are

$$B = \frac{2^{1/2}}{24\pi}\left(9\sin\tfrac{1}{2}\alpha + 2\sin^3\tfrac{1}{2}\alpha\right)$$

$$C = \frac{2^{1/2}}{6\pi}\left(3\sin\tfrac{1}{2}\alpha + 2\sin^3\tfrac{1}{2}\alpha\right)$$

$$D = \frac{2^{1/2}}{2\pi}3\sin\tfrac{1}{2}\alpha$$

The functions $v_j(1, \lambda)$ are now known explicitly and since

$$v_j(1, \lambda) = \frac{2^{3/2}}{\pi}\sum_{n=1}^{\infty}A_n^j\sin\left(n + \tfrac{1}{2}\right)\lambda$$

the Fourier coefficient A_n^j is given by

$$A_n^j = 2^{-1/2}\int_0^{\pi}v_j(1, \lambda)\sin\left(n + \tfrac{1}{2}\right)\lambda\, d\lambda$$

On calculation

$$A_n^1 = \frac{1}{3\pi}\left[\frac{\sin(n-1)\alpha}{n-1} - \frac{\sin(n+2)\alpha}{n+2}\right] + \frac{2^{1/2}C}{2n+1}\cos\left(n + \tfrac{1}{2}\right)\alpha$$

$$+ \frac{D}{2^{1/2}}\left[\frac{\cos(n + \tfrac{3}{2})\alpha}{2n+3} + \frac{\cos(n - \tfrac{1}{2})\alpha}{2n-1}\right]$$

A_n^2 has the same form as A_n^1 with C replaced by B and D replaced by $\tfrac{3}{4}D$. When $n = 1$, $\sin(n-1)\alpha/(n-1)$ is interpreted as α. These expressions for A_n^j can now be substituted in [1.3.222] to give infinite series expansions for $V_j(r, \theta)$.

The drag on the cap can be computed from a formula due to Payne & Pell (1960b). If $\bar{U}_\infty$ is the speed of the uniform stream at infinity and a is the radius of the cap, the drag is

$$F = 8\pi\rho_0\nu\bar{U}_\infty a \lim_{r\to\infty} \frac{\psi - \frac{1}{2}r^2\sin^2\theta}{r\sin^2\theta} = -\bar{U}_\infty a\rho_0\nu(6\alpha + 8\sin\alpha + \sin 2\alpha)$$

[1.3.224]

where ρ_0 and ν are the density and kinematic viscosity, respectively. This expression was first given by Collins (1963) and later by Dorrepaal et al. (1976b). It predicts the correct drag in the case of a sphere $\alpha = \pi$ and the disk $\alpha \to 0$, $a \to \infty$, $a\alpha \to b$.

To describe the flow structure, the question of interest is whether the flow bends around the rim or separates at the rim. It is convenient to define a local coordinate system (η, ϵ) at the rim by

$$r = 1 - \epsilon \qquad \theta = \alpha + \eta$$

and local polar coordinates by $\rho e^{i\lambda} = \eta + i\epsilon$. The inner surface of the cap is described by $\lambda = \pi$ and the outer surface by $\lambda = -\pi$. Without describing the details, which are given in Dorrepaal et al. (1976b), the stream function locally in a neighborhood of the rim is given by

$$\psi = 4\pi^{-1}(2\sin\alpha)^{1/2}\rho^{3/2}\cos^3\tfrac{1}{2}\alpha\cos^3\tfrac{1}{2}\lambda(\tfrac{1}{3} - \tan\tfrac{1}{2}\alpha\tan\tfrac{1}{2}\lambda)$$

illustrating that the flow separates at the rim at angle $\lambda = \lambda_0$, where

$$\tan\tfrac{1}{2}\lambda_0 = \tfrac{1}{3}\cot\alpha \qquad\qquad [1.3.225]$$

Again, it is fairly straightforward to show that there is a stagnation point on the axis for all values of $\alpha > 0$. Thus the flow separates at the rim and there is an eddy or ring vortex attached to the cap. For the case of a hemispherical cap $\alpha = \frac{1}{2}\pi$, it is readily shown that

$$u_r(r, \tfrac{1}{2}\pi) = 0$$

$$u_\theta\left(r, \frac{1}{2}\pi\right) = \frac{1}{2} - \frac{1}{4\pi}(3r^{-1} + r^{-3})\sin^{-1}r - \frac{1}{4\pi}(3 - r^{-2})(1 - r^2)^{1/2}$$

and moreover that u_θ vanishes on $r = r_0 = 0.687$. So there is a stagnation ring at $r = 0.687$, $\theta = \frac{1}{2}\pi$. The axial fluid velocity within the wake attains a maximum of $u_m = 5/3\pi - \frac{1}{2} = 0.0305$ and this occurs at $r = 0$.

Figure 1.3.14 shows the streamlines past a hemispherical cap $\alpha = \pi/2$. Since Stokes flow is reversible, the vortex is located in the same position regardless of the direction of the uniform stream. It seems likely that if a body is sufficiently concave, separation will take place. Michael & O'Neill (1977) studied the separation produced by a concave lens. There are no examples of smooth axisymmetrical bodies that exhibit separation, even though the phenomenon is likely to be present. This is borne out by Michael & O'Neill's study. They found that only when the concave lens degenerates into a cap does the separation streamline detach from the rim. In all other cases separation takes place from the concave surface of the rim, in

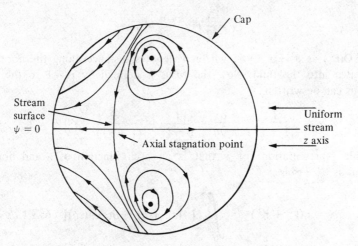

Figure 1.3.14   Streamlines past a hemispherical cap $\alpha = \pi/2$.

general very close to the rim. Michael & O'Neill also showed that separation can occur for a thin planoconvex or biconvex lens, suggesting that separation can occur from a single convex body.

1.3.7.2   The Closed Torus

The closed torus is the solid of revolution formed by rotating a circle about one of its tangent lines. Stokes flow past this obstacle was first solved by Dorrepaal et al. (1976a). Let the circles each have radius a and a system of cylindrical polar coordinates $(2ar, \phi, 2az)$ be chosen so that the z axis lies along the common tangent as shown in figure 1.3.15. It is appropriate to introduce tangent sphere coordinates by

$$r = \frac{\eta}{\xi^2 + \eta^2} \qquad z = \frac{\xi}{\xi^2 + \eta^2} \qquad -\infty < \xi < \infty \qquad 0 \leqslant \eta < \infty$$

and it is observed that the torus with unit cross-sectional diameter is defined by $\eta = 1$. The space outside this torus is given by $-\infty < \xi < \infty$, $0 \leqslant \eta < 1$, with points infinitely distant given by $\xi = \eta = 0$, while the origin $r = z = 0$ is approached by $|\xi| \to \infty$. The fluid velocity components can again be expressed in terms of a Stokes stream function:

$$4a^2 u_r = -\frac{1}{r}\frac{\partial\psi}{\partial z} \qquad 4a^2 u_z = \frac{1}{r}\frac{\partial\psi}{\partial r}$$

The equation satisfied by ψ is

$$L^2_{-1}\psi = \left(\frac{\partial^2}{\partial r^2} - \frac{1}{r}\frac{\partial}{\partial r} + \frac{\partial^2}{\partial z^2}\right)^2 \psi = 0$$

Writing $\psi = 4a^2 \bar{U}_\infty(\frac{1}{2}r^2 - \chi)$, it is clear that $L^2_{-1}(\chi) = 0$ and the boundary conditions are satisfied on the torus if

$$\chi = \frac{1}{2}r^2 \qquad \frac{\partial \chi}{\partial n} = r\frac{\partial r}{\partial n}$$

and $\chi = O(r^2)$ as $r^2 + z^2 \to \infty$, where n denotes distance along the normal to the torus drawn into the fluid. Now the torus is defined by $\eta = 1$ so the boundary conditions can be written

$$\chi = \frac{1}{2(1 + \xi^2)} \qquad \frac{\partial \chi}{\partial \eta} = \frac{1}{1 + \xi^2} - \frac{2}{(1 + \xi^2)^3} \qquad \text{at } \eta = 1$$

A suitable representation for χ that is an even function of ξ and bounded on $\eta = 0$ and as $|\xi| \to \infty$ is

$$\chi = \eta(\xi^2 + \eta^2)^{-3/2} \int_0^\infty [A(s)I_1(s\eta) + B(s)I_0(s\eta)] \cos s\,\xi\, ds$$

where $I_1(x)$, $I_0(x)$ are Bessel functions of imaginary argument of order 1 and 0, respectively, and s is a parameter of integration. Employing the results

$$\int_0^\infty \frac{\cos s\,\xi\, d\xi}{(1 + \xi^2)^{1/2}} = K_0(s) \qquad \int_0^\infty \frac{\cos s\,\xi\, d\xi}{(1 + \xi^2)^{3/2}} = sK_1(s)$$

and the boundary conditions are satisfied if

$$\pi A(s)I_1(s) + \pi B(s)I_0(s) = K_0(s)$$

$$\pi sA(s)I_1'(s) + \pi B(s)[I_0(s) + sI_0'(s)] = K_0(s) - sK_1(s)$$

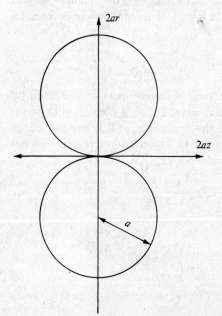

Figure 1.3.15 Cross section of the closed torus in an axial plane.

where K_1 and K_0 are the Bessel functions of imaginary argument and of the second kind. The functions $A(s)$, $B(s)$ are

$$\pi s A(s) = \frac{1}{[I_1(s)]^2 - I_0(s)I_2(s)}$$

$$\pi B(s) = \frac{I_1(s)K_1(s) + K_0(s)I_2(s)}{[I_1(s)]^2 - I_0(s)I_2(s)}$$

The drag on the torus is determined by the formula given by Payne & Pell (1960b) and is

$$\frac{F}{8\pi\mu\bar{U}_\infty a} = \int_0^\infty [sA(s) + 2B(s)]\ ds = \frac{1}{\pi}\int_0^\infty \frac{1 - 2[I_1(s)K_1(s) + I_2(s)K_0(s)]}{[I_1(s)]^2 - I_0(s)I_2(s)}\ ds$$

On evaluating the integral numerically it is found that

$$F = 35.26\ \mu\bar{U}_\infty a \qquad\qquad [1.3.226]$$

The drag on a closed torus is compared below with that on a disk, a hemispherical cup, and a sphere.

Body	Drag ratio
Disk	0.849
Torus	0.935
Hemispherical cup	0.925
Sphere	1

Consider now the flow properties when the torus is at rest in an axisymmetrical stream. On the boundary the tangential stress is equal to the vorticity $\bar{U}_\infty\omega/2a$ and in terms of ψ this is expressed by

$$\omega = r^{-1}L_{-1}\ \psi = -r^{-1}L_{-1}\chi = \frac{2(1 + \xi^2)^{3/2}}{\pi}\int_0^\infty \frac{I_2(x)\ \cos x\xi\ dx}{[I_1(x)]^2 - I_0(x)I_2(x)}$$

Introducing spherical polar coordinates $(2aR, \theta, \phi)$, it is readily shown that

$$R = (\xi^2 + \eta^2)^{-1/2} \qquad r = R\ \sin\theta \qquad z = R\ \cos\theta$$

and on the torus, $\eta = 1$ or $R = \sin\theta$

$$w|_{R=\sin\theta} = \frac{2}{\pi\ \sin^3\theta}\int_0^\infty \frac{I_2(x)\ \cos(x\ \cot\theta)\ dx}{[I_1(x)]^2 - I_0(x)I_2(x)}$$

at $\theta = \frac{1}{2}\pi$, assuming the value unity at $x = 0$ and behaving as $(2\pi)^{1/2}x^{3/2}e^{-x}$ as $x \to \infty$. However, as $\theta \to 0$, $\cot\theta \to +\infty$, and the cosine term oscillates very rapidly.

Numerical methods are inadequate for analyzing the boundary vorticity and an asymptotic analysis for small θ is required to show where the vorticity and tangential stress change sign. The asymptotic analysis is described in Dorrepaal et al. (1976a) and it is found that

$$w|_{R=\sin\theta} = -\frac{2}{\sin^3\theta}\, \text{Im} \sum_{n=0}^{\infty} \frac{\zeta_n e^{i\zeta_n|\cot\theta|}}{I_0(\zeta_n)}$$ [1.3.227]

where ζ_n are the roots of

$$[I_1(\zeta)]^2 - I_0(\zeta)I_2(\zeta) = 0$$

The values $I_0(\zeta_n)$ can be computed from tables and it is found that

$$I_0(\zeta_0) = -0.6677 - i\,0.4847 \qquad I_0(\zeta_1) = 0.625 + i\,0.516$$

After some simplification, the first two terms of [1.3.227] are given by

$$w|_{R=\sin\theta} = \frac{11.3962}{\sin^3\theta}\, e^{-4.4663|\cot\theta|} \sin(\beta + 1.4675\,|\cot\theta|)$$

$$-\frac{19.468}{\sin^3\theta}\, e^{-7.693|\cot\theta|} \sin(\gamma + 1.727|\cot\theta|)$$ [1.3.228]

where $\beta = 0.6254$ rad and $\gamma = 0.613$ rad. The concave region of the closed torus lies in the range $0 \leqslant \theta \leqslant \frac{1}{4}\pi$. Thus $|\cot\theta| \geqslant 1$ and the ratio of the magnitudes of the two items is of order

$$\frac{19.468e^{-7.693|\cot\theta|}}{11.3962e^{-4.4663|\cot\theta|}} \sim 1.7e^{-3.227|\cot\theta|} \leqslant 1.7e^{-3.227} \sim 0.07$$

It follows that in the cusp region the first term is at least one order of magnitude larger than the second, so an accurate description of the flow in the concave region can be obtained by analyzing the first term in [1.3.228]. It is obvious that the boundary vorticity in the cusp region decays exponentially and changes sign infinitely many times as $\theta \to 0$. The points on the boundary where separation occurs are solutions of

$$\beta + 1.4675 \cot\theta_n = n\pi \qquad n = 1, 2, 3$$

that is,

$$\theta_n = \tan^{-1} \frac{1.4675}{n\pi - \beta}$$

The first two solutions of this equation are given in table 1.3.3.

Table 1.3.3 Solutions for θ_n

n	1	2	3	4	5	6
θ_n	30.25°	14.54°	9.47°	7.01°	5.56°	4.60°

The infinite number of separation points on the boundary of the closed torus indicates the presence of nested vortices. The cusp region is divided into infinitely many cells, each of which contains a toroidal vortex. To envisage the flow structure more clearly a similar analysis can be performed with the axial velocity. The velocity on the axis is calculated as

$$w|_{R=0} = \bar{U}_\infty - \frac{\bar{U}_\infty}{\pi z} \int_0^\infty \frac{1 - 2[K_1(x)I_1(x) + K_0(x)I_2(x)]}{[I_1(x)]^2 - I_0(x)I_2(x)} \cos \frac{x}{2} \, dx$$

In this case, the integrand has a logarithmic singularity at $x = 0$. The leading terms in the asymptotic expansion are

$$w|_{R=0} \sim \frac{6.9064}{z} \bar{U}_\infty e^{-4.4663/z} \sin \left(\frac{1.4675}{2} - \delta \right)$$

where $\delta = 0.0023$ rad. As in the case of the vorticity, the second term is dominated by the first term in the cusp region. Hence this expression can be used to determine the stagnation points on the axis near the cusp. These points are solutions of

$$\frac{1.4675}{z_n} - \delta = n\pi \qquad n = 1, 2, 3, \ldots$$

that is,

$$z_n = \frac{1.4675}{\delta + n\pi}$$

The first few solutions are given in table 1.3.4.

Expression [1.3.227] predicts that there are an infinite number of stagnation points on the axis. Each stagnation point marks the spot where a dividing stream surface originating from the boundary intersects the axis. If the separation points from table 1.3.3 are paired off with the corresponding stagnation points in table 1.3.4, a more complete picture of the shape and curvature of the dividing stream surfaces is determined. To investigate the data contained in the two tables, the projection of each separation point can be computed and compared with the z_n in table 1.3.4.

From figure 1.3.16 it is clear that the projection of the nth separation point onto the axis is

$$\sigma_n = \sin \theta_n \cos \theta_n = \tfrac{1}{2} \sin 2\theta_n$$

Table 1.3.5 compares σ_n and z_n. For $n = 1$, $\sigma_1 < z_1$, so that the first dividing stream surface is slightly convex to the external fluid. However, for $n > 1$, $\sigma_n > z_n$,

Table 1.3.4 Solutions for z_n

n	1	2	3	4	5	6
z_n	0.4667	0.2335	0.1557	0.1168	0.0934	0.0778

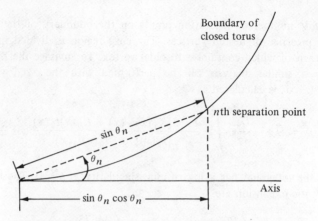

Figure 1.3.16 Projection on the axis of the nth separation point on the torus.

and the remaining stream surfaces are slightly concave. As n increases the two values tend to zero so that for large n the dividing surfaces are virtually planar. A sketch of the streamline is given in figure 1.3.17. This appears to be the first exact solution of the Stokes equations that predicts the existence of axisymmetrical Dean-Moffatt vortices. It can be expected that the same phenomenon will occur in any axisymmetrical Stokes flow past an obstacle that has a cusplike concavity, and this conjecture is verified in the numerical solution of Bourot (1975) for flow past a cardioid of revolution.

1.3.7.3 Flow Past Two Spheres

Two rigid spheres, each of radius a, are situated in a steady stream of infinite incompressible viscous fluid of constant density ρ_0 and viscosity μ so that the line of centers of the spheres, which are held at rest, is parallel to the direction of the stream. The speed of the stream is $\bar{U}_\infty$ and the distance between the centers of the spheres is $2ka$ with $k > 1$ as illustrated in figure 1.3.18.

It is appropriate to choose cylindrical polar coordinates (ar, ϕ, az) so that the centers of the spheres are at $r = 0$, $z = \pm k$. Then, since the flow is symmetrical about the z axis, the fluid velocity has cylindrical components of the form $\bar{U}_\infty(u, 0, w)$ with u and w independent of ϕ. In this case the velocity components are expressed by

$$u = \frac{1}{r} \frac{\partial \psi}{\partial z} \qquad w = -\frac{1}{r} \frac{\partial \psi}{\partial r} \qquad\qquad [1.3.229]$$

Table 1.3.5 Comparison of σ_n and z_n

n	1	2	3	4	5	6
σ_n	0.4352	0.2430	0.1622	0.1211	0.0964	0.0800
z_n	0.4667	0.2335	0.1557	0.1168	0.0934	0.0778

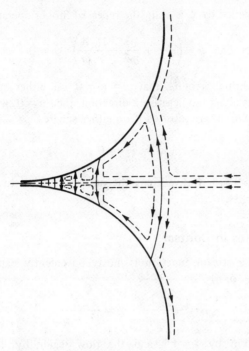

Figure 1.3.17 Structure of the flow in the neighbor-hood of either cusp of the torus.

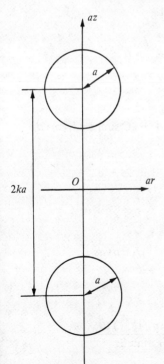

Figure 1.3.18 Geometry of the problem of flow past two spheres.

and the equation satisfied by ψ is again the repeated Stokes operator equation

$$L^2_{-1} \, \psi \equiv \left(\frac{\partial^2}{\partial z^2} + \frac{\partial^2}{\partial r^2} - \frac{1}{r} \frac{\partial}{\partial r} \right)^2 \psi = 0 \qquad [1.3.230]$$

The boundary conditions require that $u = w = 0$ on either sphere and, if the undisturbed stream is along the negative z direction, then $u = 0$, $w = -1$ at infinity. These boundary conditions are satisfied if on either sphere

$$\psi = \frac{\partial \psi}{\partial n} = 0$$

where $\partial/\partial n$ denotes the derivative along the outward normal to either sphere and $\psi \sim \frac{1}{2} r^2$ as $r^2 + z^2 \to \infty$.

1.3.7.4 Spheres in Contact

The solution for the stream function is most conveniently expressed in tangent sphere coordinates (ξ, ϕ, η)

$$r = \frac{2\eta}{\xi^2 + \eta^2} \qquad z = \frac{2\xi}{\xi^2 + \eta^2} \qquad [1.3.231]$$

The spheres are given by $\xi = \pm 1$ and the flow region by $|\xi| < 1$, $0 \leqslant \eta < \infty$, $0 \leqslant \phi \leqslant 2\pi$. The boundary conditions are equivalent to

$$\psi = \frac{\partial \psi}{\partial \xi} = 0 \qquad \xi = \pm 1$$

$$\psi - \frac{2\eta^2}{(\xi^2 + \eta^2)^2} \to 0 \qquad \xi^2 + \eta^2 \to 0$$

The solution is expressed by

$$\psi = \frac{2\eta}{(\xi^2 + \eta^2)^2} + \frac{\eta}{(\xi^2 + \eta^2)^{3/2}} \int_0^\infty (B \cosh s\xi + \xi C \sinh s\xi) J_1(s\eta) \, ds$$

where
$$B = -\frac{2 + 2s + s^{-1}(1 - e^{-2s})}{s + \sinh s \cosh s} \qquad C = \frac{1 + 2s - e^{-2s}}{s + \sinh s \cosh s}$$

By employing the Hankel transform

$$\frac{\eta}{(\xi^2 + \eta^2)^{-1/2}} = \int_0^\infty e^{-s|\xi|} (|\xi| + s^{-1}) J_1(s\eta) \, ds$$

it can be shown for $0 \leqslant \xi \leqslant 1$

$$\psi = -\frac{2\eta}{(\xi^2 + \eta^2)^{3/2}} \frac{d}{d\eta} \int_0^\infty \frac{J_0(s\eta) f(\xi, \zeta) \, ds}{2s + \sinh 2s}$$

where

$$f(\xi, s) = \xi[s^{-1} \sinh s\xi + 2 \cosh s\xi + s^{-1} \sinh (2 - \xi)s] - 2s^{-1} \sinh s\xi - 2 \cosh s\xi$$
$$- s^{-2} \cosh s\xi + s^{-2} \cosh (2 - \xi)s \qquad [1.3.232]$$

$f(\xi, s)$ is an even function of s that vanishes at $s = 0$. Using the integral representation

$$J_0(x) = \frac{2}{\pi} \int_1^\infty \frac{\sin tx}{(t^2 - 1)^{1/2}} dt \quad x > 0$$

from standard references enables the stream function to be written as

$$\psi = \frac{2\eta i}{\pi(\xi^2 + \eta^2)^{3/2}} \frac{d}{d\eta} \int_1^\infty \frac{dt}{(t^2 - 1)^{1/2}} \int_{-\infty}^\infty \frac{f(\xi, s)e^{ist\eta} ds}{2s + \sinh 2s}$$

with $f(\xi, s)$ given by [1.3.232] and $0 \leqslant \xi \leqslant 1$, the s integral can be expressed as a sum of residues at the zeros of $2s + \sinh 2s = 0$ in the upper half of the complex s plane. The zeros of $z + \sin z = 0$ are $z = \pm \lambda_n$ and $z = \pm \bar{\lambda}_n$ ($n = 1, 2, \ldots$), where each λ_n is in the first quadrant, $\bar{\lambda}_n$ is the complex conjugates of λ_n, and the ordering is according to increasing real part. The first few values of λ_n are given below to six significant figures.

$$\lambda_1 = 4.21239 + 2.25073i$$
$$\lambda_2 = 10.7125 + 3.10319i$$
$$\lambda_3 = 17.0734 + 3.55108i$$

As $n \to \infty$, λ_n can be calculated from the asymptotic expansion

$$\lambda_n \sim \alpha_n - \alpha_n^{-1} \log (2\alpha_n) + i \log (2\alpha_n)$$

where $\alpha_n = (2n - \frac{1}{2})\pi$, which can be used to start a Newton iteration procedure for finding λ_n numerically. The zeros of $2s + \sinh 2s = 0$ in the upper half of the complex s plane are evidently $s = \frac{1}{2} i\lambda_n$ and $s = \frac{1}{2} i\bar{\lambda}_n$ ($n = 1, 2, \ldots$). Hence ψ may be written as

$$(\xi^2 + \eta^2)^{3/2} \frac{\psi}{2\eta} = - \operatorname{Re} \frac{d}{d\eta} \int_1^\infty \frac{2 dt}{(t^2 - 1)^{1/2}} \sum_{n=1}^\infty \frac{f(\xi, \frac{1}{2} i\lambda_n)e^{-1/2\lambda_1 \eta t}}{1 + \cos \lambda_n}$$

In particular, in the neighborhood of the point of contact between the spheres $\eta > 2$, so with exponentially small error only the first term in the series need be retained and

$$(\xi^2 + \eta^2)^{3/2} \frac{\psi}{2\eta} \sim - \operatorname{Re} \frac{2f(\xi, \frac{1}{2} i\lambda)}{1 + \cos \lambda_1} \frac{d}{d\eta} \int_1^\infty \frac{e^{-1/2\lambda_1 \eta t}}{(t^2 - 1)^{1/2}} dt = \operatorname{Re} \frac{\lambda_1 f(\xi, \frac{1}{2} i\lambda_1)}{1 + \cos \lambda_1}$$

$$\cdot\, K_1\left(\frac{1}{2}\lambda_1\eta\right) \sim \mathrm{Re}\, \frac{\lambda_1 f(\xi, \frac{1}{2}i\lambda_1)}{1 + \cos\lambda_1}\left(\frac{\pi}{\lambda_1\eta}\right)^{1/2} e^{-1/2\lambda_1\eta}\left[1 + \frac{3}{4\lambda_1\eta} + O(\lambda_1^{-2}\eta^{-2})\right]$$

As λ_1 is complex, the exponential function is oscillatory with period $4\pi/\mathrm{Im}(\lambda_1)$. Hence for all $0 \leqslant \xi < 1$ there is an infinity of values of η for which ψ vanishes. Since the flow is symmetrical about the plane $z = 0$ and the axis $r = 0$, there exists an infinite set of stream surfaces of revolution on which $\psi = 0$. These surfaces bound an infinite set of nested ring vortices with axes along the z axis, and are attached to the spheres where

$$\chi(\eta) = \lim_{\xi\to 1}\frac{\psi(\xi, \eta)}{(1 - \xi)^2} = \lim_{\xi\to -1}\frac{\psi(\xi, \eta)}{(1 + \xi)^2} = 0$$

$\chi(\eta)$ is given asymptotically by

$$\frac{(1 + \eta^2)^{3/2}}{2\eta}\,\chi(\eta) \sim -\,\mathrm{Re}\,\frac{\lambda_1^2 \sin\frac{1}{2}\lambda_1}{1 + \cos\lambda_1}\left(\frac{\pi}{\lambda_1\eta}\right)^{1/2} e^{-1/2\lambda_1\eta}\left[1 + \frac{3}{4\lambda_1\eta} + O(\lambda_1^{-2}\eta^{-2})\right]$$

when $\eta \geqslant 2$. Hence the solutions are given asymptotically by

$$\frac{3}{2}\arg\lambda_1 + \arg\left(\sin\frac{1}{2}\lambda_1\right) - \arg(1 + \cos\lambda_1) - \frac{1}{2}\eta\mathrm{Im}\lambda_1 + \arg\left(1 + \frac{3}{4\lambda_1\eta}\right)$$

$$\sim -\left(m + \frac{1}{2}\right)\pi$$

with $m = 0, \pm 1, \pm 2, \ldots$. With these values of λ_1 the positive solutions are given asymptotically by

$$\frac{1}{2}\eta\mathrm{Im}\lambda_1 - \arg\left(1 + \frac{3}{4\lambda_1\eta}\right) \sim d_m$$

where $d_1 = 3.12411$ and $d_m - d_{m-1} = \pi$. Further insight into the flow structure can be obtained by considering the velocity in the plane $z = 0$. The velocity component u vanishes on this plane and

$$w_0 = w|_{z=0} = \frac{\eta}{4}\frac{\partial\psi}{\partial\eta}\Big|_{\xi=0}$$

The zeros of w_0 occur at the centers of the sections of the ring vortices in an azimuthal plane, while the value of w_0 at a zero of $\psi(0, \eta)$ gives the maximum velocity in the ring vortex whose outer boundary is the streamline $\psi = 0$ through the zero. Hence it is a good measure of the decay of velocity as the point of contact between the spheres is approached. For $\eta > 2$ it is found that

$$w_0 \sim -\frac{1}{4}\mathrm{Re}\,(\lambda_1 + 5\eta^{-1} + \ldots)\frac{\lambda_1 f(0, \frac{1}{2}i\lambda_1)}{1 + \cos\lambda_1}\left(\frac{\pi}{\lambda_1\eta}\right)^{1/2} e^{-1/2\lambda_1\eta}\left(1 + \frac{3}{4\lambda_1\eta} + \ldots\right)$$

$$\sim -\frac{1}{4}\,\mathrm{Re}\,\frac{\lambda_1^2 f(0,\tfrac{1}{2}i\lambda_1)}{1+\cos\lambda_1}\left(\frac{\pi}{\lambda_1\eta}\right)^{1/2}e^{-1/2\lambda_1\eta}\left[1+\frac{23}{4\lambda_1\eta}+O(\lambda_1^{-2}\eta^{-2})\right]$$

Figure 1.3.19 shows the shape of the stream surfaces $\psi = 0$ when drawn with the asymptotic expressions described in this section. The surfaces are essentially circular cylinders, the cross sections tapering slightly from the circles of intersection with the spheres to the intersection with the plane $z = 0$ except for the outermost surface, where the reverse flow occurs to preserve the near constancy of the angle of intersection of the stream surface with either sphere. It follows that in the steady axisymmetrical Stokes streaming flow past two equal spheres in contact there is a cylinder attached to both spheres within which the fluid rotates in an infinite set of nested ring vortices.

1.3.7.5 Spheres Not in Contact

The solution for the Stokes flow produced by the translation of two equal spheres along their line of centers with the same velocity was obtained by Stimson & Jeffery (1926). These authors were mainly interested in calculating the drag coefficient and did not investigate the flow structure. The solution is expressed in bispherical coordinates defined by

$$r = \frac{c\sin\eta}{\cosh\xi - \cos\eta} \qquad z = \frac{c\sinh\xi}{\cosh\xi - \cos\eta}$$

The spheres are given by $\xi = \pm\alpha(\alpha > 0)$, the radius of either sphere is $c\,\mathrm{cosech}\,\alpha$, and the distance $2k$ between the centers of the spheres is $2c\coth\alpha$. The flow

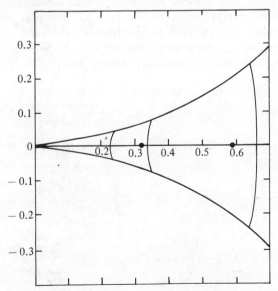

Figure 1.3.19 Meridional section of the separation stream surfaces; $\psi = 0$ when the spheres are in contact. Dots indicate points of zero velocity within the ring vortices.

region is $-\alpha < \xi < \alpha$, $0 \leqslant \eta \leqslant \pi$, $0 \leqslant \phi \leqslant 2\pi$ and the boundary conditions are equivalent to

$$\psi = \frac{\partial \psi}{\partial \xi} = 0 \qquad \xi = \pm \alpha$$

$$\psi - \frac{c^2 \sin^2 \eta}{2(\cosh \xi - \cos \eta)} \to 0 \qquad (\xi, \eta) \to 0$$

The solution for ψ satisfying the boundary conditions can be found by adding $\frac{1}{2} c^2$ $\sin^2 \eta/(\cosh \xi - \cos \eta)^2$ to the solution for ψ obtained by Stimson & Jeffery, giving

$$\psi = c^2 (\cosh \xi - \cos \eta)^{-3/2} \chi + \frac{c^2 \sin^2 \eta}{2(\cosh \xi - \cos \eta)^2}$$

where

$$\chi = \sum_{n=1}^{\infty} \bar{U}_n \bar{V}_n$$

and

$$\bar{U}_n = A_n \cosh (n - \tfrac{1}{2})\xi + C_n \cosh n + \tfrac{3}{2})\xi$$

$$\bar{V}_n = P_{n-1} (\cos \eta) - P_{n+1} (\cos \eta)$$

The coefficients A_n and C_n are given by

$$A_n = -\frac{n(n+1)}{\sqrt{2}\,(2n-1)(2n+1)} \left[\frac{2(1 - e^{-(2n+1)\alpha}) + (2n+1)(e^{2\alpha} - 1)}{2 \sinh (2n+1)\alpha + (2n+1) \sinh 2\alpha} \right]$$

For an isolated sphere in a uniform stream there is no separation of the flow from the sphere, and this is expected to be the case for flow past two widely spaced spheres. To examine the complex flow structure when the spheres are close together, consider first the behavior of the velocity at the midpoint between the spheres, i.e., $r = z = 0$. The components of velocity $(u_\xi, 0, u_\eta)$ in bispherical coordinates are

$$u_\xi = -\frac{\cosh \xi - \sigma}{c^2} \frac{\partial \psi}{\partial \sigma} \qquad u_\eta = -\frac{(\cosh \xi - \sigma)^2}{c^2(1 - \sigma^2)^{1/2}} \frac{\partial \psi}{\partial \xi}$$

where $\sigma = \cos \eta$. Now the origin $r = z = 0$ corresponds to $\xi = 0$, $\sigma = -1$, so the velocity at the origin is

$$u_\xi = w(0) = 1 - 4\left\{ \frac{\partial}{\partial \sigma} \left[(\cosh \xi - \sigma)^{-3/2} \chi \right] \right\}_{\xi=0, \sigma=-1} \qquad u_\eta = 0 = 1 - 4P(\alpha)$$

where

$$P(\alpha) = (2\sqrt{2})^{-1} \sum_{n=1}^{\infty} (-1)^n (2n+1)(A_n + c_n) = \sum_{n=1}^{\infty} \frac{(-1)^{n+1} n(n+1)}{(2n-1)(2n+3)}$$

$$\cdot \frac{2[1 - e^{-(2n+1)\alpha}] + (2n+1)^2 \sinh^2 \alpha + (2n+1) \sinh 2\alpha}{2 \sinh (2n+1)\alpha + (2n+1) \sinh 2\alpha}$$

and
$$w(0) > 1 - 8 \, \frac{2(1 - e^{-3\alpha}) + 9 \sinh^2 \alpha + 3 \sinh 2\alpha}{5(2 \sinh 3\alpha + 3 \sinh 2\alpha)}$$

Since the second term on the right vanishes as $\alpha \to \infty$, $w(0)$ remains positive for sufficiently large α and the direction of flow at the origin is the same as the stream at infinity if the spheres are sufficiently widely spaced. Examination of $w(0)$ for small α is a lengthy process and is described in Stimson & Jeffery (1926). The results will be described briefly. When $2k > 3.57$ there is no separation on either sphere. If $3.22 < 2k < 3.57$ wakes form symmetrically on both spheres and in these wakes the fluid moves in a closed eddy-type motion. For $2k < 3.22$ a cylinder of fluid links both spheres; within this cylinder the fluid rotates in one or more ring vortices, the number of vortices increasing as the distance between the spheres decreases. When the spheres are in contact, the fluid rotates in an infinite set of nested ring vortices. The types of motion are illustrated in figure 1.3.20.

1.3.7.6 Slender Body Theory

Several authors have considered the Stokes flow past a slender body of revolution, using the method of matched asymptotic expansions; see Cox (1970, 1971), Batchelor (1970), and Tillett (1970). Keller & Rubinow (1976) presented general theories for the creeping motion of long slender bodies in a viscous fluid. Geer (1976) considered a similar problem with a completely general incident Stokes flow.

1.3.7.7 Optimum Profiles in Stokes Flow

The problem of minimizing the drag at constant volume in Stokes flow has long attracted interest. In the earlier papers it was assumed that the optimum body would be axisymmetrical and smooth, but recent work disproves this. Pironneau (1973) derived the first-order optimality conditions for minimizing the drag at constant unit volume. He found that the unit-volume body with smallest drag must be such that the magnitude of the normal derivative of the velocity is constant on the boundary of the body. In a three-dimensional problem with uniform flow at infinity, the body with minimum drag has a pointed shape, being similar to a

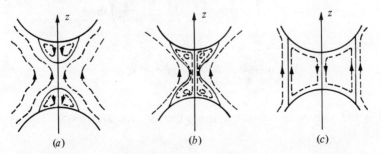

Figure 1.3.20 Flow structure in the primary wakes. (a) before coalescence, (b) immediately after coalescence, and (c) after coalescence when the two ring vortices have emerged.

prolate spheroid but with differences including conical front and rear ends of angle 120°.

1.3.7.8 Asymmetrical Flow

In the last 5 yr some progress has been made with three-dimensional Stokes flow problems. Ranger (1973) considered asymmetrical flow past a spherical cap, i.e., the flow at infinity is perpendicular to the axis of symmetry of the cap.

The Stokes equations in nondimensional form are·given by

$$\nabla p = \nabla^2 \mathbf{u} \qquad \nabla \cdot \mathbf{u} = 0$$

A representation suitable for spherical boundary conditions is

$$\mathbf{u} = \nabla \times \left(\frac{\psi}{r \sin \theta} \mathbf{r} \cos \phi \right) + \nabla \times \left(\frac{V_3}{r \sin \theta} \mathbf{r} \sin \phi \right)$$

where

$$p = \frac{1}{\sin \theta} \frac{\partial}{\partial r} L_{-1}(\psi) \cos \phi$$

ψ and V_3 satisfy

$$L_{-1}^2(\psi) = 0 \qquad L_{-1}(V_3) = 0$$

and the Stokes operator is defined in spherical polar coordinates (R, θ, ϕ) by

$$L_{-1} \equiv \frac{\partial^2}{\partial R^2} + \frac{\sin \theta}{R^2} \frac{\partial}{\partial \theta} \frac{1}{\sin \theta} \frac{\partial}{\partial \theta}$$

The components of fluid velocity are

$$u_r = -\frac{1}{R^2} \frac{\partial}{\partial \theta} \left(\frac{1}{\sin \theta} \frac{\partial \psi}{\partial \theta} \right) \cos \phi$$

$$u_\theta = \left[\frac{1}{R} \frac{\partial}{\partial \theta} \left(\frac{1}{\sin \theta} \frac{\partial \psi}{\partial R} \right) + \frac{V_3}{R \sin^2 \theta} \right] \cos \phi$$

$$u_\phi = -\left(\frac{1}{R \sin^2 \theta} \frac{\partial \psi}{\partial R} + \frac{1}{R} \frac{\partial}{\partial \theta} \frac{V_3}{\sin \theta} \right) \sin \phi$$

The boundary conditions are

$$\mathbf{u} = 0 \qquad R = 1 \qquad 0 \leqslant \theta \leqslant \alpha$$

$$\mathbf{u} \sim \mathbf{i} \qquad R \to \infty$$

where $\mathbf{i}$ is the unit vector directed along the axis $\theta = \pi/2$, $\phi = 0$. An appropriate form for ψ is

$$\psi = \frac{1}{2} R^2 \sin^2 \theta - V_1 + (R^2 - 1) \left(\frac{R}{2} \frac{\partial V_1}{\partial R} - V_2 \right)$$

where V_j, $j = 1$, 2, 3, satisfy $L_{-1}(V_3) = 0$. The outer boundary condition is satisfied if $V_j = O(1)$ as $R \to \infty$. Appropriate integral representations for $V_j(R, \theta)$ are

$$V_j(R, \theta) = R^{1/2} \int_0^\theta \frac{v_j(R, \lambda) \sin \lambda \, d\lambda}{(\cos \lambda - \cos \theta)^{1/2}} + A^j_{-1} + A^j_0 R(1 - \cos \theta)$$

$$= - R^{1/2} \int_\theta^\pi \frac{u_j(R, \lambda) \sin \lambda \, d\lambda}{(\cos \theta - \cos \lambda)^{1/2}} + A^j_{-1} + A^j_0 R(1 - \cos \theta)$$

for $R < 1$ and

$$V_j(R, \theta) = R^{1/2} \int_0^\theta \frac{v_j(1/R, \lambda) \sin \lambda \, d\lambda}{(\cos \lambda - \cos \theta)^{1/2}} + (A^j_{-1} + A^j_0 R)(1 - \cos \theta)$$

$$= - R^{1/2} \int_\theta^\pi \frac{u_j(1/R, \lambda) \sin \lambda \, d\lambda}{(\cos \theta - \cos \lambda)^{1/2}} + A^j_{-1} + A^j_0 R(1 - \cos \theta)$$

for $R > 1$, $j = 1$, 2, 3. The u_j, v_j are conjugate two-dimensional harmonics even and odd in λ, respectively, with $v_j(R, 0) = u_j(R, \pi) = 0$ and expressible in the form

$$u_j + iv_j = \frac{2^{3/2}}{\pi} \sum_{n=1}^\infty A^j_n (Re^{i\lambda})^{n+1/2}$$

where the A^j_n, $j = 1$, 2, 3, are real. In fact, u_j, v_j map into

$$V_j(R, \theta) = (A^j_{-1} + A^j_0 R)(1 - \cos \theta) + \sum_{n=1}^\infty A^j_n R^{n+1} [P_{n-1}(\cos \theta) - P_{n+1}(\cos \theta)]$$

For the velocity to be finite at the origin and behave like a uniform stream at infinity, it is found that if $A^1_0 = h$, where h is a constant to be determined, then

$$A^3_{-1} = h \qquad A^2_{-1} = 0 \qquad A^1_{-1} = 0$$

$$A^3_0 = 0 \qquad A^2_0 = \tfrac{1}{2} h$$

The boundary condition on the cap for the radial component is $u_R = 0$ at $R = 1$, $0 \leqslant \theta \leqslant \alpha$, or equivalently

$$V_1(1, \theta) = \frac{1}{2} \sin \theta + A(1 - \cos \theta) = \int_0^\theta \frac{v_1(1, \lambda) \sin \lambda \, d\lambda}{(\cos \lambda - \cos \theta)^{1/2}}$$

for $0 \leqslant \theta \leqslant \alpha$, and A is an arbitrary constant. The inverse of the Abel-type integral equation for $v_1(1, \lambda)$ is

$$v_1(1, \lambda) = \frac{2^{3/2}}{3\pi} \sin \frac{3}{2}\lambda + \frac{2^{3/2}}{\pi} A \sin \frac{1}{2}\lambda \qquad 0 \leqslant \lambda \leqslant \alpha$$

Velocity components u_θ, u_ϕ vanish on the cap if

$$\frac{\partial}{\partial\theta}\left(\frac{2\,V_2^1}{\sin\theta}\right) + \frac{V_3}{\sin^2\theta} = 0 \qquad \frac{2V_2^1}{\sin^2\theta} + \frac{\partial}{\partial\theta}\left(\frac{V_3}{\sin\theta}\right) = 0$$

at $R = 1$, $0 \leqslant \theta \leqslant \alpha$, and $V_2^1(1, \theta) = \frac{1}{2}\sin^2\theta - V_2(1, \theta)$. These equations are equivalent to

$$V_2(1, \theta) = \frac{1}{2}\sin^2\theta + \frac{b}{2}(1 - \cos\theta)$$

$$V_3(1, \theta) = b(1 - \cos\theta)$$

for $0 \leqslant \theta \leqslant \alpha$ and b an arbitrary constant. Thus on the cap

$$\frac{1}{2}\sin^2\theta + \frac{b}{2}(1 - \cos\theta) = \int_0^\theta \frac{v_2(1, \lambda)\sin\lambda\,d\lambda}{(\cos\lambda - \cos\theta)^{1/2}}$$

$$b(1 - \cos\theta) = \int_0^\theta \frac{v_3(1, \lambda)\sin\lambda\,d\lambda}{(\cos\lambda - \cos\theta)^{1/2}}$$

for $0 \leqslant \theta \leqslant \alpha$. The inverses of the Abel-type integral equations are

$$v_2(1, \lambda) = 2^{3/2}\sin\frac{1}{2}\lambda + \frac{2^{1/2}b}{\pi}\sin\frac{1}{2}\lambda$$

$$v_3(1, \lambda) = \frac{2^{3/2}}{\pi}b\sin\frac{1}{2}\lambda$$

for $0 \leqslant \lambda \leqslant \alpha$. The boundary conditions off the cap require ψ, $\partial\psi/\partial R$, $\partial^2\psi/\partial R^2$, $\partial^3\psi/\partial R^3$ to be continuous on $R = 1$, $\alpha < \theta \leqslant \pi$. The first two conditions are satisfied automatically by the use of Kelvin's inversion theorem in defining V_j. The third and fourth conditions are satisfied if

$$v_1(1, \lambda) = C + D\cos\lambda$$

$$v_2(1, \lambda) = B + \tfrac{3}{4}D\cos\lambda$$

for $\alpha < \lambda \leqslant \pi$ and B, C, and D constants. In addition, the boundary condition for V_3 off the cap is that $\partial V_3/\partial R$ be continuous at $R = 1$, $\alpha < \theta \leqslant \pi$. This results in

$$v_3(1, \lambda) = F = \text{const} \qquad \alpha < \lambda \leqslant \pi$$

The constants are determined from the condition that the velocity tends to zero at the rim of the cap, together with the Fourier series requirement

$$\int_0^\pi v_j(1, \lambda)\sin\frac{\lambda}{2}\,d\lambda = 2^{1/2}(A_{-1}^j + A_0^j)$$

for $j = 1, 2, 3$. From these conditions the constants can be determined uniquely and the A_n^j, $j = 1, 2, 3$, can be found. These will not be written explicitly. For some simplification of the results refer to Dorrepaal (1976), who also simplified Ranger's expression for the drag and torque on the cap. Dorrepaal found that the drag on the cap is

$$F = \mu \bar{U}_\infty a \left[6(\alpha + \sin \alpha) - \frac{8}{3} \frac{\sin^2 \alpha \cos^4 \frac{1}{2} \alpha}{\alpha + \sin \alpha} \right]$$

The case $\alpha = \pi$ corresponds to the sphere, giving the well-known result $F = 6\pi\mu\bar{U}_\alpha a$. The limiting situation $\alpha \to 0$, $\alpha a \to c$, gives the result for the drag on a disk edgewise to the flow, namely $F = \frac{32}{3} \mu\bar{U}_\infty c$, where c is the disk radius.

The torque on the cap about the y axis is

$$T = \mu\bar{U}_\infty a^2 \left(8 \sin \alpha \cos^2 \frac{\alpha}{2} + \frac{16}{3} \frac{\sin^2 \alpha \cos^4 \frac{1}{2} \alpha}{\alpha + \sin \alpha} \right)$$

Takagi (1974) reproduced the results of Ranger and of Dorrepaal and the expressions for the drag and torque agree. Takagi used the dual series equations approach developed by Collins for the axisymmetrical problem. He also considered the case of a cap in steady rotation about the line perpendicular to the axis of the cap.

Dorrepaal (1978) applied Brenner's general results for the force and torque experienced by an arbitrary particle simultaneously translating and rotating in a linear shear flow to the case where the particle is a spherical cap. The cap's five fundamental resistance tensors are determined and the corresponding tensors for the sphere and circular disk are recovered as special cases. The problem of a freely moving cap in a linear shear is considered and the resulting translational and rotational motions are analyzed. The cap's center of free rotation is found and trajectories of this point are plotted in a few instances. The cap is also found to possess a "point of planar motion," which always moves in a plane perpendicular to the vorticity vector of the undisturbed shear regardless of the initial orientation of the cap. It is shown that the motion of the cap serves as a model for the motions of all "oblate" asymmetrical bodies of revolution that are freely moving in a linear shear.

Finally, Tokuda (1975) examined three-dimensional viscous flow near a corner formed by the intersection of two quarter-infinite flat plates at various angles, by constructing Stokes flow solutions. Specifically, flows for intersection angles π, $3\pi/2$, and 2π correspond to flows past a semi-infinite flat plate, an external flow past a right-angle corner, and a quarter-infinite flat plate, respectively. On the basis of the Stokes solutions, various types of singularities arising in the flow field are identified over the complete range of intersection $[0, 2\pi]$.

Taylor (1969) considered the resistance to the slow motion of a long axisymmetrical body in a viscous fluid. He found the force on the body to be twice as great for motion perpendicular to the axis as for motion along it.

1.3.8 TURBULENT FLUID-PARTICLE INTERACTION

Richard L. Peskin

1.3.8.1 Role of Turbulence in Fluid–Particle Mixture Motion

Most fluid-particle motions encountered in practice are characterized by a fluid Reynolds number sufficiently high to indicate that the flow is turbulent. The same is true for a large number of other fluid multiphase systems that are found in nature or in engineering practice. In fact, for multiphase systems where the particulate phase is more dense than the fluid supporting medium, steady horizontal motion such as that occurring in pneumatic transport (see section 1.7.) would be impossible without the presence of fluid turbulence. The presence of fluctuating velocity components directed opposite to gravity provides the energy necessary to keep the particulate phase in suspension. A fundamental first step in designing a pneumatic conveying or other fluid solid system for horizontal transport is to estimate the turbulent kinetic energy per unit volume contained in the vertical components of fluid motion and to compare this with the kinetic energy per unit volume of the particulate phase at terminal settling velocity. For suspension, the fluid energy must exceed the particulate phase (terminal velocity) kinetic energy. While this may not be a sufficient condition for suspension, it is a necessary condition (Soo 1956).

This section describes the physical nature of turbulent flow and concentrates on the aspects of the distribution of turbulent energy in a fluid that are most significant in characterizing the turbulence of fluid-particle motion. Emphasis is placed on single-particle motion and its interaction with the turbulent fluid medium. This limitation allows examination of the aspects of the fluid turbulent energy spectrum that are most important in modifying the particle motion, and also of situations where the particle motion can alter some aspects of the structure of the turbulence in the fluid. Not considered are situations where extreme dense packing of solids can result in a major modification of the turbulent energy spectrum in the fluid.

One of the most important features of turbulent flow is its ability to disperse contaminants or other tracers. Thus one of the most important aspects of fluid mechanical interaction in turbulence is the dispersion or separation of the particles, and it is necessary to examine the aspects of turbulent motion that are most important in effecting such dispersion.

Fluid-particle interaction in turbulence can be classified into single- and multiple-particle study, and in each of these classifications cases can be considered where particle inertia is either negligible or significant. Although it is obvious that neglecting particle inertia amounts to studying turbulent motion by following fluid points, what is not obvious is that the importance of inertia may depend on particular coordinate directions in the flow system. For example, in studying the dispersion of solid pollutants in the atmosphere, particulate inertia is generally unimportant in the horizontal direction but of considerable significance in the vertical direction.

This section begins with a review of fundamental aspects of turbulent fluid motion and then considers single-particle motion in turbulence. Following that, boundary-layer flow where particle motion can have an effect on the turbulent structure is considered. Next, two-particle or relative separation in turbulence is considered. Finally, methods of dealing with these complex problems in actual application are discussed, including a discussion of numerical simulation techniques.

1.3.8.2 Some Fundamental Aspects of Turbulent Fluid Motion

In many circumstances of practical interest, turbulent fluid-particle interaction is passive in the sense that the behavior of the contaminant particle is very similar to that of a "fluid particle," i.e., a point tracer in the fluid flow field. This occurs under circumstances where the particle (in this section taken to mean a contaminant particle, i.e., an element in the flow field that is not a mere tracer of the motion of the fluid) is able to respond to the dynamics of the surrounding flow field in a time that is very small compared to times of interest in the overall flow field. An example might be the dispersion by turbulent motion of small, near neutrally buoyant, particles in the atmosphere. If such particles have diameters less than 50 μm they can respond to changes in flow field velocity in fractions of a second; while for determining the spread of such particles by atmospheric turbulence, times of the order of many minutes or hours or more are of interest. In this case, the fluid-particle interaction is for all practical purposes passive. Particles follow the fluid motion and their dispersion is determined primarily by the dynamics of the flow field. Thus it suffices for this type of problem to understand the fundamental dynamics of the turbulent flow field, at least as they apply to dispersion, to gain an understanding of the effect of that motion on the particles contained therein. In addition to this area of application, one must be interested in turbulent motion to understand more complex fluid-particle interactions—i.e., interactions where the particles have significant inertial properties. Even in those cases, although the particles no longer merely follow the fluid motion, their interaction with the fluid flow field is dynamically passive in most situations of practical interest.

A completely comprehensive and unambiguous definition of turbulent flow is probably not possible. In this section turbulent flow is taken to mean a viscous fluid flow occurring at high Reynolds numbers such that an ensemble of a large number of different velocity fields, each of which satisfies the boundary conditions, is an admissible solution to the governing Navier-Stokes equations. Furthermore, it is presumed that this ensemble of flow fields forms a collection that has a probability distribution. In other words, each velocity $u(x, t; \omega)$ is such that for a given value of ω there is a probability of occurrence of the aforementioned velocity field. For practical purposes, interest is directed to the various statistical measures of the velocity field rather than the attempt to describe all the individual solutions. Thus the various moments that, taken together, would completely characterize the probability distribution are the quantities of prime interest (Batchelor 1952).

Of most interest is the second moment with space and/or time lag, namely the space-time correlation of the velocity field

$$R_{ij}(\mathbf{x}, \mathbf{r}, t, \tau) = \overline{u_i(\mathbf{x}, t)u_j(\mathbf{x} + \mathbf{r}, t + \tau)} \qquad [1.3.233]$$

where $\mathbf{x}$ is a spatial position vector; $\mathbf{r}$ is a spatial displacement vector; t is time; τ is a time increment variable; and u_i and u_j are the fluctuating Eulerian velocities at points i and j, respectively.

For zero time lag, the Fourier transform of [1.3.233] is given by

$$E_{ij}(\mathbf{k}, t) = \frac{1}{8\pi^3} \iiint R_{ij} \exp{(i\,\mathbf{k}\cdot\mathbf{x})}\,d\mathbf{x} \qquad [1.3.234]$$

where $\mathbf{k}$ is the wave number vector. For isotropic velocity fields the following relation holds between the kinetic energy of the velocity field and the above transform:

$$\frac{3}{2}\bar{u}^2 = \int_0^\infty E(k, t)\,dk$$

$$[1.3.235]$$

$$E(k, t) = 2\pi k^2 E_{ij}(k, t)$$

The quantity $E(k)$ is called the spectral energy distribution or energy spectrum. Attempts to determine the energy spectrum for all values of its wave number argument are a fundamental objective of turbulence theory (Monin & Yaglom 1971).

Detailed predictions of the energy spectrum are not yet possible for more than a very few classes of idealized flows. Nevertheless, to make practical headway, it is necessary to evolve a heuristic physical picture of turbulent flow and attempt to deal with that picture by invoking scale analysis. In this section turbulence is assumed to be three-dimensional. At high enough Reynolds numbers, the statistical features of the fluctuating velocity field are characterized over the large majority of motions scales in a manner that is essentially independent of specific features of the largest of the motion scales, namely those defining the boundaries of the field and/or perhaps the scales that feed energy into the field (Kolmogorov 1941).

The smallest wave numbers or largest "eddies" are of a semipermanent nature. At their largest extreme, they are characterized by overall conditions that bound the field. The largest eddies include the length scales that are of dominant importance in the calculation of diffusion of single points in a turbulent field. Most of the turbulent energy in the spectrum is contained in the so-called energy-containing eddies. For wave numbers sufficiently above that characteristic of the peak of the spectrum, there exists the range first described by Kolmogorov, namely the universal equilibrium range. This part of the turbulent spectrum is characterized by the

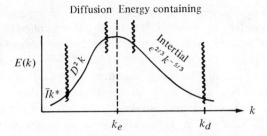

Figure 1.3.21 Schematic illustration of the energy spectrum.

overall rate of energy transfer, the viscosity, and the local wave number, and its form tends to be independent of the structure of the largest eddies in the flow field. Indicated in figure 1.3.21 is the approximate functional dependence of the spectrum on wave number. The characteristic dimensional parameters for each portion of the spectrum are:

$$\bar{I} \equiv -\frac{1}{6\pi} \int_0^\infty r^4 R_{ij}i(r,\, t)\, dr \qquad \left[\frac{L^7}{T^2}\right] \qquad [1.3.236a]$$

$$D \sim \int_k^\infty \frac{E(k,\, t)}{k^3}^{1/2} dk \qquad \left[\frac{L^2}{T}\right] \qquad [1.3.236b]$$

$$\epsilon = 2\nu \int_0^\infty k^2\, E(k,\, t)\, dk \sim (\bar{u}^2)^{3/2}\, k_e \qquad \left[\frac{L^2}{T^3}\right] \qquad [1.3.236c]$$

$$k_d \equiv \left(\frac{\epsilon}{\nu^3}\right)^{1/4} \qquad \left[\frac{1}{L}\right] \qquad [1.3.236d]$$

where D is diffusivity, ϵ is dissipation, ν is kinematic viscosity, and k_e and k_d are energy containing wave number and the dissipation wave number, respectively. Of particular interest in particle-fluid interaction is the comparison of scale lengths in each region of the spectrum in relation to some appropriately determined impulse response length for a particle. When particle inertia can be neglected, the diffusion, energy-containing, and inertial subranges of the spectrum are of most interest.

While the spectrum in figure 1.3.21 is useful for describing the energy processes in an idealized turbulent flow, its applicability to the prediction of diffusion of particles in turbulence is restricted to isotropic or homogeneous flows or the isotropic portion of turbulent flows, namely the smaller-scale characteristics of the flow (Hinze 1975). Most practical flows of interest involve at least violation of isotropy through the introduction of shear and, in most situations, nonhomogeneities as a result of shear flow variation. Turbulent energy spectra for such flows are significantly more complicated and must include the features representative of the interaction of fluctuations with the mean shear, an interaction that gives rise to spectral energy transfer. In view of the increasing complication of the spectral picture, one might look to other means of characterizing turbulent motion from a particle trajectory point of view. For many types of flow encountered in engineering practice, examination of the energy equation in physical rather than wave space yields useful information about some of the parameters that control the overall features of energy transport in the turbulent field. An approach based on physical reasoning and scale analysis is extremely useful in characterizing the relation between the mean shear gradients and the energy transport rate; it can also introduce important information about the diffusive aspect of the turbulent field as well as some information about smaller-scale features of the field.

Discussion is limited here to simpler forms of turbulent shear flows in the steady state. When the velocity field can be characterized by a single length scale, one can express the turbulent shear stress τ as

$$\tau_{xy} = -\rho \overline{u_x u_y} \tag{1.3.237}$$

where ρ is the density and x and y are spatial coordinates. The ratio of the characteristic turbulent velocity to the characteristic eddy length scale, which is a measure of characteristic vorticity, must be proportional to the mean shear (Tennekes & Lumley 1972):

$$\frac{u_y'}{l} \sim \frac{\partial U_x}{\partial y} \tag{1.3.238}$$

where u_y' is a characteristic fluctuating velocity in the y direction, l is the length scale of the energy-containing eddies, and U_x is the mean velocity in the x direction. By substitution, the shear stress then can be related to the mean gradient in the following manner:

$$\tau_{xy} = ab\rho u_y' l \frac{\partial U_x}{\partial y} \equiv \rho D \frac{\partial U_x}{\partial y} \tag{1.3.239}$$

where a and b are constants of order 1. Equation [1.3.239] is the eddy viscosity model. It has nothing to do with eddy viscosities and, in fact, is not related to the mixing length concept, but is strictly a consequence of scale analysis. Its usefulness is broad but limited to flows with a single length and velocity characteristic. These include important engineering flows such as flows with mean shear, jets, wakes, and so forth. It should be noted that the relation between characteristic vorticity and mean shear can be used to predict one form of the logarithmic profile in the vicinity of the constant stress layer (the layer close to the wall in most turbulent boundary layers). This is done by substituting distance from the wall for characteristic length and integrating to yield

$$\frac{U_x}{u_*} = \frac{1}{k} \ln y + \text{const} \tag{1.3.240}$$

with
$$l = a_2 y \qquad u_*^2 = \frac{\tau_{xy}(0)}{\rho}$$

where a_2 is another constant and $\tau_{xy}(0)$ is the shear stress at the wall. The characteristic length l is also related to the mean square displacement of a point moving in the turbulent fluid or of a particle in the fluid with no inertial or other external field properties. This relation is

$$\frac{1}{2}\frac{d}{dt}\,\bar{X}^2(t) = u\,'l \sim D$$

$$u'l = \int_0^\infty \overline{v(t)v(t+\tau)}\,d\tau \qquad [1.3.241]$$

$$\frac{d}{dt}\,X = v(t)$$

where $\bar{X}^2$ is the mean square displacement and v is the velocity following a point. Equation [1.3.241] is a basic relation in determining the diffusive behavior for points in the fluid (or particles that have no interaction with the fluid other than being tracers of the fluid motion).

In some applications of particulate diffusion in turbulence, it is necessary to estimate certain parameters controlling various regions in the turbulent energy spectrum. The length scale above is related to the eddy diffusion portion of the spectrum and for many applications can be used as an estimate of the energy-containing eddies. An examination of the turbulent energy yields the following relations between the production of fluctuating energy and its dissipation.

$$P \equiv \text{production} \sim -\overline{u_i u_j}\,S_{ij}$$

$$\epsilon \equiv \text{dissipation} \sim 2\nu\,\overline{S_{ij}S_{ij}} \qquad [1.3.242]$$

$$P = \epsilon$$

where S_{ij} is the mean stress rate. This production-dissipation balance can then be used with scaling relations to obtain the following estimation for the energy dissipation:

$$\epsilon \sim \frac{(\bar{u}^2)^{3/2}}{l} \qquad [1.3.243]$$

The characteristic length and velocities for the higher wave number portion of the spectrum where dissipation begins to exert control are obtained from the characteristic (Kolmogorov) length and velocity:

$$l_d \equiv \frac{1}{k_d} = \left(\frac{\nu^3}{\epsilon}\right)^{1/4} \qquad [1.3.244]$$

$$v_d \equiv (\nu\epsilon)^{1/4}$$

In effect, the critical parameters for estimating the characteristic features of isothermal turbulence are (1) the turbulent kinetic energy, which can be measured; (2) the characteristic length scales for the energy-containing eddies, which can be inferred from the geometry or other features of the flow or estimated as the Eulerian length scale defined by

$$l \sim \int_0^\infty \frac{R_{11}(r, t)\, dr}{R_{11}(0, t)} \qquad [1.3.245]$$

(3) the energy dissipation rate; and (4) the kinematic viscosity.

The discussion above applies to turbulence characterized primarily by a single length scale and a single velocity scale, and thus excludes many important areas such as atmospheric turbulence, where buoyant forces introduce additional controlling scale parameters. However, it does apply to a wide category of engineering-type flows.

1.3.8.3 Single-Particle Dispersion in Turbulent Motion

Where the inertia of the particulate phase can be neglected, one can infer particle diffusion from kinematic considerations. As previously mentioned, practical applicability need not depend entirely on neglecting the inertial aspects of the interaction. For example, for three-dimensional motion in a gravity field, the inertial features are unimportant in the horizontal plane but they do determine the particulate motion in the vertical direction (section 1.3.8.7). The most direct route to studying particulate motion under the assumption that inertia can be neglected is through the Lagrangian description, i.e., a description following the particle (Taylor 1921). Assuming that the particle's position is a function only of time and its initial position (which is suppressed in this discussion), one has the following relation between the derivative of position and velocity:

$$\frac{d}{dt} X(t) = v(t)$$

Multiplication of both sides of this equation by the position function and integration yields the expression relating the mean square particle displacement to the autocorrelation (assumed to be statistically stationary) of the particulate velocity:

$$\frac{1}{2} \frac{\overline{dX^2(t)}}{dt} = \int_0^t \overline{v(t)v(t + \tau)}\, d\tau = \bar{v}^2 \int_0^t R_L(\tau)d\tau \equiv D_L \qquad [1.3.246]$$

where R_L is the Lagrangian correlation, v is the Lagrangian velocity, and D_L is the Lagrangian diffusivity. Remember that the autocorrelation in [1.3.246] is the autocorrelation of the velocity following the particle. This quantity is normally not easily measurable, nor is it inferred from correlations usually measured in the turbulent flow field, namely the (Eulerian) velocity correlation. The applicability of the previous result depends entirely on the ability to specialize the form of the correlation.

The first application to be considered is that of diffusion in homogeneous isotropic turbulent flow. When the particle inertia can be totally neglected, and if one assumes that the Lagrangian correlation has a finite integral scale, [1.3.246] can be integrated to obtain the relation between mean square particle displacement and the integral scale.

$$\int_0^t R_L(\tau)\, d\tau \ \sim \bar{v}^2 T_L t \qquad [1.3.247]$$

$$D_p = \bar{v}^2 T_L = (\bar{v}^2)^{1/2} l_L$$

where T_L is the Lagrangian time scale, D_p is the particle diffusivity, and l_L is the Lagrangian length scale. This length scale has been related to the more easily obtainable Eulerian length scale empirically and by use of an analytic model that relates the Lagrangian correlation to the Eulerian correlation (Corrsin 1959). The analytic model indicates that the relation between the Lagrangian and Eulerian scales depends on the intensity of turbulence. Using this model, Philip (1967) obtained the following relation between the scales:

$$\frac{T_L}{T_U} = \left(1 + \frac{\alpha^2}{I^2}\right)^{1/2} F(\alpha)$$

$$T_U = \int_0^\infty R_{11}(-Ut, 0, t)\, dt \qquad [1.3.248]$$

$$\alpha = \frac{(\bar{u}^2)^{1/2}}{l}\,(T_u)|_{u=0}$$

$$I = \frac{(\bar{u}^2)^{1/2}}{U}$$

$$F(\alpha) = \text{universal function}$$

These results can be used to obtain diffusivity and provide the means of supplying the diffusivity parameter for the concentration partial differential equation (Csanady 1972).

The kinematic results in the previous section can be extended to nonisotropic homogeneous flows in the case where there is uniform shear by introducing a pseudo-Lagrangian velocity in the downstream direction (Corrsin 1959). Integration then proceeds as in the isotropic case, but the computations are somewhat more involved. The following expressions are obtained for the diffusivity in the downstream $D_{p\,11}$ and cross-stream $D_{p\,12}$ directions (Monin & Yaglom 1971):

$$D_{p11} = \frac{2}{3}\left(\frac{\partial U_x}{\partial y}\right)^2 \bar{u}^2 T_L t^3$$

$$\qquad [1.3.249]$$

$$D_{p12} = \frac{\partial U_x}{\partial y}\,\bar{u}^2 T_L t^2$$

The results show that the presence of the shear dominates the diffusional behavior in the downstream direction. Riley & Corrsin (1974) obtained the Eulerian concentration equation diffusion tensor from the appropriate Lagrangian correlation tensor in the presence of the shear. Their results show that the appropriate Eulerian tensor is not symmetric.

Another practical problem that can be considered with the kinematic-type analysis is that of longitudinal dispersion in channel flow. In this case, the difference between the fluid point position and initial position is given by

$$X_1(\mathbf{a},\, t) - a_1 = \int_0^t [U_x(Y) + v_1(t')]\, dt' \qquad [1.3.250]$$

where $\mathbf{a}$ is the initial position vector and a is the x component of $\mathbf{a}$. The mean square displacement is given by the following expression, which is similar in form to that for the isotropic case:

$$\overline{(X_1 - \bar{X}_1)^2} = 2\bar{v}_1^2 t\, T_L \qquad [1.3.251]$$

This result depends on the fact that lateral displacement inside a channel is stationary because the particles are confined to the boundaries of the system. The appropriate velocity variance in [1.3.251] is that for channel flow:

$$\bar{v}_1^2 = \frac{1}{2h} \int_{-h}^{h} [\bar{u}_1^2 + (U_x - U_b)^2]\, dy \qquad [1.3.252]$$

where the velocity defect law is employed:

$$\frac{U_x - U_b}{u_*} = F(\tilde{\eta}) \qquad \frac{\bar{u}_1^2}{u_*^2} = g(\tilde{\eta})$$

to obtain the Lagrangian variance. One obtains for the downstream dispersion

$$\overline{(X_1 - \bar{X}_1)^2} = cu_* h t \qquad [1.3.253]$$

The scale factor c has been shown to be approximately 10.

1.3.8.4   Nonstationary Flows

Nonstationary flows for which the solution of the diffusion problem is possible are now considered. These are the self-preserving flows such as decay behind a grid in a wind tunnel and in downstream regions of jets, wakes, and mixing layers. Analysis of these flows from the point of view of turbulent diffusion has been considered by Batchelor (1957) and Monin & Yaglom (1971). The basic assumption is that the same transformation of variables that allows the Eulerian characteristics to be reduced to dimensionless form independent of downstream position can be used for the Lagrangian information. That is, it is assumed that there exists a variable velocity scale and time scale:

$$U_1(\tau) = U_1[X_1(x, t_0 + \tau)]$$

$$T(\tau) = \frac{\hat{L}(X_1)}{U_1(\tau)} \qquad [1.3.254]$$

where $\hat{L}$ is a characteristic length scale. Motion of the particle is measured in terms of the time scale by introducing a new time variable η

$$d\eta = \frac{d\tau}{T(\tau)} \qquad [1.3.255]$$

The Lagrangian fluctuation velocity is assumed to be a stationary random function of the new variable as follows:

$$\frac{V(x, t_0 + \tau)}{U_1(\tau)} = F(\eta) \qquad [1.3.256]$$

Introducing the new variables into the general expression for mean square displacement:

$$\overline{X_i X_j} = \int_{t_0}^{t_0 + \tau} \int_{t_0}^{t_0 + \tau} \overline{V_i(x, t_1) V_j(x, t_2)} \, dt_1 \, dt_2 \qquad [1.3.257]$$

one can obtain appropriate forms for the mean square displacement function. For example, in the flow behind the grid in a wind tunnel, the velocity and length scales are

$$F(\eta) \sim (x_1 - x_0)^{-1/2}$$

$$\hat{L} \sim (x_1 - x_0)^{1/2} \qquad [1.3.258]$$

The scaling assumptions above imply that the Lagrangian velocity correlation has the form

$$\overline{V_i V_j} = U_0^2 \tau_0 (\tau_1 \tau_2)^{-1/2} \hat{S}_{ij} \left(\ln \frac{\tau_1}{\tau_0} - \ln \frac{\tau_2}{\tau_0} \right)$$

$$\hat{S}_{ij} \equiv \overline{F_i F_j} \qquad [1.3.259]$$

and one finds the following expression for the mean square displacement. For sufficiently large times, the mean square displacement is again proportional to time, as in the homogeneous case:

$$\overline{X_i X_j} = 2U_0^2 \tau_0 \, \Theta_{ij} \tau$$

$$\Theta_{ij} = \frac{1}{2} \int_0^\infty [\hat{S}_{ij}(\theta) + \hat{S}_{ji}(\theta)] \, e^{-\theta/2} \, d\theta \qquad [1.3.260]$$

Similar analysis for the wake yields the mean square displacement for the long time limit:

$$\overline{X_i X_j} \sim \begin{cases} \tau^{2/3} & \text{three dimensions} \\ \tau & \text{two dimensions} \end{cases} \quad [1.3.261]$$

and for the jet:

$$\overline{X_i X_j} \sim \begin{cases} \tau & \text{three dimensions} \\ \tau^{4/3} & \text{two dimensions} \end{cases} \quad [1.3.262]$$

These results have been applied to two- and three-dimensional convective jets over heated bodies and the mixing layer between two plane parallel turbulent flows:

$$\overline{X_i X_j} \sim \begin{cases} \tau^2 & \text{two dimensions} \\ \tau^{3/2} & \text{three dimensions} \end{cases} \quad [1.3.263]$$

These results for nonstationary flows are extremely useful. However, caution must be employed in applying them to diffusion of particulates in turbulent flows. The results are for fluid points with no inertia. A condition that allows particulate inertia to be ignored in larger-scale stationary flows, such as certain types of atmospheric flows, may not be applicable for these evolving flows. First, the length scale and time scale of such evolving flows are generally more commensurate with important particulate phase scales such as the relaxation time. In addition, the form employed above implies self-similarity at some distance from inlet conditions, i.e., the flow has relaxed with self-similar conditions. When particles are present in the flow, even if their inertia can be neglected after the flow has fully evolved, the length scale downstream to achieve self-similarity for the particulate phase need not be the same as that to achieve self-similarity for the fluid phase.

1.3.8.5 Contaminant Dispersion from the Continuum Point of View

The mean square displacements as a function of time, or alternatively the diffusivities computed from the Lagrangian framework, can be incorporated into the concentration equation normally associated with the Eulerian description of concentration dispersion. For the homogeneous flow, the relation between the diffusivity tensor and the Lagrangian mean square displacement can be seen from the relation,

$$K_{ij} \equiv \frac{1}{2} \frac{d}{dt} \overline{X_i X_j} = \frac{1}{2} \int_0^t [R_{Lij}(\tau) + R_{Lji}(\tau)] \, dt \quad [1.3.264]$$

$$\frac{d}{dt} c = K_{ij}(t) \frac{\partial^2 c}{\partial x_i \partial x_j} \quad [1.3.265]$$

where c is concentration and K_{ij} is the diffusion tensor.

When one considers complications such as the presence of shear, the relation becomes considerably more involved. Riley & Corrsin (1974) treated the problem of deriving an Eulerian framework concentration equation from Lagrangian information for particles in a uniform shear flow. Of particular interest is the fact that the diffusivity tensor is not symmetrical, even though the associated Lagrangian information is. The Riley & Corrsin model was employed by Hwang et al. (1979) to provide more accurate models of dispersion phenomena in ground- and low-level atmospheric releases.

When one applies the turbulent diffusion models to contaminants subject to molecular action, it becomes necessary in certain cases to consider the interaction between these molecular processes and the purely dynamical aspects of turbulent diffusion as indicated above. In effect, the straining motion of the turbulence enhances the molecular diffusion. However, this effect is of small significance if the points under consideration are not subject to molecular action, which is the usual situation when one is applying the turbulent diffusion equations to the motion of a particulate phase neglecting inertia. Also, for sufficiently small particles Brownian motion may be important; in most cases Brownian diffusivity can be treated as an additive effect.

1.3.8.6 Effect of Free-Fall Fields on Particle Diffusion

To this point it has been presumed that the particulate diffusion follows that of a fluid. It is now necessary to introduce the first effect that would arise from the particle inertia, namely the effect of free fall such as would occur in a uniform gravity field. In applications such as pollutant fallout from atmospheric flow or fallout from horizontal gas-solid transport, one of the most direct approaches to considering the inertial effect is to endow the particle with a free-fall velocity in one direction (the vertical direction) while allowing it to follow fluid point motions in the horizontal plane. The first approximation ignores the characteristic response time of the particle under acceleration, but recognizes that because of the particle's independent motion, namely free-fall velocity, it can encounter a different structure of turbulent field than it would if it followed the fluid points exactly. This is the crossing trajectory effect (Csanady 1963). The problem has also been considered by Yudine (1959), and by Meek & Jones (1973). Meek & Jones modified the usual turbulent Lagrangian analysis by considering a free-fall velocity component and its effect on the reduction in correlation. In other words, rather than the particle's being confined to single eddy regions in the fluid, the free fall allows it to sample various and presumably less correlated regions of fluid in the vertical direction. Particle inertia was considered by incorporating the particle response function into the specification of the Lagrangian energy spectrum. (As will be shown in the next section, incorporation of such a response function has no effect on the asymptotic diffusivity if the particle is constrained to sample the full spectrum of available turbulent fluctuation.) The particle energy spectrum was appropriately modified to account for the crossing trajectory effect in free fall and the following results were obtained for the mean square diffusivity primarily as a function of the fluid Lagrangian integral time scale:

$$\bar{X}_{p11}^2 = \frac{\bar{v}_p^2 \tau T_p}{11 - \xi} [1 - e^{-\tau/T_p} - \xi^2 (1 - e^{-\tau/\xi T_p})] \qquad [1.3.266]$$

$$\frac{v_p^2}{\bar{u}^2} = \frac{1}{1 + \xi}$$

where

$$T_p = \frac{T_L}{(1 + f^2/\bar{v}_p^2)^{1/2}}$$

$$\xi = \frac{1}{\alpha \beta T_L}$$

$$\alpha = \frac{3v}{a_p^2}$$

$$\beta = \frac{3}{2(\rho_p/\rho_p) + 1}$$

and f is the particle free-fall velocity.

The results of Meek & Jones compare favorably with experiments by Snyder & Lumley (1971) and thus should be considered the appropriate format for the diffusivity in the case of homogeneous turbulence in the absence of shear, including effects of particle free fall. The results illustrate the major role that crossing trajectory effects have when one considers finite inertia and its relation to single-particle motion in turbulent flow.

1.3.8.7   Effects of Particle Inertia

The problem of particle motion in a turbulent fluid is now considered from a more general point of view to determine whether the simplification made previously can be extended to a larger class of flows and particles. Unfortunately, the problem of particulate motion in a turbulent fluid, even for a single particle and with the simplification that only Stokes drag forces are important, remains unsolved. The reason can be seen on examination of the appropriate equation of motion:

$$X_{pi}(\mathbf{a}, t) - \mathbf{a}_0 = \int_0^t G(t - \tau) u_i[X_{pj}(\mathbf{a}, \tau)j\ \tau]\ d\tau \qquad [1.3.267]$$

This equation has been discussed by Lumley (1957) and others, yet there is no satisfactory algorithm to obtain a solution even in the statistical sense. The problem is that the finite particle inertia, which causes the particle to lag behind the initially coincident fluid parcel, implies that the sequence of fluid velocities encountered by the particle may have a different statistical characterization than the sequence of velocities achieved by the initially coincident fluid parcel. This is evident in the right-hand side of [1.3.267], where the fluid velocity encountered by the particle is that determined by the (local Eulerian) fluid field at the particle's instantaneous position. Equation [1.3.267] is limited to linear drag law flow, and therefore the impulse response function is not written as a function of encountered velocity.

More complex dynamic equations may yield nonlinear dependence on the fluid velocity, but the fundamental problem remains, namely that the appropriate fluid velocity is that found at the particle's instantaneous position. The same difficulties occur when one attempts to determine the Lagrangian characteristics of the turbulent field from knowledge of the Eulerian statistics. In that case, the impulse response function is unity.

One may look at the problem in terms of filtering. Essentially, the solid particle responds only to a certain sequence of fluid velocities. In addition, from a frequency point of view, the particulate dynamics restricts the particle to responses that are characteristic only of certain portions of the available frequencies in the fluid motion. In one limiting case an extremely heavy particle would be almost stationary in the field. In that sense it would encounter a wide spectrum of fluid velocities, namely all the fluid velocity components that pass by its location; however, its ability to respond to any of these is limited. The other limit is the very small light particle, which follows the fluid parcels exactly. Although these can respond to all the frequencies available in the fluid motion, the relation of this sequence of velocities to the statistical information available in Eulerian form is not known. In the latter case, the particle undergoes diffusion equivalent to that of a fluid particle, whereas in the former case there is no observable diffusion; the realistic situations are somewhat in between. To deal with this problem, simplifications are required or experimental or numerical simulation is necessary. Turning first to possible simplifications, one of those most commonly used retains the impulse response function characteristic of a particle of finite inertia but presumes that the particle follows an initially coincident fluid parcel precisely. In that case, the basic equation of motion can be written

$$X_{pi}(\mathbf{a}, t) - \mathbf{a}_0 = \int_0^t G(t - \tau) v_f(\tau) \, d\tau \qquad [1.3.268]$$

This equation was employed by Soo (1956) and others. In this limit, while the mean square particulate velocity is less than the mean square fluid velocity (Soo 1956), the effect of finite inertia is limited to small or intermediate diffusion times, but a long-time asymptotic diffusivity (which is the one normally employed in the definition of diffusivity in the concentration equations) is equal to the fluid diffusivity (Peskin 1960). In other words, for this model the ratio of particle phase diffusivity to fluid diffusivity is 1 for long times from release:

$$\frac{1}{2} \frac{d}{dt} \bar{X}_p^2 = \frac{1}{2} \frac{d}{dt} \bar{X}^2 = \bar{u}^2 T_L \qquad [1.3.269]$$

The result above is true strictly for isotropic homogeneous turbulent supporting fields and for the long-time limit in the homogeneous uniform shear case. It is probably true for any other circumstance where the particle can remain in the fluid long enough to encounter all the available values of fluid velocity that would be encountered by a fluid parcel itself. A word of caution is necessary here, inasmuch as the required times may be considerably longer than other important physical characteristics such as decay time for nonstationary fluid fields.

The inability of the solid particles to follow an initially coincident fluid particle is a generalization of the concept of crossing trajectory. While the mere presence of a crossing trajectory effect indicates that one would expect a difference in the asymptotic diffusivity, it is not clear whether an enhanced or reduced particulate diffusivity is implied. It is not even evident that the crossing-trajectory effect results in a different particulate diffusivity. In attempts to deal with this problem, model systems have been investigated that retain partial features of the complete problem. Peskin (1971) assumed that the particle never deviates too far from the initially coincident fluid parcel, and the actual velocity encountered by the particle could be predicted by its stochastic estimation projection from the presumably given statistical information about the fluid parcel itself. The following result was obtained for the diffusivity ratio:

$$\frac{D_p}{D} = 1 - \frac{\bar{u}^2 T_L}{2\lambda^2}\left(\frac{3\sigma}{\sigma + 2}\right) + \cdots$$

$$\sigma = \frac{1}{9}\left(\frac{2a_p}{\nu}\,\bar{u}^2\right)^{1/2}\left(\frac{\rho_p}{\rho_\rho}\right)\frac{4a_p}{(\bar{u}^2)^{1/2}}\,T_L$$

[1.3.270]

where λ is the Eulerian microscale. This implies that the particulate diffusivity measured against the fluid parcel diffusivity depends on the relative magnitude of the Eulerian and Lagrangian length scales in the supporting turbulence. For example, if the fluid is strongly correlated spatially (has a large Eulerian length scale), then if the solid particle fails to follow an initially coincident fluid parcel that means that it will encounter unrelated fluid velocities, and this will result in a greatly reduced solid particle diffusivity. To use such results, it is necessary to have information about the relative length scales associated with the Eulerian and Lagrangian descriptions of turbulence. Unfortunately, this also remains an unsolved problem, but the results of Philip (1967) (see [1.3.248]) seem to correlate well with known information.

Lumley (1957) analyzed the small particle diffusivity problem and indicated the difficult problem of arriving at an algorithm to compute the solid particle diffusivity, given necessary statistical information about the supporting fluid fields. Margolin (1977) reconsidered the problem but assumed that a solid particle encountered a velocity sequence equivalent to that of a fluid particle. He did, however, treat the effects of shear on solid particle diffusion.

The difficulties encountered with analysis of the crossing-trajectory problem indicate that study by numerical simulation is a fruitful approach. Such simulations depend on the ability to produce a reasonably realistic model of the turbulent velocity field, and introduce particles into the field controlled by an appropriate equation of motion. In one such experiment (Kau 1972; Peskin 1975) a channel flow was considered for numerical simulation and particle trajectories were followed in the numerically simulated channel flow for high Reynolds number. Because the basic flow developed the expected mean velocity profile for channels, the results are not comparable to those calculated by assuming homogeneous isotropic turbulence. In addition, the significant inertial factor employed for the particulate phase (density ratio in excess of 2500) indicated that the theoretical assumptions used for the diffusivity equation (Peskin 1971) were not comparable. Numerical simulation indicated that the particulate phase had an asymptotic diffusivity approximately 40% greater than that of the fluid parcels. The significant discrepancy cannot be totally explained by the lack of isotropy or homogeneity in the flow. Unfortunately, the expense and complexity of numerical simulation indicate that, at present, the technique should be employed primarily for basic research questions. It is not yet a practical technique for a wide variety of engineering applications. Among its limitations are the need for a sufficient number of grid points in the simulation to realistically represent the fluid field and a sufficient number of particles to realistically estimate the mean square displacement without excessive statistical error. Furthermore, the inertia of the particle implies that simulations involving particulate motion require considerably more time to attain statistical equilibrium than simulations that follow fluid points only. This translates into very extensive and expensive computation times.

1.3.8.8 Effect of Particulate Phase on Fluid Turbulence

Discussion thus far has implied that the structure of the turbulent flow remains unaffected by the presence of particles. This is true for dilute suspensions away from the wall region and is a good assumption for a large variety of applications. The effects of particle motion on the turbulent structure are now considered. Studies by Peskin & Baw (1971) and experimental work by Wallace (1966) indicated that the effect of the presence of particles away from the wall is to shift the energy spectrum toward higher wave numbers. However, the effect seems to be small for solid particle loadings of less than 5% by volume. Peskin & Rin (1967) considered the effect of the presence of solids on the eddy diffusivity of the turbulence. They found that the presence of solids moderately increased the randomness of the fluid turbulence and thereby decreased the eddy diffusivity. However, this result presupposes that the mean square velocity of the turbulence, i.e., the kinetic energy, remains constant. In practical situations, while the presence of particles may increase the randomness of fluid motion, there can be an attendant decrease in turbulent kinetic energy since the eddy diffusivity depends on both the kinetic energy and the correlation length scale. The resulting decrease in eddy diffusivity may not be negligible.

The most interesting effect of particles on the flow structure occurs in the boundary-layer region. There have been numerous studies of the effect of particles on friction factor and heat transfer coefficients, e.g., by Dwyer & Peskin (1965), Briller & Peskin (1968), and Kane (1973). While these studies were concerned with lightly loaded situations, the conclusions concerning dilute suspensions of particles were basically the same, namely that significant effects on the structure of the turbulent boundary layer can occur if the characteristic particle response time is commensurate with characteristic time scales in the boundary layer. These conclusions are similar to those of Lumley (1969) in a study of the effect of polymer additives on the turbulent boundary layer. Essentially, if the particle response times are commensurate with characteristic times scales in the boundary layer, a thickening of the boundary layer can occur. This gives rise to a decrease in friction factor and an enhanced heat transfer coefficient. These effects will not be present for an arbitrary set of inertial particle characteristics and boundary-layer characteristics, and the flow system must be appropriately designed if such boundary-layer interaction effects are to be expected.

1.3.8.9 Two-Particle or Relative Dispersion in Turbulence

In many cases of practical engineering interest, such as the spreading rate of jets and plumes of contaminants, the relative motion of two particles is of concern. In air pollution technology the spreading rate of jets is an important characteristic, and for large-scale atmospheric contamination the relative diffusivity determines the spreading rate of clouds. While the inertial effects associated with particles of finite size and mass are significant in the analysis of one-particle diffusion, it is generally thought that they are less important in the relative two-point dispersion considerations. While this remains unproved, it seems plausible in view of the fact that two-point dispersion is dominated by the imposed shear mechanisms acting jointly on two particles. In view of the absence of concrete results on relative dispersion for two particles with inertia, the following discussion concentrates on situations where particulate inertia parameters can be neglected.

The dynamic equations controlling the relative separation of two particles can be written as

$$\bar{Y}_i(\mathbf{A}, t) = X_i(\mathbf{a} + \mathbf{A}, t) - X_i(\mathbf{A}, t)$$

For $\mathbf{u} = 0$

$$X_1' = A_1 + \int_0^t v_1'(\mathbf{A}, \tau) \, d\tau$$

$$X_1 = \int_0^t v_1(0, \tau) \, d\tau$$

$$\frac{1}{2} \frac{d}{dt} \bar{Y}_1^2 = \int_0^t \tilde{R}_{11}(\tau, t, \mathbf{A}) \, d\tau$$

[1.3.271]

$$\tilde{R}_{ij}(\tau, t, \mathbf{A}) \equiv \overline{w_i(\mathbf{A}, t) \, w_j(\mathbf{A}, t + \tau)}$$

$$\mathbf{w} = \mathbf{v}' - \mathbf{v}$$

Unlike the corresponding equations for a single particle, the relative velocity autocorrelation that appears in the relative dispersion equation is not stationary; this can be seen physically from the fact that two particles initially close together

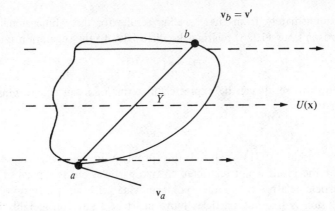

Figure 1.3.22 Schematic of two-particle analysis.

eventually move far enough apart to become independent. Thus the relative dispersion behavior does change in time. The problem is further complicated by the fact that the results are not independent of initial separation. For very large initial separations, the particles behave independently for all time. The most straight-forward approach to a two-particle analysis is the use of scale analysis.

The fundamental assumption employed in scale analysis is that two particles separated by some distance r (figure 1.3.22) tend to move relative to each other under the action of the locally determined fluid strain field. If one scales the relative velocity in terms of the imposed strain field and presumes that the characteristic correlation time for relative velocity is that characterized by that strained field, then one can invoke the following scaling equations relating the relative velocity and time scale to the energy spectrum of a three-dimensional turbulent field:

$$\frac{1}{2}\frac{d}{dt}\bar{Y}^2 \equiv D_R = \int_0^t \overline{w(t)w(t+\tau)}\, d\tau$$

$$D_R \sim \overline{w^2}\,\tau(t)$$

$$\tau(t) \sim \left(\frac{\partial U_i}{\partial x_j}\right)^{-1} \equiv S^{-1}$$

$$w \sim [kE(k)]^{1/2} \tag{1.3.272}$$

If the particles are sufficiently close to be confined to the energy transfer regions of the turbulence, the appropriate relations for the energy spectrum can be inserted to determine the relative velocity and the characteristic time scale in terms of the characteristic features of the turbulence spectrum, namely the energy cascade rate and the wave number.

$$E(k) \sim \epsilon^{2/3} k^{-5/3}$$

$$S \sim [k^3 E(k)]^{1/2} \tag{1.3.273}$$

$$\tau(t) \sim k^{-2/3} \epsilon^{-1/3}$$

It follows immediately from these scaling results for three-dimensional turbulence that Richardson's law (1926) relating the diffusivity to the separation rate is

$$D_R \sim (\bar{Y}^2)^{2/3} \qquad [1.3.274]$$

Alternatively, this result can be expressed in terms of mean square separation as a function of time

$$\bar{Y}^2 \sim \epsilon t^3 \qquad [1.3.275]$$

Krasnoff & Peskin (1971) analyzed this problem in somewhat more detail and showed that the result is not restricted to two particles but is typical of the motion of one particle relative to another point moving with an arbitrary velocity. The main conclusion is that the particles move apart at a rate considerably in excess of the mean square displacement of either particle alone.

Some interesting limiting cases are available. In particular for very large separations the scaling analysis shows

$$\overline{w^2} \rightarrow 2\bar{v}^2 \sim 2\bar{u}^2$$

$$S \sim \frac{(\bar{u}^2)^{1/2}}{l} \qquad [1.3.276]$$

$$D_R \sim 2(\bar{u}^2)^{1/2} l \sim 2D$$

The appropriate independent motion case is recovered.

For very small separations, in particular for separations less than the Kolmogorov microscale, the two points tend to see a constant strain characterized by the Kolmogorov scale, and the separation is characterized by the exponential spreading rate

$$\bar{Y}^2 \sim \exp t \left(\frac{\epsilon}{\nu}\right)^{1/2} \qquad [1.3.277]$$

One other limit of interest is that for extremely small separations where the particles are subject to translation by the flow field (Hinze 1975):

$$\bar{Y}^2 \sim R(r)t^2 \qquad [1.3.278]$$

where $R(r)$ is the Eulerian space correlation.

The above results are for isotropic flow. For uniformly applied shear flow similar results are obtained.

$$\bar{Y}^2 \sim \frac{2}{3}\left(\frac{\partial U_i}{\partial x_j}\right)^2 \bar{u}^2 l t^3 \qquad [1.3.279]$$

The main conclusion here is that in the presence of shear the downstream spreading rate goes as t^3. A similar result was found by Deardorff & Peskin (1970) for flow in a channel simulated by computer modeling.

Although little work has been reported on the modification of the relative diffusion results by finite inertia, there is reason to suspect that these effects are most important at large separations, where the finite inertia affects the sequence of fluid velocities that act on a given particle. Another conceivable effect of finite inertia may be the inability of smaller-scale applied turbulence strain fields to induce any relative motion of two heavy particles. That is, the inertial feature of a particle may filter out its response to small-scale turbulence strain fields because they are not sufficiently persistent. In this case, the particles are responsive at small separation only to the larger-scale persistent fields, and thus the separation proceeds exponentially. This contention is yet to be tested by theoretical analysis, numerical simulation, or experimentation.

In many engineering applications, particle-particle interactions may have a greater effect on the structure of the imposed turbulent field than they do on particle motion itself. Exceptions are packed beds and other highly dense particulates. Nevertheless, for moderately dilute particle suspensions, particle-particle interaction can have an effect on diffusivity. In particular, the presence of other particles induces relative motion with respect to the single particle under consideration that gives rise to various hydrodynamic force fields. Such force field interaction has been examined for both viscous and inviscid flow. For moderately dilute suspensions inviscid flow approximations are probably sufficient, and Peskin (1960) obtained the following relation for diffusivity caused by particle-particle interaction due to hydrodynamic field induction:

$$\frac{D_{p\,\text{interaction}}}{D} = S_L \hat{\delta} \, (1 - G)$$

$$1 - G \approx \exp\left(-\frac{\bar{v}_p^2}{\bar{u}^2}\right)$$

[1.3.280]

with $S_L = 0.0011 \, \text{Re} \, \phi^{8/3}$, where Re is the Reynolds number and ϕ is the volume fraction, i.e., volume of solids divided by volume of fluid, and $\hat{\delta}$ is a parameter that depends on particle-particle interaction forces.

1.3.8.10 Features Important for Practical Application

The most important characteristic to be considered in determining the particle-fluid interaction is the turbulent characteristic of the supporting flow field. The intensity of the turbulent field in the direction of gravity determines whether there is a suspension. In particular, this component of turbulent energy must exceed the square of the terminal velocity. When particle inertia can be neglected, as in the majority of air pollution cases and many other practical applications, two important characteristics control the mean square displacement or its time derivative, the diffusivity. These are the kinetic energy of turbulence and the characteristic scale length of turbulence, determined primarily by the area under the Lagrangian correlation curve. For engineering applications, an estimate of the intensity of turbulence obtained as some percentage of the mean flow velocity can be used together with an estimate of the characteristic length scales for the larger features of the flow. For typical flows such as channel flows and pipe flows, such length scale estimates can be found in turbulence texts such as Hinze (1975). For unbounded turbulent flows such as wakes, jets, and mixing layers, the appropriate length scale is the characteristic width of the turbulent shear region. For relative or two-particle separation, more detailed knowledge of the turbulent energy spectrum is necessary to estimate the relative dispersion rate. In general, this can be obtained in the laboratory by measurement of the turbulent energy spectrum.

The most important characteristic of the particle to be considered is its effective inertial response time for whatever particulate drag law is employed. For example, for Stokes drag this characteristic time is

$$\tau_{\text{characteristic}} = \frac{2}{9} \frac{a_p^2}{\nu} \frac{\rho_p}{\rho} \qquad [1.3.281]$$

The greater the characteristic response time, the more difficult it is for the particle to respond to fluctuations in the turbulent field. That is, it tends to filter out motions with frequencies higher than some characteristic frequency determined by the inverse of the particle response time. This means that the particle with inertia cannot actually follow the fluid motion but is acted on only by a subset of velocities of that fluid field. Since the mean square displacement or diffusivity is determined by the autocorrelation of the velocities that act on the particle, the diffusive characteristic of a particle with inertia depends entirely on the auto-correlation of the sequence of velocities to which that particle responds. If the fluid flow field is highly correlated spatially, this sequence closely approximates the actual sequence of fluid Lagrangian velocities. Unfortunately, in many cases where particle inertia is important, such a high degree of correlation is not present and little guidance is given to the appropriate particle diffusivity. If the response time of the particles is sufficiently small, approximations that imply that the particle almost, but not exactly, follows the fluid particle indicate that there is a reduction in particle diffusivity. However, this result was obtained for isotropic homogeneous turbulent fields. Numerical simulations in configurations such as channel flows do not necessarily corroborate this result. Finally, in the presence of applied shear, the diffusivity in the direction of the shear flow is greatly enhanced.

1.3.9 HYDRODYNAMICS OF DROPS AND BUBBLES

J. R. Grace and M. E. Weber

1.3.9.1 Drops and Bubbles in Liquids

Shape Regimes

Drops and bubbles rising or falling freely under gravity in a Newtonian liquid are commonly considered to belong to one of three broad shape regimes: spherical, ellipsoidal, or spherical cap. In reality, these regimes cover shapes that are not strictly spheres, ellipsoids, or spherical caps. To be included within the spherical regime, the fluid particle must be rounded with a minimum aspect (height-to-width) ratio of about 0.9. The ellipsoidal regime includes flattened drops and bubbles with a concave surface (viewed from inside) around the entire periphery. The shapes may, however, lack fore-and-aft symmetry, and oscillations, dilations, or wobbling may occur. The distinguishing feature of the spherical cap regime is that the rear surface must be either flat or convex (i.e., indented) when viewed from inside. This regime includes cases where a thin annular "skirt" of the dispersed fluid is trailed and where the leading edge is ellipsoidal rather than spherical.

Grace (1973) and Grace et al. (1976) showed that a convenient mapping of these three principal regimes, as well as of certain subregimes (e.g., where skirts or wobbling occur), can be obtained by plotting the fluid particle Reynolds number,

$$Re = \frac{\rho d_e u_T}{\mu} \qquad [1.3.282]$$

versus the Eötvös number,

$$Eo = \frac{g \Delta \rho d_e^2}{\sigma} \qquad [1.3.283]$$

with a fluid property group,

$$M = \frac{g \mu^4 \Delta \rho}{\rho^2 \sigma^3} \qquad [1.3.284]$$

as parameter. Here u_T is the terminal rising or falling velocity of the drop or bubble, d_e the sphere volume-equivalent diameter $[d_e = (6V_p/\pi)^{1/2}]$, and $\Delta \rho = |\rho - \rho_p|$. Unsubscripted properties refer to the outer liquid phase, while the subscript p is used to denote the fluid particle (i.e., dispersed) phase.

The regime map given by Grace et al. (1976) appears in figure 1.3.23. The range of fluid properties and particle volumes covered by the diagram is very wide indeed. Each liquid-liquid or gas-liquid system corresponds to a constant value of M. Hence each of the lines running upward and to the right could correspond to a particular fluid-liquid combination with the appropriate value of M. The other heavy lines delineate the three principal shape regimes. Subregimes are shown within the ellipsoidal and spherical cap regimes corresponding to wobbling conditions, skirt formation, and ellipsoidal caps. Drops and bubbles are spherical if either interfacial tension forces or viscous forces are dominant over gravity and inertia forces (i.e., at low Eo or low Re). For continuous liquids of low viscosity, e.g., water and low-molecular-weight organic liquids, M is generally in the range 10^{-10}-10^{-12} and there is a substantial particle size range corresponding to the ellipsoidal regime. For very viscous liquids where $M > 10^2$, drops or bubbles pass directly from the spherical to the spherical cap regime with increasing d_e, without any intermediate ellipsoidal regime. Note that the viscosity of the dispersed fluid, μ_p, plays an insignificant role in determining the shape regime and does not appear in figure 1.3.23.

Of the three dimensionless groups that appear in figure 1.3.23, only Re involves the terminal velocity u_T. Hence this diagram provides a simple means for estimating terminal rising or settling velocities for drops and bubbles in liquids. More accurate predictions can usually be obtained from the correlations given in later sections.

Other shapes can be observed in cases where one or both of the phases is non-Newtonian, especially if the outer liquid is viscoelastic (e.g., Carreau et al.

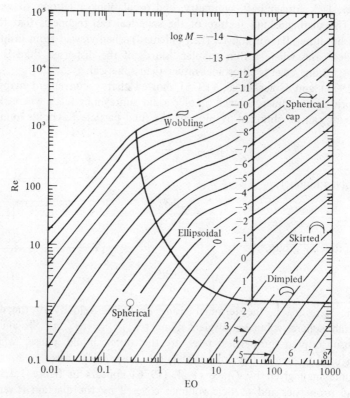

Figure 1.3.23 Shape regimes and subregimes for liquid drops and gas bubbles rising or falling freely through liquids under gravity; adapted from Clift et al. (1978) with permission.

1974). Bubbles and drops in non-Newtonian liquids are not considered further in this chapter.

Spherical or Nearly Spherical Drops and Bubbles at Low Reynolds Number

The problem of the free steady rise of a spherical droplet of radius a in an infinite expanse of liquid in creeping flow was solved independently by Hadamard (1911) and Rybczynski (1911). The Stokes stream functions for the outer and inner fluids are given, respectively, by

$$\psi = -\frac{ur^2 \sin^2 \theta}{2}\left[1 - \frac{(3\kappa + 2)a}{2(\kappa + 1)r} + \frac{\kappa a^3}{2(\kappa + 1)r^3}\right] \qquad [1.3.285]$$

$$\psi_p = \frac{ur^2(a^2 - r^2)\sin^2 \theta}{4(\kappa + 1)a^2} \qquad [1.3.286]$$

where $\kappa = \mu_p/\mu$ is the viscosity ratio. The flow fields given by [1.3.285] and

[1.3.286] have fore-and-aft symmetry, with the internal motion corresponding to a Hill's spherical vortex (Hill 1894). The boundary conditions imposed in obtaining the Hadamard-Rybczynski solution are uniform streaming at a velocity u far from the sphere, no flow across the spherical boundary, continuity of tangential velocity at the interface, and continuity of shear stress at $r = a$. Although continuity of normal stress could not be imposed because of the prior assumption of a spherical particle shape, normal stresses are balanced along the interface if the neglect of inertia terms (inherent in the use of the creeping flow equations) is justified. Hence drops and bubbles are spherical at low Re even in the absence of surface or interfacial tension forces. This behavior is consistent with figure 1.3.23.

Integration of the normal and shear stresses over the surface of the sphere leads to an expression for the drag coefficient,

$$C_D = \frac{2F_D}{\pi\rho u^2 a^2} = \frac{8}{Re}\frac{3\kappa + 2}{\kappa + 1} \qquad [1.3.287]$$

By equating the net drag force F_D to the absolute value of the weight minus buoyancy force, the terminal rising or settling velocity is derived as

$$u_T = \frac{2}{3}\frac{ga^2\Delta\rho}{\mu}\frac{\kappa + 1}{3\kappa + 2} \qquad [1.3.288]$$

When the viscosity of the internal fluid is much greater than that of the outer liquid, i.e., for $\kappa \to \infty$, [1.3.285], [1.3.287] and [1.3.288] simplify to the corresponding Stokes results for creeping flow past a rigid sphere.

Hetsroni & Haber (1970) generalized the above analysis to the case where the velocity field at infinity is an arbitrary solution to the creeping flow equations, rather than uniform. As a first stage in an iterative procedure, the droplet or bubble is assumed to be spherical and the velocity fields inside and outside are solved subject to six boundary conditions, not including the normal stress condition at $r = a$. The normal stress condition can then be used to give an estimate of deformation from the spherical, where deviation from the spherical is described by a sum of surface harmonics. Further iterations could then be carried out to revise the flow fields, then the shape, and so on. The analysis was used to rederive well-known results for a neutrally buoyant drop in a Couette shear flow and in a hyperbolic flow field (Taylor 1934) and to treat the case of a droplet in an unbounded Poiseuille flow. The second iteration (Haber & Hetsroni 1971) does not alter the terminal settling velocity from the first iteration, but leads to lateral migration of the drop.

In practice, drops and bubbles seldom obey the predictions of the Hadamard-Rybczynski analysis, since even minute traces of surface-active impurities are usually sufficient to damp out most internal circulation of the dispersed fluid. When a drop or bubble falls or rises under gravity through a liquid, adsorbed surface-active contaminants are swept to the rear, leaving the forward surface relatively uncontaminated. Hence a concentration gradient of surface-active agents is established, and this causes a surface gradient in tangential stress that opposes surface motion (Frumkin & Levich 1947; Levich 1962). These gradients are especially significant for small drops and bubbles.

Attempts to relate the retardation of fluid particles to the degree of contamination have been reviewed by Harper (1972) and Clift et al. (1978). The most common approach (e.g., Savic 1953, Harper 1973) for gas bubbles ($\kappa \to 0$) has been to assume a stagnant cap of contaminant at the rear of the particle with the forward surface being completely mobile. Since the quantity and type of surface-active contaminant are seldom known in practice, approximate methods must generally be applied. For many systems, the transition from Stokes' law to the Hadamard-Rybczynski drag given by [1.3.287] has been found to occur over a relatively narrow range of d_e corresponding to Eo ≈ 4 (Bond & Newton 1928). Since Eo reaches this value at low Re only for systems of very high M (see figure 1.3.23), Stokes' law should be assumed at low Re for most systems. The Hadamard-Rybczynski analysis provides an upper limit on u_T and a lower limit on drag that are only achieved for systems of exceptionally high purity or for $M > 10^3$. The presence of surfactants has a much more profound effect on terminal velocity and internal circulation than on the shape of fluid particles.

Inertial effects lead to deformation of fluid particles. The Reynolds number Re based on external liquid properties is much more important than another Reynolds number $\mathrm{Re}_p = \rho_p d_e u / \mu_p$ based on dispersed fluid properties (Pan & Acrivos 1968). Taylor & Acrivos (1964) used a matched asymptotic expansion for high M that predicts that the initial deformation is toward an oblate ellipsoidal form. Further terms in the expansion were derived by Brignell (1973).

Wall effects tend to retard the motion of drops and bubbles and to cause some elongation in the vertical direction. Consider a spherical droplet or bubble of radius a moving at velocity u with its center a distance b ($b < R - a$) from the axis of a vertical cylindrical tube of radius R. Consider also a parabolic flow far from the sphere with centerline velocity u_0. Both fluids are Newtonian, incompressible, isothermal, and governed by the creeping flow equations. Hetsroni et al. (1970) found a general expression for the drag force in the axial direction,

$$
F_D = 2\pi\mu a \, \frac{2 + 3\kappa}{1 + \kappa} \left\{ [u_0(1 - \beta^2) - u] \left[1 + \frac{\lambda}{3} \frac{2 + 3\kappa}{1 + \kappa} f(\beta) + \frac{\lambda^2}{9} \left(\frac{2 + 3\kappa}{1 + \kappa} \right)^2 f^2(\beta) \right] \right.
$$

$$
\left. - \frac{2\kappa}{2 + 3\kappa} u_0 \lambda^2 + \mathbf{O}(\lambda^3) \right\} \tag{1.3.289}
$$

where $\lambda = a/R$, $\beta = b/R$, and values of $f(\beta)$ from Greenstein & Happel (1968) are given in table 1.3.6. For $\beta = 0$, [1.3.289] simplifies to a well-known solution given by Haberman & Sayre (1958); other appropriate limits are recovered as $\lambda \to 0$ and $\kappa \to \infty$ (Hetsroni et al. 1970). The normal stress distribution can be used to estimate the degree of deformation when the deformation is small. Deformation depends on both β and λ as well as on $\mu u_0 / \sigma$ and Eo. The droplet or bubble tends to migrate radially in such a configuration. Migration is toward the wall if u_0 is in the same direction as the Hadamard-Rybczynski settling velocity given by [1.3.288], and toward the axis if these two velocities are opposed (Hetsroni et al. 1972). For particles on or near the axis of the tube, i.e., for $\beta = 0$, reasonable predictions are obtained for most cases of physical significance provided $\lambda < 0.3$ and Re < 1. For

Table 1.3.6 Values of Position Function $f(\beta)$ as Calculated by Greenstein & Happel (1968)

β	$f(\beta)$	β	$f(\beta)$	β	$f(\beta)$
0.00	2.10444	0.30	2.05687	0.55	2.10274
0.01	2.10433	0.35	2.04800	0.60	2.16980
0.02	2.10415	0.37	2.04561	0.65	2.28060
0.03	2.10381	0.39	2.04419	0.70	2.45850
0.05	2.10270	0.40	2.04388	0.75	2.742
0.10	2.09758	0.41	2.04391	0.80	3.20
0.15	2.08962	0.43	2.04522	0.85	3.96
0.20	2.07937	0.45	2.04819	0.90	5.30
0.25	2.06801	0.50	2.06557		

larger λ severe deformation occurs, and the fluid particle should be considered as a slug.

The acceleration under gravity of fluid spheres with creeping flow in both phases has been treated by Sy et al. (1970), Sy & Lightfoot (1971), and Morrison & Stewart (1976). The initial acceleration is identical to that given by unsteady potential flow theory, i.e.,

$$\mathbf{a}_0 = -\frac{g(\rho_p - \rho)\mathbf{i}}{(\rho_p + \rho/2)} \qquad [1.3.290]$$

An analytical solution is given for the special case of a gas bubble (i.e., for $\rho_p/\rho \to 0$ and $\kappa = \mu_p/\mu \to 0$) by Sy et al. (1970). The bubble remains spherical as long as inertial terms are negligible. Numerical solutions have been given (Sy & Lightfoot 1971) for other density and viscosity ratios.

The interaction of fluid spheres at low Re is treated in section 1.3.3.

Spherical Drops and Bubbles at Intermediate Reynolds Numbers

As shown in Figure 1.3.23 drops and bubbles moving freely under gravity remain spherical at Reynolds numbers of order 100 or more if the Eötvös number is small enough, i.e., if the interfacial tension is sufficiently large. Theories for circulating fluid spheres at Reynolds numbers from about 1 to 500 have been based on three different approaches: Galerkin's method, numerical solution of the complete equations of motion, and boundary-layer solutions. When internal circulation is virtually absent, due to either large values of the viscosity ratio κ or contamination of the interface by surface-active impurities, the drag on and flow around fluid spheres may be treated as if the drop or bubble were a solid sphere of the same density.

Numerical solutions provide the most complete picture of the flow outside and inside fluid spheres. Results for freely circulating air bubbles in liquids ($\kappa \to 0$) have been reported by Hamielec & Johnson (1962), Hamielec et al. (1963), LeClair & Hamielec (1971), and Brabston & Keller (1975). Internal circulation delays the onset of flow separation in the outer fluid, and the surface vorticity and wake volume are smaller than for corresponding rigid (noncirculating) spheres. Both pressure drag and skin friction are reduced as a result of the internal motion so that the overall drag coefficient for circulating fluid spheres falls below that for rigid spheres.

Numerical solutions for circulating fluid spheres at specific intermediate values of κ have been obtained as follows: $\kappa = 1$ (Rivkind et al. 1972); $\kappa = 0.10$, 0.27, 0.30, 0.55, 0.71, and 1.4 (Abdel-Alim & Hamielec 1975); $\kappa = 1$, 3, 5, 10, 100, and 1000 (Rivkind & Ryskin 1976); and $\kappa = 0.33$, 1, 3, and 10 (Rivkind et al. 1976). Whereas the Hadamard-Rybczynski internal circulation for drops and bubbles at low Re has fore-and-aft symmetry, the eye of the vortex is shifted forward as Re increases. Under some circumstances, a secondary internal circulation of opposite sense may appear at the rear of the drop (Rivkind & Ryskin 1976). A reversal of flow can occur in the outer fluid, immediately behind the drop, without separation occurring on the drop surface. When there is an attached wake, its size increases with increasing κ and with increasing Re. The numerical results for drag over the complete range $0 \leqslant \kappa \leqslant \infty$ and $2 \stackrel{.}{<} \text{Re} \stackrel{.}{<} 500$ have been fitted (Rivkind & Ryskin 1976) by

$$C_D = \frac{1}{\kappa + 1} \left[\frac{14.9}{\text{Re}^{0.78}} + \kappa \left(\frac{24}{\text{Re}} + \frac{4}{\text{Re}^{1/3}} \right) \right] \qquad [1.3.291]$$

Boundary-layer solutions for fluid particles have been reviewed by Harper (1972) and Clift et al. (1978). For bubbles or drops of low κ, the external flow is only slightly different from potential flow past a sphere, while the internal flow is similar to a Hill's spherical vortex. A first approximation for the drag

$$C_D = \frac{48}{\text{Re}} \qquad (\kappa \to 0) \qquad [1.3.292]$$

is obtained by calculating the energy dissipation for potential flow past a sphere (Levich 1962). Inclusion of dissipation in the boundary layer and wake leads to

$$C_D = \frac{48}{\text{Re}} \left[1 - \frac{2.21}{\text{Re}^{0.5}} + O(\text{Re}^{-5/6}) \right] \qquad [1.3.293]$$

for gas bubbles. This result was extended to the case of appreciable values of κ by Harper & Moore (1968).

In practice, both surface-active agents and any deformation from a spherical shape tend to increase the drag above these values. Hence [1.3.291] and [1.3.293] give lower limits, which are approached only for extremely pure systems of high interfacial tension (Harper 1974). The changes in drag caused by the tendency of surfactants to damp out internal circulation are even more marked at high Re than at low Re (Lochiel 1965; Harper 1972). Because stringent purities are seldom realized in practice, drag coefficients for spherical drops and bubbles at intermediate Re usually lie closer to the "standard drag curve" for rigid spheres than to the results given above. Nevertheless, the results of the numerical work and of the boundary-layer solutions are supported by the limited work that has been performed with ultrapure systems (see Clift et al. 1978).

Because of the difficulty in producing completely pure liquids or purified surfactant solutions of known concentrations, analytical results regarding the effects of surfactants at high Re (e.g., Lochiel 1965; Harper 1974) have not been tested experimentally. Wall effects and acceleration of circulating fluid spheres in liquids at intermediate Re have also received little attention.

The in-line rise of two identical spherical bubbles has been studied by Harper (1970), using the boundary-layer approximations that lead to [1.3.293] for a single bubble. The two bubbles rise in unison more rapidly than a single bubble when separated by a critical distance. This configuration is predicted to be stable to small vertical displacements, but not to horizontal displacements. There are no supporting data for bubbles, while for spherical drops both data and analysis are lacking.

Ellipsoidal Regime

Experimental results showing the terminal velocity of intermediate-size air bubbles in water rising freely under gravity appear in figure 1.3.24. The ellipsoidal regime for this commonly encountered system covers bubble volume-equivalent diameters ranging from about 1 to 17 mm. Note that the influence of surface-active contaminants, shown by the shaded region, is more prominent for the ellipsoidal regime than for either the spherical regime ($d_e < 1$ mm) or the spherical cap regime ($d_e > 17$ mm). Boundaries of the ellipsoidal regime are given in general cases by the regime plot that appears as figure 1.3.23.

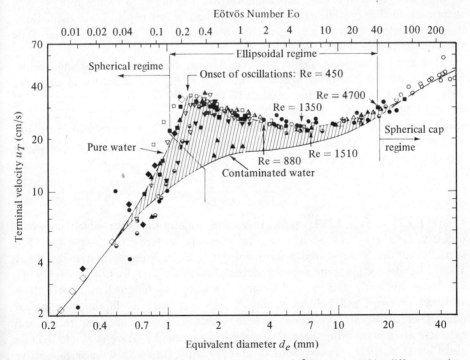

Figure 1.3.24 Terminal velocities of air bubbles in water at 20°C as measured by different workers. For identification of symbols with investigators, see Clift et al. (1978, p. 172), from whom figure has been adapted with permission.

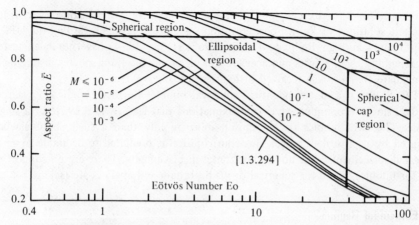

Figure 1.3.25 Shape correlation for drops and bubbles in liquids with surface-active contaminants present. Adapted from Clift et al. (1978) with permission.

The onset of deformation with increasing drop or bubble volume is due to inertia forces. Although the first stages of deformation at low Re may be toward a true oblate spheroid (Taylor & Acrivos 1964), the deformation quickly develops such that the shape lacks fore-and-aft symmetry. Flattening may be more significant at the front, or at the rear, depending on Re, Eo, and ρ_p/ρ (Wairegi 1974). The shapes are further complicated once unsteady oscillations begin. These oscillations, discussed further below, may give rise to instantaneous shapes that bear little resemblance to true oblate ellipsoids.

The simplest single parameter for characterizing the shape of drops and bubbles is the time-averaged height-to-maximum-width ratio $\bar{E}$, often called the aspect ratio. This ratio has been correlated graphically against Eo and M with extensive data from the literature (Grace et al. 1976). The result appears in figure 1.3.25. Note that the extent of deformation from the spherical ($\bar{E} = 1$) increases with increasing Eo and decreasing M group. For $M \leqslant 10^{-6}$ and Eo < 40, the time-averaged aspect ratio can be predicted from an equation proposed by Wellek et al. (1966):

$$\bar{E}, = \frac{1}{1 + 0.163 \, \text{Eo}^{0.757}} \qquad [1.3.294]$$

Figure 1.3.25 and [1.3.294] apply to normal conditions, under which no extraordinary measures have been taken to eliminate surface-active impurities. For specially purified systems, the deformation tends to be larger than given by figure 1.3.25. Results for ultrapure aqueous systems have been given by Clift et al. (1978).

There are many data in the literature pertaining to terminal rising or settling velocities of drops and bubbles in liquids that apply to the ellipsoidal regime. A number of empirical correlations are in common usage. The most recent and extensive attempt to bring these data together was made by Grace et al. (1976) (see also Clift et al. 1978). For systems of normal purity (i.e., with some surface-active contaminants inevitably present, but no addition of extra surfactants), the recommended method of predicting terminal velocities is based on 1483 data points in which wall effects are negligible. The correlation is a modification of that of Johnson & Braida (1957), which in turn involved an extension to the Hu & Kintner (1955) correlation. To obtain the terminal velocity in the ellipsoidal regime, one first calculates a dimensionless group

$$H = \frac{4}{3} \text{Eo } M^{-0.149} \left(\frac{\mu}{\mu_w} \right)^{-0.14} \qquad [1.3.295]$$

where $\mu_w = 9 \times 10^{-4}$ kg/m s is the viscosity of water in Braida's experiments. The terminal velocity is then given by

$$u_T = \frac{\mu}{\rho d_e} M^{-0.149} (J - 0.857) \qquad [1.3.296]$$

where
$$J = 0.94 \, H^{0.757} \qquad (2 < H \leqslant 59.3) \qquad [1.3.297a]$$

or
$$J = 3.42 \, H^{0.441} \qquad (H > 59.3) \qquad [1.3.297b]$$

The gradient discontinuity at $H = 59.3$ corresponds approximately to the onset of unsteady oscillations. For contaminated systems, the viscosity of the dispersed fluid is unimportant in determining the terminal velocity. The above method is recommended for systems with $M < 10^{-3}$, Re > 0.1, Eo < 40, and negligible wall effects. For higher M systems and fluid particles in the ellipsoidal regime, figure 1.3.23 can be used to estimate Re and hence u_T. Wall effects are considered below.

Drops and bubbles travel more rapidly in ultrapure systems than in contaminated systems. The increase in velocity results from increased internal circulation (Skelland & Huang 1977), which in turn gives decreased shear resistance at the interface, delayed boundary-layer separation, smaller wakes, and delayed wake shedding. The terminal velocity for ultrapure systems, denoted by a superscript p, may be obtained from

$$u_T^p = u_T \left(1 + \frac{\Gamma}{1 + \kappa} \right) \qquad [1.3.298]$$

where u_T is obtained from [1.3.295] to [1.3.297] and Γ is given by figure 1.3.26 (Grace et al. 1976). Note that the correction $\Gamma/(1 + \kappa)$ becomes small for highly viscous (i.e., high κ) systems, where internal circulation is small even in the complete absence of impurities. The correction is also seen from figure 1.3.26 to approach zero at both small and large Eo. This is in conformity with figure 1.3.24, which shows an extensive influence of purity for intermediate-size bubbles, with little effect at large and small Eo.

Predictions of the above procedures are shown in figure 1.3.27 for terminal velocities of carbon tetrachloride drops falling through water. Equations [1.3.295] – [1.3.297] give a good fit for cases in which no special purity precautions were taken, while the correction from [1.3.298] and figure 1.3.26 leads to an excellent fit to results by Thorsen et al. (1968), in which special measures were taken to ensure a high level of purity.

Moore (1965) derived an expression for the drag on an ellipsoidal bubble in which energy dissipation is calculated for irrotational flow past an oblate spheroid

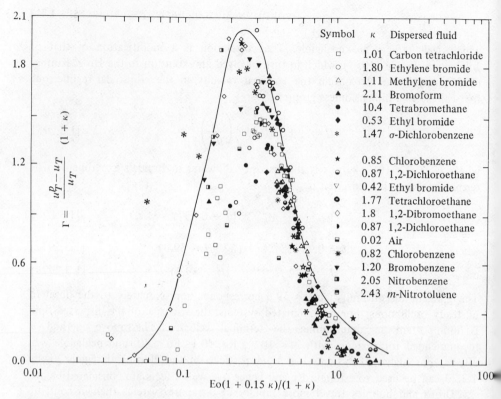

Figure 1.3.26 Correction factor Γ relating terminal velocity of drops and bubbles in pure liquids to those in corresponding contaminated systems. Adapted from Clift et al. (1978) with permission.

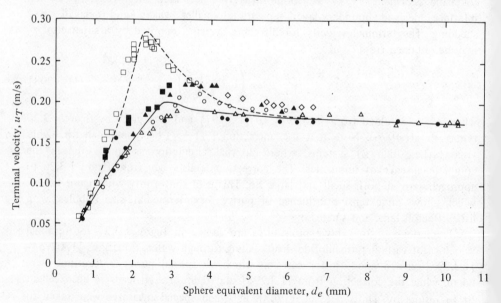

Figure 1.3.27 Terminal velocity of carbon tetrachloride drops falling through water reported by different workers with systems having different impurities. The lower curve corresponds to predictions from [1.3.295]–[1.3.297]; the upper curve corresponds to predictions from [1.3.298] and figure 1.3.26. For identification of data, see Grace et al. (1976) or Clift et al. (1978), from whom figure has been adapted with permission.

and allowance is made for additional dissipation in the boundary layer and wake. Like [1.3.293], the analogous expression for a spherical bubble, the results give lower limits on drag for ultrapure systems, but are rarely approached in practice. No extension of this approach has been reported for deformed drops of appreciable κ and ρ_p/ρ.

Wakes of drops and bubbles in the ellipsoidal regime are strongly affected by the system purity, the degree of internal circulation, the extent of deformation, and the nature of secondary motion, if any. Fully circulating drops and bubbles give delayed boundary-layer separation and smaller wakes than contaminated fluid particles (Winnikow & Chao 1966; Edge & Grant 1972). Wake configurations tend to be complex. Ellipsoidal air bubbles in water have helical vortex wakes, which discharge vorticity in a periodic manner (Lindt 1972).

The onset of secondary motion of drops and bubbles coincides with the onset of vortex shedding from the wake (Clift et al. 1978). For contaminated drops or bubbles or at large κ, this occurs at Re $\approx$ 200, but this is delayed to higher Re if κ is small and the system free of surface-active contaminants. For purified low-M systems ($M < 1.6 \times 10^{-8}$), the Reynolds number corresponding to the onset of oscillation was found to be approximately 9.0 $M^{-0.173}$ (Tsuge & Hibino 1977).

Secondary motion may involve shape dilations (usually called oscillations), rocking from side to side, spiral motion, or some combination of these three. The paths followed may be rectilinear, zigzagging in a plane, or spiral. There is some evidence that the type of motion observed is related to the manner in which the fluid particle is released. Experimental observations of the paths followed by air bubbles in water in one study (Aybers & Tapucu 1969) are given in table 1.3.7. The Strouhal number for the secondary motion (maximum width times frequency of oscillation divided by u_T) is typically in the range 0.2-0.3 (Lindt 1972; Lindt & de Groot 1974).

Although wake shedding appears to provide the impetus for shape oscillations, the frequencies of the two commonly differ. The natural frequency of the fundamental mode for fluid particles undergoing small oscillations in the absence of viscous forces is (Lamb 1932):

$$f = \left[\frac{48\sigma}{\pi^2 d_e^3 (2\rho + 3\rho_p)} \right]^{1/2} \qquad [1.3.299]$$

Observed oscillation frequencies for drops and bubbles in free rise are generally less

Table 1.3.7 Paths Followed by Air Bubbles in Water[a]

d_e (mm)	$\bar{E}$	Re	Path followed
< 1.3	> 0.8	< 565	Rectilinear
1.3-2.0	0.8-0.5	565-880	Helical
2.0-3.6	0.5-0.36	880-1350	Plane (zigzag) then helical
3.6-4.2	0.36-0.28	1350-1510	Plane (zigzag)
4.2-1.7	0.28-0.23	1510-4700	Rectilinear but with rocking

[a]From Clift et al. (1978), reprinted with permission.

than predicted by [1.3.299], typically by 10–20% for impure systems and 20–40% for pure systems (Clift et al. 1978). Oscillations may be oblate-prolate, oblate-spherical, or oblate-less oblate. The amplitude of oscillation is larger for pure systems. Although correlations of the amplitude of oscillation have been given (e.g., Schroeder & Kintner 1965), the amplitude is highly irregular and these correlations are of limited value. For cases where the shedding frequency and natural oscillation frequency are nearly equal, "beats" may even be observed. Resonance is one possible cause of bubble and drop disintegration. Oscillations of drops and bubbles may also disrupt internal circulation patterns and cause rapid mixing of the contents.

Secondary motion of fluid particles leads to an increase in drag and a decrease in terminal rising or settling velocity. The peaks in the curves shown in figures 1.3.24 and 1.3.27 are associated with the onset of secondary motion. For low-M systems, oscillations may become so extreme that the bubbles or drops are said to exhibit random wobbling (figure 1.3.23).

Wall effects tend to cause retardation of drops and bubbles and some elongation in the vertical direction. Some damping of secondary motion has also been observed. For Re > 200, the terminal velocity of an ellipsoidal drop or bubble subject to wall effects divided by that for a container of infinite cross section is given approximately (Clift et al. 1978) by

$$\frac{u_T^w}{u_T} = \left[1 - \left(\frac{d_e}{D}\right)^2\right]^{3/2} \qquad [1.3.300]$$

where D is the container diameter or hydraulic diameter (4 × cross-sectional area divided by perimeter). This relationship is recommended for $d_e/D \leqslant 0.6$, Eo < 40, and Re > 200. For $d_e/D \leqslant 0.6$, Eo < 40, and $1 \leqslant$ Re $\leqslant 200$, few data are available, but there are indications that u_T^w/u_T ratios can be based on the wall correction factors for rigid spheres (Clift et al. 1978). For $d_e/D > 0.6$, the fluid particle must be treated as a slug.

Interaction of ellipsoidal bubbles and drops is complicated by secondary motion such as zigzagging or helical rise. Hence two bubbles or drops that begin motion along a common vertical axis may not remain aligned (de Nevers & Wu 1971; Otake et al. 1977). In addition, when collision occurs it may not be followed by coalescence. Coalescence is governed by the rate of drainage of the thin film of continuous phase between the bubbles or drops at small separation. These rates are sensitive to the sizes of the fluid particles, their relative velocity, and the composition and purity of the phases (e.g., Lang & Wilke 1971; Scheele & Leng 1971; Kirkpatrick & Lockett 1974; Sagert & Quinn 1978). Only interaction before collision is considered here.

During the interaction of a pair of ellipsoidal bubbles (Yip et al. 1970; de Nevers & Wu 1971; Otake et al. 1977) or drops (Zabel et al. 1973), the velocity of the trailing fluid particle is larger than its terminal rise velocity in isolation. The incremental velocity is appreciable even at large separations. For example, for 3.7-mm air bubbles in water, the incremental velocity is about 5% of the terminal velocity at a separation of 10 equivalent diameters (Yip et al. 1970).

A prediction of the interaction has been made using a simple superposition postulate: The trailing particle rises at a velocity equal to the sum of its terminal rise velocity in isolation and the velocity in the wake of the leading particle at the position of the nose of the trailing particle. The effect of the trailing particle on the leading particle is neglected (Marks 1973; Otake et al. 1977).

The incremental velocity due to the wake has been determined for ellipsoidal bubbles from the measured velocity of the trailing bubble during interaction. Otake et al. (1977) give an empirical correlation of the axial and radial components of the wake velocity for separations less than four equivalent diameters. At the large Reynolds numbers typical of the ellipsoidal regime in low-M liquids, the wakes are turbulent and the asymptotic turbulent wake formula (Schlichting 1968) should apply for large separations. This formula predicts that the wake velocity decays with the $-\frac{2}{3}$ power of the downstream distance. Using the simple superposition postulate and the asymptotic wake expression with its one adjustable constant, Marks (1973) was able to fit data on the rise velocity of a chain of bubbles. This approach has not been tested for the interaction of pairs of bubbles or drops.

Spherical Cap Regime

The spherical cap regime covers most bubbles and drops with Eo > 40 (figure 1.3.23). In general, this means volumes greater than about 3 cm^3 or $d_e > 18$ mm. Such large bubbles are of interest in liquid-metal processing, fluidized beds, and underwater explosions. Liquid drops in this size range are of less practical importance and have received considerably less attention than large gas bubbles.

For spherical cap fluid particles with Re > 150, the front surface is very much like a segment of a true sphere, while the rear surface is almost flat, as shown schematically in figure 1.3.23. The wake angle θ_w (defined as the angle between the vertical axis and the line joining the center of curvature of an arc fitting the front portion to the outer rim of the cap) is then very nearly 50°. At lower Re, the bubble or drop is more rounded (i.e., θ_w is larger), the rear surface tends to be indented, and the leading surface is oblate ellipsoidal rather than truly spherical. The wake angle in degrees can be predicted from an empirical relationship suggested by Clift et al. (1978):

$$\theta_w = 50 + 190 \exp\left(-0.62\, \mathrm{Re}^{0.4}\right) \qquad [1.3.301]$$

The volume of continuous-phase liquid contained in the indentation at the rear increases from zero at Re ≈ 1 to a maximum of about 25% of the particle volume at Re ≈ 35, reaching zero again for Re > 150 (Hnat & Buckmaster 1976, Bhaga 1976). Theoretical treatments of wakes have been attempted by Moore (1959), Collins (1966), Rippin & Davidson (1967), and Parlange (1969).

The terminal velocity of spherical cap fluid particles may be predicted by an approach first suggested by Davies & Taylor (1950). A potential flow pressure distribution is assumed in the neighborhood of a complete sphere of which the bubble or drop forms the cap. Balancing this pressure distribution with that due to the hydrostatic pressure distribution to terms of order θ^2 leads to

$$u_T = \frac{2}{3}\left(\frac{gR_c\Delta\rho}{\rho}\right)^{1/2} \qquad [1.3.302]$$

where R_c is the radius of curvature of the bubble surface at the nose. Collins (1966) obtained a second approximation by a perturbation technique

$$u_T = 0.652 \left(\frac{g \bar{R}_c \Delta \rho}{\rho} \right)^{1/2}$$ [1.3.303]

where $\bar{R}_c$ is the average radius of curvature of the front surface over an included angle of 37.5° from the nose. Both [1.3.302] and [1.3.303] give good results for a wide range of systems provided Eo > 40 and Re $\gtrsim$ 150. For smaller Re, where the front surface is oblate spheroidal, the result corresponding to [1.3.302] is (Wairegi & Grace 1976)

$$u_T = (\sin^{-1} e - e \sqrt{1 - e^2}) \frac{(gb \Delta \rho / \rho)^{1/2}}{e^3}$$ [1.3.304]

where e is the eccentricity and b is the vertical semiaxis.

Since spherical cap fluid particles are geometrically similar with $\theta \approx 50°$ once Re exceeds about 150, [1.3.302] can be recast in terms of volume V_p or equivalent diameter d_e. Convenient forms commonly found in the literature are

$$u_T = 0.792 \left(\frac{g \Delta \rho}{\rho} \right)^{1/2} V_p^{1/6}$$ [1.3.305]

$$u_T = 0.711 \left(\frac{g d_e \Delta \rho}{\rho} \right)^{1/2}$$ [1.3.306]

and

$$C_D = \frac{4}{3} \frac{g d_e}{u_T^2} \frac{\Delta \rho}{\rho} = \frac{8}{3}$$ [1.3.307]

Note that these results apply only for Re > 150 and Eo > 40. For Re > 1.2 and Eo > 40 and gas bubbles (i.e., $\Delta \rho / \rho \approx 1$), Bhaga & Weber (1981) showed that terminal velocities for $10^{-11} < M < 10^3$ can be obtained from a simple dimensional empirical relationship:

$$u_T = \frac{10^{6m} V_p^m}{4 + 1.32 M^{0.29}}$$ [1.3.308]

where

$$m = 0.167(1 + 0.34 M^{0.24})$$ [1.3.309]

Equation [1.3.308] approaches [1.3.305] as $M \to 0$ and $\Delta \rho / \rho \to 1$.

For very viscous systems where $M > 2$, the terminal velocity can be predicted over the entire range of Re by the quadratic equation (Clift et al. 1978)

$$2 \, \mathrm{Re}^2 + 6 \, \mathrm{Re} \, \frac{2 + 3\kappa}{1 + \kappa} - \mathrm{Ar} = 0$$ [1.3.310]

where

$$\mathrm{Ar} = \mathrm{Eo}^{3/2} M^{-1/2} = \frac{g \rho \Delta \rho d_e^3}{\mu^2}$$ [1.3.311]

is the Archimedes number.

In systems with $M \gtrsim 10^{-1}$, bubbles and drops may trail thin annular films of the dispersed phase, called skirts, as shown schematically in figure 1.3.23. Skirt formation occurs when viscous forces acting on the outer rim are sufficient to overcome the restraining effect of surface or interfacial tension forces. For gas bubbles, skirt formation has been found to require $Re \gtrsim 9$ and

$$\frac{We}{Re} = \frac{\mu u_T}{\sigma} > 2.32 + \frac{11}{(Re - 9)^{0.7}} \qquad [1.3.312]$$

while the corresponding conditions for liquid drops are $Re \gtrsim 4$ and $We/Re \gtrsim 2.3$ (Clift et al. 1978). The highest Re at which skirts have been reported is 500 (Hnat & Buckmaster 1976).

The skirt thickness is of order $(6\mu_p u_T/g\Delta\rho)^{1/2}$ (Guthrie & Bradshaw 1969). The local skirt thickness tends to decrease with increasing distance from the rear of the bubble or drop, while the overall skirt length increases with increasing Re (Wairegi 1974; Hnat & Buckmaster 1976; Bhaga 1976). Skirts may be steady, growing with time, wavy, or exfoliating (Wairegi & Grace 1976). The length of steady skirts is controlled by a balance between viscous and capillary forces (Bhaga 1976), while the length of wavy skirts is limited by the growth of Helmholtz instability waves (Hnat & Buckmaster 1976). Whatever their configuration, skirts have little influence on the terminal velocity or drag on large fluid particles.

Surface-active agents play a minor role in determining the hydrodynamics of the spherical cap regime, as noted in the preceding section (see figure 1.3.24).

At $Re > 110$, wakes behind spherical cap bubbles and drops are turbulent and unbounded. At lower Re, closed recirculating wakes are formed with volumes given by

$$\frac{V_w}{V_p} = 0.037 \, Re^{1.4} \qquad (3 \leqslant Re \leqslant 110) \qquad [1.3.313]$$

(Clift et al. 1978). Bhaga (1976) used hydrogen bubbles to trace the motion in the wake and external flow fields, while Wairegi (1974) studied the motion of tracer particles inside large drops. Closed wakes are commonly assumed to complete the sphere or spheroid of which the fluid particle forms the cap, but this tends to overestimate the wake size for $Re \lesssim 5$ and underestimate wake volumes at larger Re (Bhaga 1976). Shedding from wakes at $Re \gtrsim 150$ is responsible for the secondary motion (rocking or wobbling) often observed for spherical cap bubbles.

Containing walls lead to elongation, smaller wakes, and a reduction in the terminal velocity of large fluid particles. Experimental results of Collins (1967) for $0.125 \leqslant d_e/D \leqslant 0.6$ giving the reduction in terminal velocity have been fitted (Wallis 1969) by

$$\frac{u_T^w}{u_T} = 1.13 \, \exp\left(-\frac{d_e}{D}\right) \qquad [1.3.314]$$

For $d_e/D < 0.125$, there is negligible retardation. Bhaga (1976) showed that [1.3.314] gives good results down to $Re \approx 10$, even if skirts are being trailed.

Only in-line interactions of spherical cap bubbles have been studied. In general, spherical cap bubbles coalesce immediately on collision, although if the resulting bubble is large it may break into several fragments (Bhaga 1976). For $Re < 2$, the interaction is best described by the interaction of two rigid spheres, which is considered in section 1.3.3 (Narayanan et al. 1974). For $10 < Re < 100$, where the wake is closed, the trailing bubble has essentially no effect on the velocity of the leading bubble until coalescence occurs (Crabtree & Bridgwater 1971; Narayanan et al. 1974; Bhaga & Weber 1980). This enables prediction of the interaction through the simple superposition postulate used for ellipsoidal bubbles in the preceding section. In the range of Re where the wake is closed, the asymptotic laminar wake formula of Batchelor (1967) should apply for large separations. This formula predicts that the wake velocity on the axis of rise decays as the reciprocal of the separation. The velocity measured behind a spherical cap bubble is smaller than the asymptotic laminar wake velocity, even 20–30 equivalent diameters downstream (Bhaga 1976). A semiempirical wake velocity correlation, which approaches Batchelor's formula for very large separations, was presented by Bhaga & Weber (1980) for $10 < Re < 110$. There is good agreement between this correlation and the earlier empirical correlations (Crabtree & Bridgwater 1971; Narayanan et al. 1974) in their ranges of overlap.

For spherical caps at higher Reynolds numbers, the trailing bubble encounters the open wake of the leading bubble, which distorts the trailing bubble and makes it move erratically (Bhaga & Weber 1980). Two spherical cap bubbles in water with open wakes take longer to collide than the same bubbles starting with the same separation in a viscous liquid, where $Re < 10^2$ and the wakes are closed (Crabtree & Bridgwater 1971). This is due in part to the fact that the trailing bubble at larger Re moves horizontally out of the region of highest wake velocity. No models for the interaction of spherical caps at $Re > 110$ have been proposed.

1.3.9.2 Drops in Gases

Drops falling freely under gravity through air remain very nearly spherical for $Eo = g d_e^2 \Delta\rho/\sigma \lesssim 0.4$. Because of the large viscosity ratios $\kappa = \mu_p/\mu$, internal circulation tends to be very slow, and the drag on such spherical drops follows closely the standard drag curve for rigid spheres. Careful experimental results have been reported by Beard & Pruppacher (1969).

Numerical solutions for spherical water drops falling through air have been obtained by LeClair et al. (1972). Internal circulation delays somewhat the onset of boundary-layer separation and causes wakes to be slightly smaller than for corresponding rigid spheres. Departure from fore-and-aft symmetry of the inner and outer flow fields becomes more significant as Re increases. For $Re > 300$, a small secondary internal circulation vortex of opposite sense to the main pattern is predicted.

As Eo increases above 0.4, some distortion from the spherical can be detected. Flattening occurs primarily at the leading (lower) surface, so that the shape then lacks fore-and-aft symmetry. The shape can be represented by two half-spheroids sharing a common horizontal circular cross section of radius a and having semiminor axes b_1 and b_2. The height-to-maximum-width ratio is given approximately by

$$\bar{E} = \frac{b_1 + b_2}{2a} = [1.0 + 0.18 \, (\text{Eo} - 0.4)^{0.8}]^{-1} \quad (0.4 < \text{Eo} < 8) \quad [1.3.315]$$

This ratio is given for water drops in air in figure 1.3.28. The ratio of the lower vertical semiaxis to the total height is

$$\frac{b_1}{b_1 + b_2} = [2.0 + 0.24 \, (\text{Eo} - 0.5)^{0.8}]^{-1} \quad (0.5 < \text{Eo} < 8) \quad [1.3.316]$$

(Clift et al. 1978). This ratio gives a measure of the lack of fore-and-aft symmetry.

Terminal velocities have been determined for a number of different liquids in atmospheric air. Results are rare for cases in which the continuous phase is other than air. The best results for water drops in air are shown in figure 1.3.28. For Eo < 0.5, terminal velocities can be calculated as for rigid spheres, as noted above. For larger drops, the following equations (Clift et al. 1978) are recommended:

$$\text{Re}_T = 1.62 \, \text{Eo}^{0.755} M^{-0.25} \quad (0.5 \leqslant \text{Eo} \leqslant 1.84) \quad [1.3.317]$$

$$\text{Re}_T = 1.83 \, \text{Eo}^{0.555} M^{-0.25} \quad (1.84 \leqslant \text{Eo} \leqslant 5.0) \quad [1.3.318]$$

and
$$\text{Re}_T = 2.0 \, \text{Eo}^{0.5} M^{-0.25} \quad (\text{Eo} \geqslant 5.0) \quad [1.3.319]$$

In dimensional form [1.3.319] gives

$$u_T = 2.0 \left(\frac{g \sigma \Delta \rho}{\rho^2} \right)^{0.25} \quad (\text{Eo} \geqslant 5.0) \quad [1.3.320]$$

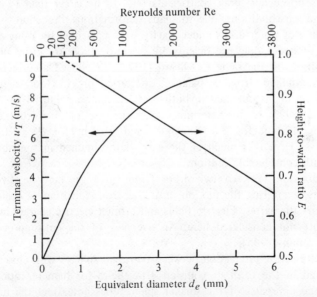

Figure 1.3.28 Terminal velocity and height-to-width ratio for water drops falling through air at 293 K and 0.1013 MPa. Data sources: Gunn & Kinzer (1949), Beard & Pruppacher (1969), Pruppacher & Beard (1970). Adapted from Clift et al. (1978) with permission.

so that the terminal velocity of large drops in gases eventually becomes independent of both drop size and gas viscosity. Drops tend to become unstable and break up in stagnant media when Eo reaches or exceeds about 16 (Grace et al. 1978).

For water drops in air under normal atmospheric conditions, Berry & Pranger (1974) proposed a single equation, accurate to within approximately 3%:

$$\text{Re}_T = \exp \left[-3.126 + 1.013 \ln N_D - 0.01912 (\ln N_D)^2 \right]$$

$$(2.4 < N_D < 10^7 \qquad 0.1 < \text{Re} < 3550) \qquad\qquad [1.3.321]$$

where $N_D = C_D \text{Re}_T^2 = 4gd_e^3 \rho \Delta\rho / 3\mu^2$. Corrections for noncontinuum effects are required for $d_e \overset{<}{\sim} 20$ μm (Beard 1976).

Quantities of surfactants sufficient to lower σ appreciably cause greater flattening of falling drops, and this leads to increased drag and decreased u_T (Ryan 1976). Traces of surfactants too small to lower σ appreciably have been claimed to influence u_T (Buzzard & Nedderman 1967), but this is questionable in view of the minor extent and influence of internal circulation with high-κ systems.

Wall effects are seldom of concern for drops in gases, and no experimental results appear to have been published about these effects.

Drops accelerating in airstreams may split up, commonly by a mechanism whereby the drop forms an inverted bag shape, which is inflated and then shatters into many pieces (Lane 1951). For water drops accelerated by a shock wave of velocity u, Reichman & Temkin (1974) found that breakup occurs for We = $\rho d_e u^2 / \sigma \geqslant 6.5$. For extremely high velocities, liquid is torn from the surface of the drop in what is called boundary-layer stripping (Fishburn 1974). When drop breakup does not occur, drag coefficients tend to be larger than for rigid spheres under accelerating conditions, due to shape deformations. Procedures for predicting the acceleration of water drops under gravity were presented by Wang & Pruppacher (1977). Instantaneous drag coefficients are based on those for drops under terminal settling conditions at the same Re. Beard (1977) introduced a correction for shape distortion determined from a balance of static forces. Good agreement with experimental results is obtained in both cases. Distances required for freely falling drops to reach 99% of their terminal velocities are of the order of 5.4 m for $d_e = 1.0$ mm, 12.6 m for $d_e = 2.0$ mm, and 18.1 m for $d_e = 6.0$ mm. These distances are so large that much of the early data obtained in the laboratory must be treated with considerable caution.

The interaction between two drops falling in a gas may be divided into an interaction stage covering the motion until the drops touch and a coalescence stage covering events thereafter. Electric fields and droplet electric charges influence both stages, but are not considered here. An overview of the entire process has been presented by Gunn (1965).

The results of the interaction between two rigid spheres with closed wakes have been presented in the form of collision efficiencies for diameter ratios of 1/10 or less, where the approach of the smaller sphere does not affect the motion of the larger sphere (e.g., Davies 1974). Attention is confined here to drops of more nearly equal size. The collision efficiency for a vertically falling drop is defined as the square of the ratio of the horizontal center-to-center offset for a grazing trajectory with another drop to the sum of the radii of the two drops. Schlamp et al. (1976)

calculated collision efficiencies for ratios of droplet diameters up to 1.0 over a range of Re from 0.02 to 4, corresponding to drop diameters of 20–150 μm in air. Assuming that each drop moved in the flow field from the other drop in isolation, they used the numerical solutions of the Navier-Stokes equations for solid spheres of LeClair et al. (1970). For the larger drops $(100 \overset{\cdot}{<} d_e \overset{\cdot}{<} 150 \, \mu\text{m})$, the calculated collision efficiencies lie between 0.8 and 1.1 for diameter ratios above 0.5. Hence these drops will collide with essentially all nearly equal-sized drops in their paths of descent. For smaller drops, the efficiencies are lower and more complex functions of diameter ratio. No matter what the size, the collision efficiency decreases as diameter ratio decreases, reflecting the fact that smaller drops follow the fluid motion better. For larger drops with open wakes, the wake extends many diameters downstream (Cataneo et al. 1971; List & Hand 1971). This wake is important in the interaction of drops of diameter larger than 1 mm (Magarvey & Geldart 1962; Cotton & Gokhale 1967; Spengler & Gokhale 1973). No models of the interaction of large drops have been proposed.

When two drops collide, they may coalesce permanently either completely or partially, they may "bounce" and separate, or they may coalesce temporarily before the resulting drop disintegrates into several fragments (McTaggart-Cowan & List 1975; Levin & Machnes 1977; Bradley & Stow 1978). The fate of the colliding droplets depends on the angle of the collision and the sizes and velocities of the original drops. No studies exist of the effect of surface-active agents on collision behavior.

1.4 Interfacial Phenomena

John C. Slattery and Raymond W. Flumerfelt

Interfacial phenomena are all effects associated with momentum, energy, and mass transfer at phase interfaces. We begin by examining the nature of the phase interface and associated common lines. We then examine separately the manners in which momentum, energy, and mass transfer are described at these phase interfaces and common lines.

1.4.1 DIVIDING SURFACE

A *phase interface* is the region separating two phases in which the properties or behavior of the material differ from those of the adjoining phases. There is considerable evidence that density and the concentrations of species present are appreciably different in the neighborhood of an interface (Defay et al. 1966, p. 29). As the critical point is approached, density is a continuous function of position in the direction normal to the interface (Hein 1914; Winkler & Maass 1933; Maass 1938; McIntosh et al. 1939; Palmer 1952). This suggests that the phase interface is a three-dimensional region, whose thickness may be several molecular diameters or more.

Molecular models for the interfacial region are not discussed here. It is perhaps sufficient to mention that the three-dimensional character of the phase interface is explicitly recognized in statistical mechanical calculations (Ono & Kondo 1960).

There are two continuum models for the phase interface. The most obvious model is a three-dimensional region of finite thickness. Korteweg (1901) suggested that the stress-deformation behavior in such a region could be described by saying that the stress tensor is a function of the rate of deformation tensor, the gradient of density, and the second gradient of density. No dynamic problems have been solved with his model for interfacial behavior. Deemer & Slattery (1978) modeled a dilute solution of surfactant molecules in the interfacial region by a dilute suspension of rigid bodies. In particular, they worked out the interfacial tension and interfacial shear viscosity attributable to a dilute suspension of spheres and to a dilute suspension of chains of spheres.

As a model for a phase interface in a body at rest or at equilibrium, Gibbs (1928, p. 219) proposed a two-dimensional dividing surface that sensibly coincides with the phase interface and separates two homogeneous phases. By a homogeneous phase, he meant one in which all variables, such as mass density and temperature, assume uniform values. He suggested that the cumulative effects of the interface on the adjoining phases be taken into account by assigning to the dividing surface any mass or energy not accounted for by the adjoining homogeneous phases.

Gibbs' approach may be extended to include dynamic phenomena, if we define a homogeneous phase as one throughout which each constitutive equation or description of material behavior applies uniformly. As in the static case, the cumulative effects of the interface on the adjoining phases can be described by associating densities and fluxes with the interface.

To describe how this dividing surface moves as a function of time, one must be able to locate it at some reference time. It is not sufficiently precise to say that the dividing surface is sensibly coincident with the phase interface (Defay et al. 1966, p. 25). The location of the reference dividing surface is normally made with respect to the mass distribution or the concentration distribution.

Deemer & Slattery (1978) developed expressions for the densities, fluxes, and source terms appropriate to the dividing surface model in terms of the densities, fluxes, and source terms arising in the context of the three-dimensional model for the interfacial region.

1.4.2 COMMON LINE

A common line (*contact line* or *three-phase line of contact*) is the curve formed by the intersection of two dividing surfaces. Of primary concern here is the motion of common lines.

Sometimes a very thin film or *foot* is observed to precede the advance of a macroscopic film. During the spontaneous spreading of hydrocarbon liquids on horizontal and vertical surfaces, Bascom et al. (1964) observed a foot as much as several millimeters long but less than 50Å thick. They attributed the formation and movement of the foot to capillary flow in microscratches on the surface and to surface diffusion. Radigan et al. (1974) detected a foot on the order of 1 μm high during the spreading of drops of glass on Fernico metal at 1000°C. In studies described by Williams (1977), the leading edge of this foot had a periodic structure. Depending on the liquid, either it assumed a scalloped periodic structure or it moved by a series of random advances with some approximate periodicity. In contrast, Schonhorn et al. (1966), who studied the wetting of aluminum, mica, and Teflon surfaces by two polymer melts, were not able to detect a foot up to 10 μm of the apparent leading edges of their films.

In cases where a foot does precede the advance of a macroscopic film, the leading edge of the macroscopic film should be taken as the common line and the foot treated as an adsorbed film.

A common line does not always move smoothly. Poynting & Thomson (1902) forced mercury up a capillary tube and then gradually reduced the pressure. Instead of falling, the mercury first adjusted itself to the reduced pressure by altering the curvature of the air-mercury interface. When the pressure gradient finally grew too large, the configuration of the meniscus became unstable and the mercury fell a short distance in the tube before stopping, repeating the deformation of the interface, and falling again when a new instability developed. Yarnold (1938) saw the same sticking phenomenon as a liquid index moved slowly through a glass capillary tube. Wilson (1975) pointed out that the irregular jerking and sticking of the common line seen by Elliott & Riddiford (1967) was due to a hydrodynamic instability. In some experiments, episodic movements of the common line may be attributable to contact angle hysteresis. Irregularities may be caused by variations in the contact angle along the common line, which in turn may be due to a nonuniform distribution of contaminants. In other cases, the multiphase flow may be hydrodynamically unstable and no amount of cleaning can alter the situation.

In the displacement of one fluid by another on a solid surface, Dussan & Davis (1974) always saw a rolling motion exhibited by one of the phases. In some cases this was a "forward rolling motion," in which material adjacent to the fluid-fluid interface moves down the interface to the common line and is left adjacent to the fluid-solid interface (see phase A in figure 1.4.1a). In other cases they saw a "backward rolling motion," in which material originally adjacent to the fluid-solid interface is lifted off as the common line passes and is transported up along the fluid-fluid interface (see phase B in figure 1.4.1b). Allen & Benson (1975) observed more complicated three-dimensional rolling motions during the passage of a drop down an inclined plane. The conditions determining which phase assumes a rolling

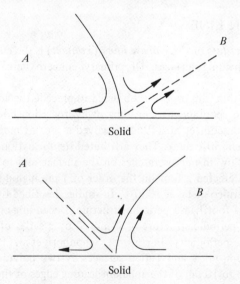

Figure 1.4.1   (a) Phase A exhibits a forward rolling motion and material is ejected from the immediate neighborhood of the common line into phase B along either side of a material surface (indicated by the dashed line). (b) Phase B exhibits a backward rolling motion and material is injected into the immediate neighborhood of the common line from phase A along either side of a material surface.

motion during a displacement have not been defined. Often the more viscous phase adopts the rolling motion, but contact angle and the relative magnitudes of inertial forces, viscous forces, gravity, and interfacial forces should be significant factors as well.

Dussan & Davis (1974) suggested by a few simple experiments and a theoretical argument that if one phase exhibits a rolling motion as a common line passes, the character of the motion in the other phase is quite different. If phase A exhibits a forward rolling motion as in figure 1.4.1a, there will be ejection of material from the neighborhood of the common line into the interior of phase B along both sides of a material surface originating at the common line and dividing the flow field within the phase. If phase B exhibits a backward rolling motion as in figure 1.4.1b, there will be injection of material from the interior of phase A into the immediate neighborhood of the common line along both sides of such a surface.

The motions of common lines and the flows resulting from their motions are not well understood. Current research should be consulted in the hope of further clarification.

1.4.3 GENERAL BALANCE EQUATIONS

Assuming that the effect of the interface may be attributed to a dividing surface, the general balance or general conservation law for some quantity (momentum, energy, mass, etc.) associated with a multiphase, multicomponent material body takes the form

$$\frac{d}{dt}\left(\int_R \psi \, dV + \int_\Sigma \psi^{(\sigma)} \, dA \right) = - \int_S \phi \cdot \mathbf{n} \, dA$$

$$- \int_C \phi^{(\sigma)} \cdot \boldsymbol{\mu} \, dl + \int_R \rho \zeta \, dV + \int_\Sigma \rho^{(\sigma)} \zeta^{(\sigma)} \, dA \qquad [1.4.1]$$

With reference to figure 1.4.2, R denotes the region occupied by the body, S the closed surface bounding the body, Σ the dividing surfaces enclosed by S, C the lines formed by the intersection of Σ with S, t time, ψ the density of the quantity per unit volume within the bulk phases, $\psi^{(\sigma)}$ the density of the quantity per unit area on Σ, ϕ the flux of the quantity (per unit area) through S, $\mathbf{n}$ the unit vector normal and outwardly directed with respect to S, $\phi^{(\sigma)}$ the flux of the quantity (per unit length of line) through C, $\boldsymbol{\mu}$ the unit vector normal to C that is both tangent and outwardly directed with respect to Σ, ρ the mass density within the bulk phases, $\rho^{(\sigma)}$ the mass density (per unit area) on Σ, ζ the rate of production of the quantity per unit mass at each point within the bulk phases, and $\zeta^{(\sigma)}$ the rate of production of the quantity per unit mass at each point on Σ; dV indicates a volume integration, dA an area integration, and dl a line integration. A multicomponent material body is one whose material particles travel with the local mass-averaged velocity of the material.

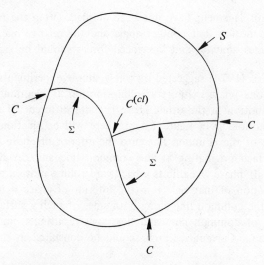

Figure 1.4.2 For any multiphase, multicomponent material body occupying a region R, one can speak about the closed surface S bounding the body, the union of all dividing surfaces Σ enclosed by S, the lines C formed by the intersection of Σ with S, and the union of all common lines $C^{(cl)}$ formed by the intersection of dividing surfaces.

As written, [1.4.1] does not account for the accumulation and production of the quantity concerned in the common lines or for the flux of this quantity along the common lines. There is little evidence at present that any of these effects are significant in the context of momentum, energy, and mass transfer.

Deemer & Slattery (1978) showed that, in addition to implying the well-known balance equation at each point in each phase, [1.4.1] requires a local balance at each point on a dividing surface

$$\frac{d_{(s)}\psi^{(\sigma)}}{dt} + \psi^{(\sigma)}\,\mathrm{div}_{(\sigma)}\mathbf{U}^{(\sigma)} + \mathrm{div}_{(\sigma)}\phi^{(\sigma)} - \rho^{(\sigma)}\zeta^{(\sigma)} + [\psi(\mathbf{U} - \mathbf{U}^{(\sigma)})\cdot\boldsymbol{\xi} + \phi\cdot\boldsymbol{\xi}] = 0$$

[1.4.2]

and a local balance at each point on a common line

$$(\psi^{(\sigma)}[\mathbf{U}^{(\sigma)} - \mathbf{u}^{(cl)}]\cdot\boldsymbol{v} + \phi^{(\sigma)}\cdot\boldsymbol{v}) = 0$$

[1.4.3]

Here
$$\frac{d_{(s)}\psi^{(\sigma)}}{dt} \equiv \left(\frac{\partial\psi^{(\sigma)}}{\partial t}\right)_{y^1,y^2} + \nabla_{(\sigma)}\psi^{(\sigma)}\cdot(\mathbf{U}^{(\sigma)} - \mathbf{u})$$

[1.4.4]

is the surface material derivative,

$$\mathbf{u} \equiv \left(\frac{\partial\mathbf{p}^{(\sigma)}}{\partial t}\right)_{y^1,y^2}$$

[1.4.5]

is the velocity of a fixed point on the dividing surface,

$$\mathbf{z} = \mathbf{p}^{(\sigma)}(y^1, y^2, t) \qquad [1.4.6]$$

is the parametric equation for the moving and deforming dividing surface, y^1 and y^2 are the surface coordinates denoting position on the dividing surface, $\mathbf{U}$ the mass-averaged velocity vector, $\mathbf{U}^{(\sigma)}$ the mass-averaged surface velocity vector, $C^{(cl)}$ the union of all the common lines or three-phase lines of contact formed by the intersection of dividing surfaces, $\nabla_{(\sigma)}$ the surface gradient operator (Hopke & Slattery 1975), and $\text{div}_{(\sigma)}$ the surface divergence operator (Hopke & Slattery 1975). Boldface brackets are used on the dividing surface between phases i and j as a shorthand notation

$$[B\,\xi] \equiv B^{(i)}\xi^{(i)} + B^{(j)}\xi^{(j)} \qquad [1.4.7]$$

with the understanding that $B^{(i)}$ is evaluated within phase i in the limit as the dividing surface is approached and $\xi^{(i)}$ is the unit normal to the dividing surface pointing into phase i. Similarly, boldface parentheses are used on the common line formed by phases i, j, and k as a shorthand notation

$$(B^{(\sigma)}\nu) \equiv B^{(\sigma,ij)}\nu^{(ij)} + B^{(\sigma,ik)}\nu^{(ik)} + B^{(\sigma,jk)}\nu^{(jk)} \qquad [1.4.8]$$

where $B^{(\sigma,\,ij)}$ is evaluated on the dividing surface between phases i and j in the limit as the common line is approached and $\nu^{(ij)}$ is the unit normal to the common line that is tangent to and directed into this dividing surface. The scalar $\mathbf{U}^{(\sigma)} \cdot \xi$ is the speed of displacement of the dividing surface in the direction ξ. Also, $\mathbf{u}^{(cl)}$ is the velocity of a fixed point on the common line; $\mathbf{u}^{(cl)} \cdot \nu$ is the speed of displacement of the common line in the direction ν.

1.4.4   CONSERVATION OF MASS

Conservation of mass requires that

The mass of a multicomponent material body is independent of time.

In order that [1.4.1] describes conservation of mass, identify

$$\psi \equiv \rho \qquad \psi^{(\sigma)} \equiv \rho^{(\sigma)}$$
$$\phi \equiv \mathbf{0} \qquad \phi^{(\sigma)} \equiv \mathbf{0} \qquad [1.4.9]$$
$$\zeta \equiv 0 \qquad \zeta^{(\sigma)} \equiv 0$$

Here ρ is the local mass density within a phase and $\rho^{(\sigma)}$ is the local surface mass density.

Equation [1.4.2] gives the jump mass balance

$$\frac{d_{(s)}\rho^{(\sigma)}}{dt} + \rho^{(\sigma)}\,\text{div}_{(\sigma)}\mathbf{U}^{(\sigma)} + [\rho(\mathbf{U} - \mathbf{U}^{(\sigma)}) \cdot \xi] = 0 \qquad [1.4.10]$$

describing mass conservation at every point on a dividing surface. If there is no mass transfer to or from the phase interface, this reduces to

$$\frac{d_{(s)}\rho^{(\sigma)}}{dt} + \rho^{(\sigma)}\text{div}_{(\sigma)}U^{(\sigma)} = 0 \tag{1.4.11}$$

Occasionally $\rho^{(\sigma)}$ may be a constant, in which case [1.4.11] becomes

$$\text{div}_{(\sigma)}U^{(\sigma)} = 0 \tag{1.4.12}$$

Similarly, [1.4.3] and [1.4.9] imply the mass balance at the common line, which gives the requirement of mass conservation at every point on the common line. If there is no mass transfer across the common line, it is automatically satisfied.

1.4.5 MOMENTUM TRANSFER

The two fundamental postulates of momentum transfer are Euler's first law

> In an inertial frame of reference, the time rate of change of the momentum of a multicomponent body is equal to the applied force.

and Euler's second law

> In an inertial frame of reference, the time rate of change of the moment of momentum of a multicomponent body is equal to the applied torque.

For [1.4.1] to take the form of Euler's first law, one must identify

$$\psi \equiv \rho U \qquad \psi^{(\sigma)} \equiv \rho^{(\sigma)}U^{(\sigma)}$$

$$\phi \equiv -T \qquad \phi^{(\sigma)} \equiv -T^{(\sigma)} \tag{1.4.13}$$

$$\zeta \equiv b \qquad \zeta^{(\sigma)} \equiv b$$

Here, T is the stress tensor, $T^{(\sigma)}$ the surface stress tensor, and b the body force vector (gravity).

Equation [1.4.2] gives the jump momentum balance

$$\frac{d_{(s)}(\rho^{(\sigma)}U^{(\sigma)})}{dt} + \rho^{(\sigma)}U^{(\sigma)}\text{div}_{(\sigma)}U^{(\sigma)} = \text{div}_{(\sigma)}T^{(\sigma)} + \rho^{(\sigma)}b$$

$$+ [-\rho U(U - U^{(\sigma)}) \cdot \xi + T \cdot \xi] \tag{1.4.14}$$

expressing the implications of Euler's first law at every point on a dividing surface. Often the effects of inertia, of the body force, and of mass transfer may be neglected in the dividing surface, in which case [1.4.14] reduces to

$$\text{div}_{(\sigma)}T^{(\sigma)} + [T \cdot \xi] = 0 \tag{1.4.15}$$

Equation [1.4.3] takes the form of the momentum balance at the common line

$$(\rho^{(\sigma)}U^{(\sigma)}[U^{(\sigma)} - u^{(cl)}] \cdot \nu - T^{(\sigma)} \cdot \nu) = 0 \tag{1.4.16}$$

Normally, the effect of mass transfer on momentum transfer at the common line is neglected, and this simplifies to

$$(T^{(\sigma)} \cdot \nu) = 0 \qquad\qquad [1.4.17]$$

Similarly, one can examine the implications of Euler's second law and conclude that the surface stress tensor is symmetrical and surface forces act tangential to the interface.

To determine the motion of a single phase, one must describe the stress-deformation behavior of the material through a constitutive equation for the stress tensor T. Similarly, to use the jump momentum balance [1.4.14] and the momentum balance at the common line [1.4.16] in determining the motion of a multiphase body, one must specify the stress-deformation behavior of the dividing surface through a constitutive equation for the surface stress tensor $T^{(\sigma)}$.

1.4.5.1 Interfacial Tension

The simplest constitutive equation for the surface stress tensor is

$$T^{(\sigma)} = \sigma P \qquad\qquad [1.4.18]$$

where σ is the interfacial tension and P is the projection tensor that transforms any vector defined on the dividing surface into its tangential components. The interfacial tension is a function of the local temperature and the composition of the dividing surface.

Consider an arbitrary line in a dividing surface. Equation [1.4.18] requires

$$T^{(\sigma)} \cdot \mu = \sigma\mu \qquad\qquad [1.4.19]$$

In words, the force per unit length of line that the dividing surface to one side of this line exerts on this line is both tangent to the interface and normal to this line. The magnitude of this force is the interfacial tension.

Equation [1.4.18] is valid under all known static conditions and at least an excellent approximation in most dynamic problems.

If we adopt [1.4.18], the reduced form of the jump momentum balance [1.4.15] becomes, for example,

$$\nabla_{(\sigma)}\sigma + 2H\sigma\xi + [T \cdot \xi] = 0 \qquad\qquad [1.4.20]$$

in which H is the mean curvature (McConnell 1957, p. 205) of the interface at the point in question. Similarly, the reduced form of the momentum balance at the common line [1.4.17] simplifies to the Neumann triangle:

$$(\sigma\nu) = 0 \qquad\qquad [1.4.21]$$

1.4.5.2 Measurement of Interfacial Tension

Numerous methods are available for the measurement of σ, and reviews are given by several authors (Padday 1969; Wu 1974; Adamson 1976; Hartland & Hartley 1976).

The most reliable methods are those involved with static interfaces. Typical of this group are the three methods illustrated in figures 1.4.3 and 1.4.4.

In the sessile and pendant drop methods, the interfacial tension is obtained from certain characteristic shape measurements coupled with solutions of the appropriate hydrostatic form of the jump momentum balance, i.e., [1.4.20] with σ constant and $[\mathbf{T} \cdot \xi] = -[p\,\xi]$. The nonlinear nature of the equation requires numerical solutions. For the sessile drop, solutions have been tabulated by several authors [see Padday (1969) for a collation of tables by Bashforth & Adams (1892), Blaisdell (1940), and Tawde & Parvatikar (1958)]. More recently, Hartland & Hartley (1976) provided extensive tabular solutions for both the sessile drop and the pendant drop. Additional tabular solutions for the pendant drop have been given by Fordham (1948), Mills (1953), Neiderhauser & Bartell (1950), and Stauffer (1965). These agree closely with those of Hartland & Hartley, but are not as extensive.

Application of the tabular solutions varies depending on the shape of the drop and the particular table used. Ordinarily, either x_{90} and z_{90} or x_c and z_c are

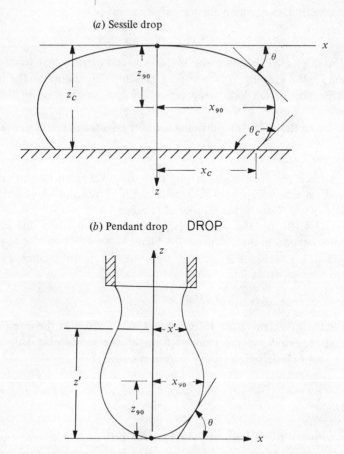

(a) Sessile drop

(b) Pendant drop   DROP

Figure 1.4.3 Illustrations of (a) sessile drop and (b) pendant drop methods for measuring interfacial tension.

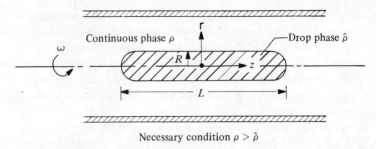

Figure 1.4.4 Spinning drop method for measuring interfacial tension.

measured in the sessile drop method. In the pendant drop method two measurements of x are used, ordinarily those corresponding to x_{90} and x' in figure 1.4.3b. Here x' is the value of x at $z' = \alpha x_{90}$, where $\alpha = 2$ or 2.5 depending on the tabular solution used.

A number of other tabular approaches have been used involving shape parameter measurements other than those indicated above as well as full profile shapes (Padday 1969; Hartland & Hartley 1976, chap. 8). Also, various authors have presented approximate solutions that can be used in place of the tabular results (Hartland & Hartley 1976, chap. 9).

The sessile and pendant drop methods are relatively simple and effective for determining σ and are applicable to a wide range of systems and temperatures (high-tension liquid melts to low-tension surfactant solutions). Their accuracies are limited only by the experimental accuracy to which the shape parameters and $\Delta\rho$ can be measured.

In recent years, the spinning drop method (figure 1.4.4) has received extensive use, particularly for low-tension systems, and theory and methods for its accurate application have been developed (Vonnegut 1942; Princen et al. 1967; Cayias et al. 1975; Manning & Scriven 1977; Manning & Puig 1978; Slattery & Chen 1978). The method involves shape measurements of drops and bubbles spinning in capillary tubes filled with another, more dense phase. Specifically, R, L, ω, and $\rho - \hat{\rho}$ are measured and σ determined from

$$\sigma = \frac{1}{2}\left(\frac{R}{r^*_{max}}\right)^3 (\rho - \hat{\rho})\omega^2 \qquad [1.4.22]$$

where r^*_{max} is a function of $2R/L$, which can be determined from the tables and figures of Slattery & Chen (1978); see also Princen et al. (1967), Cayias et al. (1975), and Manning & Puig (1978). When $2R/L < 0.25$, $r^*_{max} = 2^{1/3}$ with less than 0.4% error. The attractive feature of the spinning drop is that accurate values of σ can be obtained rapidly and somewhat routinely. The method is particularly valuable in making low-tension measurements ($\sim 10^{-1}$ mN/m or less).

Other static methods are available. The capillary rise method, as described by Harkins & Brown (1919), Sugden (1921), and Hartland & Hartley (1976, pp. 595–602), is quite accurate for determining σ when small contact angles are achieved. The rotating meniscus method of Princen & Aronson (1976) represents a variation of the capillary rise method; it gives good results when the capillary is completely wetted by the lower fluid. With the Wilhelmy plate (Padday 1957; Dettre & Johnson 1966; Pike & Bonnet 1970), a force measurement is required. With the meniscus break-off technique (Kovitz 1975), one slowly draws a meniscus out of a flat interface with a circular knife-edge and observes that there is a maximum height of the meniscus beyond which static solutions to the problem do not exist and the meniscus must break.

Finally, some of the more common dynamic methods are the ring pull method (Harkins & Jordan 1930; Freud & Freud 1930; Padday & Russell 1960); the drop weight method (Harkins & Brown 1919; Hartland & Srinivasan 1974; Pierson & Whitaker 1976a, 1976b); maximum bubble pressure (Sugden 1922, 1924; Johnson & Lane 1974; Ramakrishnan et al. 1976); the oscillating jet method (Sutherland 1954; Hansen & Wallace 1959; Hansen 1964); capillary ripples (Lucassen & Hansen 1966; Milgram & Bradley 1971); and others mentioned in the general review of Defay & Petrie (1971). Although not always fundamentally sound (see Padday 1976), such methods give quick and satisfactory results for many applications.

1.4.5.3 Prediction of Interfacial Tension

Goodrich (1971) reviewed the progress that has been made in using liquid-state theories and statistical mechanics to predict interfacial tension. As with most property predictions, more rigorous statistical mechanics treatments provide considerable insight into the various molecular interactions at the interface, but are generally too complex to be widely utilized for prediction.

Accurate predictions of surface tensions of pure liquids and mixtures of liquids against their vapors are possible with various empirical and semiempirical approaches. [Reid et al. (1977) summarize approaches and specific recommendations covering both nonpolar and polar systems.] For liquid-liquid systems the available predictive methods are much less exact. The methods based on thermodynamics are largely limited by the availability of accurate activity data and the specification of phase interactions at the interface. The strictly empirical methods are limited by the respective range of validity. Typical of the methods available are those given by Fowkes (1964), Girifalco & Good (1957), Good & Elbing (1970), Aveyard & Haydon (1973, pp. 78–83), Wu (1974), and Davis (1975).

Interfacial tension is a function of temperature and surface composition. For pure liquids against their vapors, σ decreases with temperature. For mixtures, σ can either increase or decrease with temperature; it can show a significant implicit dependence on pressure because the surface composition is a function of pressure, particularly near the critical point.

1.4.5.4 Interfacial Viscosities

After [1.4.18], the next simplest constitutive equation for the surface stress tensor is the Boussinesq surface fluid (Boussinesq 1913; Ericksen 1952; Oldroyd 1955; Scriven 1960)

$$\mathbf{T}^{(\sigma)} = [\sigma + (\kappa - \epsilon) \, \mathrm{div}_{(\sigma)}\mathbf{U}^{(\sigma)}]\mathbf{P} + 2\epsilon\mathbf{D}^{(\sigma)} \qquad [1.4.23]$$

in which

$$\mathbf{D}^{(\sigma)} \equiv \tfrac{1}{2} \, [\mathbf{P} \cdot \nabla_{(\sigma)}\mathbf{U}^{(\sigma)} + (\nabla_{(\sigma)}\mathbf{U}^{(\sigma)})^{T} \cdot \mathbf{P}] \qquad [1.4.24]$$

is the surface rate of deformation tensor, κ the interfacial dilatational viscosity, and ϵ the interfacial shear viscosity. The Boussinesq surface fluid is directly analogous to Newton's law of viscosity, a simple description of the stress-deformation behavior of bulk fluids. It says that the stresses arising within a dividing surface are attributable not only to the effects of interfacial tension but also to the local rate at which the surface deforms. The second law of thermodynamics requires that both κ and ϵ be positive.

Assuming the Boussinesq surface fluid, Scriven (1960) (see also Aris 1962, p. 242; for typographical errors see Slattery 1964) gives the three components of the jump momentum balance in the form of [1.4.15] for a stationary plane interface, a stationary cylindrical interface, and a stationary spherical interface.

The interfacial viscosities can often strongly influence the velocity distribution within the immediate neighborhood of the phase interface. This suggests that they can be significant parameters in problems concerned with the interface itself, for example in mass transfer. They can also be important when most of the fluid is within the neighborhood of an interface, as in foams.

The interfacial viscosities have been suggested as being important parameters in foam stability (Brown et al. 1953; Joly 1964; Kanner & Glass 1969), emulsion stability (Sherman 1953; Kanner & Glass 1969; Cairns et al. 1976), and coalescence (Barber & Hartland 1976). Some theoretical work (Oldroyd 1955) indicates that they may affect the stress-deformation behavior of emulsions. Both experimental (Lewis 1954a, 1954b, 1958; Plevan & Quinn 1966; Sada & Himmelblau 1967; Springer & Pigford 1970; Mudge & Heideger 1970; McFerrin & Davison 1971) and theoretical (Sternling & Scriven 1959; Scriven & Sternling 1964) investigations suggest that they may play a role in the suppression by surfactants of interfacial turbulence and of mass transfer across fluid-fluid phase interfaces. Interfacial viscosities may also play significant roles in the tertiary displacement of residual oil by microemulsions (Slattery 1974; Wasan et al. 1977) and by foams (Kanda & Schechter 1976; Slattery 1979).

1.4.5.5 Measurement of Interfacial Viscosities

Several experiments have been proposed for measuring the interfacial shear viscosity at liquid-gas interfaces. The most widely used device at this time is the deep channel surface viscometer (Burton & Mannheimer 1967; Mannheimer & Schechter 1968, 1970a; Pintar et al. 1971; Hegde & Slattery 1971b, Wei & Slattery 1976). Other geometries for which suitable analyses have appeared recently are the circular knife-edge surface viscometer (Mannheimer & Burton 1970; Lifshutz et al. (1971), the blunt knife-edge viscometer (Goodrich & Allen 1972; Briley et al. 1976), the disk viscometer (Goodrich 1969; Goodrich & Chatterjee 1970; Briley et al. 1976; Oh & Slattery 1978, the rotating wall knife edge viscometer (Goodrich et al. 1975;

Poskanzer & Goodrich 1975a, 1975b), and the surface relaxation method (Krieg et al. 1981).

A linear combination of the two interfacial viscosities at a liquid-gas interface can be determined from the damping characteristics of capillary waves (Hegde & Slattery 1971a). The two interfacial viscosities can be individually determined with the spinning drop interfacial viscometer (Slattery et al. 1979).

Fewer suggestions have been made about measurement of the interfacial viscosities at liquid-liquid interfaces. There have been three suggestions for using the deep channel geometry in measuring the interfacial shear viscosity at liquid-liquid interfaces (Mannheimer & Schechter 1970a; Wasan et al. 1971; Hegde 1971). Analyses are available for other geometries with the disk and biconical bob interfacial viscometers (Oh & Slattery 1978). The biconical interfacial viscometer has been proposed and used without a complete analysis in studying emulsion stability (Wibberley 1962; Shotten et al. 1971; Gladden & Neustadter 1972; Cairns et al. 1974).

A linear combination of the interfacial viscosities at a liquid-liquid interface can be measured by studying the velocity distribution in a drop rotating in a constant shear field (Wei et al. 1974). In a similar experiment, drop deformation and orientation measurements can provide individual values of κ and ϵ (Flumerfelt 1980; Phillips et al. 1980). The spinning drop interfacial viscometer may also be used to determine the two interfacial viscosities individually (Slattery et al. 1979).

1.4.5.6 Prediction of Surface Viscosities

There are no methods available for predicting measurable interfacial viscosities. The structural models for interfacial shear viscosity constructed by Deemer & Slattery (1978) are consistent with experimental data for dilute surface solutions only insofar as they predict interfacial shear viscosities below the sensitivity of current methods of measurement.

Available experimental data and these structural models for interfacial shear viscosity suggest that, for the surface shear viscosity to be appreciable (larger than 10^{-4} mN s/m), there must be considerable interaction between the surfactant molecules in the dividing surface. This interaction might be visualized as taking two forms. The surfactant molecules may be so large and of such concentration that intermolecular entanglements result. Interactions may also result with mixtures of surfactants, where the molecular weight distribution is such as to allow the interface to be more fully packed with surfactant.

In dilute solutions of nonionic surfactants below the critical micelle concentration (CMC point), the interfacial shear viscosity should increase with increasing concentration of surfactant, while the interfacial tension decreases. With anionic surfactants and cationic surfactants, even these simple rules may fail.

1.4.5.7 Contact Angle

Consider a common line formed by two fluids A and B on a solid S. Usual practice is to ignore the slight deformation of the solid (Lester 1961; Wickham & Wilson

1975) and write the component of [1.4.21] tangent to the undeformed solid surface in the form of Young's equation (Young 1805)

$$\cos \theta = \frac{1}{\sigma^{(AB)}} (\sigma^{(BS)} - \sigma^{(AS)})$$ [1.4.25]

where θ is the contact angle measured through phase A. The component of [1.4.21] normal to the (assumed) undeformed solid is ignored. The apparent interfacial tensions $\sigma^{(AS)}$ and $\sigma^{(BS)}$ can be measured, but one should be cautious in interpreting them as thermodynamic quantities.

In practice, the momentum balance at a common line on a solid surface is replaced by a specification of the contact angle. The magnitude of a contact angle is influenced by a number of factors.

Normally, a contact angle will depend on the direction of recent movement of the common line. This difference between advancing and receding contact angles is referred to as *contact angle hysteresis*. Surface roughness has been demonstrated to be one cause (Dettre & Johnson 1964; Morrow 1975; Huh & Mason 1977b). In some cases, the system requires a finite time to reach adsorption equilibrium (Elliott & Riddiford 1965), and the rate at which adsorption equilibrium is approached depends on the direction in which the common line moved recently (Yarnold & Mason 1949). When roughness is absent and adsorption equilibrium is reached quickly, contact angle hysteresis appears to be eliminated (Morrow 1975).

The contact angle is known to depend on the speed of displacement of the common line (Ablett 1923; Rose & Heins 1962; Elliott & Riddiford 1965, 1967; Schonhorn et al. 1966; Ellison & Tejada 1968; Coney & Masica 1969; Schwartz & Tejada 1970, 1972; Hansen & Toong 1971; Radigan et al. 1974; Hoffman 1975; Burley & Kennedy 1976a, 1976b; Kennedy & Burley 1977). Several distinct regimes are possible.

If the speed of displacement of the common line is sufficiently small, the contact angle will be independent of it, since the solid in the immediate neighborhood of the common line will nearly have achieved adsorption equilibrium with the adjoining phase [Elliott & Riddiford (1967); see also Wilson (1975), who argues that their measurements of the receding contact angle are in error].

If the speed of displacement of the common line is too large for adsorption equilibrium to be attained but too small for viscous effects within the adjoining fluid phases to play a significant role, the advancing contact angle increases with increasing speed of displacement (Hansen & Miotto 1957; Elliott & Riddiford 1967; Ellison & Tejada 1968; Blake & Haynes 1969; Schwartz & Tejada 1970, 1972). Often the contact angle will approach an upper limit with increasing speed of displacement (Ellison & Tejada 1968; Schwartz & Tejada 1970, 1972). Under these conditions, the common line is moving too rapidly for adsorption to have a significant effect on the contact angle but still too slowly for viscous effects within the adjoining phases to play a significant role.

If the speed of displacement of the common line is sufficiently large for the effects of the viscous forces to be important but too small for inertial effects within the adjoining fluid phases to be considered, the advancing contact angle increases with increasing speed of displacement (Hoffman 1975; Cherry & Holmes 1969). Under these conditions, the contact angle approaches as an upper limit 180°.

As this upper limit is reached, a continuous, visible film of the fluid originally in contact with the solid is entrained and the common line necessarily disappears (Burley & Kennedy 1976a, 1976b; Kennedy & Burley 1977). This is referred to as *dynamic wetting.* Inertial forces probably become more important than surface forces under these conditions.

The character of the solid surface plays an important role. Roughness, scratches, or grooves affect both advancing and receding contact angles (Morrow 1975; Huh & Mason 1977b; Oliver et al. 1977). Chemical heterogeneities undoubtedly also play a significant role (Cassie 1948; Johnson & Dettre 1969; Neumann & Good 1972).

A number of techniques have been used to study the effect of the speed of displacement of the common line on the contact angle (Ablett 1923; Rose & Heins 1962; Hansen & Toong 1971; Hoffman 1975; Coney & Masica 1969; Schonhorn et al. 1966; Radigan et al. 1974; Ellison & Tejada 1968; Schwartz & Tejada 1970, 1972; Burley & Kennedy 1976a, 1976b; Kennedy & Burley 1977; Elliott & Riddiford 1967; Wilson 1975). While the static contact angle is independent of measurement technique or, equivalently, geometry, the effect of geometry on dynamic measurements of the contact angle is unsettled. The analyses of Dussan (1976) and Huh & Mason (1977a) suggest that, if there is a slip within the immediate neighborhood of the common line, the significance of current measurements of the dynamic contact angle is in doubt. The configuration of the interface within the immediate neighborhood of the contact line can be quite different than one would observe with a microscope at X10. In contrast, there is the apparent success of Jiang et al. (1979) in correlating experimental data from two different geometries.

1.4.5.8 Measurements of Contact Angles

In figure 1.4.5, various methods for the measurement of contact angles are shown. Such measurements may be direct, where θ is obtained by constructing tangents on projected images of photographs or using a telemicroscope with a goniometer eyepiece; or they may be indirect, where θ is obtained from dimension or profile measurements of the drop meniscus shape, coupled with a knowledge of the interfacial tension and the density difference. In most cases, accurate measurements are possible by either approach; however, reproducibility of results requires extreme care in cleaning and preparing the surfaces.

The common observation of hysteresis in contact angle measurements necessitates the measurement of both advancing and receding angles. The difference between these quantities indicates the magnitude of the hysteresis. Depending on the system and the conditions, the hysteresis may be quite small (even zero) or quite large; values of $\theta_a - \theta_r$ as high as 154° have been measured for mercury on steel (Adamson 1976, p. 347).

Probably the most common methods for measuring contact angles are those associated with sessile drops and bubbles (Bigelow et al. 1946; Bartell & Bjorklund

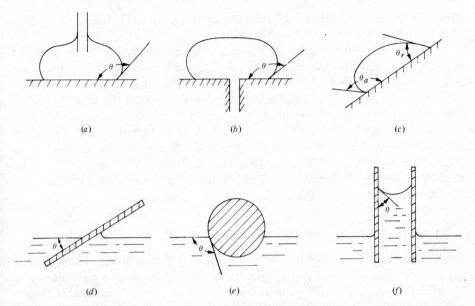

Figure 1.4.5 Methods for measuring contact angles. (*a* and *b*) Sessile drop or bubble injected from above or below; (*c*) variation with tilted plate; (*d*) tilted plate immersed in liquid; (*e*) variation with cylindrical body immersed in liquid; (*f*) capillary rise method.

1952; Gaudin & Witt 1964; Johnson & Dettre 1965; Adamson et al. 1970). Such methods are illustrated in figure 1.4.5*a*, *b*. To obtain advancing angles, the drop (or bubble) volume is increased by injecting fluid from a syringe from above or from below through a small hole in the support surface. Caution must be used; Wilson (1975) pointed out the possibility of instabilities developing as the common line advances. He argued that instabilities will always develop in the experiment in which receding angles are obtained by reversing this process. Both direct and indirect approaches are possible, and in the case of indirect measurements a number of tables and approaches are available (Hartland & Hartley 1976, pp. 562–593, 654–659; Ferguson 1913; Mack & Lee 1936; Staicopolus 1962; Padday 1963; Parvatikar 1967). A variation of the method involves tilting the plate and directly measuring the advancing and receding angles just before drop mobilization (Macdougall & Ockrent 1942) (figure 1.4.5*c*).

A more conventional approach utilizing a tilting plate is that shown in figure 1.4.5*d*. Here a plate is immersed in the liquid and the angle of inclination adjusted to give a horizontal liquid surface. The contact angle is obtained from the slope of the plate to the horizontal liquid surface. Advancing and receding angles are obtained by immersion and emersion of the plate, respectively, in the direction of inclination. A variation of the method involves the use of a horizontal cylinder, which is immersed in the liquid to a point where the liquid contact surfaces are horizontal (Ablett 1923) (figure 1.4.5*e*). A similar approach is possible with a spherical body (Yarnold 1946; Yarnold & Mason 1949).

Another method that has been widely used is the capillary rise method (figure 1.4.5*f*). Very accurate contact angle measurements can be made either directly

(Bartell & Merrill 1932; Rose & Heins 1962) or indirectly (Bosanquet & Hartley 1921; Bartell & Wooley 1933; Morrow 1975).

Other common methods employ tensiometric measurements; in particular, in the Wilhelmy plate method, the forces on a plate are measured during immersion and emersion cycles (Guastalla 1954, 1957; Johnson & Dettre 1965; Dettre & Johnson 1966; Funke et al. 1969). Many other methods for obtaining contact angles at solid as well as at powder interfaces are available (Johnson & Dettre 1969; Adamson 1976).

In all the methods just described, the scales of measurement and observation are macroscopic. Hence the contact angles obtained are the apparent values. As pointed out by a number of authors (see Huh & Mason 1977b) and established by electron microscopy (Oliver & Mason 1977), the actual (microscopic) contact angle can be quite different from the apparent value on a rough surface.

1.4.5.9 Prediction of Contact Angles

Because the nature and condition of the support surface are critically important to the contact angles observed and are not easily quantified, accurate predictions of θ by thermodynamically based methods, which assume smooth, equilibrated, homogeneous surfaces, are rare. It is possible, however, with low-energy surfaces (e.g., polytetrafluoroethylene) to correlate the advancing angles with the surface tensions of the wetting liquids alone (Zisman 1964). The surface tension at which $\cos \theta_a = 1$ is the critical surface tension and is correlated with the chemical structure of the solid surface (Shafrin & Zisman 1960; Zisman 1964). The critical surface tension can be used as a measure of relative wettability of surfaces (see references just noted and Johnson & Dettre 1969).

1.4.5.10 Boundary Conditions

The boundary condition of no relative velocity which requires continuity of the tangential components of velocity at a dividing surface, is well established in fluid mechanics (Goldstein 1938, p. 676), with two possible exceptions.

There is relative velocity at boundaries in the flow of rarefied gases. It is preferable to use kinetic theory to describe these flows, since the usual constitutive equations for stress-deformation behavior are probably no longer applicable.

Difficulties can also arise in describing the motion of a common line over a solid surface. If the solid is assumed to be rigid, forces become unbounded in the immediate neighborhood of the common line. This difficulty can be removed by allowing relative velocity in this region (Dussan & Davis 1974; Dussan 1976; Hocking 1976; Huh & Mason 1977a). It is not clear whether the introduction of relative velocity in this manner leads to other difficulties, such as in representing mass transfer of surfactant through a moving common line.

1.4.6 ENERGY TRANSFER

The two fundamental postulates of energy transfer are the energy balance (first law of thermodynamics)

The time rate of change of internal energy of a multicomponent body is equal to the rate at which work is done on the body by the system of forces acting on it (including the force of inertia) plus the rate of energy transmission to the body.

and the Clausius-Duhem inequality (second law of thermodynamics)

The rate of production of entropy in a multicomponent body beyond that due to external and mutual energy transmission must be greater than or equal to zero.

To our knowledge, the energy associated with the dividing surface has no observed influence on energy transfer. The existence of interfacial tension proves that there is internal energy associated with the dividing surface and that it depends on both temperature and composition. But the effect of this interfacial internal energy on energy transfer must normally be very small. For this reason, all interfacial effects are ignored in applying the results of section 1.4.3 to the energy balance. Equation [1.4.2] gives the usual form for the jump energy balance (Slattery 1981, pp. 295, 465). When all interfacial effects are ignored, there is no energy balance at the common line corresponding to [1.4.3].

The differential Clausius-Duhem inequality places a constraint on the relationships used to describe the behavior of the bulk phases (Slattery 1981, pp. 299, 466, 473). The jump Clausius-Duhem inequality corresponding to [1.4.2] places a limitation on the constitutive equations employed to describe the behavior of the dividing surface. For example, this inequality allows us to prove that the two interfacial viscosities κ and ϵ are positive. The implications of the Clausius-Duhem inequality at a common line corresponding to [1.4.3] have not been investigated, since interfacial effects associated with the common line have generally been neglected.

Just as we normally consider the tangential components of velocity to be continuous across a dividing surface, we require temperature to be continuous as well. Just as this assumption concerning tangential components of velocity fails for rarefied gases such as metal vapors, the assumption concerning temperature fails as well [see discussions of the accommodation coefficient (Rohsenow 1973; Necmi & Rose 1976)]. This is not an interfacial effect, since it is not associated with either the existence or absence of energy associated with the dividing surface.

1.4.7 MASS TRANSFER

The fundamental postulate of mass transfer is the mass balance for an individual species i:

The time rate of change of the mass of each species i ($i = 1, 2, \ldots, N$) in a multicomponent body is equal to the rate at which mass of species i is produced by chemical reaction.

For [1.4.1] to take the form of the mass balance for species i, identify

$$\Psi \equiv \rho_i \qquad \Psi^{(\sigma)} \equiv \rho_i^{(\sigma)}$$

$$\phi \equiv j_i \qquad \phi^{(\sigma)} \equiv j_i^{(\sigma)} \qquad\qquad [1.4.26]$$

$$\rho\zeta \equiv r_i \qquad \rho^{(\sigma)}\zeta^{(\sigma)} \equiv r_i^{(\sigma)}$$

Here ρ_i is the mass concentration of species i, $\rho_i^{(\sigma)}$ the interfacial mass concentration of species i, j_i the mass flux relative to the mass-averaged velocity, $j_i^{(\sigma)}$ the interfacial mass flux relative to the mass-averaged velocity, r_i the rate at which species i is produced by homogeneous chemical reactions per unit volume, and $r_i^{(\sigma)}$ the rate at which species i is produced by heterogeneous chemical reactions per unit area.

Equation [1.4.2] gives the jump mass balance for an individual species i:

$$\frac{d_{(s)}\rho_i^{(\sigma)}}{dt} + \rho_i^{(\sigma)}\text{div}_{(\sigma)}\mathbf{U}^{(\sigma)} + \text{div}_{(\sigma)}j_i^{(\sigma)} = r_i^{(\sigma)} - [\rho_i(\mathbf{U} - \mathbf{U}^{(\sigma)})\cdot\xi + j_i\cdot\xi]$$

$$[1.4.27]$$

The first two terms on the left describe convection within the dividing surface; the third describes interfacial diffusion or motion of i relative to the mass-averaged velocity.

Equations [1.4.3] and [1.4.26] similarly imply the mass balance at the common line for an individual species. This could be used to describe, for example, the rate at which an adsorbed layer of a surfactant species i is deposited as a common line moves across a solid. To our knowledge, problems of this character have not been investigated in sufficient detail to permit demonstration of its use.

To determine the concentration distributions within the bulk phases as well as at the interface, we must supplement the mass balance given by [1.4.27] with certain constitutive relations:

1. Relation for the bulk phase mass flux j_i such as Fick's first law.
2. Relation for the surface mass flux $j_i^{(\sigma)}$. In the absence of definitive published treatments, a constitutive equation analogous to the extension of Fick's first law for dilute multicomponent mixtures is suggested (Slattery 1981, p. 480):

$$j_i^{(\sigma)} = - \rho^{(\sigma)}D_{i,\text{mix}}^{(\sigma)}\nabla_{(\sigma)}\omega_i^{(\sigma)} \qquad\qquad [1.4.28]$$

Here $D_{i,\text{mix}}^{(\sigma)}$ may be referred to as the *interfacial diffusion coefficient* for i in the multicomponent dividing surface; $\omega_i^{(\sigma)}$ is the interfacial mass fraction of i in the dividing surface. Often the effects of surface diffusion are small relative to those of surface convection and may be neglected.

3. Relations describing the rate of adsorption between the interface and the adjacent substrates (portions of the bulk phases in the immediate neighborhood of the interface). If the rate of adsorption is much higher than the rate of mass transfer within the adjacent bulk phases, the dividing surface will be nearly in equilibrium with the substrates and the only relations required are the adsorption isotherms relating the substrate concentrations to the surface concentrations at equilibrium. If the rate of adsorption is of the same order as (or less than) the

rate of mass transfer within the bulk phases, it must be specified. It is common practice to describe adsorption and desorption as first-order kinetic processes, which is equivalent to

$$[j_i + \rho_i(U - u)] \cdot \xi = k(\rho_i^{(\sigma)} - \rho_i^{(\sigma)*}) \qquad [1.4.29]$$

Here $\rho_i^{(\sigma)*}$ is the interfacial mass concentration of species i that would be in equilibrium with the existing substrate concentration ρ_i.

4. Equations relating the intrinsic bulk phase and interfacial properties to the thermodynamic state variables. Note particularly here the need for an interfacial equation of state relating interfacial tension to temperature and interfacial concentrations. It is this dependence of interfacial tension on interfacial composition that couples the momentum and mass transfer processes and often gives rise to interfacial tension-driven flows (see section 1.4.7.3).

Finally, it should be noted that the mass balance for an individual species within a bulk phase can be written in both mass and molar terms (Bird et al. 1960, p. 496; Slattery 1981, p. 452). Alternative mass and molar forms for [1.4.27] and [1.4.28] can be readily written by analogy.

1.4.7.1 Interfacial Equations of State and Adsorption Isotherms

The molar interfacial chemical potential for species i $(i = 1, 2, \ldots, N)$ relative to some standard state can be represented by [this is an extension of similar relationships given by Lucassen-Reynders (1976) and Butler (1932)]

$$\mu_i^{(\sigma)} = \mu_i^{(\sigma)0} + RT \ln (b_i^{(\sigma)} x_i^{(\sigma)}) + A_i(\sigma^{0(i)} - \sigma) \qquad [1.4.30]$$

where $b_i^{(\sigma)}$ is the interfacial activity coefficient, $x_i^{(\sigma)}$ is the interfacial mole fraction of species i, $\sigma^{0(i)}$ is the interfacial tension in the standard state for species i in the interface, R is the gas constant, and T is the temperature. The partial molar area A_i is defined by analogy with partial molar quantities for bulk phases (Slattery 1981, p. 286). Note that

$$\sum_{i=1}^{N} A_i c_i^{(\sigma)} = 1 \qquad [1.4.31]$$

in which $c_i^{(\sigma)}$ is the surface molar concentration of species i. In deriving [1.4.30], the only assumption made is that A_i is independent of interfacial tension.

Assuming local equilibrium and equating $\mu_i^{(\sigma)}$ with the corresponding chemical potential $\mu_i = \mu_i^0 + RT \ln(b_i x_i)$ for the substrate, it follows that

$$x_i^{(\sigma)} = \frac{b_i x_i}{a_i^0 b_i^{(\sigma)}} \exp \left[-\frac{A_i(\sigma^{0(i)} - \sigma)}{RT} \right] \qquad [1.4.32]$$

where

$$a_i^0 \equiv \exp \frac{\mu_i^{(\sigma)0} - \mu_i^0}{RT} \qquad [1.4.33]$$

The definitions of the excess interface concentration variables $x_i^{(\sigma)}$ and $c_i^{(\sigma)}$ are still arbitrary, since the position of the dividing surface has not been defined. Given the dependence of $x_i^{(\sigma)}$ in [1.4.30], any selection of the dividing surface position where $x_i^{(\sigma)}$ was zero or negative would invalidate the use of [1.4.30]. Many of the more widely used conventions for locating the dividing surface give zero or negative values for one or more of the corresponding surface mole fractions. To avoid such difficulties, Lucassen-Reynders & van den Tempel (1964) suggested a convention for which

$$\sum_{i=1}^{N} c_i^{(\sigma)} = c^{(\sigma)\infty} \qquad [1.4.34]$$

Here $c^{(\sigma)\infty}$ is a constant saturation value slightly in excess of the highest measured surfactant adsorption. In this convention

$$A_i = \frac{1}{c^{(\sigma)\infty}} \quad \text{all } i \qquad [1.4.35]$$

Consider some results for binary systems involving a solvent (component 1) and a surfactant (component 2) that are sufficiently dilute to justify $b_1^{(\sigma)} \doteq 1$ and $b_1 x_1 \doteq 1$. With the standard state defined as that corresponding to infinite dilution, such conditions imply that $a_1^0 = 1$ and $\sigma^{0(1)} = \sigma_1^0$, where σ_1^0 is the interfacial tension of pure solvent at the system temperature. If [1.4.32] is written for species 1 and $x_1^{(\sigma)}$ is replaced by $1 - x_2^{(\sigma)}$, one discovers the Frumkin equation of state (Frumkin 1925; Lucassen-Reynders & van den Tempel 1964; Lucassen-Reynders 1976)

$$\sigma = \sigma_1^0 + RT c^{(\sigma)\infty} \ln\left(1 - \frac{c_2^{(\sigma)}}{c^{(\sigma)\infty}}\right) \qquad [1.4.36]$$

If $x_1^{(\sigma)}$ and $x_2^{(\sigma)}$ are eliminated between [1.4.32] applied to each component, one finds the Szyszkovski equation of state (Szyszkovski 1908; Lucassen-Reynders & van den Tempel 1964; Lucassen-Reynders 1976)

$$\sigma = \sigma_1^0 - RT c^{(\sigma)\infty} \ln\left(\frac{b_2 x_2}{a_2^0 b_2^{(\sigma)}} + 1\right) \qquad [1.4.37]$$

If σ is eliminated between [1.4.32] applied to each component, one obtains the Langmuir adsorption isotherm (Langmuir 1917; Lucassen-Reynders & van den Tempel 1964; Lucassen-Reynders 1976)

$$\frac{c_2^{(\sigma)}}{c^{(\sigma)\infty}} = \frac{x_2}{x_2 + a_2^0 b_2^{(\sigma)}/b_2} \qquad [1.4.38]$$

Such methods can be applied to more complex systems and more complete equations of state and adsorption isotherms can be developed. In particular, extensions to multicomponent electrolyte systems have been presented by Lucassen-Reynders (1976).

Before leaving this section, it is desirable to note the generalized form of the Gibbs adsorption isotherm equation:

$$c_i^{(\sigma,G)} = -\frac{b_i x_i}{RT}\left[\frac{\partial \sigma}{\partial(b_i x_i)}\right]_{b_j x_j (j \neq i)} \qquad [1.4.39]$$

For ideal solutions, this reduces to

$$c_i^{(\sigma,G)} = -\frac{x_i}{RT}\left(\frac{\partial \sigma}{\partial x_i}\right)_{x_j (j \neq i)} \qquad [1.4.40]$$

These equations, which are based on the Gibbs convention for locating the dividing surface (i.e., locating the surface such that $c_j^{(\sigma)} = 0$ for one species j), provide relatively easy methods for determining the relationship between c_i and $c_i^{(\sigma)}$ from equilibrium interfacial tension data at different bulk concentrations. For nearly ideal solutions that are also dilute, the values of $c_i^{(\sigma,G)}$ are quite close to those appropriate for the Lucassen-Reynders & van den Tempel (1964) convention and can be used interchangeably (see Lucassen-Reynders 1976, pp. 282–283).

1.4.7.2 Rates of Adsorption

A basic concern in describing the mass transfer between a bulk phase and an interface is whether it is adsorption-controlled or controlled by mass transfer within the adjacent bulk phases (in nearly stagnant systems, "diffusion controlled"). Further, when the process is adsorption-controlled, the rate of adsorption must be characterized.

For moderate rates of mass transfer, in which the effects of diffusion-induced convection at the interface can be neglected, [1.4.29] reduces to

$$-\rho D_{i,\text{mix}} \nabla \omega_i \cdot \xi = k(\rho_i^{(\sigma)} - \rho_i^{(\sigma)*}) \qquad [1.4.41]$$

in which j_i is represented by Fick's first law for diffusion Slattery 1981, pp. 480, 483). Here $D_{i,\text{mix}}$ is the diffusion coefficient for species i within the adjacent bulk phase and ω_i is the mass fraction of i in this phase. This suggests that if

$$\frac{D_{i,\text{mix}}}{kL^2} \gg 1 \qquad [1.4.42]$$

the rate of mass transfer at the interface is limited by the rate of adsorption rather than by the concentration gradient developed in the substrate. Here L is a characteristic length. When there is no convection in the adjacent bulk phase, L can be chosen as a length characteristic of the dimensions of this phase. When there is forced convection in the adjacent bulk phase, L can be chosen by setting either the Peclet number (the product of the Schmidt and Reynolds numbers) or the Reynolds number equal to unity. Effects of the rate of adsorption are believed to have been observed by Tung & Drickamer (1952), Lewis (1954a), Sinfelt & Drickamer (1955), Blokker (1957), McManamey (1961), Ward & Quinn (1965), England & Berg (1971), Tsonopoulos et al. (1971), and Pierson & Whitaker (1976a, 1976b).

Care is required in interpreting experimental data. Any effects of convection within the interface and within the adjacent phases that are not explicitly taken into account will alter the resistance to mass transfer attributed to the rate of adsorption. It is particularly easy to overlook the effects of interfacial turbulence (natural convection in the immediate neighborhood of the phase interface induced by concentration or temperature gradients).

1.4.7.3 Marangoni Effects

All phenomena attributable to local gradients of interfacial tension are called Marangoni effects. Gradients in interfacial tension (and in the two interfacial viscosities) arise as the result of gradients in surfactant concentration and temperature within the interface. Gradients in surfactant concentration, in turn, can exist only through a complex interplay of adsorption, diffusion, and convection.

These effects can be important, normally more important than those attributable to the interfacial viscosities. For a survey of situations in which they appear, see Sternling & Scriven (1959).

1.5 Nomenclature for Chapter 1

ROMAN LETTERS

A	surface area
$\mathbf{A}$	initial position vector
A_i	partial molar area
$A(t)$	closed surface
$A_m(t)$	material surface area
A_n^j	Fourier coefficient
$\mathbf{A}_t, \mathbf{A}_z$	matrices given by tables 1.2.3 and 1.2.4
$\mathbf{a}$	acceleration
a	radius of sphere
a	horizontal half-width of drop
a_i^0	defined by [1.4.33]
$\mathbf{a}_0$	initial acceleration
a_p	radius of particle
$\mathbf{B}$	vector field
$\mathbf{b}$	body force vector per unit mass
b	distance from column axis to center of drop or bubble, minor semiaxis of spheroid
b_1, b_2	lower and upper vertical semiaxes of drop falling in gas
b_i	molar activity coefficient of i
$b_i^{(\sigma)}$	molar interfacial activity coefficient of i
C	interface, closed curve
$C^{(cl)}$	union of common lines of contact formed by intersection of dividing surfaces
C_D	drag coefficient
$C_{n+1}^{-1/2}(\sigma)$	Gegenbauer polynomial of order $n+1$ and degree $-\frac{1}{2}$
c	concentration
$c_i^{(\sigma)}$	surface molar concentration of species i
$c^{(\sigma)\infty}$	defined after [1.4.34]

$c_i^{(\sigma, G)}$	surface molar concentration based on Gibbs convention for locating dividing surface
D	column or hydraulic diameter
$\mathbf{D}^{(\sigma)}$	surface rate of deformation tensor
$\mathbf{D}$	rate of strain tensor
D	drag
D	instantaneous rate of energy dissipation in Stokes flow
D	diffusivity
$D_{i,\text{mix}}^{(\sigma)}$	interfacial diffusion coefficient for species i in dividing surface
D_L	Lagrangian diffusivity
D_p	particle diffusivity
D_R	relative two-particle diffusivity
d	distance of sphere from wall
d_e	volume-equivalent sphere diameter
E	energy spectrum
$\bar{E}$	time mean height-to-width ratio
e	eccentricity of spheroid
$\mathbf{e}_1, \mathbf{e}_2, \mathbf{e}_3$	unit vectors in body frame
$\mathbf{F}$	drag force vector
F^*	dimensionless force
F	force coefficient
f^*	value of F^* obtained from asymptotic theory
F_D	component of drag force vector
f	frequency
$f(\beta)$	displacement function (table 1.3.6)
f_k	arbitrary quantity pertaining to phase k
$\mathfrak{F}$	force-torque vector
$\mathbf{G}$	velocity gradient
G^*	dimensionless couple
G	couple coefficient
G_A, G_B	couples
g	arbitrary function [1.2.23]
$\mathbf{g}$	gravity vector
g	specific Gibbs free energy
g^*	value of G^* obtained from asymptotic theory
g_k	free enthalpy of phase k [1.2.76]
H	mean curvature of surface
h	specific enthalpy [1.2.27]
h	channel height
$\mathbf{i}_1, \mathbf{i}_2, \mathbf{i}_3$	unit vectors in right-handed Cartesian axes
$I_1(x), I_0(x)$	Bessel functions of imaginary argument of order 1 and 0, respectively
$\mathbf{I}$	unit tensor
$\mathbf{J}_k$	flux term
$\mathbf{j}_i$	bulk phase mass flux
$\mathbf{j}_i^{(\sigma)}$	surface mass flux
K_1, K_0	Bessel functions of imaginary argument of the second kind

$K_s^1(\cosh \xi_i)$	Mehler function of rank 1
$\mathbf{K}_{ij}$	diffusivity tensor
$\mathbf{k}$	wave number vector
k	absorption rate constant
k	phase $(= 1, 2)$
k	eigenvalues
L	characteristic length
L	drop length
L_ρ	inertial length
L_μ	viscous length
l	length
l	curvilinear abscissa along interface
l	energy-containing eddy length scale
M	mass
$\mathbf{M}$	tensor field
$\dot{m}_k$	mass transfer per unit area of interface and per unit time [1.2.17]
$\mathbf{n}$	unit normal vector
n	number of particles
P	pressure including variation due to gravity
$P_n(\cos \theta)$	Legendre polynomial of degree n
$\mathbf{P}$	projection tensor
$\mathbf{p}^{(\sigma)}$	position vector of material element on dividing surface
p	pressure
p	fluid pressure
p_k	pressure within phase k, defined by [1.2.31]
Q	total rate of heat transfer
$\mathbf{q}$	heat flux vector
$\mathbf{q}^R$	radiant energy heat flux vector
$\mathbf{R}$	grand resistance matrix
$\mathbf{R}$	antisymmetrical tensor corresponding to $\mathbf{r}$
R	gas constant
R	drop radius
R	region occupied by body
R	column radius
R	radius of curvature
R_c	radius of curvature
R_{ij}	Eulerian correlation
R_{k2}	area fraction of phase k [1.2.132]
R_L	Lagrangian correlation
$\mathbf{r}$	point
$\mathbf{r}$	spatial displacement vector
r_i	rate of production of i by homogeneous chemical reactions per unit volume
$r_i^{(\sigma)}$	rate of production of i by heterogeneous chemical reactions per unit area
r_{max}^*	dimensionless function of $2R/L$ [1.4.22]

S	shear vector
S	shear rate
S	closed surface bounding a body
S_{ij}	mean strain rate
s	entropy per unit mass
s	arc length
s_{ij}	fluctuating strain rate
T	absolute temperature [1.2.32]
T	temperature
T	time interval
T	stress tensor
$\mathbf{T}^{(\sigma)}$	surface stress tensor
T_{ij}	scalar components of stress tensor
T_L	Lagrangian time scale
T_z	torque
t	time
$\mathbf{t}_{(n)}$	stress vector
U	velocity-spin vector
U	mass-averaged velocity vector
Ū	time-averaged velocity vector
U'	fluctuating velocity
U	unit tensor
$\mathbf{U}^{(\sigma)}$	mass-averaged surface velocity vector
$\mathbf{U}_b$	bulk velocity
$\mathbf{U}_I$	velocity of surface point (u, v) defined by [1.2.2]
$\mathbf{U}_k$	velocity vector of phase k
U, V, W	scalar components of **U**
u	internal energy per unit mass
u	velocity of fixed point on dividing surfaces
u	Eulerian fluctuating velocity vector
$u^{(cl)}$	velocity of fixed point on common line
u'	characteristic fluctuating velocity
u_0	centerline velocity for parabolic velocity profile
u_m	maximum axial fluid velocity
u_T	terminal settling or rising velocity of drop or bubble
u, v	coordinates of surface point
u, v, w	scalar components of **U**
V	fixed control volume
$V(t)$	geometric volume, figure 1.2.1
V_p	fluid particle volume
V_s	Stokes velocity of sphere
V_w	wake volume
v	Lagrangian velocity
v	fluid velocity
w	relative velocity
w_k	projection of $\mathbf{U}_k$

X	vector of main dependent variables
x_i	mole fraction of i
x_1, x_2, x_3	spatial coordinates
x, y, z	spatial coordinates
x	quality
$x_i^{(\sigma)}$	interfacial mole fraction of i
y^1, y^2	contravariant surface coordinates
Z	distance
z	position vector of material element on dividing surface
$\daleth(\mathbf{r})$	local specific area [1.2.139]
$\daleth_3(t)$	integral specific area [1.2.140]

DIMENSIONLESS GROUPS

BC^I	parameters in dimensionless form of boundary conditions
Ar	Archimedes number
Ec	Eckert number
Eo	Eötvös number
Fo	Fourier number
Fr	Froude number
H	dimensionless group defined by [1.3.295]
J	dimensionless group obtained from [1.3.297a] or [1.3.297b]
M	dimensionless property group ($= g\mu^4 \Delta\rho/\rho^2 \sigma^3$)
N_D	dimensionless drop diameter ($= C_D \mathrm{Re}_T^2$)
Nu	Nusselt number
Pe	Peclet number
Pr	Prandtl number
Re	Reynolds number
Re_p	Reynolds number corresponding to internal particle properties
Re_T	Reynolds number under terminal settling or rising conditions
We	Weber number

GREEK LETTERS

α	film heat transfer coefficient
α	normal stress
α_k	residence time of phase k [1.2.117]
β	coefficient of thermal expansion
β	dimensionless displacement
β	shear stress
Γ	dimensionless coefficient [1.3.298]
γ	shear stress
Δ	local entropy source per unit volume and per unit time
δ_{ij}	Kronecker delta
ϵ	unit isotropic alternating triadic

ϵ	interfacial shear viscosity
ϵ	minimum clearance
ϵ	dissipation
ϵ/D	wall roughness parameter
ζ	rate of production per unit mass at each point within bulk phase
$\zeta^{(\sigma)}$	rate of production per unit mass at each point on dividing surface
η	ratio
η	time variable
$\tilde{\eta}$	defect parameter (dimensionless)
η_0	angle of intersection in Dean-Moffatt flows
θ	contact angle
θ	angular coordinate
θ_w	wake angle, measured from the nose
κ	bulk coefficient of viscosity
κ	viscosity ratio, μ_p/μ
κ	von Karman constant (dimensionless)
κ	interfacial dilatational viscosity
λ	unit vector tangent to streamline
λ	ratio of viscosities of immiscible fluids
λ	dimensionless drop or bubble size
$\lambda*$	critical value of λ
μ	unit vector tangent to Σ, normal to C
μ	shear coefficient of viscosity
μ_i	molar chemical potential of i
μ_i^0	molar chemical potential of i in standard state
μ_p	dispersed-phase shear viscosity
$\mu_i^{(\sigma)}$	molar interfacial chemical potential for i
$\mu_i^{(\sigma)0}$	molar interfacial chemical potential of i in standard state
ν	kinematic viscosity
ν	unit normal to common line
ξ	dimensionless drag force
ξ	drag coefficient
ξ	friction factor
ξ	unit normal to dividing surface
π	stress dyadic
ρ	continuous-phase density
ρ_p	dispersed-phase density
$\rho^{(\sigma)}$	local surface mass density
ρ_i	mass concentration of i
$\rho^{(\sigma)}$	interfacial mass concentration of i
$\rho_i^{(\sigma)*}$	interfacial mass concentration of i in equilibrium with substrate
ρ_k	density of phase k
Σ	dividing surface
σ	interfacial or surface tension
σ	particle response parameter (dimensionless) [1.3.270]
$\sigma^{0\,(i)}$	interfacial tension in standard state for i in the interface
$\bar{\sigma}_x$	normal stress

τ	time increment variable
τ	unit tangential vector
τ	deviatoric stress tensor
τ	viscous stress tensor
τ_k	viscous stress tensor [1.2.28]
τ_{xy}	tangential stresses
$\Upsilon(t)$	relative separation time scale
Φ	source or sink of electromagnetic energy
Φ	shear resistance matrix
ϕ	flux of quantity per unit area
$\phi^{(\sigma)}$	surface flux of a quantity per unit length
ϕ_k	source term
ψ	Stokes stream function for outer fluid
ψ	density of quantity per unit volume within bulk phases
ψ_k	specific quantity
ψ_p	Stokes stream function for dispersed fluid
$\psi(x, y)$	Earnshaw stream function
$\psi^{(\sigma)}$	density of surface quantity per unit area
ω	angular velocity
ω_f	fluid spin (= half the vorticity of the fluid)
$\omega_i^{(\sigma)}$	interfacial mass fraction, species i

OPERATORS

div	divergence operator
$\text{div}_{(\sigma)}$	surface divergence operator
∇	gradient operator
$\nabla_{(\sigma)}$	surface gradient operator
L_{-1}	Stokes operator
L_m^2	operators ($m = 0, 1, 2$)

SUBSCRIPTS

f	fluid
G	gas
I	interface
i, j	species i, j
i, j	coordinate notation
j	jth interface
k	phase index
L	liquid
L	Lagrangian
M	center of mass
n	index
n	noise
p	interface particle

s	signal
s	Stokes
sat	saturated
W	wall
(σ)	surface or interface

SUPERSCRIPTS

(cl)	common line
G	Gibbs
$(i), (j)$	ith and jth phases
(ij)	quantity on dividing surface between phases i and j
m	index
n	normal
p	ultrapurified system
t	transpose, tangential
w	wall effects present
(σ)	surface or interface
(σ, ij)	surface quantity on dividing surface between phases i and j
$+$	dimensionless term
$\dagger$	transposition operator
$\wedge$	dimensionless
$*$	dimensionless
0	standard state

1.6 References for Chapter 1

Abdel-Alim, A. H. & Hamielec, A. E. 1975 A Theoretical and Experimental Investigation of the Effect of Internal Circulation on the Drag of Spherical Droplets Falling at Terminal Velocity in Liquid Media, *Ind. Eng. Chem. Fundam.* **14**:308-312.

Ablett, R. 1923 An Investigation of the Angle of Contact between Paraffin Wax and Water, *Philos. Mag.* **46**:224-256.

Adamson, A. W. 1976 *Physical Chemistry of Surfaces,* 3d ed., Wiley, New York.

Adamson, A. W., Shirley, F. P., & Kunichika, K. T. 1970 Contact Angles on Molecular Solids. 1. Ice, *J. Colloid Interface Sci.* **34**:461-468.

Allen, R. F. & Benson, P. R. 1975 Rolling Drops on an Inclined Plane, *J. Colloid Interface Sci.* **50**:250-253.

Andersen, P. S., Astrup, P., Eget, L., & Rathmann, O. 1978 Numerical Experience with the Two-Fluid Model RISQUE, *Proc. Topical Meet. Thermal Reactor Safety, Sun Valley, July 31-Aug. 4, 1977* **2**:409-423.

Aris, R. 1962 *Vectors, Tensors, and the Basic Equations of Fluid Mechanics,* pp. 242-244, Prentice-Hall, Englewood Cliffs, N.J.

Aveyard, R. & Haydon, D. A. 1973 *An Introduction to the Principles of Surface Chemistry,* Cambridge Univ. Press, London.

Aybers, N. M. & Tapucu, A. 1969 Studies on the Drag and Shape of Gas Bubbles Rising through a Stagnant Liquid, *Waerme Stoffuebertrag.* **2**:171-177.

Barber, A. D. & Hartland, S. 1976 The Effects of Surface Viscosity on the Axisymmetric Drainage of Planar Liquid Films, *Can. J. Chem. Eng.* **54**:279-284.

Bart, E. 1959 M.Ch.E. thesis, New York Univ., New York.

Bart, E. 1968 The Slow Unsteady Settling of a Fluid Sphere Towards a Flat Fluid Interface, *Chem. Eng. Sci.* **23**:193-210.

Bartell, F. E. & Bjorklund, C. W. 1952 Hysteresis of Contact Angles. A Study of Interfacial Contact Angles in the Mercury-Benzene-Water System, *J. Phys. Chem.* **56**:453-457.

Bartell, F. E. & Merrill, E. J. 1932 Determination of Adhesion Tension of Liquids against Solids. A Microscopic Method for the Measurement of Interfacial Contact Angles, *J. Phys. Chem.* **36**:1178-1190.

Bartell, F. E. & Wooley, A. D. 1933 Solid-Liquid-Air Contact Angles and Their Dependence upon the Surface Condition of the Solids, *J. Am. Chem. Soc.* **55**:3518-3527.

Bascom, W. D., Cottington, R. L., & Singleterry, C. R. 1964 Dynamic Surface Phenomena in the Spontaneous Spreading of Oils on Solids in *Dynamic Surface Phenomena in the Spontaneous Spreading of Oils on Solids, Contact Angles, Wettability and Adhesion,* ed. R. F. Gould, pp. 355-379, American Chemical Society, Washington, D.C.

Bashforth, F. & Adams, J. C. 1892 *An Attempt to Test the Theory of Capillary Action,* Cambridge Univ. Press, London.

Batchelor, G. K. 1952 *A Theory of Homogeneous Turbulence,* p. 20, Cambridge Univ. Press, London.

Batchelor, G. K. 1957 Diffusion in Free Turbulent Shear Flows, *J. Fluid Mech.* 3:67–80.

Batchelor, G. K. 1967 *An Introduction to Fluid Dynamics,* Cambridge Univ. Press, London.

Batchelor, G. K. 1970 Slender-Body Theory for Particles of Arbitrary Cross-Section in Stokes Flow, *J. Fluid Mech.* 44:419–439.

Batchelor, G. K. 1972 The Mechanics of Two-Phase Systems, *Prog. Heat Mass Transfer* 6.

Beard, K. V. 1976 Terminal Velocity and Shape of Cloud and Precipitation Drops Aloft, *J. Atmos. Sci.* 33:851–864.

Beard, K. V. 1977 On the Acceleration of Large Water Drops to Terminal Velocity, *J. Appl. Meteorol.* 16:1068–1071.

Beard, K. V. & Pruppacher, H. R. 1969. A Determination of the Terminal Velocity and Drag of Small Water Drops by Means of a Wind Tunnel, *J. Atmos. Sci.* 26:1066–1072.

Berry, E. X. & Pranger, M. R. 1974 Equations for Calculating Terminal Velocities of Water Drops, *J. Appl. Meteorol.* 13:108–113.

Bhaga, D. 1976 Bubbles in Viscous Liquids: Shapes, Wakes and Velocities, Ph.D. thesis, McGill Univ., Montreal, Quebec, Canada.

Bhaga, D. & Weber, M. E. 1980 In-Line Interaction of a Pair of Bubbles in a Viscous Liquid, *Chem. Eng. Sci.* 35:2467–2474.

Bhaga, D. & Weber, M. E. 1981 Bubbles in Viscous Liquids: Shapes, Wakes and Velocities, *J. Fluid Mech.*, in press.

Bigelow, W. C., Pickett, D. L., & Zisman, W. A. 1946 Oleophobic Monolayers. I. Films Adsorbed from Solution in Nonpolar Liquids, *J. Colloid Sci.* 1:513–538.

Bird, R. B., Stewart, W. E., & Lightfoot, E. N. 1960 *Transport Phenomena,* Wiley, New York.

Birkhoff, G. 1960 *Hydrodynamics: A Study in Logic, Fact and Similitude,* Princeton Univ. Press, Princeton, N. J.

Birkhoff, G. 1964 Averaged-Conservation Laws in Pipes, *J. Math. Anal. Appl.* 8:66–77.

Blaisdell, B. E. 1940 The Physical Properties of Fluid Interfaces of Large Radius of Curvature. *J. Math. Phys.* 19:186–216 (I), 217–227 (II), 228–245 (III).

Blake, T. D. & Haynes, J. M. 1969 Kinetics of Wetting of Surfaces by Polymers, *J. Colloid Interface Sci.* 29:174–176.

Blokker, P. C. 1957 On Mass Transfer across Liquid/Liquid Interfaces in Systems with and without Surface Active Agents, *Proc. Second Int. Congr. Surface Activity,* ed. J. H. Schulman, vol. 1, p. 503, Academic, New York.

Bohlin, T. 1960 On the Drag on a Rigid Sphere Moving in a Viscous Liquid inside a Cylindrical Tube, *K. Tek Hogsk. Handl.* 155.

Bond, W. N. & Newton, D. A. 1928 Bubbles, Drops and Stokes' Law, *Philos. Mag.* 5:794–800.

Bosanquet, C. H. & Hartley, H. 1921 The Angle of Contact, *Philos. Mag.* 42:456–462.

Bouré, J. A. 1975 On a Unified Presentation of the Non-Equilibrium Two-Phase Flow Models, in *Non-Equilibrium Two-Phase Flows,* eds. R. T. Lahey & G. B. Wallis, ASME G 00094, pp. 1–9, ASME, New York.

Bouré, J. A. 1978a On the Constitutive Laws of 1-D, Two-Fluid, Two-Phase Flow Models: Possible Mathematical Forms, Restrictions Resulting from Basic Principles, *OECD/NEA Specialists' Meet. Transient Two-Phase Flow, Paris.*

Bouré, J. A. 1978b Nonequilibrium Phenomena and Nonequilibrium Variables in Two-Phase Flows, in *Two-Phase Momentum, Heat and Mass Transfer in Chemical, Process, and Energy Engineering Systems,* eds. F. Durst, G. V. Tsiklauri, & N. H. Afgan, pp. 187–204, Hemisphere, Washington, D.C.

Bouré, J. A. 1978c Mathematical Modeling of Two-Phase Flows. A Review of Its Bases and Problems, in *Transient Two-Phase Flow,* eds. S. Banerjee & K. R. Weaver, *Proc. CNSI Specialists Meet., Toronto, Aug. 3–4, 1976* 1:85–111.

Bouré, J. A. & Latrobe, A. 1976–77 Two-Phase Flow Models and Well-posed Problems, *Trans. Can. Soc. Mech. Eng.* 4:167–173.

Bourot, J. M. 1975 Sur le Calcul de l'Ecoulement Irrotational et de l'Ecoulement de Stokes

Autour d'un Obstacle de Révolution de Méridienne Cardioïde; sur la Structure du Champ au Voisinage du Point de Rebroussement, *C. R. Acad. Sci. Ser. A* **281**:178–182.

Boussinesq, J. 1913 Sur l'Existence d'une Viscosite Superficielle, dans la Mince Couche de Transition Separant un Liquide d'un Autre Fluide Contigu, *C. R. Acad. Sci.* **156**:983–989.

Brabston, D. C. & Keller, H. B. 1975 Viscous Flows past Spherical Gas Bubbles, *J. Fluid Mech.* **69**:179–189.

Bradley, S. G. & Stow, C. D. 1978 Collisions between Liquid Drops, *Philos. Trans. R. Soc. London* **287**:635–678.

Brenner, H. 1961 On the Slow Motion of a Sphere through a Viscous Fluid towards a Plane Surface, *Chem. Eng. Sci.* **16**:242–264.

Brenner, H. 1963 The Stokes Resistance of an Arbitrary Particle, *Chem. Eng. Sci.* **18**:1–25.

Brenner, H. 1964a The Stokes Resistance of an Arbitrary Particle. Part II. An Extension, *Chem. Eng. Sci.* **19**:599–629.

Brenner, H. 1964b The Stokes Resistance of an Arbitrary Particle. Part III. Shear Fields, *Chem. Eng. Sci.* **19**:631–651.

Brenner, H. 1966 Hydrodynamic Resistance of Particles at Small Reynolds Numbers, *Adv. Chem. Eng.* **6**:287–438.

Brenner, H. 1970 Pressure Drop due to the Motion of Neutrally Buoyant Particles in Duct Flows, *J. Fluid Mech.* **43**:641–660.

Brenner, H. 1972a Dynamics of Neutrally Buoyant Particles in Low Reynolds Number Flows, *Prog. Heat Mass Transfer* **6**:509–574.

Brenner, H. 1972b Rheology of Two-Phase Systems, *Annu. Rev. Fluid Mech.* **2**:137–176.

Brenner, H. & Bungay, P. M. 1971 Rigid-Particle and Liquid-Droplet Models of Red Cell Motion in Capillary Tubes, *Fed. Proc.* **30**:1565–1570.

Brenner, H. & Happel, J. 1958 Slow Viscous Flow past a Sphere in a Cylindrical Tube, *J. Fluid Mech.* **4**:195–213.

Brenner, H. & O'Neill, M. E. 1972 On the Stokes Resistance of Multiparticle Systems in a Linear Shear Field, *Chem. Eng. Sci.* **27**:1421–1439.

Brignell, A. S. 1973 The Deformation of a Liquid Drop at Small Reynolds Number, *Q. J. Mech. Appl. Math.* **26**:99–107.

Briley, P. B., Deemer, A. R., & Slattery, J. C. 1976 Blunt Knife-Edge and Disk Surface Viscometers, *J. Colloid Interface Sci.* **56**:1–18.

Briller, R. & Peskin, R. L. 1968 Gas Solid Suspension Convective Heat Transfer at a Reynolds Number of 130,000. *Trans. ASME, J. Heat Transfer,* **90**:464–469.

Brown, A. G., Thuman, W. C., & McBain, J. W. 1953 The Surface Viscosity of Detergent Solutions as a Factor in Foam Stability. *J. Colloid Sci.* **8**:491–507.

Bungay, P. M. & Brenner, H. 1973a Pressure Drop due to the Motion of a Sphere in Proximity to the Wall Bounding a Poiseuille Flow, *J. Fluid Mech.* **60**:81–96.

Bungay, P. M. & Brenner, H. 1973b The Motion of a Closely-fitting Sphere in a Fluid-filled Tube, *Int. J. Multiphase Flow* **1**:25–56.

Burley, R. & Kennedy, B. S. 1976a A Study of the Dynamic Wetting Behavior of Polyester Tapes, *Br. Polym. J.* **8**:140–143.

Burley, R. & Kennedy, B. S. 1976b An Experimental Study of Air Entrainment at a Solid/Liquid/Gas Interface, *Chem. Eng. Sci.* **31**:901–911.

Burton, R. A. & Mannheimer, R. J. 1967 Analysis and Apparatus for Surface Rheological Measurements, *Adv. Chem. Ser.* **63**:315–328.

Butler, J. A. V. 1932 The Thermodynamics of the Surfaces of Solutions, *Proc. R. Soc. London Ser. A* **135**:348–375.

Buzzard, J. F. & Nedderman, R. M. 1967 The Drag Coefficients of Liquid Droplets Accelerating through Air, *Chem. Eng. Sci.* **22**:1577–1586.

Cairns, R. J. R., Grist, D. M., & Neustadter, E. L. 1976 The Effect of Crude Oil-Water Interfacial Properties on Water-Crude Oil Emulsion Stability, in *Theory and Practice of Emulsion Technology*, ed. A. L. Smith, pp. 135–151, Academic, New York.

Callen, H. B. 1960 *Thermodynamics*, Wiley, New York.

Carreau, P. J., Devic, M., & Kapellas, M. 1974 Dynamique des Bulles en Milieu Viscoélastique, *Rheol. Acta* 13:477–489.

Cassie, A. B. D. 1948 Contact Angles, *Discuss. Faraday Soc.* 3:11–16.

Cataneo, R., Adam, J. R., & Semonin, R. G. 1971 Interactions between Equal Sized Droplets due to the Wake Effect, *J. Atmos. Sci.* 28:416–418.

Cayias, J. L., Schechter, R. S., & Wade, W. H. 1975 Measurement of Low Interfacial Tension via the Spinning Drop Technique, in *Adsorption at Interfaces,* ed. K. L. Mittal, *ACS Symp. Ser.* 8:234–247.

Chen, T.-C. & Skalak, R. 1970 Stokes Flow in a Cylindrical Tube Containing a Line of Spheroidal Particles, *Appl. Sci. Res.* 22:403–441.

Cherry, B. W. & Holmes, C. M. 1969 Kinetics of Wetting of Surfaces by Polymers, *J. Colloid Interface Sci.* 29:174–176.

Clift, R., Grace, J. R., & Weber, M. E. 1978 *Bubbles, Drops and Particles,* Academic, New York.

Coleman, B. D. 1964 Thermodynamics of Materials with Memory, *Arch. Rational Mech. Anal.* 17:1–46.

Coleman, B. D. & Mizel, V. J. 1964 Existence of Caloric Equations of State in Thermodynamics, *J. Chem. Phys.* 40:1116–1125.

Collins, R. 1966 A Second Approximation for the Velocity of a Large Gas Bubble Rising in an Infinite Fluid, *J. Fluid Mech.* 25:469–480.

Collins, R. 1967 The Effect of a Containing Cylindrical Boundary on the Velocity of a Large Gas Bubble in a Liquid, *J. Fluid Mech.* 28:97–112.

Collins, W. D. 1963 A Note on the Axisymmetric Stokes Flow of Viscous Fluid past a Spherical Cap, *Mathematika* 10:72–78.

Coney, T. A. & Masica, W. J. 1969 Effect of Flow Rate on the Dynamic Contact Angle for Wetting Liquids, *NASA Tech. Note* TND-5115.

Cooley, M. D. A. 1971 The Slow Rotation in a Viscous Fluid of a Sphere Close to Another Fixed Sphere about a Diameter Perpendicular to the Line of Centers, *Q. J. Mech. Appl. Math.* 24:237–250.

Cooley, M. D. A. & O'Neill, M. E. 1968 On the Slow Rotation of a Sphere about a Diameter Parallel to a Nearby Plane Wall, *J. Inst. Math. Appl.* 4:163–173.

Cooley, M. D. A. & O'Neill, M. E. 1969a On the Slow Motion Generated in a Viscous Fluid by the Approach of a Sphere to a Plane Wall or Stationary Sphere, *Mathematika* 16:37–49.

Cooley, M. D. A. & O'Neill, M. E. 1969b On the Slow Motion of Two Spheres in Contact along Their Line of Centres through a Viscous Fluid, *Proc. Cambridge Philos. Soc.* 66:407–415.

Corrsin, S. 1959 Progress Report on Some Turbulent Diffusion Research, *Adv. Geophys.* 6:161–164.

Cotton, W. R. & Gokhale, N. R. 1967 Collision, Coalescence and Breakup of Large Water Drops in a Vertical Wind Tunnel, *J. Geophys. Res.* 72:4041–4044.

Courant, R. & Hilbert, D. 1961 *Methods of Mathematical Physics,* Interscience, New York.

Cox, R. G. 1970a The Motion of Small Particles in a Moving Fluid, *Rept.* PGRL/25, Pulp and Paper Research Inst. of Canada, Pointe Claire, Quebec.

Cox, R. G. 1970b The Motion of Long Slender Bodies in a Viscous Fluid. Part 1. General Theory, *J. Fluid Mech.* 44:791–810.

Cox, R. G. 1971 The Motion of Long Slender Bodies in a Viscous Fluid. Part 2. Shear Flow, *J. Fluid Mech.* 45:625–657.

Cox, R. G. & Brenner, H. 1967 The Slow Motion of a Sphere through a Viscous Fluid Towards a Plane Surface. II. Small Gap Widths, Including Inertial Effects, *Chem. Eng. Sci.* 22:1753–1777.

Cox, R. G. & Brenner, H. 1968 The Lateral Migration of Solid Particles in Poiseuille Flow. I. Theory, *Chem. Eng. Sci.* 23:147–176.

Cox, R. G. & Mason, S. G. 1971 Suspended Particles in Fluid Flow through Tubes, *Annu. Rev. Fluid Mech.* 3:291–316.

Crabtree, J. R. & Bridgwater, J. 1971 Bubble Coalescence in Viscous Liquids, *Chem. Eng. Sci.* 26:839–851.

Csanady, G. T. 1963 Diffusion of Heavy Particles in the Atmosphere. *J. Atmos. Sci.* 20:201–208.

Csanady, G. T. 1972 *Turbulent Diffusion in the Environment,* pp. 61–65. Reidel, Boston.

Dahl, H. 1925 Appendix to Faxén, H. (1925), *Arkiv. Mat. Astron. Fys.* 19A:No. 13.

Davies, C. N. 1974 *Air Filtration,* Academic, New York.

Davies, R. M. & Taylor, G. I. 1950 The Mechanics of Large Bubbles Rising through Extended Liquids and through Liquids in Tubes, *Proc. R. Soc. London Ser. A* 200:375–390.

Davis, A. M. J. & O'Neill, M. E. 1977a Separation in a Slow Linear Shear Flow past a Cylinder and a Plane. *J. Fluid Mech.* 81:551–564.

Davis, A. M. J. & O'Neill, M. E. 1977b Separation in a Stokes Flow past a Phase with a Cylindrical Ridge or Trough, *Q. J. Mech. Appl. Math.* 30:355–368.

Davis, A. M. J., O'Neill, M. E., & Ranger, K. B. 1975 Some Properties of Multi-Fluid Stokes Flows, *Int. J. Multiphase Flow* 2:1–8.

Davis, A. M. J., O'Neill, M. E., Dorrepaal, J. M., & Ranger, K. B. 1976 Separation from the Surface of Two Equal Spheres in Stokes Flow, *J. Fluid Mech.* 77:625–644.

Davis, B. W. 1975 Contact Angles for Two Liquids and a Solid in the Presence of Adsorbed Layers, *J. Colloid Interface Sci.* 52:150–154.

Davis, M. H. 1969 The Slow Translation and Rotation of Two Unequal Spheres in a Viscous Fluid, *Chem. Eng. Sci.* 24:1769–1776.

Davis, M. H. 1971 Two Unequal Spheres in a Slow Linear Shear Flow, *Rept.* NCAR-TN/STR-64, Natl. Center for Atmospheric Research, Boulder, Colo.

Dean, W. R. 1944 On the Shearing Motion of Fluid past a Projection, *Proc. Cambridge Philos. Soc.* 40:18–36.

Dean, W. R. & Montagnon, P. E. 1949 On the Steady Motion of Viscous Liquid in a Corner, *Proc. Cambridge Philos. Soc.* 45:389–394.

Dean, W. R. & O'Neill, M. E. 1963 A Slow Motion of Viscous Liquid Caused by a Slowly Rotating Solid Sphere, *Mathematika* 10:13–24.

Deardorff, J. & Peskin, R. L. 1970 Lagrangian Statistics on Numerically Integrated Turbulent Shear Flow. *Phys. Fluids* 13:584–595.

Deemer, A. R. & Slattery, J. C. 1978 Balance Equations and Structural Models for Phase Interfaces, *Int. J. Multiphase Flow* 4:171–192.

Defay, R. & Petrie, G. 1971 Dynamic Surface Tension, *Surf. Colloid Sci.* 10:27–81.

Defay, R., Prigogine, I., Bellemans, A., & Everett, D. H. 1966 *Surface Tension and Adsorption,* Wiley, New York.

Delhaye, J. M. 1968 Equations Fondamentales des Ecoulements Diphasiques, *Rept.* CEA-R 3429, Commissariat à l'Energie Atomique, Paris.

Delhaye, J. M. 1974 Jump Conditions and Entropy Sources in Two-Phase Systems. Local Instant Formulation, *Int. J. Multiphase Flow* 1:395–409.

Delhaye, J. M. 1976 Sur les Surfaces Volumiques Locale et Intégrale en Ecoulement Diphasique, *C. R. Acad. Sci. Ser. A* 283:243–246.

Delhaye, J. M. & Achard, J. L. 1977 On the Use of Averaging Operators in Two-Phase Flow Modeling, in *Thermal and Hydraulic Aspects of Nuclear Reactor Safety,* vol. 1, *Light Water Reactors,* eds. O. C. Jones & S. G. Bankoff, pp. 289–332, ASME, New York.

Delhaye, J. M. & Achard, J. L. 1978 On the Averaging Operators Introduced in Two-Phase Flow Modeling, in *Transient Two-Phase Flow,* eds. S. Banerjee & K. R. Weaver, *Proc. CSNI Specialists Meet.,* Toronto, Aug. 3–4, 1976 1:5–84.

Dettre, R. H. & Johnson, R. E. 1964 Contact Angle Hysteresis. II. Contact Angle Measurements on Rough Surfaces, *Adv. Chem. Ser.* 43:136–144.

Dettre, R. H. & Johnson, R. E. 1966 Surface Properties of Polymers. I. The Surface Tensions of Some Molten Polyethylenes, *J. Colloid Interface Sci.* 21:367–377.

Dorrepaal, J. M. 1976 Asymmetric Stokes Flow past a Spherical Cap, *J. Appl. Math. Phys.* 27:739–748.

Dorrepaal, J. M. 1978a The Stokes Flow past a Smooth Cylinder, *J. Eng. Math.* 12:177–185.

Dorrepaal, J. M. 1978b The Stokes Resistance of a Spherical Cap to Translational and Rotational Motions in a Linear Shear Flow, *J. Fluid Mech.* 84:265–278.

Dorrepaal, J. M., Majumdar, S. R., O'Neill, M. E., & Ranger, K. B. 1976a A Closed Torus in Stokes Flow, *Q. J. Mech. Appl. Math.* 29:381–397.

Dorrepaal, J. M., O'Neill, M. E., & Ranger, K. B. 1976b Axisymmetric Stokes Flow past a Spherical Cap, *J. Fluid Mech.* 75:273–286.

Dussan, E. B., V. 1976 The Moving Contact Line: The Slip Boundary Condition, *J. Fluid Mech.* 77:665–684.

Dussan, E. B., V. & Davis, J. H. 1974 On the Motion of a Fluid-Fluid Interface along a Solid Surface, *J. Fluid Mech.* 65:71–103.

Dutton, J. A. 1976 *The Ceaseless Wind: An Introduction to the Theory of Atmospheric Motion*, McGraw-Hill, New York.

Dwyer, H. & Peskin, R. L. 1965 A Study of the Mechanics of Turbulent Gas Solid Shear Flows, ASME paper 65-FE-24.

Edge, R. M. & Grant, C. D. 1972 The Motion of Drops in Water Contaminated with a Surface Active Agent, *Chem. Eng. Sci.* 27:1709–1721.

Einstein, A. 1956 in *Investigations on the Theory of the Brownian Movement*, ed. R. Fürth, Dover, New York.

Elliott, G. E. P. & Riddiford, A. C. 1965 Contact Angles, *Recent Prog. Surf. Sci.* 2:111–128.

Elliott, G. E. P. & Riddiford, A. C. 1967 Dynamic Contact Angles. I. The Effect of Impressed Motion, *J. Colloid Interface Sci.* 23:389–398.

Ellison, A. H. & Tejada, S. B. 1968 Dynamic Liquid/Solid Contact Angles and Films on Contaminated Mercury, *NASA Contract Rept.* CR72441.

England, D. C. & Berg, J. C. 1971 Transfer of Surface-active Agents across a Liquid-Liquid Interface, *AIChE J.* 17:313–322.

Ericksen, J. L. 1952 Thin Liquid Jets, *J. Ration. Mech. Anal.* 1:521–538.

Eveson, G. F., Hall, E. W., & Ward, S. 1959 *Br. J. Appl. Phys.* 10:43.

Faxén, H. 1927 Die Geschwindigkeit zeven Kugeen, die unter Ein wirkung der Schwere in einen zahen Flussigkeit fallen, *Z. Angew. Math. Mech.* 7:79–92.

Ferguson, A. 1913 On the Theoretical Shape of Large Bubbles and Drops with Other Allied Problems, *Philos. Mag.* 25:507–520.

Finn, R. & Noll, W. 1957 On the Uniqueness and Nonexistence of Stokes Flow, *Arch. Ration. Mech. Anal.* 1:97–106.

Fishburn, B. D. 1974 Boundary Layer Stripping of Liquid Drops Fragmented by Taylor Instability, *Acta Astron.* 1:1267–1284.

Flumerfelt, R. W. 1980 Effects of Dynamic Interfacial Properties on the Deformation and Orientation of Drops in a General Flow Field, *J. Colloid Interface Sci.* 76:330–349.

Fordham, S. 1948 On the Calculation of Surface Tension from Measurement of Pendant Drops, *Proc. R. Soc. London Ser. A* 194:1–16.

Fowkes, F. M. 1964 Attractive Forces at Interfaces, *Ind. Eng. Chem.* 56:40–52.

Frankel, N. A. & Acrivos, A. 1967 On the Viscosity of a Concentrated Suspension of Spheres, *Chem. Eng. Sci.* 22:847–853.

Freud, B. B. & Freud, H. Z. 1930 A Theory of the Ring Method for the Determination of Surface Tension, *J. Am. Chem. Soc.* 52:1772–1782.

Frumkin, A. 1925 Surface Tension Curves of the Higher Fatty Acids and the Equation of Condition of the Surface Layer, *Z. Phys. Chem.* 116:466–484.

Frumkin, A. & Levich, V. G. 1947 The Effects of Surface Active Matter on Movement in the Boundaries of Liquid Media, *Zh. Fiz. Khim.* 21:1183–1204.

Funke, W., Hellwig, G. E. H., & Neumann, A. W. 1969 Determination of Solidification Temperature of Polymers from the Temperature Dependence of Wetting, *Angew. Makromol. Chem.* 8:185–193.

Gaudin, A. M. & Witt, A. F. 1964 Hysteresis of Contact Angles in the System Mercury-Benzene-Water, *Adv. Chem. Ser.* 43:202–210.

Geer, J. 1976 Stokes Flow past a Slender Body of Revolution, *J. Fluid Mech.* 78:577–600.

Germain, P. 1973 *Cours de Mécanique des Milieux Continus, Vol. 1, Théorie Générale*, Masson, Paris.

Gibbs, J. W. 1928 *The Collected Works of J. Willard Gibbs*, vol. 1, Longmans, New York.

Girifalco, L. A. & Good, R. J. 1957 A Theory for the Estimation of Surface and Interfacial Energies. I. Derivation and Application to Interfacial Tension, *J. Phys. Chem.* 61:904.

Gladden, G. P. & Neustadter, E. L. 1972 Oil/Water Interfacial Viscosity and Crude Oil Emulsion Stability, *J. Inst. Pet. London* 58:351.

Goldman, A. J., Cox, R. G., & Brenner, H. 1966 The Slow Motion of Two Identical Arbitrarily Oriented Spheres through a Viscous Fluid, *Chem. Eng. Sci.* **21**:1151–1170.

Goldman, A. J., Cox, R. G., & Brenner, H. 1967 Slow Viscous Motion of a Sphere Parallel to a Plane Wall. I. Motion through a Quiescent Fluid, *Chem. Eng Sci.* **22**:637–651.

Goldsmith, H. L. & Mason, S. G. 1967 The Microrheology of Dispersions, in *Rheology: Theory and Applications*, ed. F. R. Eirich, vol. 4, pp. 85–250, Academic, New York.

Goldstein, S. 1938 *Modern Developments in Fluid Dynamics*, Oxford Univ. Press, London.

Good, R. J. & Elbing, E. 1970 Generalization of Theory for Estimation of Interfacial Energies, *Ind. Eng. Chem.* **62**:54–78.

Goodrich, F. C. 1969 The Theory of Absolute Surface Shear Viscosity. I. *Proc. R. Soc. London Ser. A* **310**:359–372.

Goodrich, F. C. 1971 Statistical Mechanics of the Capillary Layer, *Surf. Colloid Sci.* **3**:1–26.

Goodrich, F. C. & Allen, L. H. 1972 The Theory of Absolute Surface Shear Viscosity. V. The Effect of Finite Ring Thickness, *J. Colloid Interface Sci.* **40**:329–336.

Goodrich, F. C. & Chatterjee, A. K. 1970 The Theory of Absolute Surface Shear Viscosity. II. The Rotating Disk Problem, *J. Colloid Interface Sci.* **34**:36–41.

Goodrich, F. C., Allen, L. H., & Poskanzer, A. 1975 A New Surface Viscometer of High Sensitivity. I. Theory, *J. Colloid Interface Sci.* **52**:201–212.

Goren, S. L. & O'Neill, M. E. 1971 On the Hydrodynamic Resistance to a Particle of a Dilute Suspension when in the Neighbourhood of a Large Obstacle, *Chem. Eng. Sci.* **26**:325–338.

Grace, J. R. 1973 Shapes and Velocities of Bubbles Rising in Infinite Liquids, *Trans. Inst. Chem. Eng.* **51**:116–120.

Grace, J. R., Wairegi, T., & Nguyen, T. H. 1976 Shapes and Velocities of Single Drops and Bubbles Moving Freely through Immiscible Liquids, *Trans. Inst. Chem. Eng.* **54**:167–173.

Grace, J. R., Wairegi, T., & Brophy, J. 1978 Break-up of Drops and Bubbles in Stagnant Media, *Can. J. Chem. Eng.* **56**:3–8.

Greenstein, T. & Happel, J. 1968 Theoretical Study of the Slow Motion of a Sphere and a Fluid in a Cylindrical Tube, *J. Fluid Mech.* **34**:705–710.

Greider, K. 1973 *Invitation to Physics*, Harcourt, New York.

Gross, W. A. 1962 *Gas Film Lubrication*, Wiley, New York.

Guastalla, J. 1954 Study of Wetting. II. Tensiometric Technique, *J. Chem. Phys.* **51**:583–589.

Guastalla, J. 1957 Wetting Balance Method and Its Application, *Proc. Second Int. Congr. Surface Activity*, vol. 3, pp. 143–152, Academic, New York.

Gunn, R. 1965 Collision Characteristics of Freely Falling Water Drops, *Science* **150**:695–701.

Gunn, R. & Kinzer, G. D. 1949 The Terminal Velocity of Fall for Water Droplets in Stagnant Air, *J. Meteorol.* **6**:243–248.

Guthrie, R. I. L. & Bradshaw, A. V. 1969 The Stability of Gas Envelopes Trailed Behind Spherical-Cap Bubbles Rising through Viscous Liquids, *Chem. Eng. Sci.* **24**:913–917.

Haber, S. & Hetsroni, G. 1971 The Dynamics of a Deformable Drop Suspended in an Unbounded Stokes Flow, *J. Fluid Mech.* **49**:257–277.

Haber, S., Hetsroni, G., & Solan, A. 1974 On the Low Reynolds Number Motion of Two Droplets, *Int. J. Multiphase Flow* **1**:57–71.

Haberman, W. L. & Sayre, R. M. 1958 Motion of Rigid and Fluid Spheres in Stationary and Moving Liquids inside Cylindrical Tubes, *David Taylor Model Basin Rept.* 1143, U.S. Navy Dept., Washington, D.C.

Hadamard, J. S. 1911 Mouvement Permanent Lent d'une Sphère Liquide et Visqueuse dans un Liquide Visqueux, *C. R. Acad. Sci.* **152**:1735–1738.

Hamielec, A. E. & Johnson, A. I. 1962 Viscous Flow around Fluid Spheres at Intermediate Reynolds Numbers, *Can. J. Chem. Eng.* **40**:41–45.

Hamielec, A. E., Storey, S. H., & Whitehead, J. H. 1963 Viscous Flow around Fluid Spheres at Intermediate Reynolds Numbers, *Can. J. Chem. Eng.* **41**:246–251.

Hancox, W. T., Mathers, W. G., & Kawa, D. 1975 Analysis of Transient Flow-boiling Application of the Method of Characteristics, AIChE paper 42, 15th National Heat Transfer Conf., San Francisco, Calif.

Hansen, R. J. & Toong, T. Y. 1971 Interface Behavior as One Fluid Completely Displaces Another from a Small-Diameter Tube, *J. Colloid Interface Sci.* **36**:410–413.

Hansen, R. S. 1964 The Calculation of Surface Age in Vibrating Jet Measurements, *J. Phys. Chem.* 68:2012–2014.

Hansen, R. S. & Miotto, M. 1957 Relaxation Phenomena and Contact Angle Hysteresis, *J. Am. Chem. Soc.* 79:1765.

Hansen, R. S. & Wallace, T. C. 1959 The Kinetics of Adsorption of Organic Acids at the Water-Air Interface, *J. Phys. Chem.* 63:1085–1091.

Hansford, R. E. 1970 On Converging Solid Spheres in a Highly Viscous Fluid, *Mathematika* 17:250–254.

Happel, J. & Brenner, H. 1965 *Low Reynolds Number Hydrodynamics,* Prentice-Hall, Englewood Cliffs, N.J.

Harkins, W. D. & Brown, F. E. 1919 The Determination of Surface Tension (Free Surface Energy) and the Weight of Falling Drops. The Surface Tension of Water and Benzene by the Capillary Height Method, *J. Am. Chem. Soc.* 41:499–524.

Harkins, W. D. & Jordon, H. F. 1930 A Method for the Determination of Surface Tension from the Maximum Pull on a Ring, *J. Am. Chem. Soc.* 52:1951–1972.

Harper, J. F. 1970 On Bubbles Rising In-Line at Large Reynolds Numbers, *J. Fluid Mech.* 41:751–758.

Harper, J. F. 1972 The Motion of Bubbles and Drops through Liquids, *Adv. Appl. Mech.* 12:59–129.

Harper, J. F. 1973 On Bubbles with Small Immobile Adsorbed Films Rising in Liquids at Low Reynolds Numbers, *J. Fluid Mech.* 58:539–545.

Harper, J. F. 1974 On Spherical Bubbles Rising Steadily in Dilute Surfactant Solutions, *Q. J. Mech. Appl. Math.* 27:87–100.

Harper, J. F. & Moore, D. W. 1968 The Motion of a Spherical Liquid Drop at High Reynolds Number, *J. Fluid Mech.* 32:367–391.

Hartland, S. & Hartley, R. W. 1976 *Axisymmetric Fluid-Liquid Interfaces,* Elsevier, New York.

Hartland, S. & Srinivasan, P. 1974 The Basis of Theoretical Correction Factors for the Drop Weight Method, *J. Colloid Interface Sci.* 49:318–320.

Hegde, M. G. 1971 The Measurement of Surface Viscosities, Ph.D. Thesis, Northwestern Univ., Evanston, Ill.

Hegde, M. G. & Slattery, J. C. 1971a Capillary Waves at a Gas-Liquid Phase Interface, *J. Colloid Interface Sci.* 35:183–203.

Hegde, M. G. & Slattery, J. C. 1971b Studying Nonlinear Surface Behavior with the Deep Channel Surface Viscometer, *J. Colloid Interface Sci.* 35:593–600.

Hein, P. 1914 Investigations on the Critical State, *Z. Phys. Chem.* 86:385–426.

Hetsroni, G. and Haber, S. 1970 The Flow in and around a Droplet or Bubble Submerged in an Unbounded Arbitrary Velocity Field, *Rheol. Acta* 9:488–496.

Hetsroni, G. & Haber, S. 1978 Low Reynolds Number Motion of Two Drops Submerged in an Unbounded Arbitrary Velocity Field, *Int. J. Multiphase Flow* 4:1–17.

Hetsroni, G., Haber, S., & Wacholder, E. 1970 The Flow Fields in and around a Droplet Moving Axially within a Tube, *J. Fluid Mech.* 41:689–705.

Hetsroni, G., Haber, S., Brenner, H., & Greenstein, T. 1972 A Second Order Theory for a Deformable Drop Suspended in a Long Conduit, *Prog. Heat Mass Transfer* 6:591–612.

Hill, M. J. M. 1894 On a Spherical Vortex, *Philos. Trans. R. Soc. London Ser. A* 185:213–245.

Hinze, J. O. 1975 *Turbulence,* McGraw-Hill, New York.

Hnat, J. G. & Buckmaster, J. D. 1976 Spherical-Cap Bubbles and Skirt Formation, *Phys. Fluids* 19:182–194 & 611.

Hocking, L. M. 1976 A Moving Fluid Interface on a Rough Surface, *J. Fluid Mech.* 76:801–817.

Hoffman, R. L. 1975 A Study of the Advancing Interface. I. Interface Shape in Liquid-Gas Systems, *J. Colloid Interface Sci.* 50:228–241.

Hopke, S. W. & Slattery, J. C. 1975 Bounding Principles for Two-Phase Flow Systems, *Int. J. Multiphase Flow* 1:727–742.

Houdayer, G., Pinet, B., & Vigneron, M. 1978 HEXECO Code, A Six-Equation Model *OECD/NEA Specialists' Meet. Transient Two-Phase Flow, Paris.*

Hu, S. & Kintner, R. C. 1955 The Fall of Single Liquid Drops through Water, *AIChE J.* 1:42–50.

Huh, C. & Mason, S. G. 1977a The Steady Movement of a Liquid Meniscus in a Capillary Tube, *J. Fluid Mech.* 81:401–419.

Huh, C. & Mason, S. G. 1977b Effects of Surface Roughness on Wetting (Theoretical), *J. Colloid Interface Sci.* 60:11–38.

Hwang, B. C., Peskin, R. L., & So, R. M. C. 1979 Concentration Distribution in a Turbulent Shear Flow, *J. Atmos. Sci.* 36(10):1955–1966.

Ishii, M. 1975 *Thermo-Fluid Dynamic Theory of Two-Phase Flow,* Eyrolles, Paris.

Ishii, M. 1977 One-Dimensional Drift Flux Model and Constitutive Equations for Relative Motion between Phases in Various Two-Phase Flow Regimes, *Rept.* ANL-77-47, Argonne National Laboratory, Argonne, Ill.

Jeffery, D. J. 1978 To be published.

Jeffery, G. B. 1915a On the Steady Rotation of a Solid of Revolution in a Viscous Fluid, *Proc. London Math. Soc.* 14:327–341.

Jeffery, G. B. 1915b The Slow Motion of Axisymmetric Bodies in a Viscous Liquid, *Proc. London Math. Soc.* 14:327–341.

Jeffery, G. B. 1915c The Motion of a Viscous Fluid around Axisymmetric Bodies, *Proc. London Math. Soc.* 14:327–352.

Jeffery, G. B. 1922a The Motion of Ellipsoidal Particles Immersed in a Viscous Fluid, *Proc. R. Soc. London Ser. A* 102:161–179.

Jeffery, G. B. 1922b The Rotation of Two Circular Cylinders in a Viscous Fluid, *Proc. R. Soc. London Ser. A* 169–174.

Jiang, T. S., Oh, S. G., & Slattery, J. C. 1979 Correlation for Dynamic Contact Angle, *J. Colloid Interface Sci.* 69:74–77.

Johnson, A. I. & Braida, L. 1957 The Velocity of Fall of Circulating and Oscillating Liquid Drops through Quiescent Liquid Phases, *Can. J. Chem. Eng.* 35:165–172.

Johnson, C. H. J. & Lane, J. E. 1974 Surface Shape and the Calculation of Surface Tension from Maximum Bubble Pressure, *J. Colloid Interface Sci.* 47:117–121.

Johnson, R. E., Jr. & Dettre, R. H. 1965 The Temperature Dependence of Wettability; Hexadecane on Fluoropolymer, *J. Colloid Interface Sci.* 20:173–176.

Johnson, R. E., Jr. & Dettre, R. H. 1965 Wettability and Contact Angles, *Surf. Colloid Sci.* 2:85–153.

Joly, M. 1964 Surface Viscosity, *Recent Prog. Surf. Sci.* 1:1–50.

Kanda, M. & Schechter, R. S. 1976 On the Mechanism of Foam Formation in Porous Media, paper 6200, Society of Petroleum Engineers of the AIME, Dallas, Tex.

Kane, R. S. 1973 Drag Reduction in Dilute Flow in Gas Solid Suspensions, Ph.D. thesis, City Univ. of New York, New York.

Kanner, T. & Glass, J. E. 1969 Surface Viscosity and Elasticity, *Ind. Eng. Chem.* 61:31–41.

Kau, C. J. 1972 Numerical Study of Turbulent Diffusion in Three-dimensional Channel Flow, Ph.D. thesis, Rutgers University, New Brunswick, N.J.

Keller & Rubinow 1976 The Transverse Force on a Spinning Sphere Moving in a Viscous Fluid, *J. Fluid Mech.* 11:447–459.

Kennedy, B. S. & Burley, R. 1977 Dynamic Fluid Interface Displacement and Prediction of Air Entrainment, *J. Colloid Interface Sci.* 62:48–62.

Kenning, D. B. 1968 Two-Phase Flow with Non-uniform Surface Tension, *Appl. Mech. Rev.* 21:1101–1111.

Kirchhoff 1876 The Slow Rotation of a Sphere in a Viscous Fluid, in Lamb, H. 1945 *Hydrodynamics,* Dover, New York.

Kirkpatrick, R. D. & Lockett, M. J. 1974 The Influence of Approach Velocity on Bubble Coalescence, *Chem. Eng. Sci.* 29:2363–2373.

Kocamustafaogullari, G. 1971 Thermo-Fluid Dynamics of Separated Two-Phase Flow, Ph.D. thesis, Georgia Inst. of Technology, Atlanta, Ga.

Kolmogorov, A. N. 1941 Local Structure of Turbulence in an Incompressible Fluid at Very High Reynolds Numbers, *Dokl. Akad. Nauk SSSR* 30:299–303.

Korteweg, D. J. 1901 *Arch. Neerl. Sci. Exactes Nat.* 6:1, as reported by C. Truesdell and W. Noll. The Non-linear Field Theories of Mechanics, in *Handbuch der Physik,* ed. S. Flugge, vol. 3, pt. 3, p. 513, Springer-Verlag, Berlin.

Kovitz, A. A. 1975 Static Fluid Interfaces External to a Right Circular Cylinder–Experiment and Theory, *J. Colloid Interface Sci.* 50:125–142.

Krasnoff, E. & Peskin, R. L. 1971 The Langevin Model for Turbulent Diffusion, *Geophys. Fluid Dyn.* 2:123–146.

Krieg, R. D., Son, J. E., & Flumerfelt, R. W. 1981 A New Method for Surface Shear Viscosity Measurements: Decay of Surface Motions at a Rotated Gas-Liquid Interface, *J. Colloid Interface Sci.* 79:14–20.

Ladyzhenskaya, D. A. 1963 *Viscous Incompressible Flow,* chap. 2, Gordon & Breach, New York.

Lamb, H. 1932 *Hydrodynamics,* 6th ed., Cambridge Univ. Press, London.

Lane, W. R. 1951 Shatter of Drops in Streams of Air, *Ind. Eng. Chem.* 43:1312–1317.

Lang, S. B. & Wilke, C. R. 1971 A Hydrodynamic Mechanism for the Coalescence of Liquid Drops, *Ind. Eng. Chem. Fundam.* 10:341–352.

Langmuir, I. 1917 Constitution and Fundamental Properties of Solids and Liquids. II. Liquids, *J. Am. Chem. Soc.* 39:1848–1906.

LeClair, B. P. & Hamielec, A. E. 1971 Viscous Flow through Particle Assemblages at Intermediate Reynolds Numbers–A Cell Model for Transport in Bubble Swarms, *Can. J. Chem. Eng.* 49:713–720.

LeClair, B. P., Hamielec, A. E., & Pruppacher, H. R. 1970 A Numerical Study of the Drag on a Sphere at Low and Intermediate Reynolds Numbers, *J. Atmos. Sci.* 27:308–315.

LeClair, B. P., Hamielec, A. E., Pruppacher, H. R., & Hall, W. D. 1972 A Theoretical and Experimental Study of the Internal Circulation in Water Drops Falling at Terminal Velocity in Air, *J. Atmos. Sci.* 29:728–740.

Lester, G. R. 1961 Contact Angles of Liquids at Deformable Solid Surfaces, *J. Colloid Sci.* 16:315–326.

Levich, V. G. 1962 *Physicochemical Hydrodynamics,* Prentice-Hall, Englewood Cliffs, N.J.

Levich, V. G. & Krylov, V. S. 1969 Surface-Tension-driven Phenomena, *Annu. Rev. Fluid Mech.* 1:293–316.

Levin, Z. & Machnes, B. 1977 Experimental Evaluation of the Coalescence Efficiencies of Colliding Water Drops, *Pure Appl. Geophys.* 115:845–867.

Lewis, J. B. 1954a The Mechanism of Mass Transfer of Solutes across Liquid-Liquid Interfaces. Part I: The Determination of Individual Transfer Coefficients for Binary Systems, *Chem. Eng. Sci.* 3:248–259.

Lewis, J. B. 1954b The Mechanism of Mass Transfer of Solutes across Liquid-Liquid Interfaces. Part II: The Transfer of Organic Solutes between Solvent and Aqueous Phases, *Chem. Eng. Sci.* 3:260–278.

Lewis, J. B. 1958 The Mechanism of Mass Transfer of Solutes Across Liquid-Liquid Interfaces. Part III: The Transfer of Uranyl Nitrate between Solvent and Aqueous Phases, *Chem. Eng. Sci.* 8:295–308.

Lifshutz, N., Hegde, M. G., & Slattery, J. C. 1971 Knife-Edge Surface Viscometer, *J. Colloid Interface Sci.* 37:73–79.

Lin, C. J., Lee, K. J., & Sather, N. F. 1970 Slow Motion of Two Spheres in a Shear Field, *J. Fluid Mech.* 43:35–47.

Lindt, J. T. 1972 On the Periodic Nature of the Drag on a Rising Bubble, *Chem. Eng. Sci.* 27:1775–1781.

Lindt, J. T. & de Groot, R. G. 1974 Drag on a Single Bubble Accompanied by a Periodic Wake, *Chem. Eng. Sci.* 29:957–962.

List, R. & Hand, M. J. 1971 Wakes of Freely Falling Water Drops, *Phys. Fluids* 14:1648–1655.

Lochiel, A. C. 1965 The Influence of Surfactants on Mass Transfer around Spheres, *Can. J. Chem. Eng.* 43:40–44.

Lucassen, J. & Hansen, R. S. 1966 Damping of Waves on Monolayer-covered Surfaces, *J. Colloid Interface Sci.* 22:32–44.

Lecassen-Reynders, E. H. 1976 Adsorption of Surfactant Monolayers at Gas/Liquid and Liquid/Liquid Interfaces, *Prog. Surf. Membr. Sci.* 10:253–360.

Lucassen-Reynders, E. H. & van den Tempel, M. 1964 Surface Equation of State for Adsorbed Surfactants, *Proc. 4th Int. Congr. Surface Active Substances, Brussels* 2:779–791.

Lumley, J. L. 1957 Some Problems Connected with the Motion of Small Particles in a Turbulent Fluid, Ph.D. thesis, Johns Hopkins Univ., Baltimore, Md.

Lumley, J. L. 1969 Drag Reduction by Additives, *Annu. Rev. Fluid Mech.* 1:367–384.

Lyczkowski, R. W., Gidaspow, D., Solbrig, C. W., & Hugues, E. D. 1978 Characteristics and Stability Analysis of Transient One-dimensional Two-Phase Flow Equations and Their Finite Difference Approximations, *Nucl. Sci. Eng.* 66:378–396.

Maass, O. 1938 Changes in the Liquid State in the Critical Temperature, *Chem. Rev.* 23:17–28.

Macdougall, G. & Ockrent, C. 1942 Surface-Engery Relations in Liquid/Solid Systems. I. The Adhesion of Liquids to Solids and a New Method of Determining the Surface Tension of Liquids, *Proc. R. Soc. London Ser. A* 180:151–173.

Mack, G. L. & Lee, D. A. 1936 The Determination of Contact Angles from Measurements of the Dimensions of Small Bubbles and Drops. II. The Sessile Drop Method for Obtuse Angles, *J. Phys. Chem.* 40:169–176.

MacKay, G. D. M. & Mason, S. G. 1961 The Sedimentation of Solid Particles on to a Rigid Plane, *J. Colloid Sci.* 16:632–635.

Magarvey, R. H. & Geldart, J. W. 1962 Drop Collisions under Conditions of Free Fall, *J. Atmos. Sci.* 19:107–113.

Majumdar, S. R. & O'Neill, M. E. 1972 On the Stokes Resistance of Two Spheres in Contact in a Linear Shear Field, *Chem. Eng. Sci.* 27:2017–2028.

Majumdar, S. R., O'Neill, M. E., & Brenner, H. 1974 Note on the Slow Rotation of a Concave Spherical Lens or Bowl in Two Immiscible Semi-infinite Viscous Fluids, *Mathematika* 21:147–154.

Mannheimer, R. J. & Burton, R. A. 1970 A Theoretical Estimation of Viscous-Interaction Effects with a Torsional (Knife-Edge) Surface Viscometer, *J. Colloid Interface Sci.* 32:73–80.

Mannheimer, R. J. & Schechter, R. S. 1968 A Comparison of Linear and Annular Canal Viscometers for Surface Rheological Measurements, *J. Colloid Interface Sci.* 27:324–327.

Mannheimer, R. J. & Schechter, R. S. 1970a An Improved Apparatus and Analysis for Surface Rheological Measurements, *J. Colloid Interface Sci.* 32:195–211.

Mannheimer, R. J. & Schechter, R. S. 1970b Shear Dependent Surface Rheological Measurements of Foam Stabilizers in Nonaqueous Liquids, *J. Colloid Interface Sci.* 32:212–224.

Manning, C. D. & Puig, J. E. 1978 Description and Operation of the UTSDIT (University of Texas Spinning Drop Interfacial Tensiometer), Research Rept., Dept. of Chemical Engineering and Materials Science, Univ. of Minnesota, Minneapolis.

Manning, C. D. & Scriven, L. E. 1977 On Interfacial Tension Measurement with a Spinning Drop in Gyrostatic Equilibrium, *Rev. Sci. Instrum.* 48:1699–1705.

Margolin, L. G. 1977 Turbulent Diffusion of Small Particles, *Los Alamos Scientific Laboratory Rept.* LA-7040-T, Los Alamos, N.M. (also Ph.D. thesis, Univ. of Michigan, Ann Arbor).

Marion, J. B. 1970 *Classical Dynamics of Particles and Systems,* Academic, New York.

Marks, C. H. 1973 Measurements of the Terminal Velocity of Bubbles Rising in a Chain, *Trans. ASME, J. Fluids Eng.* 95:17–22.

Maude, A. D. 1961 End Effects in a Falling-Sphere Viscometer, *Br. J. Appl. Phys.* 12:293–305.

McConnell, A. J. 1957 *Applications of Tensor Analysis,* Dover, New York.

McFerrin, A. R. & Davison, R. R. 1971 The Effect of Surface Phenomena on a Solvent Extraction Process, *AIChE J.* 17:1021–1027.

McIntosh, R. L., Dacey, J. R., & Maass, O. 1939 Pressure, Volume, Temperature Relations of Ethylene in the Critical Region. II. *Can. J. Res. Sect. B* 17:241–250.

McManamey, W. J. 1961 Interfacial Resistances in the Liquid Extraction of Inorganic Nitrates, *Chem. Eng. Sci.* 15:210–219.

McTaggart-Cowan, J. D. & List, R. 1975 Collision and Breakup of Water Drops at Terminal Velocity, *J. Atmos. Sci.* 32:1401–1411.

Meek, C. C. & Jones, B. G. 1973 Studies of the Behaviour of Heavy Particles in a Turbulent Fluid Flow, *J. Atmos. Sci.* 30:239–244.

Michael, D. H. 1967 The Steady Motion of a Sphere in a Dusty Gas, *J. Fluid Mech.* 31:175–192.

Michael, D. H. & O'Neill, M. E. 1977 The Separation of Stokes Flows, *J. Fluid Mech.* 80:785–794.

Milgram, J. H. & Bradley, R. G. 1971 Determination of the Interfacial Tension between Two Liquids, *J. Fluid Mech.* 50:469–480.

Mills, O. S. 1953 Tables for Use in the Measurement of Interfacial Tension between Liquids with Small Density Difference, *Br. J. Appl. Phys.* 4:247–252.

Modell, M. & Reid, R. C. 1974 *Thermodynamics and Its Applications,* Prentice-Hall, Englewood Cliffs, N.J.

Moffatt, H. K. 1964 Viscous and Resistive Eddies near a Sharp Corner, *J. Fluid Mech.* 18:1–18.

Monin, A. S. & Yaglom, A. M. 1971 *Statistical Fluid Mechanics,* p. 558, M.I.T. Press, Cambridge, Mass.

Moore, D. W. 1959 The Rise of a Gas Bubble in a Viscous Liquid, *J. Fluid Mech.* 6:113–130.

Moore, D. W. 1965 The Velocity of Rise of Distorted Gas Bubbles in a Liquid of Small Viscosity, *J. Fluid Mech.* 23:749–766.

Morrison, F. A. & Stewart, M. B. 1976 Small Bubble Motion in an Accelerating Liquid, *Trans. ASME, J. Appl. Mech.* 43:399–403.

Morrow, N. R. 1975 The Effects of Surface Roughness on Contact Angle with Special Reference to Petroleum Recovery, *J. Can. Pet. Technol.* 14:42–53.

Mudge, L. K. & Heideger, W. J. 1970 The Effect of Surface Active Agents on Liquid-Liquid Mass Transfer Rates, *AIChE J.* 16:602–608.

Narayanan, S., Goossens, L. H. J., & Kossen, N. W. F. 1974 Coalescence of Two Bubbles Rising in Line at Low Reynolds Numbers, *Chem. Eng. Sci.* 29:2071–2082.

Necmi, S. & Rose, J. W. 1976 Film Condensation of Mercury, *Int. J. Heat Mass Transfer* 19:1245–1256.

Neiderhauser, D. O. & Bartell, F. E. 1950 A Corrected Table for the Calculation of Boundary Tensions by the Pendant Drop Method. Fundamental Research on Occurrence and Recovery of Petroleum, 1948–1949, American Petroleum Inst., Washington, D.C.

Neumann, A. W. & Good, R. J. 1972 Thermodynamics of Contact Angles. I. Heterogeneous Solid Surfaces, *J. Colloid Interface Sci.* 38:341–358.

Nevers, N. de & Wu, J.-L. 1971 Bubble Coalescence in Viscous Fluids, *AIChE J.* 17:182–186.

Oh, S. G. & Slattery, J. C. 1978 Disk and Biconical Interfacial Viscometers, *J. Colloid Interface Sci.* 67:516–526.

Oldroyd, J. G. 1955 The Effect of Interfacial Stabilizing Films on the Elastic and Viscous Properties of Emulsions, *Proc. R. Soc. London Ser. A* 232:567–577.

Oliver, J. F. & Mason, S. G. 1977 Microspreading Studies on Rough Surfaces by Scanning Electron Microscopy, *J. Colloid Interface Sci.* 60:480–487.

Oliver, J. F., Huh, C., & Mason, S. G. 1977 The Apparent Contact Angle of Liquids on Finely-grooved Solid Surfaces—A SEM Study, *J. Adhes.* 8:223–234.

O'Neill, M. E. 1964a A Slow Motion of Viscous Liquid Caused by a Slowly Moving Solid Sphere, *Mathematika* 11:67–74.

O'Neill, M. E. 1964b Ph.D. thesis, Univ. of London.

O'Neill, M. E. 1967 A Slow Motion of Viscous Liquid Caused by a Slowly Moving Solid Sphere. An Addendum, *Mathematika* 14:170–173.

O'Neill, M. E. 1969 On Asymmetrical Slow Viscous Flows Caused by the Motion of Two Equal Spheres Almost in Contact, *Proc. Cambridge Philos. Soc.* 65:543–555.

O'Neill, M. E. 1970 On Asymmetrical Slow Viscous Flows Caused by the Motion of Two Equal Spheres, *Appl. Sci. Res.* 21:452–466.

O'Neill, M. E. 1977 On the Separation of a Slow Linear Shear Flow from a Cylindrical Ridge or Trough in a Plane *Z. Angew. Math. Phys.* 28:439–448.

O'Neill, M. E. & Dorrepaal, J. M. 1978 The Existence and Free Eddies in a Streaming Stokes Flow, *Q. J. Mech. Appl. Math.,* in press.

O'Neill, M. E. & Majumdar, S. R. 1970a Asymmetrical Slow Viscous Fluid Motions Caused by the Translation or Rotation of Two Spheres. Part I: The Determination of Exact Solutions for Any Values of the Ratio of Radii and Separation Parameters, *Z. Angew. Math. Phys.* 21:164–179.

O'Neill, M. E. & Majumdar, S. R. 1970b Asymmetrical Slow Viscous Fluid Motions Caused by the Translation or Rotation of Two Spheres. Part II: Asymptotic Forms of the Solutions when the Minimum Clearance between the Spheres Approaches Zero, *Z. Angew. Math. Phys.* 21:180–187.

O'Neill, M. E. & Ranger, K. B. 1979 Rotation of a Sphere in Two Phase Flow, *Int. J. Multiphase Flow* 5:143–148.

O'Neill, M. E. & Stewartson, K. 1967 On the Slow Motion of a Sphere Parallel to a Nearly Plane Wall, *J. Fluid Mech.* 27:705–724.

O'Neill, M. E., Ranger, K. B., & Brenner, H. 1978 The Motion of a Sphere in Two Phase Flow, in press.

Ono, S. & Kondo, S. 1960 Molecular Theory of Surface Tension in Liquids, in *Handbuch der Physik,* ed. S. Flugge, vol. 10, pp. 134–280, Springer-Verlag, Berlin.

Otake, T., Tone, S., Nakao, K., & Mitsuhashi, Y. 1977 Coalescence and Breakup of Bubbles in Liquids, *Chem. Eng. Sci.* 32:377–383.

Padday, J. F. 1957 A Direct Reading Electrically Operated Balance for Static and Dynamic Surface Tension Measurement, *Proc. Second Int. Congr. Surface Activity,* ed. J. H. Schulman, vol. 1, pp. 1–6, Academic, New York.

Padday, J. F. 1963 Heights of Sessile Drops and Meniscus Properties, *Nature (London)* 198:378–379.

Padday, J. F. 1969 Theory of Surface Tension, *Surf. Colloid Sci.* 1:39–251.

Padday, J. F. 1976 The Equilibrium and Stability Properties of Menisci: The Measurement of Surface Tensions by Exact Methods, *Pure Appl. Chem.* 48:485–494.

Padday, J. F. & Russell, D. R. 1960 The Measurement of the Surface Tension of Pure Liquids and Solutions, *J. Colloid Interface Sci.* 15:503–511.

Palmer, H. B. 1952 Ph.D. thesis, Univ. of Wisconsin, as reported in Hirschfelder, J. O., Curtis, C. F., & Bird, R. B. 1954 *Molecular Theory of Gases and Liquids,* 2d corrected printing, Wiley, New York.

Pan, F. Y. & Acrivos, A. 1968 Shape of a Drop or Bubble at Low Reynolds Number, *Ind. Eng. Chem. Fundam.* 7:227–232.

Parlange, J.-Y. 1969 Spherical-Cap Bubbles with Laminar Wakes, *J. Fluid Mech.* 37:257–263.

Parvatikar, K. G. 1967 Verification of Empirical Equation of Computing Contact Angle by the Sessile Drop Method, *J. Colloid Interface Sci.* 23:274–276.

Payne, L. E. & Pell, W. H. 1960a The Stokes Flow about a Spindle, *Q. Appl. Math.* 18:257–262.

Payne, L. E. & Pell, W. H. 1960b The Stokes Flow Problem for a Class of Axially Symmetric Bodies, *J. Fluid Mech.* 7:529–549.

Pell, W. H. & Payne, L. E. 1960 On Stokes Flow about a Torus, *Mathematika* 7:78–92.

Peskin, R. L. 1960 Some Effects of Particle-Particle Interaction in Two Phase Flow Systems, Ph.D. thesis, Princeton Univ., Princeton, N.J.

Peskin, R. L. 1970 Stochastic Estimation Applications to Turbulent Diffusion, Stochastic Hydraulics, *Proc. Int. Symp. Stochastic Hydraulics,* pp. 251–267, Univ. of Pittsburgh Press, Pittsburgh, Pa.

Peskin, R. L. 1975 Digital Computer Simulation of Turbulent Diffusion, in *Advances in Computer Methods for Partial Differential Equations,* pp. 207–214, Int. Assoc. for Mathematics and Computers in Simulation, Rutgers Univ., New Brunswick, N.J.

Peskin, R. L. & Baw, P. S. 1971 Some Aspects of Gas Solid Suspension Turbulence, *Trans. ASME, J. Fluids Eng.,* 93:631–635.

Peskin, R. L. & Rin, C. H. 1967 The Effect of Suspended Solids on Turbulent Dispersion, ASME paper 67-FE-17.

Philip, J. R. 1967 Relation between Eulerian and Lagrangian Statistics, *Phys. Fluids Suppl.* S69–S71.

Phillips, W., Graves, R., & Flumerfelt, R. W. 1980 Experimental Studies of Drop Dynamics in Shear Fields: Role of Dynamic Interfacial Effects, *J. Colloid Interface Sci.* 76:350–370.

Pierson, F. W. & Whitaker, S. 1976a Studies of the Drop-Weight Method for Surfactant Solutions.

I. Mathematical Analysis of the Adsorption of Surfactants at the Surface of a Growing Drop, *J. Colloid Interface Sci.* 54:203–218.

Pierson, F. W. & Whitaker, S. 1976b Studies of the Drop-Weight Method for Surfactant Solutions. II. Experimental Results for Water and Surfactant Solutions, *J. Colloid Interface Sci.* 54:219–230.

Pike, F. P. & Bonnet, J. C. 1970 The End-Correction in the Wilhelmy Technique for Surface Tension Measurements, *J. Colloid Interface Sci.* 34:597–605.

Pinkus, O. & Sternlicht, B. 1961 *Lubrication Theory,* McGraw-Hill, New York.

Pintar, A. J., Israel, A. B., & Wasan, D. T. 1971 Interfacial Shear Viscosity Phenomena in Solutions of Macromolecules, *J. Colloid Interface Sci.* 37:52–67.

Pironneau, O. 1973 On Optimum Profiles in Stokes Flow, *J. Fluid Mech.* 59:117–128.

Plevan, R. E. & Quinn, J. A. 1966 The Effect of Monomolecular Films on the Rate of Gas Absorption into a Quiescent Liquid, *AIChE J.* 12:894–902.

Poskanzer, A. M. & Goodrich, F. C. 1975a A New Surface Viscometer of High Sensitivity. II. Experiments with Stearic Acid Monolayers, *J. Colloid Interface Sci.* 52:213–221.

Poskanzer, A. M. & Goodrich, F. C. 1975b Surface Viscosity of Sodium Dodecyl Sulfate Solutions with and without Added Dodecanol, *J. Phys. Chem.* 79:2122–2126.

Poynting, J. H. & Thomson, J. J. 1902 *A Textbook of Physics–Properties of Matter,* Griffin, London.

Princen, H. M. & Aronson, M. P. 1976 Determination of Surface and Interfacial Tensions from Rotating Menisci in a Vertical Tube, in *Colloid and Interface Science,* ed. M. Kerker, vol. 3, pp. 359–373, Academic, New York.

Princen, H. M., Zia, I. Y. Z., & Mason, S. G. 1967 Measurement of Interfacial Tension from the Shape of a Rotating Drop, *J. Colloid Interface Sci.* 23:99–107.

Proudman, I. & Pearson, J. R. A. 1957 Expansions at Small Reynolds Numbers for the Flow Past a Sphere and a Circular Cylinder, *J. Fluid Mech.* 2:237–262.

Pruppacher, H. R. & Beard, K. V. 1970 A Wind Tunnel Investigation of the Internal Circulation and Shape of Water Drops Falling at Terminal Velocity in Air, *Q. J. R. Meteorol. Soc.* 96:247–256.

Radigan, W., Ghiradella, H., Frisch, H. L., Schonhorn, H., & Kwei, T. K. 1974 Kinetics of Spreading Glass on Fernico Metal, *J. Colloid Interface Sci.* 49:241–248.

Remakrishnan, S., Mailliet, K., & Hartland, S. 1976 Measurement of Surface and Interfacial Tension from Maximum Pressure in Sessile and Pendant Bubbles and Drops, *Proc. Indian Acad. Sci. Sect. A.* 73(3):107–118.

Ranger, K. B. 1965 A Stokes Flow Treated by the Method of Inversion, *Q. J. Mech. Appl. Math.* 18:277–285.

Ranger, K. B. 1973 The Stokes Drag for Asymmetric Flow past a Spherical Cap, *J. Appl. Math. Phys.* 24:801–809.

Ranger, K. B. 1977 The Stokes Flow around a Smooth Cylinder with an Attached Vortex, *J. Eng. Math.* 11:81–88.

Ranger, K. B. 1978. The Circular Disk Straddling the Interface of a Two-Phase Flow, *Int. J. Multiphase Flow* 4:263–277.

Ranger, K. B. & O'Neill, M. E. 1978 Rotation of a Cylinder and Sphere in the Presence of a Solid Plane and Interface, *Int. J. Multiphase Flow,* in press.

Reichman, J. M. & Temkin, S. 1974 A Study of the Deformation and Breakup of Accelerating Water Droplets, *Proc. Int. Colloquium on Drops and Bubbles,* vol. 2, pp. 446–464, California Inst. of Technology and Jet Propulsion Laboratory, Pasadena, Calif.

Reid, R. C., Prausnitz, J. M., & Sherwood, T. K. 1977 *The Properties of Gases and Liquids,* 3d ed., McGraw-Hill, New York.

Richardson, L. S. 1926 Atmospheric Diffusion Shown on a Distance Neighbor Graph, *Proc. R. Soc. Ser. A* 110:709–737.

Richardson, S. 1977 Axisymmetric Slow Viscous Flow about a Body of Revolution Whose Section Is a Cardioid, *Q. J. Mech. Appl. Math.* 30:369–374.

Riley, J. J. & Corrsin, S. 1974 The Relation of Turbulent Diffusivities to Lagrangian Velocities; Statistics for the Simplest Shear Flow, *J. Geophys. Res.* 79:1768–1771.

Rippin, D. W. T. & Davidson, J. F. 1967 Free Streamline Theory for a Large Gas Bubble in a Liquid, *Chem. Eng. Sci.* **22**:217-228.

Rivkind, V. Y. & Ryskin, G. M. 1976 Flow Structure in Motion of a Spherical Drop in a Fluid Medium at Intermediate Reynolds Number, *Fluid Dyn. (U.S.S.R.)* **11**:5-12.

Rivkind, V. Y., Ryskin, G. M., & Fishbein, G. A. 1972 The Motion of a Spherical Drop in the flow of a Viscous Fluid, *Fluid Mech. Sov. Res.* **1**:142-151.

Rivkind, V. Y., Ryskin, G. M., & Fishbein, G. A. 1976 Flow around a Spherical Drop at Intermediate Reynolds Numbers, *Appl. Math. Mech.* **40**:687-691.

Rohsenow, W. M. 1973 Film Condensation of Liquid Metals, *Prog. Heat Mass Transfer* **7**:469-484.

Rose, W. & Heins, R. W. 1962 Moving Interfaces and Contact Angle Rate-Dependency, *J. Colloid Sci.* **17**:39-48.

Rushton, E. & Davies, G. A. 1970 The Quasi-steady Motion of Two Fluid Spheres, presented at the International Fluid Dynamics Symposium, McMaster Univ., Hamilton, Ontario, Canada.

Rushton, E. & Davies, G. A. 1973 The Slow Unsteady Setting of Two Fluid Spheres along Their Line of Centres, *Appl. Sci. Res.* **28**:37-61.

Rushton, E. & Davies, G. A. 1978 The Slow Motion of Two Spherical Particles along Their Line of Centres, *Int. J. Multiphase Flow*, in press.

Ryan, R. T. 1976 The Behaviour of Large Low Surface Tension Water Drops Falling at Terminal Velocity in Air, *J. Appl. Meteorol.* **15**:157-165.

Rybczynski, W. 1911 Ueber die fortschreitende Bewegung einer Flüssigen Kugel in einem zähen Medium, *Bull. Int. Acad. Sci. Cracovie* A:40-46.

Sada, E. & Himmelblau, D. M. 1967 Transport of Gases through Insoluble Monolayers, *AIChE J.* **13**:860-865.

Sagert, N. H. & Quinn, M. J. 1978 The Coalescence of Gas Bubbles in Dilute Aqueous Solutions, *Chem. Eng. Sci.* **33**:1087-1095.

Savic, P. July 1953 Circulation and Distortion of Liquid Drops Falling through a Viscous Medium, *Natl. Res. Counc. Can. Rept.* MT-22.

Scheele, G. F. & Leng, D. E. 1971 An Experimental Study of Factors which Promote Coalescence of Two Colliding Drops Suspended in Water, *Chem. Eng. Sci.* **26**:1867-1879.

Schlamp, R. J., Grover, S. N., Pruppacher, H. R., & Hamielec, A. E. 1976 A Numerical Investigation of the Effect of Electric Charges and External Electric Fields on the Collision Efficiency of Cloud Drops, *J. Atmos. Sci.* **33**:1747-1755.

Schlichting, H. 1968 *Boundary-Layer Theory,* 6th ed., McGraw-Hill, New York.

Schneider, J. C., O'Neill, M. E., & Brenner, H. 1973 On the Slow Rotation of a Body Straddling the Interface between Two Immiscible Semi-infinite Fluids. *Mathematika* **20**:175-196.

Schonhorn, J., Frisch, H. L., & Kwei, T. K. 1966 Kinetics of Wetting of Surfaces by Polymer Melts, *J. Appl. Phys.* **37**:4967-4973.

Schroeder, R. R. & Kintner, R. C. 1965 Oscillation of Drops Falling in a Liquid Field, *AIChE J.* **11**:5-8.

Schubert 1967 *J. Fluid Mech.* **274**:647-656.

Schwartz, A. M. & Tejada, S. B. 1970 Studies of Dynamic Contact Angles on Solids, *NASA Contract Rept.* CR72728.

Schwartz, A. M. & Tejada, S. B. 1972 Studies of Dynamic Contact Angles on Solids, *J. Colloid Interface Sci.* **38**:359-375.

Schwiderski, E. W., Lugt, H. J., & Ugincius, P. 1966 Axisymmetric Viscous Fluid Motions around Conical Surfaces, *SIAM J. Appl. Math.* **14**:191-208.

Scriven, L. E. 1960 Dynamics of a Fluid Interface: Equation of Motion for Newtonian Surface Fluids, *Chem. Eng. Sci.* **12**:98-108.

Scriven, L. E. & Sternling, C. V. 1964 On Cellular Convection Driven by Surface-Tension Gradients: Effects of Mean Surface Tension and Surface Viscosity, *J. Fluid Mech.* **19**:321-340.

Shafrin, E. G. & Zisman, W. A. 1960 Constitutive Relations in the Wetting of Low Energy Surfaces and the Theory of the Retraction Method of Preparing Monolayers, *J. Phys. Chem.* **64**:519-524.

Sherman, P. 1953 Studies in Water-in-Oil Emulsions. III. The Properties of Interfacial Films of Sorbitan Sesquioleate, *J. Colloid Sci.* 8:35–37.

Shotton, E., Wibberley, L., Warburton, B., Davis, S. S., & Finaly, P. L. 1971 A Versatile Surface Rheometer, *Rheol. Acta* 10:142–152.

Sinfelt, J. H. & Drickamer, H. G. 1955 Resistance in a Liquid-Liquid Interface. III. The Effect of Molecular Properties, *J. Chem. Phys.* 23:1095–1099.

Skelland, A. H. P. & Huang, Y. F. 1977 Effects of Surface Active Agents on Fall Velocities of Drops, *Can. J. Chem. Eng.* 55:240–245.

Slattery, J. C. 1964 Surfaces. I. Momentum and Moment-of-Momentum Balances for Moving Surfaces, *Chem. Eng. Sci.* 19:379–385.

Slattery, J. C. 1972 *Momentum, Energy, and Mass Transfer in Continua*, McGraw-Hill, New York.

Slattery, J. C. 1974 Interfacial Effects in the Entrapment and Displacement of Residual Oil, *AIChE J.* 20:1145–1154.

Slattery, J. C. 1977 Limiting Criteria for Intrinsically Stable Equilibrium in Multiphase Multi-Component Systems, *AIChE J.* 23:275–285.

Slattery, J. C. 1979 Interfacial Effects in the Displacement of Residual Oil by Foam, *AIChE J.* 25:283–289.

Slattery, J. C. 1981 *Momentum, Energy and Mass Transfer in Continua*, 2d ed., Krieger, Huntington, N. Y.

Slattery, J. C. & Chen, J. D. 1978 Alternative Solution for Spinning Drop Interfacial Tensiometer, *J. Colloid Interface Sci.* 64:371–373.

Slattery, J. C. & Gaggioli, R. A. 1962 The Macroscopic Angular Momentum Balance, *Chem. Eng. Sci.* 17:893–895.

Slattery, J. C., Chen, J. D., Thomas, C. P., & Fleming, P. D. 1979 Spinning Drop Interfacial Viscometer, 73:483–499.

Smoluchowski, M. 1911 On the Mutual Action of Spheres which Move in a Viscous Liquid, *Bull. Int. Acad. Pol. Sci. Lett. Cl. Sci, Math. Nat. Ser. A* 1:28.

Snyder, W. H. & Lumley, J. L. 1971 Some Measurements of Particle Velocity Autocorrelation Functions in the Turbulent Flow, *J. Fluid Mech.* 48:41–71.

Solbrig, C. W., McFadden, J. H., Lyczkowski, R. W., & Hughes, E. D. 1975 Heat Transfer and Friction Correlations Required to Describe Steam-Water Behavior in Nuclear Safety Studies, AIChE paper 21, 15th Natl. Heat Transfer Conf., San Francisco, Calif.

Soo, S. L. 1956 Statistical Properties of the Momentum Transfer in Two Phase Flow, *Chem. Eng. Sci.* 5:57–64.

Spengler, J. D. & Gokhale, N. R. 1973 Wake Effect Interactions of Freely Suspended Large Water Drops, *J. Geophys. Res.* 78:497–503.

Spindler, B., Solesio, J. N. & Delhaye, J. M. 1978 On the Equations Describing the Instabilities of Liquid Films with Interfacial Phase Change, *ICHMT 1978 Int. Seminar Momentum, Heat Mass Transfer Two-Phase Energy Chemical Systems, Dubrovnik, Sept. 4–9.*

Springer, T. G. & Pigford, R. L. 1970 Influence of Surface Turbulence and Surfactants on Gas Transport through Liquid Interfaces, *Ind. Eng. Chem. Fundam.* 9:458–465.

Staicopolus, D. N. 1962 The Computation of Surface Tension and of Contact Angle by the Sessile-Drop Method, *J. Colloid Sci.* 17:439–447; 1963 *J. Colloid Sci.* 18:793–794; 1967 *J. Colloid Sci.* 23:453–456.

Stauffer, C. E. 1965 The Measurement of Surface Tension by the Pendant Drop Technique, *J. Phys. Chem.* 69:1933–1938.

Sternling, C. V. & Scriven, L. E. 1959 Interfacial Turbulence: Hydrodynamic Instability and the Marangoni Effect, *AIChE J.* 5:514–523.

Stimson, M. & Jeffery, G. B. 1926 The Motion of Two Spheres in a Viscous Fluid, *Proc. R. Soc. London Ser. A* 111:110–116.

Stokes, G. G. 1851 On the Effect of the Internal Friction of Fluids on the Motion of Pendulums, *Trans. Cambridge Philos. Soc.* 9:8–106 (also in *Scientific Papers,* vol. 3, pp. 1–141, University Press, Cambridge, 1901).

Sugden, S. 1921 The Determination of Surface Tension from the Rise in Capillary Tubes, *J. Chem. Soc. Trans.* 119:1483-1492.

Sugden, S. 1922 The Determination of Surface Tension from Maximum Pressure in Bubbles. *J. Chem. Soc. Trans.* 121:858-866(I); 125:27-31(II).

Sugden, S. 1924 The Variation of Surface Tension with Temperature and Some Related Functions, *J. Chem. Soc. Trans.* 125:32-41.

Sutherland, K. L. 1954 The Oscillating Jet Method for the Measurement of Surface Tension, *Aust. J. Chem.* 7:319-328.

Sy, F. & Lightfoot, E. N. 1971 Transient Creeping Flow around Fluid Spheres, *AIChE J.* 17:177-181.

Sy, F., Taunton, J. W., Lightfoot, E. N. 1970 Transient Creeping Flow around Spheres, *AIChE J.* 16:386-391.

Szyszkowski, B. von 1908 Experimental Studies of the Capillary Properties of Aqueous Solutions of Fatty Acids, *Z. Phys. Chem.* 64:385-414.

Takagi, H. 1974 Slow Motion of a Spherical Cap in a Viscous Fluid. 1. Uniform Translation and Rotation, *J. Phys. Soc. Jpn.* 37:229-236.

Tanner, R. I. 1958 The Spherical Journal-Bearing, *Appl. Sci. Res. Sect. A* 8:45-59.

Tawde, N. R. & Parvatikar, K. G. 1958 A Table for the Calculation of Surface Tension from Measurements of Sessile Drops, *Indian J. Phys.* 28:345-348.

Taylor, J. D. & Acrivos, A. J. 1964 Deformation and Drag of a Falling Drop, *J. Fluid Mech.* 18:466-476.

Taylor, G. I. 1921 Diffusion by Continuous Movements, *Scenes London Math. Soc.* 20:196-211.

Taylor, G. I. 1934 The Formation of Emulsions in Definable Fields of Flow, *Proc. R. Soc. London Ser. A* 146:501-523.

Taylor, G. I. 1969 Motion of Axisymmetric Bodies in Viscous Fluids, in *Problems of Hydrodynamics and Continuous Mechanics,* vol. 10 pp. 718-724, Society for Industrial and Applied Mathematics, Philadelphia, Pa.

Teletov, S. G. 1958 Two-Phase Flow Hydrodynamics. 1. Hydrodynamics and Energy Equations (in Russian), *Bull. Moscow Univ.* 2.

Tennekes, H. & Lumley, J. L. 1972 *A First Course in Turbulence,* p. 48, M.I.T. Press, Cambridge, Mass.

Thorsen, G., Stordalen, R. M., & Terjesen, S. G. 1968 On the Terminal Velocity of Circulating and Oscillating Liquid Drops, *Chem. Eng. Sci.* 23:413-426.

Tillett, J. P. K. 1970 Axial and Transverse Stokes Flow past Slender Axisymmetric Bodies, *J. Fluid Mech.* 44:401-417.

Tokuda, N. 1975 Stokes Solutions for Flow near Corners in Three Dimensions, *J. Phys. Soc. Jpn.* 38:1187-1194.

Truesdell, C. 1968a The Creation and Unfolding of the Concept of Stress, in *Essays in the History of Mechanics,* chap. 4, Springer-Verlag, New York.

Truesdell, C. 1968b A Program toward Rediscovering the Rational Mechanics of the Age of Reason, in *Essays in the History of Mechanics,* chap. 2, Springer-Verlag, New York.

Truesdell, C. 1969 *Rational Thermodynamics,* McGraw-Hill, New York.

Truesdell, C. A. & Toupin, R. A. 1960 The Classical Field Theories, in *Encyclopedia of Physics,* ed. S. Flugge, vol. 3, part 1, *Principles of Classical Mechanics and Field Theory,* pp. 226-858, Springer-Verlag, New York.

Tsonopoulos, C., Newman, J., & Prausnitz, J. M. 1971 Rapid Aging and Dynamic Surface Tension of Dilute Aqueous Solutions, *Chem. Eng. Sci.* 26:817-827.

Tsuge, H. & Hibino, S. 1977 The Onset Conditions of Oscillatory Motion of Single Gas Bubbles Rising in Various Liquids, *J. Chem. Eng. Jpn.* 10:66-68.

Tung, L. H. & Drickamer, H. G. 1952 Diffusion through an Interface, *J. Chem. Phys.* 20:6-12.

Vernier, Ph. & Delhaye, J. M. 1968 General Two-Phase Flow Equations Applied to the Thermohydrodynamics of Boiling Water Nuclear Reactors, *Energie Primaire* 4:5-46.

Veteau, J. M. 1979 Quelques Méthodes pour Mesurer la Surface Volumique Intégrale Moyenne dans les Ecoulements Diphasiques, CEAR, Centre d'Etudes Nucleaires de Grenoble, France.

Vonnegut, B. 1942 Rotating Bubble Method for the Determination of Surface and Interfacial Tensions, *Rev. Sci. Instrum.* 13:6-9.

Wacholder, E. & Weihs, D. 1972 Slow Motion of a Fluid Sphere in the Vicinity of Another Sphere or a Plane Boundary, *Chem. Eng. Sci.* 27:1817-1828.

Wairegi, T. 1974 The Mechanics of Large Drops and Bubbles Moving through Extended Liquid Media, Ph.D. thesis, McGill Univ., Montreal, Quebec, Canada.

Wairegi, T. & Grace, J. R. 1976 The Behaviour of Large Drops in Immiscible Liquids, *Int. J. Multiphase Flow* 3:67-77.

Wakiya, S. 1967 Slow Motions of Viscous Fluid around Two Spheres, *J. Phys. Soc. Jpn.* 22:1101-1109.

Wakiya, S. 1975 Application of Bipolar Co-ordinates to the Two-dimensional Creeping Motion of a Liquid. I. Flow over a Projection or a Depression on a Wall, *J. Phys. Soc. Jpn.* 39:1113-1120.

Wallace, J. P. 1966 A Study of the Fluid Turbulence Energy Spectrum in a Gas Solid Suspension, Ph.D. thesis, Rutgers Univ., New Brunswick, N.J.

Wallis, G. B. 1969 *One-dimensional Two-Phase Flow,* McGraw-Hill, New York.

Wang, H. & Skalak, R. 1969 Viscous Flow in a Cylindrical Tube Containing a Line of Spherical Particles, *J. Fluid Mech.* 38:75-96.

Wang, P. K. & Pruppacher, H. R. 1977 Acceleration to Terminal Velocity of Cloud and Raindrops, *J. Appl. Meteorol.* 16:275-280.

Wannier, G. H. 1950 A Contribution to the Hydrodynamics of Lubrication, *Q. Appl. Math.* 8:1-18.

Ward, W. J. & Quinn, J. A. 1965 Diffusion through the Liquid-Liquid Interface III. Interfacial Resistance in Three-Component Systems, *AIChE J.* 11:1005-1011.

Wasan, D. T., Gupta, L., & Vora, M. K. 1971 Interfacial Shear Viscosity at Fluid-Fluid Interfaces, *AIChE J.* 17:1287-1295.

Wasan, D. T., Shah, S., Aderangi, N., Chan, M., McNamara, J. J., Paolicchi, R., Patel, P., & Mohan, V. 1977 The Mechanism of Oil Bank Formation and Coalescence in Porous Media, *Proc. ERDA Symp. Enhanced Oil Gas Recovery Improved Drilling Methods,* ed. B. Linville, vol. 1, pp. b-4/1-B-4/14, Petroleum Publishing, Tulsa, Okla.

Wei, L. Y. & Slattery, J. C. 1976 Experimental Study of Nonlinear Surface Stress-Deformation Behavior with the Deep Channel Surface Viscometer, in *Colloid and Interface Science,* ed. M. Kerker, vol. 4, pp. 399-420, Academic, New York.

Wei, L. Y., Schmidt, W., & Slattery, J. C. 1974 Measurement of the Surface Dilatational Viscosity, *J. Colloid Interface Sci.* 28:1-9.

Wellek, R. M., Agrawal, A. K., & Skelland, A. H. P. 1966 Shape of Liquid Drops Moving in Liquid Media, *AIChE J.* 12:854-862.

Weyl, P. K. 1970 *Oceanography: An Introduction to the Marine Environment,* Wiley, New York.

Whitaker, S. 1981 *Introduction to Fluid Mechanics,* Krieger, Huntington, New York.

Whitaker, S. 1977 *Fundamental Principles of Heat Transfer,* Pergamon, Elmsford, N.Y.

Wibberley, K. 1962 Some Physical Properties of Interfacial Films of Potassium Arabate, *J. Pharm. Pharmacol.* 14:87T-92T.

Wickham, G. R. & Wilson, S. D. R. 1975 The Deformation of an Elastic Solid by a Sessile Drop, *J. Colloid Interface Sci.* 51:189-190.

Williams, R. 1977 The Advancing Front of a Spreading Liquid, *Nature (London)* 266:153-154.

Wilson, S. D. R. 1975 A Note on the Measurement of Dynamic Contact Angles, *J. Colloid Interface Sci.* 51:532-534.

Winkler, C. A. & Maass, O. 1933 Density Discontinuities at the Critical Temperature, *Can. J. Res.* 9:613-629.

Winnikow, S. & Chao, B. T. 1966 Droplet Motion in Purified Systems, *Phys. Fluids* 9:50-61.

Wu, S. 1974 Interfacial and Surface Tensions of Polymers, *J. Macromol. Sci. Rev. Macromol. Chem.* C10(1):1-73.

Yarnold, G. D. 1938 The Motion of a Mercury Index in a Capillary Tube, *Proc. Phys. Soc. London* 50:540–552.

Yarnold, G. D. 1946 The Hysteresis of the Angle of Contact of Mercury, *Proc. Phys. Soc. London* 58:120–125.

Yarnold, G. D. & Mason, B. J. 1949 The Angle of Contact between Water and Wax, *Proc. Phys. Soc. London Sect. B* 62:125–128.

Yip, F., Venart, J., & Govier, G. 1970 The Motion of Small Air Bubbles in Stagnant and Flowing Water, *Can. J. Chem. Eng.* 48:229–235.

Young, T. 1805 An Essay on the Cohesion of Fluids, *Philos. Trans. R. Soc. London* 95:65–87.

Yudine, M. I. 1959 Physical Considerations on Heavy Particle Diffusion, *Adv. Geophys.* 6:185–191.

Zabel, T., Hanson, C., & Ingham, J. 1973 The Influence of System Purity, Drop Separation and Heat Transfer on the Terminal Velocity of Falling Drops in Liquid-Liquid Systems, *Trans. Inst. Chem. Eng.* 51:162–164.

Zisman, W. A. 1964 Relation of the Equilibrium Contact Angle to Liquid and Solid Constitution, *Adv. Chem. Ser.* 43:1–51.

2 LIQUID–GAS SYSTEMS

2.1 Flow Regimes

G. F. Hewitt

2.1.1 INTRODUCTION

Of the four types of two-phase flow (gas-liquid, gas-solid, liquid-liquid, and liquid-solid), gas-liquid flows are the most complex, since they combine the characteristics of a deformable interface and the compressibility of one of the phases. For given flows of the two phases in a given channel, the gas-liquid interfacial distribution can take any of an infinite number of possible forms. Fortunately, several factors tend to limit the range of possibilities:

1. Depending on the flow conditions, there exist regions of the channel where one phase is continuous and the other discontinuous, e.g., a flow of a mist of droplets in a continuum of gas or the flow of a dispersion of bubbles in a continuum of liquid.
2. Where there are regions of liquid or gas continua, the discontinuous phase (bubbles or drops) tends to assume a spherical shape under the influence of surface tension. Clearly, the influence of surface tension is greater, the smaller the discontinuous element; larger bubbles or drops tend to be subjected to distorting influences in the flow field and become nonspherical.
3. In general, there is a tendency for the wall to be wetted by the liquid phase and for the gas phase to concentrate, in many cases, in the center of the channel. Important exceptions to this general rule include those cases where vapor generated due to boiling at the channel wall remains close to the wall, where wetting of the channel surface is inhibited owing to the fact that the channel is at a high temperature, and where there is preferential concentration of bubbles near the wall due to special hydrodynamic effects.

These factors combine to make it possible, in principle, to delineate certain classes of interfacial distribution, commonly called *flow regimes* or *flow patterns*.

Examples of flow patterns are as follows:

Author acknowledges permission from the United Kingdom Atomic Energy Authority (UKAEA) to reproduce figures 2.1.1, 2.1.2, 2.1.3, 2.1.4, 2.1.5, 2.1.8, 2.1.9, 2.1.11, 2.1.12, 2.1.13, 2.1.14, 2.1.17, 2.1.18, 2.1.19, 2.1.20, 2.1.21, 2.1.25, 2.2.1, 2.2.2, 2.2.7, 2.2.8, 2.2.9, 2.2.10, 2.2.11, 2.2.12, 2.2.13, 2.2.14, which remain UKAEA copyright material.

1. Bubble flow. The gas phase flows as bubbles dispersed in the liquid. Bubble flow occurs typically at low gas superficial velocities and high liquid velocities.
2. Stratified flow. This pattern occurs typically in horizontal or inclined channels. It is characterized by the liquid flowing in a layer at the bottom of the channel, with the gas flowing above it. Stratified flow occurs at low gas velocities, increases in gas flow leading to the generation of interfacial waves and the breakdown of the regime.
3. Annular flow. This pattern occurs at higher gas velocities. The liquid phase flows partly as a liquid film on the channel wall, with the gas flowing in the channel core. Usually, part of the liquid phase flows as droplets entrained in the gas core.

Many different regimes have been defined in the literature, and the nature of the regimes varies with channel geometry and orientation. More detailed definitions for the various cases are given in sections 2.1.3–2.1.6.

In two-phase flow studies, the question is often asked, Are flow-regime maps helpful in practical design? Certainly, the vast majority of technical calculations on two-phase flow are made without any reference whatsoever to flow-pattern maps. This is true, for instance, of pressure drop calculations (see section 2.2), and one can argue that the invocation of flow patterns is an unnecessary complication. However, the relationships for pressure drop are likely to be different for a flow consisting of a dispersion of bubbles (bubbly flow) than for a flow consisting of a liquid film on the channel wall with a central gas core (annular flow). Recent work has demonstrated that more accurate results can be obtained by giving attention to specific flow patterns; furthermore, models that have a sound theoretical basis are likely to be more applicable than those that are purely empirical. It seems likely that calculation methods based on flow-pattern delineation will ultimately supersede those that take no account of the nature of the flow. Thus, the understanding and delineation of flow patterns are likely to be increasingly important in the future.

Assessment of the flow regime occurring in a given channel is necessarily a somewhat subjective matter. Thus, it is important to assess information on flow patterns in the light of the methods used to obtain the information, namely, the measurement technique. Therefore, the various methods for flow-pattern determination are discussed next.

2.1.2 DETERMINATION OF FLOW REGIMES

Most of the earlier work on the determination of flow regimes was carried out using direct visual observation; later, this was supplemented by evidence obtained through high-speed photography. The necessarily subjective nature of the interpretation of visual and photographic evidence has led to the search for more specific methods. A general review of the techniques employed is given by Hewitt (1978).

The objective here is not to review all the methods, but rather to give some recommendations concerning techniques for flow-pattern delineation. The recommended methods fall into three categories:

1. Visualization methods, including photographic methods (section 2.1.2.2).
2. Methods depending on the measurement of fluctuating quantities and statistical characterization of the results in terms of flow patterns (section 2.1.2.3). Here,

the use of pressure fluctuations and fluctuations in X-ray absorption are recommended. However, observations of other fluctuating quantities have been employed, such as conductance between a needle placed in the flow and the channel wall [see, for example, Fiori & Bergles (1966), Dsarasov et al. (1974), and Reimann & John (1978)] or wall shear stress (Kutateladze 1973).

3. Methods dependent on radiation-absorption measurement of density distribution (section 2.1.2.4). Included here are X-radiography measurements and multibeam gamma densitometry.

The recommended procedure for choosing a method of flow-pattern determination is given in section 2.1.2.1. There are, however, no *absolute* methods for the determination of flow pattern. All data on flow patterns should be treated with some reserve.

2.1.2.1   Selection of Method for Delineation of Flow Pattern

A selection chart is shown in figure 2.1.1. The main questions raised are as follows:

1. Are the flows slow enough to be observed visually in transparent channels? Obviously, if the flow pattern can be recognized by direct viewing, then this is the simplest and cheapest method. However, circumstances may prevent the use of transparent test sections, or the flow may be so complex that it cannot be clearly observed except with the aid of high-speed photography.

2. Is visualization possible and adequate with special photographic techniques? Where transparent channels can be used or suitable windows employed, but where the motion of the flow is too rapid to discern the flow regime clearly, it is often possible to use high-speed flash or cine photography. However, even with very-high-speed photography, it is often not possible to discern clearly what is happening in the channel. This is because, if there is a complex pattern of interfaces in the channel, the refraction and reflection of light from the interfaces obscures the view of the flow from outside. Here, alternative techniques such as X-radiography may be used.

3. Are methods involving radiation acceptable? In many laboratories, it is not feasible to use X-ray or gamma-ray densitometry or radiography. In this case, and where visualization techniques are inapplicable, an alternative technique must be sought. If feasible, it is recommended that pressure fluctuation analysis (section 2.1.2.3) be employed in this case.

4. Is X-radiography feasible? This technique may be employed if absorption by the channel wall is relatively small. The method is not suitable for thick-walled channels; nor is it suitable if high-speed motion radiography is necessary to identify the flow patterns. The method is described further in section 2.1.2.4.

5. Are the measurements being made in a transient or steady-state flow? In steady-state flows, statistical fluctuations in void fraction occur, and these can be measured using the X-ray absorption method. These statistical fluctuations can be used to characterize the flow pattern as described in section 2.1.2.3. For transient measurements, a general idea of the flow pattern may be obtained by using multibeam densitometry (section 2.1.2.4).

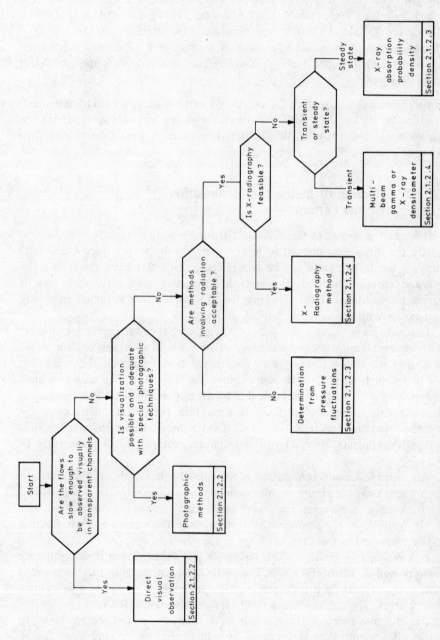

Figure 2.1.1 Selection chart for flow regime delineation method.

2.1.2.2 Determination of Flow Regime by Visualization

Direct Visual Observation

Principle of method The principle of the method is obvious; a two-phase flow is set up in a channel that is either transparent or has visual access windows, and the flow is observed directly.

Problems in applications Clearly, the delineation of flow patterns by direct visual observation is only applicable to low-speed flows and where suitable visual access can be facilitated. For higher-speed flows, and where objects such as waves or bubbles are moving along the channel at relatively constant velocity, the applicability of visual observation can be extended by using scanning devices of the type illustrated in figure 2.1.2. This type of device has been used by Hewitt & Lovegrove (1969) for tracking waves in annular flows, and by Roumy (1969) for tracking bubbles in bubbly and slug flows. The image in the rotating mirror is tracked along the channel at a fixed velocity and is seen by the observer in the fixed mirror; by adjusting the rotation speed, it is possible to keep a given wave or bubble in the image. The device can be used also for measuring the velocities of waves or bubbles by noting the speed of rotation.

Photographic Methods

Principle of method A wide variety of high-speed photographic techniques have been employed in studying two-phase flows. Reviews of developments in photography are given by Cooper et al. (1963), Arnold & Hewitt (1967), Hewitt & Whalley

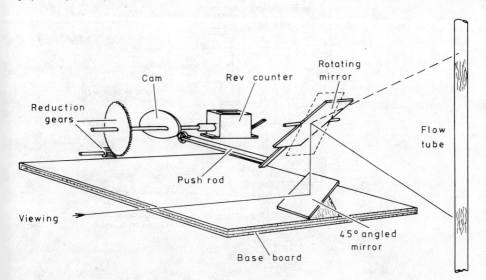

Figure 2.1.2 Mirror-scanner device for following bubbles or waves in two-phase flow (Hewitt & Lovegrove 1969).

(1980), and Delhaye (1979). It is sufficient here to make a few comments about various aspects of the application of high-speed photography:

1. Illumination. When the viewing direction is normal to the channel, the illumination can be either from the side (dark ground) or from the back of the channel (light ground). In general, diffuse light-ground illumination seems to give the best results, although information obtained from dark-ground illumination is often useful.

2. Axial-view methods. For annular flow in particular, an improved view of the phenomena may be obtained by viewing axially. A device for viewing the flow in an upstream cross-sectional plane is illustrated in figure 2.1.3. At the end of the channel, the flow is diverted to allow viewing through an air-purged viewing tube as shown. Motions of the liquid phase can be clearly observed in the plane of illumination, and they throw considerable light on the mechanisms of droplet entrainment from interfacial waves in annular flow. Applications of this device are discussed by Arnold & Hewitt (1967), Hewitt & Roberts (1969b), Azzopardi & Lacey (1974), Whalley et al. (1977), Mayinger & Langner (1977), and Suzuki & Ueda (1977). In the axial-view method illustrated in figure 2.1.3, phenomena are observed only in the zone of focus and illumination. An alternative method (which, for instance, allows the droplets to be followed from their time of creation from interfacial waves to their final deposition) is the parallel-light technique described by Hewitt & Whalley (1980) and Whalley et al. (1979) and illustrated in figure 2.1.4. Here, glass windows are arranged at the bottom and top of the test section, with suitable flow separators to keep the windows free of impinging liquid. The

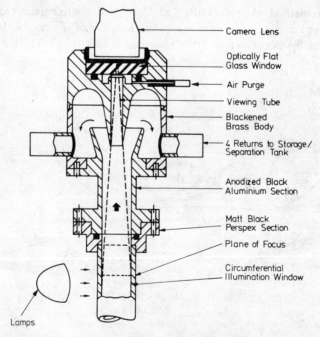

— Camera Lens

— Optically Flat Glass Window

— Air Purge

— Viewing Tube

— Blackened Brass Body

— 4 Returns to Storage/ Separation Tank

— Anodized Black Aluminium Section

— Matt Black Perspex Section

— Plane of Focus

— Circumferential Illumination Window

Lamps

Figure 2.1.3 Device for axial-view photography of annular two-phase flow in a 32-mm-bore tube (Hewitt & Roberts 1969b).

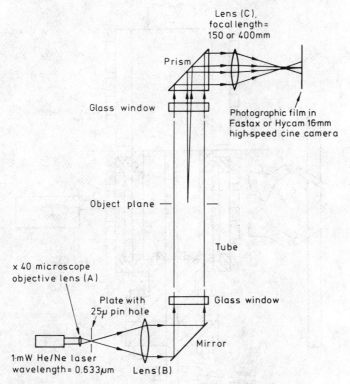

Figure 2.1.4 Optical arrangement for parallel-light viewing technique
(Whalley et al. 1979).

technique has proved useful not only in studying droplet behavior in annular flow,
but also in studying flooding in countercurrent flow.

3. Visualization at high pressure. Many situations of practical importance
concern high-pressure vapor-liquid flows, and particularly steam-water flows. Here,
there are special difficulties in visualization, owing to the fact that high-pressure
water tends to attack window material. However, special windows (e.g., of sapphire
or calcium fluoride) can be constructed; alternatively, ordinary borosilicate glass
windows can be used for short periods. An example of the latter technique is
illustrated in figure 2.1.5. Here, the high-pressure steam-water flow is observed in an
ordinary borosilicate glass tube mounted in a water-filled pressure vessel with glass
windows for illumination and viewing.

Often, better visualization can be obtained using a colored liquid, but this is
not always feasible.

Problems in applications The main intrinsic limitation on the application of
photographic methods is the influence of complex interfacial structures in giving
multiple reflection and refraction effects that obscure the view, particularly of the
center regions of the channel. Thus, for example, a high-speed cine or flash
photograph may indicate the presence of bubbly two-phase flow, whereas, in fact,
what one is seeing is merely a bubble-rich layer adjacent to the wall, with other

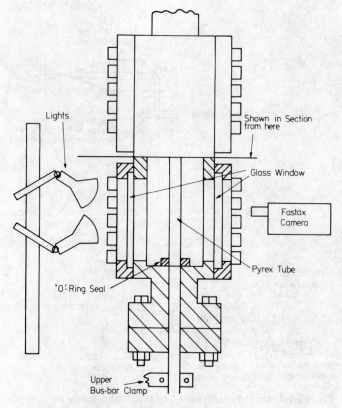

Figure 2.1.5 High-pressure viewing section used for flow-pattern studies in steam-water flows (Bennett et al. 1965).

(unseen) structures in the center region. This problem is particularly severe at high mass fluxes and low qualities. Another problem with high-speed cinematography is the enormous amount of information produced and the difficulty of analyzing and interpreting it. Again, there is a strong element of subjectivity in the deduction of flow patterns from high-speed cine records.

2.1.2.3 Methods Depending on the Statistical Analysis of Fluctuating Quantities

Analysis of Local Pressure Fluctuations

Principle of method This method has been used by Hubbard & Dukler (1966) and Simpson et al. (1977); continuous measurements are made of the local pressure $p(t)$ as a function of time. A useful technique for analyzing fluctuating signals is that of autocorrelation. The autocorrelation function for the signal $p(t)$ is given by the time average of the product of the pressure at time t [that is, $p(t)$] and the pressure at time $t + \tau$ [that is, $p(t + \tau)$]:

$$R_{pp}(\tau) = \lim_{T \to \infty} \frac{1}{T} \int_0^T p(t)\, p(t + \tau)\, dt \qquad [2.1.1]$$

The power spectral density of the pressure signal, indicating its distribution within the frequency domain f, is obtained by a Fourier transform of the autocorrelation function $R_{pp}(\tau)$ as follows:

$$G_{pp}(f) = 2 \int_{-\infty}^{\infty} R_{pp}(\tau) \exp\left(- i\, 2\pi f \tau\right) d\tau = 4 \int_0^{\infty} R_{pp}(\tau) \cos 2\pi f \tau\, d\tau$$

$$[2.1.2]$$

Hubbard & Dukler (1966) distinguished essentially three types of power-spectral-density distribution obtained from pressure fluctuation measurements in horizontal air-water flows. These are illustrated in figure 2.1.6 and are as follows:

1. Separated flow: There is a peak at zero frequency. This type of response is obtained from stratified, wavy, and cresting flows.
2. Dispersed flows: There is a flat, relatively uniform spectrum.
3. Intermittent flows: There is a characteristic peak in the power spectral density. This type of result is obtained for plug, slug, and slug-annular flows.

Problems in applications The interpretation of pressure fluctuations is not always as clearcut as figure 2.1.6 might indicate. Unfortunately, the conditions that are most difficult to interpret (i.e., complex high mass flow, low-quality flows) are also those that are most difficult to interpret using visual means. Another problem with pressure fluctuation measurement is that pressure waves can reflect from the outlet of the test section, giving spurious signals (Webb 1970).

Void Fraction Fluctuations Determined by Using X-Ray Absorption

Principle of method The method (Jones & Zuber 1975) is illustrated schematically in figure 2.1.7. An X-ray beam is passed through the flow and is absorbed by it to

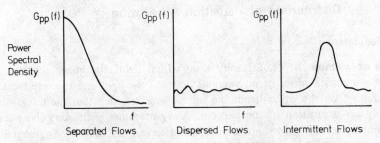

Figure 2.1.6 Relation between power-spectral-density function and flow type (Hubbard & Dukler 1976).

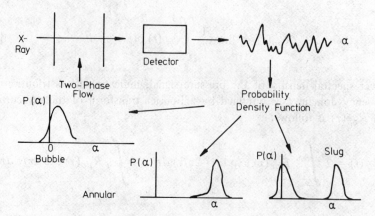

Figure 2.1.7 X-ray-absorption method for flow-pattern detection (Jones & Zuber 1975).

an extent that increases with instantaneous density (that is, the absorption decreases with instantaneous void fraction). In X-ray absorption measurements of void fraction (section 10.2.1.2) for flow-regime determination, the output from the detector is converted into a signal representing the instantaneous void fraction; in turn, this signal is analyzed to give a probability distribution $P(\alpha)$ for void fraction. A single peak at low void fraction indicates bubble flow; a single peak at high void fraction, annular flow; and double peaks, slug flow (figure 2.1.7). In bubble flow and slug flow, void fractions of less than zero are indicated by the signal. This is due to the inherent scatter resulting from the statistical nature of the absorption and detection (see section 10.2.1.2).

Problems in applications The problems inherent in radiation-absorption methods are discussed in detail in section 10.2.1.2. Even if radiation techniques are acceptable, X-ray methods require a reasonably high degree of in-house electronics expertise. Although the patterns seen in figure 2.1.7 are clearcut, complex flows may give a less productive indication. Nevertheless, this technique is one of the most promising nonvisual techniques for the delineation of flow regimes. Further work is needed to extend its range.

2.1.2.4 Methods Depending on the Spatial Distribution of Radiation Absorption

X-Radiography

Principle of method In photography using visual light, the image received is the result of a complex series of interactions between the light and the interfaces. With X-radiography, on the other hand, the interactions are such that the image depends principally on absorption of the photons. X-ray machines giving very-short-duration (for example, $0.1\text{-}\mu s$) pulses are available and have been used in X-radiography of two-phase flow (Bennett et al. 1965; Hewitt & Roberts 1969a; Mayinger & Zetsmann 1977). Although repetitive-flash X-ray equipment is available for cine studies, this is normally somewhat limited. X-ray fluoroscopy can be used directly for visual observation of the flows, although the time resolution is often insufficient (Johanns 1964; Baker 1965).

Problems in applications This method entails the usual problems of handling radiation (see section 10.2.1.2). The main difficulty with X-radiography is that of obtaining sufficient resolution. With plastic-walled channels, excellent time and spatial resolution can be obtained (Hewitt & Roberts 1969a), but the most useful area of application for this technique is in visualizing flows in nontransparent (typically metal-walled) channels, including those cases in which there is a heat flux. If high-pressure operation is required, then there is a conflict between pressure integrity and the need to maintain the walls as thin as possible to reduce their absorption of the X-rays. Bennett et al. (1965) used a ribbed titanium test section, as illustrated in figure 2.1.8. The ribs provided the pressure strength, allowing the intervening wall to be made thin enough to give minimum absorption of X-rays. Typical radiographs of high-pressure boiling flows are included in figure 2.1.8.

Multibeam Densitometry

Principle of method The importance of transiently varying flows in nuclear reactor safety and the need to predict such flows in more detail have led to the development of multibeam radiation-absorption techniques that are capable, in principle, of distinguishing flow regimes. The multibeam-adsorption system used by Smith (1975) is illustrated in figure 2.1.9; here an X-ray source is used (note the inclusion of reference beams to account for the effect of fluctuations in effective

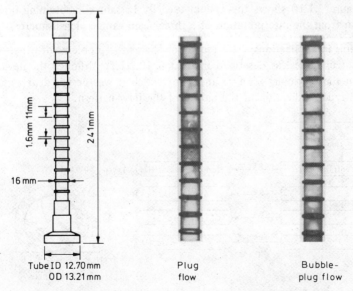

Figure 2.1.8 Ribbed titanium test section for X-radiography of steam-water flow at pressures up to 7.0 MPa, with examples of flow-pattern pictures taken using this test section (Bennett et al. 1965).

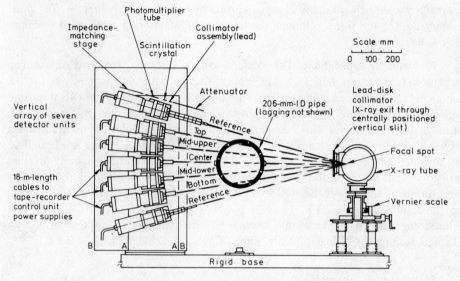

Figure 2.1.9 Multibeam X-ray system for determination of chordal mean void fractions and identification of flow patterns during blowdown from a horizontal tube (Smith 1975).

source strength). Alternatively, multibeam gamma-absorption devices can be used (Ybarrondo 1975; Lassahn 1977; Reiman & John 1978). Good time response is obtainable from such systems by using a high-strength source (e.g., a 30-Ci ^{137}Cs source); figure 2.1.10 shows the system used by Lassahn for obtaining flow-pattern information from the interpretation of a three-beam gamma densitometer.

Problems in applications This technique shares the problems of other radiation-absorption techniques, as described in section 10.2.1.2. Although the device is very effective in the particular circumstances for which it was designed, it can, at best, give only a crude indication of the nature of the flow pattern.

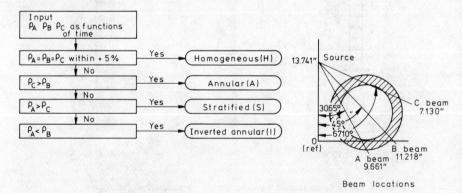

Figure 2.1.10 "Truth diagram" for determining flow regime from the response of the LOFT three-beam gamma densitometer (Lassahn 1977).

2.1.3 REGIMES IN VERTICAL FLOW

2.1.3.1 Definitions of Regimes

A very wide variety of flow regimes have been defined in the literature; this results partly from the subjective nature of flow-regime definitions and partly from a variety of names being given to essentially the same regime. It is convenient to define the following five regimes for vertical flow (figure 2.1.11):

1. Bubble flow. The liquid phase is continuous, and a dispersion of bubbles flows within the liquid continuum.
2. Slug or plug flow. At higher gas flows, bubble coalescence occurs, and eventually the bubble diameter approaches that of the tube. When this occurs, large, characteristically bullet-shaped bubbles are formed, which may be separated by regions containing dispersions of smaller bubbles. Typically, the liquid phase flows down the outside of the large bubbles in the form of a falling film, although the *net* flow of both liquid and gas can be upward.
3. Churn flow. With increasing flow velocity, a breakdown of the slug flow bubbles leads to an unstable flow regime in which there is, in wide-bore tubes, an oscillatory motion of the liquid upward and downward in the tube; thus the name churn flow. The oscillation may not occur in narrow-bore tubes, and a smoother transition between the slug flow and annular flow regimes may be observed.
4. Annular flow. The liquid flows on the wall of the tube as a film, and the gas phase flows in the center. Usually, some of the liquid phase is entrained as small droplets in the gas core; it is also possible (although less common) for bubbles to be entrained in the liquid film.
5. Wispy annular flow. As the liquid flow rate is increased, the concentration of drops in the gas core increases; ultimately, droplet coalescence in the core leads

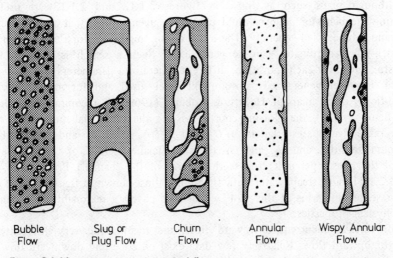

| Bubble Flow | Slug or Plug Flow | Churn Flow | Annular Flow | Wispy Annular Flow |

Figure 2.1.11 Flow patterns in vertical flow.

to large lumps or streaks (wisps) of liquid in the gas core. This regime is characteristic of flows with high mass flux.

2.1.3.2   Data for Flow-Pattern and Generalized-Flow-Pattern Maps

Many flow-pattern data exist within the literature, but, unfortunately, most are for air-water flows. There is a dearth of information for other systems. The data have to be treated with some reserve when they depend on visual or photographic evidence. For example, many early workers indicated the existence of a transition between annular flow and "mist" flow, the apparent transition probably being ascribable to the limits to which a visually observable film existed. With high-speed photography, the liquid film can be observed well beyond this limit. Of course, partial entrainment of the flow is the rule rather than the exception, and, in many circumstances, a very large fraction of the liquid phase can be entrained as droplets. However, in unheated systems, complete entrainment, without a liquid film present, is unlikely to occur.

In addition, many authors have designated a "froth" flow regime. This is defined as being an emulsion-type flow without noticeable structure. However, flash X-ray pictures show that within this region there is noticeable structure, ranging from developing structure in a high-speed bubbly flow at one extreme to wispy-annular-type flow at the other. At high liquid flow rates, the transition from bubbly flow to annular flow occurs gradually as the gas flow rate is increased.

The normal practice in presented flow-pattern data is to classify the flow pattern by visual or other means and to plot the data as a *flow-pattern map* in terms of system parameters. Parameters that are commonly used are the phase superficial velocities or, alternatively, the total mass flux and quality; examples of these two forms of plotting are illustrated in figures 2.1.12 and 2.1.13, both for upward vertical flow in round tubes.

Although maps such as those in figures 2.1.12 and 2.1.13 are useful in indicating the behavior of given fluid pairs in a given geometry at a given pressure, they cannot be applied generally. There is a continuing search for flow-pattern maps in which the coordinates can be generalized. Such a search is unlikely to be successful, since, for each transition, different generalized parameters are likely to be relevant. However, generalized maps are still widely used, and, for vertical flows, the general-flow-pattern map of Hewitt & Roberts (1969a) is recommended. On this map (figure 2.1.14), the plotting coordinates are the superficial momentum fluxes of the respective phases (that is, $\rho_L U_L^2$ and $\rho_G U_G^2$, where ρ_L and ρ_G are the gas and liquid densities, and U_G and U_L the superficial velocities, or the volume flow rates of the phases per unit cross-sectional area of the channel). Both the air-water (figure 2.1.11) and steam-water data (including those shown in figure 2.1.12) could be represented in terms of this plot, which thus covers a reasonably wide range of fluid physical properties.

For vertical cocurrent downward flow, the regimes are very different from those for upward flow. Relatively few data exist on cocurrent downward flow. The main characteristic of such flow is the preponderance of the annular flow regime. It

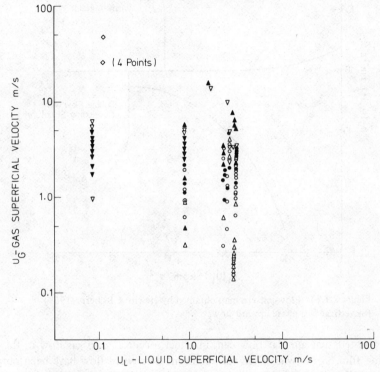

o Bubble
△ Bubble with plug
▼ Churn flow (bubbly liquid film)
▽ Annular with bubbly film
◇ Annular with bubble-free film
▲ Annular with wisps and bubble film
● Evidence of structure (bubble flow)

Figure 2.1.12 Flow-pattern data obtained by Hewitt & Roberts (1969a) for air-water flows at atmospheric pressure, using simultaneous flash photography and flash X-radiography.

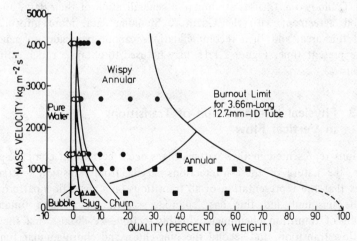

Figure 2.1.13 Flow-pattern data obtained by Bennett et al. (1965) for steam-water flow at 6.89 MPa pressure.

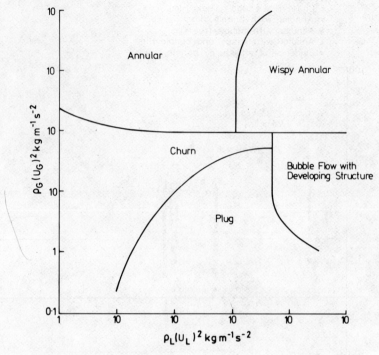

Figure 2.1.14   Flow-pattern map obtained by Hewitt & Roberts (1969) for vertical two-phase upward flow.

should be noted that annular flow can, in effect, occur at zero gas flow in the form of a falling film on the wall. Data for cocurrent downward flow have been obtained by Golan & Stenning (1969) and by Oshinowo & Charles (1974). The Golan & Stenning map for air-water systems is shown in figure 2.1.15. The oscillatory regime shown may be a characteristic specifically of the U-tube test section used by Golan & Stenning. Oshinowo & Charles attempted a generalization of their data, but this is not in good agreement with the Golan & Stenning data. More information is required in this area, and firm recommendations cannot be made on generalized maps at the present time. Figure 2.1.15 may be used to obtain a rough estimate of a flow pattern.

2.1.3.3 Physical Interpretation of Transitions in Vertical Flow

The transitions represented in flow-pattern maps occur because of complex physical interactions, the nature of these interactions varying from transition to transition. This implies that the representation of all transitions on a given flow-pattern map is likely to be unsound and this has led to a search for a more fundamental understanding of transition phenomena. In this section, we discuss first the bubble flow–plug flow transition, and second the plug-churn and churn-annular transitions in the context of flooding and flow-reversal phenomena.

The Bubble Flow-Plug Flow Transition
in Vertical Upward Cocurrent Flow

In bubble flow, the bubbles undergo random motions in passing through the channel; from time to time, two bubbles collide and may coalesce to form a larger bubble. This process of collision and coalescence ultimately leads to plug flow. Radovcich & Moissis (1962) consider a simplified model of bubble flow in which the bubbles are disposed in a cubic lattice, moving randomly with respect to adjacent bubbles in the lattice with a mean fluctuating velocity. They show that, in such a system, the bubble collision frequency would vary with void fraction in the manner illustrated in figure 2.1.16. The collision frequency is small for void fractions of 10%, but increases rapidly in the region 20–30%; for void fractions higher than 30%, collision and consequent coalescence of bubbles becomes very rapid, and bubble flow is very unstable. As a rule of thumb, therefore, 30% void fraction may be taken as a limit for bubble flow. However, plug flow can exist at very low void fractions (for example, individual plug flow bubbles can be introduced into the channel), and bubbly flow can exist at high void fractions owing to a number of factors, which include

1. Inhibition of bubble coalescence. Surface-active contaminants tend to prevent coalescence. An example of this is the case of detergent froth, where, in effect, bubble flow exists at a void fraction close to unity.

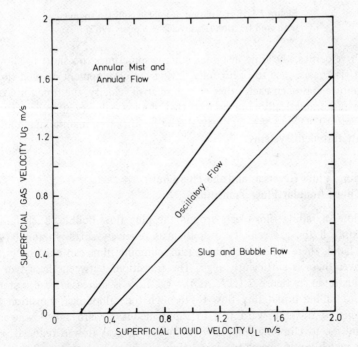

Figure 2.1.15 Flow-regime map for vertical cocurrent downward flow (Golan & Stenning 1969). Reprinted by permission of the Council of the Institution of Mechanical Engineers from *The Proceedings of the Institution of Mechanical Engineers.*

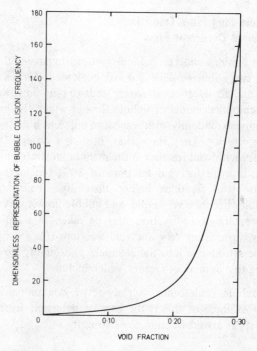

Figure 2.1.16 Variation of bubble collision frequency
with void fraction (Radovcich & Moissis 1962).

2. At high velocities, the time in the channel is sometimes too short to allow bubble
growth via coalescence to occur fully, giving the development of plug flow. When
two bubbles approach each other at high relative velocity, the time for coalescence
is increased dramatically compared to that of a low-velocity approach (Kirkpatrick
& Lockett 1974), and this fact may also be significant in maintaining bubbly flows
in highly turbulent systems.

Flooding, Flow Reversal, and the Plug-Churn and Churn-Annular Flow Transitions

In plug flow, a falling film exists around the plug flow bubble. Such falling films
can exist only if the gas velocity over them is relatively small. In annular flow, on
the other hand, there exists a climbing film; climbing films can exist only if the gas
velocity over them is sufficiently high. The transitions between these two extreme
cases is illustrated in figure 2.1.17. As the gas flow is increased, the system passes
from one of falling liquid film flow (*a*) through the "flooding" transition at which
liquid begins to travel upward (*b*), to simultaneous upward and downward liquid
flow (*c* and *d*), to climbing film flow (*e*). When the gas flow is reduced, a point is
reached at which liquid begins to creep below the injection point, and this is termed
"flow reversal." The relation between the flooding and flow-reversal transitions,
and the flow-regime transitions between plug (slug) and churn flow and between
churn flow and annular flow, are discussed below. First, however, it is appropriate

to discuss correlations for the prediction of the transitions illustrated in figure 2.1.17.

Apart from its interest in the context of flow-pattern transitions, the flooding transition has industrial relevance in contexts that include

1. Reflux condensation. Here, the flooding transition represents the limit of vapor flow that can enter the condenser in countercurrent flow to the condensate reflux.
2. Falling-film mass transfer equipment. In this case, it is economical to operate the equipment with a countercurrent (rising) gas flow, and again flooding is a limitation. A similar phenomenon limits the countercurrent operation of packed towers.
3. Reactor safety. In a loss-of-coolant accident (LOCA) in a pressurized water reactor, the emergency cooling-water stream may have to enter in downward flow that is countercurrent to steam flow leaving the reactor vessel. Here, the rate at which emergency cooling water can enter the reactor may be limited by the flooding phenomenon.

The technical importance of flooding has led to a wide range of studies and the development of a number of alternative correlation forms. Correlating parameters that are fairly widely used for flooding are those due to Wallis (1961):

$$U_G^* = U_G \rho_G^{1/2} \left[g d_0 (\rho_L - \rho_G) \right]^{-1/2} \qquad [2.1.3]$$

$$U_L^* = U_L \rho_L^{1/2} \left[g d_0 (\rho_L - \rho_G) \right]^{-1/2} \qquad [2.1.4]$$

where U_L and U_G are the liquid and gas superficial velocities (volume flux per unit area), ρ_L and ρ_G are the densities of the liquid and gas phases, d_0 is the tube diameter, and g is the acceleration due to gravity. Wallis correlated flooding data with a relationship of the form

$$(U_G^*)^{1/2} + (U_L^*)^{1/2} = C \qquad [2.1.5]$$

where C is a constant whose value is of the order of unity.

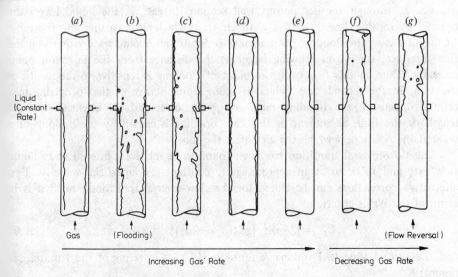

Figure 2.1.17 Flooding and flow reversal.

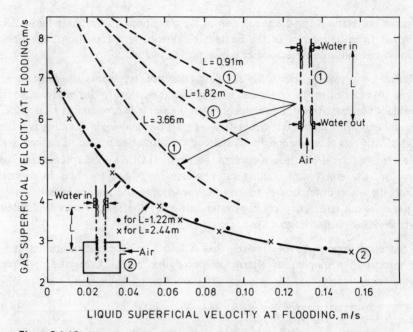

Figure 2.1.18 Flooding in air-water flow in vertical tubes. Data for case 1 taken from Hewitt et al. (1965); results for case 2 taken from recent unpublished data of Harwell.

Actually, flooding is a very complex phenomenon, and an equation as simple as [2.1.5] cannot be expected to represent it adequately. This can be illustrated by considering two cases of flooding in vertical tubes with air-water flow, as illustrated in figure 2.1.18. In both cases, the water is smoothly injected through a porous section in the channel wall. In case 1, the falling film is removed, after moving distance L, through another porous wall section. In case 2, the liquid leaves the channel by moving directly into a chamber from which air is passing into the tube. In the first case, the flooding phenomenon is due to developing wave growth on the film interface, the waves growing larger as the distance from the injection point increases. Thus, in this first case, the onset of flooding is sensitive to the length of the film. In the second case (which is more representative of that occurring in a reflux condenser), the flooding rates are much lower and are insensitive to the length of the film, as shown; in this case flooding is caused by the buildup of a wave at the position at which the air enters the tube.

The flow-reversal transition has been found to be relatively insensitive to liquid flow rate and to occur at an approximately constant gas superficial velocity. Two alternative correlations can be stated for the flow-reversal transition; the first is in terms of the Wallis criterion:

$$U_G^* = U_G \rho_G^{1/2} \, [g d_0 (\rho_L - \rho_G)]^{-1/2} \approx 1 \qquad [2.1.6]$$

and the second (due to Pushkina & Sorokin 1969) is in terms of the Kutateladz number K:

$$K = U_G \rho_G^{1/2} \left[g\sigma \left(\rho_L - \rho_G \right) \right]^{-1/4} = 3.2 \qquad [2.1.7]$$

where σ is the surface tension. Note that [2.1.6] contains the tube diameter, whereas [2.1.7] does not. The relationship between these two expressions was investigated by Wallis & Makkenchery (1974); they concluded that there are two extreme situations:

1. For large-diameter tubes (typically, greater than 5 cm), the transition gas velocity is independent of tube diameter and is given approximately by [2.1.7].
2. For small tube diameters (typically, less than 1 cm), capillarity effects begin to be important.

Between these two extremes (i.e., covering the often-used tube-diameter range of 1-5 cm) the U_G^* criterion [2.1.6] is applied.

There is a clear need for further work on flooding and flow reversal, particularly to cover a wider range of fluid physical properties and geometries.

The link between the plug-churn transition and flooding was first identified by Nicklin & Davidson (1962), who suggested that the breakdown of plug flow into churn flow occurred when flooding takes place at the base of the plug flow bubble. This situation is illustrated in figure 2.1.19. Consider the gas and liquid flows through the cross section A-A as illustrated; for incompressible flows, the total volumetric flow through A-A is $\dot{Q}_G + \dot{Q}_L$, where $\dot{Q}_G$ and $\dot{Q}_L$ are the volumetric flows of the gas and liquid, respectively. If $\dot{Q}_G'$ and $\dot{Q}_L'$ are defined as the instantaneous gas and liquid flow rates past A-A, then it follows that

$$\dot{Q}_G' = U_b \epsilon_G' A \qquad [2.1.8]$$

where U_b is the plug flow bubble velocity, ϵ_G' is the instantaneous fraction of the cross section A-A that is occupied by the gas phase, and A is the total cross-sectional area. Thus,

$$\dot{Q}_L' = \dot{Q}_L + \dot{Q}_G - \epsilon_G' A U_b \qquad [2.1.9]$$

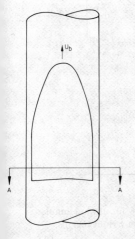

Figure 2.1.19 Parameters in plug flow.

ϵ'_G is a function of the local instantaneous flow rate; in fact, up to the point of flooding, ϵ'_G depends mainly on the liquid flow rate and can be estimated from experiments on falling films. Thus, the conditions for breakdown of plug flow can be determined by increasing either $\dot{Q}_L$ or $\dot{Q}_G$, calculating the instantaneous flows at the base of the plug-flow bubble, and estimating whether these satisfy the conditions for flooding. Nicklin & Davidson obtained quite good agreement with observed transition data using this procedure.

An interpretation of the flow-reversal transition and its link to the churn-annular flow transition is given by Hewitt et al. (1965). The relationship between pressure gradient and gas flow rate, for a given liquid flow rate, in vertical cocurrent annular flow is illustrated schematically in figure 2.1.20. As the gas flow rate is reduced, the pressure gradient decreases progressively in the region AB but reaches a minimum at B; Hewitt et al. demonstrated that this minimum corresponds approximately to the condition in which the wall shear stress τ_0 is close to zero. As the gas flow rate is further reduced, the pressure gradient increases (BC), and this corresponds to a region in which the wall shear stress is likely to fluctuate in a manner illustrated in the sketch in figure 2.1.20. Included in the fluctuations are times of *negative* shear stress, which implies local downward flow close to the wall during these periods. The liquid is flowing partly down toward the edge of the injection section (as sketched), and here it forms a "bulge" that is periodically swept away by the gas, forming a series of large waves on the gas-liquid interface. Eventually, when the flow-reversal point is reached, the down-flowing liquid can no longer be swept away by this means, and net down flow begins to occur.

The precise point of flow reversal might be expected to vary with, say, the wetting conditions of the channel near the liquid entrance and the design of the liquid-entrance device. Indeed, what is recognized as the annular flow can exist at a

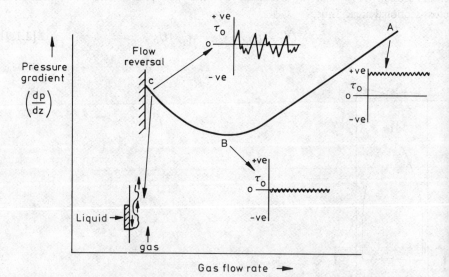

Figure 2.1.20 Relationship between pressure gradient and gas flow for upward annular flow, showing the postulated behavior of the wall shear stress in the various regions.

gas flow rate much lower than that for flow reversal in certain channels. However, it is a good rule of thumb that annular flow always exists for gas flow rates above the flow-reversal transition. It *may* exist at gas flow rates below this. If the wave-formation mechanism is insufficient to carry the liquid phase upward, then backflow of the liquid occurs with consequent "churning," and hence the existence of the churn flow regime. It will be seen immediately that region *BC* is one in which a quite different type of flow exists from that existing in region *AB*. This is borne out in studies of the interfacial wave characteristics, which are different in the two regions.

2.1.4 REGIMES IN HORIZONTAL FLOW

Flow regimes in horizontal flow tend to be somewhat more complex than those in vertical flow; this results from the asymmetry in the flow induced by the gravitational force acting normal to the direction of flow, rather than parallel to it. This makes the heavier (liquid) phase tend to accumulate at the bottom of the channel. Horizontal flows are of wide industrial importance, and examples of their application include in-tube condensers (e.g., air-cooled condensers in process plants), oil and gas pipelines, and certain types of waste-heat boilers.

2.1.4.1 Definitions

A wide variety of flow-pattern definitions have been proposed for horizontal flows; the following regime definitions are suggested here, and are illustrated in figure 2.1.21:

Stratified flow. The gravitational separation is complete; liquid flows along the bottom of the tube, and the gas along the top part of the tube.

Stratified-wavy flow. As the gas velocity is increased in stratified flow, waves are formed on the gas-liquid interface, giving the stratified-wavy or wavy flow regime.

Dispersed-bubble flow. Here, the bubbles are dispersed in a liquid continuum. In horizontal flow, the bubbles tend to congregate near the top of the tube as illustrated. At high system velocities, the bubbles may be more uniformly distributed and appear as a froth.

Annular-dispersed flow. The pattern is similar to that observed in vertical flow, with the exception that the film thickness is nonuniform, the film being much thicker at the bottom of the tube. Liquid entrainment in the gas core is the rule rather than the exception; often, a substantial fraction of the liquid phase is entrained. Earlier work, based on visual observation, led to the definition of a further regime in which the liquid phase is fully dispersed. This is unlikely to happen in adiabatic systems, and the annular-to-dispersed flow transition often shown in earlier regime maps should be treated with considerable reserve.

Intermittent flows. A variety of complex intermittent flows can exist in horizontal tubes, and it is often appropriate to treat all such flows as being of a single generic type of flow regime. However, this class of intermittent flows can often be conveniently divided into three subdivisions as follows:

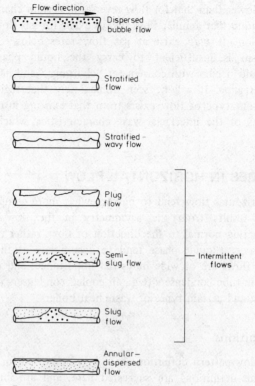

Figure 2.1.21   Flow regimes in horizontal two-phase flow.

Plug flow. As in vertical flow, the characteristic bullet-shaped bubbles are
observed, but here they tend to move along in a position closer to the top
of the tube, as illustrated in figure 2.1.21.

Slug flow. This is characterized by passage along the channel of frothy "slugs,"
in which the liquid phase is continuous, but in which a large number of gas
bubbles are entrained. The presence of these slugs can often be troublesome in practical applications (giving rise to sudden pressure pulses, causing
vibration of tubes, etc.), and the prediction of the onset of slug flow is of
considerable industrial importance. Although the distinction between plug
flow and slug flow is quite clear from the rather extreme examples in
figure 2.1.21, it is, in practice, difficult to distinguish between the regimes
in intermediate regions.

Semislug flow. Here, the frothy slug takes the form of a wave on the surface of
the stratified layer at the bottom of the tube, and does not actually touch
the top of the tube.

2.1.4.2 Data and Flow-Pattern Maps

A reasonably large amount of data on flow patterns has been accumulated and
reported in the literature. The preponderance of data are for air-water flows in

relatively narrow-bore tubes (typically 2–5 cm). Although there is a dearth of horizontal flow data covering a wide range of physical properties there are a number of current efforts to widen the data base.

A recent example of data for air-water two-phase flow patterns is those of Sakaguchi et al. (1979), who obtained data for tubes with diameters of 20–40 mm and lengths of 4–8 m. Their results are exemplified by those presented in figure 2.1.22. In addition to the regimes defined above, they also refer to a "violent-wave" regime, where violently disturbed small waves are caused by a high-speed airstream.

There is an obvious need to generalize data such as those shown in figure 2.1.22 so as to cover a wide range of fluid properties. One of the best known generalized-flow-pattern maps for horizontal flow is that of Baker (1954); since this map is still widely used, it is presented here for reference purposes. Baker took account of physical properties by introducing the following parameters:

$$\lambda_B = \left(\frac{\rho_G \, \rho_L}{\rho_A \, \rho_W}\right)^{0.5} \qquad\qquad [2.1.10]$$

$$\Psi_B = \frac{\sigma_W}{\sigma}\left[\frac{\mu_L}{\mu_W}\left(\frac{\rho_W}{\rho_L}\right)^2\right]^{1/3} \qquad\qquad [2.1.11]$$

where ρ, σ, and μ represent, respectively, density, surface tension, and viscosity, the subscripts G and L represent the gas and liquid phases, and the subscripts A and W represent the values for air and water at atmospheric conditions (typically 20°C and atmospheric pressure). Clearly λ_B and Ψ_B are equal to unity for atmospheric-pressure air-water flows. In SI units, appropriate values for the air-water standard

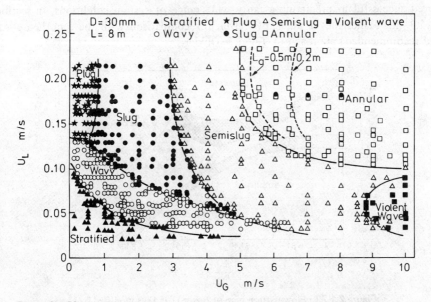

Figure 2.1.22 Flow-regime data obtained by Sakaguchi et al. (1979) for air-water horizontal flow in a 30-mm-diameter tube. L_a is the length required for the establishment of fully developed annular flow.

conditions are as follows:

$$\rho_A = 1.205 \text{ kg/m}^3 \qquad \mu_W = 0.001002 \text{ kg/m s}$$

$$\rho_W = 1000 \text{ kg/m}^3 \qquad \sigma_W = 0.0728 \text{ N/m}$$

In the original form of the Baker map, the plotting parameters were $\dot{m}_G/\lambda_B$ and $\dot{m}_L \Psi_B \lambda_B/\dot{m}_G$. This coordinate may alternatively be expressed as $\dot{m}x/\lambda_B$ and $(1-x)\lambda_B\Psi_B/x$, where x is the quality (ratio of gas mass flow to total mass flow). A modified form of the map in these original coordinates was produced by Scott (1963); this revised map (figure 2.1.23) has the advantages of showing transition regions (indicating uncertainty) between the various regimes and of omitting the transition line between annular and dispersed flow, which is invalid for the reasons described above.

A number of authors (e.g., Collier 1972; Bell 1969) have preferred to plot the Baker map in terms of the coordinates $\dot{m}_G/\lambda_B$ and $\dot{m}_L \Psi_B$. A plot in this format is shown in figure 2.1.24.

More recent data on flow patterns in horizontal flow have shown that the original Baker map is deficient in representing the effects of various system parameters. Notable among these studies are those of Schicht (1969), Al-Sheikh et al. (1970), Mandhane et al. (1974), and Fisher & Yu (1975). These studies have led to the development of a number of alternative flow maps; the map produced by Mandhane et al. being probably the most successful. However, the basic problem with all maps of this kind is that it is impossible to represent all the appropriate transitions in terms of a single set of parameters. This has been recognized by a number of authors, and a semitheoretical study by Taitel & Dukler (1976) has proved successful in predicting a fairly wide range of system conditions. In section 2.1.4.3 the Mandhane et al. map is given for comparison with the semitheoretical (and recommended) approach of Taitel & Dukler.

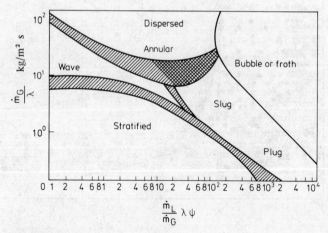

Figure 2.1.23 Flow-pattern map of Baker (1954) as modified by Scott (1963).

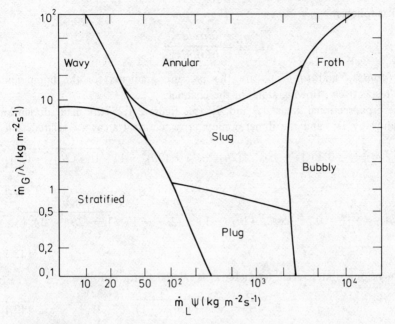

Figure 2.1.24   Flow-pattern map of Baker (1954) replotted in the form suggested by Bell (1969).

2.1.4.3   Analytic Approach to Transitions in Horizontal Flow

The earlier empirical flow-regime maps for horizontal flow show serious deficiencies, particularly in extrapolation to higher system pressures and large-bore pipes. Since the latter conditions are of considerable industrial importance (e.g., in pipelines carrying mixtures of high-pressure gas and oil), there is an evident need for a more generalized description. There have been a number of attempts at a theoretical or semitheoretical description of flow-regime transitions; clearly, for such a description to be successful, it should be suitable for extrapolation to a wide range of conditions. Perhaps the most comprehensive treatment of flow-regime transitions in horizontal flow on a semitheoretical basis is that of Taitel & Dukler (1976). It is recommended that their method be used, rather than empirical flow-regime maps, for the prediction of regimes in horizontal two-phase flow.

It is useful to define a number of dimensionless parameters that are used repeatedly for the various transitions. The nondimensionality of these variables is indicated by a tilde (~). The dimensionless liquid height $\tilde{h}_L$ is given by

$$\tilde{h}_L = \frac{h_L}{D} \qquad [2.1.12]$$

where D is the tube diameter. Taitel & Dukler analyzed smooth stratified flows (their analysis is summarized in section 2.3.5.1) and showed that, for horizontal flows, $\tilde{h}_L$ is uniquely related to the Lockhart & Martinelli (1949) parameter X, defined as follows:

$$X = \frac{(dp_F/dz)_L}{(dp_F/dz)_G} \qquad [2.1.13]$$

where $(dp/dz)_L$ and $(dp/dz)_G$ are the pressure gradients for the liquid and gas phases, respectively, flowing alone in the channel.

The cross-sectional areas A_G and A_L (see figure 2.1.25) are made dimensionless by dividing by D^2, and the dimensionless cross-sectional areas are related to $\tilde{h}_L$ by

$$\tilde{A}_L = \frac{A_L}{D^2} = 0.25 \left[\pi - \cos^{-1}(2\tilde{h}_L - 1) + (2\tilde{h}_L - 1)\sqrt{1 - (2\tilde{h}_L - 1)^2} \right] \qquad [2.1.14]$$

$$\tilde{A}_G = \frac{A_G}{D^2} = 0.25 \left[\cos^{-1}(2\tilde{h}_L - 1) - (2\tilde{h}_L - 1)\sqrt{1 - (2\tilde{h}_L - 1)^2} \right] \qquad [2.1.15]$$

The dimensionless interfacial perimeter $\tilde{P}_i$ is related to $\tilde{h}_L$ as follows:

$$\tilde{P}_i = \frac{P_i}{D} = \sqrt{1 - (2\tilde{h}_L - 1)^2} \qquad [2.1.16]$$

Dimensionless phase velocities $\tilde{u}_G$ and $\tilde{u}_L$ are defined relative to the superficial velocities of the phases U_G and U_L and are related to $\tilde{A}_L$ and $\tilde{A}_G$ as follows:

$$\tilde{u}_G = \frac{u_G}{U_G} = \frac{\tilde{A}}{\tilde{A}_G} \qquad [2.1.17]$$

$$\tilde{u}_L = \frac{u_L}{U_L} = \frac{\tilde{A}}{\tilde{A}_G} \qquad [2.1.18]$$

where u_G and u_L are the phase velocities, and $\tilde{A} = A/D^2$. The dimensionless equivalent diameter for the liquid phase $\tilde{D}_L$ is given by

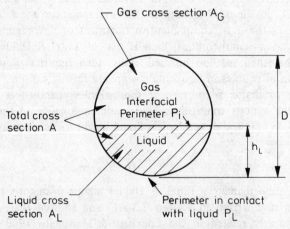

Figure 2.1.25 Stratified flow—definitions of quantities.

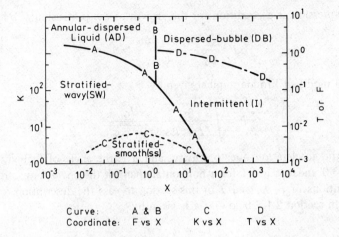

Figure 2.1.26 Generalized-flow-regime map for horizontal two-phase flow (Taitel & Dukler 1976).

$$\tilde{D}_L = \frac{4A_L}{P_L D} = \frac{4\tilde{A}_L}{\tilde{P}_L}$$ [2.1.19]

where P_L is the tube perimeter wetted by the liquid (see figure 2.1.15), and $\tilde{P}_L$, the nondimensional value of this perimeter, is given by

$$\tilde{P}_L = \frac{P_L}{D} = \pi - \cos^{-1}(2\tilde{h}_L - 1)$$ [2.1.20]

It will be noted that the dimensionless parameters used in the Taitel & Dukler analysis (namely, $\tilde{A}_L$, $\tilde{A}_G$, $\tilde{P}_i$, $\tilde{P}_L$, $\tilde{u}_G$, $\tilde{u}_L$, and $\tilde{D}_L$) are all uniquely related to $\tilde{h}_L$ and, thus, to X.

In general terms, the Taitel & Dukler approach is to express the various transitions in terms of dimensionless groups K, T, and F (to be defined below) that are uniquely related to the independent variables of the system. The transitional values of these groups are calculated in terms of the dimensionless variables defined in [2.1.14]–[2.1.20] and are thus related to $\tilde{h}_L$ and hence to X, which again can be calculated from the independent variables of the system. A plot of the transitions in terms of the nondimensional variables K, T, F, and X is shown in figure 2.1.26, which is used for reference in what follows.

Transition *A* of Figure 2.1.26

Transition A is the boundary between the stratified (S) and intermittent (I) or annular-dispersed (AD) regimes. Taitel & Dukler describe this transition in terms of the classical Kelvin-Helmholtz instability. Suppose that a small perturbation occurs on the interface in stratified flow. The gas flowing over the protrusion will accelerate, giving a drop in the gas pressure and producing a suction on the protrusion that will cause it to grow unless the suction is more than offset by the gravitational force acting downward on the protrusion. Taitel & Dukler derive the following expression as a condition for the growth of the protrusion:

$$F^2 \frac{1}{C_2^2} \frac{\tilde{u}_G d\tilde{A}_L/d\tilde{h}_L}{\tilde{A}_G} \geqslant 1 \qquad [2.1.21]$$

where F is a modified Froude number given by

$$F = \sqrt{\frac{\rho_G}{\rho_L - \rho_G}} \frac{U_G}{\sqrt{Dg \cos \alpha}} \qquad [2.1.22]$$

where g is the acceleration due to gravity, and α is the angle of inclination of the channel ($\alpha = 0$ and $\cos \alpha = 1$ for a horizontal channel; the $\cos \alpha$ terms are included in the definitions of F, K, and T in this section to ease the description for inclined tubes given in section 2.1.5 below). C_2 is given by

$$C_2 = 1 - \tilde{h}_L \qquad [2.1.23]$$

and it follows from [2.1.14] that

$$\frac{d\tilde{A}_L}{d\tilde{h}_L} = \sqrt{1 - (2\tilde{h}_L - 1)^2} \qquad [2.1.24]$$

If the wave growth criterion [2.1.21] is satisfied, then large waves are formed. Taitel & Dukler speculate that the formation of these waves can lead to formation of other flow patterns by the following mechanisms:

1. At lower values of $\tilde{h}_L$, the wave may be swept up and around the pipe to form an annulus, thus giving annular or annular-dispersed flow (some of the liquid being entrained from the wave tips); this mechanism for formation of annular flow in horizontal tubes was suggested by Butterworth (1972).
2. For large values of $\tilde{h}_L$, the waves formed on the interface may grow and be swept along by the gas phase (semislug flow) or touch the upper surface of the tube (plug or slug flow), giving a transition to the intermittent regime.

Other studies of the onset of slugging in horizontal two-phase flow are reported by Wallis & Dobson (1973), Gardner (1977), and Kubie (1979). The nature and prediction of the transition are still the subjects of active research; for instance, the transition criteria given by Kubie are probably more suitable than that of Taitel & Dukler for conditions where the liquid-to-gas denisty ratio is low (typically less than 10).

By combining [2.1.15], [2.1.17], [2.1.21], [2.1.23], and [2.1.24], the transition criterion can be expressed in terms of F and $\tilde{h}_L$; by invoking the relationship between $\tilde{h}_L$ and X (see section 2.3.5.1), transition A can be represented uniquely in terms of a plot of F against X, and this is done in figure 2.1.26.

Transition B of Figure 2.1.26

Transition B is the boundary between the intermittent (I) and annular-dispersed (AD) regimes. Here, Taitel & Dukler hypothesize that if the value of $\tilde{h}_L = h_L/D$ is greater than 0.5, then a sinusoidal wave growing on the interface touches the top of the tube before its trough reaches the bottom of the tube. For horizontal flow, $\tilde{h}_L = 0.5$ corresponds to $X = 1.6$. Some confirmation of this view of the transition is given in the work of Kubie (1979).

Transition C of Figure 2.1.26

Transition C is the boundary between the stratified-smooth (SS) and stratified-wavy (SW) regimes. The mechanisms by which waves develop as a result of gas flow over a smooth interface are not yet fully understood. The choice between a number of alternative models is still somewhat arbitrary, and the approach used by Taitel & Dukler is a modified form of the Jeffreys (1925, 1926) "sheltering" hypothesis. In the classical Kelvin-Helmholtz instability referred to above, the gas-phase pressure is 180° out of phase with the surface displacement. Although this causes the waves to grow, owing to the suction effect, it does not provide a mechanism for transferring energy to the waves. In the Jeffreys hypothesis, there is a further phase shift due to the occurrence of a recirculation zone downstream of the wave, and this leads to a distribution of normal and shear stresses that can result in the net transfer of energy and further wave growth.

To make the predictions from this method fit reasonably close to the data, it was necessary for Taitel & Dukler to use coefficients that are much lower than those employed in the original Jeffreys work. Furthermore, they assume that the velocity of the surface waves is equal to the liquid velocity. The criterion for the onset of waves (and hence the transition between smooth-stratified and wavy-stratified flow) is expressed as follows:

$$K > \frac{20}{\tilde{u}_G \sqrt{\tilde{u}_L}}$$ [2.1.25]

where K is the product of the modified Froude number F and the square root of the superficial Reynolds number of the liquid:

$$K^2 = F^2 \, \text{Re}_L = \frac{\rho_G U_G^2}{(\rho_L - \rho_G)Dg \cos \alpha} \frac{DU_L}{\nu_L}$$ [2.1.26]

where ν_L is the kinematic viscosity of the liquid. For horizontal flow, $\tilde{u}_G$ and $\tilde{u}_L$ are uniquely related to $\tilde{h}_L$ and hence to X. The transition can, therefore, be represented in terms of a plot of K against X, and the transition line is represented in this way in figure 2.1.26.

Transition D in Figure 2.1.26

Transition D is the boundary between the intermittent (I) and dispersed-bubble (DB) regimes. Taitel & Dukler equate this transition with the situation in which turbulent fluctuations within the liquid are sufficient to overcome the buoyant forces tending to keep the gas at the top of the pipe. An approximate analysis led them to the following transition criterion between intermittent and dispersed-bubble flows:

$$T^2 < \frac{8\tilde{A}_G}{\tilde{P}_i\tilde{u}_L^2(\tilde{u}_L\tilde{D}_L)^{-n}}$$ [2.1.27]

where n is the exponent in the friction factor–Reynolds number relationship (n is 0.2 for turbulent flow, and 1.0 for laminar flow). The dimensionless parameter T is given by

$$T = \left[\frac{(dp_F/dz)_L}{(\rho_L - \rho_G)g\cos\alpha}\right]^{1/2}$$ [2.1.28]

Since the dimensionless quantities on the right-hand side of [2.1.27] are all related to $\tilde{h}_L = h_L/D$, which in turn is related to X, the transition can be represented in terms of a plot of T versus X, and this is shown in figure 2.1.26.

Comparison with Other Transition Data

Mandhane et al. (1974) suggested that a correlation of regime boundaries in terms only of the superficial velocities of the phases was perhaps the best representation of the available data. However, most of the data evaluated by Mandhane et al. were for air-water flows at atmospheric pressure. A comparison of the Taitel & Dukler (1976) and Mandhane et al. (1974) correlations as applied to these air-water flows is given in the paper by Taitel & Dukler, and this comparison is reproduced as figure 2.1.27. The semitheoretical predictions of Taitel & Dukler agree moderately well

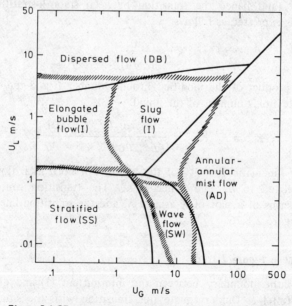

Figure 2.1.27 Comparison between the flow-regime boundaries predicted for air-water flow at atmospheric conditions in a 2.5-cm-diameter horizontal tube, using the Taitel & Dukler (1976) method and the boundaries given by Mandhane et al. (1974). The regime descriptions are as given by Mandhane et al., with the letters in brackets indicating the regime descriptions according to Taitel & Dukler.

with the experimentally derived correlation of Mandhane et al. However, the Taitel & Dukler correlation appears suitable for extrapolation to a wider range of tube diameters and physical properties; these parameters were shown by Taitel & Dukler to have a significant effect.

Although the Taitel & Dukler method represents a very useful attempt at a physical interpretation of the flow-pattern boundaries, its physical basis is not entirely secure, and it is not surprising that recent data have begun to reveal its deficiencies. In studies of flow patterns in horizontal pipes with a wide range of physical-property values, Weisman and co-workers (Husain & Weisman 1978; Choe et al. 1978; Weisman 1979) have indicated a number of deficiencies in the Taitel & Dukler model:

1. Although the Taitel & Dukler method works fairly well for the transition between the separated and intermittent flow regimes for liquids of low or moderate viscosity, it does not fit the data obtained by Weisman and co-workers for high-viscosity glycerine solutions. The Taitel & Dukler correlation predicts an effect of liquid viscosity, whereas the data indicate that there is little or no effect of viscosity on this transition.
2. A small but significant effect of surface tension was observed on the transition between intermittent and dispersed-bubble flows, which is not included in the parameters suggested by Taitel & Dukler.
3. The experimental evidence is inconsistent with the assumption of a transition between intermittent and annular-dispersed flows corresponding to $\tilde{h}_L = 0.5$ ($X = 1.6$).

Weisman and co-workers produced an alternative set of dimensionless correlations for each of the transitions, and these correlations are summarized by Weisman (1979). However, these correlations are of a somewhat arbitrary nature, so that the Taitel & Dukler (1974) semitheoretical relationships are recommended, notwithstanding their deficiencies as revealed by the recent work. It should be remembered that there is an essential arbitrariness in the interpretation of flow-pattern data, and it is unlikely that perfect prediction methods will ever emerge.

2.1.5 FLOW REGIMES IN INCLINED TUBES

Most of the available flow-pattern data are for nominally vertical or horizontal tubes. There are relatively few data on inclined tubes, notwithstanding the technical importance of such flows. The areas of interest include both steeply inclined tubes (e.g., in "A-frame" air-cooled condensers) and tubes with small angles of inclination (e.g., for pipelines on the sea bed or passing over hilly terrain). It is useful here to quote two sets of data to illustrate the effects of tube inclination:

1. Data have recently been obtained by Barnea et al. (1980) for flow patterns in tubes with inclinations in the range −10 to +10°. Figure 2.1.28 shows data obtained in this study for horizontal flow and for the extremes of the inclination angles investigated.

2. Gould (1972) studied flow patterns in vertical tubes, horizontal tubes, and tubes inclined at 45°, for air-water flow. The results for the 45° inclination (up flow) are shown in figure 2.1.29. Gould's regime names are different from those

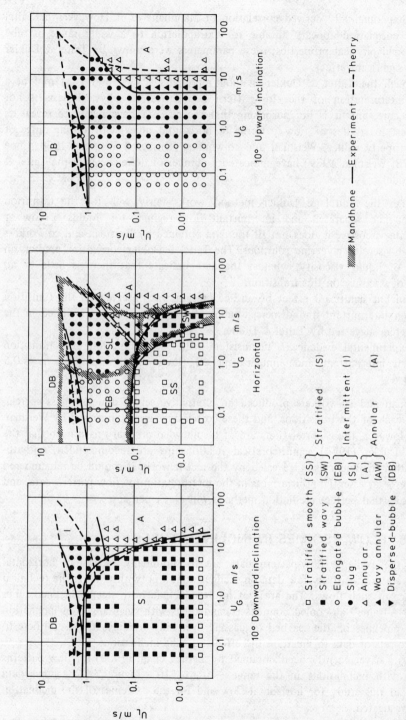

Figure 2.1.28 Data for atmospheric-pressure air-water flow in a 2.5-cm-diameter tube (Barnea et al. 1980).

Stratified smooth (SS)
Stratified wavy (SW) } Stratified (S)
Elongated bubble (EB)
Slug (SL) } Intermittent (I)
Annular (A)
Wavy annular (AW) } Annular (A)
Dispersed-bubble (DB)

▨▨ Mandhane —— Experiment ––– Theory

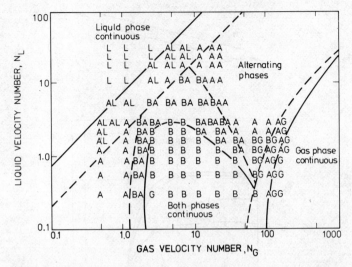

Figure 2.1.29 Flow-pattern data for upward air-water flow in a 2.5-cm-bore tube inclined at 45° (Gould 1972).

used in the rest of this chapter: His liquid phase continuous (L) corresponds to bubble flow and, for vertical flows, may also include plug flow; his alternating phases (A) corresponds to slug flow in horizontal and inclined tubes and probably corresponds to wispy annular flow for vertical tubes; and his gas phase continuous (G) corresponds to annular or annular-mist flow. The flow-pattern data shown in figure 2.1.29 are given in terms of the dimensionless liquid and gas velocity numbers N_L and N_G, defined as follows:

$$N_L = U_L \left(\frac{\rho_L}{g\sigma}\right)^{1/4} \qquad [2.1.29]$$

$$N_G = U_G \left(\frac{\rho_L}{g\sigma}\right)^{1/4} \qquad [2.1.30]$$

where ρ_L is the liquid density, g is the acceleration due to gravity, and σ is the surface tension. Regimes identified as transitional are given a double letter as shown.

The most striking feature of the results for inclined tubes is the great sensitivity of the position of the stratified-to-intermittent transition to angle of inclination. With a downward inclination there is a preponderance of the stratified regime, and with upward inclination a preponderance of the intermittent regime. This can be observed in the results illustrated in figure 2.1.28; it is further demonstrated in the plots shown in figures 2.1.30 and 2.1.31.

In figure 2.1.30 the position of the stratified-intermittent boundary is plotted from the results of Barnea et al. (1980) as a function of angle of inclination. The dramatic effect of inclination by an angle of only 0.25° is seen. It seems quite feasible that discrepancies in flow-pattern observations in the literature may be partially ascribed to the effects of adventitious departures from true horizontal in

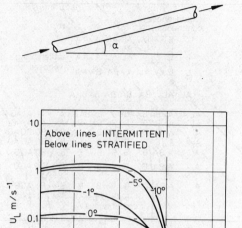

Figure 2.1.30 Effect of angle of inclination on the boundary between stratified and intermittent flows (results of Barnea et al. 1980).

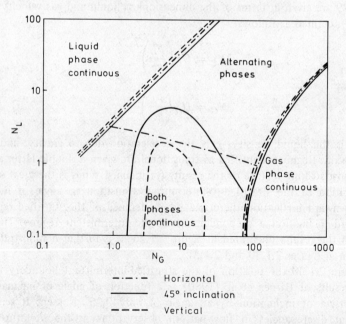

Figure 2.1.31 Effect of tube inclination on flow-regime boundaries (results of Gould 1972).

the test tubes. Certainly, small inclinations of this magnitude are commonplace in industrial applications.

Figure 2.1.31 shows a comparison of the transition lines observed by Gould (1972) for horizontal, vertical upward, and 45° upward flows. The lines in figure 2.1.31 are taken as the mean position in the transition zones as illustrated in figure 2.1.29, for example. The transition between the "both phases continuous" and "alternating phases" regions varies considerably with angle of inclination. The definition of the both-phases-continuous region for vertical flow indicates that it corresponds to the churn flow regime as defined in section 2.1.3.1. This classification of the stratified and churn flow regimes under one heading is interesting; the implication is that in both cases the gas phase is unable to support the liquid, which then progresses downward to form a stratified layer in horizontal and inclined tubes and to cause churning in the case of vertical tubes.

In contrast, the positions of the intermittent–dispersed-bubble and annular–intermittent boundaries are relatively insensitive to tube orientation, as is illustrated in figure 2.1.32 for the results of Barnea et al. (1980) and figure 2.1.31 for the results of Gould (1972). In the range of angles of inclination studied by Barnea et al., there was no significant change in the position of the intermittent–dispersed-bubble boundary with inclination, and the position of the intermittent-annular boundary is also relatively unaffected; the changes are due mainly to the changing extent of the intermittent zone itself as the angle of inclination changed. The results of Gould are even more remarkable in illustrating the very small effect that angle of

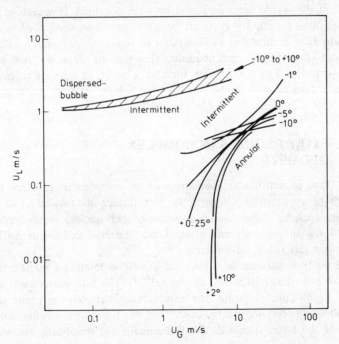

Figure 2.1.32 Effect of tube inclination on the dispersed-bubble–intermittent and intermittent-annular flow transitions; plotted from results of Barnea et al. (1980).

inclination has on the boundaries separating the liquid-phase-continuous, alternating-phases, and gas-phase-continuous regions.

The Taitel & Dukler (1976) semitheoretical treatment of flow-pattern transitions was described in detail in section 2.1.4.3, in the particular context of horizontal flow. The application of this semitheoretical method to flow in inclined tubes follows similar lines; the dimensionless equilibrium liquid-layer height $\tilde{h}_L = h_L/D$ is no longer a function only of the Martinelli parameter X, but is also a function of the group Y defined by

$$Y = \frac{-(\rho_L - \rho_G)g \sin \alpha}{(dp/dz)_G} \qquad [2.1.31]$$

where α is the angle of inclination (see figure 2.1.30).* Details of the relationships among $\tilde{h}_L$, X, and Y are given in section 2.3.5.1. Once one obtains the value of $\tilde{h}_L$ for the appropriate values of Y and X, the transition criteria given in [2.1.21], [2.1.25], and [2.1.27] can be evaluated using the dimensionless quantities (calculable from $\tilde{h}_L$) defined in [2.1.14]–[2.1.20]. Note that the definitions of the parameters F in [2.1.22], K in [2.1.25], and T in [2.1.28] include a $\cos \alpha$ term, where α is the angle of inclination of the tube.

By carrying out this solution procedure, the flow-pattern map can be calculated for any given situation. Barnea et al. (1980) present comparisons of their data for inclined tubes with the predictions of the Taitel & Dukler method. These comparisons are exemplified in figure 2.1.28; reasonable predictions of the effect of inclination on the regime boundary positions are obtained. However, in detail, the theory does not appear to correctly predict the insensitivity of some of the transitions to tube inclination, as illustrated in figures 2.1.31 and 2.1.32. Weisman (1979) states that recent inclined-tube flow-pattern data do not show good agreement with the Taitel & Dukler method. Clearly, in spite of recent advances, there is much further work to be done on the subject of flow patterns in general, and flow patterns in inclined tubes in particular.

2.1.6 FLOW REGIMES IN COMPLEX GEOMETRIES

Two-phase flows in nontubular geometries are of considerable practical importance in a number of applications. Of particular significance are parallel upward flows in rod bundles, such as those found in water-cooled nuclear reactor systems, and two-phase flows on the shell side of shell-and-tube heat exchangers. In both these areas, there is a scarcity of information.

Two-phase flow patterns in a four-rod bundle simulating a nuclear reactor fuel element have been investigated by Bergles (1969). The flow pattern was determined by using a needle-contact probe, the conductance between the probe tip and the channel wall being recorded continuously, and the flow pattern being deduced from the nature of the trace. Although this technique is not specifically recommended in

---

*The angle α is defined here as positive when the flow is upward. This is consistent with the definition in section 2.2, but opposite to the original definition of Taitel & Dukler.

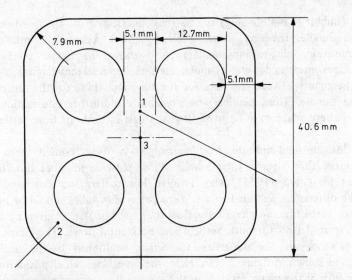

Figure 2.1.33 Test-section geometry used by Bergles (1969) for rod-bundle flow-pattern investigations.

section 2.1.2, it does have the advantage of being able to delineate local flow patterns in rod bundles, notwithstanding some ambiguities in the interpretation of the results in transition regions.

The geometry used in the Bergles experiments is illustrated in figure 2.1.33, which also indicates the positions at which the flow pattern was determined using needle-contact devices. The experiments were for high-pressure (7.0-MPa) steam-water mixtures. Results from the Bergles experiments are illustrated in figure 2.1.34; for two of the transitions investigated (namely the bubble-to-bubble–slug and the slug-to-slug–annular transitions), the results are plotted for all three positions in terms of the overall mass flux and bundle mean quality. It is seen that the first

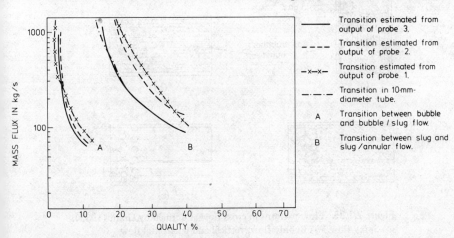

Figure 2.1.34 Effect of measurement position (see figure 2.1.33) on flow-pattern transition in the high-pressure steam-water flow studies of Bergles (1969).

transition (bubble-to-bubble–slug) is relatively unaffected by the position selected within the bundle. However, considerable variations occur with position for the second transition (slug-to-slug–annular). Also shown in figure 2.1.34 are the transition lines, measured using a similar method, for a 10-mm-diameter tube; there is good agreement between the data for the tube and those for the center position of the rod bundle. Thus, pending the availability of further information, vertical-tube flow-pattern maps may be used to give a first estimate of flow patterns in rod bundles.

The flow in shell-and-tube heat exchangers is often thought of in terms of idealized cross flow over a tube bundle. Flow patterns in cross flow have been investigated by Grant (1975), who defined flow patterns as illustrated in figure 2.1.35. The differences and analogies to flow patterns in tubes should be noted. The flow-pattern maps for two-phase cross flow over rod bundles, as given by Grant, are shown in figure 2.1.36 for both vertical and horizontal flows. The Grant maps are plotted in terms of the superficial velocities multiplied by physical-property parameters, as shown in figure 2.1.36. Here, the superficial velocity is defined as the volumetric flux of the phase divided by the average flow cross-sectional area.

Flows in heat exchangers differ from the idealized cross flows shown in figure 2.1.35, owing to a number of effects, including

1. Separation effects due to changes in direction of the flow as it proceeds through the exchanger, directed by the baffles. For instance, a gas bubble may form on the downstream side of a baffle.

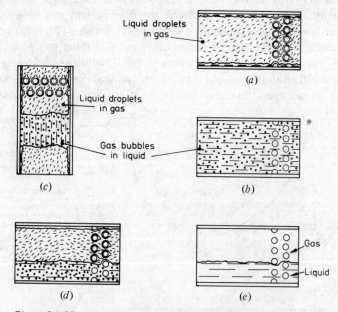

Liquid droplets in gas

(a)

Liquid droplets in gas

Gas bubbles in liquid

(c)

(b)

(d)

(e)

Gas

Liquid

Figure 2.1.35 Flow patterns in cross flow as defined by Grant (1975).
(a) Spray flow. (b) Bubbly flow, vertical and horizontal flow.
(c) Chugging flow, vertical flow. (d) Stratified flow, spray flow.
(e) Stratified flow.

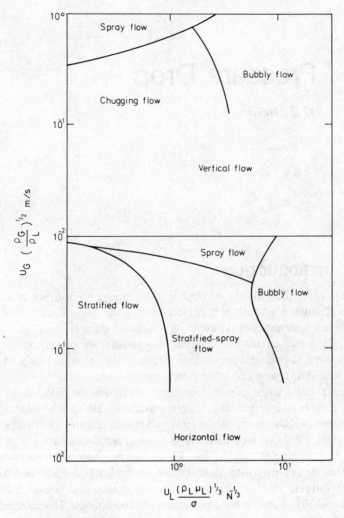

Figure 2.1.36 Flow-pattern maps for two-phase cross flow (Grant 1975).

2. Fluid leaks through the spaces between the tubes and the baffles, and the baffles and the shell. Also, bypass flow occurs around the bundle. For two-phase flows, these effects are coupled with phase separation such that the two-phase composition of the bypass and leakage streams is different from the composition of the cross-flow streams.

These factors make the prediction of two-phase flows in shell-and-tube heat exchangers extremely difficult.

2.2 Pressure Drop

G. F. Hewitt

2.2.1 INTRODUCTION

The pressure drop (that is, the change in fluid pressure occurring as a two-phase flow passes through a system) is a parameter of great importance in the design of both adiabatic systems and systems with phase change, such as boilers and condensers. In forced-circulation systems, the pressure drop governs the pumping requirement, and in natural-circulation systems, the pressure drop dictates the circulation rate and, hence, the other system parameters.

The great importance of pressure drop prediction is reflected in the large number of models and correlations that are available. Here, only selected methods that are either widely used, or of a fundamental nature, or (where they are empirical) cover a wide enough range of parameters are discussed.

None of the general correlations for two-phase pressure drop is particularly accurate. This is due partly to their failure to explicitly include factors, such as entrance conditions, that are known to be important and whose influence can persist for hundreds of diameters downstream of the entrance. The inaccuracy is also due partly to the fact that the same correlation is used to represent many different physical situations; that is, in the general correlations no particular reference is made to flow pattern, and this has a profound effect on fluid-fluid interaction, and hence on the pressure drop. In section 2.2.4 reference is made to alternative calculation methods based on modeling for a specific regime. These can lead to improved predictions for pressure gradient, but they require the prediction of the specific flow regime.

In addition to the flow-regime and entrance effects mentioned above, another factor influencing the accuracy of prediction of pressure drop data is the inherent inaccuracy of the available data. Pressure drop measurement is difficult in two-phase systems (see section 10.2.1.1).

This section is concerned with relationships for pressure drop in ducts of constant cross section. Most of the relationships are given for straight, round tubes, but they can often be applied in other cases by use of the hydraulic diameter instead of the tube diameter. Pressure drops in devices such as bends and valves are not specifically dealt with in this section. To a first approximation, such situations can often be dealt with by treating the flow as homogeneous; a brief description of relationships for orifices and venturi meters (in the context of two-phase flow measurement) is given in section 10.1.2.

2.2.2 BASIC EQUATIONS

Fundamental to the calculation of two-phase pressure drop is the derivation and use of basic conservation laws for mass, momentum, and energy. Traditionally, these have been derived on a phenomenological basis, leading to simplified equations that include the following inherent assumptions:

1. At any one cross section of the channel, the fluid pressure is constant.
2. The velocity of a phase (liquid or gas) is essentially constant across the channel, although there may be a difference between the velocities of the phases.

In recent years, there has been intense interest in developing a more fundamental approach to the conservation equations, with particular reference to problems of averaging [see section 1.2 and Ishii (1975) and Hughes et al. (1976)]. However, in what follows it is appropriate to retain the traditional phenomenological approach, since it is on this that most empirical correlations have been based. However, in section 2.2.4, reference is made to modeling methods for annular two-phase flow that involve a more detailed approach, and in section 2.3.3, models for void fraction that include radial variation of phase velocities are introduced.

2.2.2.1 Some Basic Quantities

The *pressure drop* may be defined as the integral along the channel length L of the pressure gradient dp/dz:

$$\Delta p = \int_0^L \frac{dp}{dz} \, dz \qquad [2.2.1]$$

In what follows, relationships for pressure gradient are given, and [2.2.1] must be solved in applying these relationships to predict the pressure drop in a given system.

The *void fraction* ϵ_G may be defined in several ways (see also section 1.2). For example, ϵ_G may be given by

1. The time-averaged volumetric fraction of vapor in a two-phase mixture
2. The time-averaged area fraction in a given cross section (see section 1.2.4).

Here it is assumed that the void fractions represented by both these averages are identical.

The *quality* x is defined as (see also section 10.1.2)

$$x = \frac{\dot{m}_G}{\dot{m}_L + \dot{m}_G} \qquad [2.2.2]$$

where $\dot{m}_G$ and $\dot{m}_L$ are the *mass fluxes* of the gas and liquid phases, respectively. In single-component flows it is often convenient to express quality in terms of the two-phase enthalpy h_{TP} and the saturated enthalpies h_L and h_G of the liquid and vapor phases, assuming thermodynamic equilibrium between the phases:

$$x = \frac{h_{TP} - h_L}{h_G - h_L} \qquad [2.2.3]$$

The assumption of thermodynamic equilibrium is often invalid, and situations are common in which the liquid and/or vapor phases as subcooled or superheated with respect to the saturation condition. In this section, thermodynamic equilibrium is assumed. However, the modeling of some systems (and specifically that of void fraction in subcooled boiling, section 2.3.5.5) demands a treatment of the nonequilibrium nature of the flow.

The *superficial velocities* U_G and U_L of the respective phases are defined as follows:

$$U_G = \frac{\dot{Q}_L}{A} \qquad [2.2.4]$$

$$U_L = \frac{\dot{Q}_L}{A} \qquad [2.2.5]$$

where $\dot{Q}_G$ and $\dot{Q}_L$ are the phase volume rates of flow, and A is the channel cross-sectional area.

The average *phase velocities* u_G and u_L are given by

$$u_G = \frac{U_G}{\epsilon_G} = \frac{\dot{Q}_G}{\epsilon_G A} \qquad [2.2.6]$$

$$u_L = \frac{U_L}{1 - \epsilon_G} = \frac{\dot{Q}_L}{(1 - \epsilon_G)A} \qquad [2.2.7]$$

and the *velocity ratio* S is

$$S = \frac{u_G}{u_L} = \frac{U_G}{U_L} \frac{1 - \epsilon_G}{\epsilon_G} \qquad [2.2.8]$$

The *two-phase density* ρ_{TP} is defined as the mass of fluid per unit volume of channel and is given by

$$\rho_{TP} = (1 - \epsilon_G)\rho_L + \epsilon_G \rho_G \qquad [2.2.9]$$

The above equations may be manipulated in a variety of ways. For instance, void fraction for thermodynamic equilibrium flows is related uniquely to quality and velocity ratio by

$$\epsilon_G = \frac{x}{x + S(1 - x)\rho_G/\rho_L} \qquad [2.2.10]$$

2.2.2.2 Conservation Equations for Homogeneous Flow

The simplest approach to the treatment of the flow of a gas-liquid mixture in a channel is to treat the flow as if the mixture were behaving as a homogeneous fluid, with the velocities of the two phases identical. In terms of the definitions given in section 2.2.2.1, this implies

$$u_G = u_L = u_H \qquad\qquad [2.2.11]$$

$$S = \frac{u_G}{u_L} = 1 \qquad\qquad [2.2.12]$$

As a result,

$$\epsilon_G = \frac{\dot{Q}_G}{\dot{Q}_L + \dot{Q}_G} = \frac{x}{x + (1 - x)\,\rho_G/\rho_L} \qquad\qquad [2.2.13]$$

$$\rho_{TP} = \rho_H = \frac{\rho_G \rho_L}{x\rho_L + (1 - x)\rho_G} \qquad\qquad [2.2.14]$$

where u_H and ρ_H are the homogeneous velocity and density, respectively.

For a homogeneous flow, consider the balance equations for flow through the element of channel δz, whose cross-sectional area is A and that is inclined at an angle α to the horizontal (see figure 2.2.1). The mass-balance (continuity) equation may be expressed as

$$\begin{array}{c} \text{Rate of} \\ \text{creation} = 0 = \\ \text{of mass} \end{array} \quad \begin{array}{c} \text{mass} \\ \text{outflow} \\ \text{rate} \end{array} - \begin{array}{c} \text{mass} \\ \text{inflow} \\ \text{rate} \end{array} + \begin{array}{c} \text{mass} \\ \text{storage} \\ \text{rate} \end{array} \qquad [2.2.15]$$

The respective terms are as follows:

$$0 = \left[j\rho_H A + \delta z\, \frac{\partial}{\partial z}\,(j\rho_H A) \right] - j\rho_H A + A\,\delta z\,\frac{\partial \rho_H}{\partial t} \qquad [2.2.16]$$

where j is the total volume flux, given by

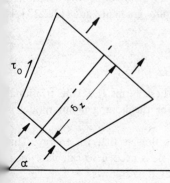

Figure 2.2.1 Element of channel for homogeneous-model balance equations.

$$j = \frac{\dot{Q}_G + \dot{Q}_L}{A} = U_G + U_L \qquad [2.2.17]$$

Rearranging gives

$$\frac{\partial}{\partial z}(j\rho_H A) + A\frac{\partial \rho_H}{\partial t} = 0 \qquad [2.2.18]$$

Referring again to figure 2.2.1, one may apply the principle of conservation of momentum to the element of channel δz:

Rate of creation of = momentum	momentum outflow – rate	momentum inflow + rate	momentum storage = rate	sum of forces acting on control volume

$$[2.2.19]$$

The momentum terms in the center portion of [2.2.19] are given by

$$\dot{m}jA + \delta z \frac{\partial}{\partial z}(\dot{m}jA) - \dot{m}jA + \frac{\partial}{\partial t}(\dot{m}jA\,\delta z) \qquad [2.2.20]$$

where $\dot{m}$ is the mass flux. The forces acting on the element are those due to the pressure gradient, gravity, and the wall shear and are summed as follows:

$$p - \left(p + \delta z\,A\,\frac{\partial p}{\partial z}\right) - g\rho_H A\,\delta z \sin \alpha - \tau_0\,\delta z\,P \qquad [2.2.21]$$

where τ_0 is the wall shear stress, and P is the channel periphery.

Equating [2.2.20] and [2.2.21] and recognizing that $\dot{m} = \rho_H j$ gives

$$\frac{\partial \dot{m}}{\partial t} + \frac{1}{A}\frac{\partial(\dot{m}^2 A/\rho_H)}{\partial z} = \frac{\partial p}{\partial z} - g\rho_H \sin \alpha - \frac{\tau_0 P}{A} \qquad [2.2.22]$$

For steady-state flow in constant-cross-section ducts, this equation simplifies to

$$-\frac{dp}{dz} = \frac{\tau_0 P}{A} + \frac{d(\dot{m}^2/\rho_H)}{dz} + g\rho_H \sin \alpha \qquad [2.2.23]$$

which is the equation most commonly used in pressure drop prediction. The three terms of the right-hand side of [2.2.23] are often denoted as the frictional, accelerational, and gravitational components of pressure gradient, and [2.2.23] is sometimes written as

$$-\frac{dp}{dz} = -\frac{dp_F}{dz} - \frac{dp_a}{dz} - \frac{dp_g}{dz} \qquad [2.2.24]$$

An empirical correlation is required for the first of these terms (i.e., the frictional pressure gradient); a discussion of such correlations for the homogeneous model is given in section 2.2.3.

The final conservation equation for homogeneous flow is that for energy. This is not directly used in pressure drop calculations, but it is needed to calculate local quality in diabatic flow. The energy balance can be stated as follows:

$$
\begin{array}{cccc}
\text{Rate of} & \text{energy} & \text{energy} & \text{energy} \\
\text{creation} = 0 = & \text{outflow} - & \text{inflow} + & \text{storage} \\
\text{of energy} & \text{rate} & \text{rate} & \text{rate}
\end{array}
\qquad [2.2.25]
$$

The three terms on the right-hand side of [2.2.25] correspond to the following:

$$
\begin{aligned}
0 = &\left[jA\rho_H e + \delta z \frac{\partial}{\partial z} (jA\rho_H e) \right] - [jA\rho_H e + \dot{q}P\,\delta z + \dot{q}_v A\,\delta z] \\
&+ \left[A\,\delta z \frac{\partial}{\partial t} \left(\rho_H \mu + \frac{j^2 \rho_H}{2} \right) \right]
\end{aligned}
\qquad [2.2.26]
$$

where $\dot{q}$ is the heat flux into the system via the channel wall, $\dot{q}_v$ is the internal heat generation rate per unit volume, μ is the specific internal energy per unit mass, and e is the energy convected per unit mass of the fluid, given by

$$
e = h + \frac{j^2}{2} + gz \sin \alpha
\qquad [2.2.27]
$$

where h is the specific enthalpy, defined as

$$
h = \mu + \frac{p}{\rho_H}
\qquad [2.2.28]
$$

and p is the system pressure.

Combining [2.2.26]–[2.2.28] and introducing the continuity relationship [2.2.18] give the following form of the energy-balance equation (Lahey & Moody 1977):

$$
\rho_H \left(\frac{\partial e}{\partial t} + j \frac{\partial e}{\partial z} \right) = \frac{\dot{q}P}{A} + \dot{q}_v + \frac{\partial p}{\partial t}
\qquad [2.2.29]
$$

2.2.2.3 Conservation Equations for Separated Two-Phase Flow

The most commonly assumed model for two-phase pressure drop calculation is that of separated flow. This situation is illustrated schematically for an annular flow in figure 2.2.2; however, the basic equations for the separated flow model are not dependent on the particular flow configuration adopted. It is assumed that the velocities of each phase are constant, in any given cross section, within the zone occupied by the phase.

It is possible to write conservation equations for mass and momentum for each phase, and this is often a useful starting point for two-phase flow analysis. However, each pair of conservation equations can be added together to give an overall balance equation for the mixture, and it is the overall balance equations that have been most commonly adopted in pressure drop prediction. Here we derive the conservation equations for each phase first, since this provides a useful background for the discussion of pressure gradient prediction in annular flow in section 2.2.4.

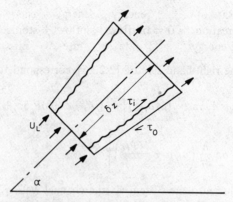

Figure 2.2.2 Element of channel for separated flow-model balance equations.

The continuity (mass-balance) equation for the liquid phase follows the form of [2.2.15], the respective terms being introduced into the equation as follows:

$$0 = \rho_L (1 - \epsilon_G) u_L A + \delta z \frac{\partial}{\partial z} [\rho_L (1 - \epsilon_G) u_L A] + \dot{m}_e \, \delta z$$

$$- \rho_L (1 - \epsilon_G) u_L A + \frac{\partial}{\partial t} [\rho_L (1 - \epsilon_G) A \, \delta z] \qquad [2.2.30]$$

where $\dot{m}_e$ is the rate of conversion of liquid to gas (i.e., vapor) per unit length. For the evaporation or condensation of a vapor under conditions of thermodynamic equilibrium, it follows that

$$\dot{m}_e = \dot{q} \frac{P}{h_{LG}} \qquad [2.2.31]$$

where h_{LG} is the latent heat of vaporization, and $\dot{q}$ is the heat flux from the surface. On simplification, [2.2.30] becomes

$$\frac{\partial}{\partial t} [\rho_L (1 - \epsilon_G) A] + \frac{\partial}{\partial z} [\rho_L u_L (1 - \epsilon_G) A] = - \dot{m}_e \qquad [2.2.32]$$

which is equivalent to [1.2.21]. A similar equation may be derived for the mass balance in the gas phase; the result is

$$\frac{\partial}{\partial t} (\rho_G \epsilon_G A) + \frac{\partial}{\partial z} (\rho_G \epsilon_G u_G A) = \dot{m}_e \qquad [2.2.33]$$

which is also equivalent to [1.2.21]. Adding [2.2.32] and [2.2.33] and remembering that

$$\dot{m} = \rho_L u_L (1 - \epsilon_G) + \rho_G \epsilon_G u_G \qquad [2.2.34]$$

give the separated flow continuity equation for the two-phase mixture,

$$\frac{\partial}{\partial t} (\rho_{TP} A) + \frac{\partial}{\partial z} (\dot{m} A) = 0 \qquad [2.2.35]$$

which is equivalent to [1.2.20].

The momentum-balance equation for the separated flow model may also be derived for the two respective phases, on lines similar to that suggested by [2.2.19]. For the liquid phase, the momentum terms equivalent to those given in the middle section of [2.2.19] are

$$\dot{M}_L u_L + \delta z \frac{\partial}{\partial z} (\dot{M}_L u_L) - \dot{M}_L u_L + \frac{\partial}{\partial t} [u_L \rho_L (1 - \epsilon_G) A \, \delta z] \qquad [2.2.36]$$

where $\dot{M}_L$ is the mass rate of flow of the liquid phase. Recognizing that

$$\dot{M}_L = u_L \rho_L (1 - \epsilon_G) A \qquad [2.2.37]$$

and simplifying give the rate of creation of liquid-phase momentum as

$$\delta z \left\{ \frac{\partial}{\partial z} [u_L^2 \rho_L (1 - \epsilon_G) A] + \frac{\partial}{\partial t} [u_L \rho_L (1 - \epsilon_G) A] \right\} \qquad [2.2.38]$$

The rate of creation of liquid-phase momentum can be balanced against the sum of the forces acting on the control volume of liquid, which are as follows:

$$p (1 - \epsilon_G) A - \left\{ p (1 - \epsilon_G) A + \delta z \frac{\partial}{\partial z} [p (1 - \epsilon_G) A] \right\} - \left\{ -p \, \delta z \frac{\partial}{\partial z} [(1 - \epsilon) A] \right\}$$

$$- g \rho_L (1 - \epsilon_G) A \, \delta z \sin \alpha - \tau_0 P \, \delta z + \tau_{im} P_i \, \delta z \qquad [2.2.39]$$

where τ_0 is the wall shear stress, τ_{im} is the rate of transfer of momentum from gas to the liquid phase per unit interfacial area, i.e., the interfacial shear stress, and P_i is the interfacial periphery. The first three terms correspond to the pressure forces on the liquid element. The first and second terms are the pressure force on the ends of the element, and the third term is the pressure force on the sloping surface of the element, occurring due to changes in the cross-sectional area of the liquid. Expanding the derivatives in the second of the pressure-force terms and equating the forces on the element to the rate of creation of liquid-phase momentum in [2.2.38] lead to the liquid-phase momentum balance:

$$- (1 - \epsilon_G) \frac{\partial p}{\partial z} - g \rho_L (1 - \epsilon_G) \sin \alpha - \frac{\tau_0 P}{A} + \frac{\tau_{im} P_i}{A} = \frac{\partial}{\partial t} [\rho_L u_L (1 - \epsilon_G)]$$

$$+ \frac{1}{A} \frac{\partial}{\partial z} [\rho_L A u_L^2 (1 - \epsilon_G)] \qquad [2.2.40]$$

A similar equation may be derived for the gas phase and is as follows:

$$- \epsilon_G \frac{\partial p}{\partial z} - g \rho_G \epsilon_G \sin \alpha - \frac{\tau_{im} P_i}{A} = \frac{\partial}{\partial t} (\rho_G \epsilon_G u_G) + \frac{1}{A} \frac{\partial}{\partial z} (\rho_G A \epsilon_G u_G^2)$$

$$[2.2.41]$$

which is equivalent to [1.2.21].

The transfer of mass from one phase to the other can significantly affect the momentum transfer; that is, τ_{im} may be significantly different from its value τ_i in the absence of interphase mass transfer. A simple method of treating the problem of estimating τ_{im} is to use the "equivalent-laminar-film" model as stated, for instance, by Bird et al. (1960). Here, it is assumed that, in the gas phase adjacent to the interface, there is a laminar boundary layer over which the velocity changes from the mean value for the gas phase u_G to the liquid interfacial velocity (assumed equal to u_L to a first approximation). The basis of the equivalent-laminar-film model is that the thickness of the boundary layer does not change appreciably as a result of the mass transfer; this certainly seems to be borne out by experimental data and by more sophisticated calculation methods, over the range of conditions encountered in most practical evaporation and condensation systems. It is convenient to define friction factors f_i and f_{im} for the cases with and without mass transfer as follows:

$$f_i = \frac{\tau_i}{\frac{1}{2}\rho_G(u_G - u_L)^2} \qquad [2.2.42]$$

$$f_{im} = \frac{\tau_{im}}{\frac{1}{2}\rho_G(u_G - u_L)^2} \qquad [2.2.43]$$

The equivalent-laminar-film model then gives the following result relating the shear stresses with and without mass transfer:

$$\frac{\tau_{im}}{\tau_i} = \frac{f_{im}}{f_i} = \frac{F}{\exp(F - 1)} \qquad [2.2.44]$$

where F is a dimensionless factor defined as

$$F = \frac{2\dot{m}_e}{P_i \rho_G f_i(u_G - u_L)} \qquad [2.2.45]$$

For $F \ll 1$ (i.e., at low condensation rates), [2.2.44] reduces to

$$\frac{\tau_{im}}{\tau_i} = 1 - \frac{F}{2} \qquad [2.2.46]$$

Introducing the above definitions and rearranging give, for this case,

$$\tau_{im} = \tau_i - \frac{\dot{m}_e}{P_i} \frac{1}{2}(u_G - u_L) \qquad [2.2.47]$$

which implies that, with evaporation, the interfacial shear stress is reduced by an amount corresponding to the product of the evaporation rate per unit interfacial area and half the velocity difference. For condensation, where $\dot{m}_e$ is negative, the interfacial shear stress is enhanced similarly.

The momentum equations for the separate phases, [2.2.40] and [2.2.41], can be added to give the mixture (separated flow) momentum equation as follows:

$$-\frac{\partial p}{\partial z} - g\rho_{TP}\sin\alpha - \frac{\tau_0 P}{A} = \frac{\partial}{\partial t}[\rho_L(1 - \epsilon_G)u_L + \rho_G\epsilon_G u_G]$$

$$+ \frac{1}{A}\frac{\partial}{\partial z}[\rho_L A(1 - \epsilon_G)u_L^2 + \rho_G A\epsilon_G u_G^2] \qquad [2.2.48]$$

Equation [2.2.48] can be rewritten in terms of mass flux $\dot{m}$ and quality x by introducing the identities

$$\dot{m} = \rho_L (1 - \epsilon_G)u_L + \rho_G\epsilon_G u_G \qquad [2.2.49]$$

$$u_L = \frac{\dot{m}(1 - x)}{\rho_L(1 - \epsilon_G)} \qquad [2.2.50]$$

$$u_G = \frac{\dot{m}x}{\rho_G\epsilon_G} \qquad [2.2.51]$$

which lead to the expression

$$-\frac{\partial p}{\partial z} - g\rho_{TP}\sin\alpha - \frac{\tau_0 P}{A} = \frac{\partial\dot{m}}{\partial t} + \frac{1}{A}\frac{\partial}{\partial z}\left\{\dot{m}^2 A\left[\frac{(1-x)^2}{\rho_L(1-\epsilon_G)} + \frac{x^2}{\rho_G\epsilon_G}\right]\right\}$$

$$[2.2.52]$$

For steady-state flow in ducts of constant cross section, [2.2.52] can be rewritten and rearranged to yield

$$-\frac{dp}{dz} = \frac{\tau_0 P}{A} + \dot{m}^2 \frac{d}{dz}\left[\frac{(1-x)^2}{\rho_L(1-\epsilon_G)} + \frac{x^2}{\rho_G\epsilon_G}\right] + g\rho_{TP}\sin\alpha \qquad [2.2.53]$$

which is the separated flow-model equivalent of [2.2.23]. The three terms on the right-hand side correspond, in order, to the frictional, accelerational, and gravitational pressure drops. Equation [2.2.53] is widely used as a basis for pressure drop calculations in two-phase flow.

The mixture form of the separated flow energy equation is given by Lahey & Moody (1977) as follows:

$$A\frac{\partial}{\partial t}\left[\rho_L h_L (1 - \epsilon_G) + \rho_G h_G\epsilon_G\right] + \frac{\partial}{\partial z}\left[\dot{m}A (h_L + xh_{LG})\right]$$

$$= \dot{q}P + \dot{q}_v A - \frac{\partial}{\partial z}\left\{\dot{m}^3 A\left[\frac{(1-x)^3}{\rho_L^2(1-\epsilon_G)^2} + \frac{x^2}{\rho_G^2\epsilon_G^2}\right]\right\} - g\dot{m}A\sin\alpha$$

$$-\frac{\partial}{\partial t}\left\{\dot{m}^2\left[\frac{(1-x)^2}{\rho_L(1-\epsilon_G)} + \frac{x^2}{\rho_G\epsilon_G}\right]\right\} + A\frac{\partial p}{\partial t} \qquad [2.2.54]$$

For steady-state flow in a constant-cross-section duct, with negligible change in physical properties, with kinetic- and potential-energy terms being negligible compared to heat input and enthalpy, and with negligible internal heat generation, the form of the energy equation most widely used in practice as a means of calculating the variation of quality with length for thermodynamic equilibrium conditions is as follows:

$$\frac{dx}{dz} = \frac{\dot{q}P}{\dot{m}Ah_{LG}} \qquad [2.2.55]$$

which for constant heat flux integrates to

$$x = x_i + \frac{\dot{q}Pz}{\dot{m}Ah_{LG}}$$

[2.2.56]

where x_i is the inlet quality (i.e., at $z = 0$). It is possible to derive many different forms of the conservation equations for separated flows (Lahey & Moody 1977).

2.2.3 EMPIRICAL RELATIONSHIPS FOR FRICTIONAL PRESSURE GRADIENT

It is convenient to define here some parameters that are used repeatedly in what follows. For both the homogeneous and separated flow models, the frictional pressure gradient is defined (see [2.2.23], [2.2.24], and [2.2.53]) as

$$-\frac{dp_F}{dz} = \frac{\tau_0 P}{A}$$

[2.2.57]

where τ_0 is the wall shear stress, P is the channel periphery, and A is the channel cross-sectional area. It is convenient to relate the frictional pressure gradient to that for the gas phase or liquid phase flowing alone in the channel, in terms of frictional multipliers ϕ_G and ϕ_L defined as follows:

$$\phi_G^2 = \frac{dp_F/dz}{(dp_F/dz)_G}$$

[2.2.58]

$$\phi_L^2 = \frac{dp_F/dz}{(dp_F/dz)_L}$$

[2.2.59]

For evaporating or condensing systems, it is often more convenient to relate the two-phase frictional pressure gradient to the frictional pressure gradient for a single-phase flow at the same total mass velocity and with the physical properties of the liquid phase, namely, $(dp_F/dz)_{LO}$. The friction multiplier ϕ_{LO} for this case is defined by

$$\phi_{LO}^2 = \frac{dp_F/dz}{(dp_F/dz)_{LO}}$$

[2.2.60]

The single-phase pressure drops used in [2.2.58]–[2.2.60] can be calculated from the standard equations:

$$\left(\frac{dp_F}{dz}\right)_G = \frac{2f_G \dot{m}^2 x^2}{D\rho_G}$$

[2.2.61]

$$\left(\frac{dp}{dz}\right)_L = \frac{2f_L \dot{m}^2 (1-x)^2}{D\rho_L}$$

[2.2.62]

$$\left(\frac{dp}{dz}\right)_{LO} = \frac{2f_{LO} \dot{m}^2}{D\rho_L}$$

[2.2.63]

where $\dot{m}$ is the mass flux, x is the quality, D is the channel equivalent diameter, and

ρ_G and ρ_L are the gas and liquid densities. The friction factors f_G, f_L, and f_{LO} are related (through standard equations and charts for single-phase flow) to the respective Reynolds numbers, defined as follows:

$$\text{Re}_G = \frac{\dot{m}xD}{\mu_G} \qquad [2.2.64]$$

$$\text{Re}_L = \frac{\dot{m}(1-x)D}{\mu_L} \qquad [2.2.65]$$

$$\text{Re}_{LO} = \frac{\dot{m}D}{\mu_L} \qquad [2.2.66]$$

where D is the tube diameter, μ_G is the gas-phase viscosity, μ_L is liquid-phase viscosity, and x is the quality. For laminar flow ($\text{Re} < 2000$), $f = 16/\text{Re}$; for turbulent flow ($\text{Re} > 2000$), the Blasius equation,

$$f = 0.079 \left(\frac{\dot{m}D}{\mu} \right)^{-1/4} \qquad [2.2.67]$$

is often used.

2.2.3.1 Calculation of Frictional Pressure Drop from Homogeneous Model

The conservation equations for homogeneous flow are given in section 2.2.2.2. The frictional pressure gradient may be expressed in terms of a two-phase friction factor f_{TP} as follows:

$$\frac{dp_F}{dz} = \frac{\tau_0 P}{A} = \frac{2 f_{TP} \dot{m}^2}{D \rho_H} \qquad [2.2.68]$$

where D, the equivalent diameter, is equal to $4P/A$, with P the wetted perimeter and A the cross-sectional area for flow.

The two-phase friction factor f_{TP} may be defined as a function of the two-phase Reynolds number Re_{TP}, which is

$$\text{Re}_{TP} = \frac{\dot{m}D}{\mu_{TP}} \qquad [2.2.69]$$

where μ_{TP} is a two-phase viscosity; provided a suitable value can be assigned to μ_{TP}, equations such as [2.2.67] can be used to calculate f_{TP}. The problem with the homogeneous model is that it is difficult to assign a universal definition for μ_{TP}; a variety of forms have been tried (McAdams et al. 1942; Cicchitti et al. 1960; Dukler et al. 1964), but none is really very satisfactory. The most commonly used form is that due to McAdams et al. (1942), which is

$$\frac{1}{\mu_{TP}} = \frac{x}{\mu_G} + \frac{1-x}{\mu_L} \qquad [2.2.70]$$

With this definition, the friction multiplier ϕ_{LO} can be calculated for turbulent

Table 2.2.1 Values of the Two-Phase Frictional Multiplier ϕ_{LO}^2 for the Homogeneous-Model Steam-Water System

Steam quality (% by weight)	Pressure (bars)								
	0.101	0.689	3.44	6.89	10.3	13.8	17.2	20.7	22.12
1	16.21	3.40	1.44	1.19	1.10	1.05	1.04	1.01	1.0
5	67.6	12.18	3.12	1.89	1.49	1.28	1.16	1.06	1.0
10	121.2	21.8	5.06	2.73	1.95	1.56	1.30	1.13	1.0
20	212.2	38.7	7.8	4.27	2.81	2.08	1.60	1.25	1.0
30	292.8	53.5	11.74	5.71	3.60	2.57	1.87	1.36	1.0
40	366	67.3	14.7	7.03	4.36	3.04	2.14	1.48	1.0
50	435	80.2	17.45	8.30	5.08	3.48	2.41	1.60	1.0
60	500	92.4	20.14	9.50	5.76	3.91	2.67	1.71	1.0
70	563	104.2	22.7	10.70	6.44	4.33	2.89	1.82	1.0
80	623	115.7	25.1	11.81	7.08	4.74	3.14	1.93	1.0
90	682	127	27.5	12.9	7.75	5.21	3.37	2.04	1.0
100	738	137.4	29.8	13.98	8.32	5.52	3.60	2.14	1.0

flow, using the Blasius equation [2.2.67] as follows:

$$\phi_{LO}^2 = \left(1 + x\,\frac{\rho_L - \rho_G}{\rho_G}\right)\left(1 + x\,\frac{\mu_L - \mu_G}{\mu_G}\right)^{-1/4} \qquad [2.2.71]$$

where ρ_L and ρ_G are the liquid- and gas-phase densities, respectively. Table 2.2.1 is a convenient table of values ϕ_{LO} for steam-water mixtures.

The homogeneous model tends to underestimate the value of the two-phase frictional pressure gradient, sometimes by a large factor, but it may give more reasonable predictions at high pressures and mass fluxes. In general, for practical calculations, it is preferable to use some form of the separated flow model.

2.2.3.2 Frictional Pressure Drop Correlations Based on the Separated Flow Model

The conservation equations for separated two-phase flow are derived in section 2.2.2.3. The key equation is [2.2.53], in which the first term on the right-hand side is the frictional pressure gradient:

$$-\frac{dp_F}{dz} = \frac{\tau_0 P}{A} = \phi_{LO}^2\left(\frac{dp_F}{dz}\right)_{LO} = \phi_G^2\left(\frac{dp_F}{dz}\right)_G = \phi_L^2\left(\frac{dp_F}{dz}\right)_L \qquad [2.2.72]$$

Historically, the most widely used correlation for the calculation of two-phase frictional pressure drop is that of Lockhart & Martinelli (1949). In spite of its deficiencies, many (and perhaps most) technical calculations are still done using this method; for that reason, it is presented, and its accuracy is discussed, below. However, more modern correlations, for example, that of Friedel (1979) (also described below), should be employed in preference to that of Lockhart & Martinelli whenever possible.

Lockhart & Martinelli related the pressure drop multipliers ϕ_L^2 and ϕ_G^2 to the parameter X^2 defined as follows:

$$X^2 = \frac{(dp_F/dz)_L}{(dp_F/dz)_G} \qquad [2.2.73]$$

where $(dp_F/dz)_L$ and $(dp_F/dz)_G$ are the pressure gradients for the liquid phase and gas phase flowing alone in the channel. Lockhart & Martinelli presented the relationship in graphic form, as illustrated in figure 2.2.3. Different curves were suggested, depending on whether the phase-alone flows were laminar ("viscous") or turbulent, and the multipliers are subscripted accordingly. For example, the multiplier ϕ_{Lvt} applies to the case in which the liquid phase flowing alone in the channel is in laminar flow and the gas phase flowing alone is turbulent. A simple and accurate analytic representation of the Lockhart & Martinelli graphic relationships for the multipliers is that of Chisholm (1967):

$$\phi_L^2 = 1 + \frac{C}{X} + \frac{1}{X^2} \qquad [2.2.74]$$

$$\phi_G^2 = 1 + CX + X^2 \qquad [2.2.75]$$

where C is a dimensionless parameter whose value is independent of x but depends on the nature (i.e., viscous or turbulent) of the phase-alone flows. Chisholm suggests values for C as given in Table 2.2.2.

Martinelli & Nelson (1948) noted that the Lockhart-Martinelli correlations did not become asymptotic to the correct value as the critical pressure was approached. They produced a revised multiplier correlation as illustrated in figure 2.2.4. This correlation was fitted to data for steam-water mixtures over a range of pressures, but the same correlation has been used for other fluids at the same ratio of pressure p to critical pressure p_c. The Lockhart-Martinelli correlation does not contain surface tension as a parameter; it seems certain that at least part of the pressure effect observed by Martinelli & Nelson was due to the variation of the surface

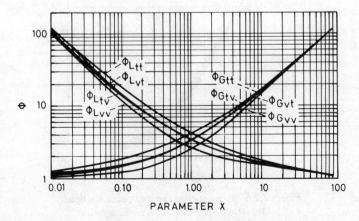

Figure 2.2.3 Correlation of Lockhart & Martinelli (1949) for pressure drop multiplier.

Table 2.2.2   Values of C to Fit the Empirical
Curves of Lockhart & Martinelli (Chisholm 1967)

Liquid	Gas	Subscript	C
Turbulent	Turbulent	tt	20
Viscous	Turbulent	vt	12
Turbulent	Viscous	tv	10
Viscous	Viscous	vv	5

tension of water with pressure, and it seems unlikely, therefore, that the arbitrary extension of the correlation shown in figure 2.2.4 to other fluids is particularly valid.

The Martinelli correlations fail to take adequate account of the influence of mass flux. This is exemplified by figure 2.2.5, in which values of ϕ_{LO}^2 calculated from actual data (Cicchitti et al. 1960) are compared with the Martinelli & Nelson and homogeneous-model curves. As will be seen, there is a systematic effect of mass flux; the Martinelli & Nelson curve is approached at low mass flux, and the homogeneous model fits more closely at high mass flux.

Thus, the traditional Martinelli-type correlations are inadequate in representing a wide range of two-phase flow pressure gradient data, and large mean and standard deviation are observed when the models are compared with large banks of experimental data. Typical standard deviations may range up to 100%, with order-of-magnitude differences for some data points.

Over the past 30 yr, continuing attempts have been made to derive better correlations for frictional pressure gradient. As more data become available, the deficiencies of earlier correlations became apparent and further correlations were

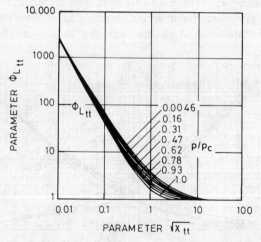

Figure 2.2.4   Pressure effect on two-phase multiplier and void fraction correlation (Martinelli & Nelson 1948).

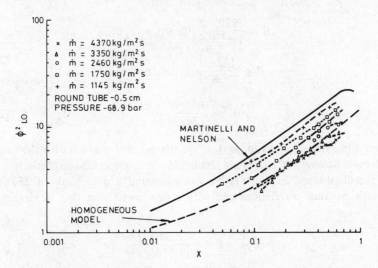

Figure 2.2.5 Effect of mass flux on pressure drop multiplier (results courtesy of CISE Laboratory, Italy).

developed. This process is a continuing one, and it reflects the fact that, for a situation as complex as two-phase flow, it is very difficult to formulate relationships that have a general physical basis. The main difficulty is that the empirical correlations are based on the assumption that the frictional pressure gradient is a function only of channel cross-sectional geometry, mass flux, and physical proper-ties. However, in two-phase flow, the effects of flow development are very considerable, and any wide-ranging data bank on two-phase flow contains data with a variety of inlet configurations and channel lengths, which will give a range of pressure gradients for the same nominal conditions. The lengths required to reach equilibrium in two-phase flow correspond typically to several hundred diameters, and thus most experiments never reach equilibrium conditions. Furthermore, in practical situations, equilibrium conditions themselves are not necessarily relevant, particularly when there is a phase conversion (i.e., evaporation or condensation) along the channel. Here, it may be preferable to use a more basic physical model (although that too presents difficulties); an example of such modeling is given in section 2.2.4.

Perhaps the most widely used advanced empirical correlation is that of Baroczy (1965). This correlation has the disadvantage of being graphic in nature, but a correlation that fits the Baroczy curves quite well and extends the range of data covered is that of Chisholm (1973), which is

$$\phi_{LO}^2 = 1 + (Y^2 - 1) \left[Bx^{(2-n)/2}(1 - x)^{(2-n)/2} + x^{2-n} \right] \qquad [2.2.76]$$

where n is the power in the friction factor–Reynolds number relationship (0.25 for the Blasius equation), the parameter B is given by

$$B = \frac{55}{\dot{m}^{1/2}} \quad \text{for } 0 < Y < 9.5 \qquad [2.2.77]$$

$$B = \frac{520}{Y\dot{m}^{1/2}} \quad \text{for } 9.5 < Y < 28$$

$$B = \frac{15,000}{Y^2\dot{m}^{1/2}} \quad \text{for } 28 < Y$$

[2.2.77]
Cont.

where

$$Y^2 = \frac{(dp_F/dz)_{GO}}{(dp_F/dz)_{LO}} \qquad [2.2.78]$$

and where $(dp_F/dz)_{GO}$ and $(dp_F/dz)_{LO}$ are the pressure gradients for the total mass in the channel flowing with gas-phase and liquid-phase properties, respectively.

In recent studies, Friedel (1979) has compared a data bank of 25,000 data points with existing correlations and with a new correlation that he developed, as follows:

$$\phi_{LO}^2 = E + \frac{3.24\,FH}{\mathrm{Fr}^{0.045}\mathrm{We}^{0.035}} \qquad [2.2.79]$$

where

$$E = (1-x)^2 + x^2\,\frac{\rho_L f_{GO}}{\rho_G f_{LO}} \qquad [2.2.80]$$

$$F = x^{0.78}\,(1-x)^{0.24} \qquad [2.2.81]$$

$$H = \left(\frac{\rho_L}{\rho_G}\right)^{0.91}\left(\frac{\mu_G}{\mu_L}\right)^{0.19}\left(1 - \frac{\mu_G}{\mu_L}\right)^{0.7} \qquad [2.2.82]$$

$$\mathrm{Fr} = \frac{\dot{m}^2}{gD\rho_{TP}^2} \qquad [2.2.83]$$

$$\mathrm{We} = \frac{\dot{m}^2 D}{\rho_{TP}\sigma} \qquad [2.2.84]$$

and f_{GO} and f_{LO} are the friction factors for the total mass flux flowing with gas and liquid properties, respectively. For this particular correlation, ρ_{TP} is given by

$$\rho_{TP} = \left(\frac{x}{\rho_G} + \frac{1-x}{\rho_L}\right)^{-1} \qquad [2.2.85]$$

The correlation [2.2.79] is for vertical upward flow and horizontal flow. A slightly different correlation is used for vertical downflow.

Figure 2.2.6 shows comparisons made by Friedel between his data bank and the predictions of the above correlation. The standard deviation was around 30% for single-component flows, and about 40–50% for two-component flows. Notwithstanding the complexity of the Friedel correlation, the deviations are still rather large and, as figure 2.2.6 illustrates, there is a considerable spread in the data, probably due to the factors described above.

Recent evaluations (based on Heat Transfer and Fluid Flow Service proprietary data bank) have led to the following tentative recommendations with respect to the published correlations (Whalley 1980):

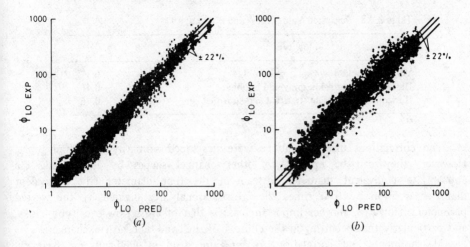

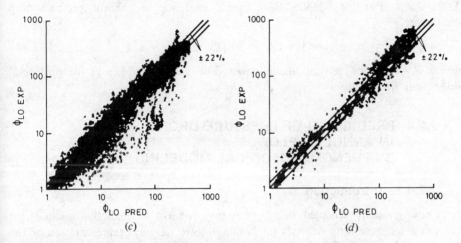

Figure 2.2.6 Comparisons between the Friedel (1979) correlation and two-phase pressure drop data for various situations. (*a*) Single-component horizontal and vertical up flow. (*b*) Two-component vertical up flow. (*c*) Two-component horizontal flow. (*d*) Single and two-component down flow.

1. For $\mu_L/\mu_G < 1000$, the Friedel (1979) correlation should be used.
2. For $\mu_L/\mu_G > 1000$ and $\dot{m} > 100$, the Chisholm (1973) correlation should be used.
3. For $\mu_L/\mu_G > 1000$ and for $\dot{m} < 100$, the Martinelli correlation (Lockhart & Martinelli 1949; Martinelli & Nelson 1948) should be used.

It should be emphasized that these recommendations are tentative and may be changed as further data appear and new correlations are developed. However, the fundamental fact remains that, unless a better physical basis is developed, an irreducible error is involved in the prediction of two-phase pressure drop.

Table 2.2.3 Suggested Values for B and n (Grant 1975)

Flow type	B	n
Vertical up-and-down spray and bubble	1	0.37
Horizontal side-to-side spray and bubble	0.75	0.46
Horizontal side-to-side stratified and stratified spray	0.25	0.46

The correlations discussed above were developed primarily for round tubes. However, they can be applied to other channel shapes by introducing the appropriate equivalent diameter instead of the tube diameter (the equivalent diameter is given by four times the cross-sectional area divided by the wetted perimeter). However, another important case is that of cross flow over tube banks, and particularly that occurring in the context of shell-and-tube heat exchangers.

Measurements and correlations of pressure drop in shell-and-tube heat exchangers are discussed by Grant (1975). For the cross-flow zone, Grant suggests the use of the Chisholm (1973) correlation [2.2.57], with values for B and n as given in Table 2.2.3. For the window flow zone, Grant suggests, as the pressure drop multiplier,

$$\phi_{LO}^2 = 1 + (Y^2 - 1) [Bx (1 - x) + x^2] \qquad [2.2.86]$$

where $B = 0.25$ for vertical up-and-down flow and $B = 2/(Y + 1)$ for horizontal side-to-side flow.

2.2.4 PREDICTION OF PRESSURE DROP IN ANNULAR FLOW BY PHENOMENOLOGICAL MODELING

2.2.4.1 Introduction

It is now generally accepted that further improvement in prediction methods for two-phase pressure drop depends on having a better physical representation of the flow. Specifically, it depends on taking account of the flow pattern or flow regime. In this section, methods of prediction of pressure drop in annular two-phase flow are discussed.

The nature of flow regimes in two-phase flow and methods for predicting the existence of a given regime are discussed in detail in section 2.1. Annular flow is the most ubiquitous of the flow regimes, occurring over a very wide range of quality and mass flux. Thus, the prediction of pressure gradient in annular flow is particularly important from a practical point of view. Furthermore, in vertical bubble and slug flow, the total pressure gradient is often dominated by the gravitational term, and the pressure drop prediction is thus mainly affected by the accuracy of the prediction of the void fraction. Prediction methods for void fraction are reviewed for these flow regimes (and others) in section 2.3.

In annular flow, it is the rule (rather than the exception) that a significant fraction of the liquid is entrained as droplets in the gas core. There is continuous interchange of liquid between the gas core and the liquid film. If the entrance conditions are such that all the liquid is initially in the film (this might be achieved, for instance, by injecting the liquid through a porous section of the wall), then some time is required for equilibrium to be reached between the droplet-entrainment and droplet-deposition processes. This has a bearing on pressure drop, as is illustrated in figure 2.2.7, where the results for a porous-wall-injection system are compared with those for a center-jet system (various forms of inlet are illustrated in the upper part of figure 2.2.7). Initially, the pressure gradient for the center-jet case is higher, owing to the need to accelerate the initially totally entrained liquid. Soon, the pressure gradient for this case becomes considerably less than that for the porous-wall-injection case, and the difference persists along the channel. Many hundreds of diameters are required to bring the pressure gradients to equality. Thus, any usable model for annular flow must take account of the droplet mass transfer processes.

If the flow rate in the liquid film is known locally, then the film thickness and pressure gradient can be calculated by combining two relationships as follows:

1. The *triangular* relationship, which allows calculation of the liquid-film thickness from a knowledge of the film flow rate and the interfacial shear stress. The interfacial shear stress itself can be calculated from the frictional pressure gradient in the gas core. The form of the triangular relationship is discussed in more detail in section 2.2.4.2.

2. The *interfacial-roughness* relationship, which is an empirical relationship between the effective roughness of the interface and the liquid-film thickness. The frictional pressure gradient is determined by the effective roughness of the

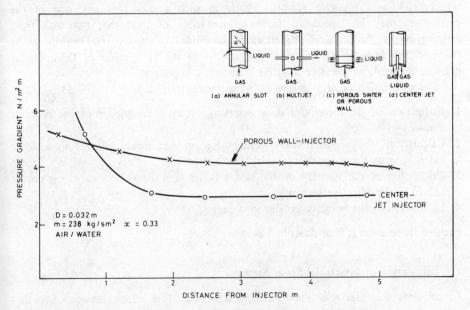

Figure 2.2.7 Pressure gradient (air-water) data obtained for identical flow conditions as a function of channel length, for center-jet and porous-wall liquid injection (Gill & Hewitt 1966).

interface. Interfacial-roughness relationships are discussed further in section 2.2.4.3.

If the liquid-film flow rate can be calculated as a function of distance along a given channel, then the frictional pressure drop may be determined by iterative solution of these relationships. To calculate the profile of film flow rate, it is necessary to solve the film mass balance equation,

$$\frac{d\dot{M}_{LF}}{dz} = P\left(\dot{m}_D - \dot{m}_E - \frac{\dot{q}}{h_{LG}}\right) \qquad [2.2.87]$$

where $\dot{M}_{LF}$ is the liquid flow rate, z is the axial distance, P is the tube periphery, $\dot{m}_D$ and $\dot{m}_E$ are the deposition and entrainment rates (mass deposited or entrained per unit peripheral area per unit time), $\dot{q}$ is the heat flux, and h_{LG} is the latent heat of evaporation. Here, $\dot{q}$ is positive for evaporation and negative for condensation.

For the prediction of annular flow, [2.2.87] must be integrated along the channel from known (or estimated) boundary conditions, with the appropriate local values of $\dot{m}_D$, $\dot{m}_E$, and $\dot{q}$ inserted. Relationships for deposition and entrainment rates are discussed in section 2.2.4.4. Some results of the application of this method are given in section 2.2.4.5, and calculations concerned with the prediction of burnout heat flux using this technique are described in section 6.4.7.

2.2.4.2 The Triangular Relationship

The triangular relationship provides an interrelation among film flow rate $\dot{M}_{LF}$, film thickness δ, and pressure gradient dp/dz in such a way that any one of the parameters may be calculated from a knowledge of the other two and from information on the physical properties of the fluids. An explicit relationship can be obtained for $\dot{M}_{LF}$ in terms of δ and dp/dz; in the calculation of thickness or pressure gradient, an iterative solution is normally necessary.

The calculation of $\dot{M}_{LF}$ proceeds in essentially four steps:

1. Estimation of the interfacial shear stress τ_{im} from a knowledge of the pressure gradient
2. Calculation of the shear-stress distribution in the liquid film from a force balance, using the value of τ_{im} calculated in step 1
3. Calculation of the velocity profile in the liquid film from the shear-stress profile and from the effective viscosity
4. Integration of the velocity profile to obtain $\dot{M}_{LF}$

Each of these steps is now described in more detail.

Calculation of Interfacial Shear Stress

To calculate the interfacial shear stress, one proceeds in a manner analogous to that for the separated flow gas-phase momentum equation [2.2.41]. For steady flow in a duct of constant cross section, this equation becomes

$$-\frac{dp}{dz} = \frac{\tau_{im}P_i}{A\epsilon_G} + \frac{1}{\epsilon_G}\frac{d}{dz}(\rho_G\epsilon_G u_G^2) + g\rho_G \qquad [2.2.88]$$

For the case of an annular flow with liquid entrainment, it is a convenient approximation to treat the gas core as a homogeneous mixture of gas and droplet occupying a fraction ϵ_c of the channel cross section. ϵ_c is related to the film thickness δ and tube radius $r_0 = D/2$ as follows:

$$\epsilon_c = \frac{(r_0 - \delta)^2}{r_0^2} \qquad [2.2.89]$$

The mean gas core density, ρ_c, calculated on the basis of homogeneous flow in the core, is given by

$$\rho_c = \frac{\dot{M}_{LE} + \dot{M}_G}{\dot{M}_G/\rho_G + \dot{M}_{LE}/\rho_L} \qquad [2.2.90]$$

where $\dot{M}_{LE}$ is the mass rate of flow of the entrained liquid, and $\dot{M}_G$ the mass rate of flow of the gas phase. For $\rho_G \ll \rho_L$, ρ_c is given approximately by

$$\rho_c \approx \rho_G \frac{\dot{M}_{LE} + \dot{M}_G}{\dot{M}_G} \qquad [2.2.91]$$

With the fraction of the total cross section occupied by the droplets defined as ϵ_d, it follows that

$$\epsilon_c = \epsilon_G + \epsilon_d = \epsilon_G + \epsilon_c \frac{\dot{M}_{LE}/\rho_L}{\dot{M}_G/\rho_G + \dot{M}_{LE}/\rho_L} \qquad [2.2.92]$$

and, thus,

$$\epsilon_c = \frac{\epsilon_G}{(\dot{M}_G/\rho_G)/(\dot{M}_G/\rho_G + \dot{M}_{LE}/\rho_L)} \qquad [2.2.93]$$

Equation [2.2.88] can be rewritten to represent the momentum balance for the (homogeneous, mixed) gas core as follows:

$$-\frac{dp}{dz} = \frac{\tau_{im}P_i}{A\epsilon_c} + \frac{1}{\epsilon_c}\frac{d}{dz}(\rho_c\epsilon_c u_c^2) + g\rho_c \qquad [2.2.94]$$

where u_c is the mean core velocity, given by

$$u_c = \frac{\dot{m}[x + F_E(1 - x)]}{\rho_c\epsilon_c} \qquad [2.2.95]$$

with $\dot{m}$ the mass flux, x the quality, and F_E the fraction of the liquid phase that is entrained. Substituting this expression for u_c into [2.2.94] and calculating P_i and A for the case of a round tube, one obtains

$$-\frac{dp}{dz} = \frac{2\tau_{im}}{r_0 - \delta} + \frac{1}{\epsilon_c}\frac{d}{dz}\left\{\frac{\dot{m}^2[x + F_E(1 - x)]^2}{\rho_c\epsilon_c}\right\} + g\rho_c \qquad [2.2.96]$$

The interfacial shear stress τ_{im} may be calculated from the total pressure gradient dp/dz via [2.2.96]. If the total pressure gradient is not known, then τ_{im} may be calculated from τ_i (the shear stress in the absence of phase change) via [2.2.44]. In turn, τ_i may be estimated from the interfacial-roughness relationships described in section 2.2.4.3.

Calculation of Shear-Stress Distribution in the Liquid Film

This shear-stress distribution is calculated by carrying out a force balance on an annular ring of outer radius r and inner radius r_i (where $r_i = r_0 - \delta$) and axial length Δz. Ignoring acceleration in the liquid film, one has

$$2\pi r\tau \, \Delta z = 2\pi r_i \tau_{im} \, \Delta z + \rho_L g\pi \, \Delta z \, (r_i^2 - r^2)$$

$$+ \pi \left[p - (p + \Delta z)\frac{dp}{dz} \right](r^2 - r_i^2) \qquad [2.2.97]$$

where τ is the shear stress at radius r. The terms on the right-hand side of [2.2.97] correspond, in order, to the interfacial shear force, the gravitational force, and the net pressure force on the element. Equation [2.2.97] simplifies to

$$\tau = \tau_{im}\frac{r_i}{r} + \frac{1}{2}\left(\rho_L g + \frac{dp}{dz}\right)\frac{r_i^2 - r^2}{r} \qquad [2.2.98]$$

which gives the interfacial shear stress as a function of radial position.

Calculation of Velocity Profile in the Liquid Film

The velocity profile within the film may be calculated by integration of the expression

$$\tau = \mu_E \frac{du}{dy} \qquad [2.2.99]$$

where u is the local liquid velocity in the film, y is the distance from the wall, and μ_E is the effective viscosity. For laminar flow, $\mu_E = \mu_L$, and integrating [2.2.99] with the boundary condition that $u = 0$ at $y = 0$ gives

$$u = \frac{1}{\mu_L}\left\{\left[\tau_{im}r_i + \frac{1}{2}\left(\rho_L g + \frac{dp}{dz}\right)r_i^2\right]\ln\frac{r_0}{r_i} - \frac{1}{4}\left(\rho_L g + \frac{dp}{dz}\right)(r_0^2 - r_i^2)\right\}$$

$$[2.2.100]$$

For turbulent flow, the effective viscosity is a function of the wall shear stress and of the distance from the wall. Commonly, the effective viscosity is calculated from the sum of the laminar and turbulent viscosities as follows:

$$\mu_E = \mu_L + \epsilon\rho_L \qquad [2.2.101]$$

where ϵ is the eddy diffusivity. The common practice has been to use single-phase flow expressions for ϵ in applying [2.2.101] in the prediction of velocity profiles in liquid films in annular flow. An example of this approach is that of Dukler (1960) for downward flow, which was adapted by Hewitt (1961) for upward flow. Here the choice of expression for ϵ is governed by the value of y^+, where

$$y^+ = u^* y \frac{\rho_L}{\mu_L}$$
[2.2.102]

where u^* is the *friction velocity*, defined by

$$u^* = \sqrt{\frac{\tau_0}{\rho_L}}$$
[2.2.103]

with τ_0 the wall shear stress. For $y^+ < 20$, the eddy diffusivity may be calculated from the Deissler expression,

$$\epsilon = n^2 u y \left[1 - \exp\left(-\rho n^2 \frac{uy}{\mu_L} \right) \right]$$
[2.2.104]

and for $y^+ > 20$, the von Karman expression may be used:

$$\epsilon = \frac{k(du/dy)^3}{(d^2 u/dy^2)^2}$$
[2.2.105]

where n and k are constants. Numerous alternative expressions exist for eddy diffusivity and/or turbulent eddy viscosity, and many of these have been applied in predicting velocity profiles in annular flow.

By using the above expressions, it is possible to integrate [2.2.99] with the boundary conditions $u = 0$ at $y = 0$, thus obtaining the velocity profile in the (turbulent) liquid film. The results of such integrations are given in detail by, for instance, Hewitt (1961).

Integration of the Velocity Profile to Obtain Film Flow Rate

The film flow rate is given by the integral

$$\dot{M}_{LF} = \int_0^\delta 2\pi r \rho_L u \, dy$$
[2.2.106]

For upward laminar flow, the following result is obtained:

$$\dot{M}_{LF} = \frac{2\pi\rho_L}{\mu_L} \left\{ \left[\tau_{im} r_i + \frac{1}{2} \left(\rho_L g + \frac{dp}{dz} \right) r_i^2 \right] \left[\frac{1}{4} (r_0^2 - r_i^2) - \frac{1}{2} r_i^2 \ln \frac{r_0}{r_i} \right] \right.$$

$$\left. - \frac{1}{16} \left(\rho_L g + \frac{dp}{dz} \right) (r_0^2 - r_i^2)^2 \right\}$$
[2.2.107]

For turbulent flow, [2.2.106] may be integrated numerically, using the velocity profile determined from the numerical integration of [2.2.99].

A convenient simplification may be obtained for the case in which the variation of wall shear stress across the film is small (i.e., where the interfacial and wall shear stresses may be assumed to be equal), and where the film is thin compared to the tube radius. In this case, and for laminar flow, the integrations of [2.2.99] and [2.2.106] yield the following results:

$$u = \frac{\tau_{im}y}{\mu_L} = \frac{\tau_0 y}{\mu_L}$$

[2.2.108]

$$\dot{M}_{LF} = \frac{\pi r_0 \rho_L \tau_{im} \delta^2}{\mu_L} = \frac{\pi r_0 \rho_L \tau_0 \delta^2}{\mu_L}$$

[2.2.109]

where τ_0 is the wall shear stress. It is convenient to define a *liquid-film friction factor* f_{LF} as follows:

$$f_{LF} = \frac{\tau_0}{\frac{1}{2}\rho_L u_{LF}^2}$$

[2.2.110]

where u_{LF} is the mean velocity in the liquid film, given by

$$u_{LF} = \frac{\dot{M}_{LF}}{2\pi r_0 \delta \rho_L} = \frac{\dot{m}_{LF} r_0}{2\rho_L \delta}$$

[2.2.111]

with $\dot{m}_{LF}$ the superficial mass flux associated with the liquid film, i.e., the mass rate of flow in the film divided by the total cross-sectional area of the tube: $\dot{m}_{LF} = \dot{M}_{LF}/\pi r_0^2$.

A liquid-film Reynolds number Re_{LF} may be defined as follows:

$$\text{Re}_{LF} = \frac{d_{HLF} u_{LF} \rho_L}{\mu_L}$$

[2.2.112]

where d_{HLF} is the equivalent diameter of the film and is given (for a film whose thickness is small compared to the tube radius) by

$$d_{HLF} = \frac{4 \text{ (cross-sectional area for flow)}}{\text{wetted perimeter}} = \frac{4 (2\pi r_0 \delta)}{2\pi r_0} = 4\delta$$

[2.2.113]

Combining [2.2.111]–[2.2.113] gives

$$\text{Re}_{LF} = \frac{2 \dot{m}_{LF} r_0}{\mu_L}$$

[2.2.114]

which is identical to the Reynolds number for full pipe flow at a liquid mass flux $\dot{m}_{LF}$. For the thin-film (constant film shear stress) case, there is a unique relationship between f_{LF} and Re_{LF}. In the limiting case of low Reynolds number, f_{LF} is given by combination of [2.2.109]–[2.2.111] and [2.2.114] as

$$f_{LF} = \frac{16}{\text{Re}_{LF}}$$

[2.2.115]

For high Reynolds numbers (turbulent liquid films), f_{LF} can be deduced from the

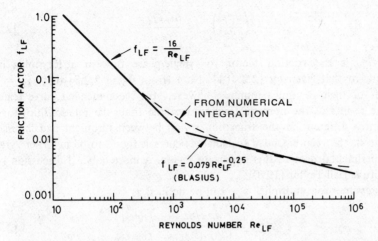

Figure 2.2.8 Liquid-film friction factor as a function of liquid-film Reynolds number. Calculated by Hewitt & Hall-Taylor (1970) from the numerical integration results (dashed line) of Hewitt (1961).

results of Hewitt (1961) as a function of liquid-film Reynolds number [see Hewitt & Hall-Taylor (1970)] and is as illustrated in figure 2.2.8.

The use of the simplified form of the triangular relationships thus consists in determining the liquid-film Reynolds number from [2.2.114], estimating the appropriate value of f_{LF} from figure 2.2.8, estimating the interfacial shear stress τ_{im} from the relationships described above, and then calculating the film flow rate from the expression

$$\dot{M}_{LF} = 2\pi r_0 \delta \sqrt{\frac{2\,\tau_{im}\rho_L}{f_{LF}}} \qquad [2.2.116]$$

It is also of interest to express the above relationships in terms of friction multipliers and void fraction. The frictional pressure gradient is given by

$$\frac{dp_F}{dz} = \frac{2\tau_0}{r_0} = \frac{\rho_L u_{LF}^2}{r_0} \frac{\tau_0}{\frac{1}{2}\rho_L u_{LF}^2} = \frac{\rho_L u_{LF}^2}{r} f_{LF} \qquad [2.2.117]$$

By defining ϵ_F as the fraction of the channel cross section that is occupied by the liquid film, the following approximate relationship for the case of a thin film is obtained:

$$\epsilon_F = 1 - \epsilon_G - \epsilon_d \approx \frac{2\pi r_0 \delta}{\pi r_0^2} \approx \frac{2\delta}{r_0} \qquad [2.2.118]$$

Combining [2.2.117] and [2.2.118] gives

$$\frac{dp_F}{dz} = \frac{\dot{m}_{LF}^2 f_{LF}}{r_0 \rho_L} \frac{1}{\epsilon_F^2} \qquad [2.2.119]$$

The pressure gradient $(dp_F/dz)_{LF}$ for single-phase liquid flow at mass flux $\dot{m}_{LF}$ is given by

$$\left(\frac{dp_F}{dz}\right)_{LF} = \frac{\dot{m}_{LF}f'_{LF}}{r_0\rho_L} \qquad [2.2.120]$$

where f'_{LF} is the friction factor for single-phase flow at a Reynolds number equivalent to that given by [2.2.114]. Note (from figure 2.2.8) that $f'_{LF} = f_{LF}$ in the limit of high Reynolds number; however, the recommended curve (calculated from the results of the numerical solution of the triangular relationship) for f_{LF} is significantly different in the transition region between turbulent and laminar flow and, indeed, the recommended (calculated) curve is found to be in closer agreement with experimental data in this important region. A more detailed discussion is given by Hewitt & Hall-Taylor (1970).

A pressure drop multiplier ϕ_{LF} can be defined as

$$\phi^2_{LF} = \frac{dp_F/dz}{(dp_F/dz)_{LF}} = \frac{f_{LF}}{f'_{LF}}\frac{1}{\epsilon^2_F} \qquad [2.2.121]$$

For the special case in which all the liquid phase is flowing in the film ($\epsilon_d = 0$),

$$\phi^2_{LF} = \frac{dp_F/dz}{(dp_F/dz)_L} = \frac{f_{LF}}{f_L}\frac{1}{(1-\epsilon_G)^2} \qquad [2.2.122]$$

where f_L is the friction factor for the total liquid-phase flow, passing alone in the channel. For $f_{LF} = f_L$, [2.2.122] is similar in form to the empirical correlation of Lockhart & Martinelli (1949) for void fraction (see section 2.3.4).

2.2.4.3 Interfacial-Roughness Relationship

In annular flow, to a first approximation, the wave configuration on the interface seems to be about the same for a given average film thickness, irrespective of the phase flow rates that produce that film thickness. Quantitative confirmation of this geometric similarity in the interface is given, for instance, by Hewitt (1969). This geometric similarity is the underlying reason why plots of the ratio of the "equivalent sand roughness" of the interface to the tube diameter, versus the ratio δ/D of film thickness to tube diameter (Gill et al. 1963), and plots of interfacial friction factor versus δ/D (Hartley & Roberts 1961; Wallis 1970), tend to correlate a rather wide range of experimental data for pressure drop. The most widely used form of the interfacial-roughness correlation is that of Wallis (1970), who defined an interfacial friction factor f_{gsci} as follows:

$$f_{gsci} = \frac{\tau_i}{\frac{1}{2}\rho_c U^2_c} \qquad [2.2.123]$$

where τ_i is the interfacial friction factor, and ρ_c is the mean gas-core density (see [2.2.90] and [2.2.91]). U_c is the superficial velocity (based on the full-tube cross section) of the gas core, and for $\rho_G \ll \rho_L$ is approximated by

$$U_c \approx \frac{4\dot{M}_G}{\pi\rho_G D^2} \qquad [2.2.124]$$

where $\dot{M}_G$ is the gas mass rate of flow, and D is the tube diameter.

The relationship suggested by Wallis for f_{gsci} is

$$f_{gsci} = f_{sgc}\left(1 + 360\,\frac{\delta}{D}\right) \qquad [2.2.125]$$

where f_{sgc} is the smooth-pipe single-phase friction factor appropriate to a Reynolds number Re_{sgc} defined by the expression

$$Re_{sgc} = \frac{U_c\rho_c D}{\mu_G} \qquad [2.2.126]$$

where μ_G is the viscosity of the gas phase. Equation [2.2.125] does not fit the data too well at high pressures, and Whalley & Hewitt (1978) suggest the modified form

$$f_{gsci} = f_{sgc}\left[1 + 24\left(\frac{\rho_L}{\rho_G}\right)^{1/3}\frac{\delta}{D}\right] \qquad [2.2.127]$$

Other, more accurate, relationships are likely to emerge as a wider range of data becomes available.

2.2.4.4 Correlations for Deposition and Entrainment Rates

Droplet deposition rates are commonly calculated from the simple expression

$$\dot{m}_D = kC \qquad [2.2.128]$$

where $\dot{m}_D$ is the rate of deposition (mass per unit peripheral area per unit time), C is the concentration of droplets in the gas core (mass per unit volume calculated on a homogeneous basis), and k is the deposition mass transfer coefficient. Methods of measurement for k (and for entrainment rate) are discussed in section 10.2.2.4. A tentative correlation of k in terms of surface tension σ is given by Whalley et al. (1974) and is illustrated in figure 2.2.9. However, it is unlikely that a simple relationship exists between deposition coefficient and surface tension, and this has

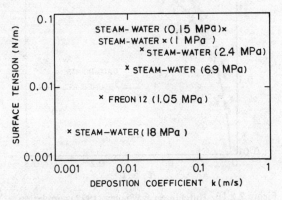

Figure 2.2.9 Tentative relationship between deposition coefficient and surface tension.

led to the search for a more general correlation, specifically in dimensionless form. For example, Hewitt (1978a) and Whalley & Hewitt (1978) report the following correlation, which appears to fit both low-pressure and high-pressure data:

$$\frac{k}{u_c^*} = 87 \sqrt{\frac{\mu_L^2}{D\sigma\rho_L}} \qquad [2.2.129]$$

where μ_L is the liquid viscosity, and u_c^* is the core friction velocity, defined as $\sqrt{\tau_i/\rho_c}$. There is no particular physical justification for this relationship, and, again, one may expect to see further development of equations in this area.

As is mentioned in section 10.2.2.1, the methods for measuring the entrainment rate $\dot{m}_E$ are rather unsatisfactory. The entrainment rate is normally deduced from data for entrainment flow rate under conditions of hydrodynamic equilibrium, where

$$\dot{m}_E = \dot{m}_D = kC_E \qquad [2.2.130]$$

where C_E is the equilibrium concentration of droplets (calculated on a homogeneous basis) in the core. Hutchinson & Whalley (1972) suggest correlation of C_E as a function of the dimensionless group S, given by

$$S = \frac{\tau_i \delta}{\sigma} \qquad [2.2.131]$$

This correlation is illustrated in figure 2.2.10. It is assumed that, even for nonequilibrium conditions, under which $\dot{m}_E \neq \dot{m}_D$, the entrainment rate is still given by $\dot{m}_E = kC_E$, where C_E is obtained from figure 2.2.10 for the appropriate value of S.

Again, the correlation shown in figure 2.2.10 is not dimensionless, and it shows

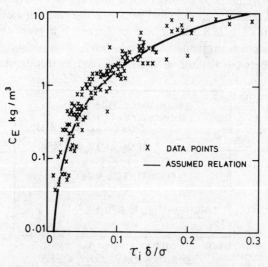

Figure 2.2.10 Hutchinson & Whalley (1972) correlation for equilibrium entrained-droplet concentration.

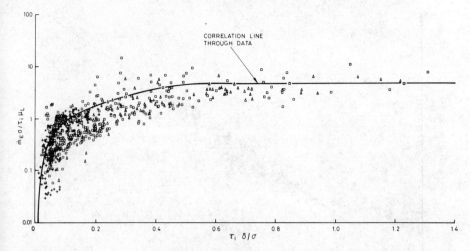

Figure 2.2.11 Tentative correlation of Whalley & Hewitt (1978) for entrainment rate in annular flow.

certain inconsistencies when expressed in terms of entrainment rate rather than homogeneous mean equilibrium concentration. Studies of alternative correlation forms for entrainment are reported by Whalley & Hewitt (1978), and a tentative nondimensional correlation is illustrated in figure 2.2.11. Clearly, there is considerable scatter in the correlation, and better correlations are being sought; probably, these will have to take account of the formation of disturbance waves on the interface and the interaction of the gas phase with waves. Initial velocity of droplets on release from film may be important (James et al. 1980). Notwithstanding the scatter, reasonable predictions of the parameters of annular flow may be made using this correlation, as is described next.

2.2.4.5 Some Results

The analytic methods described above for predicting annular flow have now been used extensively for a variety of purposes. Perhaps one of the most important applications is that of prediction of burnout, which corresponds to the point at which the liquid film flow becomes zero in an evaporation situation. The results of such calculations are reviewed in section 6.4.7. The analysis leads to the prediction of interfacial shear stress τ_i, from which the frictional pressure gradient may be calculated directly (see [2.2.96]); indeed, for thin films, the frictional pressure gradient is proportional to the interfacial shear stress (see [2.2.117]). Whalley & Hewitt (1978) present comparisons of predicted and experimental values of interfacial shear stress obtained by using the simplified form of the triangular relationship (figure 2.2.8), the modified interfacial-roughness correlation [2.2.127], the nondimensional deposition-coefficient correlation [2.2.129], and the entrainment correlation illustrated in figure 2.2.11. The comparisons are illustrated in figure 2.2.12. The agreement obtained is comparable with that observed in empirical correlations (compare figure 2.2.6), and some of the scatter is likely the result of residual entrance effects of the type illustrated in figure 2.2.7.

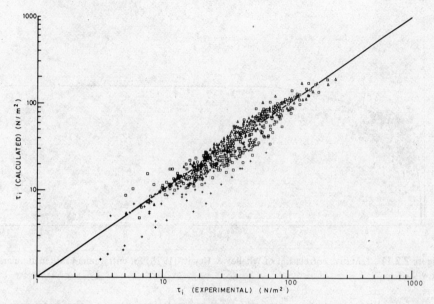

Figure 2.2.12 Comparison of experimental and calculated values of interfacial shear stress in annular flow (Whalley & Hewitt 1978).

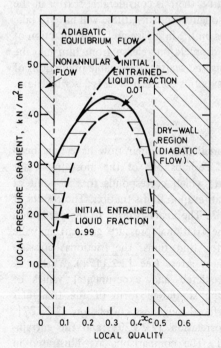

Figure 2.2.13 Predicted local pressure gradients in the evaporation of water at 9.8 MPa pressure with a mass flux of 1500 kg/m² s.

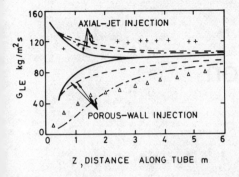

Figure 2.2.14 Comparison of predicted entrained-liquid mass fluxes with those observed in air-water flow for two different injectors (Hutchinson et al. 1974).

For evaporating flows, the calculation proceeds by integration of the mass balance equation [2.2.87], and the frictional pressure gradient is calculated locally as a function of distance along the channel. Results obtained from calculations of this type are illustrated in figure 2.2.13. Note that the pressure gradient passes through a maximum and falls as the burnout point is approached. This occurs because the liquid film is thinning due to evaporation at a rate that cannot be compensated for by net deposition. Also shown in figure 2.2.13 is the line calculated for adiabatic equilibrium flow; very large differences in calculated pressure gradients at the same local quality, between adiabatic and diabatic flow, may be observed. It is in the prediction of such differences that these methods are particularly powerful.

It is interesting to compare predictions of the analytic methods with the data presented by Gill & Hewitt (1968) for the two extreme forms of entrance condition (i.e., liquid injection through a center jet and through a porous wall section). The comparisons are shown in figure 2.2.14. The analysis predicts too rapid a rate of achievement of equilibrium, compared to the experimental results. Slightly better agreement is obtained if a transient analysis of the effect of entrance conditions on the mass transfer coefficient k is carried out. However, it is evident that, for the porous-wall-injection system, the rate of entrainment is initially less than is predicted from the correlations shown in figures 2.2.10 and 2.2.11. Hutchinson et al. propose an exponential equation for the growth of entrainment capacity due to wave growth. This has some physical logic, but it was, of course, fitted to the data empirically.

2.3 Void Fraction

G. F. Hewitt

2.3.1 INTRODUCTION

Void fraction is defined as either of

1. The fraction of the channel volume that is occupied by the gas phase
2. The fraction of the channel cross-sectional area that is occupied by the gas phase

For present purposes, it is assumed that these two quantities are identical and designated as ϵ_G. A detailed discussion of the averaging processes associated with the definition of void fraction is given in section 1.2, and a review of measuring techniques for the determination of void fraction is given in section 10.2.1.2.

The primary purpose of this section is to present prediction methods for void fraction. These can be expressed either in terms of void fraction itself or, alternatively, in terms of the velocity ratio S, which is defined as the ratio of the average gas and liquid velocities u_G and u_L and is thus related to void fraction as follows:

$$S = \frac{u_G}{u_L} = \frac{\dot{Q}_G/A\,\epsilon_G}{\dot{Q}_L/A(1-\epsilon_G)} = \frac{\dot{Q}_G(1-\epsilon_G)}{\dot{Q}_L\epsilon_G} \qquad [2.3.1]$$

$$S = \frac{u_G}{u_L} = \frac{U_G/\epsilon_G}{U_L/(1-\epsilon_G)} = \frac{U_G(1-\epsilon_G)}{U_L\epsilon_G} \qquad [2.3.2]$$

$$S = \frac{u_G}{u_L} = \frac{\dot{m}x/A\,\epsilon_G\rho_G}{\dot{m}(1-x)/A\,(1-\epsilon_G)\rho_L} = \frac{\rho_L x(1-\epsilon_G)}{\rho_G(1-x)\epsilon_G} \qquad [2.3.3]$$

where $\dot{Q}_G$ and $\dot{Q}_L$ are the volumetric rates of flow of the gas and liquid phases, A is the cross-sectional area of the channel, U_G and U_L are the superficial velocities of the phases, x is the quality, $\dot{m}$ is the mass flux, and ρ_L and ρ_G are the liquid- and gas-phase densities. From the above, it follows that

$$\epsilon_G = \frac{\dot{Q}_G}{S\dot{Q}_L + \dot{Q}_G} \qquad [2.3.4]$$

$$\epsilon_G = \frac{U_G}{SU_L + U_G} \qquad [2.3.5]$$

$$\epsilon_G = \frac{\rho_L x}{S\rho_G(1-x) + \rho_L x} \qquad [2.3.6]$$

For the homogeneous model, $u_G = u_L$, $S = 1$, and $\epsilon_G = \beta$, where β is the ratio of the gas volume flow to the total volume flow. Thus,

$$\epsilon_G = \beta = \frac{\dot{Q}_G}{\dot{Q}_L + \dot{Q}_G} \qquad [2.3.7]$$

The void fraction approaches that calculated from the homogeneous model at high pressure and high mass flux, but normally deviates significantly from the homogeneous value. A simple (and sometimes physically reasonable) approach to the calculation of void fraction is to assume that there is, over the whole channel cross section, a constant relative velocity between the phases. This so-called one-dimensional treatment is reviewed in section 2.3.2 and can be a powerful tool in analyzing, say, bubbly flows. The next level of sophistication is to develop models that take account of the radial distribution of velocity and relative velocity by using simple (empirical) distribution factors. Such models are reviewed in section 2.3.3. The failure of these simple models to accurately represent a wide range of void fraction data has led to a number of empirical correlations, and section 2.3.4 gives some examples of these. To provide more detailed and accurate models, it is necessary to consider the physics of specific flow regimes, and models of this type are reviewed in section 2.3.5 for stratified flow, bubble flow, slug flow, and annular flow, and for voids in subcooled boiling.

2.3.2 ONE-DIMENSIONAL FLOW CALCULATION METHOD

The objective of this method is to calculate the void fraction ϵ_G in a given channel, knowing the volumetric flows $\dot{Q}_L$ and $\dot{Q}_G$. The main assumptions of the method (Wallis 1969) are that (1) the shear stress at the channel wall may be ignored, and consequently (2) there is no variation in void fraction or velocity across the channel.

A total superficial velocity U is defined as

$$U = U_L + U_G \qquad [2.3.8]$$

and, in the general case,

$$u_G \neq u_L \neq U \qquad [2.3.9]$$

If we consider a plane moving along the channel at a velocity U, it is possible to define a drift velocity for each phase with respect to this plane as follows:

$$u_{GU} = u_G - U \qquad [2.3.10]$$

$$u_{LU} = u_L - U \qquad [2.3.11]$$

Furthermore, it is possible to define *drift fluxes*, j_{GL} and j_{LG} for the flux of each phase through the plane moving at velocity U. These drift fluxes are obtained by multiplying the drift velocities u_{GU} and u_{LU} by the area fraction of the plane occupied by each phase:

$$j_{GL} = \epsilon_G u_{GU} \qquad [2.3.12]$$

$$j_{LG} = (1 - \epsilon_G) u_{LU} \qquad [2.3.13]$$

It follows from the continuity that there is no net drift through the plane moving at velocity U, and thus

$$j_{GL} + j_{LG} = 0 \qquad [2.3.14]$$

From the above equations, it follows that

$$j_{GL} = \epsilon_G u_{GU} = \epsilon_G(u_G - U) = \epsilon_G\left(\frac{U_G}{\epsilon_G} - U_G - U_L\right) = U_G(1 - \epsilon_G) - \epsilon_G U_L$$

$$[2.3.15]$$

$$j_{LG} = (1 - \epsilon_G)u_{LU} = (1 - \epsilon_G)(u_L - U) = (1 - \epsilon_G)\left(\frac{U_L}{1 - \epsilon_G} - U_G - U_L\right)$$

$$= - u_G(1 - \epsilon_G) + \epsilon_G U_L = - j_{GL} \qquad [2.3.16]$$

Equations [2.3.15] and [2.3.16] arise purely from continuity arguments, but it could also be reasoned that the drift fluxes are a representation of the physics of the system and that, for instance,

$$j_{GL} = f(\epsilon_G, \text{physical properties, flow pattern}) \qquad [2.3.17]$$

Clearly, when the void fraction approaches zero, j_{GL} also approaches zero. Also, for very high void fractions, it could be argued that j_{GL} would again approach zero (for example, in foam flow). Thus, j_{GL} passes through a maximum as the void fraction increases from zero to unity. A combination of the physics expression [2.3.17] with the expression [2.3.15] arising from continuity gives the required solution for void fraction. It is convenient to illustrate the solution graphically, as in figure 2.3.1, which gives the solution for four cases of vertical flow. It should be noted that, from [2.3.15], if $\epsilon_G = 0$, then $j_{GL} = U_G$, and if $\epsilon_G = 1$, then $j_{GL} = - U_L$. Between these two values, the continuity relationship is linear. Considering the four cases shown in figure 2.3.1, we have the following:

1. Vertical cocurrent upward flow. Here, U_G and U_L are both positive, the continuity expression [2.3.15] giving a negative value of j_{GL} at $\epsilon_G = 1$. Only one solution is obtained in this case.
2. Vertical cocurrent downward flow. Here again, only one solution for ϵ_G is obtained, but the ϵ_G value is a much higher value than that for vertical upward flow for the same phase flow rates.
3. Countercurrent flow (upward gas flow, downward liquid flow). Here there can be two solutions or, in the limiting case, one solution. For high values of liquid

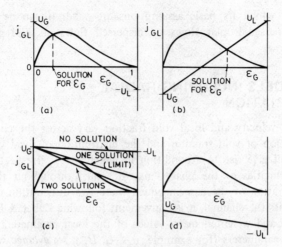

Figure 2.3.1 Solutions for void fraction in vertical flow using the one-dimensional analysis method. (*a*) Vertical cocurrent up flow. (*b*) Vertical cocurrent down flow. (*c*) Vertical countercurrent flow (liquid down, gas up). (*d*) Vertical countercurrent flow (liquid up, gas down).

velocity, no solutions are available, indicating that the gas must be swept downward.

4. Countercurrent flow (gas downward, liquid upward). Here, it is physically obvious that there can be no solutions, and this is confirmed by the diagram.

Figure 2.3.2 shows the regions of possible operation. As will be seen, cocurrent upward flow and cocurrent down flow are always possible, and countercurrent flow with the gas flowing down is always impossible. For countercurrent flow with the gas flowing up, there is a region of impossible operation bounded by a line that is sometimes referred to as the "locus of flooding."

Relationships for j_{GL} for bubble flow are discussed in section 2.3.5.2. However, the one-dimensional flow method is not restricted to bubble flow; it can be used for

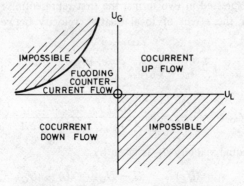

Figure 2.3.2 Regions of possible operation based on simplified one-dimensional flow treatment.

any situation in which its basic assumptions are valid. It can be employed, for instance, for dispersed-droplet flows or dispersed flows of solid particles (Wallis 1969).

2.3.3 MODELS INCLUDING RADIAL VARIATION

In practice, local velocity and local void fraction vary across the channel. The fact that the distribution of void fraction and the distribution of local velocity may be different can itself give rise to a condition in which $S \neq 1$, irrespective of the fact that the local velocities of the phases may be equal throughout the channel. To facilitate consideration of the case in which there is a distribution of velocity and void fraction across the channel, it is convenient, following Zuber & Findlay (1975), to define average and weighted mean values of the local parameters. Let F be any one of the local parameters (for example, u_G, U, U_L). An *average* value for F over a channel cross section A can be defined as follows:

$$\langle F \rangle = \frac{1}{A} \int_A F \, dA \qquad [2.3.18]$$

A *weighted mean* value for F may be defined as follows:

$$\bar{F} = \frac{\langle \epsilon_G F \rangle}{\langle \epsilon_G \rangle} = \frac{(1/A) \int_A \epsilon_G F \, dA}{(1/A) \int_A \epsilon_G \, dA} \qquad [2.3.19]$$

With a notation similar to that used in [2.3.8]–[2.3.13] but now with parameters that can vary across the channel, expressions for the average gas velocity and the weighted mean gas velocity are obtained as follows:

$$\langle u_G \rangle = \langle U \rangle + \langle u_{GU} \rangle \qquad [2.3.20]$$

$$\bar{u}_G = \frac{\langle U_G \rangle}{\langle \epsilon_G \rangle} = \frac{\langle \epsilon_G u_G \rangle}{\langle \epsilon_G \rangle} = \frac{\langle \epsilon_G U \rangle}{\langle \epsilon_G \rangle} + \frac{\langle \epsilon_G u_{GU} \rangle}{\langle \epsilon_G \rangle} \qquad [2.3.21]$$

$\bar{u}_G$ is conveniently expressed in two terms, the first representing the velocity-profile effect and the other the effect of local relative velocity between the phases, as follows:

$$\bar{u}_G = C_0 \langle U \rangle + \frac{\langle \epsilon_G u_{GU} \rangle}{\langle \epsilon_G \rangle} \qquad [2.3.22]$$

where

$$C_0 = \frac{\langle \epsilon_G U \rangle}{\langle \epsilon_G \rangle \langle U \rangle} = \frac{(1/A) \int_A \epsilon_G U \, dA}{(1/A^2) \int_A U \, dA \int_A \epsilon_G \, dA} \qquad [2.3.23]$$

The weighted mean liquid velocity $\bar{u}_L$ is given by

$$\bar{u}_L = \frac{\langle U_L \rangle}{\langle 1 - \epsilon_G \rangle} = \frac{\langle U - U_G \rangle}{\langle 1 - \epsilon_G \rangle} = \frac{\langle U \rangle - \langle U_G \rangle}{\langle 1 - \epsilon_G \rangle} \qquad [2.3.24]$$

Using [2.3.21], [2.3.22], and [2.3.24], we obtain the following expression for the velocity ratio S:

$$S = \frac{\bar{u}_G}{\bar{u}_L} = \frac{\langle 1 - \epsilon_G \rangle}{1/(C_0 + \langle u_{GU}\epsilon_G \rangle/\langle \epsilon_G \rangle \langle U \rangle) - \langle \epsilon_G \rangle} \qquad [2.3.25]$$

For the case of no local relative velocity between the phases ($u_{GU} = 0$),

$$S = \frac{\langle 1 - \epsilon_G \rangle}{1/C_0 - \langle \epsilon_G \rangle} \qquad [2.3.26]$$

This is a form of equation for velocity ratio derived originally by Bankoff (1959).

If the relative velocity u_{GU} is constant across the channel, then [2.3.25] may be transformed into a void-quality relationship of the form

$$\langle \epsilon_G \rangle = \frac{x\rho_L}{C_0[x\rho_L + (1 - x)\rho_G] + \rho_L\rho_G u_{GU}/\dot{m}} \qquad [2.3.27]$$

where ρ_L and ρ_G are the liquid- and gas-phase densities, $\dot{m}$ is the mass flux, and x is the quality.

The value of C_0 varies with the flow regime. Thus, in fully developed bubble and/or slug flow, $C_0 = 1.1/1.2$; for qualities approaching unity, $C_0 = 1.0$; and, as the void fraction approaches zero, $C_0 = 0$. For void fractions greater than 0.1, Rouhani (1969) suggests the following expression for C_0:

$$C_0 = 1 + 0.2 (1 - x)\left(\frac{gD\rho_L^2}{\dot{m}^2}\right)^{0.25} \qquad [2.3.28]$$

where g is the acceleration due to gravity, and D is the tube diameter. For the "churn-turbulent" bubble flow regime, Zuber & Findlay (1965) give the following expression for u_{GU}:

$$u_{GU} = 1.18 \left(\sigma g \frac{\rho_L - \rho_G}{\rho_L^2}\right)^{0.25} \qquad [2.3.29]$$

where σ is the surface tension.

Alternative expressions for C_0 and u_{GU} may be derived in terms of void fraction, although they are less convenient because they often require iterative solution of [2.3.27] to calculate the void fraction. Some of these expressions are discussed in sections 2.3.5.2 and 2.3.5.5.

2.3.4 EMPIRICAL CORRELATIONS FOR VOID FRACTION

In section 2.2.3.2, the Lockhart & Martinelli (1949) relationships for frictional pressure drop were reviewed. Lockhart & Martinelli also give a graphic relationship (illustrated in figure 2.3.3) for void fraction ϵ_G in terms of the Martinelli parameter X, defined in [2.2.73]. In a manner similar to that for frictional pressure gradient, Martinelli & Nelson (1948) introduce a pressure correction to the relationship

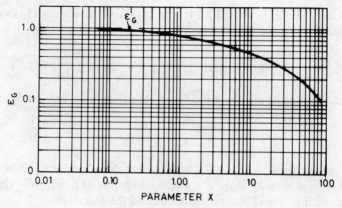

Figure 2.3.3 Correlation of Lockhart and Martinelli (1949) for void fraction.

between X and void fraction; this is illustrated in figure 2.3.4. Again, this relationship has been used for fluids other than water at the same ratio of pressure p to critical pressure p_c.

The curve relating ϵ_G to X in figure 2.3.3 is well fitted (for the turbulent-turbulent region) by the expression

$$\epsilon_G = \frac{\phi_L - 1}{\phi_L} \qquad [2.3.30]$$

where ϕ_L is the friction multiplier defined by [2.2.59]. For the case of annular flow with all the liquid flowing in the film, and for $f_{LF} = f_L$, this corresponds to the triangular relationship result, [2.2.122].

In practice, Martinelli-type correlations do not fit void fraction data well, as is exemplified in figure 2.3.5. A number of alternative empirical correlations have been

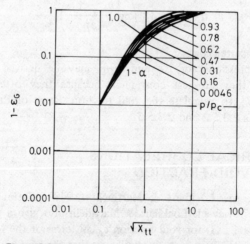

Figure 2.3.4 Correlation of Martinelli & Nelson (1948) for void fraction.

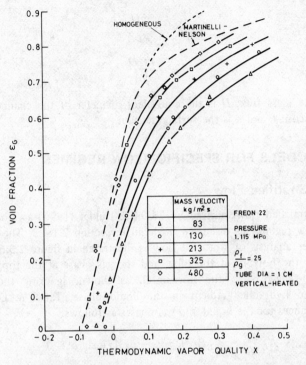

Figure 2.3.5 Results of Zuber et al. (1967), illustrating the influence of mass velocity on void fraction.

suggested; that of Premoli et al. (1971) covers a reasonably wide range of data and takes account of the mass flux effects illustrated in figure 2.3.5. The correlation is in terms of velocity ratio S (see [2.3.3]), from which the void fraction may be calculated using [2.3.6]. The correlation has the form

$$S = 1 + E_1 \left(\frac{y}{1 + yE_2} - yE_2 \right)^{1/2} \qquad [2.3.31]$$

where

$$y = \frac{\beta}{1 - \beta} \qquad [2.3.32]$$

where β is the volume flow ratio, defined in [2.3.7], and

$$E_1 = 1.578 \ \text{Re}^{-0.19} \left(\frac{\rho_L}{\rho_G} \right)^{0.22} \qquad [2.3.33]$$

$$E_2 = 0.0273 \ \text{We} \ \text{Re}^{-0.51} \left(\frac{\rho_L}{\rho_G} \right)^{-0.08} \qquad [2.3.34]$$

where ρ_L and ρ_G are the liquid- and gas-phase densities, and the Reynolds and Weber numbers, Re and We, are defined as follows:

$$\text{Re} = \frac{\dot{m}D}{\mu_L} \qquad [2.3.35]$$

$$\text{We} = \frac{\dot{m}^2 D}{\sigma \rho_L} \qquad [2.3.36]$$

where $\dot{m}$ is the mass flux, D is the equivalent diameter of the channel, μ_L is the liquid-phase viscosity, and σ is the surface tension.

2.3.5 MODELS FOR SPECIFIC FLOW REGIMES

2.3.5.1 Stratified Flow

A model for stratified flow, derived by Taitel & Dukler (1976) as a basis for their models for flow regimes, is discussed in detail in section 2.1.4.3. The basis of the Taitel & Dukler analysis of stratified flow is illustrated in figure 2.3.6. The liquid phase flows at the bottom of the tube, and the gas phase at the top; the tube is inclined at an angle α to the horizontal, as shown. Ignoring the effects of acceleration and hydraulic gradient in the liquid phase, Taitel & Dukler wrote momentum balances for the liquid and gas phases as follows:

$$-A_L \frac{dp}{dz} - \tau_{0L} P_L + \tau_i P_i - \rho_L A_L g \sin \alpha = 0 \qquad [2.3.37]$$

$$-A_G \frac{dp}{dz} - \tau_{0G} P_G - \tau_i P_i - \rho_G A_G g \sin \alpha = 0 \qquad [2.3.38]$$

where A_L and A_G are the cross-sectional areas for flow over the liquid and gas phases, respectively, τ_{0L} and τ_{0G} are the wall shear stresses for those parts of the perimeter that are in contact with the gas and liquid, respectively, τ_i is the interfacial shear stress, P_L and P_G are the tube perimeters in contact with the liquid and gas phases, respectively, and P_i is the interfacial perimeter. Eliminating the pressure gradient dp/dz from [2.3.37] and [2.3.38] gives

$$\tau_{0G} \frac{P_G}{A_G} - \tau_{0L} \frac{P_L}{A_L} + \tau_i P_i \left(\frac{1}{A_L} + \frac{1}{A_G} \right) - (\rho_L - \rho_G)g \sin \alpha = 0 \qquad [2.3.39]$$

It is convenient to express the wall and interfacial shear stresses in terms of friction factors that were defined by Taitel & Dukler as follows:

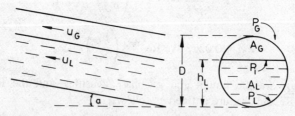

Figure 2.3.6 Parameters in equilibrium stratified flow.

$$\tau_{0L} = \frac{f_L \rho_L u_L^2}{2} \qquad [2.3.40]$$

$$\tau_{0G} = \frac{f_G \rho_G u_G^2}{2} \qquad [2.3.41]$$

$$\tau_i = \frac{f_i \rho_G (u_G - u_L)^2}{2} \qquad [2.3.42]$$

Following Agrawal et al. (1973), Taitel & Dukler evaluated f_L and f_G as

$$f_L = C_L \left(\frac{D_L u_L \rho_L}{\mu_L} \right)^{-h} \qquad [2.3.43]$$

$$f_G = C_G \left(\frac{D_G u_G \rho_G}{\mu_G} \right)^{-m} \qquad [2.3.44]$$

where C_L and C_G are constants and where the equivalent diameters D_L and D_G for the liquid and gas phases, respectively, are given by

$$D_L = \frac{4 A_L}{P_L} \qquad [2.3.45]$$

$$D_G = \frac{4 A_G}{P_G + P_i} \qquad [2.3.46]$$

Taitel & Dukler assumed that $C_G = C_L = 0.046$ and $n = m = 0.2$ for turbulent flow, and that $C_G = C_L = 16$ and $n = m = 1.0$ for laminar flow. They introduced the expressions for friction factor into [2.3.39] and then proceeded to nondimensionalize the equation by the procedure introduced in section 2.1.4.3. With nondimensional quantities denoted by a tilde ($\tilde{\ }$), the momentum balance reduces to

$$X^2 (\tilde{u}_L \tilde{D}_L)^{-n} \tilde{u}_L^2 \frac{\tilde{P}_L}{\tilde{A}_L} - (\tilde{u}_G \tilde{D}_G)^{-m} \tilde{u}_G^2 \left(\frac{\tilde{P}_G}{\tilde{A}_G} + \frac{\tilde{P}_L}{\tilde{A}_L} + \frac{\tilde{P}_i}{\tilde{A}_G} \right) - 4Y = 0$$

$$[2.3.47]$$

where $\tilde{u}_L = u_L/U_L$ and $\tilde{u}_G = u_G/U_G$; $\tilde{D}_L = D_L/D$ and $\tilde{D}_G = D_G/D$ (where D is the tube diameter); $\tilde{P}_L = P_L/D$, $\tilde{P}_G = P_G/D$, $\tilde{P}_i = P_i/D$, $\tilde{A}_G = A_G/D^2$, and $\tilde{A}_L = A_L/D^2$. X is the Martinelli parameter (see [2.1.13]), and Y is a parameter defined by Taitel & Dukler to represent the effect of channel inclination as follows:

$$Y = \frac{-(\rho_L - \rho_G) g \sin \alpha}{(dp_F/dz)_G} \qquad [2.3.48]$$

where $(dp_F/dz)_G$ is the frictional pressure gradient for the gas phase flowing alone in the channel.

In [2.3.47], all the dimensionless quantities with a tilde ($\tilde{\ }$) are functions of the dimensionless liquid height $\tilde{h}_L = h_L/D$. The appropriate expressions for $\tilde{A}_L$, $\tilde{A}_G$, $\tilde{P}_i$, $\tilde{u}_G$, $\tilde{u}_L$, $\tilde{D}_L$, and $\tilde{P}_L$ are given in [2.1.14]–[2.1.20]. The remaining dimensionless variables in [2.3.47] are $\tilde{D}_G$ and $\tilde{P}_G$, and these are given as follows:

$$\tilde{D}_G = \frac{4 A_G}{D(P_G + P_i)} = \frac{4 \tilde{A}_G}{\tilde{P}_G + \tilde{P}_i} \qquad [2.3.49]$$

$$\tilde{P}_G = \frac{P_G}{D} = \cos^{-1}(2 \tilde{h}_L - 1) \qquad [2.3.50]$$

These relationships can be introduced into [2.3.47], and, for given values of X and Y (corresponding to the known flow conditions), the appropriate value of $\tilde{h}_L$ may be estimated as that giving a solution (by iteration) of [2.3.47]. The solutions obtained by Taitel & Dukler are illustrated in figure 2.3.7. They found that— expressed in this dimensionless form—the results were remarkably similar whether the gas-phase flow was assumed laminar or turbulent. Of course, the actual liquid height would vary, since, for a given set of flow conditions, X and Y are different for laminar and turbulent gas flow.

Once $\tilde{h}_L$ is estimated from the above equations or by interpolation of figure 2.3.7, the void fraction ϵ_G may be calculated as follows:

$$\epsilon_G = \frac{1}{\pi} \left[\cos^{-1}(2 \tilde{h}_L - 1) - (2 \tilde{h}_L - 1) \sqrt{1 - (2 \tilde{h}_L - 1)^2} \right] \qquad [2.3.51]$$

2.3.5.2 Bubble Flow

For bubble flow, it is often sufficiently accurate to use the one-dimensional flow method outlined in section 2.3.2. A model like [2.3.17] is needed for the calculations of the drift flux j_{GL}. It is convenient to relate j_{GL} to the rise velocity u_∞ of a bubble in an infinite pool of liquid. At low void fraction, j_{GL} is given by the product of the bubble rise velocity and the fraction of the cross section occupied by the bubbles, namely ϵ_G. As the bubble concentration increases, bubble-to-bubble interference increases, and at very high void fractions, if bubble

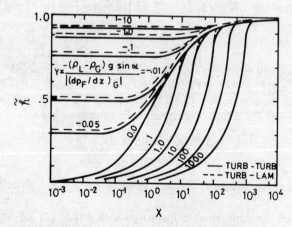

Figure 2.3.7 Equilibrium liquid level for stratified flow. (Taitel and Dukler 1976).

Table 2.3.1 Expressions for u_∞ and n for Use in [2.3.52]

Range	u_∞	n
$\mathrm{Re}_b < 2$	$\dfrac{2r_b^2(\rho_L - \rho_G)g}{9\mu_L}$	2
$2 < \mathrm{Re}_b < 4\,\mathrm{Ga}_L^{-2.2}$	$0.33g^{0.76}\left(\dfrac{\rho_L}{\mu_L}\right)^{0.52} r_b^{1.28}$	1.75
$\mathrm{Re}_b > 3\,\mathrm{Ga}_L^{-0.25}$	$1.5\left(\dfrac{g\sigma}{\rho_L}\right)^{0.25}$	1.5–2.0
$r_b > 2\left(\dfrac{\sigma}{g\rho_L}\right)^{1/2}$	$1.0\,(gr_b)^{1/2}$	0

flow still exists, a foam is obtained. For this case, j_{GL} would be expected to go to zero as $\epsilon_G \to 1$. A suitable functional form, suggested by Wallis (1969), is

$$j_{GL} = \epsilon_G u_{GU} = u_\infty \epsilon_G (1 - \epsilon_G)^n \qquad [2.3.52]$$

where n is an exponent in the range 0–2. The bubble rise velocity is influenced considerably by the cleanliness of the fluid, particularly at small values of r_b, the bubble radius. For clean fluids, the values of u_∞ and n can be derived from the expressions given in table 2.3.1, where the bubble Reynolds number Re_b and the liquid Galileo number Ga_L are defined by

$$\mathrm{Re}_b = \frac{2\rho_L u_\infty r_b}{\mu_L} \qquad [2.3.53]$$

$$\mathrm{Ga}_L = \frac{g\mu_L^4}{\rho_L \sigma^3} \qquad [2.3.54]$$

where ρ_L is the liquid density, μ_L is the liquid viscosity, σ is the surface tension, and g is the acceleration due to gravity.

Although the use of the one-dimensional flow method, employing [2.3.52] and table 2.3.1 in the calculation of j_{GL}, is recommended here for bubble flow, there are a number of disadvantages, as follows:

1. The functional relationship between j_{GU} and ϵ_G is such as to demand an iterative or graphic solution of [2.3.52] and [2.3.15]; see section 2.3.2.
2. To evaluate u_∞ from the expressions shown in table 2.3.1, the bubble radius r_b is required. Usually, this is not known although it can sometimes be estimated). An alternative general expression (which is not so accurate) is that of Zuber & Findlay (1965) for u_{GU} $(= j_{GL}/\epsilon_G)$ given as [2.3.29]. This expression implies, in contrast to [2.3.52], a constant value of u_{GU} independent of ϵ_G. Rouhani (1969) suggested the following modification of the Zuber-Findlay expression:

$$u_{GU} = 1.18[g\sigma(\rho_L - \rho_G)/\rho_L^2]^{0.25}(1 - x) \qquad [2.3.55]$$

where x is the quality. This expression gives $u_{GU} \to 0$ as $x \to 1$ (that is, as $\epsilon_G \to 1$). It has the additional advantage of not including ϵ_G, and its use avoids the need for an iterative or graphic solution.

3. The use of the one-dimensional method implies that the distribution is uniform (that is, $C_0 = 1.0$; see section 2.3.2). In practice, the void fraction is nonuniform in bubbly flow. Even in adiabatic flow, voids may be concentrated near the wall, particularly in vertical upward flow. In this case, $C_0 < 1$. Alternatively, in fully developed bubble flow, the voids may be peaked near the center of the tube, with the distribution factor C_0 having values in the range 1.1-1.2. We may thus take C_0 as unity for a first approximation to many practical situations, but the possibility of distribution effects should be borne in mind, and some calculations on the sensitivity of the calculated void fraction to these effects are usually worthwhile. An expression (Rouhani 1969) relating C_0 to quality, given as [2.3.28], fits data for steam-water flows at void fractions greater than 0.1. Alternative expression for C_0 in evaporating channels (including subcooled boiling) are given in section 2.3.5.5.

2.3.5.3 Plug Flow

In plug flow, the mean gas velocity is given by

$$u_G = C_0 U + u_S \qquad [2.3.56]$$

where $U = U_G + U_L$ is the total superficial velocity, u_S is the rise velocity of a single slug flow bubble in a static liquid, and C_0 is a distribution parameter. Nicklin et al. (1962) found that $C_0 = 1.2$ for slug flow. The void fraction is readily calculated from the expression:

$$\epsilon_G = \frac{U_G}{u_G} \qquad [2.3.57]$$

A generalized expression for u_S was developed by Wallis (1962b), who defined two dimensionless groups as follows:

$$Vi = \frac{[D^3 g(\rho_L - \rho_G)\rho_L]^{1/2}}{\mu_L} \qquad [2.3.58]$$

$$E\ddot{o} = \frac{gD^2(\rho_L - \rho_G)}{\sigma} \qquad [2.3.59]$$

where D is the tube diameter, ρ_L and ρ_G are the liquid- and gas-phase densities, μ_L is the liquid viscosity, g is the acceleration due to gravity, and σ is the surface tension. The viscosity number Vi accounts for the effect of viscosity, and the Eötvos number Eö accounts for the effect of surface tension. Wallis's expression for u_s is

$$\frac{u_S}{\sqrt{gD}} = 0.345 \, [1 - \exp{(0.029 \, Vi)}] \left(1 - \exp{\frac{3.37 - E\ddot{o}}{m}}\right) \qquad [2.3.60]$$

where m depends on the value of Vi as follows:

$$m = 10 \quad \text{for Vi} > 250$$

$$m = 69 \ \text{Vi}^{-0.35} \quad \text{for } 18 < N < 250 \qquad [2.3.61]$$

$$m = 25 \quad \text{for Vi} < 18$$

For low-viscosity fluids (e.g., water) and wide-bore tubes (wider than 1 cm, say), [2.3.60] reduces to

$$u_s = 0.345 \ \sqrt{gD} \qquad [2.3.62]$$

which is the expression for the slug flow bubble rise velocity obtainable from a potential flow solution.

2.3.5.4 Annular Flow

The analysis of annular flow is described in detail in section 2.2.4. For this case, the void fraction ϵ_G is given by $(1 - \epsilon_F - \epsilon_D)$. ϵ_F is the fraction of the channel cross section occupied by the liquid film and may be calculated from the triangular relationship (e.g., from the approximate form given by [2.2.119]). ϵ_d is the fraction of the cross section occupied by the core droplets and may be calculated approximately by assuming a homogeneous flow in the core (see [2.2.92]).

2.3.5.5 Void Fraction in Subcooled Boiling

The generally accepted picture of void generation in subcooled boiling is illustrated in figure 2.3.8. We may define a mean fluid enthalpy $h(z)$ that is a function of the

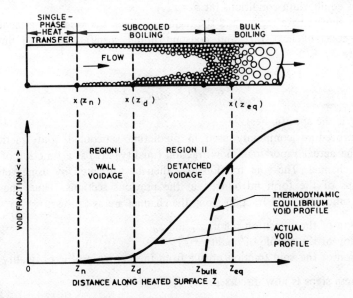

Figure 2.3.8 Void formation in subcooled boiling.

distance z along the channel. Correspondingly, a thermodynamic equilibrium quality $x_e(z)$ may also be defined according to the equation

$$x_e(z) = \frac{h(z) - h_L}{h_{GL}} \qquad [2.3.63]$$

where h_L is the liquid saturation enthalpy, and h_{GL} is the latent heat of vaporization. For a constant heat flux $\dot{q}$ and a circular channel,

$$h(z) = h_i + \frac{4\dot{q}z}{\dot{m}D} \qquad [2.3.64]$$

where h_i is the inlet liquid enthalpy, $\dot{m}$ is the mass flux through the channel, and D is the channel diameter.

At a distance z_n along the channel, nucleate boiling commences at the wall. Initially, the bubbles condense near the wall without detaching, and the void fraction associated with these attached bubbles is usually considered to be negligible. At a distance z_d, bubbles begin to detach from the wall and can flow along the channel with the liquid. These bubbles condense, but their rate of condensation is often slow enough to allow a substantial void fraction to be generated as shown. Ultimately, a situation is reached at which $h(z) = h_L$; that is, $x_e(z) = 0$. If thermodynamic equilibrium conditions had been maintained, then no voids would have been formed until this condition had been reached. The thermodynamic equilibrium void profile is sketched in figure 2.3.8; owing to the formation of subcooled voids, the void fraction is higher than that predicted from equilibrium, and, as a consequence, the liquid-phase temperature is *below* that expected for equilibrium. The distance at which the mean bulk enthalpy reaches the value of the saturated liquid enthalpy is denoted z_{bulk} in figure 2.3.8. Eventually, the flow approaches equilibrium conditions (at $z = z_{eq}$).

In the single-phase region and the region in which the voids are attached to the wall, for constant heat flux and constant liquid specific heat, the bulk liquid temperature T_L is

$$T_L = T_i + \frac{4\dot{q}z}{\dot{m}DC_{pL}} \qquad [2.3.65]$$

where C_{pL} is the specific heat.

The procedure commonly used in predicting subcooled void fraction is to estimate the actual vapor mass flow fraction (quality) $x(z)$ as a function of position along the channel. The void fraction may then be estimated by using void-quality relationships of the form introduced in the previous sections. Thus, the steps in predicting subcooled void fraction along the channel are as follows:

1. Prediction of the transition points z_n and z_d
2. Prediction of the profile of quality $x(z)$
3. Prediction of the void fraction profile from the known profile of quality

Each of these steps is now discussed.

Prediction of z_n and z_d

The prediction of z_n is of secondary interest in subcooled-void prediction, since it is normally assumed that the void fraction in the attached bubble region is negligible. However, the presence of nucleate boiling in the region between z_n and z_d leads to a considerable increase in the heat transfer coefficient in that zone. If the wall temperature (rather than the wall heat flux) is controlled, then this can obviously lead to a reduction in $z_d - z_n$. For constant heat flux conditions, the position of z_d is unaffected, according to the correlations suggested below, by the previous attached bubble zone.

To predict z_n, one may use the Davis & Anderson (1966) criterion to predict the wall superheat $(\Delta T_{sat})_n$ at the onset of nucleation:

$$(\Delta T_{sat})_n = \sqrt{\frac{8\,\sigma\dot{q}T_{sat}v_G}{k_L h_{GL}}} \qquad [2.3.66]$$

where T_{sat} is the saturation temperature, v_G is the specific volume of the vapor, and k_L is the thermal conductivity of the liquid.

Suppose that the heat transfer coefficient for single-phase heat transfer between the wall and the liquid is α_L; then it follows that the wall temperature T_W in the single-phase heat transfer region is given by

$$T_W = T_L + \frac{\dot{q}}{\alpha_L} \qquad [2.3.67]$$

The wall superheat ΔT_{sat} is thus given by

$$\Delta T_{sat} = T_W - T_{sat} = T_L + \frac{\dot{q}}{\alpha_L} - T_{sat} \qquad [2.3.68]$$

For constant heat flux, one may combine [2.3.65], [2.3.66], and [2.3.68] to obtain the following expression for the distance along the channel z_n at which nucleate boiling starts:

$$z_n = \frac{\dot{m}DC_{pL}}{4}\left(\sqrt{\frac{8\,\sigma T_{sat}v_G}{k_L h_{GL}\dot{q}}} - \frac{1}{\alpha_L} + \frac{T_{sat} - T_i}{\dot{q}}\right) \qquad [2.3.69]$$

Over the years, a number of relationships have been proposed for the conditions leading to departure of bubbles from the wall, i.e., the prediction of z_d. A survey of the alternative relationships is given by Lahey & Moody (1977); here, the correlation due to Saha & Zuber (1974) is recommended as representing a wide range of data for a variety of fluids. The results are represented in terms of a Stanton number, defined as

$$St = \frac{\dot{q}}{\dot{m}C_{pL}\left[T_{sat} - T_L(z_d)\right]} \qquad [2.3.70]$$

where $T_L(z_d)$ is the bulk liquid temperature (calculated from [2.3.65]) at z_d.

Saha & Zuber plotted St as a function of the Peclet number

$$Pe = \frac{\dot{m}DC_{pL}}{k_L} \qquad [2.3.71]$$

and obtained results as illustrated in figure 2.3.9. The data could be represented by the expression

$$St = \begin{cases} \dfrac{455}{Pe} & \text{for Pe} \leqslant 70000 \\[2ex] 0.0065 & \text{for Pe} > 70000 \end{cases} \qquad [2.3.72]$$

The thermodynamic equilibrium quality $x_e(z_d)$ at the bubble departure point is given by

$$x_e(z_d) = -\frac{C_{pL}[T_{\text{sat}} - T_L(z_d)]}{h_{GL}} \qquad [2.3.73]$$

and the criterion for bubble departure given by [2.3.72] can be expressed in terms of equilibrium quality as follows:

$$x_e(z_d) = \begin{cases} -0.0022 \dfrac{\dot{q}DC_{pL}}{h_{GL}k_L} & \text{for Pe} < 70000 \\[2ex] -154 \dfrac{\dot{q}}{\dot{m}h_{GL}} & \text{for Pe} > 70000 \end{cases} \qquad [2.3.74]$$

For constant heat flux, the distance to the point of bubble departure is given, from [2.3.63] and [2.3.64] as

$$z_d = \frac{\dot{m}D[h_{GL}x_e(z_d) + h_L - h_i]}{4\dot{q}} \qquad [2.3.75]$$

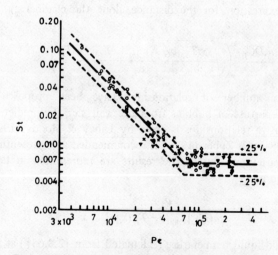

Figure 2.3.9 Stanton number versus Peclet for bubble detachment in subcooled boiling (Saha & Zuber 1974).

Calculation of Actual Flow Quality

The two main approaches that have been followed in the calculation of flow quality $x(z)$ are:

1. Mechanistic modeling. Here, an attempt is made to describe the processes of bubble formation and condensation. Surveys of such methods are given by Mayinger (1978) and Lahey & Moody (1977). Although these models are capable of qualitative description of the phenomena, they contain, of necessity, a number of empirical functions describing the rates of the various processes. There is no completely general mechanistic model, and, for this reason, these models are not described further here.

2. Profile-fit models. In these models, no attempt is made to describe the detailed local processes, and an arbitrary interpolation formula is used to fit the void profile from z_d onward. Here, the void-profile fit suggested by Levy (1966) is described. The main problem with the profile-fit technique is that it is, implicitly, based on an assumption of uniform heat flux. For example, if the heat flux were decreasing with length, then the void fraction might actually fall in the subcooled region, owing to a preponderance of vapor condensation over detached vapor generation.

Any model for the calculation of flow quality must satisfy the conditions that $x(z) = 0$ at $z = z_d$ and that $x(z)$ should approach $x_e(z)$ in the quality region, as indicated in figure 2.3.8. Levy (1966) suggested the following relationship, which meets these criteria and which appears to give good results when applied to the prediction of subcooled void fraction:

$$x(z) = x_e(z) - x_e(z_d) \exp\left[\frac{x_e(z)}{x_e(z_d)} - 1 \right] \qquad [2.3.76]$$

Calculation of Subcooled Void Fraction from Flow Quality

The Zuber & Findlay expression [2.3.27] for void fraction may be used to calculate void fraction from $x(z)$ as follows:

$$\epsilon_G = \frac{x(z)\rho_L}{C_0 \{x(z)\rho_L + [1 - x(z)]\rho_G\} + \rho_L \rho_G u_{GU}/\dot{m}} \qquad [2.3.77]$$

Values of the distribution constant C_0 and the mean relative velocity u_{GU} must be chosen to suit the void profiles found in subcooled boiling; as will be seen from figure 2.3.8, the subcooled voids tend to be concentrated near the wall of the channel, where the fluid velocity is low. In the limit, as void fraction approaches 0, $C_0 \to 0$. An expression that fits the appropriate trends for the variation of C_0 with quality is that of Dix (1971):

$$C_0 = \beta \left[1 + \left(\frac{1}{\beta} - 1 \right)^b \right] \qquad [2.3.78]$$

where β is the volumetric flow ratio, which is related to local flow quality by the expression

$$\beta = \frac{x(z)}{x(z) + [1 - x(z)]\rho_G/\rho_L} \tag{2.3.79}$$

where ρ_G and ρ_L are the vapor and liquid densities. The exponent b is related to the density ratio as follows:

$$b = \left(\frac{\rho_G}{\rho_L}\right)^{0.1} \tag{2.3.80}$$

If [2.3.78] is used in the calculation of subcooled voids, then one must select an expression for u_{GU} that is consistent in fitting empirical void data. Lahey & Moody (1977) suggest the following expression (which is similar to [2.3.29] but with a different constant):

$$u_{GU} = 2.9\left[\frac{(\rho_L - \rho_G)og}{\rho_L^2}\right]^{0.25} \tag{2.3.81}$$

Thus, to summarize, the recommended procedure for the calculation for subcooled void profile with uniform heat flux is to calculate $x_e(z_d)$ from [2.3.74], calculate the quality profile from [2.3.76], and calculate the void fraction profile from [2.3.77], using [2.3.78] and [2.3.81] for the estimation of C_0 and u_{GU}, respectively.

2.4 Wave Phenomena and Two-Phase Flow Instabilities

M. Ishii

2.4.1 INTERFACIAL WAVES AND INSTABILITIES

2.4.1.1 Mechanisms

There are several possible mechanisms for energy transfer across an interface. Based on the dominant hydrodynamic forces involved, the causes of the generation of surface waves can be classified as the inviscid flow pressure (Kelvin-Helmholtz instability), viscous shear (Jeffreys 1925), inviscid Reynolds stress (Miles 1957; Benjamin 1959), viscous Reynolds stress (Benjamin 1959), and turbulent fluctuations of pressure (Phillips 1957). Miles (1962) states that turbulent fluctuations of pressure and inviscid Reynolds stress are important for the generation of longer waves on deep water. On the other hand, for viscous fluids, wave formation is well predicted by the Kelvin-Helmholtz instability. Capillary and short gravity waves appear to be generated initially by the viscous Reynolds stress, which is also important for waves over a thin liquid film.

A large number of experimental and theoretical reports on interfacial waves can be found in the literature. These are reviewed by Hughes & Stewart (1961), Miles (1962), Levich (1962), Ostrach & Koestel (1965), and Brodkey (1967), among others.

2.4.1.2 Kelvin-Helmholtz Instability

The Kelvin-Helmholtz instability arises at the interface of two fluid layers of different densities ρ_1 and ρ_2 flowing horizontally with velocities u_1 and u_2. By use of a potential-flow approximation and a small-perturbation method, the stability of the interface has been analyzed mathematically in terms of the propagation velocity C of surface waves (Helmholtz 1868; Kelvin 1871; Lamb 1945; Chandrasekhar 1961; Yih 1969). The solution for the wave velocity is given by

$$C = \frac{\rho_2 u_2 + \rho_1 u_1}{\rho_2 + \rho_1} \pm \left[C_\infty^2 - \rho_1 \rho_2 \left(\frac{u_1 - u_2}{\rho_2 + \rho_1} \right)^2 \right]^{1/2} \qquad [2.4.1]$$

in which
$$C_\infty^2 = \frac{g}{k}\frac{\rho_2 - \rho_1}{\rho_2 + \rho_1} + \frac{\sigma k}{\rho_2 + \rho_1}$$

[2.4.2]

Where k is the wave number, σ is the surface tension, and the subscript 1 indicates the upper fluid. The displacement of the interface from the equilibrium configuration is proportional to $\exp[ik(z - Ct)]$. When the root in the expression for the wave velocity C has a nonzero imaginary part, then the interfacial disturbance can grow exponentially. Hence, the flow is unstable if

$$\frac{g}{k}\frac{\rho_2 - \rho_1}{\rho_2 + \rho_1} + \frac{\sigma k}{\rho_2 + \rho_1} < \rho_1\rho_2\left(\frac{u_1 - u_2}{\rho_2 + \rho_1}\right)^2$$

[2.4.3]

There are several important points to be recognized in this stability criterion. First, the viscosities of the fluids are neglected; therefore, the Reynolds number plays no role in this type of interfacial instability. The stability of the system then is governed by three effects—namely, the gravity force, surface-tension force, and relative motion. The relative-motion term reflects the effect of the pressure through the Bernoulli principle. The gravity term is stabilizing only if the upper fluid is lighter than the lower fluid ($\rho_2 > \rho_1$). The surface-tension force is always stabilizing, since the flat interface has the minimum surface area, and the surface-tension force acts to resist any deformation from the equilibrium configuration. On the other hand, relative motion between the fluids is destabilizing.

The propagation velocity C_∞ in the absence of the flows (or the left-hand side of the stability criterion) is a function of the wave number k. Therefore, as the wavelength $\lambda = 2\pi/k$ changes from zero to infinite, the wave velocity decreases to the minimum value and then increases. This minimum value of C_∞^2 is given by $C_{\infty c}^2 = 2[\sigma g(\rho_2 - \rho_1)/(\rho_2 + \rho_1)^2]^{1/2}$, which occurs at $k_c^2 = g(\rho_2 - \rho_1)/\sigma$. This corresponds to the critical wavelength of $\lambda_c = 2\pi/k_c$. Then the system is stable for small disturbances of all wavelengths if the relative velocity is sufficiently small to satisfy

$$(u_1 - u_2)^2 < \frac{2(\rho_1 + \rho_2)}{\rho_1\rho_2}\sqrt{\sigma g(\rho_2 - \rho_1)}$$

[2.4.4]

For a relative velocity larger than this limit, the system is only conditionally stable for a certain range of wavelengths. When the wavelength is large, the value of C_∞^2 in [2.4.2] is mainly determined by the gravity term. Conversely, if λ is sufficiently small, the capillary force governs the wave motion.

For a system with finite depths of h_1 and h_2, modified densities of $\rho_1' = \rho_1$ coth kh_1 and $\rho_2' = \rho_2$ coth kh_2 should be used in [2.4.1] and [2.4.2]. Furthermore, it is possible to develop a similar stability criterion based on the one-dimensional two-phase flow equations (Wallis 1969; Kocamustafaogullari 1971). It is noted (Miles 1959) that the Kelvin-Helmholtz instability theory tends to overpredict the critical relative velocity for the initial generation of surface waves, except in the case of highly viscous fluids. However, the Kelvin-Helmholtz instability mechanism is important in wave-propagation phenomena, particularly for flows in a confined channel (Kordyban 1977). Based on the analysis, Kelvin proposed the word "ripples" to describe waves having a wavelength of less than $\lambda_c = 2\pi\sqrt{\sigma/g(\rho_2 - \rho_1)}$.

2.4.1.3 Rayleigh-Taylor Instability

The Rayleigh-Taylor instability is the interfacial instability between two fluids of different densities that are stratified in the gravity field or accelerated normal to the interface. It is commonly observed that the boundary between two stratified fluid layers at rest is not stable if the upper-fluid density ρ_1 is larger than the lower-fluid density ρ_2. Since the Rayleigh-Taylor instability can lead to the destruction of the single common interface, it is important in the formation of bubbles or droplets. In particular, the critical wavelength predicted by the related stability analysis is one of the most significant length scales for two-phase flows.

The Rayleigh-Taylor instability can be considered as a special case of the Kelvin-Helmholtz instability with zero flows and $\rho_1 > \rho_2$. Hence the propagation velocity can be obtained from [2.4.1] by setting $u_1 = u_2 = 0$:

$$C^2 = \frac{g}{k} \frac{\rho_2 - \rho_1}{\rho_2 + \rho_1} + \frac{\sigma k}{\rho_2 + \rho_1} \qquad [2.4.5]$$

The system is unstable if the root of the propagation velocity has a nonzero imaginary part. Therefore, [2.4.5] shows that the gravitational force is destabilizing for $\rho_1 > \rho_2$, whereas the surface-tension force is stabilizing. There is a critical wavelength λ below which C^2 is always positive. This is given by $\lambda_c = 2\pi \sqrt{\sigma/g(\rho_1 - \rho_2)}$. If the wavelength of a disturbance is larger than the critical wavelength $(\lambda > \lambda_c)$, then C^2 becomes negative and the interface is unstable. For fluids that are unlimited laterally, the wavelength of the disturbance can be as large as desired; therefore such a system is always unstable. However, if the fluids are confined laterally, the maximum wavelength is limited to twice the system dimension. This implies that a system is stable if the lateral characteristic dimension is less than half the critical wavelength λ_c. For an air-water system, this characteristic dimension is 0.86 cm. A similar dimension can be obtained for fluids contained in a vertical cylinder by using polar coordinates in the stability analysis.

For an unstable system, any disturbance having a wavelength greater than λ_c can grow in time. However, the dominant waves are those having the maximum growth factor. Since the wave amplitude grows with $\exp(-ikCt)$, the predominant wavelength should be

$$\lambda_m = 2\pi \sqrt{\frac{3\sigma}{g(\rho_1 - \rho_2)}} \qquad [2.4.6]$$

These unstable waves can be observed as water droplets dripping from a wire in a rainy day, or condensed water droplets falling from a horizontal downward-facing surface. Quite regular waveforms and generation of bubbles due to the Rayleigh-Taylor instability can be observed in film boiling. Note that this instability is not limited to the gravitational field. Any interface, and fluids that are accelerated normal to the interface, can exhibit the same instability. In such a case the acceleration should replace the gravity field g in the analysis.

2.4.1.4 Waves Generated by Viscous Force

Jeffreys (1925) assumed that the pressure profile along a wave is a function of the relative velocity of the wind with respect to the wave and the slope of the wave profile. Then, considering the viscosity effect only in the perturbed flow, he obtained the minimum wind velocity that could sustain the wave motion. This can be given as

$$u_1 - u_2 = 3\left(\frac{\mu_2 g}{\beta \rho_1}\right)^{1/3} \qquad\qquad [2.4.7]$$

where β is the sheltering coefficient, which takes the approximate value 0.3. When this sheltering model of Jeffreys is applied to an air-water system, the minimum wind velocity is 107 cm/s. This value is considerably smaller than the 650 cm/s given by the Kelvin-Helmholtz instability analysis.

2.4.1.5 Nonlinear Waves and Entrainment

In a film-flow system, several hydrodynamic transitions leading to the entrainment of liquid film into gas flow are possible (Brodkey 1967; van Rossum 1959; Hewitt & Hall-Taylor 1970). When the gas velocity is increased, the initially stable film becomes wavy. The order of magnitude of the wavelength is $3\pi\sigma/\rho_G(u_G - u_L)^2$, and these capillary waves are known as ripples. As the relative velocity is increased further, the waves become irregular (van Rossum 1959; Hanratty & Hershman 1961). At a sufficiently high gas velocity, large-amplitude concentration waves appear. These are the roll waves studied by Hanratty & Hershman (1961), Hanratty & Engen (1957), and Chung & Murgatroyd (1965), among others. Approximately at the roll-wave transition or at a still higher gas velocity, the onset of entrainment can occur. However, entrainment may also occur in the absence of large-amplitude roll waves. Experimentally observed transitions of these types are shown in figure 2.4.1.

Reviews of experimental and analytic work on the inception of entrainment are given by Zuber (1962), Hewitt & Hall-Taylor (1970), Wallis (1969), Kutateladze (1972), and Ishii & Grolmes (1975). A wavy liquid film can be entrained into a gas flow in a number of different ways, and Zuber's work was also directed toward exploring possible entrainment mechanisms. By the use of simple models based on force balances, several similarity criteria are derived in Zuber (1962). The extensive review work of Hewitt & Hall-Taylor (1970) summarizes various experimental data and correlations. It is shown there that large discrepancies exist among the various correlations and among the experimental data. For example, the critical gas velocity predicted by the correlation of Chien & Ibele (1960) can be five times as high as the one given by Zhivaikin (1962) (figure 2.4.2). These results are not surprising, since several completely different methods of defining the experimental point of entrainment inception have been used. Experimental results based on sampling probes (Cousins et al. 1965; Steen & Wallis 1964; Wallis 1962; Yablonik & Khaimov 1972; Ueda & Tanaka 1973) show that the mass fraction entrained increases rather slowly with increasing gas velocity near the inception point. Furthermore, the

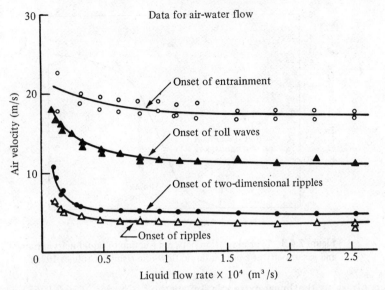

Figure 2.4.1 Several hydrodynamic transitions for film flow in a 30 × 13 cm duct (Wallis et al. 1964).

position of the entrainment versus flow curve can be easily shifted in the low-entrainment region by changing the inlet conditions or the position of the sampling probes. However, at a relatively high entrainment fraction, the amount of entrainment increases linearly with the gas velocity. Consequently, some investigators (Steen & Wallis 1964; Wallis 1962; Yablonik & Khaimov 1972) used a linear extrapolation from the high-entrainment-fraction region to the zero-entrainment condition (figure 2.4.3).

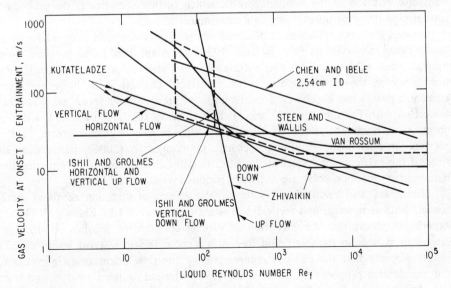

Figure 2.4.2 Comparison of various entrainment correlations for water-air flow (Ishii & Grolmes 1975).

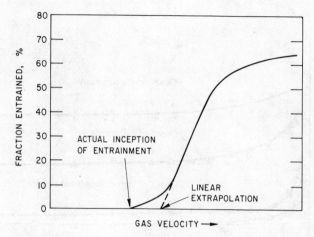

Figure 2.4.3   Typical relation between fraction of liquid mass entrained and gas velocity at constant liquid flow rate (Ishii & Grolmes 1975).

In contrast to the linear-extrapolation method, Cousins et al. (1965) and Ueda & Tanaka (1973) carefully followed the actual entrainment curve by measuring the liquid fraction entrained at lower gas velocities; thus, it can be expected that their data indicate smaller critical gas velocities than those based on linear extrapolation. The difference between the critical gas velocity at the actual onset and that based on linear extrapolation can be as high as 100%, even under controlled inlet conditions that effectively eliminate the entrainment caused by liquid injection into the system. It was also pointed out (Cousins et al. 1965; Wallis 1969; Yablonik & Khaimov 1972) that the measured critical gas velocity depends on the axial and transverse position of the sampling probe, which further complicates the procedure for defining the experimental onset of entrainment.

Several different entrainment detection methods and inception criteria have been used. Visual observations (van Rossum 1959; Zhivaikin 1962) and pressure drop measurements (Chien & Ibele 1960; Zhivaikin 1962) are useful means of identifying the change in the flow regime or in the interfacial characteristics. In general, two transition points can be observed in the curve of pressure drop versus gas flow, one associated with the transition of smooth film to wavy film and the other with the onset of entrainment. Both transitions are characterized by an increase in the pressure drop gradient, signifying a change in momentum transfer mechanism. In spite of the existence of several methods, difficulties encountered in determining the entrainment inception point are noted by various investigators.

There are also conflicting results on the effects of direction of flows—horizontal, vertical upward, and vertical downward (see figure 2.4.1). Zhivaikin's (1962) experiment shows that the inception of droplet entrainment depends on the flow direction, at least in the low liquid Reynolds number region, whereas Wallis' (1962) result indicates that the onset is independent of the flow orientation. In contrast, the correlations proposed by Kutateladze (1972) depend on the flow direction over the whole range of liquid Reynolds number. The critical gas velocity is given by

$$u_G = C \frac{\sigma}{\mu_L} \sqrt{\frac{\rho_L}{\rho_G}} N_\mu \, \mathrm{Re}_L^{-1/3} \qquad C = \begin{cases} 36 \text{ (horizontal)} \\ 54 \text{ (vertical)} \end{cases} \qquad [2.4.8]$$

where the viscosity number is defined as $N_\mu \equiv \mu_L/(\rho_L \sigma \sqrt{\sigma/g \, \Delta\rho})^{0.5}$ and the Reynolds number by $\mathrm{Re}_L \equiv \rho_L j_L D/\mu_L$. Here $\Delta\rho$ is the density difference, and j_L is the liquid volumetric flux.

In countercurrent film flow, the situation is further complicated by the flooding phenomenon. Near the flooding point, the interface is extremely unstable, and large-amplitude waves appear. These waves can be carried up by a gas flow or, in small diameter channels, extend to form a liquid bridge that can be entrained into a gas stream. The mechanism of entrainment can be quite different in this case from that occurring in a cocurrent gas-liquid flow.

Detailed experimental work using various liquids was carried out by van Rossum (1959). His data indicate that there are several different mechanisms of entrainment. He was apparently the first to realize that for sufficiently high liquid-film Reynolds numbers, the critical gas velocity approaches a constant value, which he correlated in terms of the liquid surface-tension parameter as

$$u_G \text{ (m/s)} \approx 0.25\sigma \text{ (dyne/cm)} \qquad [2.4.9]$$

His empirical rule, however, has a dimensional form, and its general use is questionable, particularly for liquid metals (Ishii & Grolmes 1975). At smaller Reynolds numbers, the experimental data appear to converge to a single curve when they are plotted in the dimensionless plane of liquid Reynolds number versus $u_G \mu_L/\sigma$, or in the plane of Weber number versus $u_G \mu_L/\sigma$, which van Rossum presented as a graphic correlation (figure 2.4.4.).

The experimental results of Zhivaikin (1962) for a cocurrent downward flow were expressed as three correlations in terms of the liquid Reynolds number. The generality of these correlations is also questionable, owing to their dimensional form. Steen & Wallis (1964) examined the effects of inlet conditions on the onset of entrainment, as well as the effects of the tube diameter. The liquid properties and the gas density have been varied in their experiment, however, because of their liquid injection method, the experiment tends to produce high inlet entrainment inception. The correlation proposed by Steen & Wallis is independent of the liquid Reynolds number, but it includes the density ratio of the gas and the liquid. It is given in terms of the gas volumetric flux as

$$j_G = 2.46 \times 10^{-4} \frac{\sigma}{\mu_G} \left(\frac{\rho_L}{\rho_G}\right)^{1/2} \qquad [2.4.10]$$

In view of the experimental observations of Zhivaikin (1962) and van Rossum (1959), it can be concluded that the correlation of Steen & Wallis (1964) is applicable only at relatively large Reynolds number. Furthermore, because of the method of defining the inception point, the correlation tends to give a larger gas velocity than the actual critical velocity. It would also appear that the correlation is not valid for liquid metals.

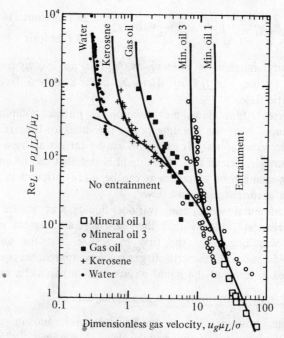

Figure 2.4.4 Correlation for onset of entrainment (van Rossum 1959).

A wavy liquid film can be entrained into a gas flow in a number of different ways. Hydrodynamic and surface-tension forces govern the motion and deformation of the wave crests. Under certain conditions, these forces lead to an extreme deformation of the interface, which results in breakup of a portion of a wave into several droplets. The forces acting on the wave crests depend on the flow pattern around them as well as on the shape of the interface. In general, the following five basic types of entrainment mechanisms, which are shown in figure 2.4.5, can be considered.

1. Shearing off of the tops of roll waves by gas flow
2. Undercutting of the liquid film by gas flow
3. Bursting of gas bubbles
4. Impingement of large drops
5. Disintegration of liquid bulge by gas flow in countercurrent situations

The last mechanism is strongly related to the flooding and flow-reversal phenomena discussed in other chapters.

For most practical applications, the inception of entrainment in cocurrent flows via the first and second mechanisms is important. A detailed entrainment-inception model was developed by Ishii & Grolmes (1975) by considering these two mechanisms and several different regimes based on the liquid Reynolds number $Re_L = \rho_L j_L D/\mu_L$. The onset of entrainment occurs when the gas velocity exceeds the critical velocity. By considering the inception of entrainment due to the shearing off of the roll wave crest, a criterion was obtained. For the range in which the film Reynolds number exceeds about 1500–1750, the film flow becomes completely rough-turbulent. In this case, the critical gas flux j_G becomes independent of the liquid Reynolds number and is given by

$$\frac{\mu_L j_G}{\sigma}\sqrt{\frac{\rho_G}{\rho_L}} = \begin{cases} N_\mu^{0.8} & \text{for } N_\mu < \frac{1}{15},\ \text{Re}_L > 1635 \\ 0.115 & \text{for } N_\mu > \frac{1}{15},\ \text{Re}_L > 1635 \end{cases} \qquad [2.4.11]$$

where the viscosity number N_μ is defined as before. For Reynolds numbers below 1635, the flow within the film becomes important, and the critical gas flux is given as a function of Re_L:

$$\frac{\mu_L j_G}{\sigma}\sqrt{\frac{\rho_G}{\rho_L}} = \begin{cases} 11.78\, N_\mu^{0.8}\ \text{Re}_L^{-1/3} & \text{for } N_\mu < \frac{1}{15} \\ 1.35\ \text{Re}_L^{-1/3} & \text{for } N_\mu > \frac{1}{15} \end{cases} \qquad [2.4.12]$$

A comparison of these results with various experimental data is shown in figure 2.4.6.

Below Reynolds numbers of 160 (for horizontal flow) and 2 (for vertical flow), an inception criterion based on the wave-undercut mechanism becomes preferable. A Weber number criterion for wave disintegration is used to develop the correlation,

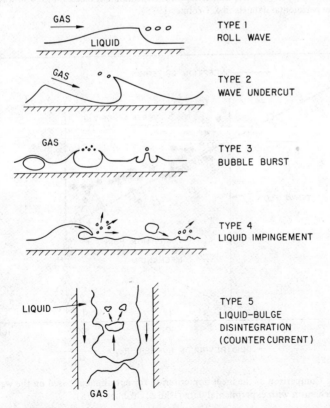

Figure 2.4.5 Various mechanisms of entrainment (Ishii & Grolmes 1975).

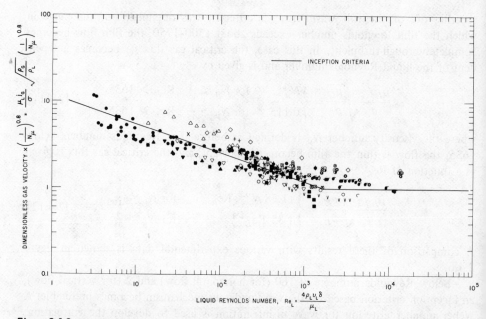

Figure 2.4.6 Comparison of the inception criterion for entrainment based on the roll-wave breakup mechanism with experimental data (Ishii & Grolmes 1975).

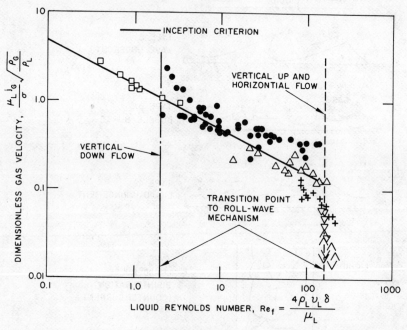

Figure 2.4.7 Comparison of the inception criterion for entrainment based on the wave-undercut mechanism with experimental data (Ishii & Grolmes 1975).

which is given by

$$\frac{\mu_L j_G}{\sigma} \sqrt{\frac{\rho_G}{\rho_L}} = 1.5 \, Re_L^{-1/2} \qquad [2.4.13]$$

A comparison of this inception criterion with various experimental data is given in figure 2.4.7.

There is a minimum Reynolds number below which no entrainment is possible. For full dynamic interaction between the turbulent gas core and film, the wave should penetrate through the gas boundary layer. The amount of energy transferred between phases can be characterized by the ratio of the film thickness to the gas boundary-layer thickness. From this, the following minimum Reynolds number is obtained:

$$(Re_L)_{min} = 155 \left(\frac{\rho_L}{\rho_G}\right)^{0.75} \left(\frac{\mu_G}{\mu_L}\right)^{1.5} \qquad [2.4.14]$$

2.4.2 CONCENTRATION WAVES AND SHOCKS

The ability to predict the unsteady flow and transient behavior of a two-phase flow system is of considerable importance. Many transient processes are governed by wave propagation. Therefore, wave theory is a powerful technique for understanding and analyzing various unsteady or instability phenomena. In addition to interfacial waves, two completely different wave propagation mechanisms are essential to two-phase flow analyses. These are concentration waves and dynamic or pressure waves. Pressure waves and related critical flows are discussed in detail in section 2.5.

The theory of concentration waves was developed by Lighthill & Whitham (1955) for analyzing flood waves and traffic flows as a kinematic wave theory, and by Kynch (1952) for the problem of sedimentation as a continuity wave theory. As explained by Lighthill & Whitham, concentration waves occur when there is a functional relation between the flux and the concentration. The characteristics of the waves, then, can be predicted directly from the continuity equation. Concentration waves have only one velocity, in contrast to dynamic waves, which can propagate in both directions. Since the concentration wave velocity is a function of the local flux, it is possible that successive waves may overtake other waves and coalesce. When this happens, a kinematic or concentration shock wave is formed. At a shock front a very steep concentration gradient is observed.

The concentration wave velocity can be derived from the one-dimensional form of the phase continuity equations. These are given by

$$\frac{\partial \epsilon_k \rho_k}{\partial t} + \frac{\partial}{\partial z} (\epsilon_k \rho_k u_k) = \Gamma_k \qquad [2.4.15]$$

where the subscript k stands for either the vapor phase ($k = G$) or the liquid phase ($k = L$), and ϵ, ρ, u, and Γ denote the void fraction, phase density, phase velocity, and mass source due to phase changes, respectively. By introducing the concept of the drift velocity (Zuber et al. 1967) these two continuity equations can be transformed into the flux and void propagation equations. First the total flux is defined as $j \equiv \epsilon u_G + (1 - \epsilon)u_L$, and the drift velocity as $u_{Gj} \equiv u_G - j$. Then, by eliminating the time deviation between the two continuity equations, the flux equation becomes

$$\frac{\partial j}{\partial z} = \frac{\Gamma_G}{\rho_G} \frac{\rho_L - \rho_G}{\rho_L}$$ [2.4.16]

where, for simplicity, each phase has been considered as incompressible. A detailed analysis without this assumption can be found elsewhere (Zuber et al. 1967). Equation [2.4.16] describes the center of volume velocity. On the other hand, if the vapor drift velocity u_{Gj} is a function only of j and ϵ, as

$$u_{Gj} = u_{Gj}(j, \epsilon)$$ [2.4.17]

then the vapor continuity equation can be transformed into the void propagation equation:

$$\frac{\partial \epsilon}{\partial t} + C_k \frac{\partial \epsilon}{\partial z} = \frac{\Gamma_G}{\rho_G} \left[1 - \epsilon \left(1 + \frac{\partial u_{Gj}}{\partial j} \right) \frac{\rho_L - \rho_G}{\rho_L} \right]$$ [2.4.18]

Here C_k is the concentration wave velocity, given by

$$C_k \equiv j + u_{Gj} + \epsilon \frac{\partial u_{Gj}}{\partial \epsilon}$$ [2.4.19]

The right-hand side of [2.4.18] is the source term due to phase change. The left-hand side of the void propagation equation shows that any small change in the void fraction will propagate with velocity C_k. Furthermore, in the absence of phase change, that is, for $\Gamma_G = 0$, the void fraction ϵ is constant on waves that propagate with velocity C_k. A comparison of predictions based on concentration wave theory with experimental data is shown in figure 2.4.8.

The basis of the concentration wave theory in two-phase flow is the constitutive assumption given by [2.4.17]. Recall that the drift velocity is the vapor velocity with respect to the volume center of the mixture. Therefore, from the definition, u_{Gj} is related to the relative velocity between phases by $u_{Gj} = (1 - \epsilon)u_r$, where $u_r = u_G - u_L$. Hence the constitutive equation [2.4.17] specifies the relative motion between phases algebraically. This assumption is based on the concept of the drift-flux model (Zuber 1967; Ishii 1975) in which the mixture is considered as a whole, rather than as two separate phases. The formulation of the drift-flux model is simpler than the more rigorous two-fluid model (Vernier & Delhaye 1968; Bouré & Réocruex 1972; Ishii 1975) based on two separate momentum equations. However, because of its simplicity and its applicability to a wide range of two-phase flow problems of practical interest, the drift-flux model is of considerable importance. Since the rates of momentum transfer at the interfaces depend on the structure of two-phase flows, the constitutive relation [2.4.17] for the drift velocity is a function of the flow regimes. The correlation for u_{Gj} for bubbly and slug flows has been studied by Zuber & Findlay (1965) and Zuber et al (1967). A more extended study (Ishii 1977) covering various two-phase flow regimes is also available. Some of the results are:

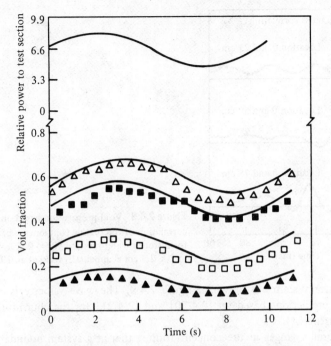

Figure 2.4.8 Comparison of calculated and measured void fraction at various axial locations under oscillating heat input condition (Zuber et al. 1967).

Distorted bubble:

$$u_{Gj} = (C_0 - 1)j + \sqrt{2} \left(\frac{\sigma g \Delta \rho}{\rho_L^2} \right)^{1/4} (1 - \epsilon)^{1.75}$$

Churn-turbulent:

$$u_{Gj} = (C_0 - 1)j + \sqrt{2} \left(\frac{\sigma g \Delta \rho}{\rho_L^2} \right)^{1/4} \qquad [2.4.20]$$

Annular:

$$u_{Gj} = \frac{1 - \epsilon}{\epsilon + 4\sqrt{\rho_G/\rho_L}} \left[j + \sqrt{\frac{\Delta \rho \, gD(1 - \epsilon)}{0.015 \, \rho_L}} \right]$$

where the distribution parameter for an adiabatic flow is given by $C_0 = 1.2 - 0.2\sqrt{\rho_G/\rho_L}$, $\Delta\rho$ is the density difference, and D is the hydraulic diameter. By substituting the above relation into [2.4.19], the concentration wave velocity can be obtained. For example, in the churn-turbulent flow regime,

$$C_k = \left(1.2 - 0.2\sqrt{\frac{\rho_G}{\rho_L}} \right)j + \sqrt{2} \left(\frac{\sigma g \Delta \rho}{\rho_L^2} \right)^{1/4} \qquad [2.4.21]$$

The volumetric concentration waves observed by Miyazaki et al. (1973) in the

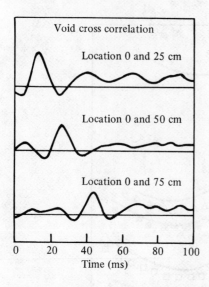

Figure 2.4.9 Void propagation based on cross correlation of fluctuating components of void fraction for nitrogen-water mixture at $\epsilon = 0.5$, $p = 0.175$ MPa in 2×2.5 cm channel (Miyazaki et al. 1973).

nitrogen-water system are shown in figure 2.4.9. The wave velocity is compared to theoretical predictions based on [2.4.20] and [2.4.21] for the churn-turbulent flow regime in figure 2.4.10.

In general, changes in the concentration, either at a system boundary or within the system, are propagated by concentration waves. Two singularities are of practical importance. One is zero propagation velocity, $C_k = 0$, and the other is the formation of concentration shock waves. When $C_k = 0$, disturbances or changes in the concentration cannot be propagated to other parts of the flow. In other words, the point at which $C_k = 0$ acts as an isolating boundary in terms of the information carried by the concentration waves. Therefore, it may be called a *kinematic choking,* paralleling the standard choking due to zero velocity of dynamic waves. Physically, kinematic choking should correspond to changes of flow regimes.

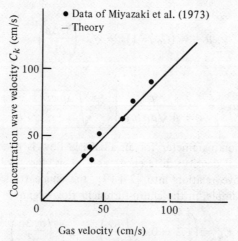

Figure 2.4.10 Prediction of concentration wave velocity based on churn-turbulent flow model.

The phenomenon of concentration shocks has been discussed in detail by various authors (Lighthill & Whitham 1955; Zuber et al. 1967; Wallis 1969; Lackme 1973; Ishii 1975; Condiff & Epstein 1976). Propagating concentration waves can develop discontinuities as slower waves are overtaken by faster-moving waves. For example, in distorted bubbly flow, the wave velocity is given by

$$C_k = \left(1.2 - 0.2\sqrt{\frac{\rho_G}{\rho_L}}\right) j + \sqrt{2}\,(1 - 2.75\epsilon)(1 - \epsilon)^{0.75} \left(\frac{\sigma g \Delta\rho}{\rho_L^2}\right)^{1/4}$$

$$[2.4.22]$$

This shows that the wave velocity decreases with increasing void fraction at low concentrations. Then lower-concentration waves are propagated faster than waves with higher concentrations, and the waves tend to coalesce and form a shock wave. The concentration shock is stable when the waves move in the direction of the shock at both sides of the shock. From the continuity relation, the shock velocity is given by $C_s = (j_G^+ - j_G^-)/(\epsilon^+ - \epsilon^-)$ if there is no phase change within the shock and the phase densities are continuous. (j_G is the vapor volumetric flux, defined as $j_G \equiv \epsilon u_G$, and the $+$ and $-$ denote the front and back of the shock.) The shock velocity can also be expressed in terms of j and u_{Gj} as

$$C_s = j + \frac{\epsilon^+ u_{Gj}^+ - \epsilon^- u_{Gj}^-}{\epsilon^+ - \epsilon^-}$$

$$[2.4.23]$$

Concentration shocks can be observed in bubbly flows (a glass of beer, for example), flood flows, sedimentation, and highway traffic flows. The experimental data of Lackme (1973), shown in figure 2.4.11, clearly indicate two possible void fraction values at the same liquid and vapor volumetric fluxes and the existence of the concentration shock wave.

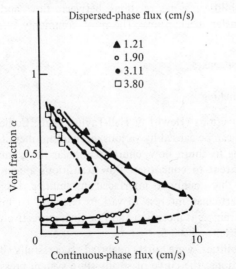

Figure 2.4.11 Void fraction versus flow rates for nitrogen (kerosene-heptane) in 3.2-cm-ID tube (Lackme 1973).

The theory of concentration waves and shocks is quite important in the analyses of bubble columns, fluidization, flow-regime transitions, and density wave instabilities.

2.4.3 TWO–PHASE FLOW INSTABILITIES

2.4.3.1 Introduction

Two-phase flow instabilities may result in operational and safety problems involving various components of interest to power, heat transfer, and process systems. Not only can these instabilities degrade the performance of the system, but sustained oscillations may result in mechanical vibrations, premature burnout, and control problems, which can be destructive. Systems and components that can be affected by two-phase flow instabilities include nuclear reactors, steam generators, liquid rocket engines, heat exchangers, cryogenic equipment, boilers, evaporators, and various chemical process units. A considerable amount of analytic and experimental research on flow instabilities has been carried out; various references can be found in the reviews by Bouré et al. (1973), Bergles (1976), Ishii (1976), Hsu & Graham (1976), and Yadigaroglu & Chan (1979).

2.4.3.2 Static Two-Phase Flow Instabilities

Two-phase flow instabilities can be divided into two main categories: static instabilities and dynamic (or oscillatory) instabilities. Static instabilities are related to discontinuous changes in steady-state operational conditions. In other words, a steady-state flow becomes unstable under certain conditions, and it translates to another quite different operational condition. The causes of static flow instabilities are interfacial instabilities, some relations between flow and pressure drop, and changes in heat transfer mechanisms. The most commonly observed static instabilities are

1. Flow-regime transitions
2. Flow excursions
3. Burnout and quenching

Flow-regime transitions (Hewitt & Hall-Taylor 1970; Collier 1972; Wallis 1969; Govier & Aziz 1972) can be caused by various mechanisms mentioned previously. Bubbly to slug flow, slug to churn flow, churn to annular flow, annular to drop-annular flow, and countercurrent to concurrent flow transitions are important examples of flow-regime changes due mainly to interfacial instabilities. The last two flow-regime transitions are of particular interest to various chemical engineering fields and are known as droplet-entrainment inception and flooding, respectively. These are discussed in detail in sections 2.1.3 and 2.3.5.

Excursive instabilities were first analyzed successfully by Ledinegg (1938). Under certain conditions, the curve of steady-state system pressure drop versus flow has a negative slope (see figure 2.4.12); hence, since the flow rate is not a single-valued function of the pressure drop, a flow excursion may occur. In his

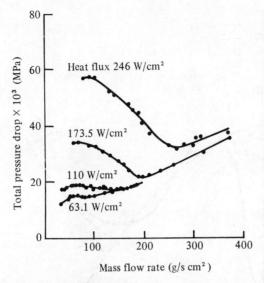

Figure 2.4.12 Pressure drop–flow rate curve for water at 3.45 MPa in 1-cm tube with inlet temperature of 124°C (Bergles et al. 1967).

analysis, Ledinegg assumed that the heat flux was uniform, but later other investigators (Chilton 1957; Profos 1947) extended this criterion to more general cases. It is also known that flow-excursion instability can induce cyclic oscillations called pressure drop oscillations (Maulbetch & Griffith 1965; Stenning & Veziroglu 1965). The excursive stability criterion can be obtained from the steady-state pump characteristic $\Delta p_{ext} = f_1(u)$ and the internal pressure drop characteristic $\Delta p_{int} = f_2(u)$. The difference between Δp_{ext} and Δp_{int} results in a transition. For a stable transition,

$$\frac{\partial \Delta p_{ext}}{\partial u} < \frac{\partial \Delta p_{int}}{\partial u} \qquad [2.4.24]$$

In general, the steady-state pressure drop in a heated duct with boiling can be expressed as

$$\Delta p_{int} = \Delta p_i + \Delta p_{con} + \Delta p_F + \Delta p_g + \Delta p_e \qquad [2.4.25]$$

where the right-hand terms are the inlet, convective-acceleration, frictional, gravitational, and exit pressure drops, respectively. Because of the convective acceleration due to boiling, the decrease in the inlet velocity does not necessarily correspond to the decrease in the channel pressure drop. In general, the channel pressure drop has approximately cubic dependence upon the inlet flow at fixed heat input. Therefore, it is possible that the curve of Δp_{int} versus u has a negative slope, as shown in figure 2.4.13. The negative slope tends to develop for a flow with large inlet subcooling (Hayama 1963). In figure 2.4.13, the pump characteristic curve is also shown. The intersections of these two curves determine the steady-state operational condition.

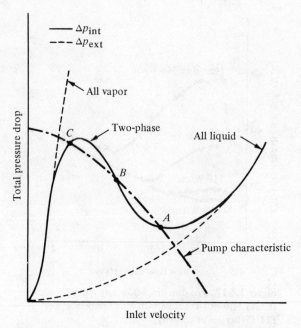

Figure 2.4.13   Two-phase pressure drop characteristic and excursion flow instability.

In figure 2.4.13, there are three intersections, denoted by A, B, and C. The excursive instability criterion given by [2.4.24] indicates that operation at point B is unstable and the steady state cannot be maintained, whereas operation at point A or C is stable. This can be explained as follows. If at point A or C the flow is increased slightly by a small perturbation, internal demand for pressure drop increases above the supply by the delivery system. Therefore, the flow decelerates and returns to the original value. Similarly, if at point A or C the flow is decreased, the pressure drop supply exceeds the demand and accelerates the flow to the original condition. On the other hand, at point B, a slight increase in the flow gives an excess supply of pressure drop from the delivery system over the internal demand of the heated duct. This leads to further acceleration of the flow until a completely new operating condition is reached at A. Conversely, if the flow at B is decreased slightly, more deceleration takes place due to insufficient pressure drop supply, until point C is reached.

A detailed study of channel pressure drop characteristics indicates that increasing the exit pressure drop is destabilizing. On the other hand, increasing the inlet flow resistance or the system pressure has a stabilizing effect. Furthermore, by steepening the pump characteristic curve sufficiently, stable operation in the negative slope region is made possible.

Burnout and quenching can be considered as flow-regime transitions due to changes in heat transfer mechanism. When a hot surface is no longer in direct contact with the liquid phase, the heat transfer is very much reduced from that of nucleate boiling or liquid-film evaporation. Burnout (Hewitt & Hall-Taylor 1970; Collier 1972;

Tong 1965) in heat-generating systems such as nuclear reactors is accompanied by a sudden rise in wall temperature, which can be destructive. A means of quenching or rewetting hot, dry surfaces is essential in emergency core-cooling systems in light-water nuclear reactors, to protect the cladding surface (Bennett et al., 1966; Yamanouchi 1968; Duffey & Porthouse 1973). When the temperature of the heating surface exceeds the so-called Leidenfrost temperature, the vapor generated by the change of phase forms a continuous film between the liquid and the solid. Unless the hot-wall temperature is reduced, rewetting cannot occur. Therefore the burnout and rewetting fronts are the flow-regime transition points that are governed by heat transfer mechanisms. These subjects are discussed in detail in sections 6.4 and 6.5.

2.4.3.3 Dynamic Two-Phase Flow Instabilities

Dynamic instabilities are rather complicated phenomena that arise from four different mechanisms:

1. Concentration wave (density wave) propagation
2. Pressure wave propagation
3. Thermodynamic nonequilibrium
4. Flow-regime change

The most common oscillations encountered in heated channels are low-frequency, i.e., density wave, oscillations. There is considerable evidence that some relationship exists between the residence time of the particle and the period of the oscillations; thus, several analyses have been formulated to consider the propagation of density waves and the attendant time-lag effects. Inlet flow perturbations in a heated channel result in delayed mixture-density changes throughout the channel. These disturbances of the mixture density affect the local mixture velocity and the total pressure drop in a channel. Under certain conditions, the inlet flow perturbations and the internal pressure drop perturbations satisfy a self-exciting relation such that sustained oscillations with considerable amplitudes appear in the system.

It was found both experimentally (Yadigaroglu & Bergles 1972) and analytically (Ishii & Zuber 1970) that several modes of density wave instability are possible. The most commonly encountered mode is the lowest-order instability (lowest frequency); however, higher-order instabilities or compound instabilities, which produce beat effects, are possible. In view of its great importance in practical applications, density wave instability will be discussed in more detail later.

Although high-frequency oscillations, which are associated with the propagation of pressure waves, have been observed in some experiments (Thurston et al. 1966), they may be of less importance for practical applications than low-frequency oscillations. The period of the oscillations is of the same order of magnitude as the residence time of the acoustic waves. These high-frequency oscillations have been encountered in subcooled boiling (Bergles et al. 1967); however, they are much more common in combustion processes. High-frequency instabilities in rocket-engine combustion systems are called "screaming," and they have been studied quite extensively (Crocco & Cheng 1956). In general, acoustic instabilities in a boiling channel do not involve destructive pressure or flow fluctuations; however, prolonged

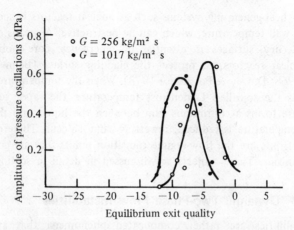

Figure 2.4.14 Amplitude of acoustic oscillations in 2.1-cm-diameter, 154-cm-long pipe at $p = 3.45$ MPa and inlet temperature of 149°C (Bergles et al. 1967).

operation under high-frequency pressure oscillations is not recommended. This is because, as observed by Bergles et al. (1967), pressure oscillations of relatively high frequency (10–100 Hz) under highly subcooled conditions can develop considerable amplitudes (see figure 2.4.14). The amplitude of the oscillations diminishes to an insignificant level in the bulk-boiling region.

The instabilities observed by Jeglic & Grace (1964) in experiments conducted with water at low pressures flowing through a smooth pipe were apparently due to thermodynamic nonequilibrium. Under these conditions and because of poor nucleation, the liquid can become highly superheated. However, once a bubble is nucleated, it grows explosively (because of the high liquid superheat), ejecting the liquid from the duct while interrupting the inlet flow. After the liquid is ejected from the duct, the pressure decreases, new liquid enters and becomes superheated, and the process repeats itself. Improving the nucleation characteristics of the heating surface should reduce the amplitude of the oscillations or stabilize the flow.

Chugging instabilities can occur for liquid metals at low pressures due to the reentry of liquid into voided channels (Singer & Holtz 1970; Grolmes & Fauske 1970). In this case, the instabilities are caused by a large ratio of liquid to vapor density and rapid evaporation from thin liquid films at the lower end of the heated section. When the liquid enters the voided channel, the high evaporation leads to a higher vapor velocity and eventual pressurization. Thus, the level of the liquid at the bottom is pushed down, reducing the evaporation rate and the vapor velocity. This depressurizes the channel, the liquid reenters from the bottom again, and the process is repeated.

Geysering instabilities occur mainly in the vertical channel of a natural-circulation loop or in a closed-end tube (Griffith 1962; Chexal & Bergles 1972). The main cause of these instabilities is the reduced total pressure drop for two-phase flow due to smaller hydrostatic head than the single phase liquid flow. As soon as sufficient vapor is generated in the channel such that the pressure drop is smaller than the liquid head, expulsion of the mixture and reentry of the liquid follow. The subcooled liquid state is restored until the boiling occurs again and the cycle is repeated.

The disturbances created by flow-regime changes can also produce oscillatory behavior. Wallis & Heasley (1961) analyzed slug flow in a long, large-diameter riser and concluded that cyclic variation of vapor content could produce periodic fluctuations in loop flow rate.

So-called thermal oscillations (Stenning & Veziroglu 1965) are associated with instability of the liquid film and are accompanied by large fluctuations in wall temperature in a constant-heat-flux system. As the heat transfer coefficient of the two-phase regime oscillates between the wet- and dry-wall conditions, the wall superheat fluctuates accordingly to accommodate the constant heat generation in the wall. In general, thermal oscillations are triggered by other hydrodynamic instabilities, such as density wave oscillations or liquid-film instabilities. The observed periods of thermal oscillations are generally quite long; however, the amplitudes of temperature waves can be very high. For example, Stenning & Veziroglu (1965) observed wall-temperature oscillations of 80°C with a period of 80 s.

2.4.3.4 Density Wave Instability

Numerous experiments (Levy & Beckjord 1959; Quandt 1961; Solberg 1966; Carver 1968; Yadigaroglu & Bergles 1972; Saha et al. 1976; Veziroglu et al. 1976; Kakaç 1976) have been concerned with density wave instabilities. It was found that the period of the oscillations is closely related to the residence time of the concentration wave (density wave), so that the product of the frequency and the residence time remains approximately constant (see figure 2.4.15). The "density" in density

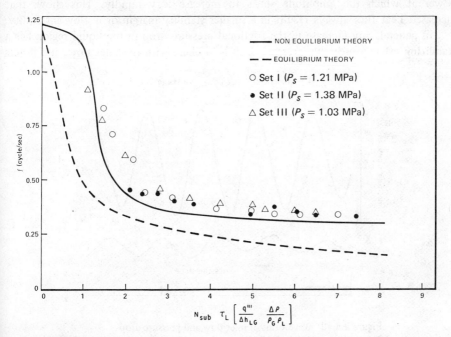

Figure 2.4.15 Relation between frequency and nondimensional residence time in the liquid region (Saha et al. 1976).

wave instability is the mixture density, and the wave propagation of concern is that of the void fraction and not that of the compressible pressure wave. In a two-phase flow system the mixture density can change, even though each constituent phase is incompressible, because the mixture density is also a function of the void fraction.

Density wave instability is caused by the finite time necessary (1) for the enthalpy wave to propagate in the subcooled-liquid region and (2) for the density or void fraction wave to propagate in the mixture region. These finite propagation times induce time-lag effects and phase-angle shifts between the channel pressure drop and the inlet flow, leading to self-exciting oscillations.

The time lag observed during unstable operation (Saha et al. 1976) is shown in figure 2.4.16. Because the period of the oscillation is approximately twice the residence time of the fluid particle in the channel (Ishii & Zuber 1970), these are low-frequency oscillations having a period of the order of seconds.

It was also observed experimentally that density wave instabilities are strongly related to the response characteristics of the total channel pressure drop and are, therefore, not caused by local phenomena. Consequently, several important parametric observations have been made on the effects of heat flux, inlet and exit flow restrictions, single- and two-phase frictional pressure drop, subcooling, inlet flow, and system pressure.

For fixed geometry, system pressure, inlet flow, and inlet subcooling, density wave oscillations can be started by increasing the test-section power (heat flux). Typical traces of inlet flow with increasing power (Saha et al. 1976) are shown in figures 2.4.17 and 2.4.18. They clearly show that the fluctuation of the flow increases with increasing power. The power at the onset of flow oscillation is the power at which the amplitude starts to increase very rapidly. This shows that increased heat flux always results in a smaller stability margin or in flow instability.

In general, any increase in the frictional pressure drop in the liquid region has a stabilizing effect, since this pressure drop is in phase with the inlet flow, and it acts

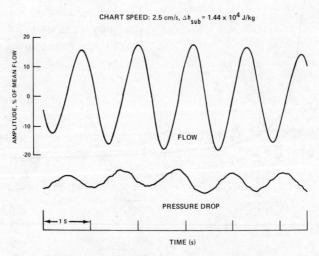

Figure 2.4.16 Waveforms of inlet-flow and pressure drop fluctuations (Saha et al. 1976).

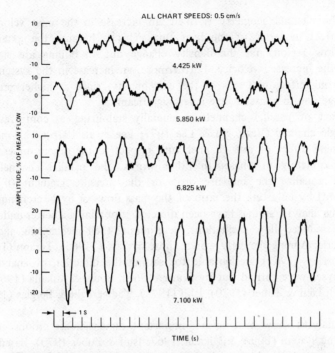

Figure 2.4.17 Inlet-flow trace with increasing power for Freon-113 system (Saha et al. 1976).

to damp the flow fluctuations. Therefore, an inlet flow restriction can be used to stabilize an unstable flow. On the other hand, an increase in two-phase region pressure drop has a destabilizing effect, since the pressure drop is out of phase with the inlet flow, owing to the finite wave-propagation time. Thus, an exit flow restriction is a strong destabilizing factor.

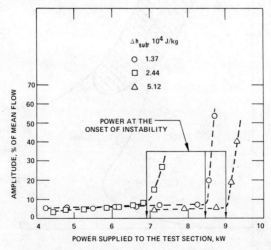

Figure 2.4.18 Point of inception of density wave oscillation (Saha et al. 1976).

When the channel geometry is fixed, an increase in the inlet velocity has a stabilizing effect in terms of the heat flux. This is because the extent of the two-phase flow region and the density change due to boiling are significantly reduced by the increased velocity. Furthermore, an increase in the system pressure has a stabilizing effect in terms of the exit quality, since at higher pressure the density change due to phase change is less significant.

The effect of parallel channels is generally stabilizing, as compared with an identical single channel (Veziroglu & Lee 1971; Lee et al. 1976). This may be due to the damping effect of one channel with respect to the others, unless they are oscillating completely in phase. In other words, the parallel channels have a tendency to equalize the pressure drop or the pressure gradient (if they are interconnected) by adjusting the ratio of the mass flows or by interchannel mixing.

Numerous analytic studies have been directed at obtaining a better understanding of thermally induced flow oscillations, determining their mechanism, and deriving stability criteria. Among the early works, those of Serov (1965), Terano (1960), and Wallis & Heasley (1961) are notable for setting the direction of analyses. More detailed analyses were carried out by Bouré (1966), Bouré & Mikaila (1967), Zuber (1966, 1967), Ishii & Zuber (1970), Ishii (1971), Yadigaroglu & Bergles (1969), and Saha (1974).

These analyses show that several important dimensionless groups govern the stability of the system (Bouré & Mikaila, 1967; Ishii & Zuber 1970). Based on these governing parameters, stability maps that indicate the stable and unstable operational regions can be obtained. Bouré & Mikaila (1967) used a dimensionless velocity-enthalpy plane as shown in figure 2.4.19, where v^* and h^* are defined by

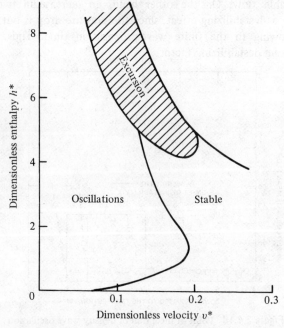

Figure 2.4.19 Stability map (Bouré & Mikaila 1967).

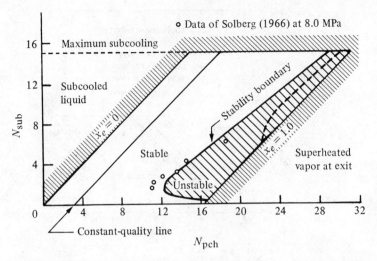

Figure 2.4.20 Stability plane (Ishii & Zuber 1970) and comparison of predicted stability boundary with experimental data.

$$v^* \equiv \frac{u_{in}\rho_{in}h_0}{Lq'''} \qquad h^* \equiv \frac{\Delta h_{in}}{h_0} \qquad\qquad [2.4.26]$$

where u_{in}, ρ_{in}, Δh_{in}, L, q''', and h_0 are the inlet velocity, density, and subcooling, and the heated length, power density, and reference enthalpy, respectively. Ishii & Zuber (1970) used a stability plane based on the subcooling and phase-change numbers given by

$$N_{sub} \equiv \frac{\Delta h_{in}}{h_{LG}}\frac{\Delta\rho}{\rho_G} \qquad N_{pch} \equiv \frac{q'''L}{u_{in}h_{LG}}\frac{\Delta\rho}{\rho_G\rho_L} \qquad [2.4.27]$$

A typical stability boundary is shown in figure 2.4.20. Here the data indicate the points of onset of the instability. The solid curve corresponds to the first-order stability boundary, and any operation within the unstable region is oscillatory. The dashed line within the unstable region indicates the onset of second-order instability. The number of undamped frequencies increases with the order of instability; thus more violent instabilities are expected in higher-order instability regions. In addition to the stability boundaries, some important operational characteristics can be represented in simple form on the stability plane. For example, the constant-exit-quality line is given by

$$N_{sub} = N_{pch} - x_e \frac{\Delta\rho}{\rho_G} \qquad\qquad [2.4.28]$$

The density group $\Delta\rho/\rho_G$ takes into account the effect of the system pressure on the stability boundary. Therefore, as shown in figure 2.4.21, the effect of the system pressure on the stability boundary is essentially absorbed by the subcooling and phase-change numbers when the system geometries are fixed. This is a definite advantage of using this stability plane.

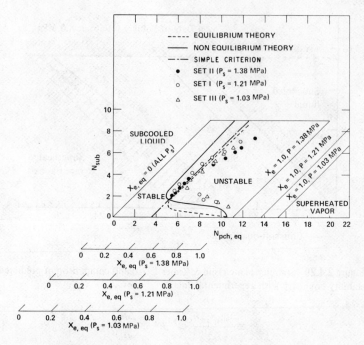

Figure 2.4.21 Stability boundary and experimental data at various pressure levels (Saha et al. 1976).

Some of the analytic studies (Bouré & Mikaila 1967; Ishii & Zuber 1970; Saha 1974) give reasonably good predictions of the onset of density wave instability. In all these analyses, the system of partial differential equations is linearized by assuming small disturbances about the steady state. The response of the system to perturbations, as well as the characteristic equation, are obtained by standard techniques. Since the stability criterion is based on the conservation laws, these analyses give considerable insight and understanding of the physical phenomena and the mechanism of flow instability.

Bouré (1966) used a thermodynamic equilibrium and homogeneous flow model and obtained a characteristic equation that is a fifth-order exponential polynomial with two time delays. Ishii & Zuber (1970) included the effect of the relative velocity between the two phases using the drift flux model, and Saha (1974) considered the effect of thermal nonequilibrium on density wave oscillations. The differences between the equilibrium and nonequilibrium theories are shown in figure 2.4.21.

Several computer codes were developed to study flow instabilities (Meyer & Rose 1963; Jones & Dight 1964; Currin et al. 1961; Efferding 1968; Carver 1968). The direct methods require expensive computer time and great care in programming, to avoid numerical instabilities. A good review of various computer codes for predicting density wave oscillations is given by Bouré et al. (1973). These codes are applicable to channels with variable heat fluxes, but without cross flows. They are more flexible in terms of heat flux profile and system geometry than the stability analyses based on the small-perturbation method described above. In these codes, the set of simultaneous partial differential equations is solved step by step in the time domain with changing conditions. It should be noted that this approach, in addition to being expensive for parametric studies, does not provide an insight into the physical aspects of the problem. However, the computer codes can be useful as a design tool for complex systems such as nuclear reactors. Furthermore, with computers, nonlinear analysis is also possible. This has an advantage over linear theory when the ultimate nonlinear response in an unstable region or the response to rapid transients is required. STABLE (Jones & Dight 1964), DYNAM-A (Effering 1968), HYDNA (Currin et al. 1961), RAMONA (Solberg & Bakstad 1967) and POISE (Carver 1968) are some of the typical codes for studying flow instabilities.

In contrast to the computer codes, very simplified algebraic criteria that can be useful for design and experimental purposes have been also developed (Ishii 1971; Saha 1974). These are obtained from the characteristic equation based on the linear-perturbation method. The asymptotic limit of the low-frequency oscillations is introduced to greatly simplify the characteristic equation; then the solution for the stability boundary is obtained analytically.

A simple criterion of Ishii (1971) is given by

$$x_e \leqslant \frac{2(k_i + f_m/2D^* + k_e)}{1 + \frac{1}{2}(f_m/2D^* + 2k_e)} \frac{\rho_G}{\rho_L - \rho_G} \qquad [2.4.29]$$

where x_e is the equilibrium exit quality, k_i and k_e are the inlet and exit orifice coefficients $(k \equiv \Delta p/\rho u^2)$, f_m is the two-phase friction factor, and D^* is the dimensionless hydraulic diameter (D/L). Under standard conditions f_m may be approximated by 1.5–2.0 times the liquid friction factor in the single-phase region. The angular frequency ω of the oscillations is approximately given by

$$\omega \leqslant \pi \left(\frac{q'''}{\rho_L \, \Delta h_{sub}} \right) \qquad [2.4.30]$$

where Δh_{sub} and q''' are the subcooling at the inlet and the power density, respectively. This criterion indicates that the exit quality calculated from the steady-state condition should be less than the value given by the right-hand side of [2.4.29] for system stability. Here the exit quality is related to operational parameters by [2.4.27] and [2.4.28]. This simple criterion has proved to be almost as good as the exact solution, except for very low inlet subcooling (Ishii 1971; Saha et al. 1976). A typical comparison of this criterion with the exact solution and experimental data is shown in figure 2.2.21. The criterion shows the basic destabilizing effect of increased power, exit flow restriction, and heated length. On the other hand, increases in inlet subcooling, flow, pressure, and inlet flow restriction have stabilizing effects. These predictions agree with more complicated analyses and experimental observations.

For very low inlet subcooling, the criterion is not satisfactory. As can be seen from figures 2.4.20 and 2.4.21, there is a particular subcooling number $(N_{sub})_c$ such that increased subcooling is stabilizing when $N_{sub} > (N_{sub})_c$ and destabilizing when $N_{sub} < (N_{sub})_c$. The simple stability analysis shows that this subcooling number is approximately

$$(N_{sub})_c \equiv \frac{(\Delta h_{in})_c \, \Delta \rho}{h_{LG} \rho_G} \leqslant \pi \qquad [2.4.31]$$

Therefore, the applicable range of [2.4.29] is limited by $N_{sub} > (N_{sub})_c$.

The effect of very low subcooling on stability is considerably different from the effect of high subcooling (see figures 2.4.20 and 2.4.21). Furthermore, Saha (1974) showed that the thermal nonequilibrium effect can be very important owing to subcooled boiling. In this region, both the nonequilibrium theory and experimental data indicate that the system is considerably more stable than is predicted by the equilibrium theory. It appears that this subcooled-boiling effect is more pronounced at low system pressures. Saha (1974) devised a simple graphical method to predict the stability boundary at low subcooling based on the exact solution at zero subcooling.

2.5 Nomenclature for Chapter 2

ROMAN LETTERS

A	channel cross-sectional area, m^2
A_G	cross-sectional area of gas phase, m^2
$\tilde{A}_G$	dimensionless cross-sectional area of gas phase, [2.1.15]
A_L	cross-sectional area of liquid phase, m^2
$\tilde{A}_L$	dimensionless liquid cross section, [2.1.14]
b	exponent in [2.3.78]
B	parameter in [2.2.76]
C	Chisholm constant, [2.2.74]
C	constant in [2.1.5]
C	mean concentration of drops in gas core, kg/m^3
C	propagation velocity, m/s
C_E	concentration of drops in gas core at hydrodynamic equilibrium, kg/m^3
C_k	concentration wave velocity, m/s
C_L	constant in [2.1.21], defined by [2.1.23]
C_0	distribution parameter
C_{pL}	liquid specific heat, J/kg K
d_{HLF}	hydraulic mean diameter of liquid film, m
d_0	tube diameter, m
D	tube diameter, m
D	hydraulic diameter, m
D^*	dimensionless hydraulic diameter
$\tilde{D}_G$	dimensionless hydraulic mean diameter for gas phase, [2.3.49]
$\tilde{D}_L$	dimensionless liquid-phase equivalent diameter, [2.1.19]
e	energy convected for unit mass of fluid, J/kg
E	parameter defined by [2.2.80]
E_1	parameter defined by [2.2.33]
E_2	parameter defined by [2.3.34]
f	frequency
f	friction factor

f_G	friction factor for gas phase flowing alone in channel
f_{gsci}	Wallis interfacial friction factor, [2.2.123]
f_i	interfacial friction factor in absence of interface mass transfer, [2.2.42]
f_{im}	interfacial friction factor in presence of mass transfer, [2.2.43]
f_L	friction factor for liquid phase flowing alone in channel
f_m	two-phase friction factor
f_{LF}	liquid-film friction factor, [2.2.110]
f_{L0}	friction factor for total mass flow with liquid properties
f_{sgc}	smooth-pipe friction factor for gas core
f_{TP}	two-phase friction factor
F	dimensionless parameter defined by [2.1.22]
F	factor defined by [2.2.45]
F	parameter defined by [2.2.81]
F_E	fraction of liquid phase entrained in gas core
g	acceleration due to gravity, m/s^2
G_{pp}	power spectral density, [2.1.2]
h	depth, m
h	enthalpy, J/kg
h^*	dimensionless enthalpy
h_G	saturated-vapor enthalpy, J/kg
h_i	inlet enthalpy, J/kg
h_L	liquid depth in stratified flow, m
h_L	saturated-liquid enthalpy, J/kg
$\tilde{h}_L$	dimensionless liquid depth in stratified flow, [2.1.12]
h_{LG}	latent heat of vaporization, J/kg
h_{sub}	subcooling at inlet, J/kg
h_{TP}	two-phase enthalpy, J/kg
$h(z)$	enthalpy at distance z, J/kg
h_0	reference enthalpy, J/kg
H	parameter defined by [2.2.82]
j	total volume flux, m^3/m^2 s
j_G	gas volumetric flux, m^3/m^2 s
j_{GL}	drift flux for gas phase, [2.3.12], m^3/m^2 s
j_L	liquid volumetric flux, m^3/m^2 s
j_{LG}	drift flux for liquid phase, m/s [2.3.13]
k	wave number
k	droplet mass transfer coefficient, m/s
k	orifice coefficient
k	von Karman constant, [2.2.105]
K	dimensionless group defined by [2.1.26]
L	heated length, m
m	parameter in [2.3.60]
$\dot{m}$	total mass flux, kg/m^2 s
$\dot{m}_D$	droplet deposition rate per unit peripheral area, kg/m^2 s
$\dot{m}_e$	rate of conversion of liquid to vapor per unit length of channel, kg/m s
$\dot{m}_E$	droplet entrainment rate per unit peripheral area, kg/m^2 s

$\dot{m}_G$	gas mass flux, kg/m^2 s
$\dot{m}_L$	liquid mass flux, kg/m^2 s
$\dot{M}_G$	mass rate of flow of gas phase, kg/s
$\dot{M}_L$	mass rate of flow of liquid phase, kg/s
$\dot{M}_{LE}$	mass rate of flow of entrained drops, kg/s
$\dot{M}_{LF}$	mass rate of flow in liquid film, kg/s
n	constant in [2.2.104]
N_G	gas velocity number, [2.1.30]
N_L	liquid velocity number, [2.1.29]
N_{pch}	phase-change number
N_{sub}	subcooling number
N_μ	viscosity number
p	pressure, N/m^2
Δp_{ext}	external pressure drop, N/m^2
Δp_{int}	internal pressure drop, N/m^2
P	channel perimeter, m
$\tilde{P}_G$	dimensionless perimeter for gas phase, [2.3.50]
P_i	interfacial perimeter, m
$\tilde{P}_i$	dimensionless interfacial perimeter, [2.1.26]
$\tilde{P}_L$	dimensionless value of perimeter in contact with liquid phase, [2.1.20]
P_L	tube perimeter in contact with liquid phase, m
dp_a/dz	acceleration and pressure gradient, N/m^2 m
dp_F/dz	frictional pressure gradient, N/m^2 m
dp_g/dz	gravitational pressure gradient, N/m^2 m
dp/dz	total pressure gradient, N/m^2 m
$(dp_F/dz)_{G0}$	frictional pressure gradient for flow with total mass flux and gas-phase properties, N/m^2 m
$(dp_F/dz)_L$	frictional pressure gradient for liquid phase flowing alone in channel, N/m^2 m
$(dp_F/dz)_{L0}$	frictional pressure gradient for flow with total mass flux and liquid-phase properties, N/m^2 m
$(dp_G/dz)_G$	frictional pressure gradient for gas phase flowing alone in channel, N/m^2 m
$\dot{q}$	heat flux, W/m^2
$\dot{q}_v$	internal heat generation rate per unit volume, J/m^3 s
q'''	power density
$\dot{Q}_G$	volumetric gas flow rate, m^3/s
$\dot{Q}'_G$	instantaneous gas volumetric flow rate, m^3/s
$\dot{Q}_L$	volumetric liquid flow rate, m^3/s
$\dot{Q}'_L$	instantaneous liquid volumetric flow rate, m^3/s
r	radius, m
r_b	bubble radius, m
r_i	interfacial radius, m
r_0	tube radius, m
R_{pp}	autocorrelation function, [2.1.1]
s	dimensionless group defined by [2.2.131]

S	velocity ratio
t	time, s
T	dimensionless parameter defined by [2.1.28]
T	total time, s
T_L	liquid bulk mean temperature, K
T_{sat}	saturation temperature, K
u	velocity, m/s
u^*	friction velocity, [2.2.103], m/s
u_c	gas core velocity, m/s
u_c^*	core friction velocity, m/s
$\tilde{u}_G$	dimensionless gas velocity
u_G	gas-phase velocity, m/s
u_{Gj}	drift velocity, m/s
u_{GU}	drift velocity for gas phase, m/s
u_H	homogeneous velocity, m/s
$\tilde{u}_L$	dimensionless liquid-phase velocity
u_L	liquid-phase velocity, m/s
u_{LF}	mean velocity in liquid film, m/s
u_{LU}	drift velocity for liquid phase, m/s
u_s	slug flow bubble rise velocity, m/s
u_∞	bubble rise velocity, m/s
U_b	plug flow bubble rise velocity, m/s
U_c	core superficial velocity, m/s
U_G	gas superficial velocity, m/s
U_G^*	dimensionless superficial velocity
U_L	liquid superficial velocity, m/s
U_L^*	dimensionless superficial velocity
v^*	dimensionless velocity
x	quality
x_e	equilibrium exit quality
$x_e(z)$	thermodynamic equilibrium quality at distance z
x_i	inlet quality
$x(z)$	actual quality at distance z
X	Martinelli parameter, [2.1.13]
y	distance from wall, m
y	parameter defined by [2.3.32]
y^+	dimensionless distance parameter, [2.2.102]
Y	Chisholm parameter, defined by [2.2.78]
Y	dimensionless group defined by [2.1.31]
z	axial distance, m
z_d	distance at which bubble departure commences, m
z_n	distance at which nucleate boiling commences, m

DIMENSIONLESS GROUPS

Eö	Eötvos number
Fr	Froude number

Ga_L	liquid Galileo number
K	Kutateladze number, [2.1.7]
Pe	Peclet number
Re_b	bubble Reynolds number
Re_G	gas-phase Reynolds number
Re_L	liquid-phase Reynolds number
Re_{LF}	liquid-film Reynolds number
Re_{Lo}	Reynolds number for total mass flux and liquid-phase properties
St	Stanton number
Vi	viscosity number, [2.3.58]
We	Weber number

GREEK LETTERS

α	angle of inclination of channel to the horizontal, degrees
α_L	heat transfer coefficient to liquid, $W/m^2\ K$
β	volumetric flow fraction of gas phase
β	sheltering coefficient
Γ	mass source due to phase changes
δ	film thickness, m
ϵ	void fraction
ϵ	eddy diffusivity, m^2/s
ϵ_c	fraction of cross section occupied by gas core in annular flow
ϵ_d	fraction of cross section occupied by entrained drops in annular flow
ϵ_F	fraction of cross section occupied by liquid film
ϵ_G	void fraction
ϵ_G'	instantaneous cross-sectional average void fraction
ϵ_k	void fraction of k phase
λ	wavelength, m
λ_B	Baker parameter, [2.1.10]
μ	specific internal energy, J/kg
μ	viscosity, $kg/m\ s$
μ_E	effective viscosity, $kg/m\ s$
μ_G	gas-phase viscosity, $kg/m\ s$
μ_L	liquid viscosity, $kg/m\ s$
μ_L	liquid-phase viscosity, $kg/m\ s$
μ_{TP}	two-phase viscosity, $kg/m\ s$
μ_W	water viscosity at ambient conditions, $kg/m\ s$
ν_L	kinematic viscosity, m^2/s
ρ	density, kg/m^3
ρ_A	air density at ambient conditions, kg/m^3
ρ_c	gas core density, kg/m^3
ρ_G	gas density, kg/m^3
ρ_H	homogeneous density, [2.2.14], kg/m^3
ρ_L	liquid density, kg/m^3
ρ_{TP}	two-phase density, kg/m^3
ρ_W	water density at ambient conditions, kg/m^3

σ	surface tension kg/s^2
σ_W	water surface tension at ambient conditions, kg/s^2
τ	time delay, s
τ_i	interfacial shear stress in absence of interface mass transfer, N/m^2
τ_{im}	interfacial shear stress in presence of mass transfer, N/m^2
τ_0	wall shear stress, N/m^2
τ_{0G}	wall shear stress in region of stratified flow in contact with gas, N/m^2
τ_{0L}	wall shear stress in region of stratified flow in contact with liquid, N/m^2
ϕ_G	pressure drop multiplier, [2.2.58]
ϕ_L	pressure drop multiplier, [2.2.59]
ϕ_{L0}	pressure drop multiplier, [2.2.60]
Ψ_B	Baker parameter, [2.1.11]
ω	angular frequency

2.6 References for Chapter 2

Agrawal, S. S., Gregory, G. A., & Govier, G. W. 1973 An Analysis of Horizontal Stratified Two-Phase Flow in Pipes, *Can. J. Chem. Eng.* **51**:280–286.

Al-Sheikh, J. N., Saunders, D. E., & Brodkey, R. S. 1970 Prediction of Flow Patterns in Horizontal Two-Phase Type Flow, *Can. J. Chem. Eng.* **48**:21–29.

Arnold, C. R. & Hewitt, G. F. 1967 Further Developments in the Photography of Two-Phase Gas-Liquid Flow, *Rept.* AERE-R5318, UKAEA, Harwell.

Azzopardi, B. J. & Lacey, P. M. C. 1974 Determining the Structure of Complex Film Flow, *European Two-Phase Flow Group Meet., Harwell,* paper A3.

Baker, J. L. L. 1965 Flow Regime Transitions at Elevated Pressures in Vertical Two-Phase Flow, *Rept.* ANL-7093, Argonne Natl. Lab.

Baker, O. 1954 Simultaneous Flow of Oil and Gas, *Oil Gas J.* **53**:185.

Bankoff, S. G. 1959 A Variable-Density Single-Fluid Model for Two-Phase Flow with Particular Reference to Steam-Water Flow, ASME paper 59-HT-7.

Barnea, D., Shohan, O., Taitel, Y., & Dukler, A. E. 1980 Flow Pattern Transition for Horizontal and Inclined Pipes: Experimental and Comparison with Theory, *Int. J. Multiphase Flow,* **6**:217–225.

Baroczy, C. J. 1965 A Systematic Correlation for Two Phase Pressure Drop, *Chem. Eng. Prog. Symp. Ser.* **62**:232–249.

Bell, K. J., Taborek, J., & Fenoglio, F. 1969 Interpretation of Horizontal In-Tube Condensation Heat Transfer Correlations with a Two-Phase Flow Regime Map, *Chem. Eng. Prog. Symp. Ser.* **66**:150–163.

Benjamin, B. T. 1959 Shearing Flow over a Wavy Boundary, *J. Fluid Mech.* **6**:161–205.

Bennett, A. W., Hewitt, G. F., & Kearsey, H. A. 1965 Flow Visualization Studies of Boiling at High Pressure, *Proc. Inst. Mech. Eng.* **180**(3C):1–11.

Bennett, A. W., Hewitt, G., Kearsey, H., & Keeys, R. 1966 The Wetting of Hot Surfaces by Water in a Steam Environment at High Pressure, *Rept.* AERE-R5146, UKAEA, Harwell.

Bergles, A. E. 1969 Two Phase Flow Structure Observations for High Pressure Water in a Rod Bundle, *Proc. ASME Symp. Two Phase Flow Heat Transfer Rod Bundles,* pp. 47–55.

Bergles, A. E. 1976 Review of Instabilities in Two-Phase Systems, *Proc. NATO Advanced Study Institute, Istanbul* **1**:383–422.

Bergles, A. E., Goldberg, P., & Maulbetsch, J. S. 1967 Acoustic Oscillations in a High Pressure Single Channel Boiling System, *Proc. Symp. Two-Phase Flow Dynamics, Eindhoven,* **1**:535–550.

Bird, R. B., Stewart, W. E., & Lightfoot, E. N. 1960 *Transport Phenomena,* Wiley, New York.

Bouré, J. 1966 The Oscillatory Behavior of Heated Channels, An Analysis of Density Effects, *Rept.* CEAR-3049, Centre d'Etudes Nucleaires de Grenoble, France.

Bouré, J. & Mikaila, A. 1967 The Oscillatory Behavior of Heated Channels, *Proc. Symp. Two-Phase Flow Dynamics, Eindhoven* **1**:695–720.

Bouré, J. & Réocreux, M. 1972 General Equations of Two-Phase Flows, *4th All Union Heat Mass Transfer Conf., Minsk, USSR.*

Bouré, J., Bergles, A. E., & Tong, L. S. 1973 Review of Two-Phase Flow Instability, *Nucl. Eng. Design* 25:165–192.

Brodkey, R. S. 1967, *The Phenomena of Fluid Motion*, pp. 456–465, 539–618, Addison-Wesley, Reading, Mass.

Butterworth, D. 1972 A Visual Study of Mechanism in Horizontal Air-Water Flow, *Rept.* AERE-M2556, UKAEA, Harwell.

Carver, M. B. 1978 An Analytical Model for the Prediction of Hydrodynamic Instability in Parallel Heated Channels, *Rept.* AECL-2681, Atomic Energy of Canada, Ltd.

Chandrasekhar, S. 1961 *Hydrodynamic and Hydromagnetic Stability,* Oxford Univ. Press, New York.

Chexal, V. K. & Bergles, A. E. 1972 Two-Phase Instabilities in a Low Pressure Natural Circulation Loop, *13th Natl. Heat Transfer Conf., Denver, AIChE Symp. Series* 69:37–45.

Chien, S. F. & Ibele, W. 1960 Pressure Drop and Liquid Film Thickness of Two-Phase Annular and Annular-Mist Flows, ASME paper 62-WA-170.

Chilton, H. 1957 A Theoretical Study of Stability in Water Flow through Heated Passages, *J. Nucl. Energy* 5:273–284.

Chisholm, D. 1967 A Theoretical Basis for the Lockhart-Martinelli Correlation for Two-Phase Flow, *Int. J. Heat Mass Transfer* 10:1767–1778.

Chisholm, D. 1973 Pressure Gradients due to Friction during the Flow of Evaporating Two-Phase Mixtures in Smooth Tubes and Channels, *Int. J. Heat Mass Transfer* 16:347–348.

Choe, W. G., Weinberg, L., & Weisman, J. 1978 Observation and Correlation of Flow Pattern Transitions in Horizontal Cocurrent Gas-Liquid Flow, in *Two-Phase Transport and Reactor Safety* eds. T. N. Veziroğlu & S. Kakaç, pp. 1357–1393, Hemisphere, Washington, D. C.

Chung, H. S. & W. Murgatroyd 1965 Studies of the Mechanism of Roll Wave Formation on Thin Liquid Films, *Proc. Symp. Two-Phase Flow, Exeter, England* 1:paper A201.

Cicchitti, A., Lombardi, C., Silvestri, M., Soldaini, G., & Zavattarelli, R. 1960 Two Phase Cooling Experiments: Pressure Drop, Heat Transfer and Burnout Measurements, *Energ. Nucl.* 7:407–425.

Collier, J. G. 1972 *Convective Boiling and Condensation,* McGraw-Hill, New York.

Condiff, D. W. & Epstein, M. 1976 Transient Volumetric Pool Boiling, I and II, *Chem. Eng. Sci.* 31:1139–1161.

Cooper, K. D., Hewitt, G. F., & Pinchin, B. 1963 Photography of Two-Phase Flow, *Rept.* AERE-R4301, UKAEA, Harwell.

Cousins, L. B., Denton, W. H., & Hewitt, G. F. 1965 Liquid Mass Transfer in Annular Two-Phase Flow, *Proc. Symp. Two-Phase Flow, Exeter, England,* 2:paper C4.

Crocco, L. & Cheng, S. I. 1956 *Theory of Combustion Instability in Liquid Propellant Rocket Motors,* Pergamon, Oxford.

Currin, H. B., Hunin, C. M., Rirlin, L., & Tong, L. S. 1961 HYDNA–Digital Computer Program for Hydrodynamic Transients in Pressure Tube Reactor or a Closed Channel Core, *USAEC Rept.* CVNA-77.

Davis, E. J. & Anderson, G. H. 1966 The Incipience of Nucleate Boiling in Forced Convection Flow, *AIChE J.* 12:774–780.

Delhaye, J. M. 1979 Optical Methods in Two-Phase Flow, *Proc. Dynamic Flow Conf., 1978, Dynamic Measurements Unsteady Flow,* pp. 321–343.

Dix, G. E. 1971 Vapour Void Fractions for Forced Convection with Subcooled Boiling at Low Flow Rates, *Rept.* NEDO-10491, General Electric Co.

Dsarasov, Y. I., Kolchugin, B. A., & Liverant, E. I. 1974 Experimental Study of Relation between Heat and Mass Transfer Characteristics in Evaporating Channels, *Proc. 5th Int. Heat Transfer Conf., Tokyo,* paper B5.3 4:195–199.

Duffey, R. & Porthouse, D. 1973 The Physics of Rewetting in Water Reactor Emergency Core Cooling, *Nucl. Eng. Design* 25:379–394.

Dukler, A. E. 1960 Fluid Mechanics and Heat Transfer in Falling Film Systems, *Chem. Eng. Prog. Symp. Ser.* 56:1–10.

Dukler, A. E., Wicks, M., & Cleveland, R. G. 1964 Pressure Drop and Hold-up in Two-Phase Flow. *AIChE J.* **10**:38–51.

Efferding, L. E. 1968 DYNAM—A Digital Computer Program for Study of the Dynamic Stability of Once-through Boiling Flow and Superheat, *USAEC Rept.* GAMD-8656, Atomic Energy Commission.

Fiori, M. P. & Bergles, A. E. 1966 A Study of Boiling Water Flow Regimes at Low Pressure, *M.I.T. Rept.* 3582-40.

Fisher, S. A. & Yu, S. K. W. 1975 Dryout in Serpentine Evaporators. *Int. J. Multiphase Flow* **1**:771–791.

Friedel, L. 1979 Improved Friction Pressure Drop Correlations for Horizontal and Vertical Two Phase Pipe Flow, *European Two Phase Flow Group Meet., Ispra, Italy,* paper E2.

Gardner, G. C. 1977 Motion of Miscible and Immiscible Fluids in Closed Horizontal and Vertical Ducts, *Int. J. Multiphase Flow* **3**:305–318.

Gill, L. E. & Hewitt, G. F. 1968 Sampling Probe Studies of the Gas Core in Annular Two-Phase Flow, III: Distribution of Velocity and Droplet Flow Rate after Injection through an Axial Jet, *Chem. Eng. Sci.* **23**:677–686.

Gill, L. E., Hewitt, G. F., & Hitchon, J. W. 1963 Sampling Probe Studies of the Gas Core in Annular Two Phase Flow, I: The Effect of Length on Phase and Velocity Distribution, *Chem. Eng. Sci.* **18**:525–535.

Golan, L. P. & Stenning, A. H. 1969 Two Phase Vertical Flow Maps, *Proc. Inst. Mech. Eng.* **184**(3C):110–116.

Gould, T. L. 1972 Vertical Two-Phase Flow in Oil and Gas Wells, Ph.D. thesis, Univ. of Michigan, Ann Arbor.

Govier, G. W. & Aziz, K. 1972 *The Flow of Complex Mixtures in Pipes,* Van Nostrand Reinhold, New York.

Grant, I. D. R. 1975 Flow and Pressure Drop with Single-Phase and Two-Phase Flow on the Shell-Side of Segmentally Baffled Shell-and-Tube Heat Exchangers, *Advances in Thermal and Mechanical Design of Shell and Tube Heat Exchangers, NEL Rept.* 590, pp. 1–22, National Engineering Laboratory, East Kilbride, Scotland.

Griffith, P. 1962 Gysering in Liquid-Filled Lines, ASME paper 62 HT-39.

Grolmes, M. A. & Fauske, H. K. 1970 Modeling of Sodium Expulsion with Freon-11, ASME paper 70-HT-24.

Hanratty, T. J. & Engen, J. M. 1957 Interaction between a Turbulent Air Stream and a Moving Water Surface, *AIChE J.* **3**:299–304.

Hanratty, T. J. & Hershman, A. 1961 Initiation of Roll Waves, *AIChE J.* **7**:488–497.

Hartley & Roberts 1961 A Correlation of Pressure Drop Data for Two-Phase Annular Flow in Vertical Channels, *Nucl. Res.* Mem. Q6, Queen Mary's College, London.

Hayama, S. 1963 A Study on the Hydrodynamic Instability in Boiling Channels, *Bull. JSME* **6**:549–556.

Helmholtz, H. 1868 Uber discontinuirliche Flüssigkeitsbewegungen, *Monatsber. Dtsch. Akad. Wiss. Berlin,* pp. 215–228.

Hewitt, G. F. 1961 Analysis of Annular Two Phase Flow: Application of the Dukler Analysis to Vertical Upward Flow in a Tube, *Rept.* AERE-R3680, UKAEA, Harwell.

Hewitt, G. F. 1969 Disturbance Waves in Annular Two-Phase Flow, *Proc. Inst. Mech. Eng.* **184**:142–150.

Hewitt, G. F. 1978a Liquid Mass Transport in Annular Two-Phase Flow, *Seminar Int. Center Heat Mass Transfer, Dubrovnik.*

Hewitt, G. F. 1978b *Measurement of Two Phase Flow Parameters,* Academic, New York.

Hewitt, G. F. & Hall-Taylor, N. S. 1970 *Annular Two-Phase Flow,* Pergamon, Oxford.

Hewitt, G. F. & Lovegrove, P. C. 1969 A Mirror-Scanner Velocimeter and Its Application to Wave Velocity Measurement in Annular Two-Phase Flow, *Rept.* AERE-R3598, UKAEA, Harwell.

Hewitt, G. F. & Roberts, D. N. 1969a Studies of Two-Phase Flow Patterns by Simultaneous X-Ray and Flash Photography, *Rept.* AERE-M2159, UKAEA, Harwell.

Hewitt, G. F. & Roberts, D. N. 1969b Investigation of Interfacial Phenomena in Annular Two-Phase Flow by Means of the Axial View Technique, *Rept.* AERE-R6070, UKAEA, Harwell.

Hewitt, G. F. & Whalley, P. B. 1980 Advanced Optical Instrumentation Methods, *Int. J. Multiphase Flow* 6:139–156.

Hewitt, G. F., Lacey, P. M. C., & Nicholls, B. 1965 Transitions in Film Flow in a Vertical Tube, *Proc. Symp. Two Phase Flow, Exeter, England* 2:

Hsu, Y. Y. & Graham, R. W. 1976 *Transport Processes in Boiling and Two-Phase Systems,* p. 261–289, Hemisphere, Washington, D.C.

Hubbard, M. G. & Dukler, A. E. 1966 The Characterization of Flow Regimes for Horizontal Two Phase Flow: I. Statistical Analysis of Wall Pressure Fluctuations, in *Proceedings of the Heat Transfer and Fluid Mechanics Institute,* eds. M. A. Saad & J. A. Miller, Stanford Univ. Press, Stanford, Calif.

Hughes, B. A. & Stewart, R. W. 1961 Interaction between Gravity Waves and a Shear Flow, *J. Fluid Mech.* 10:385–400.

Hughes, E. D., Lyczkowski, R. W., & McFadden, J. H. 1976 An Evaluation of the State-of-the-Art of Two-Velocity Two-Phase Flow Models and Their Applicability to Nuclear Reactor Transient Analysis, *EPRI Rept.* NP143, Electric Power Research Inst., Palo Alto, Calif.

Husain, A. & Weisman, J. 1978 Applicability of Homogeneous Flow Model to Two-Phase Pressure Drop in Straight Pipe and across Area Changes, *Chem. Eng. Prog. Symp. Ser.* 74:205–214.

Hutchinson, P. & Whalley, P. B. 1972 A Possible Characterization of Entrainment in Annular Flow, *Rept.* AERE-R7126, UKAEA, Harwell.

Hutchinson, P., Whalley, P. B., & Hewitt, G. F. 1974 Transient Flow Redistribution in Annular Two-Phase Flow, *Int. J. Multiphase Flow* 1:383–393.

Ishii, M. 1971 Thermally Induced Flow Instabilities in Two-Phase Mixtures in Thermal Equilibrium, Ph.D. thesis, Georgia Institute of Technology, Atlanta.

Ishii, M. 1975 *Thermo-Fluid Dynamic Theory of Two-Phase Flow,* Eyrolles, Paris.

Ishii, M. 1976 Study on Flow Instabilities in Two-Phase Mixtures, *Rept.* ANL-76-23, Argonne Natl. Lab.

Ishii, M. 1977 One-Dimensional Drift Flux Model and Constitutive Equations for Relative Motion between Phases in Various Two-Phase Flow Regimes, *Rept.* ANL-77-47, Argonne Natl. Lab.

Ishii, M. & Grolmes, M. A. 1975 Inception Criteria for Droplet Entrainment in Two-Phase Concurrent Film Flow, *AIChE J.* 21:308–318.

Ishii, M. & Zuber, N. 1970 Thermally Induced Flow Instabilities in Two-Phase Mixtures, *4th Int. Heat Transfer Conf., Paris,* paper B5.11.

James, P. W., Hewitt, G. F., & Whalley, P. B. 1980 Droplet Motion in Two Phase Flow, *ANS Topical Meet., Saratoga, N.Y.,* October.

Jeffreys, H. 1925 On the Formation of Water Waves by Wind, I and II, *Proc. R. Soc. London* A107:189–206.

Jeffreys, H. 1926 On the Formation of Water Waves by Wind. *Proc. R. Soc. London* A110:241.

Jeglic, F. A. & Grace, T. M. 1964 Onset of Flow Oscillations in Forced Flow Subcooled Boiling, *NASA TN* 2821.

Johanns, J. 1964 Development of a Fluoroscope for Studying Two-Phase Flow Patterns, *Rept.* ANL-6958, Argonne Natl. Lab.

Jones, A. B. & Dight, A. G. 1964 Hydrodynamic Stability of a Boiling Channel, *USAEC Rept.* KAPL-2170 and KAPL-3070, Knoll Atomic Power Laboratory.

Jones, A. B. & Zuber, N. 1975 The interrelation between Void Functions Fluctuation and Flow Patterns in Two Phase Flow, *Int. J. Multiphase Flow,* 2:273–306.

Kakaç, S. 1976 Boiling Flow Instabilities in Multi-Channel Upflow Systems, *Proc. NATO Advanced Study Inst.* 1:511–547.

Kelvin, W. 1871 Hydrokinetic Solutions and Observations, *Phil. Mag.* 4:374.

Kirkpatrick, R. D. & Lockett, M. J. 1974 The Influence of Approach Velocity on Bubble Coalescence, *Chem. Eng. Sci.* 29:2363–2373.

Kocamustafaogullari, G. 1971 Thermo-Fluid Dynamics of Separated Two-Phase Flow, Ph.D. thesis, Georgia Inst. of Technology, Atlanta.

Kordyban, E. 1977 Some Characteristics of High Waves in Closed Channels Approaching Kelvin-Helmholtz Instability, *J. Fluids Eng.* 99:389–346.

Kubie, J. 1979 The Presence of Slug Flow in Horizontal Two-Phase Flow, *Int. J. Multiphase Flow* 5:327–339.

Kutateladze, S. S. 1972 Elements of the Hydrodynamics of Gas-Liquid System, *Fluid Mech. Sov. Res.* 1:29–50.

Kutateladze, S. S. 1973 *Study of Turbulent Two-Phase Flow,* Inst. of Heat Physics, Siberian Academy of Sciences, Novisibirsk.

Kynch, G. J. 1952 A Theory of Sedimentation, *Trans. Faraday Soc.* 48:166–176.

Lackme, C. 1973 Two Regimes of a Spray Column in Countercurrent Flow, *14th Natl. Heat Transfer Conf.,* AIChE paper 7.

Lahey, R. T. & Moody, F. J. 1977 *The Thermal Hydraulics of a Boiling Water Nuclear Reactor,* American Nuclear Society.

Lamb, H. 1945 *Hydrodynamics,* Dover, New York (originally published in 1879).

Lassahn, G. D. 1977 LOFT 3-Beam Densitometer Data Interpretation, *Rept.* TREE-NUREG-1111.

Ledinegg, M. 1938 Instabilität der Strömung bei Natürlichen und Zwangumlauf, *Warme* 61(8):891–898.

Lee, S. S., Veziroğlu, T. N., & Kakaç, S. 1976 Sustained and Transient Boiling Flow Instabilities in Two Parallel Channel Systems, *Proc. NATO Advanced Study Institute* 1:467–510.

Levich, V. G. 1962 *Physiochemical Hydrodynamics,* pp. 591–700, Prentice-Hall, Englewood Cliffs, N.J.

Levy, S. 1966 Forced Convection Subcooled Boiling–Prediction of Vapour Volumetric Fraction. *Rept.* GEAP-5157, General Electric Co.

Levy, S. & Bekjord, E. S. 1959 Hydraulic Instability in a Natural Circulation Loop with Net Steam Generation at 1000 psia, *Rept.* GEAP-3215, General Electric Co.

Lighthill, M. J. & Whitham, G. B. 1955 On the Kinematic Waves, I and II, *Proc. R. Soc. London* 229A:281–345.

Lockhart, R. W. & Martinelli, R. C. 1949 Proposed Correlation of Data for Isothermal Two-Phase, Two-Component Flow in Pipes, *Chem. Eng. Prog.* 45:39–48.

Mandhane, J. M., Gregory, G. A., & Aziz, K. A. 1974 A Flow Pattern Map for Gas-Liquid Flow in Horizontal Pipes, *Int. J. Multiphase Flow* 1:537–553.

Martinelli, R. C. & Nelson, D. B. 1948 Prediction of Pressure Drop during Forced-Circulation Boiling of Water, *Trans. ASME* 70:695–702.

Maulbetsch, J. S. & Griffith, P. 1965 A Study of System-Induced Instabilities in Forced Convection Flow with Subcooled Boiling, *M.I.T. Engineering Project Laboratory Rept.* 5382-35, Massachusetts Inst. of Technology, Cambridge.

Mayinger, F. 1978 Subcooled Boiling, in *Two Phase Flows and Heat Transfer with Application to Nuclear Reactor Design Problems* ed. J. J. Ginoux, pp. 339–410, Hemisphere, Washington, D.C.

Mayinger, F. & Langner, H. 1977 Use of An Optical Measurement Technique to Determine the Entrainment Behaviour of a Two-Phase Flow in Steady-State and Non-stationary Blowdown Conditions. *Proc. Specialist Conf., Hanover,* Interatom, Berg-Gladbach, West Germany.

Mayinger, F. & Zetzmann, K. 1977 Vapour Content Measurement Using the X-Ray Flash Technique, *Proc. Specialist Conf., Hannover,* Interatom, Berg-Gladbach, West Germany.

McAdams, W. H., Woods, W. K., & Heroman, L. C. 1942 Vapourisation inside Horizontal Tubes, 2: Benzene-Oil Mixtures, *Trans. ASME* 64:193–200.

Meyer, J. & Rose, R. 1963 Application of a Momentum Integral Model to the Study of Parallel Channel Boiling Flow Oscillations, *J. Heat Transfer* 85:1–9.

Miles, J. W. 1957 On the Generation of Surface Waves by Shear Flows, I–IV, *J. Fluid Mech.* 3:185–204; 6:568–582 (1959); 6:583–598 (1959); 13:433–448 (1962).

Miyazaki, K., Isogai, K., Fujue, Y., & Suita, T. 1973 Measurement of Propagation Velocities of Pressure and Void by Cross-Correlation of Fluctuations in Nitrogen-Water Flow, *J. Nucl. Sci. Technol.* 10:323–325.

Nicklin, D. J. & Davidson, J. F. 1962 The Onset of Instability in Two-Phase Slug Flow, *Proc. Symp. Two-Phase Flow,* paper 4.

Nicklin, D. J., Wilkes, J. O., & Davidson, J. F. 1962 Two-Phase Flow in Vertical Tubes, *Trans. Inst. Chem. Eng.* 40:61–68.

Oshinowo, T. & Charles, M. E. 1974 Vertical Two-Phase Flow, 1: Flow Pattern Correlations, *Can. J. Chem. Eng.* 52:25–35.

Ostrach, S. & Koestel, A. 1965 Film Instability in Two-Phase Flow, *AIChE J.* 11:294–303.

Phillips, O. M. 1957 On the Generation of Waves by Turbulent Wind, *J. Fluid Mech.* 2:417–445.

Premoli, A., Francesco, D., & Prina, A. 1971 A Dimensionless Correlation for Determining the Density of Two-Phase Mixtures, *Termotecnica* 25:17–26.

Profos, P. 1947 Die Stabilität der Wasserverteilung in Zwanglauf-Heizflächen, *Sulzer Tech. Rev.* 1:1.

Pushkina, O. L. & Sorokin. Y. L. 1969 Breakdown of Liquid Film Motion in Vertical Tubes, *Heat Transfer Sov. Res.* 1:56–64.

Quandt, E. R. 1961 Analysis and Measurement of Flow Oscillations, *Chem. Eng. Progress Sym.* Ser. 57 No. 32, 111–126.

Radovcick, N. A. & Moissis, R. 1962 The Transition from Two Phase Bubble Flow to Slug Flow, *M.I.T. Rept.* 7-7673-22.

Reimann, J. & John, H. 1978 Measurements of the Phase Distribution in Horizontal Air-Water and Steam-Water Flow, *CNSI Meet. Transient Two Phase Flow, Paris.*

Rouhani, S. Z. 1969 Subcooled Void Fraction, *AB Atomenergi (Sweden) Rept.* AE-RTV 841.

Roumy, R. 1969 Structure of Air-Water Two-Phase Flow: Study of the Void Fraction and Flow Configuration, *Rept.* CEAR-3892, Centre d'Etudes Nucleaires de Grenoble, France.

Saha, P. 1974 Thermally Induced Flow Instabilities Including the Effect of Thermal Non-Equilibrium between Phases, Ph.D. thesis, Georgia Inst. of Technology, Atlanta.

Saha, P. & Zuber, N. 1974 Point of Net Vapour Generation and Vapour Void Fraction in Subcooled Boiling, *5th Int. Heat Transfer Conf., Tokyo* 4:175–179.

Saha, P., Ishii, M., & Zuber, N. 1976 An Experimental Investigation of the Thermally Induced Flow Oscillations in Two-Phase Systems, *J. Heat Transfer,* ser. C 98:616–622.

Sakaguchi, T., Akagawa, K., Hamaguchi, H., Imoto, M., & Ishida, S. 1979 Flow Regime Maps for Developing Steady Air-Water Two-Phase Flow in Horizontal Tubes. *Mem. Fac. Eng. Kobe Univ.* 25:191–202.

Schicht, H. H. 1969 Flow Patterns for Adiabatic Two-Phase Flow of Water and Air within a Horizontal Tube, *Verfahrenstechnik* 3:153–161.

Scott, D. S. 1963 Properties of Co-Current Gas-Liquid Flow, in *Advances in Chemical Engineering,* vol. 4, pp. 199–277, Academic, New York.

Serov, E. P. 1953 The Operation of Once-Through Boilers in Variable Regimes, *Tr. Mosk. Energ. Inst.* 11:204–227.

Serov, E. P. 1965 Analytical Investigation of the Boundary Conditions for the Formation of Pulsation in Steaming Pipes during Forced Circulation, *High Temp.* 3:545–549.

Singer, R. M. & Holtz, R. E. 1970 Comparison of the Expulsion Dynamics of Sodium and Nonmetallic Fluids, ASME paper 70-HT-23.

Smith, A. V. 1975 Fast Response Multi-Beam X-Ray Absorption Technique for Identifying Phase Distribution during Steam-Water Blowdowns, *J. Br. Nucl. Energy Soc.* 14:227–235.

Solberg, K. 1966 Results des essais d'instabilities sur la boucle 'culine' et comparisons avec un code de calcul, CENG note 225, Centre d'Etudes Nucleaires de Grenoble, France.

Solberg, K. O. & Bakstad, P. 1967 A Model for the Dynamics of Nuclear Reactors with Boiling Coolant with a New Approach to the Vapor Generation Process, *Proc. Symp. Two-Phase Flow Dynamics, Eindhoven,* 1:871–933.

Steen, D. A. & Wallis, G. B. 1964 The Transition from Annular to Annular-Mist Cocurrent Two-Phase Down Flow, *USAEC Rept.* NYO-3114-2.

Stenning, A. H. & Veziroglu, T. N. 1965 Flow Oscillation Modes in Forced Convection Boiling, *Proc. 1965 Heat Transfer Fluid Mechanics Inst.* pp. 301–316, Stanford Univ. Press, Stanford, Calif.

Suzuki, S. & Ueda, T. 1977 Behaviour of Liquid Films and Flooding in Counter-Current Two-Phase Flow, I: Flow in Circular Tubes, *Int. J. Multiphase Flow* 3:517–532.

Taitel, Y. & Dukler, A. E. 1976 A Model for Predicting Flow Regime Transitions in Horizontal and Near Horizontal Gas-Liquid Flow, *AIChE J.* 22:47–55.

Terano, T. 1960 Kinetic Behaviour of Monotube Boiler, *Bull. JSME* 3:540–546.

Thurston, R. S., Rogers, J. D., & Skoglund, V. J. 1966 Pressure Oscillations Induced by Forced Convection Heating of Dense Hydrogen, in *Advances in Cryogenic Engineering*, vol. 12, p. 438.

Tong, L. S. 1965 *Boiling Heat Transfer and Two-Phase Flow*, Wiley, New York.

Ueda, T. & Tanaka, T. 1973 Studies of Liquid Film Flow in Two-Phase Annular and Annular-Mist Flow Regions, I and II *Trans. JSME* 39:2842–2852.

van Rossum, J. J. 1959 Experimental Investigation of Horizontal Liquid Films, *Chem. Eng. Sci.* 11:35–52.

Vernier, P. & Delhaye, J. 1968 General Two-Phase Flow Equations Applied to the Thermodynamics of Boiling Nuclear Reactors, *Energ. Primarie* 4:1–43.

Veziroğlu, T. N. & Lee, S. S. 1971 Boiling Flow Instabilities in a Cross-Connected Parallel Channel Upflow System, ASME paper 71-HT-12.

Veziroğlu, T. N., Lee, S. S., & Kakaç, S. 1976 Fundamentals of Two-phase Flow Oscillations and Experiments in Single Channel Systems, *Proc. NATO Advanced Study Inst.* 1:423–466.

Wallis, G. B. 1961 Flooding Velocities for Air and Water Vertical Tubes, *Rept.* AEEW-R123, UKAEA, Winfrith.

Wallis, G. B. 1962a The Onset of Droplet Entrainment in Annular Gas-Liquid Flow, *Rept.* 62 GL 127, General Electric Co.

Wallis, G. B. 1962b General Correlations for the Rise Velocity of Cylindrical Bubbles in Vertical Tubes, *Rept.* 62 GL 130, General Electric Co.

Wallis, G. B. 1969 *One-dimensional Two-Phase Flow*, McGraw-Hill, New York.

Wallis, G. B. & Dobson, J. E. 1973 The Onset of Slugging in Horizontal Stratified Air-Water Flow, *Int. J. Multiphase Flow* 1:173–193.

Wallis, G. B. & Heasley, J. H. 1961 Oscillation in Two-Phase Flow System, *J. Heat Transfer, Trans. ASME*, ser C 83:363–369.

Wallis, G. B. & Makkenchery, S. 1974 The Hanging Film Phenomenon in Vertical Annular Two-Phase Flow, *J. Fluids Eng.* 96:297–298.

Wallis, G. B., Turner, J. M., Bemberis, I., & Kaufmann, D. 1964 Two-Phase Flow and Boiling Heat Transfer, *USAEC Rept.* NYO-3114-4.

Webb, D. R. 1970 Two Phase Phenomena, Ph.D. thesis, Cambridge Univ. Cambridge, Mass.

Weisman, J. 1979 Flow Pattern Identification in Concurrent Vapour-Liquid Flow, *Proc. Japan-US Seminar Two Phase Flow Dynamics*, Inter-University Seminar House, Kansai, Japan.

Whalley, P. B. & Hewitt, G. F. 1978 The Correlation of Liquid Entrainment Fraction and Entrainment Rate in Annular Two Phase Flow, *Rept.* AERE-R9187, UKAEA, Harwell.

Whalley, P. B. 1980 Private communication.

Whalley, P. B., Hutchinson, P., & Hewitt, G. F. 1974 The Calculation of Critical Heat Flux in Forced Convective Boiling, *Proc. 5th Int. Heat Transfer Conf., Versailles* 4:290–294.

Whalley, P. B., Azzopardi, B. J., Pshyk, L., & Hewitt, G. F. 1977 Axial View Photography of Waves in Annular Two-Phase Flow, *European Two Phase Flow Group Meet., Grenoble*, paper A5.

Whalley, P. B., Hewitt, G. F., & Terry, J. W. 1979 Photographic Studies of Two-Phase Flow Using a Parallel Light Technique, *Rept.* AERE-R9389, UKAEA, Harwell.

Yablonik, R. M. & Khaimov, V. A. 1972 Determination of the Velocity of Inception of Droplet Entrainment in Two-Phase Flow, *Fluid Mech. Sov. Res.* 1:130–134.

Yadigaroglu, G. & Bergles, A. E. 1969 An Experimental and Theoretical Study of Density-Wave Oscillation in Two-Phase Flow, *M.I.T. Rept.* DSR74629-3.

Yadigaroglu, G. & Bergles, A. E. 1972 Fundamental and Higher-Mode Density-Wave Oscillations in Two-Phase Flow, *J. Heat Transfer* 94:189–195.

Yadigaroglu, G. & Chan, K. C. 1979 Analysis of Flow Instabilities, *Proc. Japan-U.S. Seminar Two Phase Flow Dynamics*, Inter-University Seminar House, Kansai, Japan.

Yamanouchi, A. 1968 Effect of Core Spray Cooling in Stationary State after Loss of Coolant Accident, *J. Nucl. Sci. Technol.* 5(9):498–508.

Ybarrondo, L. 1975 Dynamic Analysis of Pressure Transducer and Two-Phase Flow Instrumentation, *Third Water Reactor Safety Research Information Meet., Washington, D.C.,* Nuclear Regulatory Commission.

Yih, C. S. 1969 *Fluid Mechanics,* McGraw-Hill, New York.

Zhivaikin, L. Y. 1962 Liquid Film Thickness in Film-Type Units, *Int. Chem. Eng.* 2:337–341.

Zuber, N. 1962 On the Atomization and Entrainment of Liquid Films in Shear Flow, *Rept.* 62 GL 153, General Electric Co.

Zuber, N. 1966 Analysis of Thermally Induced Flow Oscillations in the Near Critical and Supercritical Thermodynamic Region, *NASA* CR 80609.

Zuber, N. 1967 Flow Excursions and Oscillations in Boiling Two-Phase Flow Systems with Heat Additions, *Proc. Symp. Two-Phase Flow Dynamics, Eindhoven* 1:1071–1089.

Zuber, N. & Findlay, J. A. 1965 Average Volumetric Concentration in Two-Phase Flow Systems, *J. Heat Transfer* 87:453–468.

Zuber, N., Staub, F. W., Bijwaard, G., & Kroeger, P. G. 1967 Steady State and Transient Void Fraction in Two-Phase Flow Systems, *Rept.* GEAP-5417, General Electric Co.

3 GAS–SOLID SYSTEMS

3.1 General Description

S. L. Soo

The validity of conservation of mass, momentum, and energy of a suspension based on a mixture has been demonstrated by analysis (Chao et al. 1978; Soo 1977) and by experiments with high-velocity flows (Eddington 1967). Computations for mixtures suffer from lack of accurate information on their thermodynamic and transport properties. These properties of mixtures are readily determined without considering the dynamics of the system only in cases where the phases have identical mass velocities and static temperatures (Pfeffer et al. 1966; Gorring & Churchill 1961; Happel 1957). In general, computations using basic or elementary thermodynamic and transport properties call for formulation in terms of equation of phases. Identical mass velocities of phases are not to be expected when the phases have different densities and hence inertia forces. Moreover, thermal equilibrium between phases with different specific heats, thermal conductivities, etc. does not exist when a flowing suspension undergoes heat transfer with a wall, for instance. We have to treat the specific heat and thermal conductivity of a suspension when the temperatures and temperature gradients of the phases are different, and the viscosity of a suspension when the velocity gradients of the phases are different (Soo 1967). Therefore, any logical treatment of a suspension must account for the following facts:

1. For particles greater than 1 μm in diameter ($2a$), random Brownian motion is negligible. The particles do not contribute to the static pressure of the system, and the particle velocity $\mathbf{U}_p$ arises from the interaction of the viscous drag force exerted by the fluid with the inertia of the particle. In general, $\mathbf{U}_p \neq \mathbf{U}$, the velocity of the fluid.

2. The fluid phase and the particle phase may have different families of streamlines. Thus, total derivatives with respect to time t must be identified by

$$\frac{d}{dt} = \frac{\partial}{\partial t} + U_j \left(\frac{\partial}{\partial x_j} \right) \qquad [3.1.1]$$

for the fluid phase and

$$\left(\frac{d}{dt}\right)_p = \frac{\partial}{\partial t} + U_{pj}\left(\frac{\partial}{\partial x_j}\right) \qquad [3.1.2]$$

for the particle phase.

3. Particles accelerate at the expense of the kinetic energy of the fluid, but their deceleration does not necessarily raise the static pressure or mass velocity of the fluid. Especially for a dilute suspension, dissipation in the wakes of particles simply adds heat to the system. This is a characteristic of free particles, not just a matter of coordinate transformation.

4. A solid or liquid particle 1 μm in diameter may contain on the order of 10^{10} molecules or atoms. The energy of such a particle is given by its body temperature T_p, although the temperature T of the gaseous phase represents the kinetic energy of random motion of its molecules. Because of the large heat capacity of a particle compared to a similar volume of the gas, in general $T_p \neq T$.

5. Because of the small size and high thermal conductivity of a particle compared to a gas, the temperature is uniform throughout the particle at a given instant. For example, for a magnesia particle whose thermal diffusivity α_p is of the order of 5×10^{-7} m^2/s, the time constant for transient heat conduction is $\alpha_p/a^2 = 2 \times 10^2$ s^{-1}, where a is the particle radius, even for a 100-μm particle.

6. Although addition of heat to a gas increases its total temperature (through its thermal energy and kinetic energy of mass motion), addition of heat to a cloud of particles simply increases its static temperature. The kinetic energy of a cloud of particles arises from fluid drag only.

In this section, unless otherwise stated, we consider a suspension of particles of one species and uniform size. We identify the mass of dispersed particulate matter per unit volume in space as the density of the particulate cloud ρ_p for a density of the particulate material $\bar{\rho}_p$. Thus the volume fraction of the particulate phase ϕ is defined by

$$\rho_p = \phi \bar{\rho}_p \qquad [3.1.3]$$

Excluding the volume fraction occupied by the particles, the mass of fluid in a given overall volume is correspondingly reduced, and we identify the density of the fluid phase as ρ for a density of fluid material $\bar{\rho}$; thus

$$\rho = (1 - \phi)\bar{\rho} \qquad [3.1.4]$$

The density of the mixture is then $\rho + \rho_p$.

For n spherical particles of radius a per unit volume

$$\rho_p = nm_p = n\,\frac{4\pi}{3}a^3\bar{\rho}_p \qquad [3.1.5]$$

where m_p is the mass of a particle and the mean interparticle spacing is given by

$$n^{-1/3} = \left(\frac{4\pi}{3\phi}\right)^{1/3} a \qquad [3.1.6]$$

Therefore, for $\phi = \frac{1}{100}$, particles are three to four diameters apart. Because of the large density of the particulate phase in a gaseous suspension, however, we note that the mass ratio is given by

$$m^* = \frac{\rho_p}{\rho} = \frac{\bar{\rho}_p}{\bar{\rho}} \frac{\phi}{1 - \phi} \qquad\qquad [3.1.7]$$

A monodisperse dilute gas-solid suspension is the simplest form of a multiphase flow system. This enables straightforward formulation, a minimal number of correlation parameters for various interactions of flow and field forces, and rigorous mathematical solutions or simple computer programs for studying physical cases. Correlation parameters have been rigorously derived and many physical systems are readily scaled. These features make a gas-solid system a suitable model for understanding the nature of multiphase mechanics. Knowledge of the behavior of a gas-solid suspension is directly applied in designing a pneumatic conveying system (section 7.1).

3.2 Fluid Mechanics of Suspensions

S. L. Soo

Previous chapters have dealt with the fundamentals of the formulation of two-phase flows. Some aspects of the basic equations involve unsettled questions and discussion of these (Sha & Soo 1977a) is outside the scope of a handbook. A dilute gas-solid suspension, however, embodies such simplifying features that its formulation is uncontroversial:

1. Because of the large material density of particles compared to the gas and the effect of pressure gradient on the flow field around the particle (Soo 1975, 1976), the effect of pressure gradient on particle motion is negligible. Pressure inside a solid particle never enters the formulation.
2. Because of the small differences in velocity between phases, the inertial coupling term can be neglected (Soo 1976).
3. Because of the small diffusivity, the gradient of the volume fraction of solid particles has a negligible effect on momentum balance.
4. Motion of the particle phase is produced by that of the fluid phase and the characteristics of the fluid phase are real (Soo 1977a, 1977b; Rudinger & Chang 1964).
5. Velocity of the particle phase is that of the particle cloud, not that inside a phase.

We further note that the virtual mass force is negligible because of the large ratio of densities of materials constituting the particle and the fluid; and the force due to an unsteady flow field is small. Formulations of individual phases that emphasize averaging over the interface are in agreement with that based on the mean velocity of a phase. The mean velocity of the particle cloud is the mean velocity of the interface. We can further simplify by neglecting the mass transfer between the phases.

3.2.1 BASIC FORMULATION

Based on the behavior of a suspension described above, we now present the simplest nontrivial formulations for the general motion of a dilute suspension ($\rho_p/\rho \ll 1$ and

$\rho \sim \bar{\rho}$). The continuity equations of the phases are

$$\frac{\partial \rho}{\partial t} + \frac{\partial \rho U_i}{\partial x_i} = 0 \tag{3.2.1}$$

$$\frac{\partial \rho_p}{\partial t} + \frac{\partial \rho_p \, U_{pi}}{\partial x_i} = 0 \tag{3.2.2}$$

where U_i is the fluid velocity in the x_i direction and U_{pi} is the velocity of the particles (i, $j = 1, 2, 3$). Equation [3.2.1] is the continuity condition of the fluid. Equation [3.2.2] formulates the basic behavior of a suspension, i.e., ρ_p does not arise from a state parameter such as temperature and pressure, but varies with the particle motion that is produced by the fluid motion. When the particle phase is slowed down ρ_p increases regardless of whether the fluid is compressible. It was demonstrated experimentally in steady pipe flow that the particle-to-fluid mass ratio and mass flow ratio are different (Soo 1970).

The momentum equations of the phases are

$$\frac{dU_i}{dt} = -\frac{\partial P}{\partial x_i} + \frac{\partial}{\partial x_j}\left[\bar{\mu}\Delta_{ji} + \left(\bar{\zeta} - \frac{2}{3}\,\bar{\mu}\right)\theta\delta_{ji}\right]$$

$$+ K\left[\rho_p\,\tau^{-1}(U_i - U_{pi}) + \rho_p f'_{pi}\right] + \rho f_i \tag{3.2.3}$$

where $\bar{\mu}$ is the viscosity of material constituting the fluid phase; $\bar{\zeta}$ is the bulk modulus of the fluid; the deformation tensor and the dilation are

$$\Delta_{ji} = \frac{\partial U_i}{\partial x_j} + \frac{\partial U_j}{\partial x_i} \qquad \theta = \frac{1}{2}\,\Delta_{kk}$$

$$\frac{dU_{pi}}{dt_p} = \tau^{-1}(U_i - U_{pi}) + f'_{pi} + f_{pi} + \frac{1}{\rho_p}\frac{\partial}{\partial x_j}(\rho_p D_p)\left[(\Delta_p)_{ji} - \frac{2}{3}\theta_p\delta_{ji}\right] \tag{3.2.4}$$

f_i and f_{pi} are the field forces per unit mass of fluid acting on the fluid and the particles, respectively; f'_{pi} is the unsteady fluid force acting on the particles; τ is the relaxation time for momentum transfer from fluid to particle; and K is the "effectiveness" of momentum transfer: $K = 1$ for $|U_i| > |U_{pi}|$ and $1 > K \geqslant 0$ for $|U_i| < |U_{pi}|$. Note that this does not constitute a discontinuity in a natural phenomenon because K changes from 1 to 0 at $U_i = U_{pi}$ and $f'_{pi} = 0$.

The energy equations of the phases are

$$\rho\frac{d}{dt}\left(\frac{U^2}{2} + CT\right) + \rho_p\frac{d}{dt_p}\frac{U_p^2}{2} = \frac{\partial P}{\partial t} + \frac{\partial}{\partial x_j}\left[\bar{\mu}U_j\Delta_{ji} + \left(\bar{\zeta} - \frac{2}{3}\,\bar{\mu}\right)\theta U_j\delta_{ji}\right]$$

$$+ \frac{\partial}{\partial x_j}\left(\bar{\lambda}\frac{\partial T}{\partial x_j}\right) - C_p\rho_p G(T - T_p) + \rho F(U_j - U_{pj})^2 + \rho q \tag{3.2.5}$$

and

$$\frac{dT_p}{dt_p} = \tau_q^{-1}(T - T_p) + \frac{q_p}{C_p} + \frac{1}{C_p \rho_p} \frac{\partial}{\partial x_j} \left(C_p \rho_p D_p \frac{\partial T_p}{\partial x_j}\right) \qquad [3.2.6]$$

where C is the specific heat at constant pressure of the fluid and C_p is that of the particles; q is the rate of heat generated per unit mass of the fluid, including radiative input, τ_q is the relaxation time for energy transfer from fluid to particles; and D_p is the particle diffusivity. Equation [3.2.5] signifies that U_p arises from U and [3.2.6] states that heat added to a particle cloud raises the body temperature of the particles. See section 3.3 for details of transport properties.

The terms including ρ_p in [3.2.3] and [3.2.5], of course, are negligible when $\rho_p \to 0$; i.e., for a very dilute suspension. In this case, the state of the fluid and its motion are entirely unaffected by the presence of particles although the state and motion of the particle phase still arise due to fluid motion and fluid temperature. It cannot be overemphasized that ρ_p can be taken to be uniform only for one-dimensional uniform motion.

A further relation is that of diffusion of particles under the influence of field forces. For a dilute suspension, [3.2.2] may be replaced by

$$\frac{d\rho_p}{dt} = -\frac{\partial}{\partial x_j} \left[-D_p \frac{\partial \rho_p}{\partial x_j} + \rho_p(U_{pj} - U_j)\right] \qquad [3.2.7]$$

where the flux $\rho_p(U_{pj} - U_j)$ is given by [3.2.4]. This is the basic relation for diffusion under field forces.

3.2.2 LIFT AND DEPOSITION AT THE BOUNDARY

The general condition at the boundary of a flowing suspension includes diffusion of particles, field forces per unit mass f_p with sticking probability σ for deposition, surface force per unit mass f_W and sticking probability σ_W before complete deposition of a monolayer, and lift force f_L per unit mass due to fluid shear, which enhances or reduces deposition. In general, f_L should be included over the whole shear layer, and it is insignificant for both $2a \ll \delta$ and $2a \gg \delta$ (δ being the boundary-layer thickness). The flux of particles produced by erosion from a bed is given by (probability of lift) $\times$ (mass per unit area of surface layer of particles) $\times$ (frequency of lifting of particles). The mass per unit area of the surface layer is given by $(4\pi/3)^{1/3} \phi_b^{2/3} a\bar\rho_p$, where ϕ_b is the volume fraction of particles in the bed. Since the frequency of lifting is given by the lift velocity (f_L/τ) divided by the mean distance between successive particles lifted, the flux of particles produced by erosion is thus $\sigma_W' \rho_{pb} f_{LR}/\tau$, where the probability σ_W' accounts for the difference between bed density ρ_{pb} and the above quantity of mass per unit area divided by the mean distance between lifted particles. Thus f_L is accounted for and the boundary condition (Soo & Tung 1972) is

$$-D_p \nabla\rho_p|_W = (1 - \sigma) \, f_p \tau \rho_{pW} - \sigma_W(f_W\tau) \, \rho_{pW}$$
$$+ [(1 - \sigma)\rho_{pW} + \sigma_W'\rho_{pb}] \, f_L\tau + J_s \qquad [3.2.8]$$

where ρ_{pW} is the density of the suspension over the deposit layer on the wall and

f_W is directed toward the wall. The effect of splashing (Bagnold 1951) by larger particles of species r colliding with the deposit layer at flux J_s is given in the next section.

When treating cases that include an erodible bed of solid particles, the lift force per unit mass f_L acting on a particle by fluid shear is given by

$$f_L = -\frac{3}{8} C_L \frac{\bar{\rho}}{\bar{\rho}_p} \frac{U_r^2}{a} \qquad [3.2.9]$$

where U_r is the local relative velocity of particles to gas and C_L is the lift coefficient, which can be represented in the form (y normal to wall):

$$C_L = c_1 \left(\frac{\bar{\nu}}{2aU_r}\right)^m \left|\frac{2a}{U_r}\frac{du}{dy}\right|^n \qquad [3.2.10]$$

where $\bar{\nu}$ is the kinematic viscosity and the coefficient c_1 and exponents m and n are given below.

Source	c_1	m	n	Condition
Saffman (1965) (theoretical)	$12.92/\pi$	$\frac{1}{2}$	$\frac{1}{2}$	Very small particles and slow relative motion
Correlated from Graf & Acaroglu (1968) and Gral (1971)	50	1	$\frac{1}{2}$	Erodible bed of sand in turbulent fluid

The relative velocity is given by

$$U_r = U_p - U + \Delta U \qquad [3.2.11]$$

where $\Delta u \sim (dU/dy)2a$.

We define the shear response number N_s as

$$N_s = \frac{3}{4} c_1 \frac{\bar{\rho}}{\bar{\rho}_p} \left(\frac{\bar{\nu}}{LU_0}\right)^m \left(\frac{L}{2a}\right)^{1+m-n} \qquad [3.2.12]$$

where L is a characteristic dimension of the system, U_0 is a characteristic flow velocity outside the shear layer, and

$$f_L = -N_s \frac{U_0^m}{L^{1-n}} \left|\frac{dU}{dy}\right|^n U_r^{2-m-n} \qquad [3.2.13]$$

For substantial relative motion, based on experimental results compiled by Graf & Acaroglu (1968) and Graf (1971),

$$N_s = \frac{3}{4} c_1 \frac{\bar{\rho}}{\bar{\rho}_p} \frac{\nu}{LU_0} \left(\frac{L}{2a}\right)^{3/2} \qquad [3.2.14]$$

and

$$f_L = -N_s \frac{U_0}{L} \left|\frac{L}{U_r}\frac{dU}{dy}\right|^{1/2} U_r \qquad [3.2.15]$$

3.2.3 EFFECT OF SPLASHING OF DEPOSITED LAYER

Bagnold (1951) observed splashing of particles when a traveling particle hit a nonsticking layer of deposit. Seman & Penny (1965) noted that particles striking a layer of electrostatically deposited dust caused splashing and reentrainment. Such an effect is readily accounted for by considering the particle-to-particle interaction when a cloud of particles of species 2 collides with a deposit layer of species 1 and bed density ρ_{pb1}. We note that

1. In a monodisperse suspension, because of the indistinguishability of similar particles, any splashing that occurs constitutes exchange of particles with the deposit layer, which is accounted for by terms in [3.2.8] other than the splashing term.

2. Splashing is produced mainly by particles larger than those of the species (1) under consideration in the deposit layer, since the fraction of kinetic energy of a particle of species 2 transferred by collision with a particle of species 1 is proportional to the ratio of their masses, m_2/m_1, when $m_2 \ll m_1$.

For particles of species 2 traveling at velocity U_{pW2} and colliding with a bed including species 1, the relaxation time τ_{12} for momentum transfer is given (Soo 1967) by

$$\rho_{p2}\tau_{21}^{-1} = \rho_{pb1}\,\tau_{12}^{-1} \qquad [3.2.16]$$

and

$$\tau_{12}^{-1} = \frac{3}{4}\,\eta_{12}\frac{[(a_1/a_2)^{1/2} + (a_2/a_1)^{1/2}]^2 U_{pW2}\,\bar\rho_{p2}}{(a_1a_2)^{1/2}(\bar\rho_{p1}\bar\rho_{p2})^{1/2}[(m_1/m_2)^{1/2} + (m_2/m_1)^{1/2}]} \qquad [3.2.17]$$

where U_{pW2} is the velocity of particle cloud 2 at the wall, η_{12} is the fraction of particle 1 impacted by cloud 2 ($\eta_{12} \cong 1$), a_1 and a_2 are the radii of particles 1 and 2, m_1 and m_2 are their masses, and $\bar\rho_p$ is the density of material of each species. The flux of particles of species 1 produced by splashing of particles of species 2 at probability σ_s is given by (τ_1 for transfer from fluid to particle 1):

$$J_s = [\rho_{pW1}(U_{p1} - U)]_{\text{splash}} = \sigma_{s12}(\rho_{pb1}\tau_1)(\tau_{12}^{-1}U_{pW2})$$

$$\sim \sigma_{s12}(\rho_{pb1}\tau_1)\frac{\rho_{pW2}\,U_{pW2}^2}{a_2\bar\rho_{p2}} \qquad [3.2.18]$$

for $m_2 > m_1$. Equation [3.2.18] gives the last term of [3.2.8]. Note that the flux of species 1 enhanced by splashing is proportional to a force per unit mass represented by U_{pW2}^2/a. Note also that we have neglected the 1 2 collision in the dilute suspension in [3.2.4] but accounted for the 1 2 collision in the layer of deposit (Soo 1973c). τ_{12} is the relaxation time for momentum transfer from particles of species 2 to particles of species 1, and τ_1 is that from fluid to particles.

3.3 Basic Interactions and Transport Properties

S. L. Soo

Leaving out chemical reaction, interactions in a gas-solid suspension include effects of momentum, heat, mass, and charge transfer [see Blake et al. (1976) for reactive suspensions). When treating a suspension, we are concerned mainly with fluid-fluid, fluid-particle, and particle-particle interactions. The transport properties include diffusivity, viscosity, and thermal conductivity of the phases; the relaxation times for momentum, energy, and charge transfer; the interaction length for particle-fluid interactions; and the accommodation coefficient for particle-wall interactions.

3.3.1 TRANSPORT PROPERTIES

Because of dissimilar gradients of velocity and temperature of phases (Soo 1970), identify the viscosity, bulk viscosity, and thermal conductivity of the fluid phase in the mixture as μ, ζ, and λ and those of the particle phase in the mixture as μ_p, ζ_p, and λ_p; they are, in general, different from those of materials constituting the phase, $\bar{\mu}$, $\bar{\lambda}$, and $\bar{\mu}_p$, $\bar{\lambda}_p$. It was shown that for a gaseous suspension with $\phi \ll 1$ (Soo 1967; Murray 1965)

$$\frac{\rho_p}{\rho} < 1$$

$$\mu_{\text{mixture}} \lessgtr \bar{\mu}$$

$$\lambda_{\text{mixture}} \lessgtr \bar{\lambda}$$

$$\mu_p \sim \bar{\mu}\frac{\rho_p}{\rho} \quad \zeta_p \sim \bar{\mu}\left(\frac{\rho_p}{\rho}\right)^3$$

$$\lambda_p \sim \bar{\lambda}\frac{C_p\rho_p}{C\rho}$$

and for the case $\rho_p/\rho \ll 1$ (Soo and Tung 1972),

$$\mu \sim \bar{\mu} \quad \zeta \sim \bar{\zeta}$$

$$\lambda \sim \bar{\lambda}$$

$$\mu_p \sim \rho_p D_p \qquad \zeta_p \sim 0$$

$$\lambda_p \sim C_p \rho_p D_p$$

where transfer of momentum and energy is by diffusion of the particles (Soo 1971). The situation is such that shear stress of the mixture arises due to the viscosity of the fluid phase and the momentum transferred by diffusion of particles. The transport properties for the case $\rho_p/\rho \ll 1$ may be considered as the definition for a truly dilute suspension (see section 3.3.3).

Particle diffusivity D_p arises from Brownian motion, wall interaction, and perturbation of the flow field by the particles. In a suspension in a turbulent fluid, D_p is the particle diffusivity in the mixture and is related to the eddy diffusivity of the fluid and the parameters of fluid-particle interaction (Soo 1978). In relation to the fluid diffusivity D, $D_p/D < 1$ for particles in a free turbulent fluid and it approaches 1 for submicrometer particles. In pipe flow of a dilute suspension $D_p \sim \langle U_{p2}^2 \rangle^{1/2} R$ in the limit, where $\langle U_p^2 \rangle^{1/2}$ is the intensity of random motion of particles and R is the pipe radius, when particle-wall collision predominates or $R \leqslant L_p$. L_p is the interaction length of particles to fluid (section 3.3.3).

Measurements of diffusivities of particles in shear flow were made by Eckstein et al. (1977). Experimental results show relations between the volume fraction of particles versus $D_p/a^2 (dU/dy)$, dU/dy being the local shear rate. Test points were not correlated. It is not clear why D_p does not approach an asymptotic value at their low volume fraction of particles.

Viscosities due to interaction of particle phases are also given for binary interaction of species 1 and 2 (Soo 1967).

$$\mu_{12} \propto n_1 n_2 a_1 a_2 \bar{\rho}_p |\Delta_1 \Delta_2|^{1/2} \qquad [3.3.1]$$

where Δ's are the shear tensors and the n's are the number densities of the phases; i.e., the viscosity due to particle-particle collision is non-Newtonian. Schugel (1971) postulated a correlation of experimental data obtained by shear viscosity measurements to give for the mixture

$$\mu_m = \frac{4a^2 \bar{\rho}_p}{2.65 \times 10^{-2}} \left(4.25 + 0.13 \frac{\phi}{\phi_0 - \phi} \right) = \frac{4a^2 \bar{\rho}_p}{2.65 \times 10^{-2}} \mu_s^* \text{ kg/m s} \qquad [3.3.2]$$

where ϕ is the solid volume fraction; ϕ_0 is its maximum value ($\phi_0 \sim 0.60$); and μ^* is given in the following.

Schugel's data cover only moderate bed expansion (section 8.1.2), $2 < \phi/(\phi_0 - \phi) < 25$. He recognized that for $\phi/(\phi_0 - \phi) > 100$ non-Newtonian behavior is seen. Blake et al. (1976) accounted for the difficulty that μ_m does not reduce the μ_G of the gas phase alone by postulating that for $0 < \phi/(\phi_0 - \phi) < 2$

$$\mu_s^* = 0.5 \mu_{s2}^* \frac{\phi}{\phi_0 - \phi} \qquad [3.3.3]$$

where μ_{s2}^* is the value of μ_s at $\phi/(\phi_0 - \phi) = 2$. Note that in this way the dependence of μ_m on n^2 is accounted for, or

$$\mu_s^* = \frac{4.61}{4} \left(\frac{\phi}{\phi_0 - \phi} \right)^2 \tag{3.3.4}$$

and an empirical correlation (in kg/m s) is

$$\mu_m = \bar{\mu} + \frac{4a^2 \bar{\rho}_p}{2.65 \times 10^{-2}} \mu_s^* = \bar{\mu} + 150 \, a^2 \bar{\rho}_p \mu_s^* \tag{3.3.5}$$

In general, a polynomial expression for μ_s^* is recommended to account for higher-order collisions (Sha and Soo 1977b):

$$\mu_s^* = a_2 \left(\frac{\phi}{\phi_0 - \phi} \right)^2 + a_3 \left(\frac{\phi}{\phi_0 - \phi} \right)^3 + a_4 \left(\frac{\phi}{\phi_0 - \phi} \right)^4 \tag{3.3.6}$$

Fitting $2 < \phi/(\phi_0 - \phi) < 14$ gives, for $\phi = 0.52$,

$$a_2 = 1.650 \quad a_3 = -0.2709 \quad a_4 = 0.01114 \tag{3.3.7}$$

The non-Newtonian nature of the suspension was treated by Gabor (1972) using a Bingham-plastic fluid model for the particle phase and was verified with particle trajectories.

Apparent thermal conductivity of particle clouds was treated in Soo (1967); again, experimental data on individual interactions are meager. The average thermal conductivity was corrected by Gelperin & Einstein (1971) to give, for mean thermal conductivity of the solid $\bar{\lambda}_p$ and of the fluid $\bar{\lambda}$, the value of λ_m for the mixture

$$\frac{\lambda_m}{\bar{\lambda}} = 1 + \frac{\phi(1 - \bar{\lambda}/\bar{\lambda}_p)}{\bar{\lambda}/\bar{\lambda}_p + 0.28(1 - \phi)^{0.63} (\bar{\lambda}_p/\bar{\lambda})^{0.18}} \tag{3.3.8}$$

for ϕ denoting volume fraction of solid. This relation was given for a fixed bed and therefore is not satisfactory, but it is the only one available.

3.3.2 PARTICLE-FLUID INTERACTIONS

Interactions of momentum and energy between the phases must be accounted for even for heat transfer calculations. For a dilute suspension, the fluid-particle interactions are given by the momentum and energy equations of the particles (when velocity and temperature gradients are absent):

$$\frac{d\mathbf{U}_p}{dt_p} = \tau^{-1}(\mathbf{U} - \mathbf{U}_p) + \mathbf{f}_p' + \mathbf{f}_p \tag{3.3.9}$$

$$\frac{dT_p}{dt_p} = \tau_q^{-1}(T - T_p) + \frac{q_p}{C_p} \tag{3.3.10}$$

where $\mathbf{f}_p$ is the field force per unit mass of the particle phase and $\mathbf{f}_p'$ is the force due to the relative motion to fluid: apparent mass, relative acceleration, change in flow field, and fluid shear and q_p is the heat generated per unit mass of the particle phase including radiative input. τ is the relaxation time or time constant for momentum transfer from the fluid to the particle; τ_q is the relaxation time for convective heat transfer between the phases. For mass m_p of a particle, τ and τ_q are defined by

$$\tau^{-1} = \frac{\text{drag force}}{m_p|U - U_p|} \qquad [3.3.11]$$

$$\tau_q^{-1} = \frac{\text{heat exchanged}}{C_p m_p |T - T_p|} \qquad [3.3.12]$$

It is seen that only for small relative motion or the particle Reynolds number

$$\text{Re}_p = \frac{2a|U - U_p|\bar{\rho}}{\bar{\mu}} \leqslant 1$$

i.e., motion in the Stokes law range, τ and τ_q are constants, for $\bar{\rho}_p \gg \bar{\rho}$

$$\tau^{-1} = \frac{9\bar{\mu}}{2a^2 \bar{\rho}_p} \qquad [3.3.13]$$

$$\tau_q^{-1} = \frac{3\bar{\lambda}}{C_p a^2 \bar{\rho}_p} \qquad [3.3.14]$$

Modification of these relations for large Re_p and high particle concentration $\phi > 0.08$ has been extensively treated. Observations by Adachi et al. (1978) of the motion of a cluster of particles in a viscous liquid showed that the swarm of particles took various shapes: ring, hat, or expanding outlines. It was shown that the terminal velocity of fall is proportional to the square of the diameter of the boundary of the cluster. For the case of glass particles of 30 μm (specific gravity 2.5) at 0.4% by mass in a glycerol-water solution (specific gravity 1.258 and viscosity 0.848 kg/m s), the terminal velocity of the swarm was found to be half of that of a single sphere of the same material and outer diameter. However, the drag of an individual particle is only half of that of a single particle.

In identifying U, U_p and T, T_p we refer to the mass character of the fluid and the particle cloud; the distribution of fluid velocity and fluid temperature around each particle is accounted for in terms of τ and τ_q.

When corrected for apparent mass and large Re, a general form of τ is

$$\tau^{-1} = F^* \frac{9\bar{\mu}}{2a^2 \bar{\rho}_p} \qquad [3.3.15]$$

including the effect of apparent mass, and the non-Stokesian correction factor $F^* = (C_D/24) \, [2a(\bar{\rho}|U - U_p|)/\bar{\mu}]$ accounts for the deviation from the Stokes law of drag. Also, $\bar{\mu}$ is the viscosity of the fluid material, U and U_p are velocity vectors, and C_D is the drag coefficient for a sphere influenced by both Re and the cloud density. $F^* = 1$ in the Stokes law range. The nonsphericity of a particle may be accounted for by modifying C_D, but may also cause lift and moment depending on orientation in the flow field.

For $\phi < 0.08$, the following curve fitting is recommended:

$$F^* = 1 + 0.0975 \, \text{Re}_p - 0.636 \times 10^{-3} \, \text{Re}_p^2 \qquad [3.3.16]$$

and
$$Re_p = \frac{2a|U - U_p|\bar{\rho}}{\bar{\mu}} \leqslant 100 \qquad [3.3.17]$$

For $\phi > 0.08$, correlation of data in Soo (1967) gives:

$$\tau^{-1} = \frac{75}{2} \frac{\phi}{(1 - \phi)^2} \frac{\mu_g}{\bar{\rho}_p a^2} + \frac{1.75}{2(1 - \phi)} \frac{\bar{\rho}}{\bar{\rho}_p} \frac{|U - U_p|}{a} \qquad [3.3.18]$$

Note that $g\tau$ is the terminal settling velocity of particle p in the gas. For the gas-particle heat transfer we have

$$\tau_q^{-1} = \frac{3G^*\bar{\lambda}}{C_p \bar{\rho}_p a^2} \qquad [3.3.19]$$

and further,

$$G_p^* = \tfrac{1}{2} \text{ Nu Re } |_p \rightarrow 1 \qquad [3.3.20]$$

where Nu is the Nusselt number.

For the dense phase

$$\tau_q^{-1} = \frac{3h}{\bar{\rho}_p a C_p} \qquad [3.3.21]$$

where
$$h = jC\bar{\rho}|U - U|Pr^{-2/3} \qquad [3.3.22]$$

and the j factor is given by

$$j = 1.77 \text{ Re}_p^{-0.4} \qquad (\text{Re}_p > 30) \qquad [3.3.23]$$

$$j = 5.7 \text{ Re}_p^{-0.78} \qquad (\text{Re}_p < 30) \qquad [3.3.24]$$

3.3.3 INTERACTION LENGTH AND DYNAMIC MEANING OF DILUTE SUSPENSION

In a dilute particulate suspension, the effect of particle-particle interactions is negligible. However, there is an interaction length L_p for particles with the fluid due to Brownian motion, wall interaction, wake effects or fluid turbulence, or their combinations:

$$L_p \sim \langle \Delta U^2 \rangle^{1/2} \tau \qquad [3.3.25]$$

where $\langle \Delta U^2 \rangle^{1/2}$ is the root-mean-square relative velocity of the particles and the fluid. L_p may become large compared to the characteristic physical dimension of a system.

The frequency of particle-fluid interaction is given by $\langle \Delta U^2 \rangle^{1/2}/L_p = \tau^{-1}$ where $\langle \Delta U^2 \rangle^{1/2}$ is the intensity of relative motion between the phases and L_p is the corresponding interaction length. The frequency of particle-particle interaction is given by $\langle U_p^2 \rangle^{1/2}/\Lambda_p$, where Λ_p is the mean free path between collisions, given by $\Lambda_p = (\sqrt{2} \ 4n\pi a^2)^{-1}$, n being the number density of particles and $2a$ the particle diameter. The ratio of these two frequencies, $R^* = (\sqrt{2} \ 4n\pi a^2 \langle U_p^2 \rangle^{1/2} \tau)^{-1}$, has to be much greater than 1 for a suspension to be considered dilute. Denoting the volume fraction of particles by ϕ, which is $n(4\pi/3)a^3$, we have the condition

$$R^* = \frac{a}{3\sqrt{2}\,\langle U_p^2\rangle^{1/2}\tau\phi} \gg 1 \qquad [3.3.26]$$

for a dilute suspension. As noted in Soo (1967), the ratio of particle diffusivity to fluid diffusivity in a dilute suspension depends on a particle-fluid interaction parameter $\kappa = 2\langle U^2\rangle^{1/2}\,\tau/\Lambda$; $\langle U^2\rangle^{1/2}$ is the intensity of fluid motion and Λ is its Lagrangian microscale.* Accordingly, [3.3.26] can be rewritten as

$$\phi \ll \frac{2a/\Lambda}{3\sqrt{2}\kappa}\frac{\langle U^2\rangle^{1/2}}{\langle U_p^2\rangle^{1/2}} \qquad [3.3.27]$$

for a dilute suspension. The ratio $\langle U_p^2\rangle/\langle U^2\rangle = \sqrt{\pi}\,\kappa^{-1}\exp\kappa^{-2}\,\mathrm{erfc}\,\kappa^{-1}$ is nearly 1 for small κ and is $\sqrt{\pi}/\kappa$ for large κ (Soo 1978). Thus, we have for small κ (small particles for a given state of fluid:

$$\phi \ll \frac{2a/\Lambda}{3\sqrt{2}\kappa} = \frac{3\sqrt{\pi}}{2\sqrt{2}}\frac{\bar{\nu}}{D}\frac{\Lambda}{2a}\frac{\bar{\rho}}{\bar{\rho}_p} \qquad [3.3.28]$$

since $\tau^{-1} = 9\bar{\nu}\bar{\rho}/\bar{\rho}_p a^2 2$; $\bar{\nu}$ is the kinematic viscosity of the fluid and $D = (\sqrt{\pi}/2)\Lambda$ $\langle U^2\rangle^{1/2}$ is the fluid diffusivity. For large κ we have

$$\phi \ll \frac{2a}{\Lambda}3\sqrt{2}\,\pi^{1/4}\kappa^{1/2} = \frac{1}{2}\left(\frac{\bar{\nu}}{D}\frac{\bar{\rho}}{\bar{\rho}_p}\right)^{1/2} \qquad [3.3.29]$$

which is independent of particle size. The order of magnitude of this limiting volume fraction of particles is illustrated by the example of a gas-solid suspension for which $2a = 5\ \mu m$, $\bar{\nu} = 2\times10^{-5}\ m^2/s$, and $\langle U^2\rangle^{1/2} = 2\ m/s$; for small κ, $\phi < 0.5\%$ when $\bar{\rho}_p/\bar{\rho} = 1000$ and $\phi < 5\%$ when $\bar{\rho}_p/\bar{\rho} = 100$. For large κ, as for 500-μm particles, the limiting ϕ remains 0.5% when $\bar{\rho}_p/\bar{\rho} = 1000$ but is 1.5% when $\bar{\rho}_p/\bar{\rho} = 100$.

In addition, an upper limit of ϕ is expected to be that the mean free path of particle-particle interaction should be greater than the mean interparticle spacing. This limits ϕ to $(\frac{1}{2})^{3/4}/6\sqrt{\pi}$, or 5.5% of the total volume, based on a cubic pattern of spheres of uniform size regardless of the density ratio of the phases. Above this range, mutual collisions of particles contribute more significantly to transport of the particle phase in the mixture. A distribution of particle sizes allows a significantly higher volume fraction because of the reduced collision cross section for particles of different sizes.

3.3.4 PARTICLE-PARTICLE INTERACTIONS

Particle-particle interactions were treated in detail by Soo (1967) and more recently by Sha & Soo (1977b) when dealing with dynamics of a fluidized bed with particles of various sizes. The relaxation times τ and τ_q of particle-particle interactions arise

---

*In the sense defined by G. I. Taylor (see Hinze 1959).

from collision, deformation, contact, and separation. To determine τ_{12} (for collision of 1 and 2, $a_1 > a_2$ or $m_1 > m_2$), Langmuir & Blodgett (1946) introduced the functions

$$\Psi_{12} = \left(1 + \frac{a_2^3 \rho_2}{a_1^3 \bar{\rho}_1}\right)^{-1} \frac{\bar{\rho}_2 (U_1 - U_2)}{2(a_1 + a_2)18\bar{\mu}} (2a_2)^2 \qquad [3.3.30]$$

$$\Phi_{12} = \left(1 + \frac{a_2^3 \bar{\rho}_2}{a_1^3 \bar{\rho}_1}\right) \frac{9\bar{\rho}^2}{\bar{\mu}\bar{\rho}_2} (U_1 - U_2) 2 (a_2 + a_1) \qquad [3.3.31]$$

which give the fraction impacted

$$\eta_{12} = \eta_{12}(\Psi_{12}, \Phi_{12}) \qquad [3.3.32]$$

To facilitate numerical computation, an approximation to fit the curves, given by Langmuir & Blodgett for relative potential motion is as follows (Sha & Soo 1977b):

$$-\ln \eta_{12} = \frac{3.243 \times 10^5}{\Phi_{12} + 1.617 \times 10^5} \ln \left[1 + \frac{7.5 \ln(\Phi_{12} + 1.617 \times 10^5) - 89.16}{\Psi_{12}^{1/2}}\right]$$

$$[3.3.33]$$

and

$$\tau_{12}^{-1} = \frac{3}{4} \eta_{12} \frac{(a_1 + a_2)^2 |(U_1 - U_2)| \bar{\rho}_2}{a_1^3 \bar{\rho}_1} \left(1 + \frac{a_2^3 \bar{\rho}_2}{a_1^3 \bar{\rho}_1}\right)^{-1} \qquad [3.3.34]$$

A modification of η_{12} due to particle diffusivity was given by Soo (1973b). These transfers between solid phases include physical contact and heat transfer within that duration. For solid-solid interaction, the relaxation times τ_q are given by

$$\tau_{q12}^{-1} = C_{12} \frac{\rho_2}{\bar{\rho}_2} \frac{(\lambda_1 \lambda_2)^{1/2}}{C_1 \bar{\rho}_1 a_2 a_1} \qquad [3.3.35]$$

where

$$C_{12} = 2.94 \frac{45}{2^{2/5} 32\pi} \eta_{12} \left[\left(\frac{m_1}{m_2}\right)^{1/2} + \left(\frac{m_2}{m_1}\right)^{1/2}\right]^{-4/5}$$

$$\cdot \left[\left(\frac{a_2}{a_1}\right)^{1/2} + \left(\frac{a_1}{a_2}\right)^{1/2}\right]^{7/5} \left[\left(\frac{k_1}{k_2}\right)^{1/2} + \left(\frac{k_2}{k_1}\right)^{1/2}\right]^{4/5} Im^{4/5}$$

where m is the particle mass $[m_1 = (4\pi/3) a_1^3 \bar{\rho}_1]$, C is the specific heat of solids, $k = (1 - \nu^2)/\pi E$ where ν is the Poisson ratio of the solid material and E is its modulus of elasticity, λ_1 and λ_2 are the thermal conductivity of the materials of the solids, and the impact number

$$Im = 5\pi^2 [U_1 - U_2]^2 \bar{\rho}_2 (k_1 k_2)^{1/2} \frac{1 + r^*}{2} \qquad [3.3.36]$$

where $r^* \sim 1/2$, the ratio of rebound speed to incoming speed. In general,

$$\rho_1 C_1 \tau_{q12}^{-1} = \rho_2 C_2 \tau_{q21}^{-1} \qquad [3.3.37]$$

The heat transfer by impact of particles on a surface (2) becomes important for

$m_2 \gg m_1$ and $a_2 > a_1$, as in the case of the tube bank and solid wall $(2 = W)$. The heat transfer coefficient h_{1W} is given by

$$h_{1W} = \alpha_1 2.94 \frac{3}{4} 2^{2/5} \rho_{p1} \frac{\bar{\lambda}_1}{\bar{\rho}_1 a_1} \left[\left(\frac{k_1}{k_W} \right)^{1/2} + \left(\frac{k_W}{k_1} \right) \right]^{4/5} \operatorname{Im}_W^{4/5} \qquad [3.3.38]$$

and

$$\operatorname{Im}_W = 5\pi^2 (U_s)^2 \bar{\rho}_s (k_s k_W)^{1/2} \frac{1 + r^*}{2} \qquad [3.3.39]$$

where α_{1W} is the accommodation coefficient of impact of particles 1 with the wall; $\alpha_{1W} < 1$.

Agglomeration occurs when colliding particles do not rebound. Some understanding of the agglomeration of similar particles due to their relative motion or of scavenging of dust particles by liquid droplets can be achieved from a one-dimensional treatment. Relative motion may be produced by acceleration of a suspension of particles of different sizes, by acoustic waves acting on the suspension, or by a liquid spray countercurrent to a dusty gas. We illustrate the basic interactions by taking a one-dimensional model with finite and constant relative velocity ΔU between species 1 and species 2 particles, consider $a_2 \gg a_1$ and treat species 2 particles as the collector, and use a mean sticking probability σ for each collision.

The collection rate of particles 1 and particles 2 for cloud density ρ_{p1} of a_1 particles is given by $\sigma \eta_{12} \Delta U \rho_{p1} \pi a_2^2$ per a_2 particle per unit time. For each volume of particle clouds of number density n_2 of a_2 particles, $n_2 \sigma \eta_{12} \Delta U \rho_{p1} \pi a_2^2$ is the rate of agglomeration per unit volume. The mass rate of flow through cross-sectional area A of a duct is given by

$$\dot{m}_2 = n_2 \frac{4\pi}{3} a_2^3 \bar{\rho}_{p2} U_{p2} A = \rho_{p2} U_{p2} A \qquad [3.3.40]$$

$$\dot{m}_1 = n_1 \frac{4\pi}{3} a_1^3 \bar{\rho}_{p1} U_{p1} A = \rho_{p1} U_{p1} A \qquad [3.3.41]$$

where the U_p's are the particle velocities, $\Delta U = |U_{p1} - U_{p2}|$, and

$$\dot{m}_2 = \frac{\text{number of } a_2}{\text{area} \times \text{time}} \frac{4\pi}{3} a_2^3 \bar{\rho}_{p2} A \qquad [3.3.42]$$

We get

$$\frac{\text{Mass rate of agglomeration of } a_1}{\text{area} \times (\text{time})^2} = \frac{\dot{m}_2 \ \sigma \eta_{12} \Delta U \rho_{p1} \pi a_2^2}{(4\pi/3) a_2^3 \bar{\rho}_{p2} A} \qquad [3.3.43]$$

$$\frac{\text{Flow of } a_1}{\text{Area} \times \text{time}} = \frac{\dot{m}_1}{A} \qquad [3.3.44]$$

The ratio of these two quantities gives the mass fraction of a_1 agglomerated per unit time:

$$\alpha_{m1} = \frac{3}{4} \frac{\dot{m}_2}{\dot{m}_1} \frac{\rho_{p1}}{\bar{\rho}_{p2}} \sigma \eta_{12} \frac{\Delta U}{a_2} = \frac{3}{4} \frac{U_{p2}}{U_{p1}} \frac{\rho_{p2}}{\bar{\rho}_{p1}} \sigma \eta_{12} \frac{\Delta U}{a_2} \qquad [3.3.45]$$

Over a distance dx swept by species 2 particles, the mass fraction of a_1

agglomerated is given by

$$\alpha_{m1} = \frac{3}{4} \frac{\dot{m}_2}{\dot{m}_1} \frac{\rho_{p1}}{\bar{\rho}_{p2}} \sigma \eta_{12} \frac{\Delta U}{a_2} \frac{dx}{U_{p2}}$$ [3.3.46]

As the collection proceeds, particles 2 will have fewer particles 1 to collect; the collection efficiency over a distance L traversed by each particle of species 2 is

$$\eta_c = 1 - \exp\left(-\frac{3}{4} \frac{\dot{m}_2}{\dot{m}_1} \frac{\rho_{p1}}{\bar{\rho}_{p2}} \sigma \eta_{12} \frac{\Delta U}{a_2} \frac{L}{U_{p2}}\right) \equiv 1 - \exp\left(-L^*\right)$$ [3.3.47]

L^* in [3.3.47] can be expressed in a more convenient form for collection of dust particles (species 1) by droplets in a water spray (species 2) where $\sigma \sim 1$ in terms of

$$\text{Volume flow rate of liquid} = \dot{Q}_L = \frac{\dot{m}_2}{\bar{\rho}_{p2}}$$

$$\text{Volume flow rate of gas} = \dot{Q}_G = \frac{\dot{m}_1}{\rho_{p1}}$$

We get

$$L^* = \frac{3}{4} \frac{\dot{Q}_L}{\dot{Q}_G} \sigma \eta_{12} \frac{\Delta U}{a_2} \frac{L}{U_{p2}}$$ [3.3.48]

For a liquid spray into a bulk of dusty gas, $\Delta U = U_{p2}$, L is then the stopping distance, $\dot{Q}_L/\dot{Q}_G$ can be replaced by the volume of liquid used to clean a given volume of gas, Q_L/Q_G (Soo 1973a). The case of pipe flow of a dusty gas over a conical spray was treated by Zaitsev et al. (1975); numerical solution is only applicable to specific cases.

Unless the dust density is very high, agglomeration by relative velocity is not effective. Collection efficiency can be improved by using charged droplets (Zebel 1968; Green & Lane 1964).

Relative motion of particles of different or similar sizes can be produced acoustically (Green & Lane 1964). The collection efficiency varies with frequency and with the size of the particles. It should be noted that particle diffusivity plays an important role here, besides Brownian motion of small particles. Recent experiments by Scott (1975) and Scott et al. (1977) showed that high efficiency can be achieved by using pulses of 250–400 Hz to agglomerate 1-μm ZnO particles to 8 μm in a gaseous suspension of mass ratio of 10^{-3}–10^{-2}. For further details see Shaw (1979).

3.3.5 PARTICLE-WALL INTERACTIONS

Basic particle-wall interactions are momentum and heat transfer and deposition (see section 3.2.2). Erosion of the wall and attrition of particles are also significant effects, of which our knowledge is largely empirical at present; they are treated in section 7.1.

3.3.5.1 Particle Velocity at the Wall

Consider flow over a flat plate along the x direction. We have $x = 0$ at the leading edge, $U_i = U$, $U_{pi} = U_p$, $x_i = x$, $x_j = y$, and free-stream velocity U. The boundary condition of particle velocity at the wall is

$$U_{pW} = U(1 - \xi) + L_p \left(\frac{\partial U_p}{\partial y}\right)_{y=0} \qquad [3.3.49]$$

where $\xi = x/U\tau$; $\xi = 1$ for $x/U\tau > 1$. The interaction Knudsen number

$$Kp = \frac{L_p}{x} \qquad [3.3.50]$$

Hence, not only may the particles have different streamlines from the fluid, but the phases may exist in different flow regimes (Soo 1962). For example, in a turbulent fluid the motion of suspended particles could be in a regime analogous to that of a rarefied gas.

3.3.5.2 Heat Transfer and Accommodation

For similar reasons, the interaction length for convection heat transfer between the particle and the fluid is

$$L_T = \langle \Delta U^2 \rangle^{1/2} \tau_q = L_p \frac{\tau_q}{\tau} \qquad [3.3.51]$$

For flow over a flat plate as in the above example with temperatures T_W at the wall and T_∞ in the free stream, we have the boundary condition for particle temperature

$$T_{pW} - T_W = (T_\infty - T_W)(1 - \xi_T) + L_T \left(\frac{\partial T_p}{\partial y}\right)_{y=0} \qquad [3.3.52]$$

with

$$\xi_T = \frac{x}{U\tau_q} = \xi \frac{\tau_q}{\tau}$$

and $\xi_T = 1$ at $x/U\tau_q > 1$; T_{pW} is the temperature of the particles at the wall. Further, since the temperature of the particle phase is the body temperature of the particles, heat conduction by surface contact must be accounted for (Soo 1969). For elastic collision of particles with a wall, an accommodation coefficient α is given by

$$\alpha \sim \frac{15(2.94)}{16(2)^{2/5}} \frac{(\bar{\lambda}_p \bar{\lambda}_W)^{1/2}}{C_p \bar{\rho}_p a \Delta U_W} \text{Im}^{4/5} \qquad [3.3.53]$$

where

$$\text{Im} = \frac{5\pi^2}{2} (\Delta U_W)^2 (1 + r^*) \bar{\rho}_p k_p \left(1 + \frac{k_p}{k_W}\right) \qquad [3.3.54]$$

r^* is the ratio of the reflected speed to the incoming speed ΔU_W, $k = (1 - v^2)/\pi E$, v is the Poisson ratio, and E is the modulus of elasticity. The temperatures of an incoming particle T_{pi} and a reflected particle T_{pr} are related by

$$\frac{T_{pr} - T_{pi}}{T_W - T_{pi}} = \alpha \qquad [3.3.55]$$

Since $T_{pW} \sim (T_{pi} + T_{pr})/2$, the heat flux J_{qp} due to impaction of particles at the wall is given by

$$\frac{J_{qp}}{C_p \dot{m}_{pW}} = T_r - T_i = \frac{-2\alpha}{2 - \alpha} (T_{pW} - T_W) \qquad [3.3.56]$$

where $\dot{m}_{pW}$ is the mass flux of impact at the wall. Equations [3.3.52] and [3.3.56] account for both the effect of conduction by surface contact at the wall and the effect of convection heat transfer with the fluid.

3.3.5.3 Surface Forces and Sticking Probability

The force of adhesion of particles on a clean surface or a surface with a layer of deposited particles influences deposition or further deposition of particles. In a review, Corn (1961) showed that adhesive forces are either electrical or liquid [viscosity (Eley 1961) and surface tension (Pietsch et al. 1969)] in origin. The electrical forces include those due to contact potential difference and dipole effect (Penny & Klingler 1962; Niedra & Penny 1965), space charges (Kottler et al. 1968), and electronic structure (Czichos 1969).

The adhesive force between a plane solid and a spherical solid particle is given by (Krupp 1967)

$$F_v = \frac{\hbar \omega a}{8 \pi z_0^2} \qquad [3.3.57]$$

where $\hbar \omega$ is the Lifschitz-van der Waals constant, $\hbar$ is Planck's constant divided by 2π, and ω is a frequency; z_0 is the distance between the adherents at the instant of maximum attraction during separation $\sim 4 \times 10^{-8}$ cm.

The phenomenon of adhesion of particles is influenced by many factors. Löffler & Muhr (1972) first reported that the sticking probability σ_W of 2.8-μm quartz particles on polyamide and glass fibers of 19 μm diameter decreases with particle velocity. Experimental values (Löffler 1977) of σ_W for quartz and glass particles 5 and 10 μm in diameter on 20-μm polyamide and glass fibers are shown in Fig. 3.3.1; it was noted that rebounding starts at about 5–15 cm/s. As speed increases, σ_W decreases rapidly; σ_W is also less for 10-μm than for 5-μm particles.

In the adhesion of an individual particle to particle multilayers adhering to a substrate, a space charge effect exists between individual particles giving a force equal to $Q\mathbf{E}_e$; Q is the charge of a particle and $\mathbf{E}_e$ is the electric field. In particle multilayers, the interparticle distance is large compared to the particle diameter and there is a force due to repulsion of like charges. The force of adhesion between polymer particles (5 and 30 μm in diameter) and a layer of amorphous selenium was measured by centrifuging after a contact time of 1 h. Charges obtained triboelectrically were 3×10^4 to 4×10^5 e per particle, where e is the electron charge. Forces for both multilayers and selenium surfaces were measured. An

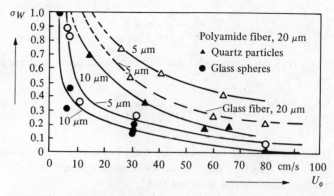

Figure 3.3.1   Sticking probability of quartz particles and glass spheres on 20μm fibers of polyamide and glass as a function of velocity (Löffler 1977).

effective particle charge—a portion of the total charge Q that is seen by the partner of adhesion—was measured with $\hbar\omega \sim 2$ eV (Krupp 1967).

3.3.6   EFFECT OF RADIATION

Even though the fluid phase might be transparent to radiation at temperatures above say, 500°C, heat transfer to a suspension by radiation is usually significant. In an optically thin dilute phase, where every particle sees the wall with which it exchanges heat by radiation, a simple radiation heat balance is adequate. In the dense phase, closely spaced particles emit independently, although radiative transfer depends on the condition of the particle cloud. An appropriate radiation model must be chosen (Soo 1967). The absorption coefficient α'_m (m^{-1}) is given by

$$\alpha'_m = \alpha_r \pi a^2 N_p \tag{3.3.58}$$

where α_r is the absorptivity of the surface for radiation, and N_p is number density of particles.

The radiation exchange constitutes a heat source in a given volume

$$\rho_p \frac{4\pi a^2}{m_p} \int_0^\infty \alpha_\lambda \left(E_{b\lambda} - \int_{4\pi} I_\lambda d\Omega \right) d\lambda \tag{3.3.59}$$

where λ is the wavelength, $E_{b\lambda}$ is the blackbody radiation at wavelength λ (energy per unit area per unit time), and I is the intensity of radiation, given (for spherical coordinates s, θ, and ϕ) by

$$\frac{dI(s, \theta, \phi)}{ds} = -\alpha'_m [I(s, \theta, \phi) - \hat{n}_m^2 I_b(s)] \tag{3.3.60}$$

where I_b is the intensity of blackbody radiation. Since the solid particles in the present system are opaque, the index of refraction $\hat{n}_m$ of the mixture is that of the gas phase. Viskanta & Grosh (1961) suggested introducing a radiative conductivity of magnitude

$$\lambda_{rad} = \frac{16\,\hat{n}_m^2\,\sigma_r T^3}{3\alpha_m'} \tag{3.3.61}$$

where σ_r is the Stefan-Boltzmann constant of radiation and T is the temperature of the phase under consideration.

This radiative conductivity is added to λ_m of [3.3.8] to account for the effect of diffuse radiation. For a distribution of particle sizes, use

$$\alpha_m' = \alpha_r \pi \sum_s a_s^2 N_s = \alpha_r \frac{3}{4} \sum_s \frac{1}{a_s} \frac{\rho_s}{\bar{\rho}_s} \tag{3.3.62}$$

The heat flux due to diffuse radiation J_{Ep} therefore takes the form

$$J_{Ep} = \frac{\partial}{\partial x_j}\left[\lambda_{rad}\frac{\partial}{\partial x_j}\left(\frac{\rho_p C_p T_p}{\rho_m C_m}\right)\right] \tag{3.3.63}$$

3.3.7 ELECTROSTATIC EFFECTS

The smaller the particles in a suspension, the more significant is the effect of the electric charges it carries. An uncharged micrometer-sized particle is a special case. Particles collect charges by contact with a surface, from atmospheric electricity, from an ionized gas, or by emission (Soo 1971).

Charge transfer by collision of a cloud of particles with a surface is illustrated by the relation for the electrostatic ball probe given in Cheng & Soo (1970). Corresponding to [3.3.35] and [3.3.10] for the collision with sphere 2 of a cloud of spherical particles 1, we have the inverse relaxation time for charge transfer H_{21} given by

$$\frac{dV_2}{dt_2} = -H_{21}(V_2 - V_1) \tag{3.3.64}$$

where V is the electric potential and

$$H_{21} = K_{21}\frac{h_{21}}{\epsilon_2}\frac{\rho_1}{\bar{\rho}_1}a_2^2(a_2 a_1)^{-1/2} \tag{3.3.65}$$

h_{21} is the change transfer coefficient and K_{21} is a dimensionless constant given by

$$K_{21} = \frac{15}{32}\,2.97\,\eta_{21}\left[\left(\frac{m_2}{m_1}\right)^{1/2} + \left(\frac{m_1}{m_2}\right)^{1/2}\right]^{4/5}\left[\left(\frac{a_2}{a_1}\right)^{1/2}\right.$$
$$\left. + \left(\frac{a_1}{a_2}\right)^{1/2}\right]^{7/5}\left[\left(\frac{k_2}{k_1}\right)^{1/2} + \left(\frac{k_1}{k_2}\right)^{1/2}\right]^{4/5}Im_{21}^{4/5} \tag{3.3.66}$$

and the impact number is given by

$$Im_{21} = 5\pi^2(\Delta U)^2\,(\bar{\rho}_1\bar{\rho}_2)^{1/2}\,(k_1 k_2)^{1/2}\frac{1 + r^*}{2} \tag{3.3.67}$$

consisting of elastic and dynamic properties only (Soo et al. 1970; Cheng & Soo 1970).

3.4 Pipe Flow

S. L. Soo

Pipe flow has been the basic means through which our current understanding of the fluid dynamics of suspensions has been developed. We now treat pipe flow, considering general relations, fully developed motion, sedimentary motion, and vapor lift. A direct application is discussed in section 7.1 on pneumatic conveying.

Gravity was shown to be important in the flow of a suspension of sand in water (Newitt et al. 1962), where the effect of electric charge would not be prominent. In the case of a gas-particle suspension in pipe flow, the particle charge effect is significant but the gravity effect is small for small pipes or large Froude numbers (Soo 1969). However, for flow of a gas-particle suspension in large pipes, both effects are significant; the general case consists of a pipe at any inclination to the direction of gravity.

3.4.1 GENERAL RELATIONS

The flow system consists of a circular pipe with its axis at angle θ to the direction of gravity, as shown in figure 3.4.1. In the figure z, r, and ϕ are the axial, radial, and azimuthal coordinates; U, V, and W are the conjugate components of velocity of the fluid; and U_p, V_p, and W_p are those of the particle phase. We treat only the case of a monodisperse suspension of spherical particles of a single species with radius a, although extension to include a distribution of particle sizes is readily accomplished.

For a dilute suspension, the transport of momentum of particles is given by the gradient of "stress" given by the tensor (alternate form of [3.2.4]):

$$\tau_p = \rho_p D_p(\nabla \mathbf{V}_p + \nabla \tilde{\mathbf{V}}_p) - \tfrac{2}{3}\rho_p D_p(\nabla \cdot \mathbf{V}_p)\mathbf{U} \qquad [3.4.1]$$

where $\mathbf{U}$ is a unitary tensor. In a dilute suspension—i.e., a free path of particle-particle collision $> L_p >$ interparticle spacing $> 2a$—the fluid motion is unaffected by the presence of the particles. This assumption is still valid for deposition of particles when the thickness of the layer of deposit is much smaller than the pipe radius.

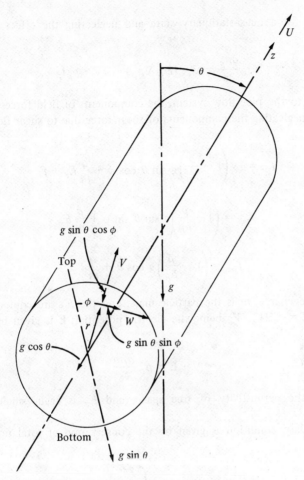

Figure 3.4.1 Coordinate system and components of
gravitational acceleration g.

We first consider cases where the fluid motion is unaffected by the presence of
particles. This means that the motion of the particle phase corresponds to viscous
slip motion and particles are not correlated with each other even when the fluid is
turbulent (Soo 1970). We treat the case where the axial gradient of the total
particle flow is small enough that a quasi-stationary state can be assumed for
transient deposition; i.e., $\partial/\partial t = 0$. Moreover, since the particle velocity distribution
over a pipe is not strongly influenced by different loading of similar particles (Soo
1971), all the inertia terms can be neglected.

The flux of particles due to field and fluid forces is now given by

$$\rho_p(\mathbf{V}_p - \mathbf{V}) = \mathbf{f}_p \rho_p \tau + \tau \nabla \cdot \tau_p \qquad [3.4.2]$$

where $\mathbf{f}_p$ is the force per unit mass.

Where deposition may occur, conservation of mass has to be accounted for by
the diffusion equation for a dilute suspension given by [3.2.7], and substitution of

[3.4.2] gives, for a quasi-stationary state and neglecting the effect of τ_p (Soo & Tung, 1972),

$$\mathbf{V} \cdot \frac{\partial \rho_p}{\partial \mathbf{r}} = \nabla \cdot (D_p \, \nabla \rho_p) - \tau \nabla \cdot \rho_p \mathbf{f}_p \qquad [3.4.3]$$

When applied to the pipe flow system, the components of field forces and the fluid force f_L are (neglecting the components of shear force due to shear flow in the ϕ, z directions):

$$f_{pr} = -\left(1 - \frac{\bar{\rho}}{\rho_p}\right) g \sin \theta \, \cos \phi + \frac{q}{m} E_r + f_L \qquad [3.4.4]$$

$$f_{p\phi} = \left(1 - \frac{\bar{\rho}}{\rho_p}\right) g \sin \theta \, \sin \phi + \frac{q}{m} E_\phi \qquad [3.4.5]$$

$$f_{pz} = \left(1 - \frac{\bar{\rho}}{\rho_p}\right) g \cos \theta + \frac{q}{m} E_z \qquad [3.4.6]$$

where q is the charge, m is the particle mass, and the E's are components of the electric field $\mathbf{E} = - \nabla V_e$, V_e being the electric potential; $\mathbf{E}$ is given by the Poisson equation

$$\nabla \cdot \mathbf{E} = \rho_p \frac{q/m}{\epsilon_0} \qquad [3.4.7]$$

where ϵ_0 is the permittivity of free space, and E_z is again small for gradual deposition.

The boundary condition is given by the conservation of total flow through a circular pipe:

$$\frac{\partial}{\partial z} \int_0^{2\pi} \int_0^R \rho_p U_p r \, dr d\phi = - \sigma R \int_0^{2\pi} V_{pR} \rho_{pR} d\phi - \sigma_w 2\pi R \rho_{pR} f_W \tau$$

$$+ \sigma_w' 2\pi R \rho_{pb} f_L \tau, \qquad [3.4.8]$$

where the terms were explained in section 3.2.2.

Since we assume that the motion of the fluid phase is fully developed ($\partial U/\partial z = 0$), we have for $E_z = 0$

$$\frac{\partial}{\partial z} (\rho_p U_p) = \frac{\partial}{\partial z} [\rho_p (U_p - U)] + U \frac{\partial \rho_p}{\partial z}$$

$$= \left[U - \tau \left(1 - \frac{\bar{\rho}}{\rho_p}\right) g \cos \theta\right] \frac{\partial \rho_p}{\partial z} \qquad [3.4.9]$$

Substitution of [3.4.9] and [3.4.3] into [3.4.8] gives, with $V_{pR} \sim f_{pr}\tau$,

$$D_p \left. \frac{\partial \rho_p}{\partial r} \right|_R = -(1 - \sigma)\left(1 - \frac{\bar{\rho}}{\bar{\rho}_p}\right) g\tau \sin\theta \cos\phi \, \rho_{pR}$$

$$+ [(1 - \sigma)\rho_{pr} + \sigma'_W \rho_{pb}] f_L\tau$$

$$+ (1 - \sigma)\frac{q}{m} \tau E_r \rho_{pR} - \sigma_W \rho_{pR} f_W \tau \qquad [3.4.10]$$

which, for $\sigma = 0$, $\sigma_W = 0$, and $\sigma'_W = 0$, reverts to the nondepositing boundary condition.

The same condition is satisfied when

$$\sigma\left(1 - \frac{\bar{\rho}}{\bar{\rho}_p}\right) g\tau \sin\theta \cos\phi + \left(-\sigma + \sigma'_W \frac{\rho_{pb}}{\rho_{pR}}\right) f_L\tau$$

$$- \sigma \frac{q}{m} E_r \tau - \sigma_W f_W \tau = 0 \qquad [3.4.11]$$

Existence of ρ_{pb} means the presence of a fixed or moving bed, or the condition of saltation.

For a dilute suspension, transport of momentum of the particulate phase is by diffusion of the particles through the fluid. When the particle-fluid interaction length L_p is not too small compared to R (Soo 1969; Tung 1971), we have

$$\tau_{pzr} = \rho_p D_p \frac{\partial U_p}{\partial r}$$

$$\tau_{pz\phi} = \rho_p D_p \frac{\partial U_p}{r\partial \phi} \qquad [3.4.12]$$

The boundary conditions are

$$V_e(R, \phi) = V_{eR}(\phi) \qquad [3.4.13]$$

$$U_{pW} = - L_p \left. \frac{dU_p}{dr} \right|_{r=R-a} \qquad [3.4.14]$$

For a conducting pipe, the surface at radius R is a Gaussian surface such that V_{eR} is uniform while $V_e = 0$ at an interior point and $V_e < 0$ elsewhere.

3.4.2 CORRELATION PARAMETERS

We treat specific cases using the dimensionless quantities

$$r^* = \frac{r}{R} \qquad z^* = \frac{z}{R} \qquad \rho_p^* = \frac{\rho_p}{\rho_{p1}} = \rho_p^*(r^*, z^*, \phi)$$

$$U^* = \frac{U}{U_0} = U^*(r^*) \qquad U_p^* = \frac{U_p}{U_0} = U_p^*(r^*, z^*, \phi) \qquad [3.4.15]$$

$$V^* = \tau \frac{q}{m} \frac{V_e}{D_p} \qquad E^* = - \nabla^* V^*$$

where U_0 is the fluid velocity at the center of the pipe and ρ_{p1} is the density of particles at the initial condition ($z^* = 0$) of fully developed motion.

We also define

$$\alpha = \frac{\rho_{p1}}{4\epsilon_0}\left(\frac{q}{m}\right)^2 \frac{R^2\tau}{D_p}$$

$$\beta = \frac{R^2}{D_p\tau}$$

$$\gamma = 2\left(1 - \frac{\bar{\rho}}{\bar{\rho}_p}\right)R^2 g \frac{\cos\theta}{D_p U_0}$$

$$\eta = 2\left(1 - \frac{\bar{\rho}}{\bar{\rho}_p}\right)\tau R g \frac{\sin\theta}{D_p}$$

the momentum transfer number N_m and particle Knudsen number Kp [3.2.51]

$$N_m = \frac{\tau U_0}{R} \qquad \text{Kp} = \frac{L_p}{R}$$

and the adhesive force parameter

$$N_{Ad} = \frac{\tau R f_W}{D_p}$$

f_W acts only on particles in the immediate vicinity of the wall.

We take the shear-lift parameter (Soo & Tung 1972) according to the correlation of data of Graf & Acaroglu (1968)

$$\varsigma = \frac{c_1'}{12}\left(\frac{a}{R}\right)^{1/2}\frac{RU_0}{D_p} \qquad c_1' \sim 0.5$$

The parameters α, β, etc. can also be expressed in terms of dimensionless numbers of interactions of two effects as follows:

$$N_{ED} = \left(\frac{\rho_{p0}}{4\epsilon_0}\right)^{1/2}\frac{q}{m}\frac{R^2}{D_p}$$

the electro-diffusion number, which is the ratio of displacement by electrostatic repulsion to that by diffusion. The diffusion-response number is

$$N_{DF} = \frac{D_p\tau}{R^2} = \beta^{-1}$$

which is the ratio of relaxation time τ to diffusion time R^2/D_p, the well-known Froude number

$$\text{Fr} = \frac{U_0}{(2Rg)^{1/2}}$$

This is the square root of the ratio of inertia force to gravity force, and the momentum transfer number is the ratio of relaxation time to transport time. In terms of these dimensionless numbers,

$$\alpha = N_{ED}^2 N_{Df}$$

$$\gamma = \mathrm{Fr}^{-2} N_{DF}^{-1} N_m \left(1 - \frac{\bar{\rho}}{\bar{\rho}_p}\right) \cos\theta$$

etc., which accounts for multiple interactions.

With these correlations, the momentum equation of the particle phase in pipe flow takes the form

$$-\frac{1}{2}\gamma\rho_p^* + \frac{1}{r^*}\frac{\partial}{\partial r^*}\left(r^*\rho_p^*\frac{\partial U_p^*}{\partial r^*}\right) + \frac{1}{r^{*2}}\frac{\partial}{\partial\phi}\left(\rho_p^*\frac{\partial U_p^*}{\partial\phi}\right)$$

$$+ \beta\rho_p^*(U^* - U_p^*) = 0 \qquad\qquad [3.4.16]$$

where the inertia effect is neglected. The diffusion equation now becomes

$$N_m\left(\beta U^* - \frac{1}{2}\gamma\right)\frac{\partial\rho_p^*}{\partial z^*} = \frac{1}{r^*}\frac{\partial}{\partial r^*}\left(r^*\frac{\partial\rho_p^*}{\partial r^*}\right) + \frac{1}{r^{*2}}\frac{\partial^2\rho_p^*}{\partial\phi^2}$$

$$-\frac{1}{r^*}\frac{\partial}{\partial r^*}(r^*\rho_p^* E_r^*) + \frac{1}{2}\eta\left(\cos\phi\frac{\partial\rho_p^*}{\partial r^*} - \frac{\sin\phi}{r^*}\frac{\partial\rho_p^*}{\partial\phi}\right)$$

$$+ \frac{1}{r^*}\frac{\partial}{\partial r^*}(r^*\rho_p^* L^*) \qquad\qquad [3.4.17]$$

where
$$L^* = \zeta\left|\frac{\partial U^*}{\partial r^*}\right|^{1/2}\frac{U_p^* - U^* + \Delta U^*}{|U_p^* - U^* + \Delta U^*|^{1/2}} \qquad [3.4.18]$$

The Poisson equation is

$$\frac{1}{r^*}\frac{\partial}{\partial r^*}\left(r^*\frac{\partial V^*}{\partial r^*}\right) + \frac{1}{r^{*2}}\frac{\partial^2 V^*}{\partial\phi^2} = -4\alpha\rho^* \qquad [3.4.19]$$

The boundary conditions are

$$\phi = \pm\frac{\pi}{2} \qquad \frac{\partial\rho_p^*}{\partial r^*}\bigg|_0 = 0$$

and, from [3.4.10], when $\bar{\rho}_p > \bar{\rho}$,

$$\frac{\partial\rho_p^*}{\partial r^*}\bigg|_1 = -(1-\sigma)\frac{1}{2}\eta\cos\phi\,\rho_p^* - \sigma_W N_{Ad}\rho_p^* - (1-\sigma)\frac{\partial V^*}{\partial r^*}\rho_p^* \qquad [3.4.20]$$

for $\pi/2 < \phi < 3\pi/2$. Since the top cannot have particles falling into the suspension, the boundary condition becomes

$$\frac{\partial\rho_p^*}{\partial r^*}\bigg|_1 = -\frac{1}{2}\eta\cos\phi\,\rho_p^* - \sigma_W N_{Ad}\rho_p^* - (1-\sigma)\frac{\partial V^*}{\partial r^*}\rho_p^* \qquad [3.4.21]$$

for $-\pi/2 < \phi < \pi/2$. Note that the reverse has to be specified when $\bar{\rho}_p < \bar{\rho}$, as in the case of buoyant particles or bubbles.

The condition of a dilute suspension permits the stipulation that U and τ of the fluid are not influenced by the presence of the particles. Further, for large Reynolds and Froude numbers of the fluid phase [$Re = U_0 R \bar{\rho}/\bar{\mu}$ and $Fr = U_0/(2Rg)^{1/2}$, U_0 being the maximum velocity of the fluid phase and R the pipe radius], gravity does not influence the velocity distribution of the fluid phase, τ_{zr} is the sheer stress, and [3.2.3] is reduced to

$$-\frac{dP}{dz} - \rho g \cos \theta + \frac{1}{r}\frac{d}{dr}(r\tau_{zr}) = 0 \qquad [3.4.22]$$

τ is just the shear stress of the fluid with $\rho \sim \bar{\rho}$. For turbulent flow, let $y = R - r$,

$$u = U_0 \left(\frac{y}{R}\right)^{1/7} \qquad [3.4.23]$$

for $y_s < y < R$ with $y_s = 60(U_0 R\rho/\bar{\mu})^{-7/8} R$, the thickness of the laminar sublayer. Under this condition, gravity contributes only to the change in static pressure along the axis of the pipe. For laminar flow, Poiseuille motion exists in the fluid phase.

3.4.3 FULLY DEVELOPED PIPE FLOW

Fully developed motion excludes deposition of the particulate phase under the field force $\mathbf{f}_p$; i.e., the fluxes due to diffusion $(-D_p\nabla\rho_p)$ and relaxation under field force $\mathbf{J}_F$ must be equal, or

$$\mathbf{J}_F + (-D_p\nabla\rho_p) = 0 \qquad [3.4.24]$$

Since $d\mathbf{U}_p/dt = \partial\mathbf{U}_p/\partial t + \mathbf{U}_p \cdot (\partial\mathbf{U}_p/\partial r) = 0$ for fully developed motion, [3.2.4] gives [3.4.2] exactly

$$\mathbf{J}_F = \rho_p(\mathbf{U}_p - \mathbf{U}) = \rho_p \mathbf{f}_p \tau \qquad [3.4.25]$$

In terms of components of the particle flux, for charge to mass ratio q/m of each particle and local electric potential V_e of the particle cloud, we have

$$-D_p \frac{\partial\rho_p}{\partial r} - \frac{q}{m}\tau\rho_p\frac{\partial V_e}{\partial r} - \rho_p\left(1 - \frac{\bar{\rho}}{\bar{\rho}_p}\right)g\tau \sin\theta \cos\phi - \rho_p f_L \tau = 0 \qquad [3.4.26]$$

$$-\frac{D_p}{r}\frac{\partial\rho_p}{\partial\phi} - \frac{q}{m}\tau\frac{\rho_p}{r}\frac{\partial V_e}{\partial\phi} + \rho_p\left(1 - \frac{\bar{\rho}}{\bar{\rho}_p}\right)g\tau \sin\theta \sin\phi = 0 \qquad [3.4.27]$$

It is readily seen that when $f_L \sim 0$ (see section 3.2.2), [3.4.26] and [3.4.27] are not independent because both integrate to

$$D_p \ln \rho_p = c_1 - \frac{q}{m}\tau V_e - (g\sin\theta)\tau r \cos\phi\left(1 - \frac{\bar{\rho}}{\bar{\rho}_p}\right) \qquad [3.4.28]$$

where the constant of integration is $c_1(\phi) = c_1(r) = c_1$.

It is readily seen from [3.4.28] that for a pipe made of an electrical conductor $V_{eR}(\phi) = $ const, and gravity gives the relation of particle density at the top $\rho_p(R, 0)$ and bottom $\rho_p(R, \pi)$ as $(R \gg a)$

$$\ln \frac{\rho_p(R, \pi)}{\rho_p(R, 0)} = \frac{2g \sin \theta \; R\tau}{D_p} \left(1 - \frac{\bar{\rho}}{\bar{\rho}_p}\right) \qquad [3.4.29]$$

Therefore, the significance of the effect of gravity depends on this dimensionless quantity and the magnitude of $\rho_p(R, \pi) - \rho_p(R, 0)$ depends on actual density and θ. Naturally, the distribution in particle density in vertical pipe flow is symmetrical with respect to the centerline of the pipe. Note that this is a basic means by which particle diffusivity in pipe flow can be determined. The values of D_p so determined from measurements (Soo et al. 1964, 1970) amount to 0.5–1.2 times the turbulent diffusivity of the fluid phase (D) in pipes 50–125 mm in diameter and ducts 75–300 mm in square section, with particles of glass, coal, and magnesia (Soo 1975).

When treating fully developed motion, [3.4.17] is replaced by $(N_{Ad} = 0)$

$$\frac{\partial \ln \rho_p^*}{\partial r^*} = -\frac{1}{2} \eta \cos \phi - \frac{\partial V^*}{\partial r^*} - L^* \qquad [3.4.30]$$

$$\frac{\partial \ln \rho_p^*}{r^* \partial \phi} = \frac{1}{2} \eta \sin \phi - \frac{\partial V^*}{r^* \partial \phi}$$

and, when the effect of L^* is negligible, they combine to

$$\ln \rho^* = -\tfrac{1}{2} \eta r^* \cos \phi - V^* \qquad [3.4.31]$$

where ρ_p is now the density of the particle cloud at $r = 0$ and the dimensionless total flow rate of the characteristic mass flow ratio is given by

$$\dot{m}^* = \frac{\dot{m}}{\pi R^2 \rho_p U_0} = \frac{1}{\pi} \int_0^{2\pi} \int_0^1 \rho_p^* U_p^* r^* dr^* d\phi \qquad [3.4.32]$$

and the average density of the particle cloud is characterized by the characteristic mass ratio

$$m^* = \frac{1}{\pi} \int_0^{2\pi} \int_0^1 \rho_p^* r^* dr^* d\phi \qquad [3.4.33]$$

m^* would be identical to those defined for the case $\rho_{po}/\rho = 1$. We also have $U^* = y^{*1/7}$ with Reynolds number $\mathrm{Re} = R U_0 \bar{\rho}/\bar{\mu}$ in the turbulent range.

Interesting cases of nondepositing pipe flow in a turbulent fluid are as follows [extensive computer programs are given in Tung (1971)]:

1. Negligible gravity and shear effects; $\eta = 0$, $\gamma = 0$, $\zeta = 0$; the distribution of particle density is given by $\rho_p^* = [1 - (\alpha/2) r^{*2}]^{-2}$. The velocity distribution computed is given in figure 3.4.2 for $\mathrm{Kp} = 1$ and $\beta = 40$, compared to experimental data. Note the slip at the boundary (Soo 1969).

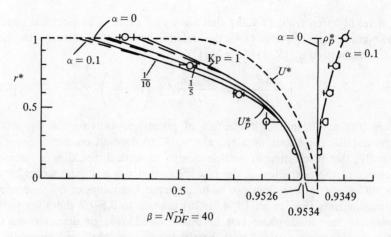

Figure 3.4.2 Velocity and density profiles in fully developed turbulent pipe flow of a suspension (Soo 1969). (○) Measured value for solid-gas mass ratio of 0.45, $U_0 = 138$ fps, 5-in pipe. (⊢⊣) Range for other mass ratios.

2. $\alpha = 0$, $\eta = 0$, $\gamma = 0$, $\zeta = 0$, velocity distribution given by [3.4.16] (Soo & Tung 1971).
3. $\alpha = 0$, finite η, $\gamma = 0$ (horizontal pipe), $\zeta = 0$. This case is illustrated in figure 3.4.3 (Wen 1966).
4. $\alpha = 0$, $\eta = 0$, finite γ (vertical pipe), $\zeta = 0$, cases of cocurrent and counter-current flow are illustrated in figure 3.4.4; the profiles are symmetrical (Soo & Tung 1971).
5. $\alpha = 0$, finite η and γ, $\zeta = 0$, combination of cases 3 and 4 (Soo & Tung 1971).
6. Finite α, η, γ, $\zeta = 0$, combination of electrical and gravity effects (Soo & Tung 1971).

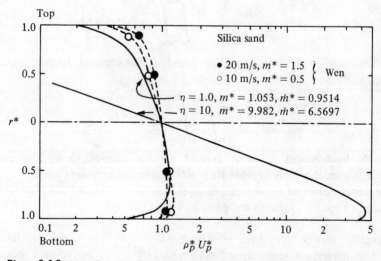

Figure 3.4.3 Mass flow distribution at various η values in horizontal pipe flow ($\gamma = 0$), $\beta = 100$, Kp = 0.1, compared with experimental data of Wen (1966).

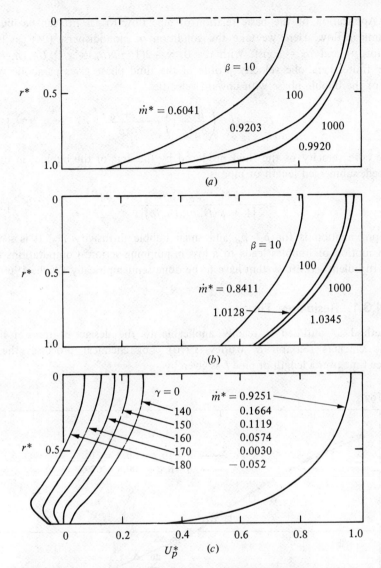

Figure 3.4.4 Vertical pipe flow ($\eta = 0$) at negligible electric charge effect ($\alpha = 0$), $m^* = 1$ (Soo & Tung 1971). (*a*) Effect of β, Kp = 0.1, $\gamma = 1.0$. (*b*) Effect of β, Kp = 1.0, $\gamma = 1.0$, $m^* = 1.0$. (*c*) Effect of γ, Kp = 0.1, $\beta = 100$.

7. $\alpha = 0$, $\gamma = 0$, finite η, ζ. The case is illustrated in figure 3.4.5. ζ is based on [3.3.14] and [3.4.15].

Interesting cases of nondepositing laminar flow are as follows:

1. $\alpha = 0$, $\eta = 0$, $\gamma = 0$, finite ζ based on Saffman (1965) for slow motion. The controversy of Einstein and Segre and Silberberg on the density distribution of particles was resolved (Soo 1969; Soo & Tung 1971), namely the disparate motion of phases gives rise to the maximum density away from the center of the pipe.

2. Application of the basic relation of pipe flow to gas lift can be illustrated with laminar flow. Here we take the condition of monodisperse (2a) gas bubbles (subscript p) and $\rho_p = $ const. With $\alpha = 0$, $\gamma = 2(1 - \bar{\rho}/\bar{\rho}_p)R^2 g/D_p U_0$, $\eta = 0$, $\beta = R^2/D_p \tau$ finite. Parabolic velocity profile of the fluid phase gives parabolic velocity profile of the bubble phase with upward velocities

$$U_p - U = \left(\frac{\bar{\rho}}{\bar{\rho}_p} - 1\right) g\tau - \frac{4U_0}{\beta}$$ [3.4.34]

and the core velocity of the fluid produced by the drag of the bubbles in the fully developed, submerged length of pipe is

$$U_0 = \frac{\phi(1 - \bar{\rho}_p/\bar{\rho})gR^2}{2[1 + \phi(D_p/\nu)(\bar{\rho}_p/\bar{\rho})]\bar{\nu}} \sim \frac{\phi gR^2}{2\bar{\nu}}$$ [3.4.35]

The approximation is for $\bar{\rho} \gg \bar{\rho}_p$ and small bubble diffusivity D_p. It is seen that random motion of bubbles leads to a loss in pumping action. Computations for the general turbulent gas lift system have to be done semiempirically (Wallis 1969).

3.4.3.1 Residence Time

The method as outlined is readily applicable to the design of transfer lines in catalytic crackers (Saxton & Worley 1970). For chemical processes the mean residence time over a length of pipe L is given by

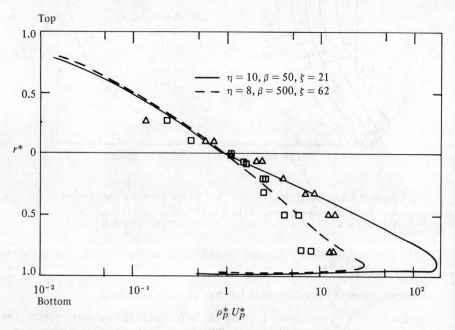

Figure 3.4.5 Mass flow distribution in vertical plane of coarse sand in water ($\gamma = 0$, $a/r = 1/35.8$, $Kp = 0.1$, $Re = 10^4$) compared to experimental results of Newitt et al. (1962) [mean volume fraction of solid: (△) 0.0550, (□) 0.0648] (Soo & Tung, 1972).

$$\int_0^L \frac{dz}{\bar{U}_p}$$

where
$$\bar{U}_p = \frac{\int_0^{2\pi} \int_0^R \rho_p U_p r \, dr \, d\phi}{\int_0^{2\pi} \int_0^R \rho_p r \, dr \, d\phi} \qquad [3.4.36]$$

i.e., the mean residence time over L is given by the total holdup in L divided by the total flow rate.

3.4.4 SEDIMENTARY FLOW

We treat cases that can be solved using [3.4.16], [3.4.17], and [3.4.19] with appropriate boundary conditions. For turbulent flow of charged suspensions without a gravity effect, we first treat the effect of particle charge on deposition with γ, η, and $\zeta = 0$. The following cases can be identified:

1. Diffusion effect alone in a dilute suspension: $\alpha = 0$; deposition is by sticking at the wall alone. This is the case studied by Friedlander & Johnstone (1957). Here we are concerned with a very dilute suspension of, say, room dust. Equation [3.4.17] becomes

$$\beta N_m U^* \frac{\partial \rho_p^*}{\partial z^*} = \frac{1}{r^*} \frac{\partial}{\partial r^*} r^* \frac{\partial \rho_p^*}{\partial r^*} \qquad [3.4.37]$$

with $U^* = U^*(r^*)$ for turbulent motion, and the boundary conditions are $r^* = 0$, $\partial \rho_p^*/\partial r^* = 0$; $r^* = 1$, $\partial \rho_p^*/\partial r^* = -\sigma_W N_{Ad} \rho_p^*$; and N_{Ad} may include the van der Waals force and the electrostatic force.

Other than the dependence of $U^* = U^*(r^*)$, the solution of [3.4.37] is straightforward. For turbulent flow, we may take $U^* \sim 1$ and we have

$$\rho_p^* = \sum_k c_k \exp\left(-k^2 \frac{z^*}{\beta N_m}\right) J_0(kr^*) \sim \exp\left(-2\sigma_W N_{Ad} \frac{z^*}{\beta N_m}\right)\left(1 - \frac{1}{2}\sigma_W N_{Ad} r^{*2}\right.$$

$$\left. + \frac{1}{16}\sigma_W^2 N_{Ad}^2 r^{*4} - \cdots\right) \qquad [3.4.38]$$

where J_0 is the zeroth-order Bessel function of the first kind and c_k is the Fourier coefficient for an eigenvalue k. The approximation is for small $\sigma_W N_{Ad}$, and $\sigma_W f_W \tau$ is the deposition velocity defined by Friedlander & Johnstone (1957), now expressed in terms of material and surface properties. An example is the adhesion and deposition of quartz particles to glass (Corn 1961). This force amounts to 0.01 dyne per micrometer of particle size. A deposition velocity of 10 cm/s in air suggests $\sigma_W = 1.5 \times 10^{-4}$. Using a stochastic model of random walk, Hutchinson et al. (1971) treated deposition in pipe flow. They gave deposition velocities of solid particles comparable to those obtained by Friedlander & Johnstone (1957) and gave additional results for liquid droplets. A large fraction of the latter was deposited.

2. Electrostatic force alone. When the electrostatic force due to self-field is significant, we can neglect both the effect of diffusion and N_{Ad}. We get, from [3.4.17],

$$\frac{\beta N_m U^*}{4\alpha} \frac{\partial \rho_p^*}{\partial z^*} = -\frac{\partial}{\partial (r^{*2})} \left[\rho_p^* \int \rho_p^* d(r^{*2}) \right]$$ [3.4.39]

For $U^* \sim 1$, we have a case similar to that of electrohydrodynamic inlet flow, which has the solution for $\xi = z^* (4\alpha/\beta N_m)$

$$\rho_p^* = (1 + \xi)^{-1} + r^{*4}(1 + \xi)^{-4} + \cdots$$ [3.4.40]

This relation is given in figure 10.16 of Soo (1967).

3. Simultaneous action of diffusion and electrostatic repulsion: [3.4.16] and [3.4.17] have to be solved numerically (Soo 1971; Wen 1966). Although any form of initial condition can be accounted for, the change from a fully developed condition at $z = 0$ is sufficiently interesting. Figure 3.4.6 shows the change in particle density at the wall along the length of the pipe. The changes in density at the center of the pipe and at the wall in the axial direction are readily seen. The particle velocity was determined from fluid velocity given by the 1/7 velocity law.

4. Attainment of packed or moving bed density. There is a limiting condition when α is large enough (that the density of a packed or moving bed ρ_{ps} of volume fraction of solid ϕ_s is reached at the wall; i.e.,

$$\frac{\rho_{pR}}{\rho_{p1}} = \left(1 - \frac{\alpha}{2}\right)^{-2} = \frac{\rho_{ps}}{\rho_{p1}} = \frac{\phi_s}{\phi_1}$$ [3.4.41]

when sedimentation occurs because of slowing down of a wall layer. For $\phi_s \gg \phi_1$, such a condition occurs when

$$\phi_1 > \frac{2}{\bar{\alpha}}$$ [3.4.42]

where

$$\bar{\alpha} = \frac{\bar{\rho}_p}{4\epsilon_0} \left(\frac{q}{m}\right)^2 \frac{R^2 \tau}{D_p}$$

In this case σ is that for particle-particle sticking and f_W is negligible.

When the bed of deposits is stationary, the rate at which its thickness is built up is given by

$$\frac{d\delta_s}{dt} = \frac{\rho_{pR} V_{pR}}{\rho_{ps}}$$ [3.4.43]

At steady state, we may have a deposit layer at the wall of thickness δ_s moving along the z direction.

We have the following cases where the effect of gravity is the contributor to sedimentation.

5. Gravity flow alone, negligible N_{Ad}. In this case $\eta \to \infty$; σ does not play a

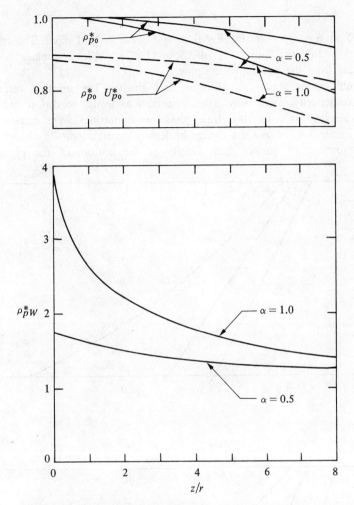

Figure 3.4.6 Electrostatic sedimentation: $\beta = 20$, $Kp = 0.2$, $N_m = 2.0$, $\sigma = 0.2$, $N_{Ad} = 0$ (Soo & Tung 1972).

role. We introduce a coordinate ξ' such that

$$d\xi' = \frac{\frac{1}{2}\eta\, dz^*}{N_m(\beta - \frac{1}{2}\gamma)} = \left[\frac{U_0}{g\tau}\left(1 - \frac{\bar{\rho}}{\bar{\rho}_p}\right)^{-1} - \cos\theta\right]^{-1} \sin\theta\, dz^* \qquad [3.4.44]$$

and, taking $U^* \sim 1$ for turbulent flow, [3.4.17] becomes

$$\frac{\partial \rho_p^*}{\partial \xi'} = \cos\phi\, \frac{\partial \rho_p^*}{\partial r^*} - \frac{\sin\phi}{r^*}\, \frac{\partial \rho_p^*}{\partial \phi} \qquad [3.4.45]$$

In this case ρ_p^* remains constant, except that, starting from fully developed motion, the top boundary of the particle phase falls according to the case of batch settling; i.e., the top surface of the suspension is

$$y = 2R - R\xi' \tag{3.4.46}$$

with $y = 0$ at $\phi = \pi$, $r = R$, for $\theta \neq 0$ ($\theta = 0$ for a vertical pipe). The relation of sedimentation follows figure 9.1 of Soo (1967), with a packed bed of ϕ_s accumulating from the bottom of the pipe.

6. Simultaneous action of diffusion and gravity. The solution can only be obtained numerically. With fully developed flow as initial condition and the 1/7 turbulent velocity law for the fluid phase, computations were carried out for $N_{\mathrm{Ad}} = 0$. Figure 3.4.7 shows the change in density distribution.

7. Attainment of packed bed density at the bottom of the pipe. This is

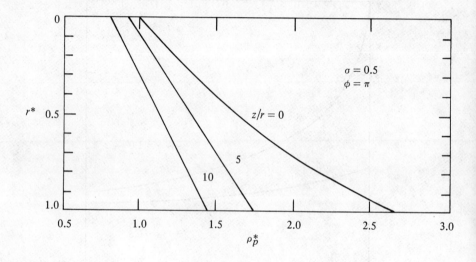

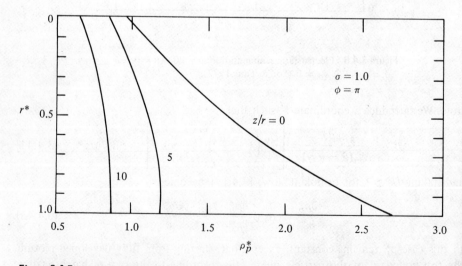

Figure 3.4.7 Density distribution when deposition occurs due to gravity and diffusion: $\beta = 10, \gamma = 1, \eta = 2, \mathrm{Kp} = 0.2, N_m = 2.0, N_{\mathrm{Ad}} = 0$ (computation by S. K. Tung).

analogous to case 4. It may lead to sliding bed motion in both the axial and peripheral directions.

It is seen that sedimentation in pipe flow may occur for a variety of reasons, although the results are often equally undesirable. The cases above show how sedimentation may start. Once it is started, three more cases may arise.

1. Transient deposition may continue until the pipe is completely plugged.
2. Transient deposition may occur together with bed movement.
3. Formation of dunes and repeated piling up of deposits may occur until a large pressure difference in the fluid is built up to blow them away (Bagnold 1953; Kennedy 1963). This causes a pulsating motion in the pipe, produced by a variation in fluid velocity due to flow restriction by the dunes.

When dealing with a gas-particle suspension, deposition in the form of dipoles (Penny & Klingler 1962; Niedra & Penny 1965) or space charges can be equally problematic unless one is interested in collecting particles. Precharged particles are deposited in pipes by space charge in the above case 2 or by instability under the image force even when there is only a single particle, because diffusion prevents a particle from staying in the middle of the pipe. By stretching a high-voltage wire along the axis of a grounded pipe conveying a suspension, one can charge the particles by a corona discharge and deposit them by the field; this constitutes an electrostatic precipitator of the wire-in-tube type (White 1968). Note that depositing flow in a precipitator of the wire-in-plate type is also readily treated (Soo & Rodgers 1971); at the collector plate

$$D_p \frac{\partial \rho_p}{\partial y} = (1 - o)KE_y\rho_p \qquad [3.4.47]$$

where y is the coordinate model to the plate and K is the mobility $(q/m)\tau$ (Soo 1973c; Soo & Rodgers 1971).

Study of pipe flow by Fortier & Chen (1976) included computation of the change in pressure and concentration along the pipe based on averaging procedures (section 1.2). Their experimental study included measurement of solid particle velocities by radioactive tracers. Based on their measurements, the friction factor of flow, the momentum loss of particles, wall interaction, and the drag coefficients of particles were determined. Some of the trend of the drag reduction model of Jokati & Tomita (1971) was demonstrated.

A theoretical analysis of laminar dispersion in fully developed pipe flow was treated by Yu (1977), including the combined effects of convection and diffusion as in [3.4.17]. The results were applicable to the condition of blood flow.

3.4.5 FLOW IN A CYCLONE COLLECTOR

A cyclone collector for separating solid particles from a gaseous suspension, which is an important adjunct of a pneumatic conveying system, is an example of flow of a gas-solid suspension in a centrifugal force field together with a simple example of a moving bed of solid particles.

The basic relations make it possible to rigorously analyze the performance of a cyclone separator. As shown in figure 3.4.8, a common configuration has dusty gas

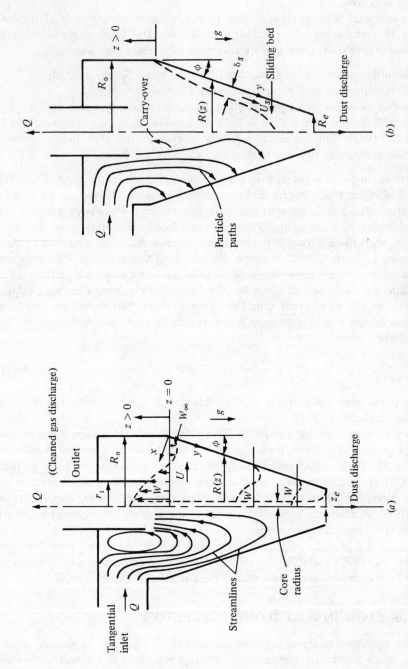

Figure 3.4.8 Conditions inside a cyclone separator and coordinates. (*a*) Fluid velocity distribution. (*b*) Particle path and sliding bed.

entering tangentially at the top of its cylindrical section to produce the vortex motion. The particles collected by the combined centrifugal and gravity forces are removed at the bottom of the conical section. The cleaned gas exits from the top.

Figure 3.4.8 shows the coordinates and dimensions of the flow system for flow volume per unit time Q; radius $R(z)$ of the inside surface with coordinate r, z in the radial and axial directions, respectively; and velocity components U, V, and W in the radial, tangential, and axial directions for the fluid phase and U_p, V_p, and W_p for the particle phase of a given species. The fluid motion is readily calculated as described in figure 3.4.8a. The vorticity of the system is C.

The density distribution of the particle phase is strongly influenced by a finite particle diffusivity D_p and field forces, together with finite interaction length L_p and sticking probability σ of particles with the wall or with a deposited layer of particles (Soo & Tung 1972). The field forces include centrifugal, gravity, and electrostatic forces. The effect of electrostatic charges is prominent in gaseous suspensions. The electric charge effect is such that much of the carry-over into the outlet pipe occurs because of electrostatic repulsion rather than turbulence alone.

For the flow system shown in figure 3.4.8a, the fluxes in the diffusion equation (neglecting inertia forces in comparison to field forces and viscous forces) are given by the equations for the radial and axial components of particle momentum:

$$\rho_p \frac{V_p^2}{r} = -\rho_p(U_p - U)\tau^{-1} + \rho_p E_r \frac{q}{m}$$

$$\rho_p g = -\rho_p(W_p - W)\tau^{-1} + \rho_p E_z \frac{q}{m}$$

[3.4.48]

where E_r and E_z are the radial and axial components of the electric field, which is given by the Poisson equation

$$\nabla \cdot \mathbf{E} = \frac{\rho_p}{\epsilon_0} \frac{q}{m} = -\nabla^2 V_e$$

[3.4.49]

At the boundary, for a small thickness of deposit or a clean wall, we have

$$-D_p \frac{\partial \rho_p}{\partial x}\bigg|_R = (1 - \sigma)\left(1 - \frac{\bar{\rho}}{\bar{\rho}_p}\right)\left(g\tau \sin \phi + \frac{V_{pW}^2 \tau}{R} \cos \phi\right)\rho_{pr}$$

$$+ [(1 - \sigma)\rho_{pR} + \sigma_W'\rho_{pb}] f_{L}\tau + (1 - \sigma)\frac{q}{m}(-E_x\tau)\rho_{pR}$$

$$- \sigma_W\rho_{pr} f_W\tau$$

[3.4.50]

The diffusion equation can be expressed in dimensionless form by introducing $W_0 = \dot{Q}/\pi R_0^2$, where $\dot{Q}$ is the total volume flow rate and R_0 is the largest radius of the cyclone:

$$r^* = \frac{r}{R} \qquad z^* = \frac{z}{R} \qquad U^* = \frac{U}{W_0}$$

$$w^* = \frac{W}{W_0} \qquad V^* = V\frac{R}{C}$$

[3.4.51]

$$V_e^* = \frac{V_e}{(\rho_{p1}/\epsilon_0)(q/m)R_0^2}$$

$$E^* = \frac{E}{(\rho_{p1}/\epsilon_0)(q/m)R_0}$$

[3.4.51]
(*Cont.*)

$$\rho_p^* = \frac{\rho_p}{\rho_{p1}}$$

giving

$$\left(\text{Pe } U^* + \alpha E_r^* + \Omega \frac{V_p^{*2}}{r^*} \right) \frac{\partial \rho_p^*}{\partial r^*} + (\text{Pe } W^* + \alpha E_z^* - \gamma)$$

$$\cdot \frac{\partial \rho_p^*}{\partial z^*} + 2\Omega \rho_p^* \frac{V_p^*}{r^*} \frac{\partial V_p^*}{\partial r^*} = \nabla^{*2} \rho_p^* - \alpha \rho_p^{*2}$$

[3.4.52]

where

$$\text{Pe} = \frac{WR_0}{D_p} \qquad \alpha = \frac{\rho_{p1}}{\epsilon_0} \left(\frac{q}{m} \right)^2 \frac{R_0^2 \tau}{D_p}$$

$$\Omega = \frac{\tau C^2}{R_0^2 D_p} \qquad \gamma = \frac{\tau g R_0}{D_p}$$

correlating convection, diffusion, and transport by various forces in relation to diffusion and relaxation phenomena. The fact that the electrostatic, centrifugal, and gravity forces give rise to drift components on particles in addition to U and W is thus shown.

When applied to a steep slant cone, the local condition can be determined by integrating [3.4.52] with the simplification

$$E_r^* \gg E_z^* \qquad W^* \cong \text{const} \qquad \gamma = 0 \qquad U^* \cong 0$$

$$-\frac{\partial}{\partial z} \int \frac{\rho_p}{\rho_{p1}} \frac{Wr}{D_p} \, dr = c_1^*$$

Integration once from 0 to r^* gives

$$r^* \frac{\partial \rho_p^*}{\partial r^*} - \Omega \rho_p^* V_p^{*2} - \alpha \rho_p^* \int \rho_p^* r^* \, dr^* - \alpha_e \rho_p^* = \text{Pe} \frac{\partial}{\partial z^*} \int \rho_p^* W_p^* r^* \, dr^*$$

[3.4.53]

where

$$\alpha_e = \frac{r_0 E_e \tau}{D_p} \frac{q}{m}$$

E_e is the external field due to potential or surface charge density of the wall, and r_0 is a characteristic dimension for the applied field. The right-hand side of [3.4.53] is the dimensionless rate of deposition of particles.

With these simplifications, and taking into account the effects given in [3.4.50], the collection efficiency η_c over a height L of the cyclone is given by integrating [3.4.53]

$$1 - \eta_c \cong \exp \left\{ - 2\sigma [\Omega + 4(2 - k^*)\, \alpha + \alpha_e] \frac{L}{R} \text{Pe}^{-1} \right.$$

$$\left. + 2 \left(1 - \sigma + \sigma'_W \frac{\rho_{pb}}{\rho_{pW}} \right) f_L \tau \frac{L}{D_p} \text{Pe}^{-1} - 2\sigma_W f_W \tau \frac{L}{D_p} \text{Pe}^{-1} \right\}$$ [3.4.54]

with the approximation for the density distribution

$$\rho_p^* \cong \rho_{pR}^* \exp \left(- \frac{\Omega}{2} \frac{1}{r^{*2}} - 1 \right)$$ [3.4.55]

and $$k^* = \frac{\Omega}{2} \exp \frac{\Omega}{2} \int_\infty^{\Omega/2} x^{-1} e^{-x} \, dx \leqslant O[1]$$

for $\Omega > O[10]$ and $\rho_{pR}^* = \rho_{pr}/\rho_{p1}$. Equation [3.4.54] shows the influence of f_L in decreasing the efficiency. Neglecting f_L and f_W, [3.4.54] can also be expressed for large Ω as

$$1 - \eta_c \cong \exp \left\{ - \sigma \left[\frac{2\pi C^2 L \tau}{\dot{Q} R^2} + 8\pi \frac{\rho_{p1}}{\epsilon_0} \left(\frac{q}{m} \right)^2 R^2 \tau \frac{L}{\dot{Q}} + 2\pi E_0 \frac{q}{m} \frac{RL\tau}{\dot{Q}} \right] \right\}$$ [3.4.56]

for length L and volume flow rate $\dot{Q}$. Note that $C^2 \tau L/18 \dot{Q} R^2$ is the cyclone number of Rietema et al. (1961). The relation also explains the choice of the Tengbergen group (Leith & Licht 1972), which is $9C\tau/R^2$. Some agreement of these chosen dimensionless groups with experimental results is hence not surprising. Other terms in [3.4.56] show that by a combination of centrifugal force and electrostatic forces a large-diameter ($2R_0$) cyclone may have the same efficiency as a small cyclone separator for a gaseous suspension. This is not the case for hydrocyclones.

In the absence of surface adhesion, sedimentation occurs when ρ_{pb} is reached at the wall. For volume fraction of solid $\phi_s = \rho_{pb}/\bar{\rho}_p$ for sedimentation, and $\phi_1 = \rho_{p1}/\bar{\rho}_p$ at the inlet, sedimentation begins at $(\bar{\alpha}/8)\phi_1 > 1 - (\phi_1/\phi_s)^{1/2}$ or

$$\bar{\alpha} = \frac{\bar{\rho}_p}{\epsilon_0} \left(\frac{q}{m} \right)^2 \frac{R_0^2 \tau}{D_p} > \frac{8}{\phi_1}$$ [3.4.57]

where $\bar{\alpha}$ is the value of α where ρ_{p1} is replaced by $\bar{\rho}_p$; α gives the minimum q/m for sedimentation by electrical effect. The most desirable condition for collection in a cyclone separator is that the sticking probability is zero and a bed density ρ_{pb} flows down the cone.

The ideal situation would be dense bed collection by either the centrifugal or the electric field, with the bed nonadhesive so that the sliding bed flows down the cone toward the dust discharge as shown in figure 3.4.8b. This is not always the case, however. Plugging of the outlet and refusal of the collected dust to unload can be the most frustrating problem to solve in an installation.

Unloading of the collected particles at the bottom of the cyclone is simple and is similar to unloading of bins and flow of solids through an orifice; often the pressure is lower inside the bottom of the cone. The difficulty is usually to get the collected layer to slide down from the upper portion of the cone.

For a sliding bed of collected particles mass balance and force balance relations give

$$\left(\frac{\delta_s}{R_0}\right)^3 \cong \frac{\sigma\mu_s D_p}{g\rho_{ps}R_0^3}\frac{\rho_{p1}}{\rho_{ps}}\frac{y}{R_0}\frac{\Omega + \pi\alpha}{\cos\phi - f\sin\phi} \qquad [3.4.58]$$

or $\delta_s \propto (-z)^{1/3}$ ($-z$ points downward), where $\delta_s = 0$ at $z = 0$, $r_1^* = r_1/R_0$ is the gravitational acceleration, ρ_{ps} is the sliding bed density, f is the Coulomb friction coefficient at the wall, μ_s is the shear resistance of the sliding bed, ρ_{p1} is the inlet density of the particles, and $\bar{\rho}_p$ is the density of solid material. δ_s increases toward the bottom of the cone. For a thin layer of deposit, the shear stress is given by

$$\tau_s = \delta_s\rho_{ps}g\,(\cos\phi - f\sin\phi) \qquad [3.4.59]$$

The larger the yield stress τ_s of the bed, the thicker is the bed. The shear stress due to fluid flow is, in general, negligible.

For the example of a cyclone of $R_0 = 0.761$ m, $\rho_{ps} = 822$ (0.6 fraction solid), and yield stress 476 n/m^2 (10 psf), [3.4.59] gives $\delta_s \cong 0.0672$ m, which is quite thick. Successful operation calls for small τ_s, and τ_s depends on consolidating pressure, which is influenced by the centrifugal and electrostatic forces driving the particles toward the wall. A large consolidating pressure and a high moisture content cause large τ_s (Soo 1973a, 1973c).

Bloor & Ingram (1975) postulated a simple set of relations for the components of fluid velocities without satisfying the condition at the wall. The tangential velocity calculated compared favorably with experiments. Variation in fluid viscosity was also taken into account. A leakage flow model of fluid was treated separately, using a boundary-layer approximation. Particle motion was not treated.

3.4.6 SCALING AND MODELING

B. T. Chao

For a complicated flow system, modeling experimentally with the aim of scaling up a successful design is in the manner of solution of dynamic equations by a physical analog. A case in point is treating the flow-gravity interaction of a suspension.

An example is the flow above a fluidized bed. In the freeboard space of a fluidized bed, the density of the particle cloud is usually such that the suspension is dilute. The dynamic equation of a small particle in a fluid is given by

$$\frac{d\mathbf{U}_p}{dt} = \tau^{-1}(\mathbf{U} - \mathbf{U}_p) + \mathbf{g} \qquad [3.4.60]$$

where $\mathbf{g}$ is the gravitational acceleration vector. In writing [3.4.60], the effects of apparent mass, Basset force, diffusion, and electric charge of the particles are ignored. For pressurized fluidized-bed combustion of coal with dolomite or limestone additive, the products of combustion have a density $\bar{\rho}$ estimated to be 3.1 kg/m^3 at 1150 K and 10 bars, and the material density of the suspended particulates $\bar{\rho}_p$ is in the neighborhood of 1600 kg/m^3. Thus, $\bar{\rho}/\bar{\rho}_0 \cong 0.002$, and according to the analysis of Chao (1964) the neglect of apparent mass and Basset force is totally justifiable. Since only the separation of larger particulates is under consideration, such an effect, if it exists, is likely to be of secondary importance.

If we denote the displacement vector of the particle by $\mathbf{x}_p$, then

$$\mathbf{U}_p = \frac{d\mathbf{x}_p}{dt} \qquad [3.4.61]$$

and the equation of motion can be written as

$$\frac{d^2 \mathbf{x}_p}{dt^2} = \tau^{-1}\left(\mathbf{U} - \frac{d\mathbf{x}_p}{dt}\right) + \mathbf{g} \qquad [3.4.62]$$

Equation [3.4.62] can be recast in dimensionless form by introducing a reference length L, a reference velocity V, and the other nondimensional quantities

$$\mathbf{x}_p^* = \frac{\mathbf{x}_p}{L} \qquad t^* = \frac{Vt}{L} \qquad \mathbf{U}^* = \frac{\mathbf{U}}{V} \text{ and } \mathbf{U}_p^* = \frac{\mathbf{U}_p}{V} \qquad [3.4.63]$$

Accordingly, [3.4.63] becomes

$$\frac{d^2 \mathbf{x}_p^*}{dt^{*2}} = \frac{L}{V\tau}\left(\mathbf{U} - \frac{d\mathbf{x}_p^*}{dt^*}\right) + \frac{Lg}{V^2}\mathbf{I} \qquad [3.4.64]$$

where $\mathbf{I}$ is a unit vector in the direction of gravitational acceleration. Thus, for geometrically similar systems with kinematically similar boundary conditions, dynamic similarity can be obtained if the following dimensionless groups are kept identical for the prototype and the model:

$$N_m = \frac{V\tau}{L} \qquad \text{Fr} = \frac{V^2}{Lg} \qquad [3.4.65]$$

The momentum transfer number N_m may be interpreted as the ratio of the relaxation time for momentum transfer to the characteristic transport time. The second group is the well-known Froude number. The expression for N_m, as it stands, is not always useful in modeling analysis because τ depends on the particle Reynolds number, which is not known a priori. However, the latter can be written as

$$\text{Re}_p = \frac{2a|\mathbf{U} - \mathbf{U}_p|\bar{\rho}}{\bar{\mu}} = \text{Re}_p^*\left|\mathbf{U}^* - \frac{d\mathbf{x}_p^*}{dt^*}\right| \qquad [3.4.66]$$

where

$$\text{Re}_p^* = \frac{2aV\bar{\rho}}{\bar{\mu}} \qquad [3.4.67]$$

which may be called a pseudo-particle Reynolds number. In view of [3.3.16] and [3.3.17], equality of N_m requires that in addition to Re_p^* the following dimensionless parameter be identical for the prototype and the model:

$$\Psi = \frac{\tau_0 V}{L} = \frac{\bar{\rho}_p V(2a)^2}{18\bar{\mu}L} \qquad [3.4.68]$$

which is referred to as the inertia parameter is Soo (1967). These parameters were identified previously by Langmuir & Blodgett (1946) in their analysis of particle impaction in potential flows over spheres, cylinders, etc. Langmuir & Blodgett's parameter Φ is related to Re_p^* and Ψ by

$$\Phi = \frac{\mathrm{Re}_p^*}{2\Psi} \qquad [3.4.69]$$

In fully developed turbulent pipe flow of dilute suspensions, the flow characteristics of the particle phase, including diffusion, momentum transfer, and gravity, were studied by Soo & Tung (1972). In the absence of electrical effects, the correlation parameters are β, γ, η given after [3.4.15]. In the definitions of these parameters, $2R$ is the pipe inside diameter, D_p is the particle diffusivity, and θ is the angle between the pipe axis and the gravitational acceleration vector. Since $\bar{\rho}/\bar{\rho}_p \cong 0.002$, the terms in parentheses in γ and η can be safely neglected. The ratio η/γ is $(V\tau/R) \tan \theta = 2N_m \tan \theta$. Thus, for geometrically similar systems, modeling requires only consideration of β and a gravity parameter

$$N_g = \frac{R^2 g}{D_p V} \qquad [3.4.70]$$

In dilute suspension, D_p arises from particle-fluid interaction only for the fluid diffusivity D. When the Reynolds number is large, D can be estimated from the fact that the Peclet number is nearly a constant, namely

$$\frac{2RV}{D} \cong 10^3 \qquad [3.4.71]$$

Prediction of the diffusivity ratio D_p/D has been the subject of study by many investigators. In general, it depends on the particle-fluid interaction parameter κ defined after [3.3.27]. It was shown (Soo 1978) that

1. For $\kappa \ll 1$, $D_p/D \cong 1 - (2\pi^{1/2})^{-1}\kappa^3$
2. For $\kappa \gg 1$, $D_p/D = a_1/\kappa$
3. For intermediate κ, $D_p/D = a_2/\kappa^{1/2}$

where a_1 and a_2 are numerical constants of order unity.

To develop some feeling about the likely range of κ in a fluidized bed, we consider spherical particles of density $\bar{\rho}_p = 1600$ kg/m^3 and diameter $2a = 7, 70,$ and 700 μm suspended in air at 1150 K and 10 bars flowing in a draft tube diameter $2R = 0.3$ m at a velocity $V = 3$ m/s. The turbulence intensity is 5%. Since $D = (\pi^{1/2}/2) \langle V^2 \rangle^{1/2} \Lambda$ and $2RV/D \cong 10^3$, we readily deduce that $\Lambda/R = 0.045$. Using the non-Stokesian correction factors $F^* = 1, 1.1,$ and 1.34, respectively, for the 7-, 70-, and 700-μm particles, the corresponding values of κ are 0.003, 0.39, and 32. Although these results are crude estimates, they demonstrate that for the system under consideration extreme values of κ have to be considered. We now examine the modeling requirements in the light of the foregoing findings:

Case 1: $\kappa \ll 1$. In this case $D_p/D \cong 1$, $F^* \cong 1$, and $\tau \cong \tau_0$. Hence

$$\beta = \frac{R^2}{D_p\tau} \cong \frac{R^2}{D\tau_0} = \frac{1}{4}\frac{2RV}{D}\frac{2R}{V\tau_0} \cong \frac{250}{\Psi}$$

$$N_g = \frac{R^2 g}{D_p V} \cong \frac{R^2 g}{DV} = \frac{1}{4}\frac{2RV}{D}\frac{2Rg}{V^2} \cong \frac{250}{\mathrm{Fr}}$$

Since both Ψ and Fr have already been identified, consideration of particle diffusion in turbulent flow leads to no additional modeling requirements.

Case 2: $\kappa \gg 1$. Here $D_p/D = a_1/\kappa$. Hence

$$\beta = \frac{R^2}{D_p\tau} = \frac{1}{a_1}\frac{R^2\kappa}{D\tau} = \frac{\pi^{1/2}}{a_1}\frac{R^2\langle V^2\rangle}{D^2} = \frac{\pi^{1/2}}{4a_1}\left(\frac{2RV}{D}\right)^2\frac{\langle V^2\rangle}{V^2}$$

$$\cong \frac{\pi^{1/2}}{4a_1}10^6\frac{\langle V^2\rangle}{V^2}$$

In turbulent flows of large Reynolds numbers $\langle V^2\rangle/V^2$ is not expected to have significant variation. Thus, the requirement of identical β's for the prototype and the model is automatically satisfied.

$$N_g = \frac{R^2 g}{D_p V} = \frac{1}{a_1}\frac{R^2 g\kappa}{DV} = \beta\frac{g\tau}{V} = \frac{\beta}{F^*}\frac{\Psi}{\mathrm{Fr}}$$

Since F^* is a function only of Re_p^*, which has also been identified, there is no additional modeling requirement.

Case 3: intermediate κ. Since $D_p/D = a_2/\kappa^{1/2}$, we have

$$\beta = \frac{1}{a_2}\frac{R^2\kappa^{1/2}}{D\tau} = \frac{\pi^{1/4}}{4a_2}\left(\frac{2RV}{D}\right)^{3/2}\left(\frac{\langle V^2\rangle^{1/2}}{V}\right)F^{*1/2}\left(\frac{2R}{V\tau_0}\right)^{1/2}$$

$$= \frac{\pi^{1/4}}{4a_2}10^{9/2}\frac{\langle V^2\rangle^{1/2}}{V}\left(\frac{F^*}{\Psi}\right)^{1/2}$$

$$N_g = \frac{1}{a_2}\frac{R^2 g\kappa^{1/2}}{DV} = \beta\frac{g\tau}{V} = \frac{\pi^{1/4}}{4a_2}10^{9/2}\frac{\langle V^2\rangle^{1/2}}{V}\left(\frac{\Psi}{F^*}\right)^{1/2}\mathrm{Fr}^{-1}$$

Once again, no new modeling requirement arises.

From the analysis presented we may conclude that modeling of dilute suspension flows in geometrically similar systems with kinematically similar boundary conditions, in which the dynamics is governed by momentum transfer, gravity, and diffusion, requires consideration of the three dimensionless parameters Ψ [3.4.68], Re_p^* [3.4.67], and Fr [3.4.65].

Modeling can be carried out with air at the same temperature and pressure in the model and the protoype, using particles of different sizes and apparent densities (e.g., hollow particles). The system can also be used to model a prototype at different operating temperatures and pressures. Therefore, broad usage of the correlation and methodology is expected.

As an example, consider a scale model of a fluidized bed of 1:10; i.e.,

$L_P/L_M = 10$. The prototype (P) operates at temperature $T_P = 1150$ K and pressure $P_P = 10$ bars. The operating temperature of the model (M) is $T_M = 300$ K. We assume that the viscosity of the products of combustion is the same as that of air; thus, $\bar{\mu}_P = 4.56 \times 10^{-5}$ kg/m s and $\bar{\mu}_M = 1.98 \times 10^{-5}$ kg/m s.

Equation [3.4.65] requires that

$$\frac{V_M}{V_P} = \left(\frac{L_M}{L_P}\right)^{1/2} = \frac{1}{(10)^{1/2}} = \frac{1}{3.16}$$

Equation [3.4.68] requires that (for the same particulate material)

$$\frac{(2a)_M}{(2a)_P} = \left(\frac{L_M\, V_P\, \bar{\mu}_M}{L_P\, V_M\, \bar{\mu}_P}\right)^{1/2} = \left(\frac{1}{10}\, 3.16\, \frac{1.98}{4.56}\right)^{1/2} = \frac{1}{2.70}$$

Equation [3.4.67] requires that (assuming the products of combustion follow the equation of state of an ideal gas)

$$\frac{\bar{\rho}_M}{\bar{\rho}_P} = \frac{P_M}{P_P}\frac{T_P}{T_M} = \frac{\bar{\mu}_M}{\bar{\mu}_P}\frac{(2a)_P}{(2a)_M}\frac{V_P}{V_M} = \frac{1.98}{4.56}(2.70)(3.16) = 3.71$$

Thus,
$$\frac{P_M}{P_P} = 3.71\,\frac{T_M}{T_D} = 3.71\,\frac{300}{1150} = 0.968$$

This example shows that model testing may be conducted with room temperature air at 300 K and at an elevated pressure of 9.7 bars, using particles with the same size distribution as in the protoype but 2.7 times smaller.

3.5 Nomenclature for Chapter 3

ROMAN LETTERS

a	radius of particle
$a, a_1, a_2, \ldots$	constants
a, b	major and minor axes of ellipse
A	area
A	constant of mapping function
b	constant
b	width
c_1, c_1'	constants
C	specific heat at constant pressure of fluid
C_p	specific heat at constant pressure of particles
c_k	Fourier coefficients
C	vorticity
C_D	drag coefficient for sphere
C_L	lift coefficient for sphere in shear flow field
C_R	vorticity at R_c
C_y	characteristic cyclone number of Rietema
D	diffusivity
D_c	diameter
D_p	particle diffusivity
D_{pm}	Brownian diffusivity
$\mathbf{E}$	electric field
E_e	component of electric field as indicator
E	modulus of elasticity
f	force per unit mass
f_{12}	change transfer coefficient
f_L	lift force
f_p	field force per unit mass of particle phase
f_p'	force due to fluid field
$\mathbf{f}_p$	force vector per unit mass of particle
$f_{pr}, f_{p\phi}, f_{pz}$	radian, tangential, and axial force per unit mass of particle

F^*	coefficient for deviation from Stokes law
F_v	force of adhesion
g	gravitational acceleration
G	tangential turbulent universal function
$\hbar$	quantum constant
Δh	latent heat
h	Planck constant or charge transfer coefficient
H	inverse relaxation time for charge transfer between particles
i	electric current
I	intensity of radiation
$\mathbf{I}$	unit vector
$\mathbf{J}_F$	flux of particles due to field force
J_0	Bessel function of zero order
J_q	heat flux at wall
J_{qp}	heat flux due to impaction of particles at wall
k	material parameter $(1 - v^2)/\pi E$, Boltzmann constant
K	effectiveness of momentum transfer
L^*	parameter for agglomeration or lift by fluid shear
L_p	interaction length of particles with fluid
L_T	interaction length of convection heat transfer
$\dot{m}$	total flow rate of particles
$\dot{m}^*$	characteristic mass flow ratio of particle to fluid
m^*	characteristic mass ratio of particle to fluid
m_p	mass of particle
m, n	constants in exponents
n_m	index of refraction of mixture
N_{Ad}	adhesive force parameter
N_{DF}	diffusion response number
N_{ED}	electrodiffusion number
N_m	momentum transfer number
N_p	number density of particles
N_S	shear response number
P	static pressure
q	electric charge per particle
q	heat input per unit mass of fluid
q_p	heat input per unit mass of particles
Q	charge transfer
Q	volume
$\dot{Q}$	volume flow rate
r, ϕ, z	radial, azimuthal, and axial coordinates
$\mathbf{r}$	position vector
R, R_0	pipe radius or radius of wall
s	specific entropy
S	swirl ratio
t	time
T	temperature of gaseous phase

T_p	body temperature of particle
T_{pi}	temperature of incoming particle
T_{pr}	temperature of reflected particle
T_{pw}	temperature of particles at wall
T_w	temperature at wall
T_∞	temperature in free stream
U, V, W	components of velocity of fluid as defined
U_p, V_p, W_p	components of velocity of particle as defined
U_0	maximum or core velocity of fluid phase
U_{pw}	velocity of particles at wall
$\mathbf{U}$	unitary tensor
$\mathbf{V}$	vectorial velocity of fluid
$\mathbf{V}_p$	vectorial velocity of particle cloud
V_e	electric potential
x, y, z	Cartesian coordinates or coordinates as defined
x^*	mapping function
x	coordinate or force
z_0	distance

DIMENSIONLESS GROUPS

Fr	Froude number
Im	impact number
Kp	Knudsen number of particle phase
Pe	Peclet number
Re	Reynolds number

GREEK LETTERS

α	accommodation coefficient
α_p	thermal diffusivity of particle
$\bar{\alpha}, \alpha, \beta, \gamma, \zeta, \eta, \lambda_i, \Omega$	dimensionless groups
γ	ratio of specific heats
δ, θ	boundary-layer thickness
Δ	deformation tensor
ϵ_0	permittivity of free space
ϵ_1	permittivity of material 1
ζ, ζ', ξ, ξ'	dimensionless coordinates
$\bar{\zeta}$	bulk modulus of fluid
η	fraction impacted
θ	angle of inclination of pipe to direction of gravity
θ	dilatation
κ	particle-fluid interaction parameter
λ	thermal conductivity of fluid phase in mixture or wavelength
$\bar{\lambda}$	thermal conductivity of fluid material
λ_p	thermal conductivity of particle phase in mixture

Λ_p	mean free path between collisions
μ	viscosity of fluid material
$\bar{\mu}$	viscosity of material constituting fluid phase
ν	Poisson ratio
$\bar{\nu}$	kinematic viscosity
ρ	density of fluid phase
$\bar{\rho}$	density of material constituting fluid phase
ρ_p	density of particulate cloud
$\bar{\rho}_p$	density of particulate material
σ, σ_W	sticking probabilities
σ'_W	lifting probability from particle bed
τ	shear stress in fluid phase
τ	relaxation time or relaxation time constant for momentum transfer
τ_q	relaxation time for convective heat transfer between phases
τ_p	shear stress tensor of particle cloud
ϕ	azimuthal angle or slant angle or cone or work function
ϕ	volume fraction of particles
Φ, Ψ	Langmuir parameters
$\omega,$	angular velocity or circular frequency

SUBSCRIPTS

0	axial, outside boundary layer, reference value
1	initial condition
1, 2	cases as indicated
b	bed or blackbody
c	core
e	exit
e	external
G	gas
L	lift
p	particle phase
q	heat
r, z, ϕ	radial, axial, tangential
R	radius R
s	deposited phase
W	wall

SUPERSCRIPTS

$*$	dimensionless quantities
$-$	material or mean quantity

3.6 References for Chapter 3

Adachi, K., Kiriyama, S., & Yoshioka, N. 1978 The Behavior of a Swarm of Particles Moving in a Viscous Fluid, *Chem. Eng. Sci.* **33**:115–121.

Bagnold, R. A. 1951 The Movement of Dimensionless Granular Bed by Cloud Charging Over It, *Br. J. Appl. Phys.* **2**:29–34.

Bagnold, R. A. 1953 *The Physics of Blown Sand and Desert Dunes,* Methuen, London.

Blake, T. R., Garg, S. K., Levine, H. B., & Pritcher, J. W. 1976 Computer Modeling of Coal Gasification Reactors, *Rept.* SSS-R-76-2967, FE-1770-15 Dist. Category UC-90C, Systems, Science, and Software, La Jolla, Calif., prepared under ERDA Contract (49-18)-1770 (July).

Bloor, M. I. G. & Ingram, D. B. 1975 Turbulent Spin in a Cyclone, *Trans. Inst. Chem. Eng.* **53**:1–11.

Chao, B. T. 1964 Turbulent Transport Behavior of Small Particles in Dilute Suspensions, *Oesterr. Ing. Arch.* **18**:7–21.

Chao, B. T., Sha, W. T., & Soo, S. L. 1978 On Inertial Coupling in Dynamic Equations of Components in a Mixutre, *Int. J. Multiphase Flow,* **4**:219–223.

Cheng, L. & Soo, S. L. 1970 Charging of Dust Particles by Impact, *J. Appl. Phys.* **41**:585–591.

Corn, M. 1961 The Adhesion of Solid Particles to Solid Surfaces, *J. Air Pollut. Control Assoc.* **11**:523–528, 566–575, 584.

Czichos, H. 1969 Uber den Zusammenhang zwischen Adhäsion und Electronenstruktur von Metallen bei der Rollreibung im elastischen Bereich, *Z. Angew. Phys.* **27**:40–46.

Eckstein, E. C., Bailey, D. G., & Shapiro A. H. 1977 Self-diffusion of Particles in Shear Flow of a Suspension, *J. Fluid Mech.* **79**:197–208.

Eddington, R. B. 1967 Investigation of Suspension Shock Phenomena in a Two-Phase Tunnel, *NASA Tech. Rept.* 32-1096.

Eley, D. D. 1961 *Adhesion,* p. 119, Oxford Univ. Press, London.

Fortier, A. & Chen, C. P. 1976 Ecoulement turbulent stationaire biphasique air-solide dans un tube cylindrique, à forte contration massique, *J. Mec.* **15**:115–183.

Friedlander, S. K. & Johnstone, H. F. 1957 Deposition of Suspension Particles from Turbulent Gas Streams, *Ind. Eng. Chem.* **49**:1151–1156.

Gabor, J. D. 1972 On the Mechanics of Fluidized Particle Movement, *Chem. Eng. J.* **4**:118–126.

Gelperin, N. I. & Einstein, V. G. 1971 The Analogy between Fluidized Beds and Liquids, in *Fluidization,* eds. J. F. Davison & D. Harrison, pp. 471–540, Academic, London.

Gorring, R. L. & Churchill, S. W. 1961 Thermal Conductivity of Heterogeneous Materials, *Chem. Eng. Prog.* **57**:53–59.

Graf, W. H. 1971 *Hydraulics of Sediment Transport,* p. 442, McGraw-Hill, New York.

Graf, W. H. & Acaroglu, E. R. 1968 Sediment Transport in Conveyance Systems, *Int. Assoc. Sci. Hydrol.* **23**:20–39, 123–135.

Green, H. L. & Lane, W. R. 1964 *Particulate Clouds, Dusts, Smokes, and Mists*, 2d ed., chap. 5, van Nostrand, New York.

Happel, J., 1957 Viscosity of Suspensions of Uniform Spheres, *J. Appl. Phys.* 28:1288–1292.

Hinze, J. O. 1959 *Turbulence*, Chap. 5, McGraw-Hill, New York.

Hutchinson, P., Hewitt, G. F., & Dukler, A. E. 1971 Deposition of Liquid or Solid Dispersions from Turbulent Gas Stream: A Stochastic Model, *Chem. Eng. Sci.* 26:419–439.

Jokati, T. & Tomita, Y. 1971 Solids Velocities and Pressure Drops in a Horizontal Pneumatic Conveying System, *Proc. Pneumotransport* 1:B3 BHRA.

Kennedy, J. F. 1963 The Mechanics of Dunes and Antidunes in Erodible Bed Channels, *J. Fluid Mech.* 16:521–544.

Kottler, W., Krupp, H., & Rabenhorst, H. 1968 Adhesion of Electrically Charged Particles, *Z. Angew. Phys.* 24:219–223.

Krupp, H. 1967 Particle Adhesion Theory and Experiment, *Adv. Colloid Interface Sci.* 1:111–239.

Langmuir, I. & Blodgett, K. 1946 A Mathematical Investigation of Water Droplet Trajectories, *Tech. Rept.* 5418, Air Material Command, Army Air Force.

Leith, D. & Licht, W. 1972 The Collection Efficiency of Cyclone Type Particle Collectors, *AIChE Symp. Ser.* 68:196–206.

Löffler, F. 1977 Collection of Particles in Fibre Filters, *Proc. 4th Int. Clean Air Congr.*, pp. 800–804.

Löffler, F. & Muhr, W. 1972 Die Abscheidung von Feststoffteilchen und Tropfen an Kreiszylindern inforlge von Trägheitskraften, *Chem. Ing. Tech.* 8:510–514.

Murray, J. D. 1965 On the Mathematics of Fluidization, *J. Fluid Mech.* 21:465–493, 22:57–80.

Newitt, D. M., Richardson, J. F., & Shook, C. A. 1962 Hydraulic Conveying of Solids in Horizontal Pipes, in *Proceedings of a Symposium on the Interaction between Fluids and Particles*, pp. 87–100, Institution of Chemical Engineers, London.

Niedra, J. M. & Penny, G. W. 1965 Orientation and Adhesion of Particles, *IEEE Trans. Ind. Electron. Control Instrum.* IECI-12:46–50.

Penny, G. W. & Klingler, E. H. 1962 Constant Potential and the Adhesion of Dust, *IEEE Trans. Commun. Electron.* 81:200–205.

Pfeffer, R., Rossetti, S., & Lieblein, S. 1966 Analysis and Correlation of Heat Transfer Coefficient and Friction Factor Data for Dilute Gas-Solid Suspensions, *NASA Tech. Memo.* D-3603.

Pietsch, W., Hoffman, E., & Rumpf, H. 1969 Tensile Strength of Moist Agglomerates, *Ind. Eng. Chem. Prod. Res. Dev.* 8:58–62.

Rietema, K. & Verver, C. G. 1961 *Cyclones in Industry*, Elsevier, Amsterdam.

Rudinger, G. & Chang, A. 1964 Analysis of Non-Steady Two-Phase Flow, *Phys. Fluids* 7:1747–1754.

Saffman, P. G. 1965 The Lift on a Small Sphere in a Slow Shear Flow, *J. Fluid Mech.* 22:385–400, 540–533.

Saxton, A. L. & Worley, A. C. 1970 Modern Catalytic Cracking Design, *Oil Gas J.* 68:82–99.

Schugel, K. 1971 Rheological Behavior of Fluidized Systems, in *Fluidization*, eds. J. F. Richardson & D. Harrison, pp. 261–292, Academic, London.

Scott, D. S. 1975 A New Approach to the Acoustic Conditioning of Industrial Aerosol Emission, *J. Sound Vibr.* 43:607–619.

Scott, D. S., Swift, W. M. & Vogel, G. J. 1977 Pulse-Jet Acoustic Dust Conditioning in High Temperature/Pressure Application, *Proc. EPA-ERDA Symp. High Temp./Pressure Particulate Removal.*

Seman, G. W. & Penny, G. W. 1965 Photographic Records of Particle Trajectories during Electrostatic Precipitation, *Power Applic. Syst. IEEE* 86:365–368.

Sha, W. T. & Soo, S. L. 1977a Multidomain Multiphase Fluid Mechanics, *Tech. Memo.* ANL-CT-77-3, NRC-7 (March).

Sha, W. T. & Soo, S. L. 1977b Numerical Modeling of Fluidized Bed Combustor, *Tech. Memo.* ANL-CT-78-4 (Nov.).

Shaw, D. T. 1979 *Recent Developments in Aerosol Science*, Wiley-Interscience, New York.

Soo, S. L. 1962 Boundary Layer Motion of a Gas-Solid Suspension, in *Proceedings of a*

Symposium on the Interaction between Fluids and Particles, pp. 50–63, Institution of Chemical Engineers, London.

Soo, S. L. 1967 *Fluid Dynamics of Multiphase Systems,* Blaisdell (Ginn), Waltham, Mass.

Soo, S. L. 1969 Pipe Flow of Suspensions, *Appl. Sci. Res.* **21**:68–84.

Soo, S. L. 1970 Think Two-Phase in *Advances in Solid-Liquid Flow in Pipes,* ed. I. Zandi, pp. 35–38, Pergamon, New York.

Soo, S. L. 1971 Dynamics of Charged Suspensions, in *Topics in Current Aerosol Research,* eds. G. M. Hidy & J. R. Brock vol. 2, pp. 61–149, Pergamon, New York.

Soo, S. L. 1973a Flows of Suspensions, Lect. Ser. 51, von Karman Inst. for Fluid Dynamics.

Soo, S. L. 1973b Effect of Diffusion on Collection and Impaction of a Sphere, *Powder Technol.* **7**:267–269.

Soo, S. L. 1973c Particle-Gas-Surface Interactions in Collection Devices, *Int. J. Multiphase Flow,* **1**:89–101.

Soo, S. L. 1975 On Equation of Motion of a Solid Particle Suspended in a Fluid, *Phys. Fluids* **18**:263–264.

Soo, S. L. 1976 On One-dimensional Motion of a Single Component in Two Phases, *Int. J. Multiphase Flow* **3**:79–82.

Soo, S. L. 1977 Multiphase Mechanics of a Single Component Two-Phase Flow, *Phys. Fluids* **20**:568–570.

Soo, S. L. 1978 Diffusivity of Spherical Particles in Dilute Suspensions, *AIChE Symp. Ser.* **74**:184–185.

Soo, S. L. & Rodgers, L. W. 1971 Further Studies on the Electroaerodynamic Precipitator, *Powder Technol* **5**:43–50.

Soo, S. L. & Tung, S. K. 1971 Pipe Flow of Suspensions in Turbulent Fluids, *Appl. Sci. Res.* **24**:83–97.

Soo, S. L. & Tung, S. K. 1972 Deposition and Entrainment in Pipe Flow of a Suspension, *Powder Technol.* **6**:283–294.

Soo, S. L., Trezek, G. J., Dimick, R. C., & Hohnstreiter, G. F. 1964 Concentration and Mass Flow Distributions in a Gas-Solid Suspension, *Ind. Eng. Chem. Fundam.* **3**:98–106.

Tung, S. K. 1971 Flow of Suspensions under Field Forces, Ph.D. thesis, Univ. of Illinois at Urbana-Champaign; University Microfilms, Ann Arbor, Mich.

Viskanta, R. & Grosh, R. J. 1961 Heat Transfer by Simultaneous Conduction and Radiation in an Absorbing Medium, *Trans. ASME J. Heat Transfer* **84C**:63–73.

Wallis, G. B. 1969 *One-dimensional Two-Phase Flow,* p. 41, McGraw-Hill, New York.

Wen, C. Y. 1966 Pneumatic Transport of Solids, *U.S. Bur. Mines Inf. Circ.* 8314.

White, H. J. 1968 *Industrial Electrostatic Precipitation,* p. 35, Addison-Wesley, New York.

Yu, J. S. 1977 An Approximate Analysis of Laminar Dispersion in Circular Tubes, *Trans. ASME J. Appl. Mech.* 76-WA:APM-10.

Zaitsev, A. I., Gatsev, V. A., & Makarov, Yu. I. 1975 Calculation of Particle Collision in Concomitant Dispersed Flows, *J. Eng. Phys. (USSR)* **28**:11–16.

Zebel, G. 1968 Capture of Small Particles by Drops Falling in Electric Fields, *J. Colloid Interface Sci.* **27**:294–304.

4 LIQUID–LIQUID SYSTEMS

J. C. Godfrey and C. Hanson

4.1 Introduction

4.1.1 APPLICATIONS

Liquid-liquid two-phase flow problems are found in a diverse range of the process industries and are more common than might be suggested by a perusal of the literature.

Oil-water systems, in particular their separation, are frequently met in the petroleum industry, varying in scale from minor washing operations to the treatment of major spillages. The latter have been the subject of considerable recent study because of environmental concern.

Most solvent extraction processes involve liquid-liquid systems in which one or more components of a solution are separated by contacting with an immiscible solvent in which they are preferentially soluble. The various components distribute between the two phases according to their affinity for the solvent. This represents a valuable separation technique. It tends to complement distillation in that it separates by chemical type rather than molecular size. The degree of separation achieved in a single equilibration is rarely adequate for practical application and most industrial processes employ multistage countercurrent contacting.

Current industrial applications of solvent extraction are diverse. One of the longest established is the separation of aromatic from aliphatic hydrocarbons in the petroleum and petrochemicals industries. Other well-known applications in the organic chemicals field include recovery of antibiotics, dehydration of acetic acid, recovery of phenolic materials from aqueous effluents, purification of lactic acid, manufacture of vitamin C, etc. The last decade has seen a surge of interest in the use of solvent extraction for metals. It has long been used for uranium, but recent work has extended the range of metals to include copper, cobalt, nickel, tungsten, the rare earths, and various precious metals. Finally, reference should be made to its large-scale use in the purification of phosphoric acid. Solvent extraction is covered in the classic text by Treybal (1963) and more recent works by Hanson (1971a) and Laddha & Degaleesan (1976). Its applications are also covered in a recent review by Bailes et al. (1976).

Quite a high proportion of solvent extraction processes depend on a reversible reaction between the solute and the solvent, giving the solvent its selectivity for a particular solute. In addition, however, several industrially important unit processes involve reaction between two immiscible liquid phases and are conducted for synthesis rather than separation. Examples include nitration, certain sulfonation reactions, sulfation, alkylation, esterification, hydrolysis (include fat splitting), and saponification. The fluid flow problems of liquid-liquid unit processes of this type have much in common with those of solvent extraction, although there appears to have been comparatively little linking of the two. Problems of mass transfer with simultaneous chemical reaction have been considered by Hanson (1971b).

Direct liquid-liquid contacting has been considered as a means of heat transfer. Early work was reviewed by Hanson & Ingham (1965). Applications are not numerous, but there is considerable interest in the possible use of such techniques in desalination. It should also be pointed out that removal of the heat generated in some of the unit processes discussed above is a critical parameter in plant design.

4.1.2   EQUIPMENT

Selection and design of liquid-liquid extraction equipment are governed by considerations of the difficulty of the separation and the hydrodynamics of the equipment. The difficulty of the separation is principally decided by the equilibrium characteristics of the system under consideration and the rate at which the solute transfers from one liquid phase to the other. From the equilibrium characteristics, a number of ideal equilibrium stages may be determined for a given separation. However, the size of the equilibrium stage will depend on the rates of mass transfer obtainable; these rates may be either diffusion- or chemically controlled. The hydrodynamics of the process will almost certainly have an important influence on rate of mass transfer and in addition will govern the liquid handling capabilities of the equipment chosen.

There are two major types of equipment: stagewise and differential, stagewise equipment generally being mixer-settlers and differential equipment being columns.

Mixer-settlers are usually arranged in countercurrent trains with each mixer unit approximating an equilibrium stage. A dispersion is created in the mixer and sufficient residence time is allowed for the specified approach to equilibrium to be achieved. The dispersion then passes to the settler, where it forms a dispersion band lying between the clear light and heavy phases. The main design variables are the number of mixer-settler units necessary to effect the required separation, the residence time and level of agitation in the mixer necessary to achieve a suitable approach to equilibrium, and the residence time necessary to effect a phase separation in the settler.

Column contactors are usually employed as single units, providing as they do the equivalent of a number of countercurrent equilibrium stages. Columns are operated in countercurrent flow and depend on differences in density for the flow of the two liquids. There are a large number of designs and the intensity of agitation, and therefore drop size, varies considerably for the range of equipment available. However, the intensity of agitation is generally less than in a mixer-settler and the drop size therefore larger, with the consequence that there is usually less provision made for phase disengagement. Calculations can be made on the basis of the number of equilibrium stages required in some instances and, together with a value for the height of column equivalent to a theoretical stage, used to estimate required column height. However, it is probably more usual to take the column as a differential contactor and determine the number of transfer units corresponding to a specific separation. The mass transfer coefficient appears in the height of transfer unit from which the total column height may be estimated.

4.1.2.1 Mixer-Settlers

This equipment clearly serves two separate functions and the two individual items are designed separately, although some consideration must be given to their interaction. As a preliminary to equipment design, flow rates are established from equilibrium calculations. These procedures have been well documented by Treybal (1963). The main decisions to be made subsequently are related to the choice of suitable residence times for the mixer and the settler. The mixer-settler is particularly suited to liquid-liquid systems where mass transfer rates and/or coalescence rates are low. For the case of low mass transfer rates, it is usually found that rate increases with impeller speed. This is brought about by some combination of increased interfacial area and perhaps increased turbulence, but often at the cost of poorer phase separation in the settler due to smaller drop size.

Some estimate of the relationship between impeller speed and continuous extraction rate can be made from batch extraction tests (Ryon et al. 1959; Treybal 1963), provided a geometrically similar model of the proposed plant mixer is used and the equipment is not too small (approximately $3 + L$). If it is at all possible, some pilot plant work should be conducted at an intermediate scale; it should be possible to establish reasonable pilot plant working conditions from batch tests by using simple reactor theory. Test work would then be necessary to confirm the estimates made and to develop a suitable scale-up criterion—constant power per unit volume being the most usual and fairly conservative.

It is not possible to fix a maximum impeller speed without some study of settler performance; the principal effects of impeller speed on the settler will be reduced coalescence capacity—as indicated by deeper dispersion bands—and higher levels of entrainment. It is important to recognize that there is no general rule regarding impeller speed and coalescence—some systems are "sensitive" and some are not (Barnea & Mizrahi 1975). However, it is likely that increases in impeller speed will increase the entrainment of uncoalesced droplets in the two phases leaving the settler.

Mixer-settler equipment comes in a variety of forms. The Windscale format is probably one of the simplest, using turbine agitation and rectangular mixer boxes and settlers. A correct inlet and outlet arrangement allows gravity flow through the equipment, relying on the difference in density between the homogeneous dispersion in the mixer box and the classified organic in the settler. For large throughputs this design is limited by the need for very deep settlers and therefore a high solvent inventory is required. A simple alternative that overcomes the problem of the deep settler is the pump-mix impeller as used by General Mills (Agers & DeMent 1972), Holmes and Narver, and Davy Powergas (Lott et al. 1972). In these designs one impeller provides for both pumping and mixing, and some compromise must be struck between pumping and mixing requirements. In an alternative proposed for the Zambian copper industry (Orjans et al. 1977), pumping and mixing impellers are separate and one phase only is pumped while the other flows under gravity. This particular arrangement avoids the uncontrolled introduction of two phases to the impeller and may therefore give better entrainment characteristics. The design also calls for three mixer compartments in series, which should, according to simple reactor theory, give a better approach to equilibrium than a mixer of the same volume and only one compartment. A similar philosophy has been used in the Holmes and Narver design at City Services (Kennedy 1977), but this does not have an impeller in each compartment.

Where external pumps can be used, employment of static mixers can be considered (Godfrey & Slater 1978). It may also be possible to use the pump as a mixer and the pipeline to provide a suitable residence time, or even use a pipeline designed for turbulent flow instead of a static mixer.

There is also considerable variety in the approaches taken to settler design. At its simplest, all that is required is a simple rectangular tank to provide sufficient residence time for the coalescence of the appropriate throughput of dispersion. For large plants, however, the volume required may be exceedingly large, so consideration has been given to more sophisticated designs in the hope of reductions in volume. Multitray designs have been developed by Lurgi (Stönner & Wohler 1975) and IMI (Mizrahi & Barnea 1973) to exploit the characteristics of the dispersion band depth-throughput relationship. Davies et al. (1972) proposed the use of packing as a coalescence aid. IMI (Barnea & Mizrahi 1977) designed a precoalescer unit containing packing, suitable for use with either conventional settlers or their multitray design. In addition, there is the possibility of using electrostatic enhancement of coalescence. In most of these proposals consideration must be given to the cleanliness of the liquids being processed, the problems of cleaning, and the effect of deposited solids on equipment performance.

Mixer-settlers have the advantages of simplicity in design and operation, flexibility, ability to operate at high throughputs of dispersed phase, low headroom requirements, minimal back-mixing problems, potentially high stage efficiencies, and relative insensitivity to solids and contamination from feed materials. There are disadvantages, however, in that the equipment is usually large in volume, has a high solvent inventory, and occupies a large floor area. It compares unfavorably in size with column-type equipment if extraction rates and coalescence rates are high and high dispersed-phase ratios are not required.

4.1.2.2 Column Contactors

In the design of solvent extraction columns the main considerations are the mass transfer requirements, which govern column height, and the throughput requirements, which govern column diameter.

The solvent extraction column is almost always operated in a countercurrent manner and usually provides the equivalent of a number of equilibrium stages, in contrast to the mixer-settler, where one discrete unit is required for each equilibrium stage. There are simple idealized relationships between mass transfer duty and number of transfer units and between mass transfer coefficient and height of a transfer unit. The relationships are analogous to those for gas absorption and other multiphase separation processes and are well described by Treybal (1963) and many standard textbooks on separation processes.

For full-scale columns there is some difficulty in determining an actual number of transfer units. This is due to the various axial mixing phenomena that occur in liquid-liquid extraction columns and that change the flow situation from the favorable plug flow assumption used in the simple theory. In general, as column sizes increases the influence of axial mixing becomes greater, so scale-up should be treated with caution.

Mass transfer coefficients are significantly influenced by hydrodynamics, and with the wide choice of column types there is a wide range of potential hydrodynamic conditions. A considerable number of correlations are available for the mass transfer coefficient, most based on considerations of the hydrodynamic conditions of the drop.

Hydrodynamics are also important in determining the liquid handling capacity of a column and its operating characteristics. Unlike the mixer in a mixer-settler, which has an almost infinite throughput capacity if suitable pumping can be arranged, the column is ultimately dependent on gravity flow and density differences. The upper limit of throughput is usually referred to as flooding and defined as the loss of dispersed phase in the continuous-phase outlet. Flooding correlations are available for most column types, but it is usual to treat them with caution and design the column for throughputs remote from the flooding conditions.

The column is also unlike a mixer in that the working holdup is usually quite different from the feed flow ratio and is a function of operating condition. This information and data on drop size are necessary in the calculation of interfacial area when mass transfer calculations are being performed.

As already mentioned, there is even more diversity in the design of columns than of mixer-settlers. Three types of column can be defined: nonagitated columns, impeller-agitated columns, and pulsed columns.

The simplest nonagitated column is the spray column, where the dispersed phase is introduced through a distributor and either rises or falls through the continuous phase according to the density of the two phases. As there are no column internals, substantial recirculation is possible and the ideal of plug flow is very poorly approximated. In addition, the absence of any form of agitation allows drop coalescence and the consequent reduction of interfacial area. Because of these characteristics, performance is poor and the spray column tends to be used for only simple operations.

The packed column has better performance characteristics with respect to limiting recirculation and drop coalescence. The presence of packing gives good radial mixing, which offsets some of the potential problems associated with the wide drop size range produced in packed columns. Although no external agitation is applied, some droplet breakup and agitation is effected during passage through the packing, which should preferably be wetted by the continuous phase. However, the performance of the packed column is limited by low mass transfer coefficients and relatively low holdup capability.

In the sieve tray column, drops are coalesced and redispersed by the stagewise arrangement of sieve trays, and this process has a beneficial effect on mass transfer rate. The design has the advantages of minimal back mixing with low construction costs but is rather inflexible with regard to throughput.

In the impeller-agitated columns, higher local mass transfer rates are obtained by the production of smaller drops and higher levels of turbulence. However, there is a compromise to be struck: small drops have low terminal velocities and this leads to low throughput; high levels of agitation tend to increase axial mixing and thus reduce separation efficiency. In agitated columns, the impellers are employed in a stagewise manner with each impeller in a compartment formed by some form of axial flow baffle. Various combinations of impeller and baffle have been used to control drop size, agitation, and intercompartment mixing. In all cases a careful choice of impeller speed is necessary.

The Scheibel column is probably the oldest of the agitated columns, and its original form employed sections of packing or wire mesh between stages to reduce axial mixing. Packing is easily contaminated by any solids present and encourages coalescence and wider drop size distributions, which increase axial mixing. Later versions of the Scheibel column dispense with packing and use an additional set of baffles.

The Oldshue-Rushton column uses a combination of turbine impellers, radial interstage baffles with a large central aperture, and axial baffles as used in agitated tanks. Back mixing can be controlled by reducing the central aperture size but at the cost of throughput.

The interstage baffles in the Kühni column are perforated plates with large holes and occupy the full column crossection. Once again, control of back mixing is achieved by reducing free area at the expense of reduced throughput. The impeller used is shrouded above and below and consequently the flow produced is predominantly radial.

The rotating disk contactor (RDC) was developed to produce a narrow drop size distribution with drops larger than those produced by turbine-type impellers. The gentler mixing action of the rotating disk is likely to be suitable for systems with poor coalescence rates. The impeller and baffle spacing is closer than in the agitated columns previously discussed. Interstage baffles with large central apertures are used to allow for easy assembly, the apertures being larger than the rotating disks. Because of these large openings, the column can operate at a large throughput but with a corresponding increase in axial mixing. The RDC has been widely used and studied and is well documented.

The axymmetrical RDC also employs the gentle agitation characteristics of the rotating disk and seeks to improve performance by reducing back mixing with a complicated arrangement of interstage and other baffles. The rotating disks are located off center to provide a region of low-intensity agitation to promote drop coalescence. This zone is protected from the direct influence of impeller discharge by a vertical baffle and provides the only flow connection between adjacent stages, which are otherwise completely separated by horizontal baffles. The protected zone also contains horizontal baffles to prevent bypassing of the mixing compartments. Thus each mixing compartment is shielded from the axial mixing influences of the adjoining compartment, while larger drops can form by coalescence in the protected zone. The large drops formed have higher settling velocities and improve throughput.

Other impeller-agitated columns include the Lurgi design, effectively a vertical stack of mixer-settlers, which avoids problems of axial mixing.

Agitation of the contents of a column can also be achieved by pulsation—either direct pulsation of the continuous phase or oscillation of the column internals. With pulsation, the variables of frequency and amplitude are both available for independent optimization. This may provide some advantage over the single variable of rotational speed in impeller-agitated columns, but at the same time it adds an extra dimension that requires study and documentation. Application of pulsations to packed columns has been shown to improve mass transfer, although whether this is due to increased turbulence, smaller drop sizes, reduced channeling, or a combination of all three is not clear. The performance of the column is improved rather than transformed and problems of axial mixing, particularly for larger diameters, are increased. Improved performance can also be obtained from sieve tray columns by applying a pulsation to the continuous phase. In the pulsed seive tray (or pulsed perforated plate) column the trays occupy the whole column cross section and both continuous and dispersed phases must pass through the trays. Operation is favored at the maximum value of the product of amplitude and frequency that still allows the column to operate in the mixer-settler mode. In this mode of operation, coalescence and redispersion of drops occurs from stage to stage, as is the case in the absence of pulsation, and the extent of axial mixing is reduced. Although pulsation improves mass transfer performance, the column remains relatively inflexible to flow rate changes.

A number of columns have been developed in which reciprocating internals are used to provide agitation. Probably the best known of these is the Karr & Lo (1977) column, which uses reciprocating plates having a very much larger free cross-sectional area (50%) than is used in sieve columns (25%). With reciprocating plates the mass could be less than in pulsed columns; however, the mechanical complexity is greater. Back mixing is thought to be reduced if large plate perforations and low intensities of agitation are used. It is also thought that reciprocation of two sets of plates in opposing motion will reduce back mixing, and a column of this type has been developed by Landau et al. (1973).

In addition to mixer-settlers and column contactors, there are centrifugal and horizontal contactors. Contacting equipment is extensively discussed by Treybal (1963), Logsdail & Lowes (1971), Laddha & Degaleesan (1976), and in a recent review by Reissinger & Schroeter (1977).

4.2 Drop Size

The creation of drops is an essential part of all liquid-liquid contacting processes, and a knowledge of drop size is useful in the interpretation of data or in design calculations. In all equipment used for liquid-liquid contacting—columns, agitated tanks, static mixers—the level of agitation is sufficient to create dispersion of one immiscible liquid in the other. In an agitated system both droplet breakup and coalescence will be possible, depending on the level of agitation and number of drops present in various regions of the equipment.

4.2.1 TURBULENT FLOW

In the breakup of a drop there are two principal influences to be considered: a disruptive stress tending to cause deformation and breakup of the drop and a surface force tending to resist deformation. The disruptive stress could be viscous, arising perhaps in gentle flow through a packed column, but more usually would be a dynamic pressure due to turbulent flow. The surface force resisting deformation is due to interfacial tension. In turbulent flow it is thought that drop breakup is brought about by variations in velocity and therefore stress at the surface of a drop.

Most theoretically based relationships for drop size in turbulent flow are based on Kolmogorov's theory of homogeneous isotropic turbulence. It is postulated that in a turbulent system there is a wide range of eddy sizes and energy is transferred from the larger to the smaller. In an agitated system the largest eddies will be of a scale L similar to that of the impeller, and they effect the transfer of energy from the impeller to the bulk of the fluid. The smaller eddies are responsible for the greater part of the energy dissipation in the system and, for high Reynolds number, are independent of the motion of the mainstream. Under these conditions the smaller eddies, of scale Z, may be characterized by the energy dissipation per unit mass of the system, e.

For the condition that the scale of the region under consideration d is much smaller than L and much larger than Z—i.e., $L_L \gg D \gg Z$—then the root-mean-square of the velocity difference between two points D apart, $\bar{u}$, can be written

$$\bar{u} = (eD)^{1/3} \qquad [4.2.1]$$

and a relationship for the maximum stable drop size determined:

$$r_{sd} = C_1 \left(\frac{\sigma}{\rho_c}\right)^{0.6} e^{-0.4} \qquad [4.4.2]$$

In an alternative approach, Hinze (1955) defined a critical droplet Weber number at which breakup occurs:

$$We_{cr} = \frac{\bar{u}^2 D_{max}\rho}{\sigma} \qquad [4.2.3]$$

By using the value of $\bar{u}^2$ given by [4.2.1], a maximum drop size above which breakup would occur is determined:

$$D_{max} = C_2 \left(\frac{\sigma}{\rho}\right)^{0.6} e^{-0.4} \qquad [4.2.4]$$

and has the same form as the relationship proposed by Kolmogorov. Using the observation that $D_{max} = 2D_{32}$ and assuming a constant value of power number (as in a fully baffled, turbine-agitated tank), an average drop size can be expressed in terms of an impeller Weber number:

$$D_{32} = C_3 We_i^{-0.6} \qquad [4.2.5]$$

$$We_i = \frac{D_i^3 N^2 \rho_c}{\sigma} \qquad [4.2.6]$$

Equation [4.2.6] has been confirmed experimentally. However, other relationships are also possible. Glasser et al. (1976) compiled data from various sources and discussed the case of the lower stream Reynolds numbers that could exist in agitated systems. In this case $L_L \gg Z \gg r$ and the relationship for stable drop radius becomes

$$r_{sd} = C_4 \left(\frac{\sigma \mu_c}{\rho_c^2}\right)^{1/3} \left(\frac{1}{e}\right)^{1/3} \qquad [4.2.7]$$

This relationship is also supported by experimental evidence. Glasser et al. make the point that $r \cong Z$ in practice.

Shinnar & Church (1960) examined the case of the minimum drop size below which coalescence occurs and proposed the relationship

$$D_{min} = \frac{C_5 D_i^{5/8}}{We_i^{3/8} \sigma^{3/8}} \qquad [4.2.8]$$

where the constant C_5 incorporates a function $A(L_0)$ that describes the energy of adhesion between two drops.

At high values of holdup, it is argued that either coalescence or turbulence damping in the impeller region becomes important and an alternative form of relationship is required. Calderbank (1958) correlated data at various values of holdup in an agitated tank with the relationship

$$\frac{D_{32}}{D_i} = C_6(1 + C_7 h)\,\text{We}_i^{-0.6} \qquad [4.2.9]$$

and subsequently many data have been presented in this form. However, the values of the exponents found by various workers vary widely: $0.051 < C_6 < 0.081$ and $3.14 < C_7 < 9.0$.

Because of the many theoretical and experimental problems that arise in the study of drop size, discrepancies in correlating constants are not surprising. At high values of holdup it is difficult to develop techniques that can clearly discriminate all the drops present because of the large numbers in any sample. In addition, the mechanism of droplet breakup and coalescence is complex. The regions within an agitated tank where droplet breakup and coalescence occur are not yet fully established and are likely to be different for different liquid-liquid systems. Droplet breakup and coalescence are not influenced in the same way by the physical properties of the liquids; coalescence will be relatively faster in one system than another.

For these and other reasons, various correlation procedures have been used. Thornton & Bouyatiotis (1967) used the two equations

$$D_{32} = D_{32}^0 + 1.18\,h\,\frac{\sigma^2}{\mu_c^2 g}\left(\frac{\Delta\rho\sigma^3}{\mu_c^4 g}\right)^{-0.62}\left(\frac{\Delta\rho}{\rho_c}\right)^{0.05} \qquad [4.2.10]$$

$$\frac{(D_{32}^0)^3\rho_c^2 g}{\mu_c} = 29.0\left(\frac{p^3}{\rho_c^2\mu_c g^4}\right)^{-0.32}\left(\frac{\rho_c\sigma^3}{\mu_c^4 g}\right)^{0.14} \qquad [4.2.11]$$

The data were collected with a baffled agitated tank; the results obtained were the same for both batch and continuous operation. In a study of drop size in an agitated tank without baffles, Weinstein & Treybal (1973) found a difference between batch and continuous operation. They correlated their data with a modification of the Hinze (1955) theory for maximum drop size, using an empirical expression for $\bar{u}^2$, as they found that drop size lay between the inertial subrange and energy dissipation range of eddy size. The correlation used was of the form

$$D_{32} = 10^{C_8 + C_9 h}\gamma_c^{C_{10}} e^{C_{11}}\left(\frac{\sigma}{\rho_c}\right)^{C_{12}} \qquad [4.2.12]$$

where different values of the exponents were required for batch and continuous operation.

The study of drop size in turbulent flow has also included the reciprocating plate column, where Baird & Lane (1973) found

$$D_{32}\left(\frac{\rho_c}{\sigma}\right)^{3/5} e^{2/5} = 0.357 \qquad [4.2.13]$$

and flow in smooth pipes, where Kubie & Gardner (1977) found

$$D_{max} \left(\frac{\rho_c}{\sigma}\right)^{3/5} e^{2/5} = 0.725 \qquad [4.2.14]$$

When it is considered that it is frequently found that $D_{max} = 2D_{32}$, these two equations are virtually identical. However, Baird (1977) later observed that the dimensionless mean drop diameter on the left-hand side of his equation is of order 0.02 for agitated tanks and that the turbulence field is therefore far from homogeneous and isotropic.

Thus the question of the correlation of drop size data for turbulent flow is as yet unresolved, and there is considerable scope for the reexamination of existing data. In applying correlations one should choose those established for the systems most similar to those in question and be cautious of predictions beyond the regions for which the correlations were established.

4.2.2 NOZZLE FLOW

In the formation of drops at nozzles the conditions of formation are particularly important. The influence of wetting characteristics of liquid and nozzle is discussed by Treybal (1963), who advises the use of nondispersed-phase wetted nozzle materials or careful nozzle design when controlled drop sizes are required. The effect of rate of formation of drops is discussed by Heertjes & de Nie (1971), who consider four regions of behavior in the relationship between drop size and rate of formation (figure 4.2.1).

In the first of the four regions of behavior proposed by Heertjes & de Nie, where drop formation is very slow and drop size is independent of rate of formation, the relationship between drop size, nozzle size, and interfacial tension is given by a modification of Tate's law,

$$Mg = \pi D_N \sigma \qquad [4.2.15]$$

by Harkins & Brown (1919):

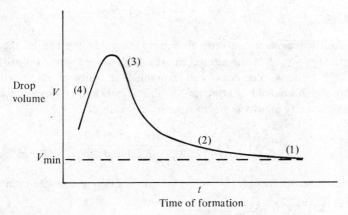

Figure 4.2.1 Drop formation as a function of time.

$$Mg = \pi D_N \sigma H \frac{D_N}{r} \qquad [4.2.16]$$

where the correction factor $H\,(D_N/r)$ makes allowance for drop shape.

In the second region, drop formation is more rapid and size is dependent on flow rate. Allowance for flow rate has been made in correlations by Hayworth & Treybal (1950) and Null & Johnson (1958), which have been used with success by others. In a theoretical model of drop formation in this region, Narasinga Rao et al. (1966) and Heertjes & de Nie (1971) considered the process in two parts: drop formation and drop release. The corresponding expression for drop volume is

$$V = V_{\min} + \dot{V} t_{RL} \qquad [4.2.17]$$

where $V_{\min}$ is the minimum drop size, as would be encountered in the first region; $\dot{V}$ is the rate of flow of liquid into the drop and is assumed constant; t_{RL} is a release time, the time taken for release subsequent to the formation of a drop of volume $V_{\min}$. Various approaches have been used to evaluate t_{RL}, and a correlation was developed by Scheele & Meister (1968) and successfully used for both mutually saturated systems and systems where mass transfer was occurring:

$$V = H \left\{ \frac{\pi \sigma D_N}{g \Delta \rho} + \frac{20 \mu \dot{V} D_N}{D^2 g \Delta \rho} - \frac{4 \rho_d \dot{V} v_n}{3 g \Delta \rho} + 4.5 \left[\frac{\dot{V}^2 D_N^2 \rho_d \sigma}{(g \Delta \rho)^2} \right]^{1/3} \right\} \qquad [4.2.18]$$

This relationship is essentially the Harkins & Brown expression for $V_{\min}$ with additional terms; a similar relationship was proposed by de Chazal & Ryan (1971):

$$V = \frac{\pi D_N \sigma}{\Delta \rho g} \left(H + 1.648 \, \frac{\Delta \rho D_N V^{1/3}}{2 \sigma v_s} - \frac{\rho_d D_N v_N^2}{2 \sigma} \right) \qquad [4.2.19]$$

This was successfully applied by Steiner et al. (1977) for spray columns. These authors proposed an empirical relationship for the data of the third region—intermediate between the slow formation (second) region and the critical velocity (fourth) region—in terms of parameters from the critical velocity region:

$$\frac{D}{D_J} = \frac{2.06}{v_N/v_{N'}} + 1.47 \ln \frac{v_N}{v_{N'}} \qquad [4.2.20]$$

In the fourth region, where drop formation occurs at the end of the Rayleigh jet, a maximum is found in the interfacial area of the drops formed. Christiansen & Hixson (1957) made a theoretical and experimental study of the production of organic drops in an aqueous continuum for this region and proposed a relationship for the nozzle velocity at which maximum area is produced:

$$v_{N'} = 2.69 \left(\frac{D_J}{D_N} \right)^2 \left[\frac{\sigma}{D_J (0.514 \rho_d + 0.472 \rho_c)} \right]^{1/2} \qquad [4.2.21]$$

They also gave empirical relationships for the nozzle/jet diameter ratio:

when $D_N/(\sigma/g\Delta\rho)^{1/2} < 0.785$:

$$\frac{D_N}{D_J} = 0.485 \left[\frac{D_N}{(\sigma/g\Delta\rho)^{1/2}}\right]^2 + 1 \qquad [4.2.22]$$

when $D_N/(\sigma/g\Delta\rho)^{1/2} > 0.785$:

$$\frac{D_N}{D_J} = \frac{1.51 D_N}{(\sigma/g\Delta\rho)^{1/2}} + 0.12 \qquad [4.2.23]$$

The average drop diameter under these conditions is approximately twice the jet diameter.

4.2.3 FLOW IN CONTACTING EQUIPMENT

For agitated tanks, as used in mixer-settlers, drop size prediction or correlation is usually performed with the turbulent relationships previously discussed. In addition to the uncertainties already raised, the difference between batch and continuous operation has not been classified, although it seems fairly certain that drop size will be larger for continuously operated tanks because of the reduced residence time.

For column contactors with rotary agitators, the methods for agitated tank prediction have been adapted. Bibaud & Treybal (1966) recommended use of the Thornton & Bouyatiotis (1967) correlation for the Oldshue-Rushton column. Strand et al. (1962) used a turbulent flow equation

$$D_{max} = C_{13} \left(\frac{\sigma}{\rho_c}\right)^{0.6} e^{-0.4} \qquad [4.2.24]$$

for the rotating disk contactor and found C_{13} in the region 0.4–0.6 for organic drops and 0.8–1.2 for water drops; the average drop diameter was approximately $0.7 D_{max}$. For intensive mixing in the RDC, Misek (1976) proposed

$$\frac{D}{D_i} = 2.7 \left(\frac{\sigma D_i}{D_K \rho_c}\right)^{1/3} e^{-2/3} \qquad [4.2.25]$$

but for mild agitation gave a relationship independent of agitation:

$$D_{max} = C_{14} \left(\frac{\sigma}{\Delta\rho g}\right)^{1/2} \qquad [4.2.26]$$

This relationship is very similar to the one that applies to packed columns.

For the packed column there is a critical packing size given by

$$D_p = 2.42 \left(\frac{\sigma}{\Delta\rho g}\right)^{1/2} \qquad [4.2.27]$$

above which drop size is independent of packing size and only slightly dependent on flow rate. With packing smaller than the critical size the drop size is larger, while packing at the critical size gives a strong dependence of drop size on flow rate.

Lewis et al. (1951) observed that the size of drops leaving the packing was independent of the size of drops entering and that, for packing larger than the critical size, drop size could be described by

$$D_{32} = C_{15} \left(\frac{\sigma}{\Delta\rho g} \right)^{1/2}$$
[4.2.28]

Later, Gayler & Pratt (1953) modified this relationship to include holdup, dispersed-phase velocity, and voidage fraction:

$$D_{32} = 0.92 \left(\frac{\sigma}{\Delta\rho g} \right)^{1/2} \frac{\bar{v}_0 bh}{V_d}$$
[4.2.29]

where $\bar{v}_0$ is a characteristic velocity, which is discussed later under holdup. Thornton & Ramshaw (1967), in a study of breakup of drops on collision with packing elements, determined a relationship for a critical drop diameter above which breakup occurs, which is approximately

$$D_c = 1.32 \left(\frac{\sigma}{\Delta\rho g} \right)^{1/2}$$
[4.2.30]

For the spray column, Steiner et al. (1977) commented that the single-drop nozzle equations previously discussed are applicable to the calculation of drop size provided the distributor is not wetted by the dispersed phase and is so constructed that drops do not touch each other.

A brief review of correlations for drop size and other design parameters is given by Korchinsky (1974) for the design of liquid-liquid extraction columns; drop size correlations are discussed by Treybal (1963) for a wide range of liquid-liquid contactors. Some additional information can be found in the later survey of Laddha & Degaleesan (1976).

4.3 Drop Phenomena

4.3.1 MASS TRANSFER

4.3.1.1 Introduction

In equipment design for liquid-liquid extraction, one of the main considerations is that adequate provision be made, usually in the form of a suitable residence time, for the mass transfer duty. At the design stage this point is usually resolved into the consideration of mass transfer coefficients or some aspect of chemical kinetics. The relationship between an overall coefficient and individual resistances is usually expressed in the conventional way:

$$\frac{1}{\beta_{oc}} = \frac{1}{\beta_c} + \frac{1}{m\beta_d} + \frac{1}{\beta_i} \qquad [4.3.1]$$

When data are collected from working extraction equipment, it is usually only possible to determine values of the overall coefficient β_{oc}. For values of the continuous- and dispersed-phase film coefficients β_c and β_d, it is usually necessary to resort to specialized experimental procedures. In most cases it is assumed that the interfacial resistance to mass transfer, as described by β_i, is negligible. The slope of the equilibrium line m is in most cases easy to determine in simple equipment.

The range of equipmental and operating conditions used for liquid-liquid extraction is very wide, with the result that there are wide variations in the hydrodynamic conditions under which mass transfer occurs in practice. Thus the need for data on mass transfer coefficients far exceeds the supply, since the complexity of two-phase flow is such that film coefficients have had to be measured under idealized experimental conditions. The interaction of fluid dynamics, interfacial phenomena, and mass transfer in extraction processes has been reviewed by Schügel et al. (1977).

In addition to the problem of the availability of mass transfer coefficient data, there is the difficulty that some mass transfer processes are accompanied by chemical reaction. Baird (1980) discusses the importance of chemical, diffusional, and hydrodynamic factors in extraction by chemical reaction.

4.3.1.2 Film Coefficients

Data are usually required for both the continuous and the dispersed phase and the range of hydrodynamic conditions of interest is very wide. Progress has been made in the study of the influence of hydrodynamics by experiments that examine the behavior of drops of various sizes falling under gravitational influence. Three broad regions of behavior can be separated by examining the relationship between drag coefficient and droplet Reynolds number (figure 4.3.1). At low Reynolds numbers, for small drops, the relationship is essentially that of a rigid sphere. At higher Reynolds numbers and layer drop sizes some departure from rigid sphere characteristics can be seen as internal circulation within the drop develops. When circulation becomes extensive at high Reynolds numbers there ceases to be any parallel with rigid sphere behavior. These three regions of hydrodynamic behavior provide a basis for the classification of mass transfer data for both the dispersed and the continuous phase.

4.3.1.3 Dispersed-Phase Coefficients

Drops falling under gravity and less than about 2 mm in diameter will experience only relatively low rates of mass transfer because of the largely stagnant condition of the liquid in the drop. For the condition where there is no significant resistance to mass transfer in the continuous phase, Newman (1931) developed a relationship between drop concentration and time from which a mass transfer coefficient can be estimated:

$$\beta_d = \frac{2\pi^2 \delta}{3D} \qquad [4.3.2]$$

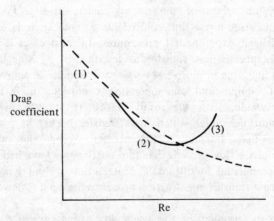

Figure 4.3.1 Drag coefficient as a function of Reynolds number.

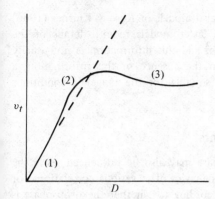

Figure 4.3.2 Terminal velocity as a function of drop size.

The relationship of Gröber (1925) permits consideration of significant resistance in the continuous phase. The values of β_d obtained for stagnant drops will be very small.

For larger drops, of 2-10 mm, some degree of internal laminar circulation will occur, giving larger values of β_d. In this regime, Re ≤ 10, a relationship similar to that of Newman was developed by Kronig & Brink (1950), once again describing changing concentration as a function of time for the condition where there is no significant resistance in the continuous phase. An approximate expression for the dispersed-phase mass transfer coefficient can be determined:

$$\beta_d \cong \frac{2\pi^2 \delta}{D} \qquad [4.3.3]$$

Once again assuming no significant resistance in the continuous phase, a model for turbulent circulation in spherical drops was given by Handlos & Baron (1957):

$$\beta_d = \frac{C_\lambda v_D}{768\,(1 + \mu_d/\mu_c)} \qquad [4.3.4]$$

where v_D is the droplet velocity and $C_\lambda = 2.88$. When continuous-phase resistance is significant, appropriate values of C_λ may be calculated by the procedure of Wellek & Skelland (1965). Appropriate conditions for the use of the Handlos & Baron equation are not easily specified, but the range Re = 100-300 and We > 3.3 are appropriate for free-falling drops. However, for drops moving through a packed column or undergoing repeated coalescence and dispersion, the equation may not be suitable and an empirical correlation has been proposed by Skelland & Wellek (1964) for nonoscillating drops. For the above conditions of turbulent circulation the value of β_d will be 5-10 times larger than that for rigid drops.

As drops of increasingly large size are considered, there comes a point where drop oscillation is observed. This drop size corresponds approximately to the maximum occurring in the terminal velocity-drop size relationship and to the region of increasing drag coefficient as a function of Reynolds number (figure 4.3.2). The region can be defined approximately by We values larger than 3.3-3.7 and drop Reynolds numbers larger than 300 (based on continuous-phase properties). The Handlos & Baron (1957) model is capable of describing data in this regime to an accuracy within experimental error; there are also models of Rose & Kintner (1966) and Angelo et al. (1966). However, the two latter models require details of the amplitude and frequency of droplet oscillation, and this information is not usually available when estimates of β_d are made. In the absence of this information, a correlation of Skelland & Wellek (1964) is suitable for the range of conditions stipulated by the authors.

4.3.1.4 Continuous-Phase Coefficients

Mass transfer conditions in the continuous phase may also be influenced, as in the dispersed-phase case, by drop size and drop behavior. The various correlations for continuous mass transfer coefficients differ according to whether the drop phase is in a rigid, nonrigid, or oscillating condition. There is an additional complication in the case of the continuous phase because it is sometimes argued that the behavior of the wake behind the moving drop should also be considered. The problem here is that, although wake formation and behavior are usually significant in laboratory studies of free-falling or suspended drops, wake behavior is less important if the continuous phase is well agitated, as is the case in much commercial equipment. The simplest relationships are usually of the form

$$Sh = C_{16} Re^{C_{17}} Sc^{C_{18}} \qquad [4.3.5]$$

For rigid drops the relationship of Linton & Sutherland (1960), also used by Thorsen (1954) and Griffith (1960), is

$$Sh = 0.582 \, Re^{1/2} \, Sc^{1/3} \qquad [4.3.6]$$

for Reynolds numbers larger than 1. An almost identical correlation with $C_{16} = 0.552$ is presented by Frössling (1938), once again for Reynolds numbers greater than 1 and Schmidt numbers much greater than 1. Data for rigid drops are also presented in the form

$$Sh = 2 + C_{19} \, Re^{1/2} Sc^{1/3} \qquad [4.3.7]$$

(where $Sh = 2$ is the theoretical lower limit for diffusion) by Rowe et al. (1965), using $C_{19} = 0.76$, and by Garner & Suckling (1958), using $C_{19} = 0.95$, for Reynolds numbers in the range 60–660 and Schmidt numbers considerably greater than 1. A third form of correlation, to account for wake behavior, is proposed by Kinard et al. (1963):

$$Sh = 2.0 + Sh_n + 0.450 \, Re^{1/2} Sc^{1/3} + 0.0484 \, Re \, Sc^{1/3} \qquad [4.3.8]$$

For nonrigid drops where there is some internal circulation, the exponent of the Schmidt number is now larger than 1/3, usually 1/2, because the velocity at the interface can no longer be considered to be zero. For this situation, as would be the case for potential flow, Boussinesq (1905) proposed

$$Sh = 1.13 \, Re^{1/2} Sc^{1/2} \qquad [4.3.9]$$

Similar relationships have been proposed by a number of authors with the value of the constant varying between 1.13 and 0.6 due to the influence of wake formation.

Thorsen et al. (1968) give a correlation for the "constant"

$$C = 1.13 \left\{ 1 - \frac{4(3\sqrt{3} - 2)}{5\sqrt{\pi}} \frac{1}{\text{Re}^{1/2}} \frac{1 + 4\mu_d/\mu_c}{1 + [(\rho_d/\rho_c)(\mu_d/\mu_c)]^{1/2}} \right\}^{1/2} \qquad [4.3.10]$$

In the Reynolds number range 8–800 the empirical correlation of Garner et al. (1959)

$$\text{Sh} = -126 + 1.8 \ \text{Re}^{1/2} \text{Sc}^{0.42}$$

describes the continuous-phase mass transfer data available for larger, nonrigid drops.

Under conditions of drop oscillation, mass transfer coefficients in the continuous phase are further increased to values above those for circulation in drops. For the experiments of Garner & Tayeban (1960),

$$\text{Sh} = 50 + 0.0085 \ \text{Re} \ \text{Sc}^{0.7} \qquad [4.3.11]$$

whereas the empirical relationship of Hughmark (1967) gives

$$\text{Sh} = 2 + 0.084 \left[\text{Re}^{0.484} \text{Sc}^{0.0339} \left(\frac{Dg^{1/3}}{\gamma^{2/3}} \right)^{0.072} \right]^{3/2} \qquad [4.3.12]$$

For the case of swarms of drops, a situation nearer the practical operating conditions of most equipment, Waslo & Gal-Or (1971) conducted a theoretical analysis for drops of uniform size assuming no dispersed-phase resistance to mass transfer. The continuous-phase film coefficient for rigid spheres—i.e., small drops or drops where there is a larger surfactant effect—is given by

$$\text{Sh} = 1.26 \left[\frac{1 - h^{5/3}}{2 \ | \ 3h^{5/3} - (3 + 2h^{5/3})h^{1/3}} \right] \text{Re}^{1/3} \text{Sc}^{1/3} \qquad [4.3.13]$$

for the condition of internal circulation within drops:

$$\text{Sh} = 0.923 \ \phi(h) \ \text{Re}^{1/2} \text{Sc}^{1/2} \qquad [4.3.14]$$

Equations for the condition of internal circulation are also given by Hadamard (1911), Heertjes et al. (1954), and Calderbank & Moo-Young (1961). Calderbank & Moo-Young also presented a relationship for agitated tank conditions:

$$\text{Sh} = 0.13 \ \text{Sc}^{-0.67} \left(\frac{p\mu_c}{\rho_c^2} \right)^{0.25} \qquad [4.3.15]$$

4.3.1.5 Application of Mass Transfer Coefficients

The correlations discussed are a good guide to the computation of coefficients under the conditions for which the correlations were established. In many cases these conditions are idealized for reasons of mathematical or experimental necessity and somewhat remote from the conditions experienced in working equipment. When consideration is being given to the use of any group of correlations, reference to the original work will be useful in making the most appropriate selection. It is also worthwhile, where possible, to estimate likely maxima and minima for the region of interest from the correlations that appear relevant. The values obtained will be useful in the sizing of pilot plant equipment, and the correlations frequently will be of assistance in the analysis of pilot data and in scale-up exercises.

4.3.2   HEAT TRANSFER

4.3.2.1   Introduction

There is a close analogy between mass transfer and heat transfer. Many workers have attempted to study the characteristics of liquid extraction contactors by using heat transfer because this is usually more easily followed than mass transfer, temperature being more conveniently measured than concentration. More recently there has been a surge of interest in direct contact liquid-liquid heat exchange in its own right, with applications proposed over a diverse range from desalination to refinery operations and the cooling of nuclear reactors. In addition, many liquid-liquid reactions such as aromatic nitration are strongly exothermic, and heat transfer from such heterogeneous dispersions is an important aspect of the design of reactors for such systems.

The whole subject of heat transfer by direct liquid-liquid contact has been reviewed comprehensively by Kehat & Sideman (1971). As with mass transfer, most fundamental work has concentrated on heat transfer to single drops in an immiscible continuous phase. Some practical data are then available on the performance of actual liquid-liquid heat exchangers.

4.3.2.2   Heat Transfer to Single Drops

Johnson & Hamielec (1960) pointed out that there are three distinct periods in the life of such a drop: (1) the period of formation, initial oscillation, and acceleration; (2) the steady fall or rise period; and (3) the period of coalescence. In most circumstances heat transfer during the latter period is likely to be small. Most investigations have concentrated on the second period.

Calderbank & Korchinski (1956) employed several column lengths so as to eliminate heat transfer during drop formation and coalescence and study the phenomenon during the free-fall period. A similar technique was employed by Zabel et al. (1974). The overall heat transfer coefficient U can be calculated by a simple balance between the heat accumulated inside the drop and that transferred from the bulk of the continuous phase to the drop, integrated for constant continuous-phase temperature. Drop temperatures (corrected for end effects) are used as integration limits. Over time t this yields

$$U = \frac{C_p \rho_d D}{6} \frac{v_d - v_c}{L_c} \ln \frac{T_i - T_c}{T_0 - T_c} \qquad [4.3.16]$$

where
$$\frac{1}{U} = \frac{1}{\alpha_d} + \frac{1}{\alpha_c} \qquad [4.3.17]$$

4.3.2.3 Continuous-Phase Coefficients

Thorsen & Terjesen (1962) claimed that the effect of internal circulation in the drop on the external coefficient is fully taken into account by the changed drop velocities. Thus the same correlation may be applied to the external transfer resistances for both stagnant drops and those with internal circulation. The major resistance to transfer is usually located within the drop, so that the effect of any deviation from this assumption should be small.

Heat transfer to solid spheres has been extensively researched and critically reviewed by Rowe et al. (1965). The data can usually be correlated by an equation of the form

$$Nu_c = C_{21} + C_{22} \, Pr_c^{C_{23}} \, Re_c^{C_{24}} \qquad [4.3.18]$$

For solid spheres in water in the range $30 < Re < 2000$, $C_{21} = 2$, $C_{22} = 0.79$, $C_{23} = 0.33$, and $C_{24} = 0.50$.

Calderbank & Korchinski (1956) used mercury drops falling through glycerol-water solutions to measure continuous-phase heat transfer coefficients. They assumed negligible internal resistance in the mercury drops so that the overall heat transfer coefficient approximates the external film coefficient.

4.3.2.4 Dispersed-Phase Coefficients

There are two well-established theoretical models based on either rigid drop behavior or drops with internal circulation.

If rigid drop behavior is assumed, heat transfer inside the drop is by conduction alone. The equation for unsteady-state diffusion into a rigid sphere was solved by Newman (1931), assuming negligible outside film resistance and constant continuous-phase temperature. Expressed in terms of a transfer efficiency term ΔT^+ representing the fractional approach to the maximum possible heat transfer over the constant velocity region, this gives

$$\Delta T^+ = \frac{T_{in} - T_{out}}{T_{in} - T_c} = 1 - \frac{6}{\pi^2} \sum_{n=1}^{\infty} \frac{1}{n^2} \exp \frac{\kappa \pi^2 n^2 t}{r^2} \qquad [4.3.19]$$

Gröber (1925) allowed for a finite external resistance, while still assuming a constant continuous-phase temperature, giving

$$\Delta T^+ = 1 - 6 \sum_{n=1}^{\infty} C_n \exp \left(- \frac{C_{\lambda n}^2 \kappa t}{r^2} \right) \qquad [4.3.20]$$

The constants C_n and $C_{\lambda n}$ are functions of the external resistance and are tabulated by Lykov & Mikhaylon (1961).

Kronig & Brink (1950) considered the case of drops involving internal circulation. This greatly increases the rate of heat transfer. Neglecting any outside film resistance and using the Hadamard stream function, they derived an equation for the inside heat transfer efficiency for $Re_c < 1$ as

$$\Delta T^+ = 1 - \frac{3}{8} \sum_{n=1}^{\infty} C_n^2 \exp\left(-\frac{16 C_{\lambda n} \kappa t}{r^2}\right) \qquad [4.3.21]$$

Handlos & Baron (1957) derived an alternative model for an extended range of Reynolds numbers ($Re_c < 1000$) by replacing the Hadamard streamlines with a system of tori and assuming a random radial motion superimposed on the circular motion, giving

$$\Delta T^+ = 2 \sum_{n=1}^{\infty} C_n^2 \exp\left[-\frac{16 C_{\lambda n} \kappa t\, Pe_d}{2048 D^2 (1 + \bar{\mu}_d/\mu_c)}\right] \qquad [4.3.22]$$

4.3.2.5 Models for Nonspherical Drops

The theoretical models discussed above were derived on the assumption of spherical drops. In practice, drops above a critical diameter will oscillate in shape. Rose & Kintner (1966) developed a model for such cases based on the concepts of interfacial stretch and assuming internal droplet mixing between oscillations. The resulting expression for the overall transfer efficiency is cumbersome to use but calculations using it show good agreement with published experimental data.

Oblate spheroids have been considered by a number of workers, who have derived theoretical models: Skelland & Cornish (1963) and Lochiel & Calderbank (1964).

4.3.2.6 Influence of the Wake Region

The wake formed behind a liquid drop moving through an immiscible second liquid plays an important part in any heat transfer process. The importance for heat transfer in liquid-liquid spray columns was first emphasized by Letan & Kehat (1968a). Zabel et al. (1974) reviewed other relevant references and showed in their own work on heat transfer to single drops that the wake has a considerable influence on the internal Nusselt number. For continuous-phase Reynolds numbers $Re_c < 20$, they found their experimental results to be in good agreement with the theoretical internal Nusselt numbers calculated from the Handlos & Baron (1957) model. Under these circumstances the wake is assumed to be small and not to play a significant role. For $Re_c > 20$ the experimental results deviated substantially from any theoretical prediction and this was ascribed to the influence of the wake behind the drop. Use of the relation for wake volume proposed by Letan & Kehat (1968a) allowed correlation of the internal Nusselt number for $6 < Re_c < 200$ by:

$$Nu_d = 0.019\, Pe_d\, \frac{\mu_c}{\mu_d + \mu_d} \left(\frac{V_W}{V}\right)^{1.8} \qquad [4.3.23]$$

This does not apply to $Re_c > 200$, where wake shedding takes place.

The study by Zabel et al. (1974) also showed that the presence of surface-active agents reduced the effective heat transfer rate to that corresponding to a solid sphere, even for drops that should have shown internal circulation and oscillation. A similar sensitivity of mass transfer rates to the presence of surfactants is well known, although this has sometimes been ascribed to the formation of a physical barrier at the interface.

4.3.2.7 Heat Transfer in Liquid-Liquid Contactors

A number of studies have been reported on heat transfer by direct liquid-liquid contact in various forms of liquid extraction equipment. Most attention has been paid to spray columns because of their simple construction and low susceptibility to blockage by solids—both considerations of importance in desalination applications. The mechanics of spray columns have been described in detail by Kehat & Sideman (1971), while Letan & Kehat (1965, 1968a, 1968b, 1969, 1970) carried out extensive research into the mechanisms of both heat and mass transfer in spray columns. Hanson et al. (1971) reported a study of direct contact heat transfer between immiscible liquids in a mixer-settler. This proved to have a very high heat transfer capacity.

Heat transfer between two immiscible liquids contacted cocurrently in a simple pipe has been studied to a limited extent by Porter et al. (1968). Use of a static mixer in the pipe should increase transfer rates.

4.3.2.8 Heat Transfer with Change of Phase

It is claimed by Kehat & Sideman (1971) that direct contact heat transfer with change of phase provides the advantages of smaller mass flow rates of the transfer fluids and convenient separation of the fluids, while giving heat transfer coefficients more than an order of magnitude greater than those for nonevaporating drops. Experimental work on single drops evaporating while rising freely in an immiscible liquid has been reported by a number of workers, including extensive studies by Sideman & Taitel (1964) and Sideman et al. (1965). The saline water conversion process of Wilke et al. (1963) involves water evaporated from a brine-oil mixture flowing cocurrently, but few data are available.

4.3.2.9 Simultaneous Heat and Mass Transfer

Many industrially important two-liquid-phase processes involve simultaneous heat and mass transfer, even though the phases may not be introduced at different temperatures. Thus solvent extraction processes are often accompanied by an enthalpy change due to differing heats of solution. While the effect on bulk temperatures may be small, temperature profiles in the interfacial region may be significant and may influence the overall mass transfer process. This has not been thoroughly researched. More immediately apparent are the temperature effects that accompany many liquid-liquid reactions such as aromatic nitration. In this example, removal of the heat of reaction can be a more critical design parameter than the mass transfer rate.

The whole subject of simultaneous heat and mass transfer in liquid-liquid systems has been critically reviewed by von Berg (1971), who is one of the few workers to have studied the process under such conditions that there is no interaction between the heat and mass transfer (Coughlin & von Berg 1966). However, experimental data are still limited and it is not possible to arrive at any generalizations on the heat transfer-mass transfer relationship in practical contactors.

4.3.3 COALESCENCE

Drop coalescence is thought to play an important role in the establishment of the steady-state drop size distribution in an agitated system. The process is viewed as an equilibrium between the opposing influences of drop breakup and drop coalescence, with the nature of that equilibrium being determined by the degree of agitation and the physical properties of the two liquids. The physical situation is very complicated and includes the problem of predicting the number of drop-drop collisions that will occur in a given situation and determining how many of these collisions will result in coalescence. Park & Blair (1975) observed that in an agitated tank only 10% of collisions lead to coalescence and, perhaps more surprisingly, that coalescence rate is proportional to turbulence level with the highest coalescence rates occurring near the impeller. Misek (1964) presented a relationship for drop-drop coalescence in the rotating disk column and Kuboi et al. (1972) presented data for coalescence in turbulent pipe flow.

Although coalescence studies in turbulent systems are of interest for considerations of drop size and mass transfer, the area of most immediate interest to the designer is likely to be the coalescence of dispersions after mass transfer has been satisfactorily effected in a contactor. In mixer-settlers, the settler is designed to provide adequate coalescence capacity for the dispersion produced by the mixer. In columns, an additional volume at the top or bottom of the column, depending on the relative density of the dispersed phase, is often sufficient to allow for the coalescence of the dispersion since operating holdup is usually low; in some cases it is necessary to employ additional settling tanks.

In coalescing dispersion bands both drop-drop and drop-interface coalescence will occur. For either case the limiting rate step will be the drainage of the continuous-phase film separating drops or drop and interface. When dispersion bands form, either in settlers or in the settling zones of column contactors, the band will have a density intermediate between the densities of the continuous and dispersed phases and will lie between the two. Consequently, there will be two boundaries: a passive interface between the dispersion and the continuous phase and an active interface between the dispersion and the coalesced dispersed phase. In columns it is possible to observe settling—i.e., movement of drops under gravitational influence—at the passive interface as drops enter the dispersion band. The main function of most "settlers" is coalescence—in most settlers an attempt is made to avoid gravity settling of drops—with the dispersion usually introduced into a region approximately midway between the active and passive interfaces.

In the study of drop-interface coalescence, a sequence of steps has been identified:

1. Deformation of drop and interface as drop approaches interface
2. Oscillation of drop and interface following deceleration of drop

3. Drainage and rupture of continuous phase film
4. Whole or partial transfer of drop contents to coalesced phase

Of these, film drainage appears to be the controlling influence; from visual observations, steps 1 and 2 do not appear to be significant in deep dispersion bands. The principal characteristic of drop-interface coalescence is the distribution of coalescence times observed. Measurement of coalescence times is particularly difficult experimentally (Liem & Woods 1974) in that the coalescence process is sensitive to a large number of variables, many of which are difficult to control—e.g., vibration and trace impurities. Correlations have been developed by Davies et al. (1971) for coalescence time for single drops:

$$\frac{\bar{t}\sigma}{r\mu_c} = 6.2 \times 10^3 \left(\frac{r^2 g \Delta \rho}{\sigma}\right)^{-1.14} \frac{\mu_c}{\mu_d} \qquad [4.3.24]$$

and for multiple drops:

$$\frac{\bar{t}\sigma}{r\mu_c} = 31 \times 10^3 \left(\frac{r^2 g \Delta \rho}{\sigma}\right)^{-1.24} \left(\frac{\mu_d}{\mu_c}\right)^{1.03} \qquad [4.3.25]$$

but the accuracy of the correlations is very much system-dependent. Of particular interest in the study of drop-interface coalescence is the influence of viscosity, temperature, mass transfer, and solids. Lower continuous-phase viscosities give more rapid film drainage and shorter coalescence times; increased temperature reduces viscosity and coalescence time. Mass transfer from drop to continuous phase decreases interfacial tension and increases film drainage rate. The presence of solids at an interface can result in decreased coalescence times but in some cases can result in drop stabilization.

Fortunately, when it comes to the study of coalescence of dispersion bands in settlers, some simplifying correlations have been possible. The scale-up procedure proposed by Ryon et al. (1959) relates settler capacity to dispersion and band depth and horizontal (i.e., active interface) area:

$$L_b = C_{25} \left(\frac{\dot{V}_d}{A_s}\right)^{C_{26}} \qquad [4.3.26]$$

The form of this empirical relationship has been confirmed in many experimental studies. There has been much debate regarding the possible range of values of the exponent C_{26}, always greater than 1, with both C_{25} and C_{26} being system-dependent. The general applicability of the relationship varies with the liquid-liquid system; in the simplest cases the relationship is independent of phase ratio and impeller speed (Barnea & Mizrahi 1975).

The fundamentals of coalescence are discussed by Jeffreys & Davies (1971), including a model for coalescence in wedge-shaped dispersion bands. A later model (Doulah & Davies 1974) deals with the case of uniform dispersion band depth. However, until the relative contributions of drop-drop and drop-interface coalescence to dispersion band behavior are better understood, it will be difficult to use the models proposed to give accurate predictions of settler behavior.

4.3.4 PHASE INVERSION

In the design of liquid-liquid extraction equipment it is usual to select the dispersed phase. This choice can be quite important in some designs and it is equally important that the desired dispersed phase be maintained. For most equipment it will be the minority phase that will be most easily dispersed, and for this reason the low-holdup characteristics of column equipment result in few phase inversion problems in normal operation. On the other hand, mixer-settlers are frequently run with high dispersed phase holdup, and in large-scale equipment problems are encountered in maintaining dispersion of the desired phase.

For mixer-settlers it is often found that a particular choice of dispersion gives very much better settler performance. A change of dispersed phase can lead to unacceptably deep dispersion bands or to large quantities of small droplets entrained in the outlet streams of the settler (Warwick et al. 1975). Less frequently, a particular dispersion will give more advantageous mass transfer characteristics. Whatever the basis of selection, it is usually desirable that a mixer should be able to maintain dispersion of the desired phase.

It is a characteristic of the continuously operated agitated tank that there is a range of flow ratios where either of the two fluids present may be established as the dispersed drop phase—termed the ambivalence region by Selker & Sleicher (1965). A number of procedures can be used to establish the desired dispersion in the ambivalence region, most depending on locating the impeller in the continuous phase before agitation is commenced. Having established a particular dispersed phase, inversion can be brought about by increasing the volume fraction of that phase. The value of the volume fraction at which inversion occurs is usually affected to a limited degree by impeller speed.

Study of phase inversion as it affects liquid-liquid contacting has attracted relatively little interest. The early studies of Quinn & Sigloh (1963) and Yeh et al. (1964) were mainly concerned with determining which phase was preferentially dispersed on the commencement of agitation. Yeh et al. proposed a direct relationship between volume fraction at inversion and viscosity ratio and presented some supporting evidence from experiments where pairs of liquids were shaken in a flask. Although both the relationship and the experiments seem too simple, it is interesting that Selker & Sleicher (1965), in a study of the ambivalent region in batch agitated tanks, observed that volume fraction at inversion was a function of kinematic viscosity ratio. The nature of the function for aqueous-to-organic inversions was different from that for organic-to-aqueous inversions. The influence of impeller speed was found to be small above a minimum speed necessary to avoid settling.

Other hypotheses have been presented to explain the relationship between phase ratio and phase inversion. It has been proposed that inversion occurs in order to reduce interfacial energy by reducing interfacial area and that consequently the phase ratio at inversion should be 0.5. This possibility is discounted by Luhning & Sawistowski (1971) and experimental data do not seem to support it. An alternative proposal is that the limiting phase ratio is governed by the degree of close packing that is possible before drops make contact with one another and coalesce. This proposal is difficult to assess because the drops present in a dispersion with a large volume fraction of dispersed phase may be very distorted. This being the case, packing characteristics would be difficult to calculate. It seems unlikely that the close-packing fraction for spheres is relevant as volume fractions considerably in excess of this value (0.7) have been recorded for stable dispersions. From the data available, it seems that viscosity (Selker & Sleicher 1965) and interfacial tension (Luhning & Sawistowski 1971) are important variables. Clarke & Sawistowski (1978) also demonstrated the importance of solute both in equilibrated systems and in systems with mass transfer.

In laboratory studies volume fractions of dispersed phase in excess of 0.9 have been recorded, while parallel studies of large commercial equipment have been limited to values of the order of 0.5 with a narrower ambivalence region. As commercial systems usually contain considerable quantities of impurities, it cannot be concluded that the difference is due to equipment size alone.

Although a number of observations have been made on the influence of physical properties and operating variables on phase inversion characteristics of agitated tanks, there is still much to be studied. As yet there seem to be no useful quantitative relationships available.

For column contactors, phase inversion has not usually been considered a major factor, but it has been discussed as a possible limit to throughput by Arnold et al. (1974) and by Misek (1974).

4.4 Equipment Characteristics

4.4.1 HOLDUP

In liquid-liquid process equipment the average volume fraction or holdup of liquids will not necessarily be equivalent to the flow ratio of the streams entering. At steady state the flow ratios of the input and output streams will be equal (although allowance for mass transfer may be necessary in some instances). However, the volume fraction of the liquids in a mixer or column will depend on operating conditions and physical properties. For agitated tanks it is usually assumed, although not always with justification, that average holdup will be equivalent to the flow ratio of the streams entering. However, for column contactors such a situation will be the exception rather than the rule.

4.4.1.1 Column Contactors

Calculation of holdup is one of the major considerations in the design of column contactors, holdup being a function of liquid flow rates, physical properties, and intensity of agitation. At constant flow rate of the continuous phase, holdup increases as dispersed-phase flow rate is increased. The ultimate throughput of dispersed phase is limited by operating considerations, this limit being the entrainment of the dispersed phase in the exiting continuous phase. This condition, usually termed flooding by analogy with gas-liquid systems, is ideally defined as the point at which the smallest dispersed-phase droplets become stationary. As flooding is approached, dispersed-phase throughput approaches a limiting value with holdup increasing rapidly (figure 4.4.1). Similar characteristics are observed when continuous-phase throughput is varied at constant dispersed-phase throughput; a limiting value of continuous-phase throughput is approached as flooding is approached.

For a packed column the dispersed-phase throughput-holdup relationship is a little more complicated. There is some similarity to the relationship for other columns up to an upper transition point where it appears that a limiting value of throughput has been reached. However, dispersed-phase throughput may be further increased and there is little change in holdup before flooding occurs. This behavior

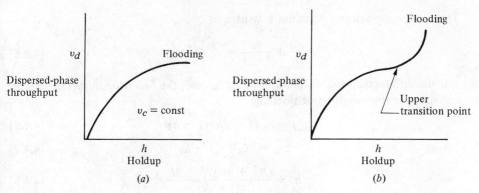

Figure 4.4.1 Column holdup as a function of throughput for (a) the general case and (b) packed columns.

is thought to be due to drop coalescence and a resulting decrease in cross-sectional area for continuous-phase flow. The basis of the interpretation of holdup and flooding data is the concept of slip velocity, the relative velocity of the two phases. In the calculation of relative velocity, allowance is made for the volume of the column occupied by the two phases and by any packing present. For columns without packing the relationship is

$$v_s = \frac{v_c}{1-h} + \frac{v_d}{h} \qquad [4.4.1]$$

where v_s is the slip velocity and v_c and v_d are the superficial velocities of the continuous and dispersed phases, respectively. For packed columns the relationship becomes

$$v_s = \frac{v_c}{b(1-h)} + \frac{v_d}{bh} \qquad [4.4.2]$$

where b is the packing voidage.

It has been demonstrated experimentally that in many cases slip velocity may be related to holdup and a characteristic velocity. In the simplest cases a relationship of the form

$$v_s = \bar{v}_0 (1-h) \qquad [4.4.3]$$

may be used, $\bar{v}_0$ being the characteristic velocity and reflecting the influence of column internals on the mean drop terminal velocity. Empirical relations have been developed to relate $\bar{v}_0$ to the true drop terminal velocity: Gayler et al. (1953) for packed columns; Logsdail et al. (1957) for rotating disk contactors; and Thornton (1957), Logsdail & Thornton (1957), and McAllister et al. (1967) for pulsed plate columns.

The slip velocity equation may be applied to the consideration of flooding. Examination of the relationships between v_d and h and v_c and h suggest that in the region of flooding

$$\frac{dv_d}{dh} \to 0 \qquad \frac{dv_c}{dh} \to 0 \qquad [4.4.4]$$

Thus, if the slip velocity equation is written as

$$\frac{v_d}{h} + \frac{v_c}{1-h} = \bar{v}_0 (1 - h) \qquad [4.4.5]$$

and the differentials dv_d/dh and dv_c/dh set to zero, the following three relations are obtained for the condition of flooding:

$$v_{cf} = \bar{v}_0 (1 - 2h)(1 - h)^2 \qquad [4.4.6]$$

$$v_{df} = 2\bar{v}_0 h^2 (1 - h) \qquad [4.4.7]$$

$$h_f = \frac{(R^2 + 8R)^{1/2} - 3R}{4(1 - R)} \qquad [4.4.8]$$

where $R = v_d/v_c$.

In addition to the assumptions that dv_d/dh and dv_c/dh may be set at zero for flooding, it is also assumed that $\bar{v}_0$ is constant. If drop size changes as flooding is approached, perhaps due to drop-drop coalescence as holdup increases, then $\bar{v}_0$ will change and the flooding relationships will no longer hold. Some account may be taken of the effect of coalescence and agitation by an alternative expression for slip velocity:

$$v_s = \bar{v}_0 (1 - h)^n \qquad [4.4.9]$$

in which case the holdup at flooding becomes

$$h_f = \frac{-R(n + 2) + \sqrt{R^2(h + 2)^2 + 4(1 - R)(n + 1)R}}{2(1 - R)(n + 1)} \qquad [4.4.10]$$

Another relationship for slip velocity, in terms of a velocity coefficient c_α and a coalescence coefficient c_z, is given by Misek (1963):

$$v_s = v_t(1 - h) \exp\left(\frac{c_z}{c_\alpha} - 4.1\right) h \qquad [4.4.11]$$

The holdup-superficial velocity relationship for packed columns is more complex and the procedure outlined above will be suitable only for making estimates regarding holdup at the upper transition point. Up to this point, experiments (Gayler et al. 1953; Wicks & Beckman 1955) have shown that the slip velocity relationship can be described by [4.4.5]. For flooding in packed columns, empirical correlations have been developed by Dell & Pratt (1951) and Hoffing & Lockhart (1954).

4.4.1.2 Agitated Tanks

In contrast to column contactors, holdup in the agitated tank of a mixer-settler should have the same numerical value as the flow ratio of the two feed streams. At steady state the outlet flow ratio from an agitated tank will be equal to the inlet ratio, but the contents of the tank will be uniform only if sufficient energy is supplied. Energy requirements vary considerably with the geometry of the tank and impeller, the position of the inlets, the properties of the two liquid phases, and the choice of phase to be dispersed. This main requirement is that the energy supplied must be above a certain minimum value, but it is not known whether the results of laboratory tests can be used in scale-up.

Miller & Mann (1944) first reported the difference between actual and nominal holdup; Treybal (1963) discussed the correlation of holdup data with impeller speed or power input. A correlation on the basis of relative velocity was developed by Thornton & Bouyatiotis (1967):

$$\frac{v_s^3 \rho_c}{\mu_c g} = 2.32 \times 10^{-8} \left(\frac{D_{32}^3 \rho_{cg}^2}{\mu_c^2}\right)^2 \frac{\rho_c \sigma^3}{\mu_c^4 g} \left(\frac{\Delta \rho}{\rho_c}\right)^{1.1} \qquad [4.4.12]$$

Since drop size is not usually known, a second form of the correlation was also proposed in terms of power per unit volume p:

$$\frac{v_s^3 \rho_c}{\mu_c g} = 1.95 \times 10^{-5} \left(\frac{p^3}{\rho_c^4 \mu_c g^4}\right)^{-0.64} \left(\frac{\rho_c \sigma^3}{\mu_c^4 g}\right)^{0.14} \left(\frac{\Delta \rho}{\rho_c}\right)^{1.1} \qquad [4.4.13]$$

Another form of correlation proposed by Weinstein & Treybal (1973) relates holdup directly to a number of dimensionless groups:

$$\frac{h}{R} = 0.764 \left(\frac{p \dot{V}_d \mu_c^2}{\rho_c^3}\right)^{0.300} \frac{\dot{V}_d \rho_c^2 \sigma}{\mu_c^3} \left(\frac{\mu_c^4 g}{\rho_c \sigma^3}\right)^{-0.276} \left(\frac{\Delta \rho}{\rho_c}\right)^{-0.074} \left(\frac{\mu_d}{\mu_c}\right)^{0.136} \qquad [4.4.14]$$

The value of these correlations is still to be proved and it should be emphasized that the influence of inlet and outlet position is important but is not included in the relationships given.

For the present, it would be wise to restrict the use of correlations to systems of physical properties and equipment geometry similar to those used in the original experimental work. The power requirements for adequate holdup characteristics will be relatively low for most agitated tanks; for good mass transfer characteristics, power levels higher than the minimum consistent with good holdup characteristics will usually be necessary.

4.4.2 AXIAL MIXING

4.4.2.1 Introduction

Studies of the performance of liquid-liquid extraction columns show that their behavior is not consistent with the simple relationship

$$L_c = L_{oc} n_{oc} \qquad [4.4.15]$$

derived for an assumed condition of countercurrent plug flow for the two phases. In particular, the concentration profiles observed in working columns show an abrupt change in concentration at the two phase inlets (figure 4.4.2). It can be seen also that the concentration profile is such that the actual driving force for mass transfer

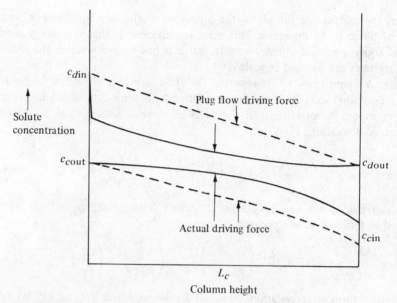

Figure 4.4.2 Comparison of actual and plug flow concentration profiles in liquid-liquid extraction column.

is less than is assumed in plug flow calculations and that the concentration gradients at the phase outlets had fallen to zero.

These conditions arise because of the distribution of residence times that may occur in both the dispersed and the continuous phase. This deviation from the ideal plug flow condition is described as axial mixing, longitudinal mixing, or back mixing. Strictly, the term back mixing should be reserved for the back transfer of material from a phase outlet toward its inlet, but the term is frequently used to describe all aspects of residence time distribution in columns.

The hydrodynamics of column contactors are complex and many factors contribute to axial mixing: velocity profiles, dead space, channeling, recirculation, drop size distribution, drop coalescence and redispersion, and drop wakes. Nevertheless, a measure of success has been achieved in modeling the effects of axial mixing with simple mathematical models of column behavior. To date, the use of simple models has been necessary as almost all of the solutions arising from the modeling process are complex. The majority of solutions and solution techniques available are for the case of a linear eqilibrium relationship between the concentrations of solute in the dispersed and continuous phases:

$$c_d = mc_c^* \qquad\qquad [4.4.16]$$

4.4.2.2 Stagewise Mixing Models

The simplest model relating axial mixing and mass transfer performance is the stagewise mixing model described by Young (1957). It is assumed that the column may be represented by a number of countercurrent, perfectly mixed stages, all of the same height. For the continuous phase a mass balance of stage i is given by

$$c_i - c_{i-1} = -\frac{\beta_{oc}aL_m}{v}(c_i - c_i^*) \qquad [4.4.17]$$

where $L_c = n_sL_m$.

The axial mixing characteristics of the column are described only by n_s, the number of stages. As n_s is increased, the character of the model approaches plug flow. An approximate description of the solute concentration profile can be achieved with this model under favorable conditions, but with only one axial mixing parameter no discrimination can be made regarding the influence of the two separate phases.

An extension of the stagewise model to consider axial mixing in the individual phases has been developed by assigning a back-mixing flow to each phase. A backflow ratio R_α is defined for both phases:

$$R_{\alpha c} = \frac{v_{Bc}}{v_c} \qquad [4.4.18]$$

$$R_{\alpha d} = \frac{v_{Bd}}{v_d} \qquad [4.4.19]$$

where v_{Bc} and v_{Bd} are superficial back-mixing flows for the continuous and the dispersed phase. The mass balance for stage i becomes

$$v_c[(1 + R_\alpha)c_{i-1} - (1 + 2R_\alpha)c_i + R_\alpha c_{i+1}]_c$$
$$= -v_d[-R_\alpha c_{i-1} + (1 + 2R_\alpha)c_i - (1 + R_\alpha)c_{i+1}]_d$$
$$= \beta_{oc}L_m a(c_i - c_i^*)_c \qquad [4.4.20]$$

As R_α is increased, the character of the model approaches the condition of complete mixing. The development of the model and solutions for special cases have been considered in detail by Hartland & Mecklenburg (1966).

4.4.2.3 Differential Model

An alternative to the stagewise modeling process is provided by the differential or diffusion model. The basis of this model is widely used in the study of systems that have a distribution of residence times and is a direct analogy with molecular diffusion. In the differential model, departures from plug flow are characterized by eddy diffusivities $(\delta_e)_c$ and $(\delta_e)_d$. For this model the material balance over an element of column height dL_c is

$$\left(-v\frac{dc}{dL_c} + \delta_e\frac{d^2c}{dL_c^2}\right)_c = \left(-v\frac{dc}{dL_c} - \delta_e\frac{d^2c}{dL_c^2}\right)_d = \beta_{oc}a(c - c^*)_c \qquad [4.4.21]$$

The axial mixing characteristics of the two phases are usually expressed in terms of Peclet numbers:

$$\text{Pe}_c = \left(\frac{vL_c}{\delta_e}\right)_c \qquad [4.4.22]$$

$$\text{Pe}_d = \left(\frac{vL_c}{\delta_e}\right)_d \qquad\qquad [4.4.23]$$

As the values of the Peclet number approach zero, the character of the model approaches the condition of complete mixing. Solutions for the case of a linear equilibrium relationship have been developed by Sleicher (1959), Miyauchi & Vermeulen (1963), McMullen et al. (1958), and Hartland & Mecklenburgh (1966).

In the modeling of column contactors, either stagewise or diffusion models can be used regardless of the stagewise or differential nature of the column being studied. An approximate relationship between the axial mixing parameters of stagewise and differential models has been developed by Miyauchi (1963):

$$\frac{1}{\text{Pe}_c} = \frac{1}{2n_s} + \frac{(R_\alpha)_c}{n_s} \qquad\qquad [4.4.24]$$

$$\frac{1}{\text{Pe}_d} = \frac{1}{2n_s} + \frac{(R_\alpha)_d}{n_s} \qquad\qquad [4.4.25]$$

The choice of model is made mainly on the basis of convenience for the solution of a particular problem.

Many workers have contributed to the development and solution of models for axial mixing and this is discussed in detail by Misek & Rod (1971). These authors list many of the solutions available and also calculation procedures. Because of the complexities involved in solutions for axial mixing models, a number of approximate methods have been developed; these are also discussed by Misek & Rod. More recently, further solution techniques have been presented by Pratt (1975, 1976, 1977), who gives examples that show the processing of published data. Steiner et al. (1977) discuss the processing of mass transfer data for the spray column.

4.4.2.4 Measurements of Axial Mixing

Application of axial mixing models to column design requires data describing column performance. The performance of a number of column contactors has been reviewed by Ingham (1971), but even now there are few data available regarding column performance during mass transfer. The application of existing data and correlations to column design is discussed by Korchinsky (1974), who concludes that the greatest need is for more experimental data; Pratt (1977) is of the same opinion. In principle, the measurement of axial mixing characteristics is straightforward, although both authors are concerned about the possible effects of coalescence and redispersion. The influence of coalescence is discussed by Komasawa & Ingham (1977) in a study of the influence of mass transfer on the hydrodynamic performance of small extraction columns.

The determination of axial mixing characteristics is virtually restricted to tracer techniques since very high accuracy is necessary if solute profiles are to be used in the calculation of Peclet numbers. Two tracer techniques have been widely used: continuous injection at a point in the column with upstream monitoring, or pulse injection with downstream monitoring. For the pulse technique the problems of imperfect pulse form and the processing of data can be avoided by the technique described by Bischoff & Levelspiel (1963), where the tracer is monitored at two downstream points. The Peclet number can be determined directly from the values of variance for the two sample points.

4.5 Nomenclature for Chapter 4

ROMAN LETTERS

a	specific (interfacial) area, m^2/m^3
A_s	settler area, m^2
$A(L_0)$	adhesion energy parameter, J/m
b	mean voidage fraction
c	concentration, kg/m^3
c_i	concentration at stage i, kg/m^3
c^*	equilibrium concentration, kg/m^3
$C_{1\text{-}24}$	experimentally determined constants
C_p	specific heat, J/kg K
C_n	constants in heat transfer equations
$C_{\lambda n}$	eigenvalues in heat transfer equations
D	drop diameter, m
D_{32}	Sauter mean drop diameter, m
D_{32}^0	Sauter mean drop diameter at zero holdup, m
D_{max}	maximum stable drop size, m
D_i	diameter of impeller, m
D_J	diameter of jet, m
D_N	diameter of nozzle, m
D_K	diameter of column, m
e	energy dissipation per unit mass, W/kg
g	gravitational acceleration, m/s^2
h	volume fraction of dispersed phase
H	Harkins & Brown correction factor
L_L	Lagrangian macroscale of turbulence, m
L_0	minimum drop separation distance, m
L_c	column height, m
L_{oc}	height of transfer unit (overall basis), m
L_b	depth of dispersion band, m
m	equilibrium constant

M	mass of drop
n	exponent in slip velocity equation
n_s	number of model stages
n_{oc}	number of transfer units (overall basis)
N	impeller speed, rev/s
p	power per unit volume, W/m^3
r	drop radius, m
R	flow ratio ($= v_d/v_c$)
R_α	backflow ratio ($= v_B/v$)
t	time, s
t_{RL}	drop release time, s
$\bar{t}$	average drop coalescence time, s
T	temperature, K
ΔT^+	transfer efficiency
$\bar{u}$	root-mean-square velocity, m/s
U	overall heat transfer coefficient, W/m^2 K
v	superficial phase velocity, m/s
v_B	superficial back-mixing flow, m/s
v_s	slip velocity, m/s
$\bar{v}_0$	characteristic velocity, m/s
v_t	terminal velocity, m/s
v_D	drop velocity, m/s
v_N	velocity in nozzle, m/s
Z	microscale of turbulence, m

DIMENSIONLESS GROUPS

Nu	Nusselt number
Pe	Peclet number (axial mixing)
Pe_d	Peclet number (heat transfer)
Pr	Prandtl number
Re	Reynolds number
Sc	Schmidt number
Sh	Sherwood number
We_i	Weber number (impeller)

GREEK LETTERS

α	heat transfer coefficient, W/m^2 K
β	mass transfer coefficient, m/s
β_{oc}	overall mass transfer coefficient (continuous phase), m/s
β_i	mass transfer coefficient (interfacial resistance), m/s
γ	kinematic viscosity, m^2/s
δ	diffusivity, m^2/s
δ_e	eddy diffusivity, m^2/s
κ	thermal diffusivity, m^2/s

λ thermal conductivity, W/m K
μ dynamic viscosity, kg/m s
ρ density, kg/m^3
$\Delta\rho$ density difference ($= |\rho_c - \rho_d|$), kg/m^3
σ interfacial tension, N/m
ϕ function of holdup

SUBSCRIPTS

b band
c continuous phase
cr   critical
d dispersed phase
i impeller, interfacial
in   inlet
J jet
max   maximum
min   minimum
N nozzle
o overall
out   outlet
p packing
RL release
s settler
sd stable drop
w wake

4.6 References for Chapter 4

Agers, D. W. & DeMent, E. R. 1972 The Evaluation of New LIX® Reagents for the Extraction of Copper and Suggestions for the Design of Commercial Mixer-Settler Plants, *Proc. Int. Symp. Solvent Extr. Metall. Processes, Technologisch Institut, Antwerp*, pp. 27–35.

Angelo, J. B., Lightfoot, E. N., & Howard, D. W. 1966 Generalisation of the Penetration Theory for Surface Stretch: Application to Forming and Oscillating Drops, *AIChE. J.* 12:751–760.

Arnold, D. R., Mumford, C. J., & Jeffreys, G. V. 1974 Drop Size Distribution and Interfacial Area in Agitated Contactors, *Proc. Int. Solvent Extr. Conf. Lyon*, pp. 1619–1650, Society of Chemical Industry, London.

Bailes, P. J., Hanson, C., & Hughes, M. A. 1976 Liquid-Liquid Extraction: The Process, the Equipment, *Chem. Eng. (N.Y.)* 83:86–100.

Baird, M. H. I. 1977 Drop Sizes and Drop Dispersion in Straight Horizontal Tubes and in Helical Coils, *Chem. Eng. Sci.* 32:981.

Baird, M. I. I. 1980 Extraction by Chemical Reaction, *AIChE 88th Natl. Meet., Solvent Extraction Research Session, Philadelphia*.

Baird, M. H. I. & Lane, S. J. 1973 Drop Size and Hold-up in a Reciprocating Plate Extraction Column, *Chem. Eng. Sci.* 28:947–957.

Barnea, E. & Mizrahi, J. 1975 Separation Mechanism of Liquid-Liquid Dispersions in a Deep Layer Gravity Settler, *Trans. Inst. Chem. Eng.* 53:75–92.

Barnea, E. & Mizrahi, J. 1977 The Effect of a Packed Bed Diffuser-Precoalescer on the Capacity of Simple Gravity Settlers and Compact Settlers, *Proc. Int. Solvent Extr. Conf., Toronto*, paper 8(f).

Bibaud, R. E. & Treybal, R. E. 1966 Axial Mixing and Extraction in a Mechanically Agitated Liquid Extraction Tower, *AIChE J.* 12:472–477.

Bischoff, K. B. & Levenspiel, O. 1963 Patterns of Flow in Chemical Process Vessels, *Adv. Chem. Eng.* 4:95–198.

Boussinesq, J. 1905 Cooling Power of a Stream, *C.R. Acad. Sci.* 140:65–70.

Calderbank, P. H. 1958 Physical Rate Processes in Industrial Fermentation, *Trans. Inst. Chem. Eng.* 36:443–463.

Calderbank, P. H. & Korchinski, I. J. O. 1956 Circulation in Liquid Drops (a Heat Transfer Study), *Chem. Eng. Sci.* 6:65–78.

Calderbank, P. H. & Moo-Young, M. B. 1961 The Continuous Phase Heat and Mass-Transfer Properties of Dispersions, *Chem. Eng. Sci.* 16:39–54.

Christiansen, R. M. & Hixson, A. N. 1957 Break-up of a Liquid Jet in a Denser Liquid, *Ind. Eng. Chem.* 49:1017–1024.

Clarke, S. I. & Sawistowski, H. 1978 Phase Inversion of Stirred Liquid/Liquid Dispersions under Mass Transfer Conditions, *Trans. Inst. Chem. Eng.* 56:50–55.

Coughlin, R. W. & von Berg, R. L. 1966 Mass and Heat Transfer to Drops in a Mixer-Settler, *Chem. Eng. Sci.* **21**:3–8.

Davies, G. A., Jeffreys, G. V., & Smith, D. V. 1971 Coalescence of Liquid Droplets—Correlation of Coalescence Times, *Proc. Int. Solvent Extr. Conf., The Hague,* pp. 385–399, Society of Chemical Industry, London.

Davies, G. A., Jeffreys, G. V., & Azfal, M. 1972 New Packing for Coalescence and Separation of Dispersions, *Br. Chem. Eng.* **17**:709–714.

De Chazal, L. E. M. & Ryan, J. T. 1971 Formation of Organic Drops in Water, *AIChE J.* **17**:1226–1229.

Dell, F. R. & Pratt, H. R. C. 1951 Liquid-Liquid Extraction, Part 1: Flooding Rates for Packed Columns, *Trans. Inst. Chem. Eng.* **29**:89–109.

Doulah, M. S. & Davies, G. A. 1974 A Queue Model to Describe Separation of Liquid Dispersion in Vertical Settlers, *Proc. Int. Solvent Extr. Conf., Lyon,* pp. 1651–1670, Society of Chemical Industry, London.

Frössling, N. 1938 The Evaporation of Falling Drops, *Beit. Geophys. Gerland* **52**:170–216.

Garner, F. & Suckling, R. 1958 Mass Transfer from a Soluble Solid Sphere, *AIChE J.* **4**:114–124.

Garner, F. H. & Tayeban, M. 1960 The Importance of the Wake in Mass Transfer from Both Continuous- and Dispersed-Phase Systems, I, *An. R. Soc. Esp. Fis. Quim. Ser. A* **568**:479–490.

Garner, F. H., Ford, H., & Tayeban, M. 1959 Mass Transfer from Circulating Liquid Drops, *J. Appl. Chem.* **9**:315–323.

Gayler, R. & Pratt, H. R. C. 1953 Liquid-Liquid Extraction, Part V: Further Studies of Droplet Behaviour in Packed Columns, *Trans. Inst. Chem. Eng.* **31**:69–77.

Gayler, R., Roberts, N. W., & Pratt, H. R. C. 1953 Liquid-Liquid Extraction, Part IV: A Further Study of Hold-up in Packed Columns, *Trans. Inst. Chem. Eng.* **31**:57–68.

Glasser, D., Arnold, D. R., Bryson, A. W., & Vieler, A. M. S. 1976 Aspects of Mixer-Settler Design, *Miner. Sci Eng.* **8**(1):23–45.

Godfrey, J. C. & Slater, M. J. 1978 Co-current Flow Systems for Liquid-Liquid Extraction, *Chem. Ind.* Oct. **7**:745–748.

Griffith, R. M. 1960 Mass Transfer from Drops and Bubbles, *Chem. Eng. Sci.* **12**:198–213.

Gröber, H. Z. 1925 The Heating and Cooling of Simple Geometric Bodies, *VDI Ber.* **69**:705–711.

Hadamard, J. 1911 Movement Permanente Lent d'une Sphere Liquide et Visqueuse dans une Liquide Visqueuse. *C. R. Acad. Sci.* **152**:1735.

Handlos, A. E. & Baron, T. 1957 Mass and Heat Transfer from Drops in Liquid-Liquid Extraction, *AIChE J.* **3**:127–136.

Hanson, C. (ed.) 1971a *Recent Advances in Liquid-Liquid Extraction,* Pergamon, Oxford.

Hanson, C. 1971b Mass Transfer with Simultaneous Chemical Reaction, in *Recent Advances in Liquid-Liquid Extraction,* ed. C. Hanson, pp. 429–454, Pergamon, Oxford.

Hanson, C. & Ingham, J. 1965 Direct Contact Liquid-Liquid Heat Exchange, *Br. Chem. Eng.* **10**:391–393.

Hanson, C., Ingham, J., & Stewardson, T. N. 1971 Direct Contact Heat Transfer between Immiscible Liquids in a Mixer-Settler Apparatus, *Proc. Int. Solvent Extr. Conf., The Hague,* vol. 1, p. 270, Society of Chemical Industry, London.

Harkins, W. D. & Brown, F. E. 1919 Detection of Surface Tension (Free Surface Energy and the Weight of Falling Drops—Surface Tension of Water and Benzene by the Capillary Height Method), *J. Am. Chem. Soc.* **41**:499–524.

Hartland, S. & Mecklenburgh, J. C. 1966 A Comparison of Differential and Stagewise Counter-current Extraction with Backmixing, *Chem. Eng. Sci.* **27**:1209–1229.

Hartland, S. & Mecklenburgh, J. C. 1973 *Theory of Backmixing,* Pergamon, Oxford.

Hayworth, C. B. & Treybal, R. E. 1950 Drop Formation in Two-Liquid Phase Systems, *Ind. Eng. Chem.* **42**:1174–1181.

Heertjes, P. M. & de Nie, L. H. 1971 Mass Transfer to Drops, in *Recent Advances in Liquid-Liquid Extractions,* ed. C. Hanson, pp. 367–406, Pergamon, Oxford.

Heertjes, P. M., Holve, W. A., & Talsma, H. 1954 Mass Transfer between Isobutanol and Water in a Spray-Column, *Chem. Eng. Sci.* **3**:122–142.

Hinze, J. O. 1955 Fundamentals of the Hydrodynamic Mechanism of Splitting in Dispersion Processes, *AIChE J.* 1:289–295.

Hoffing, E. H. & Lockhart, F. J. 1954 A Correlation of Flooding Velocities in Packed Columns, *Chem. Eng. Prog.* 50:94–103.

Hughmark, G. A. 1967 Liquid-Liquid Spray Column, Drop Size, Hold-up and Continuous Phase Mass Transfer, *Ind. Eng. Chem. Fundam.* 6:408–413.

Ingham, J. 1971 The Study of Longitudinal Mixing in Liquid-Liquid Contactors, in *Recent Advances in Liquid-Liquid Extraction*, ed. C. Hanson, chap. 8, pp. 237–292, Pergamon, Oxford.

Jeffreys, G. V. & Davies, G. A. 1971 Coalescence of Liquid Droplets and Liquid Dispersion, in *Recent Advances in Liquid-Liquid Extraction*, ed. C. Hanson, chap. 14, pp. 495–584, Pergamon, Oxford.

Johnson, A. E. & Hamielec, A. E. 1960 Mass Transfer Inside Drops, *AIChE J.* 6:145–149.

Karr, A. I. & Lo, T. C. 1977 Performance of a 36" Diameter Reciprocating-Plate Extraction Column, *Proc. Int. Solvent Extr. Conf., Toronto*, paper 8(a).

Kehat, E. & Letan, R. 1971 The Role of Wakes in the Mechanism of Extraction in Spray Columns, *AIChE J.* 17:984–990.

Kehat, E. & Sideman, S. 1971 Heat Transfer by Direct Liquid-Liquid Contact, in *Recent Advances in Liquid-Liquid Extraction*, ed. C. Hanson, chap. 13, pp. 455–494, Pergamon, Oxford.

Kennedy, A. D. 1977 The Cities Services Solvent Extraction and Electrowinning Plant at Miami, Arizona, *Proc. Int. Solvent Extr. Conf., Toronto*, paper 6(b).

Kinard, G. E., Manning, F. S., & Manning, W. P. 1963 A New Correlation for Mass Transfer From Single Spheres, *Br. Chem. Eng.* 8:326–327.

Kolmogoroff, A. N. 1949 On the Disintegration of Drops in a Turbulent Flow, *Dokl. Akad. Nauk SSSR* 66:825.

Komasawa, I. & Ingham, J. 1977 Effect of System Properties on the Performance of Liquid Extraction Columns. I—Packed Column. II—Oldshue-Rushton Column, *Chem. Eng. Sci.* 33:341–347, 479–485.

Korchinsky, W. J. 1974 Modelling of Liquid-Liquid Extraction Columns: Use of Published Model Correlations in Design, *Can. J. Chem. Eng.* 52:468–474.

Kronig, R. & Brink, J. C. 1950 On the Theory of Extraction from Falling Droplets, *Appl. Sci. Res.* A2:142–148.

Kubie, J. & Gardner, G. C. 1977 Drop Sizes and Drop Dispersion in Straight Horizontal Tubes and in Helical Coils, *Chem. Eng. Sci.* 32:195–202.

Kuboi, R., Komasawa, I., & Tsutao, O. 1972 Behaviour of Dispersed Particles in Turbulent Liquid Flow, *J. Chem. Eng. Jpn.* 5:349–354.

Laddha, G. S. & Degaleesan, T. E. 1976 *Transport Phenomena in Liquid Extraction*, Tata McGraw-Hill, New Delhi.

Landau, J., Dim, A., & Houlihan, R. 1973 A Reciprocating-Plate Extraction Column for Hydrometallurgical Applications, *Proc. AIME Int. Symp. Hydrometall., Chicago*, pp. 943–963.

Letan, R. & Kehat, E. 1965 Mixing Effects in a Spray Column Heat Exchanger, *AIChE J.* 11:804–808.

Letan, R. & Kehat, E. 1968a The Mechanism of Heat Transfer in a Spray Column Heat Exchanger, *AIChE J.* 14:398–405.

Letan, R. & Kehat, E. 1968b The Temperature Jump at the Inlet of the Continuous Phase in a Spray Column Heat Exchanger, *AIChE J.* 14:831–833.

Letan, R. & Kehat, E. 1969 Residence Time Distribution of the Dispersed Phase in a Spray Column, *AIChE J.* 15:4–10.

Letan, R. & Kehat, E. 1970 The Mechanism of Heat Transfer in a Spray Column Heat Exchanger, II. Dense Packing of Drops, *AIChE J.* 16:955–963.

Lewis, J. B., Jones, I., & Pratt, H. R. C. 1951 Part III—A Study of Droplet Behaviour in Packed Columns, *Trans. Inst. Chem. Eng.* 29:126–144.

Liem, A. J. S. & Woods, P. R. 1974 Review of Coalescence Phenomena, Water—1974: Industrial Waste Treatment No. 144, *AIChE. Symp. Ser.* 70:8–23.

Linton, M. & Sutherland, K. L. 1960 Transfer from a Sphere into a Fluid in Laminar Flow, *Chem. Eng. Sci.* 12:214–229.

Lochiel, A. C. & Calderbank, P. H. 1964 Mass Transfer in the Continuous Phase around Axisymmetric Bodies of Revolution, *Chem. Eng. Sci.* 19:471–484.

Logsdail, D. & Lowes, L. 1971 Industrial Contacting Equipment, in *Recent Advances in Liquid-Liquid Extraction*, ed. C. Hanson, chap. 5, pp. 139–168, Pergamon, Oxford.

Logsdail, D. & Thornton, J. D. 1957 Liquid-Liquid Extraction, Part XIV: The Effect of Column Diameter upon the Performance and Throughput of Pulsed Plate Columns, *Trans. Inst. Chem. Eng.* 35:331–342.

Logsdail, D., Thornton, J. D., & Pratt, H. R. C. 1957 Liquid-Liquid Extraction, Part XII: Flooding Rates and Performance Data for a Rotary Disc Contactor, *Trans. Inst. Chem. Eng.* 35:301–315.

Lott, J. B., Warwick, G. C. I., & Scuffham, J. B. 1972 Design of Large Scale Mixer-Settlers, *Trans. Soc. Min. Eng. AIME* 252:27–35.

Luhning, R. W. & Sawistowski, H. 1971 Phase Inversion in Stirred Liquid-Liquid Systems, *Proc. Int. Solvent Extr. Conf., The Hague*, pp. 873–887, Society of Chemical Industry, London.

Lykov, A. V. & Mikhaylon, Y. A. 1961 *Theory of Energy and Mass Transfer*, p. 147, Prentice-Hall, Englewood Cliffs, N.J.

McAllister, R. A., Groenier, W. S., & Ryon, A. D. 1967 Correlation of Flooding in Pulsed, Perforated-Plate Extraction Columns, *Chem. Eng. Sci.* 22:931–944.

McMullen, A. K., Miyauchi, T., & Vermeulen, T. 1958 *Univ. Calif. Radiat. Lab. Rep.* UCRL-3911.

Miller, S. A. & Mann, C. A. 1944 Agitation of Two-Phase Systems of Immiscible Liquids, *Trans. Am. Inst. Chem. Eng.* 40:709–745.

Misek, T. 1963 Hydrodynamic Behaviour of Agitated Liquid Extractors, *Collect. Czech. Chem. Commun.* 28:1631–1643.

Misek, T. 1964 Coalescence of Drops in an Agitated Liquid-Liquid Extractor, *Collect. Czech. Chem. Commun.* 29:2086–2093.

Misek, T. 1974 Design and Normal Flows through a Column Extractor, *Ind. Chem. Eng.* 14:107–112.

Misek, T. 1976 Liquid-Liquid Extraction Equipment (Comparative Study), paper presented at the World Congress on Chemical Engineering, Amsterdam.

Misek, T. & Rod, V. 1971 Calculation of Contactors with Longitudinal Mixing, in *Recent Advances in Liquid-Liquid Extraction*, ed. C. Hanson, chap. 7, pp. 197–236, Pergamon, Oxford.

Miyauchi, T. & Vermeulen, T. 1963 Longitudinal Dispersion in Two Phase Continuous Flow Operations, *Ind. Eng. Chem. Fundam.* 2:113–126.

Mizrahi, J. & Barnea, E. 1973 Compact Settler Gives Efficient Separation of Liquid-Liquid Dispersions, *Process Eng.* Jan:60–66.

Narasinga Rao, E. V. L., Kumar, R., & Kuloor, N. R. 1966 Drop Formation Studies in Liquid-Liquid Systems, *Chem. Eng. Sci.* 21:867–880.

Newman, A. B. 1931 The Drying of Porous Solid: Diffusion Calculations, *Trans. Am. Inst. Chem. Eng.* 27:310–321.

Null, H. R. & Johnson, H. F. 1958 Drop Formation in Liquid-Liquid Systems from Single Nozzles, *AIChE J.* 4:273–281.

Orjans, R. D., Notebaart, C., Godfrey, J. C., Hanson, C., & Slater, M. J. 1977 The Design of Mixer-Settlers for the Zambian Copper Industry, *Proc. Int. Solvent Extr. Conf., Toronto*, paper 6(c).

Park, J. Y. & Blair, L. M. 1975 The Effect of Coalescence on Drop Size Distribution in an Agitated Liquid-Liquid Dispersion, *Chem. Eng. Sci.* 30:1057–1064.

Porter, J. W., Goren, S. L., & Wilke, C. R. 1968 Direct Contact Heat Transfer between Immiscible Liquids in Turbulent Pipe Flow, *AIChE J.* 14:151–158.

Pratt, H. R. C. 1975 A Simplified Analytical Design Method for Differential Extractors with Backmixing, 1. Linear Equilibrium Relationship, *Ind. Eng. Chem. Process Des. Dev.* 14:74–80.

Pratt, H. R. C. 1976 A Simplified Analytical Design Method for Differential Extractors with Backmixing, II. Curved Equilibrium Line, *Ind. Eng. Chem. Process Des. Dev.* 15:34–41.

Pratt, H. R. C. & Anderson, W. 1977 On Axial Mixing and the Design of Extraction Columns from First Principles, *Proc. Int. Solvent Extr. Conf., Toronto,* paper 25(a).

Quinn, J. A. & Sigloh, D. B. 1963 Phase Inversion in the Mixing of Immiscible Liquids, *Can. J. Chem. Eng.* **41**:15–18.

Reissinger, K. H. & Schroeter, J. 1977 Modern Liquid Extractors: Review and Selection Criteria. The Present State of the Art, *Inst. Chem. Eng. Symp. Ser.* **54**:33–48.

Rose, P. M. & Kintner, R. C. 1966 Mass Transfer from Large Oscillating Drops, *AIChE J.* **12**:530–534.

Rowe, P. N., Claxton, K. T., & Lewis, J. B. 1965 Heat and Mass Transfer from a Single Sphere in an Extensive Flowing Fluid, *Trans. Inst. Chem. Eng.* **43**:T14–T31.

Ryon, A. D., Daley, D. L., & Lowrie, R. S. 1959 Scale Up of Mixer Settlers, *Chem. Eng. Prog.* **55**(10):70–75.

Scheele, G. F. & Meister, G. B. 1968 Drop Formation at Low Velocities in Liquid-Liquid Systems, *AIChE J.* **14**:9–15.

Schügel, K., Blaschke, H. G., Brunke, U., & Streicher, R. 1977 Interaction of Fluid Dynamics, Interfacial Phenomena and Mass Transfer in Extraction Processes, in *Recent Developments in Separation Science,* ed. N. N. Li, vol. 3, pt. A, pp. 71–128, CRC, West Palm Beach, Fla.

Selker, A. H. & Sleicher, C. A., Jr. 1965 Factors Affecting Which Phase Will Disperse When Immiscible Liquids Are Stirred Together, *Can. J. Chem. Eng.* **43**:298–301.

Shinnar, R. & Church, J. M. 1960 Predicting Particle Size in Agitated Dispersions, *Ind. Eng. Chem.* **52**:253–256.

Sideman, S. & Taitel, Y. 1964 Direct Contact Heat Transfer with Change of Phase: Evaporation of Drops in an Immiscible Liquid Medium, *Int. J. Heat Mass Transfer* **7**:1273–1289.

Sideman, S., Hirsch, G., & Gat, Y. 1965 Direct Contact Heat Transfer with Change of Phase (Effect of the Initial Drop Size in Three Phase Heat Exchangers), *AIChE J.* **11**:1081–1087.

Skelland, A. H. P. & Cornish, A. R. H. 1963 Mass Transfer from Spheroids to an Air Stream, *AIChE J.* **9**:73–76.

Skelland, A. H. P. & Wellek, R. M. 1964 Resistance to Mass Transfer Inside Droplets, *AIChE J.* **10**:491–496.

Sleicher, C. A. 1959 Axial Mixing and Extraction Efficiency, *AIChE J.* **5**:145–149.

Steiner, L., Horvath, M., & Hartland, S. 1977 Determination of Actual Mass Transfer Rates in Extraction Columns, *Proc. Int. Solvent Extr. Conf., Toronto,* paper 8(c).

Stönner, H. M. & Wohler, F. 1975 An Engineer's Approach to a Solvent Extraction Problem, *Inst. Chem. Eng. Symp. Ser.* **42**:14.1–14.11.

Strand, C. P., Olney, R. B., & Ackerman, G. H. 1962 Fundamental Aspects of Rotating Disc Contactor Performance, *AIChE J.* **8**:252–261.

Thornton, J. D. 1957 Liquid-Liquid Extraction, Part XIII: The Effect of Pulse Wave-Form and Plate Geometry on the Performance and Throughput of a Pulsed Column, *Trans. Inst. Chem. Eng.* **35**:316–330.

Thornton, J. D. & Bouyatiotis, B. A. 1967 Liquid Extraction Studies in Stirred Tanks, Part I: Droplet Size and Hold-up Measurements in a Seven Inch Diameter Baffled Vessel, *Inst. Chem. Eng. Symp. Ser.* **26**:43–51.

Thornton, J. D. & Ramshaw, C. 1967 Droplet Breakdown in a Packed Extraction Column, Part I: The Concept of Critical Droplet Size, *Inst. Chem. Eng. Symp. Ser.* **26**:73–79.

Thorsen, G. 1954 Ph.D. thesis, Trondheim Univ. Norway.

Thorsen, G. & Terjesen, S. G. 1962 On the Mechanism of Mass Transfer in Liquid-Liquid Extraction, *Chem. Eng. Sci.* **17**:137–148.

Thorsen, G., Stordalen, R. M., & Terjesen, S. G. 1968 On the Terminal Velocity of Circulating and Oscillating Liquid Drops, *Chem. Eng. Sci.* **23**:413–426.

Treybal, R. E. 1963 *Liquid Extraction,* 2d ed., McGraw-Hill, New York.

von Berg, R. L. 1971 Simultaneous Heat and Mass Transfer, in *Recent Advances in Liquid-Liquid Extraction,* ed. C. Hanson, chap. 11, pp. 407–428, Pergamon, Oxford.

Warwick, G. C. I., Senffham, J. B., Rowden, G. A., & Davies, G. A. 1975 Considerations of Ambivalence Range and Phase Inversions in Hydrometallurgical Solvent Extraction Processes, Hydromet., *Inst. Chem. Eng. Symp. Ser.* **42**:17.1–17.17.

Waslo, S. & Gal-Or, B. 1971 Boundary Layer Theory for Mass and Heat Transfer in Clouds of Moving Drops, Bubbles or Solid Particles, *Chem. Eng. Sci.* **26**:829–839.

Weinstein, B. & Treybal, R. E. 1973 Liquid-Liquid Contacting in Unbaffled Agitated Vessels, *AIChE J.* **19**:304–312.

Wellek, R. M. & Skelland A. H. P. 1965 Extraction with Single Turbulent Droplets, *AIChE J.* **11**:557–560.

Wicks, C. E. & Beckman, R. B. 1955 Dispersed-Phase Hold-up in Packed, Countercurrent Liquid-Liquid Extraction Columns, *AIChE J.* **1**:426–433.

Wilke, C. R., Cheng, J. C., Ledesma, V. L., & Porter, J. W. 1963 Direct Contact Heat Transfer for Sea Water Evaporation, *Chem. Eng. Prog.* **59**(12):69–75.

Yeh, G. C., Haynie, F. H., Jr., & Moses, R. A. 1964 Phase-Volume Relationship at the Point of Phase Inversion in Liquid Dispersions, *AIChE J.* **10**:260–265.

Young, E. F. 1957 New Tool Analyzes Mixing Stages, *Chem. Eng. (N.Y.)* **64**:241–242.

Zabel, T., Hanson, C., & Ingham, J. 1974 Direct Contact Heat Transfer to Single Freely Falling Liquid Drops, *Trans. Inst. Chem. Eng.* **52**:307–312.

5 CONDENSATION

5.1 Introduction

Peter Griffith

Condensation is one of the commonest modes of heat transfer. First, it is appropriate to show the orders of magnitude of the condensing heat transfer coefficients along with others that are usually found in series with them. The smallest heat transfer coefficient usually governs, so that the condensation heat transfer coefficient, which can be quite high, often has a small effect.

Typically, condensers consist of a nest of horizontal tubes with cooling water on the inside and the vapor to be condensed on the outside. Resistances to heat transfer may be caused by air, the condensing film on the outside of the tube, the tube, the scale on the inside, and the water film on the inside. Typical values of the heat transfer coefficient for air-free vapors are given in table 5.1.1. In many cases the governing resistance is not the condensing film. For unfinned air-cooled condensers, for instance, the air film governs.

Table 5.1.1 Orders of Magnitude for Condensation Heat Transfer Coefficients

Mode of condensation	α (W/m² K)
Typical values for air-free vapors	
Film condensation on surfaces	
Pure steam	6,000–30,000
Gassy steam	600–6,000
Hydrocarbons	1,000–5,000
Dropwise condensation of steam	60,000–300,000
Steam on a cold water jet	200,000–600,000
Steam jet in cold water	~10^6
Representative values of heat transfer coefficients often associated with condensing systems	
Tubes	6,000–100,000
Scale in tubes	600–12,000
Water in tubes	2,000–30,000

We open this section by deriving the heat transfer coefficient for film condensation on a vertical surface as originally performed by Nusselt. We then show the effect on it of various geometric and system changes. We proceed to a parametric study of the effects of vapor velocity, vapor superheat, noncondensable gases and condensation of mixtures, and low pressure. Finally, we look briefly at dropwise condensation.

5.2 Film Condensation

Peter Griffith

5.2.1 NUSSELT THEORY FOR FILM CONDENSATION ON A VERTICAL FLAT PLATE

A cooled, constant temperature vertical surface with a film of condensate running down it is illustrated in figure 5.2.1. Vapor flows to the interface and is condensed. The heat released by the condensation process passes through the condensate layer, with the primary resistance to the heat transfer offered by the condensate layer itself. We now relate the thickness of this layer and the resulting heat transfer coefficient to the other parameters of the problem. This development is similar to that presented by Rohsenow & Choi (1961).

The force balance on the piece of condensate film illustrated in figure 5.2.1 yields

$$\mu_L \frac{dU_z}{dz} = g\rho_L(b - y) - g\rho_G(b - y) \qquad [5.2.1]$$

where μ_L is the dynamic viscosity of the liquid, U_z is the velocity in the z direction, g is the gravitational acceleration, ρ_L and ρ_G are the densities of the liquid and vapor, and y is a coordinate. Integrating from the wall and substituting the boundary conditions of zero velocity at the wall and zero shear stress at the interface yield the velocity distribution

$$U_z = g\frac{\rho_L - \rho_G}{\mu_L}\left(by - \frac{y^2}{2}\right) \qquad [5.2.2]$$

Integrating [5.2.2] yields the film flow rate per unit width

$$\Gamma_f = g\rho_L \frac{\rho_L - \rho_G}{\mu_L}\frac{b^3}{3} \qquad [5.2.3]$$

The change in the film flow rate with thickness is then

$$\frac{d\Gamma_f}{db} = g\rho_L\frac{\rho_L - \rho_G}{\mu_L}b^2 \qquad [5.2.4]$$

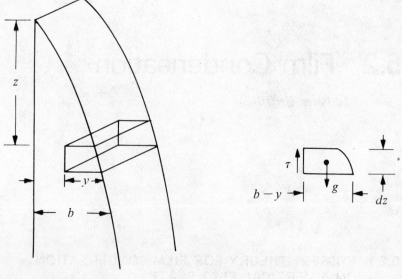

Figure 5.2.1 Coordinate system for Nusselt analysis of film condensation, showing film, control volume, and dimensions appearing in the analysis.

The average temperature of the film is slightly below saturation temperature so that the enthalpy change from saturated vapor to condensate is

$$h'_{LG} = h_{LG} + \tfrac{3}{8}C_{pL}(T_{\text{sat}} - T_W)$$ [5.2.5]

where h_{LG} is the enthalpy change from liquid to saturated vapor, C_{pL} is the specific heat of the liquid at constant pressure, T_{sat} is the saturation temperature, and T_W is the wall temperature. Then the relation between the heat transfer rate and the increment in film flow rate becomes

$$\dot{q} = \lambda_L \frac{T_{\text{sat}} - T_W}{b} = h'_{LG} \frac{d\Gamma_f}{dz}$$ [5.2.6]

where $\dot{q}$ is the heat flux and λ_L is the thermal conductivity of the liquid. Equating the expressions for $d\Gamma_f$ from [5.2.4] and [5.2.6] and integrating:

$$b = \left[\frac{4\lambda_L \mu_L (T_{\text{sat}} - T_W)z}{g\rho_L(\rho_L - \rho_G)h'_{LG}} \right]^{1/4}$$ [5.2.7]

The resulting expression for the local heat transfer coefficient is

$$\alpha_z = \left[\frac{g\rho_L(\rho_L - \rho_G)\lambda_L^3 h'_{LG}}{4z\mu_L(T_{\text{sat}} - T_W)} \right]^{1/4}$$ [5.2.8]

The average heat transfer coefficient up to the point L is

$$\alpha_{az} = \frac{1}{L}\int_0^L \alpha_z \, dz$$ [5.2.9]

so that

$$\alpha_{az} = \tfrac{4}{3}\,\alpha_z$$

This is the average heat transfer coefficient up to the distance L from the leading edge of a vertical flat plate. The vapor shear stress is assumed to be zero, the film is in laminar flow, and the vapor is free of noncondensable gases.

Figure 5.2.2 shows a comparison of the transfer coefficient of [5.2.9] in the form of a length Reynolds number:

$$\mathrm{Re}_f = \frac{\alpha_{az}L(T_{\mathrm{sat}} - T_W)}{h_{LG}\mu_L} \qquad\qquad [5.2.10]$$

The heat transfer coefficient is evidently somewhat better than calculated. This is caused by the presence of waves on the film of condensate that is running down the plate.

It is clear that as the film flow rate becomes larger, the film becomes turbulent. The heat transfer is then a complex function of the local film Reynolds number and

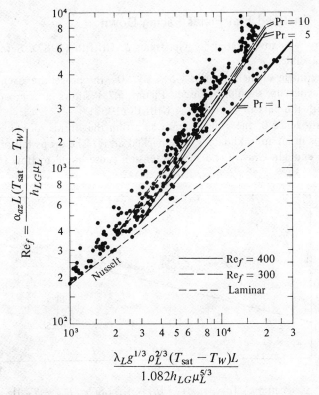

Figure 5.2.2 Comparison of Nusselt theory with data for a variety of fluids and Prandtl numbers for both laminar and turbulent flow. Fluids include water, diphenyl, CO_2, and diphenyl oxide (From *Heat and Mass Transfer* by E. R. G. Eckert and R. M. Drake. Copyright © 1959 by McGraw-Hill Book Company. Used with permission of McGraw-Hill Book Company.)

Prandtl number. It is suggested that the values for the heat transfer coefficient under these circumstances be taken from the curves shown in figure 5.2.2.

5.2.2 OTHER GEOMETRIES

An analysis similar to the preceding one has been completed for many other geometries of interest. In this section we summarize the results for these geometries in a form convenient for quick calculation. The range of values for the heat transfer coefficients given in table 5.1.1 is also appropriate for geometries other than the horizontal tube and, in fact, covers almost all heat exchanger geometries.

5.2.2.1 Inclined Flat Plates Facing Up

This case is very similar to the vertical flat plate except that g in [5.2.8] is replaced by $g \sin \gamma$, where γ is the angle of inclination measured from the horizontal. Figure 5.2.2 also applies with this transformation for both laminar and turbulent flow.

5.2.2.2 Inclined Flat Plates Facing Down

This geometry was investigated by Gerstman & Griffith (1967). Several different regimes are possible.

When the angle of inclination is $7.5 < \gamma < 90°$, the procedure given for inclined flat plates facing up should be used. Figure 5.2.3 shows a comparison of this procedure with the data of Gerstman & Griffith (1967).

As γ approaches 0, the condensation as a film that forms spontaneously into a series of drops in an approximately close-packed array. The drops fall off when they become large enough. Gravity and surface tension cause liquid to flow from the film

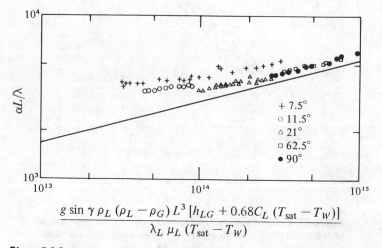

Figure 5.2.3 Effect of inclination on the average heat transfer rate for plates inclined more than 7.5° from the horizontal. The data are for refrigerant 113; the line is for a vertical plate [5.2.9] (after Gerstman & Griffith 1967).

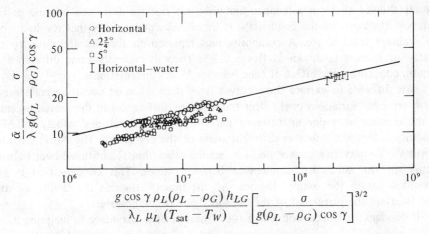

Figure 5.2.4   Effect of inclination on the average heat transfer rate for horizontal plates and plates inclined up to 7.5° from the horizontal. The best line through the data for horizontal plates is shown. Most of the points are for refrigerant 113 (after Gerstman & Griffith 1967).

surrounding the drops into the drops themselves. Figure 5.2.4 shows data taken under these circumstances (σ in the figure is surface tension). Points taken from the curve for the appropriate inclination should be used. The characteristic dimension of the problem is a function of gravity and surface tension only. The length of the plate does not affect the computation.

When the inclination of the plate is $0 < \gamma < 7.5°$, the configuration is different. The surface is covered by a series of ridges that flow down the plate and from which condensate drips off. Somewhere between 0 and 7.5° inclination, the ridges flow so slowly that they have time to form into drops that fall off before reaching the end of the plate. The plate length and the balance of surface and gravity forces provide the characteristic dimension for the problem, although the dimension arising from the balance of the surface and gravity forces is of the greatest significance. Figure 5.2.4 shows the effect of inclination under these circumstances. Although theories have been developed for these lines, it is suggested that the values be taken from figure 5.2.4 directly.

5.2.2.3 Outside Tubes

The equation for condensation outside a single horizontal tube can be derived in much the same way as that for a vertical plate. The result is

$$\alpha = 0.727 \left[\frac{g\rho_L(\rho_L - \rho_G)\lambda_L^3 h'_{LG}}{D\mu_L(T_{sat} - T_W)} \right]^{1/4} \qquad [5.2.11]$$

where D is the diameter of the tube. This value is about 15% lower than the data.

If there is more than one tube in a stack, condensate drops from the top tube to the next and so forth. The condensate layer is then thicker on subsequent tubes and the heat transfer coefficient is thus reduced. In his original development,

Nusselt showed that for a laminar film the heat transfer decreased because of the increased thickness of the condensate layer on subsequent tubes that resulted from the drainage from above. A composite plot representing theories and data from a variety of sources is shown in figure 5.2.5. There is evidently some difference of opinion concerning the effect of tube number N on condensation.

It is difficult to extract these curves from data taken on operating condensers. There are axial variations in the heat transfer rate, differences in the partial pressure of the condensing vapor in different parts of the condenser, and widely differing velocities across the tubes in different parts of the condenser. The Nusselt theory provides a conservative answer because, among other things, additional heat transfer occurs on the subcooled condensate between tubes. This condensation is not accounted for in the simple theories. All the imperfections in the simple theories tend to affect the placement of the lines in figure 5.2.5, however.

If condensation occurs outside a tube, there is little advantage in inclining it.

5.2.2.4 Inside Tubes

When condensing at low velocity, inside tube condensation is better in down-flowing inclined tubes than either vertical or horizontal tubes. (At high velocity, inclination does not matter; condensation at high velocity inside tubes considered later in this section.) This is because the layer of condensate in the bottom is quite thick in a horizontal tube, so that a small inclination in the direction of flow results in more rapid condensate flow and a much thinner condensate layer. Vertical tubes are not usually as good as inclined ones because the condensate layer is uniform around the tube; better heat transfer is obtained when the condensate layer is nonuniformly distributed. The optimum inclination for condensation is about 20° from the horizontal. It is recommended that for tubes inclined between 5 and 30° from the horizontal in down flow, [5.2.11] be used.

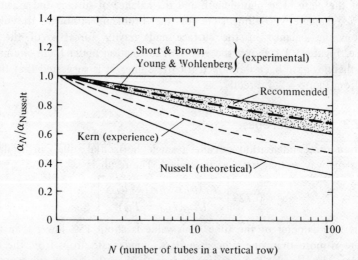

Figure 5.2.5 Ratio of the heat transfer coefficient on the Nth tube to that on the first tube for a tube bundle (Bell & Panchal 1978).

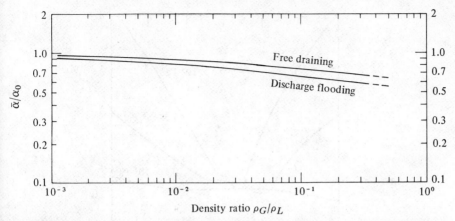

Figure 5.2.6 Degradation of heat transfer resulting from pooling of condensate in the bottom of a horizontal tube. The factor obtained from this curve should multiply the value of α obtained from [5.2.11] to obtain the value appropriate for condensation inside horizontal tubes (Kaminski 1977).

For tubes inclined more than 30°, interpolate between the formulas for horizontal and vertical tubes.

For condensation inside tubes inclined less that 5°, the formula for condensation outside horizontal tubes is appropriate as long as the effective area is reduced by the appropriate factor resulting from the pool of condensate that collects in the bottom. Figure 5.2.6 (Kaminski 1977) shows approximately how much the average heat transfer coefficient is degraded by this condensate layer.

5.2.3 EFFECT OF VARIOUS PARAMETERS ON FILM CONDENSATION

The foregoing recommendations apply, generally, to laminar and turbulent film condensation in various geometries. This section considers the effects of various other parameters: vapor velocity (or shear), noncondensable gases, vapor superheat, and low pressure. Most of these effects are accounted for by means of a correction factor on the basic laminar or turbulent heat transfer coefficient.

5.2.3.1 Vapor Velocity outside Tubes

Mikheyev (undated) and Kutateladze (1952) report data outside single tubes. At moderate velocity, the smoothed data for three different pressures are shown in figure 5.2.7. Figure 5.2.8 shows these data correlated as recommended by Kutateladze (1952). Theories for condensation outside tubes with a variety of orientations have been worked out and are compared in figure 5.2.9 (Nicol et al. 1978). When using the curves in figures 5.2.7–5.2.9 for tubes in tube bundles, the velocity should be interpreted as the gap velocity for the smallest spacing between adjoining tubes.

At very high velocity, the improvements in the heat transfer are not as large as one would expect from extrapolating these curves. This may be caused by the

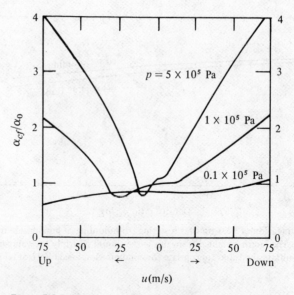

Figure 5.2.7 Effect of cross-flow velocity on heat transfer outside a single tube for steam condensing at three different pressures. The velocity in the gap should be used for tube bundles when using this curve. α_0 is from [5.2.11] and α_{cf} is for the cross flow (Mikheyev 1977).

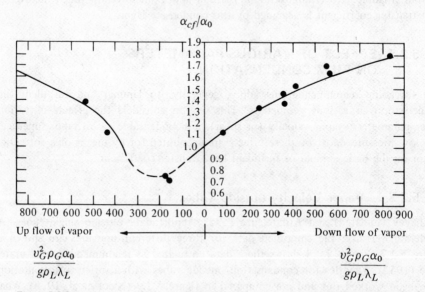

Figure 5.2.8 Correlation of data in figure 5.2.7 for use at other pressures (Kutateladze 1952).

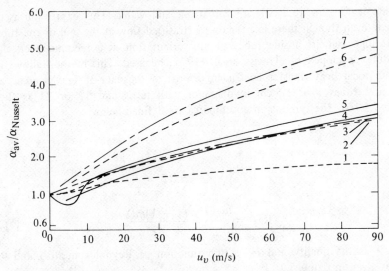

Figure 5.2.9 Comparison of different theories for condensation in the presence of vapor velocity (Nicol et al. 1978). The conditions chosen are: $p = 0.2 \times 10^5$ Pa, $T_{sat} - T_W \cong 10°C$, and $R_0 = 0.0095$ m. Curves are for (1) nonisothermal cross flow, (2) isothermal down flow (Wallace 1975), (3) isothermal cross flow, (4) cross flow with separation at 82°, (5) isothermal up flow, (6) no gravitational field, and (7) isothermal down flow (Fujii et al. 1972).

reduction in saturation temperature resulting from the low pressure in the vicinity of the tube when the cross-flow velocity is comparable to the velocity of sound. The heat transfer coefficient can be as little as 0.4 of the value calculated by extrapolation of figure 5.2.8. In general, the other resistances to heat transfer govern at high velocities and a precise answer is not usually necessary.

5.2.3.2 Vapor Velocity inside Tubes

The effect of vapor velocity inside tubes is to increase the heat transfer coefficient by thinning the film. If the velocity is high enough to ensure annular flow, tube orientation has little or no effect, as the condensate is reasonably uniformly distributed around the periphery of the tube. Under the circumstances, the following is recommended for an estimate of the average heat transfer coefficient inside a tube with 100% condensation (Boyko & Kruzhilin 1967):

$$\frac{\bar{\alpha} D}{\lambda_L} = 0.024 \left(\frac{\dot{m} D}{\mu_L}\right)^{0.8} \left(\frac{c_L \mu_L}{\lambda_L}\right)^{0.43} \frac{1 + \sqrt{\rho_L / \rho_G}}{2} \qquad [5.2.12]$$

where $\bar{\alpha}$ is the average heat transfer coefficient, D is the tube diameter, λ_L is the thermal conductivity of the liquid, μ_L is the viscosity of the liquid, ρ_L and ρ_G are the densities of the liquid and vapor, and $\dot{m}$ is the mass flow rate.

An expression as simple as [5.2.12] is adequate because the liquid film on the wall is the governing resistance and its fluid mechanics is governed by the liquid Reynolds number and density ratio. Both are included in the expression. Most of the data leading to [5.2.12] are for steam and water. This expression is usually adequate even though there is a region of stratified flow at the end of the tube.

At high velocity inside tubes of any orientation, it is recommended that the procedure developed by Traviss et al. (1971) be used. This method allows one to estimate local heat transfer coefficients. Most of the data of Traviss et al. are for horizontal tubes 1 or 1.5 cm in diameter with refrigerant 12 or 22 as the fluid (figure 5.2.10). The symbols in coordinates are defined below:

$$\mathrm{Nu} = \frac{\alpha_z D}{\lambda_L} \qquad [5.2.13a]$$

$$\mathrm{Pr}_L = \frac{C_L \mu_L}{\lambda_L} \qquad [5.2.13b]$$

$$\mathrm{Re}_L = \frac{\dot{m}_L D}{\mu_L} = \frac{(1 - X)\dot{m}D}{\mu_L} \qquad [5.2.13c]$$

where X is the quality and F_2 is the function of Reynolds number and Prandtl number given in figure 5.2.11.

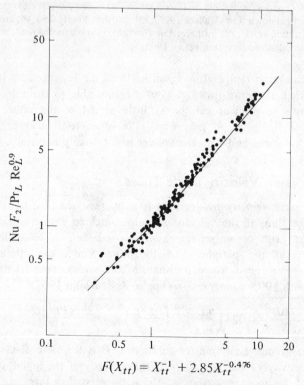

$$F(X_{tt}) = X_{tt}^{-1} + 2.85 X_{tt}^{-0.476}$$

Figure 5.2.10 Correlation of condensation heat transfer data for tubes of any orientation. This theory has worked well on tubes 1.2 cm in diameter as well as the 1-cm diameter tubes presented here for refrigerants 12 and 22 (Traviss et al. 1971).

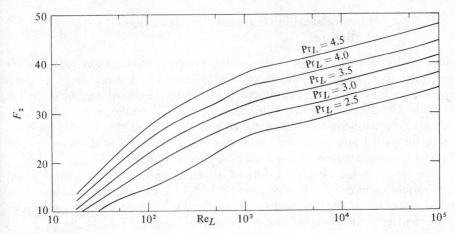

Figure 5.2.11 Factor accounting for Prandtl number variations in the theory of Traviss et al. (1971) for high-velocity condensation inside tubes of any orientation.

$$X_{tt} = \left(\frac{\mu_G}{\mu_L}\right)^{0.1} \left(\frac{1-X}{X}\right)^{0.9} \left(\frac{\rho_G}{\rho_L}\right)^{0.5} \qquad [5.2.14]$$

The dividing line between the high- and low-velocity regimes is determined by the major flow regime in the pipe. If the flow is stratified or wavy stratified, it is in the low-velocity regime (for horizontal or near-horizontal pipes) and [5.2.11] and figure 5.2.6 should be used. If the flow is annular or slug, it is in the high-velocity regime and [5.2.12] for the average value or figures 5.2.10 and 5.2.11 for the local value should be used. The recommended flow regime map is that of Taitel & Dukler as given in section 2.1.4.

As the quality changes continuously along the tube, the flow regime can change too. It is recommended that the flow regime existing at 50% quality be used to decide whether the flow is at high or low velocity for a tube in which 100% of the vapor is condensed. If only a portion is condensed, the average conditions over that section should be used to determine the approximate flow regime.

5.2.3.3 Vapor Superheat

The heat transfer from superheated vapor is calculated from the appropriate formula, using T_s in the driving temperature difference. The enthalpy change on condensation must be augmented for the superheat enthalpy. Thus in [5.2.8] or [5.2.11], h'_{LG} must be

$$h'_{LG} = h_{LG} + C_{pG}(T_s - T_{\text{sat}}) + \tfrac{3}{8} C_{pL}(T_{\text{sat}} - T_W) \qquad [5.2.15]$$

where h'_{LG} is the enthalpy change from liquid to vapor (for superheated vapor).

5.2.3.4 Noncondensable Gases and Condensation of Mixtures

Noncondensable gases seriously reduce the effective condensation heat transfer coefficient. The reason for this can be seen in figure 5.2.12, which shows the cross section of a tube on which condensation is occurring, the film of condensate on the tube, and the layer of noncondensable gas concentrated outside the tube. The vapor that is condensed must first diffuse through the layer of noncondensable gas. This means the partial pressure of the condensing vapor is reduced at the interface and the heat transfer rate through the condensate film is reduced.

For air in steam, a quick estimate of the effect of air on the condensing heat transfer coefficient can be obtained from figure 5.1.13. The weight percentage of air in the steam is evaluated in the free stream, locally. (In a once-through condenser the percentage of air would increase continually to the outlet.)

For a more precise answer to this problem and the problem of condensation of mixtures, the procedure developed by Votta (1964) is recommended. This procedure is based on the trial-and-error method originally developed by Colburn and others for sizing heat exchangers that must condense mixtures of vapors or a vapor

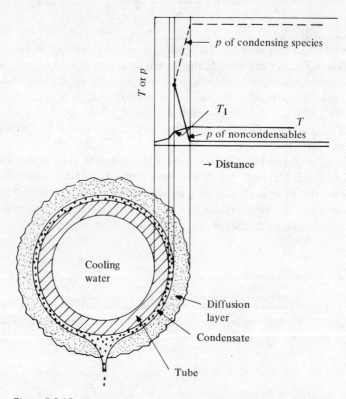

Figure 5.2.12 Temperature and partial pressure profiles in the vicinity of a tube on which condensation is occurring with a noncondensable gas present.

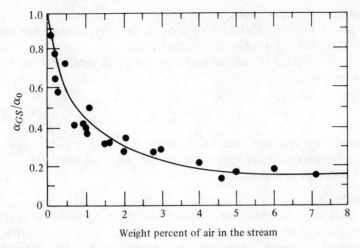

Figure 5.2.13   Effect of air on condensation heat transfer (Mikheyev 1977).

from a mixture containing a noncondensable gas. Votta's method has a good theoretical foundation and has the advantage that the trial-and-error calculation inherent in the original method is eliminated.

The essential difficulty in calculating condensation of vapors from mixtures is evident in figure 5.2.12, where the condensate resistance is joined by a diffusion resistance across which the condensing species must pass to get to the interface. The interface assumes a temperature T_I, which is less than the situation temperature for the vapor at the ambient pressure and is, in general, a function of the condensing rate.

Votta's method replaces the vapor thermal resistance plus vapor diffusion resistance with a combined equivalent thermal resistance to be used with an equivalent temperature difference. To use Votta's procedure, the following information is used.

1. Relation between temperature T and driving potential F, which is developed from

$$F_n - F_O = T_n - T_O + R_p \ln \frac{p - p_O}{p - p_N} \qquad [5.2.16]$$

where R_p is defined in [5.2.24], p is the pressure, subscript N refers to a state at T_n, and subscript O refers to an arbitrary base condition.

2. Incremental area relation

$$A = \int_0^{\dot{Q}_T} \frac{d\dot{Q}_T}{\alpha_G (F_G - F_I)} \qquad [5.2.17]$$

where $\dot{Q}_T$ is the heat transfer rate in the section of the condenser.

3. Vapor-side sensible heat transfer coefficient α_G.
4. Overall heat transfer coefficient α_{IL} (based on the condensing surface area) from the condensate-gas interface to the cooling water.
5. Interfacial temperature T_I and driving potential F_I as obtained from the $T - F$ relationship and

$$T_I = T_L + \frac{F_G - F_I}{\alpha_{IL}/\alpha_G} \qquad [5.2.18]$$

These quantities are discussed after the procedure for calculating the condenser area is described. The important assumptions of this procedure are then mentioned.

The procedure is as follows:

1. Develop the appropriate F-T curve from [5.2.16].
2. Choose a temperature level for condensation and a temperature interval over which to calculate the incremental area. Determine the amount of heat that must be transferred in passing through that temperature interval. That determines $\dot{Q}_T$.
3. Calculate α_G, the vapor-side heat transfer coefficient based on the outside condensing surface area.
4. Calculate α_{IL}, the overall heat transfer coefficient based on the condensing surface area (see item 4 above).
5. Calculate the interfacial driving potential F_I and temperature T_I, from the simultaneous solution of the F-T curve and [5.2.18].
6. Determine F_G, for the temperature level chosen, from the F-T curve.
7. Determine the incremental area needed to condense the chosen increment of vapor from [5.2.17].
8. Choose a new temperature increment and calculate the appropriate area increment as described above.

The quantities needed to implement this procedure were obtained as follows. Start with the T-F curve, which is the heart of the procedure. Look at the processes occurring across the gas-vapor boundary layer outside the tube illustrated in figure 5.2.12. The heat transfer is

$$\frac{d\dot{Q}_T}{dA} = \alpha_G(T_G - T_I) + \beta_G h_{LG}(p_v - p_I) \qquad [5.2.19]$$

where β is the mass transfer coefficient.

The first term is the sensible heat and the second is the latent heat of the diffusing species. Note that [5.2.19] concentrates on the resistance to sensible heat transfer resulting from the gas layer outside the condensate film. It is evident that even with only 1% noncondensables, as seen in figure 5.2.13, the gas layer is the most important resistance. Replace the two terms appearing above with a single term:

$$\frac{d\dot{Q}_T}{dA} = \alpha_G(F_G - F_I) \qquad [5.2.20]$$

This expression is actually the definition of the driving potential F, which, multiplying the sensible heat transfer coefficient, gives both sensible and latent heat transfer across the film. Eliminating the heat flux between [5.2.19] and [5.2.20] and rearranging:

$$F_G - F_I = T_G - T_I + \frac{\beta_G}{\alpha_G} h_{LG}(p_G - p_I) \qquad [5.2.2.1]$$

From the Chilton-Colburn analogy

$$\frac{\beta_G}{\alpha_G} = \frac{1}{C_p p_{nm}} \left(\frac{\text{Pr}}{\text{Sc}}\right)^{2/3} = \frac{1}{C_p p_{nm}} \text{Le}^{2/3} \qquad [5.2.22]$$

where C_p = specific heat at constant pressure in [5.2.21]
  Le = Lewis number, $C_p, D_q/\lambda_G$ (dimensionless)

$$p_{nm} = \frac{(p - p_I) - (p - p_G)}{\ln\left[(p - p_I)/(p - p_G)\right]} \quad \text{(the log mean pressure difference)} \qquad [5.2.23]$$

Define

$$R_p = \frac{h_{LG}}{C_p} \text{Le}^{2/3} \qquad [5.2.24]$$

Then

$$F_G - F_I = T_G - T_I + R_p \ln \frac{p - p_I}{p - p_G} \qquad [5.2.25]$$

The base condition at which the potential F is evaluated is arbitrary, as only F differences appear in the equations used. We can determine F to this arbitrary base from [5.2.16], which is [5.2.24] rewritten in terms of a general condition n. The subscript 0 refers to the base condition and n to the condition of interest, and

$$F_n - F_O = T_n - T_O + R_p \ln \frac{p - p_O}{p - p_n} \qquad [5.2.16]$$

This function has been evaluated for several mixtures and is presented in table 5.2.1 for a $T_O = 0°C$ and $p_O = 0$. Table 5.2.1 also gives R as a function of temperature.

Let us now proceed to [5.2.17], which is really just the definition of α_G rearranged. The α_G should be evaluated as though one were calculating heat transfer from a gas to the surface—that is, it should be evaluated from the chosen equation for cross flow on tubes, flow inside tubes, or flow along a bundle, whichever is appropriate.

The overall heat transfer coefficient α_{IL} shown in [5.2.18] includes the condensate film (which must be estimated), the scale resistances, and a heat transfer resistance inside. As these resistances are in series with the gas and the vapor boundary layer on the outside,

$$\alpha_{IL}(T_I - T_L) = \alpha_G(F_G - F_I)$$

from which [5.2.18] is developed.

Votta reported that this procedure gave virtually the same areas as the Colburn method for several condensers. According to Bell & Ghaly (1973), a similar method

Table 5.2.1 Magnitudes of F for Various Mixtures above a Reference State of 0°C at a Total Pressure of 101.31×10^3 Pa

Temperature (°C)	Air-water		Air-toluene		Air-benzene		Helium-water		CO_2-water	
	R (°C)	F (°C)	R (°C)	F (°C)	R (°C)	F (°C)	R (°C)	F (°C)	R (°C)	F (°C)
0	–	0	–	0	–	0	–	0	–	0
4.44	1728	8.3	678	6.1	707	14	1422	7.8	1883	8.9
10.00	1710	20.6	681	15	706	31	1422	19	1844	21
15.56	1661	34.4	672	25	699	51	1422	31	1794	36
26.67	1608	73.3	664	48	681	103	1439	69	1750	77
37.78	1472	132	644	79	663	179	1467	127	1683	140
48.89	1494	222	639	121	663	312	1556	230	1633	239
60.00	1489	377	620	183	647	522	1639	410	1567	394
71.11	1483	632	617	272	629	957	1850	798	1502	641
76.67	–	–	611	328	624	1546	–	–	–	–
82.22	1467	1222	–	–	–	–	2089	1561	1467	1121
93.33	1589	2521	–	–	–	–	2989	4611	1436	2288

gave design areas ranging from ones that were correct to ones that were as much as twice as large as necessary.

There are several limitations in this procedure. One is that there is no established way to handle a multipass arrangement. Another is that equilibrium between the condensate and the vapor phase composition is assumed, whereas the condensate probably drains to the bottom and undergoes little subsequent change in composition resulting from condensation.

An additional word should be said about the condensation of immiscible mixtures. The properties of the two components are often very different, and the way in which the immiscible condensate fractions are arranged on the condensing surface makes a substantial difference in calculating the condensation heat transfer. This problem has not been solved in general. However, Bernhardt et al. (1972) recommend simple weighting of the condensed volume flow rates of the two condensing components. That is, the weighted condensation heat transfer coefficient α_c is

$$\alpha_c = \alpha_1 \left(\frac{\dot{M}_1/\rho_1}{\dot{M}_1/\rho_1 + \dot{M}_2/\rho_2} \right) + \alpha_2 \left(\frac{\dot{M}_2/\rho_2}{\dot{M}_1/\rho_1 + \dot{M}_2/\rho_2} \right) \qquad [5.2.26]$$

where $\dot{M}$ is the mass flux and 1 and 2 refer to components 1 and 2.

5.2.3.5 Low-Pressure Interfacial Mass Transfer Resistance

At very low pressure the interfacial mass transfer resistance becomes significant. For steam, this means that the pressure must be below 3.38×10^3 Pa before the interfacial heat transfer coefficient α_I is an appreciable factor. The kinetic theory limitations to the heat transfer can be put in the form of a coefficient:

$$\alpha_I = 2 \left(\frac{\bar{M}}{2\pi RT} \right)^{1/2} \frac{h_{LG}^2}{T_{\text{sat}}(1/\rho_G + 1/\rho_L)} \qquad [5.2.27]$$

where $\bar{M}$ is the molecular weight.

The resistance arising from this heat transfer coefficient is in series with the others in the problem.

5.3 Direct Contact Condensation

Peter Griffith

Extraordinarily large heat transfer rates are possible when condensation occurs directly on a cold liquid interface with no intervening solid surface. Several different geometries are possible. One can condense a steam jet in a large pool of cold liquid, one can condense steam on drops in a spray, or one can condense on a coherent liquid jet sprayed into a steam environment.

In every case the limiting process is the heat transfer in the liquid. Consider what happens when a jet of steam is sprayed into a pool of cold water. Experiments reported by Cumo et al. (1978) and by Young et al. (1973) explore the variables of vapor mass velocity quality, pressure, and condensing water temperature.

The condensing rate of a jet of steam blowing into cold water is determined by the turbulent mixing of the water in the vicinity of the jet. The mixing is driven by the velocity difference between the almost sonic steam and the slow-moving water. The heat transfer coefficient is defined on the basis of the area of the condensing cone. Values for steam Mach numbers Ma were within the range

$$0.7 < \text{Ma} < 2.0$$

for
$$10^5 < p < 15 \times 10^5 \text{ N/m}^2$$

$$36 < T_L < 40°\text{C}$$

Heat transfer coefficients based on cone area were of the order of 3×10^6 W/m^2 with cone lengths in the range $0.5 < L/D < 5.0$. The details in predicting the cone length are complex, and for many applications the answer is not significant. Far more water was provided than was needed to condense all the steam.

As the steam mass velocity decreased, the jet became shorter until condensation sometimes occurred in the nozzle. This caused periodic ejection of hot water from the nozzle and very unsteady, noisy condensation. The vapor mass velocity in the nozzle at which this first occurred was a function of subcooling, varying from 100 g/cm² s at 20°C subcooling to 15 g/cm² s at about 75°C subcooling at 0.1 MPa pressure for steam (Cumo et al. 1978).

Condensation of steam on a cold water spray is also limited by the transfer of heat in the liquid. The key questions are the spray drop size distribution, and whether the drops circulate as they pass through the condensing vapor. As the answers are so specific to the nozzle and resulting spray geometry, no general formula can be given. Heat transfer rates are very high.

Condensation of steam on a water jet has been reported by Linehan & Grolmes (1970) and by Kutateladze (1952). The result obtained by Linehan & Grolmes is particularly simple:

$$\mathrm{St} = \frac{\alpha}{u_j \rho_L C_{pL}} = 0.012 \qquad [5.3.1]$$

where St is the Stanton number and u_j is the velocity of the jet. Their system was a coaxial water jet inside a steam jet. Condensation rates in the water jet were inferred from the wall pressure profiles. Implicit in their treatment of the data was the assumption that the turbulence in the jet results from the inlet flow rather than the shear of the condensing steam. This appears to be the case.

A more detailed study of condensation on jets is that of Kutateladze (1952). The limiting process is still the turbulent diffusion in the liquid. Turbulence in the jet, and thus diffusion, is governed by the approach Reynolds number. The coordinates for the circular, accelerating jet are shown in figure 5.2.1. Equations summarizing the results for jets of various geometries are given in table 5.3.1. The results from table 5.3.1 are to be substituted into

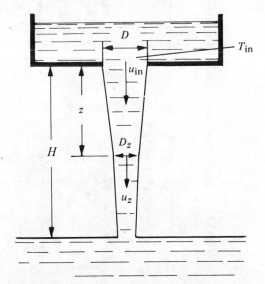

Figure 5.3.1 Coordinates for condensation of turbulent water jets (Kutateladze 1952).

Table 5.3.1 Summary of Expressions for Condensation on Coherent Jets of Various Kinds

Shape	ϵ^*	C_1	C_2	$f(z)$
Freely falling cylindrical jet	5×10^{-4}	0.160	2.52	$\dfrac{\kappa_L z}{u_{in}(D/2)^2} + \dfrac{2\epsilon^* u_{in}^2}{2\phi^{5/2} g(D/2)}$	$\left[\left(1 + \dfrac{2\phi^2 gz}{u_{in}^2}\right)^{5/4} - 1\right]$
Freely falling plane jet	5×10^{-4}	0.92	1.075	$\dfrac{4u_{in}^2}{3\phi^3 g\delta_{in}}\left(\dfrac{\kappa_L}{u_{in}\delta_{in}} + \dfrac{\epsilon^*}{2}\right)$	$\left[\left(1 + \dfrac{2\phi^2 gz}{u_{in}^2}\right)^{3/2} - 1\right]$
Plane jet with constant thickness heated on one side	5×10^{-4}	0.92	1.075	$\left(\dfrac{\kappa_L}{u\delta} + \dfrac{\epsilon^*}{2}\right)\dfrac{4z}{\delta}$	

$$\ln \frac{T_{\text{sat}} - T_I}{T_{\text{sat}} - T_x} = C_1 + C_2 f(x) \tag{5.3.2}$$

where C_1 and C_2 are dimensionless constants, the values of which are given in table 5.3.1; ϵ^* in the table is a constant (given in the table); κ is the thermal diffusivity; δ is the thickness of the jet; and ϕ is defined by

$$\phi = \frac{u_{\text{in}}}{u_z} \tag{5.3.3}$$

5.4 Pressure Drop inside Tubes with Condensation

Peter Griffith

Pressure drop must be known in condensing systems for two reasons. First, because the pressure drop is a penalty one must pay in order to transfer the heat, it must be considered if an optimum system is to be designed. Second, the pressure changes and associated saturation temperature changes can alter the heat transfer appreciably. One must use the true local saturation temperature with the preceding recommendations on heat transfer coefficients to calculate the heat transfer rate properly. The recommendations on the pressure drop are as follows.

Use the Thom friction multipliers given in section 2.2.3 for the friction pressure drop. Use the velocity ratio curve of figure 5.4.1 (Rohsenow & Hartnett 1973) and [5.4.1] to calculate the local void fraction α:

$$\frac{1-\alpha}{\alpha} = \frac{v_G}{v_L}\frac{\rho_G}{\rho_L}\frac{1-X}{X} \qquad [5.4.1]$$

where X is the quality. The void fraction, in turn, should be substituted into the following equation to calculate the gravity pressure change:

$$\Delta p_g = [\rho_L(1-\alpha) + \alpha\rho_G]gL\sin\gamma \qquad [5.4.2]$$

where γ is the inclination angle and L is the length of the tube. If there is a uniform heat flux, the integrated friction and gravity Thom multipliers of section 2.2.3 can be used. Otherwise, step-by-step integration must be used. Momentum pressure drop should be calculated from the homogeneous model [5.4.3] and [5.4.4] as follows. Calculate the mixture specific volume:

$$\frac{1}{\rho} = X\frac{1}{\rho_G} + (1-X)\frac{1}{\rho_L} \qquad [5.4.3]$$

and substitute into

$$\Delta p_m = \frac{\dot{m}^2}{g_0}\left(\frac{1}{\rho_2} - \frac{1}{\rho_1}\right) \qquad [5.4.4]$$

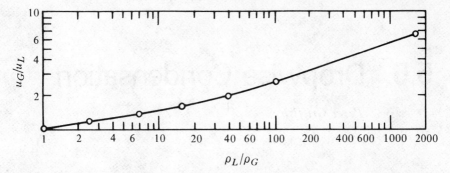

Figure 5.4.1 Velocity ratio as a function of density ratio for calculating the local gravity term in the momentum equation for condensation in tubes. The value for a whole tube must be integrated. For uniform heat flux the integrated results are presented in section 2.2.3.

The total pressure drop then becomes

$$\Delta p = \Delta p_f + \Delta p_g + \Delta p_m \qquad\qquad [5.4.5]$$

It is recommended that form factor losses be calculated by using the homogeneous model and the appropriate velocity head or equivalent L/D multipliers.

5.5 Dropwise Condensation

Peter Griffith

Dropwise condensation is an attractive mode of heat transfer because the heat transfer coefficients are so high (table 5.1.1). Application of dropwise condensation to heat exchangers usually results in such small heat transfer resistances on the condensing side that the fluid, the scale on the water side, and the tube resistances govern the heat transfer rate. For this reason, an accurate calculation of the dropwise condensation heat transfer coefficient is rarely justified.

In the next section the orders of magnitude of the dropwise condensation heat transfer coefficients for various systems are presented. This is followed by a description of mechanisms of dropwise condensation and recommended methods of calculating the dropwise condensation heat transfer coefficient. Finally, some promoters to use with steam are suggested.

5.5.1 ORDERS OF MAGNITUDE

Data for dropwise condensation on a variety of surfaces and experimental systems are displayed in figure 5.5.1. The bulk of the data is for steam condensing on vertical copper or copper alloy surfaces. The scatter is caused primarily by noncondensables, which are properly vented in the systems with high heat transfer coefficients but are not vented effectively in the systems with low heat transfer coefficients. To ensure good venting it is necessary to have a sustained, positive flow of steam from the entrance to the vent in an unambiguous path. Changes in steam flow path area and abrupt changes in flow direction lead to pockets of noncondensable gas and to deteriorated heat transfer.

Dropwise condensation occurs on surfaces that are poorly wetted (i.e., have receding contact angles measured through the liquid that appreciably exceed 0). Condensation is initiated on exceedingly small drops (of order 10^{-6} m in diameter) trapped in cavities on the surface. Immense populations of these drops (of order $10^8/cm^2$) appear at surface subcoolings of the order of $0.3°C$. They grow by condensation on themselves and by agglomeration with neighboring drops until they become so large that they fall off, run down, or are swept away by the steam from

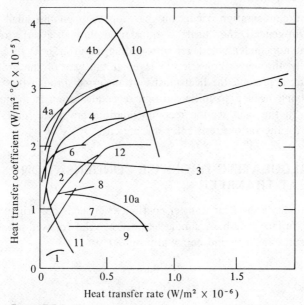

Figure 5.5.1 Dropwise condensation on various surfaces (after Tanner et al. 1968).

Curve	Orienta-tion	Surface material	Surface finish	Promoter	Venting arrange-ment	Gas concen-tration
1	Vertical	Copper	Mirror smooth	Stearic acid	Unknown	Unknown
2	Vertical	Copper	Mirror smooth	Benzyl mercap-tan and oleic acid mixed	Continuous bleed	Unknown
3	Vertical	Chromium plated on brass	Highly polished	Oleic acid	Unknown	Unknown
4 4a, 4b	Vertical	Copper	Mirror smooth	Dioctadecyl; disulfide	Blow past sur-face, various velocities	2 ppm
5	Vertical	Copper	Mirror smooth	Dioctadecyl; disulfide	Close by venting	"Very small"
6	Vertical	Copper	Mirror smooth	Dioctadecyl; disulfide	Blow past sur-face	"Very small"
7	Vertical tubes	Chromium plated on copper	Unknown	Oleic acid	Continuous bleed	Unknown
8	Vertical	Copper	Unknown	Oleic acid	Blow past surface	Unknown
9	Vertical tubes	Copper	Unknown	Benzyl mercaptan	Continuous bleed	Unknown
10, 10a	Vertical	Copper	Highly polished	Benzyl mercaptan	Blow past sur-face	Unknown
11	Vertical	Copper	Polished	Cupric oleate	Unknown	Unknown
12	Vertical	Copper	Unknown	Benzyl mercaptan	Blow past surface	Unknown

the surface. The condensation occurs on the drops, not on the small bare patches between them. In general, the "heat" is transferred through a series of resistances, first through the noncondensable layer surrounding the drop, next through the drop itself, and finally through a constriction layer at the base of the drop. If a thick layer of promoter is present, the heat must be transferred through that also.

The subcooling needed to initiate dropwise condensation is so small that it is neglected here. In the next section recommendations are made for calculating the heat transfer when the various resistances are present.

5.5.2 CALCULATING DROPWISE CONDENSATION HEAT TRANSFER

The dropwise condensation heat transfer coefficient depends only slightly on surface orientation and surface length. A simple expression valid for well-promoted copper surfaces at pressures equal to and below atmospheric is

$$\alpha = \alpha_{\text{dco}} \qquad [5.5.1]$$

where
$$\alpha = 51,104 + 2044 T_{\text{sat}} \qquad [5.5.2]$$

when
$$22 < T_{\text{sat}} < 100°C$$

but
$$\alpha_{\text{dco}} = 255,510 \qquad [5.5.3]$$

when
$$T_{\text{sat}} = 100°C$$

where α is in W/m^2 °C (Graham 1969).

Noncondensables in steam condensing on copper are accounted for by use of figure 5.5.2 (Shade & Mikic 1974). One interprets the denominator of the ordinate as the α_{dco}, which is evaluated from [5.5.2] or [5.5.3]. The velocity given in figure 5.5.2 is the local velocity past the condensing surface. In general, some extrapolation is necessary as only limited data are available. It is clear, however, that noncondensables have a major effect on dropwise condensation heat transfer.

Another resistance of consequence arises when the condensing surface is not as good a thermal conductor as copper or silver. This is the constriction resistance. Figure 5.5.3 (Hannemann & Mikic 1976) shows heat transfer data from a variety of sources. The denominator of the ordinate is the heat transfer coefficient evaluated from [5.5.2] or [5.5.3]. This resistance accounts for the additional temperature drop that occurs on low thermal conductivity surfaces because of crowding of the heat flow lines near active areas of the condensing surface.

It is not entirely clear how to calculate condensing gassy steam on a low-conductivity surface. On physical grounds, one expects to find the heat transfer coefficient reduced by both factors. Under the circumstances, it is proposed that the following equation be used:

$$\alpha = \alpha_{\text{dco}} \frac{\alpha}{\alpha_{\text{dco1}}} \frac{\alpha}{\alpha_{\text{dco2}}} \qquad [5.5.4]$$

where $\alpha/\alpha_{\text{dco1}}$ is to be obtained from figure 5.5.2 and $\alpha/\alpha_{\text{dco2}}$ from figure 5.5.3.

The promoter layer is usually so thin (of thickness x_p) that it has a negligible

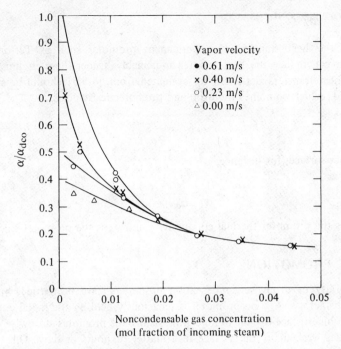

Figure 5.5.2 Effect of noncondensables on dropwise condensation on a copper surface (after Shade & Mikic 1974).

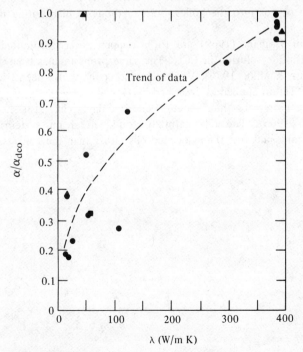

Figure 5.5.3 Effect of surface thermal conductivity on heat transfer coefficient for dropwise condensation (after Hannemann & Mikic 1976).

effect on the heat transfer. If a permanent promoter such as Teflon is used, however, it can reduce the heat transfer appreciably. Under these circumstances the promotor heat transfer coefficient α_p evaluated from [5.5.5] should be substituted into [5.5.6], which combines the drop and promoter resistances:

$$\alpha_p = \frac{\lambda_p}{x_p} \tag{5.5.5}$$

For a copper surface, for instance,

$$\frac{1}{\alpha} = \frac{1}{\alpha_{dco}} + \frac{1}{\alpha_p} \tag{5.5.6}$$

where λ_p is the promoter thermal conductivity and x_p is the promoter thickness.

5.5.3 PROMOTION

A wide variety of dropwise condensation promoters have been tried, but none is entirely satisfactory. A good promoter is tenaciously held by the metal and presents a hydrophobic surface to the water. Almost any oil promotes dropwise condensation but it is washed off the surface in a matter of hours or days. Oils containing sulfur tend to bond more tenaciously to metals. A survey of promoters is presented by Erb & Thalan (1965). Of those tested, $(C_{18}H_{37}S)_4Si$ dissolved as a 1% solution in octanoic acid was found to be most effective. The promoter could be injected into the stream or put into the boiler; both methods of distributing the promoter were effective.

The data of Graham (1969) are for a copper surface promoted with a 1% di-n-octadecyldisulfide solution in CCl_4. The same promoter has been successful on gold (Hannemann & Mikic 1976). Various promoters have also been tried, the most successful being Teflon applied as described by Graham (1969).

Gold, in an extremely thin, vacuum-deposited layer, has also shown promise (Erb & Thalan 1965). The oils naturally found in steam systems stick very tenaciously to gold, and it is the associated oils rather than the gold itself that does the promotion.

5.6 Condensing Equipment

D. Butterworth

5.6.1 TYPES OF EQUIPMENT

5.6.1.1 Subdivisions of Condenser Types

Condensers are of two main types: those in which the coolant and condensing streams are separated by a solid surface, usually a tube wall, and those in which the coolant and condensing vapor are brought into direct contact. Each of these types may be subdivided into further categories as illustrated in figure 5.6.1. The direct contact type may consist of vapor that is bubbled into a pool of liquid or of liquid that is sprayed into vapor. Those in which the streams are separated may be subdivided into three main types: air-cooled, shell-and-tube, and plate. In the air-cooled type, condensation occurs inside tubes, with cooling being provided by air that is blown or sucked across the tubes. Fins are usually provided on the air side to compensate for the low air-side coefficients by having a large surface area. The shell-and-tube type consists of a large cylindrical shell inside which there is a bundle of tubes. One fluid stream flows inside the tubes, the other on the outside or shell side. Condensation may occur outside or inside the tubes, depending on the circumstances. Because of the special circumstances in different applications, the design of these units may vary widely and it is therefore convenient to subdivide shell-and-tube condensers into process and turbine-exhaust types. A plate may be used instead of a tube wall to divide the coolant and condensing streams. In one design, the plates are corrugated to give rigidity and also to improve heat transfer. They are held together in a press or frame with gaskets between them to prevent fluid leakage. In another design, the plates are flat but corrugated metal sheets are sandwiched between them to act as fins. These units are made of aluminum and are used in cryogenic heat transfer applications.

Further details of some of these types of units are given below. The plate-and-frame type of unit is not described further here because it is not usually used as a condenser except when service steam is used to heat another stream. Information on this type of exchanger is given by Alfa Laval (1969) and Butterworth (1977).

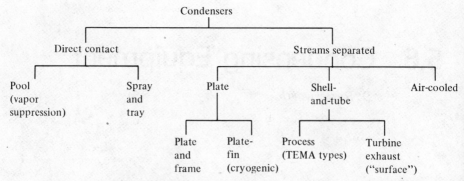

Figure 5.6.1   Subdivision of condenser types.

5.6.1.2 Shell-and-Tube Condensers for Chemical Processing

A wide variety of units fall into this category and make it possible to handle many and varied process streams. They are used for water, solvents, hydrocarbons, acids, and many other fluids, which may be condensing under vacuum or at high pressure. Single vapors, mixtures of vapors, and vapors with noncondensable gas can all be handled with a suitable choice of geometry. The design of these condensers is covered by the TEMA (1978) standards, which also cover shell-and-tube exchangers for single-phase and boiling duties.

An example of a process condenser is shown schematically in figure 5.6.2. In this instance, the hot (condensing) stream is on the shell side with the coolant on the tube side. The coolant traverses the length of the exchanger, thus giving a single tube-side pass. Multipass arrangements are possible by having U tubes or by partitioning the header boxes.

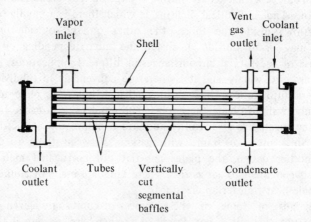

Figure 5.6.2   Example of shell-side condenser: TEMA E type with a single tube-side pass.

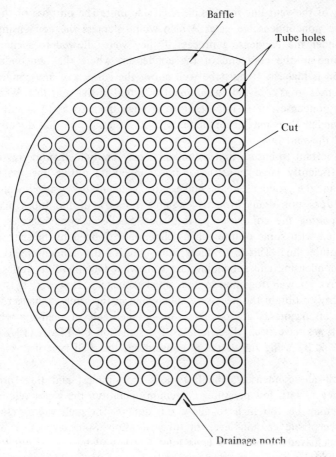

Baffle

Tube holes

Cut

Drainage notch

Figure 5.6.3 Single segmental baffle with vertical cut.

The baffles consist of circular plates with a segment cut away (figure 5.6.3) and with slightly oversized holes drilled to take the tubes when the exchanger is constructed. These baffles perform two important duties: to support the tubes and to direct the shell-side stream back and forth across the tubes. For condensation on the shell side, it is usual to have the baffles cut vertically so that the condensate can fall easily to the bottom of the shell in all baffle compartments. The baffles are usually cut horizontally if there is single-phase flow on the shell side. Notches are cut in the lowest position in the baffle to allow the unit to be drained. Other baffle types are possible and are described elsewhere (TEMA 1978).

The choice of putting the condensing stream on the tube side or the shell side is dictated by many factors. Dirty fluids are usually better on the tube side because it is easier to clean inside the tubes than outside them. Corrosive fluids are better in the tubes because then only the tubes and header boxes (but not the shell) need be of special materials. For similar reasons, it is better to have high-pressure streams on the tube side.

Venting is an important feature of all condensers, and figure 5.6.2 illustrates the location of the vent line in a simple shell-side unit. The purpose of the vent line is to remove noncondensable gases, which would depress the condensing temperature and hinder the condensing process if they were allowed to accumulate. The vent is located in the cold end of the condenser, where the noncondensable gas concentration is highest. It must be well above the surface of any condensate pool in the condenser so as to avoid entrainment of liquid in the vent line. When locating baffles in a condenser, it is important to arrange them so as to avoid dead spots where noncondensables may accumulate. A good design is one that directs the vapor flow toward the vent line.

It is important to ensure that a condenser may be drained properly. This means having a sufficiently large, constriction-free condensate outlet line that is located low down in the condenser and takes the condensate away downhill. If the condensate does not drain properly, a large fraction of the tubes may become flooded, impairing the condenser performance. Shell-side condensers are, however, often designed with some of the tubes deliberately flooded by having, say, a loop seal in the outlet line. This is to allow subcooling of the condensate. It should be noted that condensing and subcooling are somewhat incompatible duties, and they do not always go well together in the same exchanger. However, it is sometimes cheap and easy to obtain the necessary subcooling in the same exchanger.

Various arrangements are possible for the shell side of shell-and-tube condensers. These types have been given letters of designation by TEMA (1978) as shown in figure 5.6.4. By using this lettering convention, the shell type described so far is an E type.

For shell-side condensers, the E type is the simplest and therefore the first choice. However, with low-pressure or vacuum operation, the vapor velocities in the inlet region may be too high to allow this design. The high vapor velocities may lead to unacceptable erosion levels or tube vibration. Some avoidance of the high velocities is achieved by having a large inlet nozzle and by leaving out tubes in the vicinity of the inlet nozzle. If this does not lead to an acceptable reduction in vapor velocities, other shell types should be considered. The J shell could be used, because it can have two inlet nozzles and one outlet. It is shown in figure 5.6.4 as a divided-flow shell, but it can clearly be arranged in a combining-flow mode with two nozzles at the top and one at the bottom. Such shells are baffled in the same manner as E shells. H shells also have the advantage of two inlet nozzles, but they are complicated by longitudinal baffles, which are shown as a broken line in figure 5.6.4. The longitudinal baffles make it expensive to include a large number of cross baffles to support the tubes. The cross-flow or X-type exchanger is a very useful unit for vacuum operation. Figures 5.6.5 and 5.6.6 show two possible arrangements for such units. They have many inlet nozzles and a distribution space above the tubes. A perforated plate is sometimes placed above the tubes to help distribute the inlet vapor. A particular advantage of the X shell is that the cross baffles no longer have the dual role of supporting the baffles and redirecting the vapor flow. In an E shell, unless of very special design, the more baffles, the higher will be the vapor velocity. In an X shell, however, many baffles may be included without any significant effect on the vapor velocity. This is very useful when designing to avoid tube vibration, because higher velocities tend to increase the

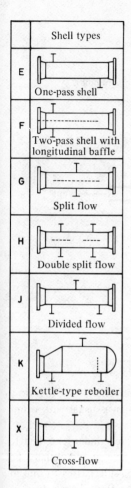

	Shell types
E	One-pass shell
F	Two-pass shell with longitudinal baffle
G	Split flow
H	Double split flow
J	Divided flow
K	Kettle-type reboiler
X	Cross-flow

Figure 5.6.4 Shell types as designated by TEMA (1978). © 1978 by Tubular Exchanger Manufacturers Association.

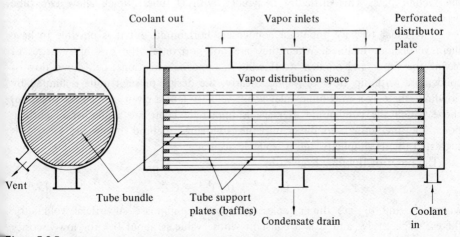

Figure 5.6.5 Main features of a cross-flow condenser (TEMA X type).

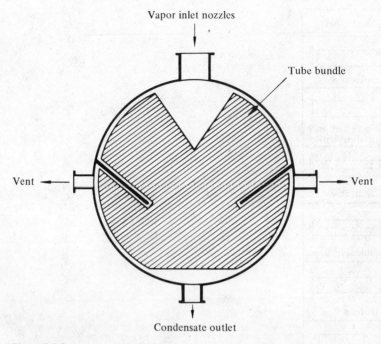

Vapor inlet nozzles

Tube bundle

Vent ←

Vent →

Condensate outlet

Figure 5.6.6   Alternative tube bundle layout for a cross-flow condenser.

chances of vibration whereas shorter tube spans reduce the chances. Cross-flow condensers also give lower pressure drops for the same duty than is usual with other types.

Any of the TEMA shell types may be used for tube-side condensers. The K type is a shell-side boiler and the condensation on the tube side would usually be from service steam. It is normal to restrict the number of tube-side passes to one in tube-side condensers because of the difficulty of knowing the flow distribution in the second pass. This difficulty is avoided with U tubes, which allow two tube passes.

It is usual to have tube-side condensers horizontal, but it is possible to have them vertical or inclined. When they are not horizontal, the possibility arises of having the vapor and condensate flowing in opposite directions; i.e., down flow of condensate with up flow of vapor. Clearly, the design of such units is limited by flooding: there is a maximum inlet vapor velocity (for a given condensate drainage) above which the condensate drainage is impaired. There are a number of correlations for predicting flooding, but the following method by Wallis (1961) is suggested for its simplicity and reasonable accuracy.

The onset of flooding is given by

$$(\dot{v}_G^+)^{1/2} + (\dot{v}_L^+)^{1/2} = C \qquad [5.6.1]$$

where $\dot{v}_G^+$ and $\dot{v}_L^+$ are dimensionless gas- and liquid-phase superficial volumetric fluxes, respectively, and C is a constant whose value is about 0.7 for low-viscosity liquids. For design purposes, a value of C of 0.6 is recommended to give a safety margin. The dimensionless fluxes are based on the ratio of inertial to gravitational forces and are defined as follows:

$$\dot{v}_G^+ = \frac{\dot{v}_G \rho_G^{1/2}}{\sqrt{(\rho_L - \rho_G)gD_i}} \qquad [5.6.2]$$

$$\dot{v}_L^+ = \frac{\dot{v}_L \rho_L^{1/2}}{\sqrt{(\rho_L - \rho_G)gD_i}} \qquad [5.6.3]$$

where $\dot{v}_G$ and $\dot{v}_L$ are the gas and liquid superficial volumetric flows per unit flow area (at the bottom of the tubes, where they have their highest values), ρ_L and ρ_G are the liquid- and gas-phase densities, g is the gravitational acceleration, and D_i is the tube internal diameter. For inclined tubes, the flooding velocity is higher than predicted by [5.6.1].

It is possible to design a condenser with up flow of both vapor and liquid. This can be done by ensuring that $\dot{v}_G^+$ is well above unity at the top of the tube. It may be difficult to ensure this in practice for all likely condenser operating conditions, and hence this mode of operation is not recommended.

5.6.1.3 Shell-and-Tube Condensers for Steam Turbine Exhausts

For historical reasons, these condensers are often referred to as surface condensers. In principle, they are no different from the shell-side condensers just described. In practice, however, there are certain severe demands placed on these units that have been overcome by special design features. These special demands arise from the large heat duties that they must perform and from the necessity to maintain a low condensing temperature to achieve the highest possible power-cycle efficiency.

The aim is to operate with a condensing temperature only a few degrees above the cooling-water temperature. Typically, the cooling water is about 20°C, with condensing taking place at around 30°C. The saturation pressure of water at this temperature is 4.2 kPa absolute, which is a normal operating pressure for these condensers. Clearly, there is little pressure available for pressure drop through the unit. There is also little temperature difference to spare in order to overcome noncondensable gases. Hence the design of surface condensers is governed by the need for good venting and low pressure drop.

Often, these condensers are very large. There may, for example, be two condensers serving a single 600-MWe turbine set. Hence each condenser must handle around 250 kg/s of steam with an approach velocity of up to 65 m/s. Surface areas are around 25,000 m², which is achieved by having, say, 15,000 tubes of 25 mm outer diameter with a length around 20 m. These very large condensers often have box-shaped shells, but the smaller ones, with surfaces of less than about 5000 m², may have cylindrical shells.

Surface condensers vary widely in their geometric details and various types are described by the Editors of Power (1967) and by Simpson (1969). Standards for their design are given by the British Electrical and Allied Manufacturers' Association (1967) and by the Heat Exchange Institute (1970). Nevertheless, there are many

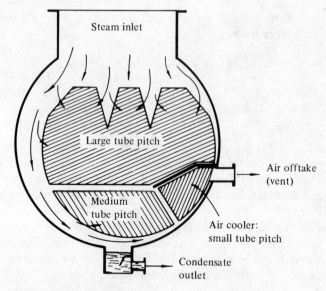

Figure 5.6.7 Small turbine exhaust condenser: areas occupied by tubes are shown shaded.

features that are common to most designs, as shown in the diagram of a relatively small surface condenser in figure 5.6.7. This is not an actual unit but a drawing illustrating some of the main items.

The vapor inlet velocity is very high because of the high thermal duty combined with the low pressure. Tubes near the inlet are therefore on a wider pitch than those elsewhere, and tubes are left out in places to provide paths or steam lanes to guide steam into the bundle. The combination of steam lanes and paths around the bundle means that there is a large bundle perimeter through which the steam may pass, thereby minimizing the effects of the large inlet velocity. As the steam passes through the bundle toward the vent line, the steam flow rate decreases and the air concentration increases. Therefore, closer tubes and less superficial flow area are used toward the exit in order to keep the steam velocities up. This improves the gas-phase heat and mass transfer and reduces the danger of stagnant pockets of air forming. There is usually a separate compartment just by the vent line that has the smallest tube pitch and the coldest cooling water in the tubes. Because most of the steam has been extracted from the air by this stage, the compartment is called the air cooler. The purpose of the section is to extract the last possible moisture from the air, which includes knocking out any entrained condensate. Some steam from the condenser inlet is allowed to pass around the bundle through any condensate falling off the tubes. This helps to deaerate the condensate.

5.6.1.4 Air-cooled Heat Exchangers

Many coolants are possible for process condensers; e.g., air, cooling-tower water, or a colder process stream that requires heating. In areas where there is a shortage of makeup water, air-cooled condensers may be favored. They can also become economic if condensation is taking place at temperatures more than about $20°C$ above ambient. They have the disadvantage, however, of occupying a relatively large ground area and of generating noise from the fans.

Figure 5.6.8 illustrates a typical air-cooled heat exchanger that may be used as a condenser. It consists of a horizontal bundle of tubes, with the air being blown across the tubes on the outside and condensation occurring inside the tubes. The unit shown is a forced-draft unit because the air is blown across. An alternative design is the induced-draft unit, which has fans on top that suck air over the tubes. The tubes have transverse fins on the outside to overcome the effects of the low air-side coefficients. There would normally be a number of tube rows and the process stream may take one or more passes through the unit. With multipass condensers, the problems arises of redistributing the two-phase mixture on entry to the next pass. This can be overcome in some cases by using U tubes or by having separate passes just for subcooling or desuperheating duties. In multipass condensers, it is important to have each successive pass below the previous one to enable the condensate to continue downward. Further information about air-cooled heat exchangers is given by Ludwig (1965) and by the American Petroleum Institute (1968).

5.6.1.5 Plate-Fin Heat Exchangers

Figure 5.6.9 shows the general form of a plate-fin heat exchanger. The fluid streams are separated by flat plates, between which are sandwiched corrugated fins. A more apt name is therefore a finned-plate exchanger. They are often used in low-temperature (cryogenic) plants and where the temperature differences between the streams are small ($1-5°C$). They are compact units having a heat transfer area per unit

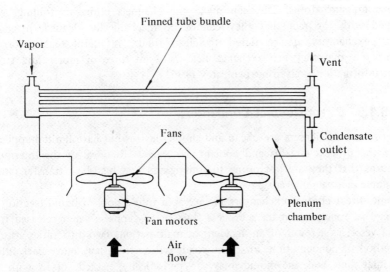

Figure 5.6.8 Forced-draft air-cooled heat exchanger used as a condenser.

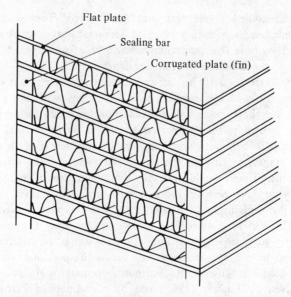

Figure 5.6.9   Basic construction of a plate-fin heat exchanger.

volume of around 2000 m²/m³. The fins may be serrated or perforated to improve heat transfer and help in the flow distribution across the plate. Special manifold devices at the inlet and the outlet provide good·flow distribution across the plates and from plate to plate. The plates are typically 0.5–1.0 mm thick and the fins 0.15–0.75 mm thick. The whole exchanger is made of aluminum alloy and the components are brazed together.

The flow channels in plate-fin exchangers are small and often contain many interruptions to flow. The flows must therefore be small (10–300 kg/m² s) to avoid excessive pressure drops. This can make the channels prone to fouling, which, combined with the fact that they cannot be mechanically cleaned, means that plate-fin exchangers are restricted to clean fluids. A useful feature of these exchangers is that they can exchange heat between three or more fluid streams. Further information is given by Lenfestey (1961).

5.6.1.6 Direct Contact Condensers

Direct contact condensers are cheap and simple devices but have limited application because the process streams and coolant are mixed. Removal of the intermediate wall means that they are not prone to fouling and very high heat transfer rates per unit volume can be achieved.

Some direct contact exchangers inject vapor into a pool of liquid (section 5.3). This may be done to heat up a process fluid or to suppress vapor released from a reaction vessel as a result of an accident or malfunction. Two difficulties arise with this method of condensation. First, the condensation front may move back into the vapor inlet line and the liquid may be periodically ejected, often with some violence. Second, a very large vapor bubble may form in the liquid pool and may

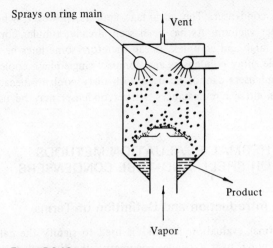

Figure 5.6.10 Spray condenser.

collapse suddenly, causing damage to the vessel. These problems may be avoided by having the vapor injected through a large number of small holes or by using special ejectors that mix the incoming vapor with liquid in a special mixing tube.

The most common type of direct contact condenser is one in which subcooled liquid is sprayed into the vapor in a large vessel. This arrangement is illustrated in figure 5.6.10. Very often, these units are used for condensing steam, using water as coolant. In these cases, the mixing of water with condensate presents no major problem. When condensing organics with water, however, a separator is usually required. Alternatively, the condensate product may be cooled and some recycled as coolant spray. At first sight, there seems to be little benefit in having a direct contact condenser and a conventional single-phase exchanger instead of using one

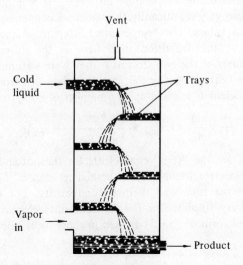

Figure 5.6.11 Tray condenser.

shell-and-tube condenser. The advantage appears, however, when the condenser is operating under vacuum. As has been seen already, tubular condensers for vacuum operation are large and complex. It can therefore sometimes be economic to replace them by simple spray condensers and compact single-phase coolers.

Spray condensers cannot be used with dirty coolants because the spray nozzle may block. In these circumstances a tray condenser may be used, as illustrated in figure 5.6.11.

5.6.2   THERMAL EVALUATION METHODS FOR SHELL-AND-TUBE CONDENSERS

5.6.2.1   Introduction and Definition of Terms

The term thermal evaluation method is used to signify the calculation process by which, for a known heat exchanger geometry, the thermal duty may be calculated or the required heat transfer area determined to suit the duty. In the latter case, the calculated heat transfer area may be incompatible with the assumed geometry. These calculations fall short of full design calculations, which involve computing stream pressure drops as well as repeating the calculations for many different assumed geometries in order to find ones that satisfy all the imposed constraints. The final stage of design is to choose the best design on the basis of, say, capital cost.

The basis of thermal evaluation methods is an equation of the form

$$\frac{d\dot{Q}}{dA} = U\theta \qquad [5.6.4]$$

where $\dot{Q}$ is the heat transfer rate, A the heat transfer area, U the overall heat transfer coefficient, and θ the temperature difference. It is important to appreciate that both U and θ can vary significantly throughout a condenser and hence [5.6.4] is based on the local values. The temperature difference θ may be defined in a number of ways, but the definition used here is the difference between the equilibrium temperatures of the two streams if they were well mixed at the point in question. The overall heat transfer coefficient U is then defined to satisfy [5.6.4].

The overall coefficient U is made up of a number of components as follows:

$$\frac{1}{U} = \frac{1}{\alpha_{\text{hot}}} + r_{\text{hot}} + \frac{\delta_W}{\lambda_W} + \frac{1}{\alpha_{\text{cold}}} + r_{\text{cold}} \qquad [5.6.5]$$

where α_{hot} and α_{cold} are the "film" coefficients for the hot and cold streams, r_{hot} and r_{cold} are the respective fouling layer thermal resistances, δ_W is the tube wall thickness, and λ_W is the tube wall thermal conductivity. For thick-walled tubes, corrections are necessary to allow for the different surface areas inside and outside the tubes. A simplified form of [5.6.5] is used in subsequent calculations:

$$\frac{1}{U} = \frac{1}{\alpha_{\text{hot}}} + r + \frac{1}{\alpha_{\text{cold}}} \qquad [5.6.6]$$

where r is the combined thermal resistance of the tube wall and fouling. The calculation of α_{cold} is discussed in chapter 6. In section 5.2 methods are given for calculating α_{hot} when condensing pure vapor. The effect of noncondensable gas on α_{hot} is discussed in section 5.2.3.4. A simple but useful method of estimating α_{hot} for vapor mixtures, or for vapor with noncondensables, is that of Silver (1947), sometimes known as the method of Bell & Ghaly (1973). In this method α_{hot} is given by

$$\frac{1}{\alpha_{\text{hot}}} = \frac{1}{\alpha_L} + \frac{1}{\alpha_G} \frac{d\dot{Q}_G}{d\dot{Q}} \qquad [5.6.7]$$

where α_L is the heat transfer coefficient for the condensate film, α_G is the heat transfer coefficient for the gas phase, and $d\dot{Q}_G$ is the heat removed from the gas phase when $d\dot{Q}$ is removed from the stream, assuming equilibrium. The gas-phase coefficient α_G is usually calculated assuming that the gas vapor mixture is flowing alone, although corrections can be applied for the effects of liquid disturbing the gas phase.

Equation [5.6.4] can be rearranged and written in an integral form as follows:

$$\int_{\dot{Q}_T} \frac{d\dot{Q}}{\theta} = \int_{A_T} U \, dA \qquad [5.6.8]$$

where the subscript T refers to the total value for the exchanger. Heat exchanger designs are usually summarized in terms of mean quantities, which are related by

$$\dot{Q}_T = U_m A_T \theta_m \qquad [5.6.9]$$

where U_m is the mean overall coefficient and θ_m the mean temperature difference. Comparing [5.6.8] and [5.6.9] suggests the following definitions for the mean quantities:

$$\frac{1}{\theta_m} = \frac{1}{\dot{Q}_T} \int_{\dot{Q}_T} \frac{d\dot{Q}}{\theta} \qquad [5.6.10]$$

$$U_m = \frac{1}{A_T} \int_{A_T} U \, dA \qquad [5.6.11]$$

In practice, it is unnecessary to evaluate both [5.6.10] and [5.6.11], because when either θ_m or U_m has been determined the other may be calculated from [5.6.9].

Equation [5.6.4] may also be written as follows:

$$A_T = \int_{\dot{Q}_T} \frac{d\dot{Q}}{U\theta} \qquad [5.6.12]$$

Combining this with [5.6.6] gives

$$A_T = \int_{\dot{Q}_T} \frac{d\dot{Q}}{\alpha_{\text{hot}}\theta} + r \int_{\dot{Q}_T} \frac{d\dot{Q}}{\theta} + \int_{\dot{Q}_T} \frac{d\dot{Q}}{\alpha_{\text{cold}}\theta} \qquad [5.6.13]$$

Dividing through by $A_T U_m$ and using [5.6.9] and [5.6.10]:

$$\frac{1}{U_m} = \frac{1}{U_m A_T} \int_{\dot{Q}_T} \frac{d\dot{Q}}{\alpha_{\text{hot}}\theta} + r + \frac{1}{U_m A_T} \int_{\dot{Q}_T} \frac{d\dot{Q}}{\alpha_{\text{cold}}\theta} \qquad [5.6.14]$$

which, on comparing with [5.6.6], suggests the following definitions for the mean film coefficients*:

$$\frac{1}{\alpha_m} = \frac{1}{U_m A_T} \int_{\dot{Q}_T} \frac{d\dot{Q}}{\alpha\theta} \qquad [5.6.15]$$

By using [5.6.4], an alternative form of this definition is

$$\frac{1}{\alpha_m} = \frac{1}{U_m A_T} \int_{A_T} \left(\frac{U}{\alpha}\right) dA \qquad [5.6.16]$$

Some special cases of [5.6.10] and [5.6.11] are useful. If θ varies linearly with $\dot{Q}$, [5.6.10] can be integrated to give

$$\theta_m = \theta_{\ln} = \frac{\theta_a - \theta_b}{\ln(\theta_a/\theta_b)} \qquad [5.6.17]$$

Where $\theta_{\ln}$ is the well-known logarithmic mean temperature difference and θ_a and θ_b are the end values of θ. It is most unusual in a condenser for θ to vary linearly with $\dot{Q}$ over the whole exchanger, but small portions of the exchanger can often be identified over which this assumption is well approximated. Examples of this are given.

If U varies linearly with A, [5.6.11] may be integrated between U_a and U_b to give

$$U_m = \tfrac{1}{2}(U_a + U_b) \qquad [5.6.18]$$

If both U and θ vary linearly with $\dot{Q}$, [5.6.11] may be integrated with the aid of [5.6.4] to give

$$U_m = \frac{U_a\theta_b - U_b\theta_a}{\theta_{\ln}\ln(U_a\theta_b/U_b\theta_a)} \qquad [5.6.19]$$

This result was first obtained by Colburn (1933). If both $1/U$ and θ vary linearly

---

*The derivation leading to [5.6.15] was proposed by R. A. Smith, heat transfer consultant, Middlesbrough.

with $\dot{Q}$, [5.6.11] may be integrated with the aid of [5.6.4] to give

$$\frac{1}{U_m} = \frac{1}{U_a}\frac{\theta_{\ln} - \theta_b}{\theta_a - \theta_b} + \frac{1}{U_b}\frac{\theta_a - \theta_{\ln}}{\theta_a - \theta_b} \qquad [5.6.20]$$

Again, these equations are not usually valid over the whole condenser but may apply to small portions of it. It is not always clear which of the above equations is valid for a given set of circumstances. However, if U_a and U_b vary by only a small amount, [5.6.18] is preferred because of its simplicity. There is a long tradition in the use of [5.6.19] but with little justification. The assumptions leading to [5.6.20] are reasonably compatible with [5.6.7], and hence [5.6.20] is recommended in situations where [5.6.18] cannot be used because of the large difference between U_a and U_b. Of course, any question about which equation is more accurate can always be avoided by dividing the exchanger into a large number of sections.

5.6.2.2 Cocurrent and Countercurrent Condensers

The procedure given here applies to TEMA E-type shells with a single tube-side pass. It also applies to a J shell, which can be divided down the middle and treated as two exchangers, one with cocurrent and the other with countercurrent flow. Countercurrent flow is more usual in E shells because it makes best use of the temperature difference between the streams. Indeed, some duties are not possible in cocurrent flow but can be handled without difficulty in countercurrent flow. The following description is in terms of countercurrent flow, but the same approach can be used for cocurrent flow; the differences in the results obtained are noted.

Figure 5.6.12 illustrates a counterflow exchanger. In this diagram and the subsequent discussion, the shell-side stream is denoted by a prime ('). Hence the shell-side stream enters with specific enthalpy h'_{in} and leaves with specific enthalpy h'_{out}. The tube-side specific enthalpy changes from h_{in} to h_{out}. The shell-side and tube-side mass flows are respectively $\dot{M}'$ and $\dot{M}$. A heat balance over area A of the exchanger gives

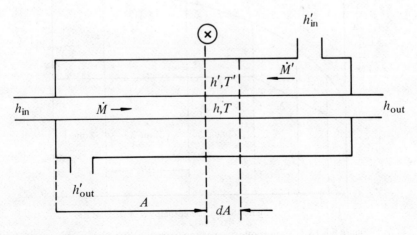

Figure 5.6.12   Counterflow heat exchanger.

$$h = h_{in} + \frac{\dot{M}'}{M}(h' - h'_{out}) \qquad [5.6.21]$$

where h' and h are the shell-side and tube-side specific enthalpies, respectively, at position X on figure 5.6.12. The corresponding equation for a cocurrent flow exchanger is obtained by replacing h'_{out} by h'_{in} and $\dot{M}'$ by $-\dot{M}'$.

The first step in the thermal evaluation is to plot the equilibrium temperature T' versus h' for the shell-side stream. The equilibrium temperature is used in accordance with the definition of the overall coefficient U. Such a plot is shown in figure 5.6.13. By using [5.6.21] and the temperature-specific enthalpy relation for the tube-side fluid, the corresponding tube-side temperature T may be plotted on figure 5.6.13 as shown. This diagram is extremely useful in condenser design and is called here the exchanger operating diagram. Figure 5.6.13 is typical of a condenser that has a desuperheating zone and condensation occurring in the presence of noncondensable gas. The tube-side curve shown would occur, say, if a pure liquid were being heated up and then boiled. The design is impossible if the two curves cross or touch anywhere.

The next step in the thermal evaluation is to divide this diagram into zones for which both the T curve and the T' curve are linear. This is shown by the vertical dashed lines in figure 5.6.13. Now, over each zone, θ (or $T' - T$) varies linearly with h'. This is the same as saying that θ varies linearly with $\dot{Q}$ because

$$\dot{Q} = \dot{M}'(h'_{in} - h') \qquad [5.6.22]$$

Thus, the logarithmic mean temperature difference, as defined by [5.6.17] applies

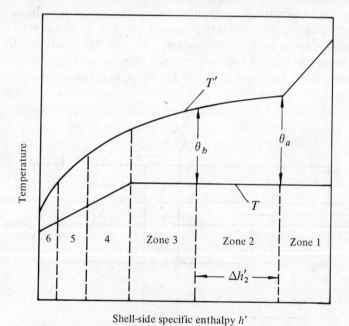

Figure 5.6.13 Example of exchanger operating diagram for a counterflow heat exchanger.

for each zone and can be evaluated. The appropriate θ_a and θ_b for zone 2 are illustrated in figure 5.6.13. Also, the overall coefficients at the zone boundaries and a mean overall coefficient for each zone may be calculated by using [5.6.18], [5.6.19], or [5.6.20], whichever is more appropriate. Equation [5.6.9] may then be applied to each zone in the form

$$A_j = \frac{\dot{M}' \Delta h'_j}{U_{m,j} \theta_{\text{ln},j}} \qquad [5.6.23]$$

where the subscript j refers to the zone number and $\Delta h'_j$ is the specific enthalpy change of the shell-side fluid in the jth zone. Clearly, the total heat transfer area is given by

$$A_T = \sum_j A_j \qquad [5.6.24]$$

Equations [5.6.10] and [5.6.11] may be expressed in summation form to give U_m and θ_m for the whole exchanger:

$$\frac{1}{\theta_m} = \frac{1}{h'_{\text{in}} - h'_{\text{out}}} \sum_j \frac{\Delta h'_j}{\theta_{\text{ln},j}} \qquad [5.6.25]$$

and

$$U_m = \frac{1}{A_T} \sum_j U_j A_j \qquad [5.6.26]$$

In the calculation above, the heat load on the exchanger is known and is given by

$$\dot{Q}_T = \dot{M}'(h'_{\text{in}} - h'_{\text{out}}) = \dot{M}(h_{\text{out}} - h_{\text{in}}) \qquad [5.6.27]$$

It is not, therefore, necessary to evaluate both [5.6.25] and [5.6.26] because U_m, θ_m, and $\dot{Q}_T$ are related by [5.6.9]. However, it is useful to evaluate [5.6.25] and [5.6.26] and substitute the results into [5.6.9] to cross-check the arithmetic.

A useful feature of the calculation procedure is that figure 5.6.13 does not depend on the heat transfer coefficient and hence is independent of details in the geometry such as the number of tubes, baffles, etc. The same applies to the zonal and exchanger mean temperature differences. These quantities may therefore need to be calculated only when the number of passes is changed.

5.6.2.3 Shell-Side, E-Type Condenser with Two Tube-Side Passes

Figure 5.6.14 illustrates the operation of an E shell with two tube-side passes. A heat balance over area A gives

$$\dot{M}'(h' - h'_{\text{out}}) = \dot{M}(h^{\text{I}} - h_{\text{in}} + h_{\text{out}} - h^{\text{II}}) \qquad [5.6.28]$$

where the superscripts I and II refer to the first and second tube-side passes respectively. Combining this with [5.6.27] gives

$$h' = h'_{\text{in}} - \frac{\dot{M}}{\dot{M}'}(h^{\text{II}} - h^{\text{I}}) \qquad [5.6.29]$$

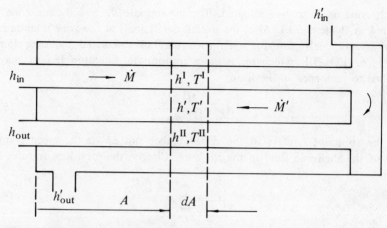

Figure 5.6.14 Exchanger with one shell pass and two tube passes.

This result is for the first tube pass countercurrent to the shell-side flow. However, if it is cocurrent the result is

$$h' = h'_{out} + \frac{\dot{M}}{\dot{M}'}(h^{II} - h^I)$$

[5.6.30]

Heat balances over area dA for passes I and II give, respectively,

$$\dot{M}\,dh^I = + U^I(T' - T^I)\frac{dA}{2}$$

[5.6.31]

and

$$\dot{M}\,dh^{II} = - U^{II}(T' - T^{II})\frac{dA}{2}$$

[5.6.32]

Dividing [5.6.32] by [5.6.31] gives

$$\frac{dh^{II}}{dh^I} = - \frac{U^{II}(T' - T^{II})}{U^I(T' - T^I)}$$

[5.6.33]

The same result is obtained if the shell-side stream is cocurrent to the first tube-side pass.

It is very convenient to simplify [5.6.33] by assuming that U^{II}/U^I is unity. This is often a reasonable approximation for shell-side condensers, provided the tube-side coefficient is constant or not controlling. With this assumption, [5.6.33] becomes

$$\frac{dh^{II}}{dh^I} = - \frac{T' - T^{II}}{T' - T^I}$$

[5.6.34]

The right-hand side of [5.6.34] is a known function of h^{II} and h^I, as becomes evident when one realizes that T' is a known function of h', T is a known function of h (whether I or II), and h' is related to h^{II} and h^I by [5.6.29] or [5.6.30]. Hence [5.6.34] can be integrated along the exchanger with the initial boundary conditions that $h^I = h_{in}$ when $h^{II} = h_{out}$.

For example, a simple numerical integration can be done by updating h^I and h^{II} as follows:

$$h^I_{new} = h^I + \delta h^I \qquad [5.6.35]$$

and

$$h^{II}_{new} = h^{II} - \frac{T' - T^{II}}{T' - T^I} \delta h^I \qquad [5.6.36]$$

where δh^I is a small change in h^I. There are, of course, more sophisticated integration methods for use with computers. This sort of integration may be used to construct the operating diagram shown in figure 5.6.15. As with the counterflow exchanger, this operating diagram is independent of detailed geometric features and therefore applies to all two-pass E shells.

The heat leaving the shell side in area dA is

$$d\dot{Q} = U^I(T' - T^I) \frac{dA}{2} + U^{II}(T' - T^{II}) \frac{dA}{2} \qquad [5.6.37]$$

which, because $U^I = U^{II} = U$ (say), gives

$$d\dot{Q} = (T' - \bar{T})U\, dA \qquad [5.6.38]$$

where

$$\bar{T} = \frac{T^I + T^{II}}{2} \qquad [5.6.39]$$

i.e., $\bar{T}$ is the average temperature between the passes at a given point along the shell.

The curve for $\bar{T}$ can be plotted on the operating diagram as illustrated by the dashed line in figure 5.6.15. Equation [5.6.38] is now identical to [5.6.4], except that θ is replaced by $T' - \bar{T}$. The remainder of the thermal evaluation is now therefore the same as for the counterflow exchanger, except that T is replaced by $\bar{T}$.

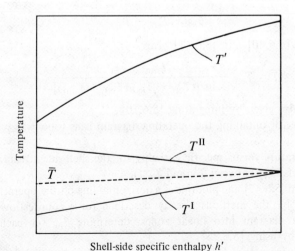

Shell-side specific enthalpy h'

Figure 5.6.15 Example of operating diagram for shell-side condenser (E type) with two tube passes.

5.6.2.4 Shell-Side, E-Type Condenser with Four or More Tube Passes

An analysis of the type described above can be applied to exchangers with 4, 6, 8, or a greater even number of passes. The calculations become progressively more complicated, however, as the number of passes is increased. Furthermore, it is found in practice that the average tube-side temperature $\bar{T}$ (now averaged over however many passes there are) does not change significantly as the number of passes is increased beyond 4 (Butterworth 1973).

Because the objective of the first part of the thermal evaluation is to construct an operating diagram containing the $\bar{T}$ curve, we could construct this for a four-pass exchanger and use it for any number of passes. There is, however, a convenient method of finding $\bar{T}$ for an infinite number of passes, which we can use instead. This method is slightly less general than that given above because it applies only when there is a linear temperature-enthalpy curve for the tube-side stream. Nevertheless, this covers the most important practical case of a single-phase coolant.

The method is that of Emerson (1973), who presented a more rigorous derivation than that given here, although he did not spot some minor algebraic manipulations that could be used to simplify the calculation procedure. It is reasonable to postulate that the tube-side stream sees a constant shell-side temperature T'_{eff} as it traverses the length of the exchanger an infinite number of times. The logarithmic mean temperature difference then applies for heating the tube-side stream because it has a linear temperature-enthalpy curve:

$$\theta_m = \frac{T_{\text{out}} - T_{\text{in}}}{\ln\,[(T'_{\text{eff}} - T_{\text{in}})/(T'_{\text{eff}} - T_{\text{out}})]} \qquad [5.6.40]$$

We know also, for a large number of tube passes, that the mean tube-side temperature $\bar{T}$ is a constant, independent of h'. We can therefore write θ_m as

$$\theta_m = T'_{\text{eff}} - \bar{T} \qquad [5.6.41]$$

Hence, combining [5.6.40] and [5.6.41] gives

$$\bar{T} = T'_{\text{eff}} - \frac{T_{\text{out}} - T_{\text{in}}}{\ln\,[(T'_{\text{eff}} - T_{\text{in}})/(T'_{\text{eff}} - T_{\text{out}})]} \qquad [5.6.42]$$

As before, θ_m is also given by integrating [5.6.10].

The procedure for obtaining the operating diagram is as follows:

1. Plot the temperature versus specific enthalpy for the shell-side stream.
2. Guess a value of T'_{eff} (between T'_{in} and T'_{out}).
3. Calculate $\bar{T}$ from [5.6.42] and plot this as a horizontal line on the operating diagram.
4. Determine θ_m by the methods already described for a counterflow exchanger; i.e., divide the diagram into linear zones, determine θ_{ln} for each zone, and combine these by using [5.6.25].
5. Recalculate T'_{eff} from [5.6.41] by using the previously calculated θ_m and $\bar{T}$.
6. Repeat the calculation from step 3 and continue the process until convergence is obtained. This usually takes two or three iterations.

The procedure described here will also give reasonable results for a multipass J shell.

5.6.2.5 Cross-Flow Condensers

Consider a single-pass cross-flow condenser as illustrated in figure 5.6.16. A heat balance over area dA of this condenser gives

$$d\dot{Q} = U\theta \, dA \qquad [5.6.43]$$

For single-phase coolant, and because the shell-side temperature is constant in area dA, θ is given as

$$\theta = \frac{T_x - T_{in}}{\ln \left[(T' - T_{in})/(T' - T_x) \right]} \qquad [5.6.44]$$

where T_x is the temperature at exit to the tubes in question. Note that this is not the same as the coolant outlet temperature to the exchanger, which is obtained after mixing the coolant from each tube. A heat balance over dN tubes sitting in area dA gives

$$\dot{m}C_p \frac{\pi D_i^2}{4}(T_x - T_{in}) \, dN = \pi D_o L U \theta \, dN \qquad [5.6.45]$$

where $\dot{m}$ is the tube-side mass flux, C_p is the coolant specific heat, D_i and D_o are the tube inside and outside diameters, respectively, and L is the tube length. This equation can be simplified to

$$T_x - T_{in} = \theta U B \qquad [5.6.46]$$

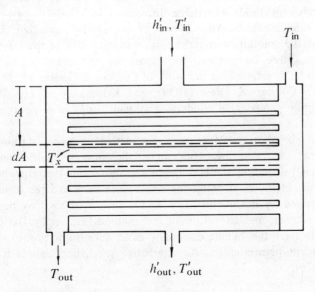

Figure 5.6.16 Cross-flow condenser with single tube-side pass.

where
$$B = \frac{4D_oL}{\dot{m}C_pD_i^2} \qquad [5.6.47]$$

Combining [5.6.46] and [5.6.44]:

$$\theta = (T' - T_{in})\frac{1 - e^{-UB}}{UB} \qquad [5.6.48]$$

Substituting this into [5.6.43]:

$$\frac{d\dot{Q}}{dA} = \frac{1}{B}(T' - T_{in})(1 - e^{-UB}) \qquad [5.6.49]$$

The heat transfer area, or the heat load for a given area, can thus be determined by integrating [5.6.49]. It must be borne in mind when doing this that both U and T' vary with $\dot{Q}$.

A cross-flow condenser with two tube passes may be treated as two cross-flow units in series and the above method may be used again. This assumes that there is good mixing over the condenser length (which is not always the case) and that there is mixing of coolant between the passes. Mixing between the passes is, of course, not possible in a U-tube condenser. Multipass units are usually arranged with tube-side passes layered and coolant flowing from lower to higher passes. Hence, a cross-flow exchanger will approximate a counterflow unit when there are many passes.

5.6.2.6 Advanced Calculation Methods

The thermal evaluation methods described above embody the assumption that equilibrium temperatures characterize the heat transfer process. This may not be the case with condensing fluids with large differences in volatility, particularly if the condensation rates are high. Also, it may be necessary to calculate disequilibrium effects such as the amount of superheating or supercooling of the vapor. To handle these problems, more complicated techniques are required than those discussed above. The reader is referred to the work of Colburn & Hougen (1934), Colburn & Edison (1941), Colburn & Drew (1937), and Krishna et al. (1976), who treat progressively more complicated condensing systems, using more rigorous calculation methods.

Additional complications arise with the design of power station condensers. Although these are cross-flow condensers, the flow is multidimensional. The one-dimensional calculation method described above can therefore be subject to significant error. Methods of predicting single-phase flow in large regular arrays of tubes are described by Butterworth (1978a, b). Such methods have been developed for condenser design, and an outline of one method is given by Davidson (1976). These methods treat the bundle essentially as an anisotropic porous medium with velocity-dependent permeabilities. An alternative subchannel approach is described by Wilson (1976).

5.6.3 THERMAL EVALUATION METHOD FOR DIRECT CONTACT CONDENSERS

5.6.3.1 Spray Condensers

These are difficult to design with any degree of precision because of uncertainties in droplet size, droplet trajectory, droplet coalescence, and flow patterns in the gas phase. However, the simplicity of the basic geometry means that they can be oversized without much additional cost.

A preliminary step in spray condenser design is the selection of nozzle type and the determination of nozzle behavior for the liquid being used. Steinmeyer (1973) described various types of spray nozzles and discussed their method of operation, advantages, and disadvantages. Spray condensers would usually operate with the simplest type of nozzle in which the source of atomization is the pressure loss in the nozzle.

Nozzle types vary so widely from one manufacturer to another that it is necessary to use the manufacturer's data to determine such quantities as the pressure drop in the nozzle, the mean droplet size, and the initial droplet velocity. Unfortunately, the data given by manufacturers are usually limited to water at around 20°C spraying into ambient air. Often, however, enough information is given to calculate the pressure drop, and then the inlet velocity u_1 may be determined as

$$u_1 = K\left(\frac{2\,\Delta p}{\rho_L}\right)^{1/2}$$

[5.6.50]

where Δp is the nozzle pressure drop, ρ_L is the liquid density, and K is a coefficient that would be unity if there were no energy losses in the nozzle. A reasonable value of K for estimation purposes is 0.8. The mean droplet diameter for water can be determined from the manufacturer's data, and Steinmeyer (1973) suggests an approximate equation for correcting this for other liquids:

$$\frac{d}{d_{\text{wat}}} = \left(\frac{\sigma}{\sigma_{\text{wat}}}\right)^{0.5}\left(\frac{\mu_L}{\mu_{\text{wat}}}\right)^{0.2}\left(\frac{\rho_{\text{wat}}}{\rho_L}\right)^{0.3}$$

[5.6.51]

when d is the droplet diameter, d_{wat} is the diameter for water sprayed with the same volumetric flow through the nozzle, μ_L is the liquid viscosity, μ_{wat} is the viscosity of water at 20°C, ρ_L is the density of the liquid, and ρ_{wat} is the density of water at 20°C. In reality, the dependence of droplet size on fluid properties is very complex, and hence the equation above should be used with caution.

The problem of subcooled droplets injected into saturated vapor was analyzed by Brown (1951). He treated the droplets as solid spheres and solved the transient conduction equation to give the temperature rise in the droplet as a function of time of exposure to the vapor. The droplet diameter is assumed to be independent of time, which is reasonable because very little vapor can condense before the droplet is heated up to, or close to, saturation.

The droplet temperature rise is given by Brown as

$$\frac{T_{\text{out}} - T_{\text{in}}}{T_{\text{sat}} - T_{\text{in}}} = 1 - \frac{6}{\pi^2} \sum_{n=1}^{\infty} \frac{1}{n^2} \exp\left(-\frac{4n^2 \pi^2 \kappa_L t_c}{d^2}\right) \qquad [5.6.52]$$

where T_{out} is the mean temperature, T_{in} is the inlet temperature, T_{sat} is the saturation temperature, κ_L is the liquid thermal diffusivity, and is t_c the contact time. Figure 5.6.17 shows this equation plotted for low-pressure water. These results may be used to determine an effective mean coefficient $\bar{\alpha}$ for a given temperature rise. The results of such a calculation are given in figure 5.6.18. This figure may be used in conjunction with the following equation to determine the desired contact time t_c:

$$t_c = \frac{d\rho_L C_{pL}}{6\bar{\alpha}} \ln\left(1 - \frac{T_{\text{out}} - T_{\text{in}}}{T_{\text{sat}} - T_{\text{in}}}\right) \qquad [5.6.53]$$

The coefficient $\bar{\alpha}$ can be very large, and indeed comparable with the interfacial coefficient discussed earlier in this chapter. This is particularly so when, as is often the case, the condenser is operating at high vacuum. In such circumstances, [5.6.53] should be evaluated with $\bar{\alpha}$ replaced by α_{eff}, where α_{eff} combines $\bar{\alpha}$ and the interfacial coefficient α_I as follows:

$$\frac{1}{\alpha_{\text{eff}}} = \frac{1}{\bar{\alpha}} + \frac{1}{\alpha_I} \qquad [5.6.54]$$

After the contact time t_c is determined, it is necessary to estimate how far the droplets will travel in this time, thus enabling one to estimate the vessel size. A force balance on the droplets for vertical downward motion yields

$$Mu \frac{du}{dz} = M \frac{du}{dt} = Mg - \xi \frac{\pi d^2}{4} \frac{\rho_G u^2}{2} \qquad [5.6.55]$$

where u is the droplet velocity, M is the droplet mass, z is the distance, t is the time, g is the gravitational acceleration, ξ is the drag coefficient, and ρ_G is the

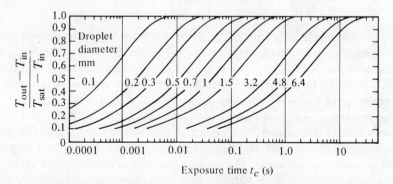

Figure 5.6.17 Temperature rise as a function of time for water droplets in saturated steam (Brown 1951). Reprinted by permission of the Council of the Institution of Mechanical Engineers from *Institution of Mechanical Engineers Proceedings of General Discussion on Heat Transfer*.

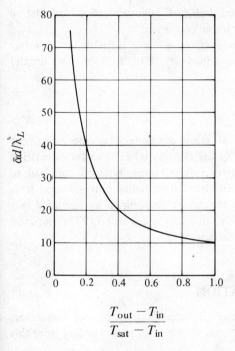

Figure axes: $\bar{\alpha} d / \lambda_L$ (vertical), $\dfrac{T_{out} - T_{in}}{T_{sat} - T_{in}}$ (horizontal)

Figure 5.6.18 Effective mean heat transfer coefficients for droplets in pure vapor (Brown 1951). Reprinted by permission of the Council of the Institution of Mechanical Engineers from *Institution of Mechanical Engineers Proceedings of General Discussion on Heat Transfer.*

gas-phase density. For horizontal flow, the same equation applies but g is zero. Also, g is often small compared with the other terms for high-velocity droplets. Pita & John (1970) integrated this equation analytically for the case when g is zero. To do this, they used the Ingebo (1951) equation for ξ, which applies for $6 < \mathrm{Re} < 400$:

$$\xi = 27\,\mathrm{Re}^{-0.84} \qquad [5.6.56]$$

where
$$\mathrm{Re} = \frac{\rho_G u d}{\mu_G} \qquad [5.6.57]$$

where μ_G is the gas-phase viscosity. Pita & John obtained the total distance traveled L in time t_c as

$$L = 0.06 \frac{d^{1.84}}{\Gamma} (u_1^{0.84} - u_2^{0.84}) \qquad [5.6.58]$$

where u_1 is the velocity at time t_c given by

$$u_2 = \left(u_1^{-0.16} - 3.23\frac{\Gamma t_c}{d^{1.84}}\right)^{-6.25} \qquad [5.6.59]$$

and Γ is a physical property grouping given by

$$\Gamma = \frac{\rho_G}{\rho_L} v_G^{0.84} \qquad [5.6.60]$$

As an alternative to this calculation method, Fair (1972) gives empirical calculation procedures based on the volumetric heat transfer coefficient.

Estimation of the effects of noncondensables is quite difficult and involves step-by-step calculations of the type described by Pita & John for droplet evaporation.

5.6.3.2 Tray Condensers

The uncertainties involved in the design of spray condensers become even more severe with tray condensers. It is possible to use the above heat transfer calculation method while using a large droplet diameter (say > 5 mm), but this can lead to error if the sheet does not break up into droplets before falling onto the next tray. The vertical distance traveled by the droplets can be determined by assuming that they fall freely under gravity. Alternatively, one can use Fair's (1972) empirical calculation methods based on volumetric coefficients.

5.6.4 REASONS FOR FAILURE OF CONDENSER OPERATION

Steinmeyer & Mueller (1974) chaired a panel discussion session on why condensers do not operate as they are supposed to. Some of the main points arising from this discussion are noted here.

1. Tubes may be fouled more than expected—a problem not unique to condensers.
2. Condensate may not be drained properly, causing tubes to be flooded; this could mean that the condensate outlet is too small or too high.
3. Venting of noncondensables may be inadequate (on the proper arrangement of vents, see section 5.6.1).
4. The condenser may have been designed on the basis of end temperatures without noticing that the design duty would involve a temperature cross in the middle of the range (see section 5.6.2).
5. Flooding limits may be exceeded for condensers with back flow of liquid against upward vapor flow (see section 5.6.1).
6. Excessive fogging may be occurring; this can be a problem when condensing high-moledular-weight vapors in the presence of noncondensable gas [further information is given by Steinmeyer (1972)].

5.7 Nomenclature for Chapter 5

A	heat transfer area, m^2
b	film thickness
B	parameters defined by [5.4.1] and [5.6.47]
C	constant in [5.6.1]
C_p	specific heat capacity at constant pressure, J/kg K
d	droplet diameter, m
D	tube or hole diameter, m
D_G	diffusion coefficient m^2/s
F	driving potential, K
g	gravitational acceleration, m/s^2
h	specific enthalpy, J/kg
h_{LG}	enthalpy change from liquid to vapor
K	parameter in [5.6.50]
L	length, m
$\dot{m}$	mass flow per unit area, kg/m^2 s
M	mass of a droplet, kg
$\dot{M}$	mass flow rate, kg/s
$\bar{M}$	molecular weight
N	number of tubes
p	pressure, Pa
$\dot{q}$	heat flux density, W/m^2
$\dot{Q}$	heat flux through exchanger surface, W
r	thermal resistance, m^2 K/W
R	universal gas constant
R	defined by [5.2.24]
t	time, s
T	temperature, K
u	velocity, m/s
U	overall heat transfer coefficient, W/m^2 K
$\mathbf{U}$	velocity vector, m/s

U_x, U_y, U_z	scalar components of velocity vector, m/s
$\dot{v}$	superficial volumetric flow rate per unit area, m/s
v	specific volume, m^3/kg
V	volume, m^3
x, y, z	coordinates
X	quality
z	distance

DIMENSIONLESS GROUPS

Le	Lewis number [5.2.22]
Ma	Mach number
Nu	Nusselt number [5.2.13a]
Nu_z	length Nusselt number [5.2.10]
Pr	Prandtl number [5.2.13b]
Re	Reynolds number [5.2.13c]
St	Stanton number [5.3.1]

GREEK LETTERS

α	void fraction (in section 5.4)
α	heat transfer coefficient (everywhere), W/m^2 K
β	mass transfer coefficient
δ	plane jet thickness
γ	angle of inclination
Γ_f	film flow rate in [5.2.3], kg/m s
Γ	physical property grouping defined by [5.6.60], $m^{1.68}/s^{0.84}$
Δ	indicates change in quantity
θ	temperature difference between streams, K
κ	thermal diffusivity, m^2/s
λ	thermal conductivity, W/m K
μ	viscosity, N s/m^2
ν	kinematic viscosity, m^2/s
ξ	drag coefficient
ρ	density, kg/m^3
σ	surface tension, N/m
τ	shear stress, N/m^2
ϕ	velocity ratio equal to u_{in}/u_z

SUBSCRIPTS

a, b	zone boundaries
c	contact, condensation, condensate
cf	cross flow
cold	cold stream
dco	dropwise condensation on copper

eff	effective value
f	film
g	gravity
G	gas phase (including vapor or gas-vapor mixtures)
GS	gassy steam
hot	hot stream
i	inside of tube
in	inlet or jet to exchanger
I	interface value, initial
j	jet
ln	logarithmic mean
L	liquid phase (or condensate)
m	mean value for exchanger
n	condition of interest
new	new value for next step
o	outside of tube
O	base conditions
out	outlet of heat exchanger
p	promoter
s	superheat
sat	saturated value
T	total for exchanger
W	wall
wat	ambient water
x	exit to tube
0	base condition
1	initial value
2	final value

SUPERSCRIPTS

$'$	shell side
I	first pass
II	second pass
$-$	average between passes
$+$	dimensionless quantities

5.8 References for Chapter 5

Alfa Laval 1969 *Thermal Handbook*, Alfa Laval, Sweden.

American Petroleum Institute 1968 Air Cooled Heat Exchangers for General Refinery Service, API Standard 661, Washington, D.C.

Bell, K. J. & Ghaly, M. A. 1973 An approximate Generalized Design Method for Multicomponent/Partial Condensers, *AIChE Symp. Ser.* 69:72–79.

Bell, K. J. & Panchal, C. B. 1978 Condensation, *Proc. 6th. Int. Heat Transfer Conf., Toronto* 6:369–375.

Bernhardt, S. H., Sheridan, T. J., & Westwater, J. W. 1972 Condensation of Immiscible Mixtures, *AIChE Symp. Ser.* 68:21.

Boyko, L. D. & Kruzhilin, G. N. 1967 Heat Transfer and Hydraulic Resistance during Condensation of Steam in a Horizontal Tube and in a Bundle of Tubes, *Int. J. Heat Mass Transfer* 10:361–373.

British Electical and Allied Manufacturers' Association 1967 *Recommended Practice for the Design of Surface Type Steam Condensing Plant*, London.

Brown. G. 1951 Heat Transmission by Condensation of Steam on a Spray of Water Drops, *Inst. Mech. Eng. Proc. Gen. Discuss. Heat Transfer*, pp. 49–52.

Butterworth, D. 1973 A Calculation Method for Shell-and-Tube Heat Exchangers in Which the Overall Coefficient Varies Along the Length, in Conferences on Advances in Thermal and Mechanical Design of Shell-and-Tube Heat Exchangers, *NEL Rept.* 590, pp. 56–71, National Engineering Laboratory, East Kilbride, Scotland.

Butterworth, D. 1977 *Engineering Design Guide: Introduction to Heat Transfer*, pp. 19–20, Oxford Univ. Press, Oxford.

Butterworth, D. 1978a The Development of a Model for Three-Dimensional Flow in Tube Bundles, *Int. J. Heat Mass Transfer* 21:253–256.

Butterworth, D. 1978b A Model for Heat Transfer during Three-dimensional Flow in Tube Bundles, *Proc. 6th Int. Heat Transfer Conf., Toronto* 4:219–223.

Colburn, A. P. 1933 Mean Temperature Difference and Heat Transfer Coefficient in Liquid Heat Exchangers, *Ind. Eng. Chem.* 25:873–877.

Colburn, A. P. & Drew, T. B. 1937 The Condensation of Mixed Vapours, *Trans. Am. Inst. Chem. Eng.* 33:197–215.

Colburn, A. P. & Edison, A. G. 1941 Prevention of Fog in Cooler-Condensers, *Ind. Eng. Chem.* 33:457–458.

Colburn, A. P. & Hougen, O. A. 1934 Design of Cooler Condensers for Mixtures of Vapours with Non-condensing Gases, *Ind. Eng. Chem.* 26:1178–1182.

Cumo, M., Farello, G. E., & Ferrari, G. 1978 Direct Heat Transfer in Pressure-Suppression Systems, *Proc. 6th Int. Heat Transfer Conf., Toronto* 4:101–106.

Davidson, B. J. 1976 Computational Methods for Evaluating the Performance of Condensers, in Meeting on Steam Turbine Condensers, *NEL Rept.* 619, pp. 152–159, National Engineering Laboratory, East Kilbride, Scotland.

Eckert, E. R. G. & Drake, R. M. 1959 *Heat and Mass Transfer,* p. 337, McGraw-Hill, New York.

Editors of Power 1967 *Power Generation Systems,* pp. 282–289, McGraw-Hill, New York.

Emerson, W. H. 1973 Effective Tube-Side Temperatures in Multi-Pass Heat Exchangers with Non-Uniform Heat-Transfer Coefficients and Specific Heats, in Conference on Advances in Thermal and Mechanical Design of Shell-and-Tube Heat Exchangers, *NEL Rept.* 590, pp. 32–55, National Engineering Laboratory, East Kilbride, Scotland.

Erb, R. A. & Thalan, E. 1965 Dropwise Condensation on Hydrophobic Metal and Metal Sulphide Surfaces, *First Int. Symp. Water Desalination, Washington, D.C.,* p. 100.

Fair, J. R. 1972 Design of Direct Contact Coolers/Condensers, *Chem. Eng. (N.Y.)* 79:91–100.

Fujii, T., Uehara, H., & Jurata, C. 1972 Laminar Filmwise Condensation on a Vertical Surface, *Int. J. Heat Mass Transfer* 15:235–246.

Gerstman, J. & Griffith, P. 1967 Laminar Film Condensation on the Underside of Horizontal and Inclined Surfaces, *Int. J. Heat Mass Transfer* 10:567–580.

Graham, C. 1969 The Limiting Heat Transfer Mechanisms of Dropwise Condensation, Ph.D. thesis, Massachusetts Inst. of Technology, Cambridge.

Hannemann, R. & Mikic, B. 1976 An Analysis of the Effect of Thermal Conductivity and the Rate of Heat Transfer in Dropwise Condensation, *Int. J. Heat Mass Transfer* 19:1309–1317.

Heat Exchange Institute 1970 *Standards for Steam Surface Condensers,* 6th ed., New York.

Ingebo, R. D. 1951 Vaporization Rates and Heat Transfer Coefficients for Pure Liquid Drops, *NACA TN* 2368.

Kaminski, D. A. 1977 *Heat Transfer and Fluid Flow Data Book,* sect. 506.3, p. 13, General Electric Co., Schenectady, N.Y.

Kern, D. G. 1958 Horizontal Condenser Theory—1. Mathematical Development of Tube Loading, *AIChE J.* 4:157.

Krishna, R., Panchal, C. B., Webb, D. R., & Coward, I. 1976 An Ackermann-Colburn & Drew Type Analysis for Condensation of Multicomponent Mixtures, *Lett. Heat Mass Transfer* 3:163–172.

Kutateladze, S. S. 1952 *Heat Transfer in Condensation and Boiling,* AEC-tr-3778, chaps. 5–7; originally published by State Scientific and Technical Publishers of Literature on Machinery, Moscow.

Lenfestey, A. G. 1961 Low Temperature Heat Exchangers, *Prog. Cryog.* 3:25–47.

Linehan, J. H. & Grolmes, M. A. 1970 Condensation of a High Velocity Vapor on a Subcooled Liquid Jet in Stratified Flow, *Proc. 4th Int. Heat Transfer Conf., Paris-Versailles,* 6:paper CS 2.6.

Ludwig, E. E. 1965 *Applied Process Design for Chemical and Petrochemical Plants,* vol. 3, pp. 146–161, Gulf Publishing Co., Houston.

McAdams, W. H. 1954 *Heat Transmission, 3d ed., p. 340, McGraw-Hill, New York.*

Mikheyev, M. 1977 *Fundamentals of Heat Transfer,* p. 145, Mir Publishers, Moscow.

Nicol, A. A., Bryce, A., & Ahmed, A. S. A. 1978 Condensation of a Horizontally Flowing Vapor on a Horizontal Cylinder Normal to the Vapor Stream, *Proc. 6th Int. Heat Transfer Conf., Toronto* 2:401–406.

Perry, J. H. 1950 *Chemical Engineers' Handbook,* 3d ed., p. 464, McGraw-Hill, New York.

Pita, E. G. & John, J. E. A. 1970 The Effect of Forced Convection on Evaporative Cooling of Sprays in Air, *Proc. 4th Int. Heat Transfer Conf., Paris-Versailles* 7:paper CT3.12.

Rohsenow, W. M. & Choi, H. 1961 *Heat, Mass and Momentum Transfer,* p. 238, Prentice-Hall, Englewood Cliffs, N.J.

Rohsenow, W. M. & Hartnett, J. P. 1973 *Handbook of Heat Transfer,* chap. 14-5, McGraw-Hill, New York.

Shade, R. & Mikic, B. 1974 The Effects of Non-condensible Gases on Heat Transfer during Dropwise Condensation, *AIChE 67th Annu. Meet.,* paper 676.

Short, B. E. & Brown, H. E. 1951 Condensation of Vapors on Vertical Banks of Horizontal Tubes, *Inst. Mech. Eng. ASME Gen. Discuss. Heat Transfer,* p. 17.

Silver, L. 1947 Gas Cooling with Aqueous Condensation, *Trans. Inst. Chem. Eng.* 25:30–42.

Simpson, H. C. 1969 Outline of Current Problems in Condenser Design, *Proc. Symp. to Celebrate the Bicentenary of the James Watt Patent, Univ. of Glasgow,* pp. 91–134.

Steinmeyer, D. E. 1972 Fog Formation in Partial Condensers, *Chem. Eng. Prog.* **68**:64–68.

Steinmeyer, D. E. 1973 Phase Dispersions: Liquid in Gas Dispersions, in *Chemical Engineers' Handbook,* 5th ed., eds. R. H. Perry & C. H. Chilton, pp. 18–62, McGraw-Hill, New York.

Steinmeyer, D. E. & Mueller, A. C. 1974 Why Condensers Don't Operate as They are Supposed To, *Chem. Eng. Prog.* **70**:78–82.

Tanner, D. W., Pope, D., Potter, C. J. & West, D. 1968 Heat Transfer in Dropwise Condensation of Low Pressures in the Absence and Presence of Non-condensable Gas, *Int. J. Heat Mass Transfer* **11**:181–190.

TEMA 1978 *Standards of Tubular Exchanger Manufacturers Association,* 6th ed., New York.

Traviss, D. P., Baron, A. B., & Rohsenow, W. M. 1971 Forced Convection Condensation inside Tubes, *Dept. of Mechanical Engineering Rept.* DSR-70591-74, Massachusetts Inst. of Technology, Cambridge.

Votta, F. 1964 Condensing from Vapor-Gas Mixtures, *Chem. Eng. (N.Y.)* **70**:223–228.

Wallace, D. J. 1975 A Study of the Influence of Vapor Velocity upon Condensation on a Horizontal Tube, Ph.D. thesis, Univ. of Strathclyde, Glasgow, Scotland.

Wallis, G. B. 1961 Flooding Velocities for Air-Water in Vertical Tubes, *Atomic Energy Establishment Rept.* AEEW-R123, AEE, Winfrith.

Wilson, J. L. 1976 Two Dimensional Condenser Computer Program in Meeting on Steam Turbine Condensers, *NEL Rept.* 619, pp. 152–159, National Engineering Laboratory, East Kilbride, Scotland.

Young, F. L. & Wohlenberg, W. J. 1942 Condensation of Saturated Freon-12 Vapor on a Bank of Horizontal Tubes, *Trans. Am. Soc. Mech. Eng.* **64**:787.

Young, J., Yang, K. C., & Novotney, J. 1973 The Interaction between a High Velocity Vapor Jet and an External Co-axial Co-current Water Flow, *Tech. Rept.* UND-73-6, Univ. of Notre Dame, Notre Dame.

6 BOILING

6.1 General Boiling

Warren M. Rohsenow

6.1.1 INTRODUCTION

The process of evaporation associated with vapor bubbles in a liquid is called boiling. Here attention is focused on boiling at solid heated surfaces of interest in engineering applications.

When a pool of liquid at saturation temperature is heated by an electrically heated wire or flat plate, data for heat flux $\dot{q}$ versus $T_W - T_{sat}$, the difference between wall and saturation temperatures, usually appear as shown by the lower curve in figure 6.1.1. As ΔT increases, the initial natural circulation regime AB changes to the nucleate boiling regime. The appearance of the first bubble at B requires a significant finite superheat.

As ΔT or heat flux is increased, more nucleation sites become active producers of bubbles. A peak nucleate boiling heat flux (called burnout heat flux, BHF) is reached when bubbles stream forth from so many nucleation sites that the liquid is unable to flow to the heated surface. The transition associated with this peak is called burnout; a further discussion is given in section 6.4.1. With electric heating ($\dot{q}$ is the independent variable) the operating condition at point C of figure 6.1.1 changes rapidly to point E', which is at a much higher temperature. Operation along the curve ED is in the film boiling regime, where a layer of vapor continually blankets the surface and liquid does not contact the surface.

If heat flux is reduced below point D at the minimum point on the curve, the operating condition reverts to nucleate boiling at point F. Then power must be increased to point C before the process can revert to film boiling.

To operate in the transition region CD between nucleate and film boiling, the surface temperature should be the independent variable, e.g., by using a condensing vapor, etc. In this region the process may be alternating between nucleate and film boiling, with the liquid touching the surface intermittently.

The dashed line shown for pool boiling of a subcooled liquid lies near the curve for saturated liquids; it may lie either to the left or the right, depending on natural convection effects resulting from different surface geometries.

Experimental data for forced convection inside ducts or across wires and plates,

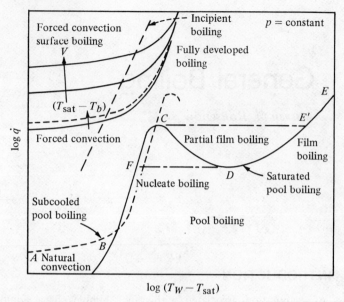

Figure 6.1.1 Regimes in boiling heat transfer.

when plotted on the same coordinates, appear as shown in figure 6.1.1. If the liquid at temperature T_b is subcooled, the heat flux is represented by

$$(\dot{q})_{\text{before boiling}} = \alpha[(T_W - T_{\text{sat}}) + (T_{\text{sat}} - T_b)] \qquad [6.1.1]$$

where α is the heat transfer coefficient.

At high heat flux, the forced convection curves for a particular pressure at various subcoolings and velocities appear to merge on log-log plots into a single curve called the fully developed boiling curve. For some systems this fully developed region lies approximately on an extension of the pool boiling line for the same surface.

The literature on boiling heat transfer is now quite voluminous. For references in addition to those cited here, the reader is referred to the annotated bibliography assembled by Gouse (1966).

6.1.2 NUCLEATION

In carefully cleaned test systems, heating of pure liquids can produce high superheat at temperatures up to a limit of stability where homogeneous nucleation (vapor formation) takes place. For the case of heat transfer associated with boiling at solid heating surfaces, observed wall temperatures are much lower than these. Further observations of nucleate boiling show bubble streams emerging at single spots on the surface. Microscopic observations of these spots revealed a scratch or a cavity where a bubble formed. Earlier, Corty & Foust (1955), Bankoff (1956), and others postulated that bubbles at a heating surface emerge from cavities in which a gas or vapor phase preexists (figure 6.1.2). As heat is added, more vapor forms in the cavity (figure 6.1.2a) and a bubble emerges and departs (figure 6.1.2b), after which liquid closes in over the cavity, trapping vapor that is the source of the next bubble. Nucleation phenomena are surveyed by Rohsenow (1966) and Griffith (1965–1966).

Consider the equilibrium of a spherical liquid-vapor interface in a capillary tube, shown in figure 6.1.3a, which would be identical to a spherical vapor bubble in a large body of liquid. Equilibrium requires equal and uniform temperatures of vapor T_G and liquid T_L:

$$T_G = T_L \tag{6.1.2a}$$

and equal chemical potentials, $\mu = h - Ts$, where h is enthalpy and s is entropy,

$$\mu_G = \mu_L \tag{6.1.2b}$$

Across the interface

$$p_G - p_L = \frac{2\sigma}{r} \tag{6.1.2c}$$

where p_G and p_L are the vapor and liquid pressures on either side of the interface, σ is surface tensions, and r is the radius of the interface. The pressure p_∞ at the flat interface is the saturation pressure, tabulated for most fluids. Except at very low subatmospheric pressures, $(p_\infty - p_G)/p_\infty \ll 1$; therefore in height y the densities ρ may be taken as uniform. Then

$$p_\infty - p_G = g\rho_G y \tag{6.1.2d}$$

$$p_\infty - p_L = g\rho_L y \tag{6.1.2e}$$

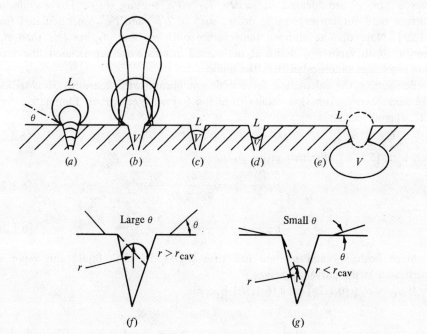

Figure 6.1.2 Formation of bubbles of vapor over cavities in a heated surface.

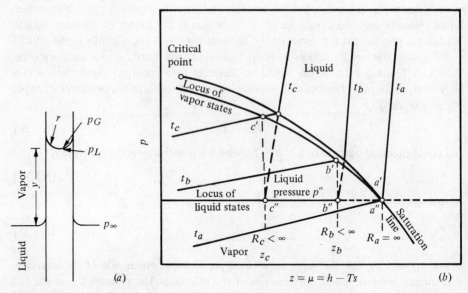

Figure 6.1.3 (a) Capillary tube; (b) approximation of vapor-liquid equilibrium at a curved interface of a vapor bubble in a one-component system.

The p versus μ graph of figure 6.1.3b shows isotherms with liquid isotherms extended into the vapor side of the saturation line as dashed lines. For various liquid states a'', b'', c'' at the same pressure the corresponding equilibrium vapor states a', b', c' are located to satisfy $T_G = T_L$ and $\mu_G = \mu_L$. The equilibrium interface radii for corresponding points such as $b'b''$ and $c'c''$ are calculated from [6.1.2c]. Note that at uniform temperature both p_G and p_L are less than p_{sat}; therefore both vapor and liquid at the curved interface are superheated, the vapor being much less superheated than the liquid.

Performing the calculation for bubble equilibrium with figure 6.1.3b is tedious. A reasonable approximation results from the following equations. Eliminate y from [6.1.2d] and [6.1.2e]:

$$\rho_L(p_\infty - p_G) = \rho_G(p_\infty - p_L) \qquad [6.1.2f]$$

Then with [6.1.2c] eliminate either p_L or p_G

$$p_\infty - p_L = \frac{\rho_L}{\rho_L - \rho_G} \frac{2\sigma}{r} \qquad [6.1.2g]$$

$$p_\infty - p_G = \frac{\rho_G}{\rho_L - \rho_G} \frac{2\sigma}{r} \qquad [6.1.2h]$$

Since both p_G and p_L are less than p_{sat} (p_∞), both liquid and vapor are superheated at the curved interface.

If $\rho_G \ll \rho_L$, [6.1.2g] and [6.1.2h] become

$$p_G \cong p_{sat}$$

$$p_{sat} - p_L \cong \frac{2\sigma}{r} \qquad [6.1.2i]$$

Calculate the ΔT corresponding to $p_\infty - p_L$ given by [6.1.2c] by integrating the Clausius-Clapeyron relation

$$\frac{dT}{dp} = \frac{T v_{LG}}{h_{LG}}$$ [6.1.3]

where v is volume and h is latent heat, along the p-T saturation curve. The results of such an integration for various assumptions are

1. If $h_{LG}/v_{LG}T$ is constant and $T = T_{sat}$

$$T = T_{sat}\left(1 + \frac{2\sigma}{r}\frac{v_{LG}}{h_{LG}}\frac{\rho_L}{\rho_L - \rho_G}\right)$$ [6.1.4a]

2. If h_{LG}/v_{LG} is constant

$$T = T_{sat}\exp\left(\frac{2\sigma}{r}\frac{v_{LG}}{h_{LG}}\frac{\rho_L}{\rho_L - \rho_G}\right)$$ [6.1.4b]

3. If $v_{LG} = v_G = R_G T/p$

$$T = \frac{T_{sat}}{1 - (T_{sat}R_G/h_{LG})\ln[1 + (2\sigma/rp_{sat})\rho_L/(\rho_L - \rho_G)]}$$ [6.1.4c]

4. Same as [6.1.4c] with $2\sigma/p_L r \ll 1$

$$T = \frac{T_{sat}}{1 - (T_{sat}R_G/h_{LG})(2\sigma/rp_{sat})[\rho_L/(\rho_L - \rho_G)]}$$ [6.1.4d]

and other alternatives follow.

5. With [6.1.2] use an empirical correlation for the saturation curve as $\log_{10}p = A - B/T$ where T is absolute temperature. With [6.1.2] this may be solved by trial and error, or with [6.1.4c]

$$\Delta T = \frac{T_{sat}^2}{B}\log_{10}\left(1 + \frac{2\sigma}{rp_{sat}}\right)\left[1 + \frac{T_{sat}}{B}\log_{10}\left(1 + \frac{2\sigma}{rp_{sat}}\right)\right]$$ [6.1.5]

for steam $B = 2156.0$ at 0.1 MPa; $B = 2004.5$ at 6.8 MPa.

6. With [6.1.2] use tabular values from properties tables for the saturation curve.

Results obtained with these calculation methods are compared in table 6.1.1 for $r = 0.00127$ cm and water at 0.1 and 6.8 MPa.

The equations above represent an approximate expression for the superheat required for equilibrium of a bubble of radius r. Nuclei of radius greater than r from [6.1.4] become bubbles and grow; those of smaller radius collapse.

Some experiments have shown that at a heated surface in water at atmospheric pressure, boiling begins around 15°C above saturation temperature. For this condition [6.1.4] predicts an equilibrium bubble radius of 2.5×10^{-6} m. This is about 10,000 times larger than the maximum cavity size expected from molecular fluctuations (Shai 1967). Volmer (1939) estimated a cavity formation rate for size

Table 6.1.1 Comparison of Calculation Methods

	T (°C) for	
Equation	$p = 0.1$ MPa $T_{sat} = 100°C$	$p = 6.8$ MPa $T_{sat} = 284.78°C$
[6.1.4a]	102.56	284.81
[6.1.4b]	102.57	284.81
[6.1.4c]	102.50	284.82
[6.1.4d]	102.62	284.82
[6.1.5]	102.44	284.81
Properties table	102.47	284.81

2.5×10^{-6} m to be approximately one per cubic centimeter per hour. From this, one readily concludes that free vapor nuclei arising from molecular fluctuations are not important as nucleation cavities. On the other hand, gas nuclei are very significant as nucleation cavities.

If inert gas at partial pressure p_g is present in the vapor space of figure 6.1.3b, the total pressure is $p_G + p_g$ and $p_\infty = p_{sat} + p_g$. Then [6.1.2c], [6.1.2g], [6.1.2h], and [6.1.4a] become

$$p_G - p_L = \frac{2\sigma}{r} - p_g \qquad [6.1.6]$$

$$p_\infty - p_G - p_g = g\rho_m y$$

$$p_\infty - p_L = g\rho_L y$$

$$p_{sat} - p_L = \frac{\rho_L}{\rho_L - \rho_m}\frac{2\sigma}{r} - p_g \qquad [6.1.6a]$$

$$p_{sat} - p_G = \frac{\rho_m}{\rho_L - \rho_m}\frac{2\sigma}{r} \qquad [6.1.6b]$$

$$T - T_{sat} = \frac{T v_{LG}}{h_{LG}}\left(\frac{\rho_L}{\rho_L - \rho_m}\frac{2\sigma}{r} - p_g\right) \qquad [6.1.6c]$$

where ρ_m is the density of the mixture of gas and vapor. Equation [6.1.6c] shows that the equilibrium superheat is less when p_g is present and may become negative if $p_g > (2\sigma/r)[\rho_L/(\rho_L - \rho_m)]$.

Except at low subatmospheric pressures, $\rho_m \ll \rho_L$ and [6.1.6b] and [6.1.6a] become, with [6.1.4a],

$$p_G \cong p_{sat}$$

$$p_{sat} - p_L \cong \frac{2\sigma}{r} - p_g$$

$$T_L - T_{sat} \cong \frac{R_G T^2}{p h_{LG}}\left(\frac{2\sigma}{r} - p_g\right) \qquad [6.1.6d]$$

Assuming that a spherical bubble contains w_g mass of gas and that it is a perfect gas, [6.1.6d] becomes

$$p_{sat} - p_L = \frac{2\sigma}{r} - \frac{3w_g R_g T}{4\pi r^3} \qquad [6.1.6e]$$

Equation [6.1.6e] is plotted in figure 6.1.4 for constant gas content w_g in the bubble. These curves represent equilibrium size bubbles. A "critical" radius, at the maxima of the curves, for which a bubble containing w_g mass of gas is stable is obtained from [6.1.6e] by setting $\partial(p_{sat} - p_L)/\partial r = 0$. Then

$$r_c = 3\sqrt{\frac{w_g R_g T}{8\pi\sigma}} \qquad [6.1.7a]$$

or
$$r_c = \frac{4\sigma}{3(p_{sat} - p_L)} \qquad [6.1.7b]$$

A pure vapor nucleus above equilibrium size continues to grow and one below equilibrium size collapses. A gas-vapor nucleus smaller than equilibrium size grows to equilibrium size; one larger than equilibrium size but smaller than the critical radius decreases to equilibrium size, and one greater than critical size continues to grow. Figure 6.1.4 shows that decreasing the mass of gas in the nucleus increases the excess pressure at the critical radius and decreases the magnitude of the critical radius.

For a given magnitude of liquid superheat the gas-vapor nuclei that exceed r_c

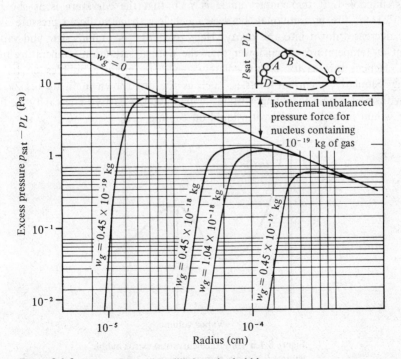

Figure 6.1.4 Effect of gas on equilibrium size bubble.

form bubbles that grow. As liquid temperature increases, the vapor pressure increases, causing the smaller gas nuclei to become active at the higher excess pressure and temperature.

The preceding calculation procedure is related to nucleation at a cavity in the heating surface in the following way. Griffith (1960, 1965) showed that the radius of curvature of a vapor interface for positions inside and outside the cavity (figure 6.1.2a) may be plotted as in figure 6.1.4 as $1/r$ versus vapor volume. In [6.1.4] and [6.1.6d] the superheat required to cause a bubble to grow was determined by $1/r$. The maximum point in the $1/r$ curve (figure 6.1.4) then determines the minimum superheat required for a bubble to grow at the cavity.

A bubble departs from a cavity nonsymmetrically and the interface goes back into the cavity, trapping vapor for the next bubble. In figure 6.1.2f and 6.1.2g the dashed line represents the trapping interface, which changes to a spherical shape of radius r. If the contact angle θ is large, $r > r_{cav}$, which represents a condition along curve abc of figure 6.1.5. Then the minimum superheat required for the next bubble to depart is calculated with the cavity radius at c. If the contact angle is small, $r < r_{cav}$, representing a condition in the region oa of figure 6.1.5. In this case r determines the required superheat, which is greater than the superheat required for the cavity radius.

Figure 6.1.6 shows the ratio of r/r_{cav} for various θ and the cavity angles β. For fluids with low θ the surface acts as though it has cavity sizes smaller than the actual ones (Singh et al. 1976; Lorenz et al. 1974; Eddington & Kenning 1978).

It is possible for a cavity to continue to contain vapor even when the surface is highly subcooled. If the contact angle is such that the curvature is as shown in figure 6.1.2d, the pressure may be very much less than the liquid pressure as the radius decreases down into the cavity. Here [6.1.2c] has a minus sign, and vapor is present at temperatures much lower than the normal saturation temperature of the liquid. Hence, this cavity is immediately ready to produce bubbles on its next heating. Similarly, reentrant cavities, such as the one shown in figure 6.1.2e, may also withstand high subcooling without collapsing the cavity. The cavity in figure 6.1.2c would immediately fill with liquid on cooling.

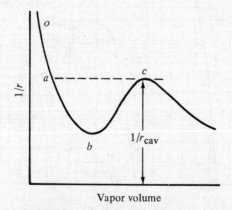

Figure 6.1.5 Interface curvature versus bubble volume for cavity shown in figure 6.1.2a.

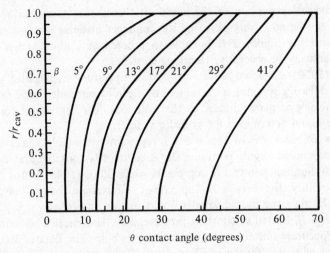

Figure 6.1.6 Effective radius of nucleation (Lorenz et al. 1974).

6.1.3 HOMOGENEOUS NUCLEATION

Nucleation in pure liquids has been treated by two different postulates. Volmer (1939) considered it to follow thermodynamic equilibrium states to an unstable condition. Others considered it to be a result of a statistical density fluctuation. Various theories are discussed by Becker (1935), Frenkel (1946), Fisher (1948), Bernath (1952), Westwater (1956), and Volmer (1939). Common to the two approaches is the requirement of a superheated liquid.

Figure 6.1.7 shows a conventional pressure-volume-temperature diagram for a single pure substance. Lines AB and FG represent isotherms in the liquid and vapor

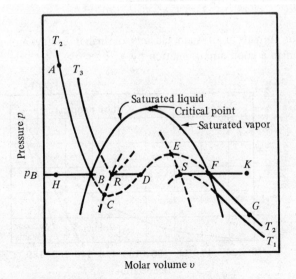

Figure 6.1.7 Typical pressure-volume diagram.

phases. Isothermal expansion of the liquid at A ordinarily results in boiling at p_B; however, if the liquid is very pure and the container material is very clean and does not react with the liquid, it is possible to proceed as a liquid down to point C, which may actually be a negative (tension) pressure.

Briggs (1950) subjected water at room temperature to negative pressures of nearly 27.0 MPa by spinning a "scrupulously clean" open-ended tube of pure water about a vertical axis perpendicular to the tube axis. The centrifugal force required to break the liquid determined the pressure at fracture.

Portions BC and EF of figure 6.1.7 represent metastable states—superheated liquid and subcooled vapor; portion CDE is completely unstable and cannot exist. The locus of limiting points CR represents what Gibbs (1948) called the limit of essential instability, $(\partial p/\partial v)_T = 0$. Approximate expressions for the line $ABCDEFG$, and hence CR, are given by the van der Waal equation and others.

A liquid at H, heated at constant pressure, may theoretically be heated to point R before it becomes unstable, forming a vapor bubble. The data of Wismer (1922) are compared with this theory in figure 6.1.8. These data were obtained under very carefully controlled conditions of cleanliness.

The kinetic view of homogeneous nucleation is presented by Cole (1974). The liquid molecules have a distribution of energies, with a fraction having energies much greater than the average. Because of density fluctuations in the liquid, there is a probability that a sufficient number of the molecules with greater than average energy can join to form a cluster with an equilibrium radius given by [6.1.2g] and [6.1.4a]:

$$r_e = \frac{2\sigma}{p_{\text{sat}} - p_L} \frac{\rho_L}{\rho_L - \rho_G} \qquad [6.1.8a]$$

or

$$r_e = \frac{2\sigma}{T - T_{\text{sat}}} \frac{T_{\text{sat}} v_{LG}}{h_{LG}} \frac{\rho_L}{\rho_L - \rho_G} \qquad [6.1.8b]$$

The rate of formation of such clusters of higher energy molecules (activated clusters) is given to a good approximation by

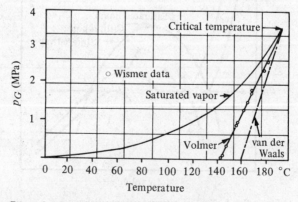

Figure 6.1.8   Attainable superheats in liquid.

$$J = n \frac{kT}{\nu} \exp\left(-\frac{4\pi r_e^2 \sigma}{3kT}\right) \qquad [6.1.9]$$

where n is the number density of molecules, k is the Boltzmann constant, and ν is Planck's constant. Combining [6.1.8b] and [6.1.9] gives

$$T - T_{\text{sat}} = \frac{T_{\text{sat}} \nu_{LG}}{h_{LG}} \frac{\rho_L}{\rho_L - \rho_G} \left[\frac{16\pi\sigma^3}{3kT \ln(nkT/\nu J)}\right] \qquad [6.1.10]$$

The magnitude of superheat required for homogeneous nucleation is calculated from [6.1.10], where the ln term does not vary much with large changes in assumed J. This occurs when J is in the range 1 to 10^{-6} clusters/cm^3 s. Agreement with measurements of maximum attainable superheats in various pure liquids is quite good (Cole 1974).

6.1.4 HETEROGENEOUS NUCLEATION

In homogeneous nucleation the formation of the critical size of vapor involves the transfer of energy from liquid molecules to vapor molecules, the work of forming the larger vapor volume, and the energy in the liquid-vapor interface. In nucleating at a solid-liquid surface (on flat surfaces, curved surfaces, or in cavities) the vapor volumes and liquid-vapor surfaces may be smaller, but energies at solid-liquid and solid-vapor interfaces must be included.

For heterogeneous nucleation at various solid surface geometries, Cole (1974) showed that [6.1.10] should be modified by

$$T - T_{\text{sat}} = \frac{T_{\text{sat}} \nu_{LG}}{h_{LG}} \frac{\rho_L}{\rho_L - \rho_g} \left[\frac{16\pi\sigma^3 f(\theta)}{3kT \ln(nkT/\nu J)}\right]^{1/2} \qquad [6.1.11]$$

At a solid surface (figure 6.1.9a), lateral force balance gives

$$\sigma \cos\theta = \sigma_{GS} - \sigma_{LS} \qquad [6.1.12]$$

Cole obtained the following expressions for $f(\theta)$. For a flat solid surface (figure 6.1.9a):

$$f(\theta) = \tfrac{1}{4}(2 + 3\cos\theta - \cos^3\theta) \qquad [6.1.13a]$$

Note for $\theta = 0$, a perfectly wet surface, $f(\theta) = 1$, which predicts the same superheat as in homogeneous nucleation. As θ increases $f(\theta)$ decreases, becoming 0 for $\theta = 180°$, a perfectly nonwet surface; however, the maximum θ observed is around 140°. At $\theta = 90°$, $f(\theta) = \tfrac{1}{2}$; so the superheat is reduced by about 30%.

For spherical projections or cavities (figure 6.1.9b and c):

$$f(\theta) = \frac{1}{2}\left[\pm\left(\frac{r_s}{r_e}\right)^3 (1 - \cos\alpha)^2(2 + \cos\alpha) - (1 - \cos\phi)^2(2 + \cos\phi)\right.$$

$$\left. + \frac{3}{2}\left(\frac{r_s}{r_e}\right)^2 (1 - \cos\alpha)\cos\theta + (1 - \cos\phi)\right] \qquad [6.1.13b]$$

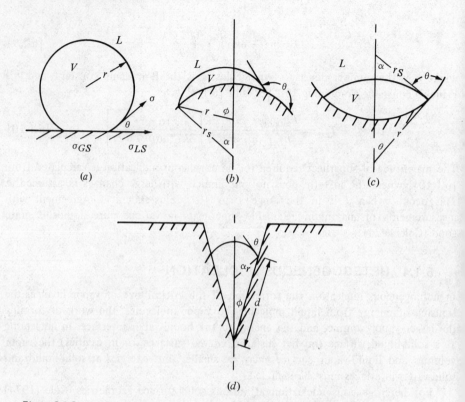

Figure 6.1.9 Heterogeneous nucleation embryo. (*a*) Plane surface. (*b*) Sphere projection. (*c*) Sphere cavity. (*d*) Conical cavity.

where the plus sign applies to the convex and the minus sign to the concave surfaces.

For a conical cavity (figure 6.1.9*d*), Kottowski (1973) obtained

$$f(\theta) = \tfrac{1}{4} \left[2 - 3 \sin (\theta - \phi) + \sin^3 (\theta - \phi) \right] \qquad [6.1.13c]$$

which reduces to [6.1.13*a*] when $\phi = 90°$, a plane surface.

The predicting equations suggest that superheat for nucleation at a solid surface is always below that for homogeneous nucleation and may be above or below that required for a bubble to grow from a cavity that contains preexisting gas or vapor.

For additional analyses and development of the phenomena in homogeneous and heterogeneous nucleation for various geometries see Kottowski (1973) and Giot (1978).

The results above apply to pure liquids and solids. Chemical impurities or dissolved gases tend to reduce the superheats below those predicted. Careful experiments have produced results in good agreement with the predictions for homogeneous nucleation. The limited data for heterogeneous nucleation suggest that the trend of the predictions is reasonable, but more data are needed.

The effect of nuclear radiation has been studied by Bell et al. (1974). Predictions and measurements for nonmetallic liquids show a significant reduction in superheat when nuclear radiation is beamed through the liquid. The predictions of the theory suggest (Kottowski 1973) that for liquid metals there would be an insignificant effect.

6.1.5 INCIPIENT BOILING IN FORCED CONVECTION

Consider a liquid flowing in a tube. As the heat flux or wall temperature is raised, boiling or nucleation begins at a particular value of the wall temperature. The following procedure was developed by Bergles and Rohsenow (1964) based on a suggestion of Hsu & Graham (1961).

The heat flux for flow inside a tube is

$$\dot{q} = \alpha(T_W - T_L) = -\lambda_L \left(\frac{\partial T}{\partial y}\right)_{y=0} \qquad [6.1.14]$$

Here α is the heat transfer coefficient, which is a function of geometry, fluid properties, and flow rate, and λ_L is the liquid thermal conductivity. For a given liquid temperature, both temperature gradient $(\partial T/\partial y)_{y=0}$ and wall temperature T_W increase as the heat flux increases. A series of curves representing the temperature distribution very near the heated wall is shown for increasing heat flux in figure 6.1.10. Also shown is a curve labeled T_G^*, which represents [6.1.4a] with the radius of the cavity plotted as the distance from the heated surface. A possible theory is that nucleation takes place when the temperature curve in the liquid is tangent to the curve representing [6.1.4a]. The implication is that the surface contains cavities of various sizes, and when the temperature at the outer surface of the bubble reaches the critical value given by [6.1.4a], the bubble grows at the cavity whose

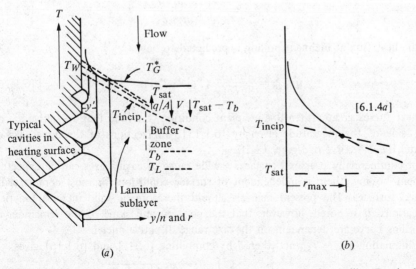

Figure 6.1.10 Initiation of bubble growth in forced convection surface boiling (Bergles & Rohsenow 1964).

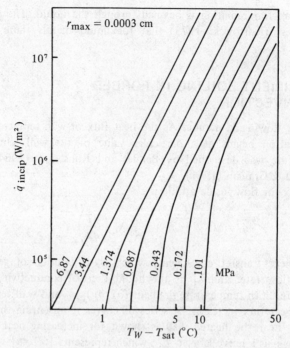

Figure 6.1.11   Incipient nucleation criteria for water.

radius is represented by the distance between the wall and the point of intersection.

At this point of tangency, the radius of the first cavity to nucleate (solving [6.1.4a] and [6.1.14] simultaneously) is

$$r_{\text{nucl}} = \sqrt{\frac{2\sigma T \upsilon_{LG}\lambda_L}{h_{LG}\dot{q}}} \qquad [6.1.15]$$

and the heat flux at incipient boiling is predicted to be

$$\dot{q}_{\text{incip}} = \frac{h_{LG}\lambda_L}{8\sigma T \upsilon_{LG}}(T_W - T_{\text{sat}})^2 \qquad [6.1.16]$$

For heat fluxes greater than this incipient condition, the radii that are active are on either side of the magnitude given by [6.1.15], intersections of the upper dashed line and the T_G^* curve of figure 6.1.10.

In commercially prepared surfaces a wide range of cavity sizes can be expected. Incipient boiling, then, is independent of surface condition for most commercially finished surfaces. The present analysis should therefore be valid in most practical applications. It is noted, however, that the position and slope of the remainder of the boiling curve are dependent on the size range of active nuclei.

Eliminating $T_W - T_{\text{sat}}$ and then $\dot{q}$ by combining [6.1.1] and [6.1.16] gives

$$(T_W - T_{\text{sat}})_{\text{incip}} = \frac{1 + \sqrt{1 + 4\Gamma(T_{\text{sat}} - T_b)}}{2\Gamma} \qquad [6.1.17]$$

$$\dot{q}_{incip} = \frac{\alpha}{2\Gamma} [1 + \sqrt{1 + 4\Gamma(T_{sat} - T_b)}] + \alpha(T_{sat} - T_b) \qquad [6.1.18]$$

$$\Gamma = \frac{h_{LG}\lambda_L}{8\sigma T v_{LG}\alpha}$$

These equations predict $\dot{q}_{incip}$ and $(T_W - T_{sat})_{incip}$ for various subcoolings $T_{sat} - T_b$ and various velocities or natural convection conditions that are embodied in the heat transfer coefficient α.

As heat flux is increased above the conditions for incipience (upper dashed line in figure 6.1.10a), a range of cavity sizes becomes nucleated, as shown. A word of caution is in order. The preceding calculation procedure assumes that cavities exist at sizes out to the point of tangency. At low heat fluxes, as in natural convection, the slope of the temperature distribution ([6.1.4b]) may be so small that the point of tangency occurs at cavity sizes larger than those present. Then the heat flux and wall superheat must be raised until the two curves intersect at the largest available active cavity. Hence for low heat fluxes, as in natural convection, the above procedure usually predicts superheats and $\dot{q}$ lower than those observed.

Approximating the temperature distribution in the liquid near the wall as linear

$$T_L = T_W - \dot{q}\,\frac{y}{\lambda_L} \qquad [6.1.19]$$

and equating this to T_L from [6.1.4a], with $y = r = r_{max}$, give

$$\dot{q}_{incip} = \frac{\lambda_L}{r_{max}} (T_W - T_{sat}) - \frac{2\sigma T_{sat} v_{LG}\lambda_L}{h_{LG}r_{max}^2} \qquad [6.1.20]$$

This equation is plotted in figure 6.1.11 as curved lines for a representative maximum cavity size of $r_{max} = 0.0003$ cm. At higher heat fluxes these curves for the intersection predictions (figure 6.1.10b) merge into straight lines on figure 6.1.11, which result from the tangency predictions (figure 6.1.10a or [6.1.16]). To determine the condition of incipient boiling, superimpose a line representing $\dot{q} = \alpha(T_W - T_b)$ on figure 6.1.11, where α is for either natural or forced convection. The intersection with the appropriate pressure curve of figure 6.1.11 predicts the incipient boiling heat flux $\dot{q}_{incip}$ and the incipient $(T_W - T_{sat})_{incip}$.

When intersection occurs in the straight upper portion of the curves, the incipient condition and the resulting boiling $\dot{q}$-ΔT curve is not sensitive to cavity size distribution (surface finish). This results for the higher α of forced convection.

When intersection occurs in the lower portion of the curves in figure 6.1.11, for the lower α associated with low-velocity forced convection or natural convection, the incipient boiling and the entire boiling curve becomes a stronger function of cavity size distribution and surface finish.

A number of other suggestions have been made for predicting the incipient boiling condition (Davis & Anderson 1966; Gaddis & Hall 1967). Most of them reduce to the scheme shown in figure 6.1.10, except that T_L is plotted against y/n with T_G^* plotted against r. In the scheme above n is taken as unity; in the other proposals n ranges from 0.67 to 2. Brown (1967) tried these suggestions with experimental data for various fluids and found n between 1 and 3.

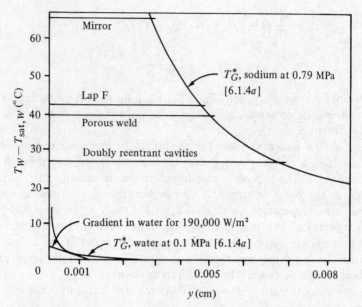

Figure 6.1.12   Incipient boiling for sodium and water (Marto & Rohsenow 1966).

The procedure above appears to provide an estimate for the lower ΔT and $\dot{q}_{incip}$ at incipience. The actual ΔT and $\dot{q}_{incip}$ may be greater. Higher wall superheats may be required to accelerate bubble growth enough to remove bubbles from the wall. Also, thermocapillarity, as described later, may provide convection currents not accounted for in this model.

Another study of nucleation (Kenning & Cooper 1965) attempted to account for flow patterns around the bubble surface protruding from the cavity in forced convection. From a comparison with a small amount of data, this study led to the following prediction for wall superheat in forced convection:

$$(T_W - T_{sat})_{incip} = 1.33 \left(\frac{\dot{q}}{\lambda}\right)^{0.4} \left(\frac{r_W}{\rho_L \nu^2}\right)^{0.1} \left(\frac{2\sigma T_{sat} \nu_{LG}}{h_{LG}}\right)^{0.6} \qquad [6.1.21]$$

Comparison with a wider variety of data is needed.

With liquid metals, which have very high thermal conductivities, the same equations predict incipient boiling. For comparison, curves for water and sodium are shown in figure 6.1.12 for incipient boiling conditions. Much greater superheats are required in the liquid metals (Marto & Rohsenow 1966). The thermal conductivity of liquid metals is so large that the temperature gradient in the liquid in the vicinity of the bubble at a cavity is essentially zero. The first cavity to nucleate should be at r_{max} if it is not inactive (filled with liquid). Then incipient boiling superheat should be predicted by [6.1.4a] with $r = r_{max}$.

Chen (1968) investigated the postulate that cavities can be deactivated to a predictable size by preconditioning, raising the pressure and temperature to specified levels of subcooling. This would establish a "negative" radius of the cavity from

[6.1.4a], assuming that oxidation in the cavity prevents further collapse to smaller radii. On subsequently reducing the pressure and increasing the degree of superheat, the radius, now taken as positive in [6.1.4a], should predict the superheat required for nucleation at the surface. The same formalism was explained by Deane and Rohsenow (1970) in terms of reentrant cavities (figure 6.1.2e), which eliminates the requirement of oxidation to aid the process. Most test results fall below the predictions of this theory, however. Singer & Holtz (1970) showed that this discrepancy was probably due to the presence of noncondensable gas. Their data showed that after extended boiling to drive gas off the surface, the measured superheats agreed well with the theory. Also, surface finish had no effect.

6.1.6 POSSIBLE MECHANISMS OF HEAT TRANSFER IN BOILING

As heat flux to a saturated liquid is increased beyond the incipient boiling point, the number of spots on the surface from which bubble columns rise increases. Photographs of Hsu & Graham (1961) suggest that a thermal layer builds up between bubbles in pool boiling and each bubble carries away the liquid in a region $2D_b$, thus pumping away the liquid superheat. In the region between bubbles at lower heat fluxes the heat transfer may be of the order of that associated with natural convection. Calculations based on this hypothesis were verified at low heat fluxes by Han & Griffith (1962).

Alternatively, Tien (1962) visualized each bubble column as inducing a stagnation-point flow away from the surface, producing a boundary layer over the surface. Using only heat transfer to this boundary layer, modest success was obtained in comparison with data.

A similar model was proposed by Beer et al. (1977) with a detailed analysis of the flow and temperature fields to calculate convective heat transfer. Evaporation to the bubble was included, as well as bubble growth and waiting times. Better agreement with data was obtained, but no useful correlation equations resulted.

As heat flux increases, nucleation site density increases and columns with discrete bubbles change to columns of continuous vapor (Moissis & Berenson 1963). The zones between these vapor columns become return passages, bringing liquid to the heating surface, where it is converted to vapor in the columns. As heat flux is increased further this situation becomes unstable and the heating surface becomes starved for liquid, causing transition to the film boiling point, C in figure 6.1.1.

A typical history of the temperature at a cavity under a bubble is shown in figure 6.1.13a. At point A the bubble begins to grow on the surface. The bubble grows in an essentially nonviscous way except near the wall, where viscosity predominates. Measurements of Cooper & Lloyd (1966) for toluene suggest that a thin liquid layer is left on the surface under the bubble (figure 6.1.9b). It is presumed that viscous force retards the motion of the liquid next to the wall as the bubble grows, thus leaving behind a liquid layer. At point B this layer has evaporated and the dry surface rises in temperature. At point C the bubble has departed and colder liquid covers the surface, reducing its temperature to D. Then the surface continues to rise in temperature to A, when a new bubble forms.

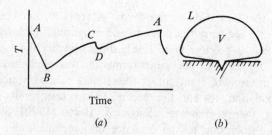

Figure 6.1.13   Temperature of wall under a bubble.

Calculations of heat flux from the surface suggest that major contributions to the heat flux occur when the thin liquid film evaporates under the bubble *AB* and when the colder liquid rushes into contact with the surface *CDA*.

Cooper (1969) showed that this microlayer is significant only at low pressure. At pressures above 0.1 MPa for fluids such as water, hydrocarbons, and cryogens, bubble growth is thermally (not dynamically) controlled; then the microlayer does not greatly influence growth and heat transfer.

For methylene cloride boiling on an oxide-coated glass surface, Judd & Hwang (1976) and Fath & Judd (1978) showed that the microlayer effect was present at low pressure but decreased as pressure was raised. Further analyses of the nature of the microlayer are surveyed by van Stralen (1978).

Measurements by Shai & Rohsenow (1969) of the temperature at a cavity in pool boiling suggest that for liquid metals the *BC* portion of the curve is essentially nonexistent and *CD* nearly coincides with *AB*. Here the primary heat transfer is to the liquid that flows in behind a departing bubble. Because of the high thermal conductivity of liquid metal, the surface temperature rise is much slower and bubble frequencies are an order of magnitude lower than in nonmetals.

Boiling from a heated surface in highly subcooled liquids may be accompanied by a different predominant effect. Cumo (1977) observed photographically long "jets" of hot liquid streaming forth in front of bubbles forming at surfaces in subcooled liquid. On the basis of heat transfer measurements and photographs in highly subcooled liquids, Brown (1967) suggested that because of evaporation at the hot side and condensation at the cold side of the bubble, a small temperature difference exists around the bubble. This results in a slightly lower surface tension at the outer edge of the bubble, producing significant flow of the interface, which induces large flows of the surrounding liquid to form the observed jets. Here the bubble appears to induce large convection currents, which are heated by the hot surface. This process has been called thermocapillarity. It should be most influential in boiling of subcooled liquids in forced convection, but is no doubt present in some degree at all times.

Thermocapillarity may tend to rapidly remove the thin layer of liquid under a bubble in figure 6.1.13*b*, reducing the time between points *A* and *B* in figure 6.1.13*a*. Also, the convection induced by thermocapillarity may require wall superheats higher than those predicted by figure 6.1.11, as observed in some test data.

Probably all of the preceding mechanisms occur simultaneously and their importance in the heat transfer process depends on the conditions. The boundaries between regions where different mechanisms predominate are not yet well established.

6.1.7 BUBBLE PARAMETERS

For liquids that wet the heating surface, the size of bubbles at departure from the surface has been studied. Fritz (1935) and Wark (1933) equated buoyancy and surface tension and obtained the following expression for *departure diameter:*

$$D_b = C_d \beta \left[\frac{2\sigma}{g(\rho_L - \rho_G)} \right]^{1/2} \qquad [6.1.22]$$

where C_d was found experimentally to be 0.0148 for water and hydrogen bubbles, and β is the contact angle.

Mikic et al. (1970) and Lien & Griffith (1969) studied bubble growth analytically and experimentally. Their results show that for all bubbles, growth is first dynamically controlled and later becomes thermally controlled, vaporization being governed by heat conduction. Mikic et al. (1970) showed that for a bubble growing at a wall with $T_W > T_{sat}$ into a liquid with $T_b < T_{sat}$

$$\frac{dR^+}{dt^+} = \left[t^+ + 1 - \theta \left(\frac{t^+}{t^+ + t_w^+} \right)^{1/2} \right]^{1/2} - (t^+)^{1/2} \qquad [6.1.23]$$

where

$$R^+ \equiv R \frac{A}{B^2} \qquad t^+ = \frac{t A^2}{B^2}$$

$$A \equiv \left[b \frac{(T_W - T_{sat})h_{LG}\rho_G}{T_{sat}\rho_L} \right]^{1/2} \qquad B \equiv \left[\frac{12}{\pi} \frac{(\text{Ja})^2 \lambda_L}{\rho_L c_L} \right]^{1/2}$$

$$\text{Ja} \equiv \frac{(T_W - T_{sat})\rho_L c_L}{h_{LG}\rho_G} \qquad \theta \equiv \frac{T_W - T_b}{T_W - T_{sat}}$$

and Ja is Jakob number. For the bubble growing at the wall $b = \pi/7$. Mikic et al. (1970) showed that the waiting time between bubbles may be approximated by

$$t_w = \frac{\rho_L c_L}{\pi \lambda_L} \left[\frac{(T_W - T_b)R_{cav}}{T_W - T_{sat}(1 + 2\upsilon_{LG}/R_{cav}h_{LG})} \right]^2$$

where R_{cav} is the radius of the cavity. Mikic et al. integrated [6.1.23] for various magnitudes of the parameters, neglecting R_{cav}, which is the bubble radius at $t = 0$, compared with R throughout the growth.

For dynamically controlled growth $t^+ \ll 1$ and $t_w^+ \gg t^+$, integration of [6.1.23] gives

$$R^+ = t^+ \qquad [6.1.24]$$

For the thermally controlled region $t^+ \gg 1$, [6.1.23] is approximated by

$$R^+ = t^{+1/2} (1 - \theta) \left[\left(1 + \frac{t_w^+}{t^+} \right)^{1/2} - \left(\frac{t_w^+}{t^+} \right)^{1/2} \right]$$ [6.1.25]

For a bubble growing in an initially uniformly superheated liquid $(t_w^+ \to \infty)$ from an initial radius greater than the critical radius given by [6.1.4a], integration of [6.1.23] gives

$$R^+ = \tfrac{2}{3} [(t^+ + 1)^{3/2} - t^{+3/2} - 1]$$ [6.1.26]

which is valid for both regimes of growth. Here $b = \tfrac{2}{3}$ in A.

For the dynamically controlled region $t^+ \ll 1$, [6.1.26] becomes

$$R^+ = t^+$$ [6.1.27]

which is the Rayleigh solution and is identical to [6.1.24].

For the thermally controlled region $t^+ \gg 1$, [6.1.26] becomes

$$R^+ = \sqrt{t^+}$$ [6.1.28]

which is the result obtained by Plesset & Zwick (1954) and by Scriven (1959).

Lien & Griffith (1969) performed definitive experiments for bubble growth in superheated water over the pressure range 0.0012–0.038 MPa, superheat range 8–15°C, and $58 < \text{Ja} < 2690$. For pressures less than around 0.003 MPa bubble growth remained in the dynamically controlled region $R^+ = t^+$; for pressures above 0.034 MPa the dynamically controlled region existed for only a short time and practically all of the growth was governed by heat conduction. Between these pressures the early stage of growth was dynamically controlled and the later stage thermally controlled. The midrange of this region existed when $t^+ = 1$. The results agreed with the prediction of [6.1.26].

Application of [6.1.26] to bubble growth in sodium suggests that for superheats around 17°C the thermally controlled region governs for pressures above about 0.17 MPa and the dynamically controlled region governs for pressures less than about 0.03 MPa.

Experimental data for growth in nonuniform temperature fields for which t_w is recorded are limited but do agree with the prediction of [6.1.25]. Data for bubble growth on heated surfaces at reduced pressures exist (Cole 1967) but magnitudes of t_w are not reported. These data fall below the prediction of [6.1.26], suggesting that [6.1.24] should apply and that the effect of waiting time on the data is significant.

Bubble departure diameters D_b as given by [6.1.22] do not agree well with data. Cole & Rohsenow (1969) correlated D_b for various fluids by using:

$$\text{Eo}^{1/2} = 1.5 \times 10^{-4} \text{ Ja}^{*5/4} \quad \text{for water}$$

$$\text{Eo}^{1/2} = 4.65 \times 10^{-4} \text{ Ja}^{*5/4} \quad \text{for other fluids}$$ [6.1.29]

where

$$\text{Eo} \equiv \frac{g(\rho_L - \rho_G)D_b^2}{\sigma}$$

$$\text{Ja}^* \equiv \frac{\rho_L c_L T_{\text{sat}}}{\rho_G h_{LG}}$$

Prediction of bubble frequency for growth at a heating surface is not well established. Jakob & Fritz (1931) suggest $fD_b = 0.078$ m/s for hydrogen and water bubbles. Zuber (1959) and Peebles & Garber (1953) observed

$$fD_b = 1.18 \left(\frac{t_c}{t_c + t_w} \right) \left[\frac{\sigma g(\rho_L - \rho_G)}{\rho_L^2} \right]^{1/4} \qquad [6.1.30]$$

where t_c and t_w are bubble growth time and waiting time between bubbles, respectively. Cole (1967) showed from data that $1.18 \, t_c/(t_c + t_w)$ ranged between 0.15 and 1.4, raising serious doubt about the validity of [6.1.30].

Ivey (1967) showed that the frequency-diameter relation depended on the regime of bubble growth:

$$D_b f^2 = \text{const} \qquad \text{dynamically controlled}$$

$$D_b f^{1/2} = \text{const} \qquad \text{thermally controlled}$$

In the intermediate region the exponent of f changes from 2 to $\frac{1}{2}$.

The analysis of Mikic et al. (1970) for the thermally controlled regime leads to

$$\frac{D_b f^{1/2}}{2 \text{Ja} \sqrt{\pi \kappa_L}} = \left(\frac{t_c}{t_c + t_w} \right)^{1/2} + \left(\frac{t_w}{t_c + t_w} \right)^{1/2} - 1 \qquad [6.1.31]$$

where $t_c + t_w = 1/f$ and κ is thermal diffusivity. Over the range $0.2 < t_c/(t_c + t_w) < 0.8$, this becomes

$$D_b f^{1/2} = \tfrac{3}{4} \sqrt{\pi \kappa_L} \, \text{Ja} \pm 10\% \qquad [6.1.32]$$

In the dynamically controlled regime, Cole (1960) suggested

$$D_b f^2 = \frac{4}{3} \frac{g(\rho_L - \rho_G)}{\xi \rho_L} \qquad [6.1.33]$$

where ξ is the drag coefficient. For steam at 0.1 MPa, $\xi = 1$, and $\rho_G \ll \rho_L$, this reduces to

$$D_b f^2 = 1.32g \qquad [6.1.34]$$

There is not much information about f versus D_b. The relations above should be considered approximate.

Effects of forced convection on D_b and f are not well established. Koumoutsos et al. (1968) showed that D_b decreased linearly with increasing velocity. No general prediction method is available.

As $\dot{q}$ increases the number of active nucleating cavities increases. Staniszewski (1959) observed

$$\dot{q} \sim n^m \qquad [6.1.35]$$

where $m = 1$ at low $\dot{q}$ and decreases to around $\frac{1}{2}$ at high $\dot{q}$.

A further discussion of the relative importance of the various forces—inertia, surface tension, buoyancy, drag—is given by Beer et al. (1977).

The discussion in this section applies to single-component fluids. In binary mixtures similar relations for bubble growth apply, but the effect of varying interface saturation temperature due to changing concentrations resulting from mass diffusion of the more volatile component must be included in integrating the equations. This phenomenon has been studied extensively by van Stralen and others (van Stralen 1968; Florscheutz & Khan 1970).

6.2 Pool Boiling

Warren M. Rohsenow

6.2.1 FACTORS AFFECTING POOL BOILING DATA

This chapter presents the results of experimental observations showing the effect on pool boiling data (figure 6.1.1) of changing the magnitude of various properties and conditions. Except as noted, all data discussed are for liquids that wet the heating surface.

Pressure and temperature difference have a marked effect on all regimes of boiling; figure 6.2.1 shows representative data. At higher pressures the curves move to lower superheat values. Imagine a cavity size distribution—the number of cavities in a particular size range versus the cavity diameter—represented by the curve in figure 6.2.2. The first cavity to be activated has an approximate diameter as calculated from the intersection, figure 6.1.10a, or the point of tangency of the curves in figure 6.1.10b. Then, in accordance with [6.1.35], as $\dot{q}$ is increased, n must increase and more cavities must become activated at diameters spread on either side of the diameter D_c (figure 6.2.2). As shown in figure 6.1.10, this requires greater wall superheat.

The slope of the $\dot{q}$ versus ΔT curve expresses the change in ΔT necessary to increase the number of activated points to accommodate the new heat flux. Although the slope is predominantly in the neighborhood of 3, observations are available that result in slopes as low as unity for contaminated surfaces and as high as approximately 25 for clean, polished surfaces. The actual slope depends on the uniformity or distribution of sizes and shapes of the nucleating cavities (figure 6.2.2).

Griffith & Wallis (1960) obtained data for a number of active nucleation sites versus wall superheat and calculated the radius corresponding to this wall superheat from [6.1.4a]. For boiling water, methanol, and ethanol on the same surface, a single curve resulted for number of active nucleation sites versus this radius, suggesting the existence of a characteristic cavity distribution (figure 6.2.2) for that surface.

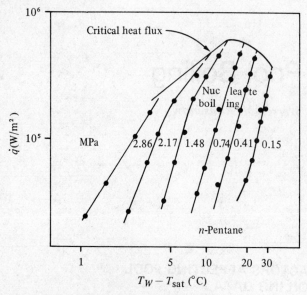

Figure 6.2.1 Effect of pressure on pool boiling curve.

6.2.1.1 Effect of Pressure

Pool boiling heat flux data plotted against wall superheat result in curves as shown in figure 6.2.1. At higher pressures the data lie at lower superheat magnitudes. Of significance in explaining this shift to lower wall superheat is that the fact that for all fluids [6.1.4a] predicts lower ΔT required to activate cavities of a given size as pressure is increased. Figure 6.2.3 presents results for pool boiling of sodium, showing the shift of lower ΔT with pressure.

Figure 6.2.1 also shows typical results for the effects of pressure on the critical (or peak) heat flux in pool boiling. This $\dot{q}_c$ typically goes through a maximum at a pressure well below the critical pressure. Data for four Freons (Bier et al. 1977) also show these effects.

6.2.1.2 Effect of Surface Finish

Changing surface finish can shift the position of the boiling curve markedly, probably because it changes the cavity size distribution (figure 6.2.2). The initial controlled experiments on this effect were performed by Corty & Foust (1955).

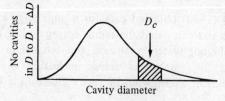

Figure 6.2.2 Cavity size distribution.

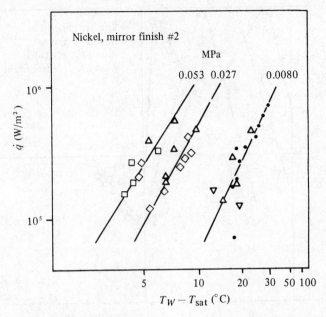

Figure 6.2.3 Effect of pressure on nucleate pool boiling of sodium (Marto & Rohsenow 1966).

Figure 6.2.4 shows typical results. The data for the rougher surfaces lie to the left, at lower wall superheat, presumably because active cavity sizes are smaller on the smoother surfaces (Berenson 1960).

The data in figure 6.2.5 show an interesting effect of direction of surface finish (or scratch) orientation on boiling. Here axial and circumferential finishing of a horizontal tube produce quite different results at low heat fluxes. At low heat flux, the liquid-vapor interface of bubbles moving circumferentially on the surface tends to fill the scratches or cavities with liquid, deactivating them. With axial scratches vapor tends to be trapped in cavities, keeping them active. For this reason, horizontal scratches require lower superheat to produce the same heat flux. At higher heat fluxes this effect disappears because the bubbles tend to move perpendicularly away from the surface. Then the roughness effect of figure 6.2.4 predominates.

Of significance is the observation from figure 6.2.4 that surface finish does not influence the position of the data or of the minimum heat flux in film boiling.

The influence of surface finish on critical heat flux is shown in figure 6.2.4 to be rather small—about a 20% reduction in $\dot{q}_c$ for very smooth surfaces.

6.2.1.3 Aging

Experience teaches that aged surfaces have higher required ΔT for a given $\dot{q}$. On metallic surfaces a scale or deposit may form from the boiling liquid, or a film may form from oxidation or other chemical reaction. In either case the vapor-trapping cavity may shrink, necessitating higher superheat for activation. Also, the tempera-

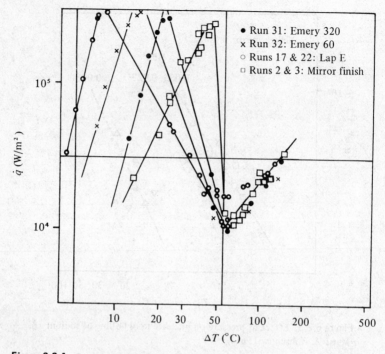

Figure 6.2.4   Copper-pentane test results: effect of roughness (Berenson 1960).

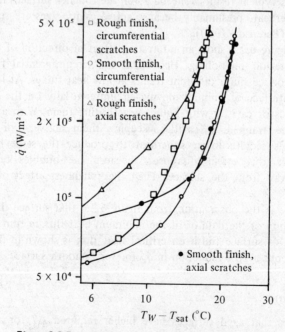

Figure 6.2.5   Influence of surface finish on pool boiling of water from the outside of a horizontal tube (Brown 1967).

ture drop across the deposit layer is included in the reported ΔT, resulting in higher ΔT values.

6.2.1.4   Surface Coating or Deposits

In addition to the effect of aging described above, a temperature drop is associated with conduction across the coating or deposit. Since coatings may be very thin and their properties unknown, this additional temperature difference is usually included in the ΔT for boiling data. Including this constant, conduction resistance causes $\dot{q}$-ΔT curves to be farther to the right and have lower slopes than those for clean surfaces. Curves for surfaces with different coatings are spread even farther apart than those of figure 6.2.4.

Various investigators have reported data for the effect of surface deposits on critical heat flux. Although there is some disagreement, the following conclusions may be reached. Surfaces coated mechanically or by oxidation may have higher $\dot{q}_c$ for small-diameter cylinders, by as much as a factor of 2-3; this effect seems to diminish as diameter increases, disappearing at diameters larger than 1 cm. No appreciable effect is noticed for flat plates.

For clean surfaces not prone to severe oxidation, such as chromel, silver, stainless steel, and nickel, data for $\dot{q}_c$ scatter with a band of about ±20% for a given wire as well as for different materials (Ivey & Morris 1962a).

6.2.1.5   Treated Surfaces

Spots of Teflon in pits were found to promote nucleation for liquids that do not wet Teflon (Young & Hummel 1964). For water, nucleation occurred at less than 1°C superheat with $\dot{q}$-ΔT curves lying at very much lower temperature differences than those for untreated surfaces. This technique was not effective for refrigerants that do wet Teflon (Bergles et al. 1968). A commercial surface, known as High Flux Surface, with a brazed porous coating containing reentrant cavities shifts the boiling curve to low wall superheats. These and other coated surfaces were surveyed by Danilova (1976).

6.2.1.6   Effect of Gases

Noncondensable gases dissolved in water tend to come out of solution at a hot surface. In general, they tend to move the $\dot{q}$-ΔT curve to the left and reduce the magnitude of $\dot{q}_c$.

Figure 6.2.6 shows the results when fresh liquid containing gas is continually brought to the heating surface by forced convection. Gas bubbles may appear at temperatures well below the normal boiling point and additional convection, probably induced by thermocapillarity, may produce higher heat fluxes as shown.

Another phenomenon that appears to be associated with the presence of gas in the nucleating cavities is a kind of unstable boiling or bumping, thus far observed only in boiling of liquid metals (Marto & Rohsenow 1966; Shai 1967). At moderate heat fluxes in nucleate boiling of sodium, the process seems to change back and

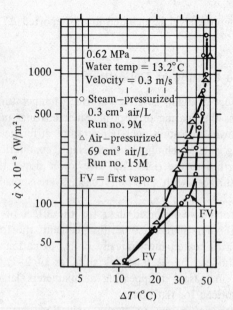

Figure 6.2.6   Effect of dissolved gas on boiling
curve (McAdams et al. 1959).

forth between nucleate boiling and natural convection as active cavities become
deactivated and reactivated. After a time during which gas is removed from the
cavity and the liquid, this oscillation ceases and steady natural convection takes
place. In the absence of gas the natural convection curve is followed until the cavity
is nucleated ([6.1.4a]); nucleate boiling occurs above this heat flux and the average
ΔT is much lower, although the surface temperature varies considerably under each
bubble in liquid metals. This minimum heat flux for nucleate boiling in the absence
of gas is also the maximum heat flux for which unstable boiling occurs when gas is
present (Shai 1967).

The effect of noncondensable gases on the critical heat flux in pool boiling
appears to be most significant at high subcooling and not very significant at
temperatures near the normal boiling point.

6.2.1.7   Hysteresis

Overshooting of the wall temperature with increasing $\dot{q}$ in natural convection and a
significant drop in ΔT when boiling begins is known as a hysteresis effect. This
overshooting is more pronounced with liquid metals—particularly alkali metals,
which wet practically all solid surfaces extemely well—and refrigerants. This tends to
deactivate cavities, as discussed in connection with figure 6.1.2c.

With liquid nonmetals overshooting occurs less frequently, since cavities such as
those of figure 6.1.2d are usually present and remain active even after the system is
cooled down. In nonmetals, if some of the cavities become deactivated, the
hysteresis overshoot can occur (Westwater & Strenge 1959); however, when the heat
flux is reduced in the nucleate boiling region the data follow smoothly down the

boiling curve to natural convection. Hysteresis in forced convection of refrigerant R-11 was observed by Abdelmessih et al. (1974).

6.2.1.8 Size and Orientation of Heating Surface

There is an effect of wire size and surface orientation on the $\dot{q}$-ΔT curve in the nucleate boiling region. This geometry effect, however, is more pronounced in the nonboiling natural convection region, which is the left asymptote of the curve, and is predicted by the normal single-phase natural convection data. Geometry also influences the data in the film boiling regime (curves for smaller wire diameters are to the left).

The burnout heat flux appears to be influenced more by geometry. There may be as much as a 25% variation in burnout flux in flat-plate data; the difference is lower for vertical heaters than for horizontal ones (Bernath 1955, 1960) and may be greater for larger heaters. Burnout heat flux appears to increase with wire size (Ivey & Morris 1962b; Bernath 1960; Costello et al. 1964; Pitts & Leppert 1966) from 0.025 to 0.25 cm and levels off above that size. For sizes from 0.025 down to 0.0075 cm the magnitude of burnout flux levels off again (Pitts & Leppert 1966). In the range where burnout changes with diameter, bubble sizes are of the order of the wire diameter. Houchin & Lienhard (1966) measured reduced burnout heat fluxes for thin-ribbon heaters with thicknesses as low as 0.0009 cm. Data for various thicknesses of aluminum, nickel, silver, tantalum, and stainless steel were correlated with $\rho c \delta$, where ρ is density, c is specific heat, and δ is the ribbon thickness with one side insulated. For water with dc heating $\dot{q}_c$ decreased from 1,000,000 to 650,000 W/m^2, when $\rho c \delta$ decreased from 1200 to 30 J/m^2 °C. A more pronounced decrease was found with ac heating. For $\rho c \delta > 1200$ both ac and dc heating gave the same $\dot{q}_c$ ($= 1,000,000$) independent of $\rho c \delta$.

6.2.1.9 Agitation

The effect of agitation, as with a propeller, is quite similar to the velocity effect shown in figure 6.1.1. Curves for greater rotational velocities are higher on the graph. This effect was studied by Austin (1903) and more recently by Pramuk & Westwater (1956). Also, burnout heat flux increases with increasing rotational velocity of the agitator. No attempt is made to correlate this information, since the effect is greatly influenced by the agitator's shape, size, and position.

6.2.1.10 Subcooling

The effect of subcooling on the position of the boiling curve is not well established but appears to depend on the geometry for convection. Data for water boiling on a 0.164-cm-diameter stainless steel tube lie farther to the right as subcooling is increased (Bergles & Rohsenow 1964). The left asymptotes are for natural convection and should have a higher $\dot{q}$ for greater subcooling at equal $T_W - T_{\text{sat}}$. By contrast, results for a horizontal flat nichrome heater 10.8 cm square and 0.0419 cm thick lie farther to the left as subcooling increases (Duke & Schrock 1961). The differences between these results may be due to different convection geometries or different nucleating conditions of the surface. Burnout heat flux increases markedly as subcooling increases.

6.2.1.11 Nonwet Surfaces

When the liquid does not wet the heating surface, very large vapor bubbles form and cover much larger portions of the heating surface (Jakob & Fritz 1931; Averin 1954). The net result is that much greater magnitudes of $T_W - T_{sat}$ are required to transfer a given $\dot{q}$. The burnout heat flux is very much reduced by factors of 10-20. The $\dot{q}$-ΔT curve may not exhibit a maximum but may increase gradually directly into film boiling.

6.2.1.12 Gravitational Field

A ribbon heater immersed in a beaker of water was photographed during free-fall conditions (Siegel & Usiskin 1959). Heat fluxes were in the nucleate boiling range under a normal gravity field. At lower heat fluxes bubbles grew while remaining attached to the ribbon, and at higher heat fluxes a very large vapor volume formed around the ribbon. This suggests that nucleate boiling is essentially nonexistent under zero-g conditions.

Subsequently, Siegel & Usiskin (1959), added a small amount of friction to the free-fall system, raising g to approximately 0.09. They reported orally that under these conditions nucleate boiling appeared to continue throughout the fall. This indicates that only a small gravity field is needed to maintain nucleate boiling.

Merte & Clark (1959) reported the results of tests on a heated surface at the bottom of a pool. The system was placed in a centrifuge and rotated so that the resultant acceleration field was normal to the surface. Their boiling tests covered the range 1–21 g. There seemed to be very little effect on the position of the $\dot{q}$ versus $T_W - T_{sat}$ curves at higher heat fluxes. The displacement of the curves at lower heat fluxes is probably due to superimposed natural convection.

6.2.1.13 Binary Mixtures

Boiling of binary mixtures is a complex process influenced by the mass diffusion of the more volatile fluid toward the liquid-vapor interface. This results in a change of interface saturation temperature with time during bubble growth. Boiling curves, $\dot{q}$ versus ΔT, for mixtures usually lie between those for the two pure components. However, burnout heat flux usually goes through a maximum at some intermediate concentration (van Stralen 1970).

6.2.2 CORRELATION OF BOILING HEAT TRANSFER DATA

The logic leading to the various forms of the correlations of pool boiling heat transfer data is omitted here, and suggested equations are presented with comments on their applicability.

Referring to figure 6.2.4, one must conclude that any correlation equation that embodies only properties of the fluid (liquid or vapor) cannot be a "universal" correlation for all fluids or, for that matter, for any particular fluid. At least the coefficient (and possibly even the exponents) must change in magnitude as the character of the solid surface changes. The data for figure 6.2.4, for example, are all for the same fluid conditions; only the solid surface condition has changed. This point cannot be overemphasized. This has led to a great deal of confusion among boiling heat transfer researchers and users.

Many proposed correlations were developed by analysis of a simplified model of boiling, leading to some dimensionless groups of quantities. Various forms of bubble Nusselt numbers, bubble Reynolds numbers, and Prandtl numbers appear in these equations. An early correlation (Rohsenow 1952) employed such groups with the characteristic dimension D given in [6.1.22]:

$$\frac{c_L(T_W - T_{sat})}{h_{LG}} = C_{sf} \left\{ \frac{\dot{q}}{\mu_L h_{LG}} \left[\frac{\sigma}{g(\rho_L - \rho_G)} \right]^{1/2} \right\}^r \left(\frac{c_L \mu_L}{\lambda_L} \right)^s \qquad [6.2.1]$$

where C_{sf} should be a function of the particular fluid-heating surface combination. From figure 6.2.7a or 6.2.7b the exponent $r = 0.33$. A cross-plot of $c_L \Delta T/h_{LG}$ versus Pr where Pr is the Prandtl number for constant values of the ordinate show $s = 1.0$ for water but $s = 1.7$ for all other fluids. The final correlation is shown in figure 6.2.7c, which results in $C_{sf} = 0.013$ with a spread of approximately ±20%. This process was repeated for other data with the results shown in table 6.2.1. The C_{sf} magnitudes in table 6.2.1 should not be associated with the metal surface, but rather with the surface condition (cavity size distribution) at the time the data were taken.

It should be emphasized that accurate values of fluid properties are essential to obtain a correlation or use [6.2.1]. Also, the heating surface should be clean. The presence of contamination or a deposit on the heating surface can shift the relative position and slope of the curve, thus changing r and s in addition to C_{sf}. It should also be noted that [6.2.1] includes a $g^{1/6}$ term, which came from the expression for D_b in [6.1.22]. There appears to be no effect of g on the position of the boiling curve.

Later, Forster & Zuber (1955) used similar dimensionless groups, but with $R\dot{R}$ of [6.1.28] as the velocity × characteristic dimension in the Reynolds number and $2\sigma/\Delta p$ as the characteristic dimension in the Nusselt number.

Forster & Greif (1959) modified the Forster & Zuber equation by not linearizing the Δp versus ΔT relation and suggested

$$\frac{\dot{q}}{h_{LG}\rho_G} \left(\frac{2\sigma}{\kappa\Delta p} \right)^{1/2} \left(\frac{\rho_L}{\Delta_p} \right)^{1/4} = C_2 \left\{ \frac{\rho_L}{\mu} \left[\frac{c\rho_L(\pi\kappa)^{1/2} T_{sat}}{(h_{LG}\rho_G)^2} \Delta p \right]^2 \right\}^{5/8} Pr^{1/3}$$

$$[6.2.2]$$

where C_2 was 0.0012 from data for water at 0.1 and 5.0 MPa, *n*-butyl alcohol at 0.33 MPa, analine at 0.23 MPa, and mercury at 0.1 and 0.3 MPa. Equation [6.2.2] in the following form approximates the data

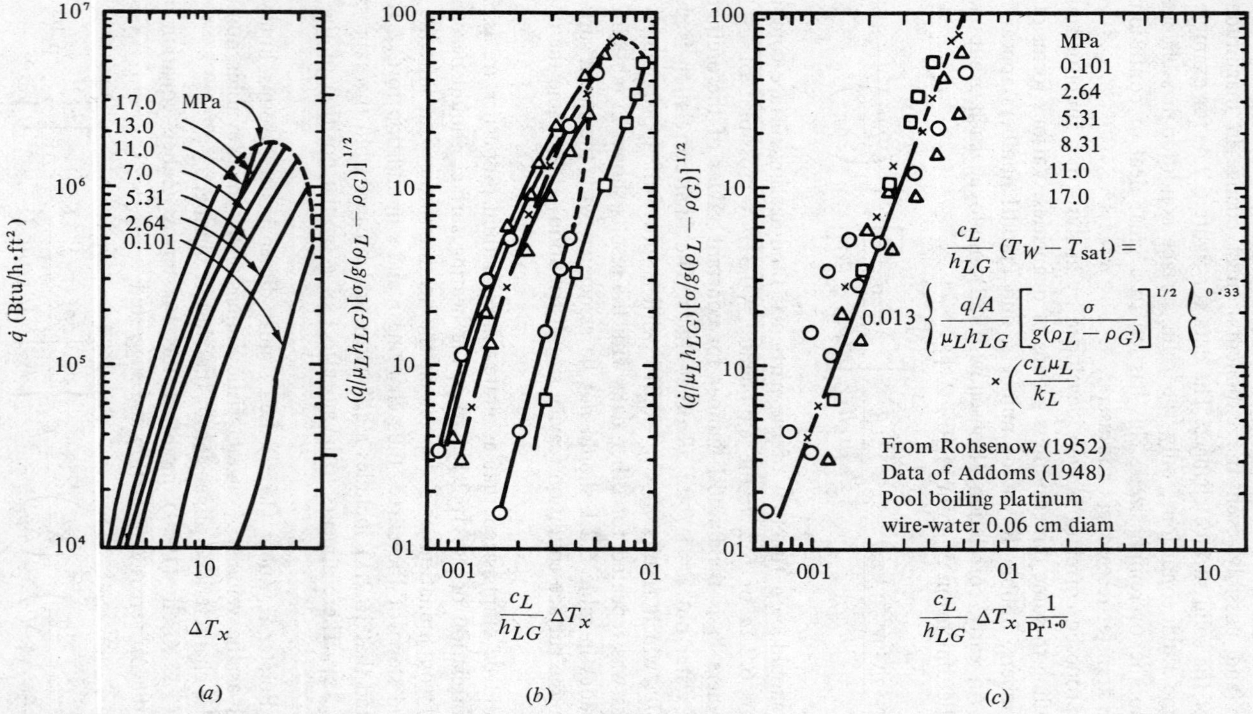

$\dot{q}$ (Btu/h·ft²)
10^7
10^6
10^5
10^4
17.0 MPa
13.0
11.0
7.0
5.31
2.64
0.101
10
ΔT_x
(a)
$(\dot{q}/\mu_L h_{LG})[\sigma/g(\rho_L - \rho_G)]^{1/2}$
100
10
10
01
001
01
$\frac{c_L}{h_{LG}} \Delta T_x$
(b)
MPa
0.101
2.64
5.31
8.31
11.0
17.0
$\frac{c_L}{h_{LG}}(T_W - T_{sat}) = 0.013 \left\{ \frac{q/A}{\mu_L h_{LG}} \left[\frac{\sigma}{g(\rho_L - \rho_G)} \right]^{1/2} \right\}^{0.33} \times \left(\frac{c_L \mu_L}{k_L} \right)$
From Rohsenow (1952)
Data of Addoms (1948)
Pool boiling platinum
wire-water 0.06 cm diam
$\frac{c_L}{h_{LG}} \Delta T_x \frac{1}{\mathrm{Pr}^{1.0}}$
(c)

Figure 6.2.7 Correlation of nucleate boiling data for water (Rohsenow 1952).

Table 6.2.1 Correlation of [6.2.1] with $r = 0.33$

Fluid and heating surface	C_{sf}	s
Water-nickel	0.006	1.0
Water-platinum	0.013	1.0
Water-copper	0.013	1.0
Water-brass	0.006	1.0
CCl_4-copper	0.013	1.7
Benzene-chromium	0.010	1.7
n-Pentane-chromium	0.015	1.7
Ethyl alcohol-chromium	0.0027	1.7
Isopropyl alcohol-copper	0.0025	1.7
35% K_2CO_3-copper	0.0054	1.7
60% K_2CO_3-copper	0.027	1.7
n-Butyl alcohol-copper	0.0030	1.7

$$\dot{q} = K_{sf} \left(\frac{\kappa c \rho_L T_S}{h_{LG} \rho_G \sigma^{1/2}} \right) \left[\frac{c T_S (\kappa)^{1/2}}{(h_{LG} \rho_G)^2} \right]^{1/4} \left(\frac{\rho_L}{\mu} \right)^{5/8} Pr^{1/3} (\Delta p)^2 \qquad [6.2.3]$$

where T_S is the saturation temperature.

Griffith & Rohsenow (1955) showed that for the data above K_{sf} should be 43×10^{-6}; they also showed that [6.2.3] agreed well with data for ethanol-chromium (Cichelli & Bonilla 1945) with $K_{sf} = 82 \times 10^{-6}$ and with data for water-platinum (Addoms 1948) with $K_{sf} = 142 \times 10^{-6}$. Hence K_{sf} is different for different surface-fluid combinations just as C_{sf} is in [6.2.1]. This is to be expected from figure 6.2.4, where surface properties alone significantly influence the position of the $\dot{q}$-ΔT curve. Since [6.2.2] and [6.2.3] contain only fluid properties, this surface effect must appear in K_{sf} as well as in C_{sf} of [6.2.3] and [6.2.1].

Equation [6.2.3] is identical to the earlier Forster & Zuber equation, except that Δp and ΔT are related by [6.1.3]. Also, [6.2.3] yields a varying exponent for $\dot{q}$ versus ΔT, increasing with ΔT in the range 2-4. In many cases the curve cuts across natural boiling data at a lower slope.

Other correlations have been suggested by Gilmour (1958), McNeilly (1953), and Levy (1959). The Gilmour correlation contains a size effect not verified by experiment. The Levy procedure is dimensional and employs an empirical curve around which data scatter by a factor of 5 or more—about the same variation observed in C_{sf} of table 6.2.1. (Readers of the Levy paper as originally published should note that the ordinate of its figure 4 should be read as multiplied by 10^{-5} instead of 10^{-6}.)

Various Russian workers have suggested correlation equations with the following form (Wallis 1961):

$$Nu_* = A \, Pr^{n_1} Pe_*^{n_2} K_p^{n_3} K_t^{n_4} Ar_*^{n_5} \qquad [6.2.4]$$

where

$$Nu_* \equiv \frac{\alpha}{\lambda} \left[\frac{\sigma}{g(\rho_L - \rho_G)} \right]^{1/2} \qquad [6.2.5]$$

$$\text{Pe}_* \equiv \frac{\dot{q}}{\kappa \rho_G h_{LG}} \left(\frac{\sigma}{g(\rho_L - \rho_G)} \right)^{1/2}$$

$$K_p \equiv \frac{p}{[g\sigma(\rho_L - \rho_G)]^{1/2}}$$

$$K_t \equiv \frac{(\rho_G h_{LG})^2}{c_L T_{\text{sat}} \rho_L [g\sigma(\rho_L - \rho_G)]^{1/2}}$$

[6.2.5]
Cont.

$$\text{Ar}_* \equiv \frac{g}{\nu^2} \left[\frac{g_0 \sigma}{g(\rho_L - \rho_G)} \right]^{3/2} \left(1 - \frac{\rho_G}{\rho_L} \right)$$

Values of the coefficients in [6.2.4] are shown in table 6.2.2. It should be emphasized again that the coefficient A in [6.2.4] is not a constant, but varies with the surface-fluid combination.

Equation [6.2.1] has correlated the pressure effect for a variety of pool boiling data. The state of knowledge is such that the coefficient C_{sf} must be determined from limited data for each fluid-surface combination. This, of course, is true for any of the other pool boiling correlations.

It should also be emphasized that the actual metal of the surface is perhaps less important than the surface character, as represented by the cavity size distribution of figure 6.2.2, which is unknown for practically all the surfaces tested.

Mikic & Rohsenow (1969) show the effect of cavity size distribution for any surface on the position of the $\dot{q}$-ΔT boiling curve in pool boiling. Starting with the description of the boiling process as outlined and assuming that the number of cavities of radius greater than r is expressible by

$$n = \left(\frac{r_s}{r} \right)^m$$

[6.2.6]

where r_s is the radius of the largest cavity present and r_s and m are determined from cavity size distribution measurements (Brown, 1967).

Postulate that when a bubble of diameter D_b departs from the surface it pumps superheated liquid away from the surface over a region $2D_b$, and colder liquid at T_{sat} replaces this superheated liquid (Hsu & Graham 1961). Between bubble departures, the transient heat conduction to the liquid in the region $2D_b$ would be

Table 6.2.2 Correlations by Russian Authors[a]

Source	A	n_1	n_2	n_3	n_4	n_5
Kichigan & Tobilevich	1.04×10^{-4}	0	0.7	0.7	0	0.125
Kutateladze	7.0×10^{-4}	-0.35	0.7	0.7	0	0
Borishanskiy & Minchenko	8.7×10^{-4}	0	0.7	0.7	0	0
Kruzhilin & Averin	0.082	-0.5	0.7	0	0.377	0
Labuntsov	0.125	-0.32	0.65	0	0.35	0

[a]From Kutateladze (1963).

$$\dot{q} = \frac{2\lambda\Delta T \sqrt{f}}{\sqrt{\pi\kappa}}$$

where f is frequency. The fraction of surface covered by n active spots per unit area is $n(\pi/4)(2D_b)^2$. Therefore the $\dot{q}$ representing the superheating of liquid at these active spots per unit total surface area is

$$\dot{q}_b = 2\sqrt{\pi(\lambda\rho c)_L f} \; D_b^2 n\Delta T \qquad [6.2.7]$$

This is taken as the heat transfer at the bubble locations that forms the vapor in the pool. This equation has been verified for many fluid-surface combinations by measuring $\dot{q}_b$, ΔT, D_b, f, and n.

The area between the active bubble sites per unit total area is

$$\frac{A_{nc}}{A} = 1 - n\pi D_b^2 \qquad [6.2.8]$$

Postulate that in this region heat is transferred by single-phase natural convection

$$\dot{q}_{nc} = h_{nc}\Delta T \qquad [6.2.9]$$

Then the total heat flux is

$$\dot{q} = (1 - n\pi D_b^2)\dot{q}_{nc} + \dot{q}_b \qquad [6.2.10]$$

The intersection of the linear temperature distribution and [6.1.4a] at any ΔT above ΔT_{incip} (figure 6.1.10b) gives

$$r = \frac{2\,T\sigma}{h_{LG}\rho_G\Delta T(1 - \dot{q}r/\lambda\Delta T)} \qquad [6.2.11]$$

For $\dot{q}r/\lambda\Delta T \ll 1$, combining [6.2.11] and [6.2.6] to eliminate r gives

$$n = r_s^m \left(\frac{h_{LG}\rho_G}{2\,T\sigma}\right)^m (\Delta T)^m \qquad [6.2.12]$$

An expression for D_b is [6.1.29] and for fD_b is [6.1.30], where $1.18 \; t_c/(t_c + t_w)$ was taken as 0.6.

Using these relations, [6.2.7] becomes

$$\frac{\dot{q}_b}{\mu_L h_{LG}}\sqrt{\frac{\sigma}{g(\rho_L - \rho_G)}} = B(\phi\Delta T)^{m+1} \qquad [6.2.13]$$

where

$$B \equiv \left(\frac{r_s J}{2}\right)^m \frac{2\sqrt{\pi}}{g^{9/8}} C_2^{5/3} C_3^{1/2} \qquad [6.2.14]$$

$$\phi^{m+1} \equiv \frac{\lambda^{1/2}\rho_L^{17/8} c_L^{19/8} h_{LG}^{m-23/8} \rho_G^{m-15/8}}{\mu_L[(\rho_L - \rho_G)]^{9/8}\sigma^{m-11/8} T_{sat}^{m-15/8}} \qquad [6.2.15]$$

The total heat flux is given by [6.2.10] with [6.2.9] and [6.2.13]. Here $C_2 = 0.00015$ for water and 0.000465 for other fluids ([6.1.29]) and $C_3 = 0.6$ ([6.1.30]); r_s and m are to be determined from the cavity size distribution

([6.2.6]). Note that B is solely a function of cavity size distribution and ϕ is a function of fluid properties and of the exponent m. Further, if the cavity size distribution has slope m, then the q/A versus ΔT curve should have slope $m + 1$. For most fluids $(q/A)_{nc} \ll (q/A)_b$ in [6.2.10] and may be neglected.

For most surfaces for which data are available a cavity size distribution has not been measured. In these cases the boiling data may be used to determine m and B. Mikic & Rohsenow (1969) showed that [6.2.10] used in this way does correlate existing boiling data.

6.2.3 POOL BOILING OF LIQUID METALS

In boiling of liquid metals, some phenomena that are unimportant in boiling of nonmetallic liquids become important. Bubble growth times are shorter, but the waiting period between bubbles is much longer, resulting in much lower bubble frequencies. The bubbles grow in the dynamic region for most of their time in contact with the surface ([6.1.27]). This rapid growth leaves a microlayer behind under the bubble. Rapid heat transfer through this thin layer evaporates only about 5% of the microlayer before departure, but causes the wall temperature to drop during the growth (figure 6.2.8). When the bubble departs the surface temperature drops sharply because $\lambda \rho c$ of the liquid metal and the solid metal surface are of the same order of magnitude.

When the colder liquid at T_{sat} replaces the bubble, transient conduction in

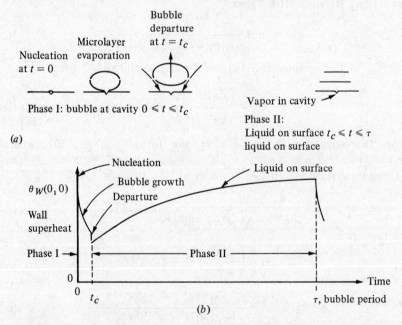

Figure 6.2.8 Model of periodic boiling behavior. (*a*) Bubble behavior. (*b*) Wall temperature-time behavior, modified from Cooper & Lloyd (1966) for the case of sodium.

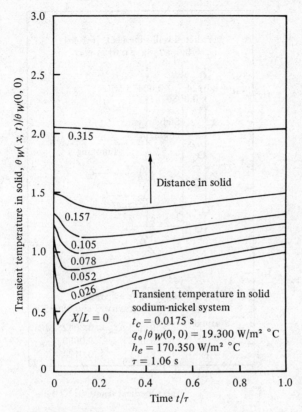

Figure 6.2.9 Transient temperature in the solid at a position, sodium-nickel system.

both the liquid metal and the solid metal occurs and the surface temperature rises in phase II (figure 6.2.8) until it reaches the temperature given by [6.1.4a] for the cavity radius. Then the process is repeated.

Deane & Rohsenow (1970) analyzed data for boiling sodium on a horizontal surface with drilled cylindrical cavities. Figure 6.2.9 shows the variation of temperature at various depths into the solid surface. Figure 6.2.10 shows the boiling curves at three pressures for boiling at a drilled cavity of $r_c = 0.0171$ cm. The vertical lines show the superheat predicted by [6.2.4a] for the drilled cavity.

The contact angle for liquid sodium is very low, less than $10°$. The cavities can become filled with liquid on cooling and become deactivated. Then on subsequent heating, higher superheats are required to initiate boiling (figure 6.2.10). When boiling begins the drilled cavity is activated (region labeled bumping) and the boiling returns to the steady vertical curves.

Data for a natural surface without drilled cavities are shown in figure 6.2.11. The overshoot to higher superheat occurs before fully developed boiling is established, but the steady-state curves have finite slope. The detailed description of the mechanism given above should apply at each active site.

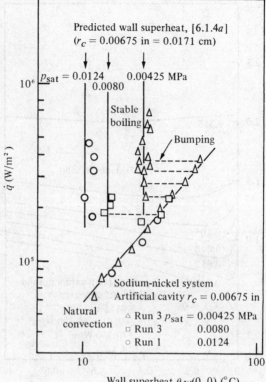

Figure 6.2.10 Effect of pressure on nucleate boiling of sodium from an artificial cavity in a nickel surface.

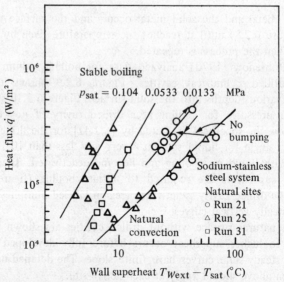

Figure 6.2.11 Effect of pressure on nucleate boiling of sodium from natural sites in stainless steel surfaces.

Subbotin et al. (1970) developed a correlation for pool boiling of sodium, potassium, and cesium:

$$\frac{\dot{q}^{1/3}}{\Delta T} = C \left(\frac{\lambda h_{LG} \rho_L \, J}{\sigma T^2} \right)^{1/3} \left(\frac{p_L}{p_c} \right)^S \qquad [6.2.16]$$

where

	$\dfrac{p_L}{p_c}$	<0.001	>0.001
C		8.0	1.0
S		0.45	0.15

The sharp discontinuity in slope with pressure at $p_L/p_c = 0.001$ is mystifying, but it clearly existed in the data for all three metals.

Dwyer (1976) presented an excellent survey of bubble growth and heat transfer in boiling of liquid metals.

6.2.4 CORRELATION OF BURNOUT POOL BOILING

As heat flux is increased in nucleate boiling, more nucleation sites become active. Equations correlating the burnout heat flux data emerge from models suggesting that (1) as nucleation sites increase, a critical "bubble packing" is reached to produce vapor blanketing (Rohsenow & Griffith 1956), (2) as nucleation sites increase, liquid flow to the heating surface is restricted sufficiently to produce vapor blanketing (Zuber 1959), and (3) as heat flux and number of nucleation sites increase, bubbles in a column overtake each other, producing a vapor column in which there are liquid droplets that fall back to the surface if it is horizontal. When the velocity is sufficient to carry these liquid droplets away from the surface, vapor blanketing occurs (Kutateladze 1952). A further discussion of pool boiling burnout mechanisms is given in section 6.4.6.

As $\dot{q}$ is increased, the streams of bubbles flowing from a nucleation site become columns of vapor. Liquid flows in the opposite direction between these columns to replace the vapor formed. Zuber (1959) suggested that at burnout the relative velocity $V_G - V_L$ reaches a magnitude that produces an unstable interface (Helmholtz instability) given by

$$V_G - V_L = \left(\frac{2\pi\sigma}{\lambda_H} \frac{\rho_L - \rho_G}{\rho_L \rho_G} \right)^{1/2}$$

where

$$\frac{\lambda_H}{2\pi} = \sqrt{\frac{N\sigma}{g(\rho_L - \rho_G)}} \qquad 1 < N < 3$$

and the burnout heat flux is

$$\frac{\dot{q}_c}{\rho_G h_{LG}} = 0.13 \left[\frac{\sigma(\rho_L - \rho_G)g}{\rho_G^2} \right]^{1/4} \left(\frac{\rho_L}{\rho_L + \rho_G} \right)^{1/2} \qquad [6.2.17]$$

Here 0.18 agrees better with the data than the value 0.13 originally suggested by Zuber.

Kutateladze (1952) gave

$$\frac{\dot{q}_c}{\rho_G h_{LG}} = 0.16 \left[\frac{\sigma(\rho_L - \rho_G)g}{\rho_G^2} \right]^{1/4} \qquad [6.2.18]$$

Chang & Snyder (1960),

$$\frac{\dot{q}_c}{\rho_G h_{LG}} = 0.145 \left[\frac{\sigma(\rho_L - \rho_G)g}{\rho_G^2} \right]^{1/4} \left(\frac{\rho_L + \rho_G}{\rho_L} \right)^{1/2} \qquad [6.2.19]$$

Rohsenow & Griffith (1956),

$$\frac{\dot{q}_c}{\rho_G h_{LG}} = 0.012 \left(\frac{g}{g_0} \right)^{1/4} \left(\frac{\rho_L - \rho_G}{\rho_G} \right)^{0.6} \qquad [6.2.20]$$

which is dimensional but agrees with most data.

The quantities on the right-hand side of [6.2.17] to [6.2.19] are essentially the same except when they are very close to the critical pressure. The relations were developed without regard to specific geometry. Lienhard and co-workers (1970, 1973, 1976) modified these relations for specific geometries, as discussed in section 6.4.3.1.

For liquid metals, Noyes & Lurie (1966) suggested

$$\dot{q}_c = 0.16 \, \rho_G h_{LG} \left[\frac{\sigma(\rho_L - \rho_G)g}{\rho_G^2} \right]^{1/4} + K_{NL} \qquad [6.2.21]$$

where $K_{NL} = 1.26 \times 10^6$ for sodium at 0.0015-0.15 MPa. Here the first group of quantities is the Kutateladze number [6.2.18] and K_{NL} is a constant that may be different in magnitude for different fluids. Potassium data (0.0012-0.15 MPa) of Balzheiser & Colver (1963) are correlated by [6.2.21] with $K_{NL} = 0.946 \times 10^6$.

The equations above apply to saturated liquids. For subcooled liquids Zuber et al. (1961) modified [6.2.17] as follows:

$$\frac{\dot{q}_{csub}}{\dot{q}_{csat}} = 1 + \frac{5.3}{\rho_G h_{LG}} \sqrt{\lambda_L \rho_L c_L} \left[\frac{\sigma(\rho_L - \rho_G)g}{\rho^2} \right]^{-1/8} \left[\frac{g(\rho_L - \rho_G)}{\sigma} \right]^{1/4} (T_{sat} - T_L)$$

$$[6.2.22]$$

This was tested and agreed with data for water and ethyl alcohol at pressures below 1.0 MPa. Ivey & Morris (1962a) suggested the simpler relation:

$$\frac{\dot{q}_{csub}}{\dot{q}_{csat}} = 1 + \frac{0.1}{\rho_G h_{LG}} \left(\frac{\rho_G}{\rho_L} \right)^{1/4} c_L \rho_L (T_{sat} - T_L) \qquad [6.2.23]$$

which was tested against and agreed with data for water, ethyl alcohol, ammonia, CCl_4, and isooctane over the pressure range 0.03-3.3 MPa.

None of the correlation equations include an effect of the condition of the solid surface. Berenson (1960) and Ivey & Morris (1962b) obtained less than a 20% variation in $\dot{q}_c$ for a wide variety of clean surface materials and surface finishes. Surfaces that are oxidized or coated, which tends to increase wettability, tend to have higher magnitudes of $\dot{q}_c$ (Ivey & Morris 1962b; Costello & Frea 1963). Parametric effects on pool boiling burnout are discussed further in section 6.4.2.1.

6.2.5 TRANSIENT POOL BOILING

Extensive tests of transient pool boiling from an electrically heated vertical thin metal strip were reported by Johnson (1971) for both stepwise and exponentially varying electrical input. Similar tests were reported for exponentially varying input by Sakurai & Shiotsu (1977), where the heater was a horizontal platinum wire 1.2 mm in diameter and 97.9 mm long. The heat flux to the liquid is

$$\dot{q} = \dot{q}_0\, e^{t/t_0} - \frac{Mc}{A}\frac{dT}{dt} \qquad [6.2.24]$$

where Mc is mass times specific heat of the heater, t_0 is a time constant of the heating, and $\dot{q}_0$ is the initial heat flux.

Figure 6.2.12 shows the change in the incipient boiling condition to higher temperatures than those for the steady state as the rate of heating is increase or t_0 is decreased. The dashed curve represents the steady-state incipient boiling condition predicted by [6.1.16] and [6.1.20] with a maximum cavity size of $r_{max} = 0.000387$ cm. At low heating rates it predicts the incipient boiling points. As

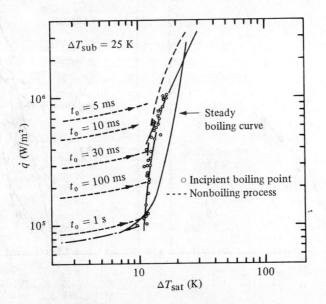

Figure 6.2.12 Relation between heat flux and superheat at incipient boiling points for subcooling of 25 K. Some of the heat transfer processes before the incipient boiling points are shown by broken lines.

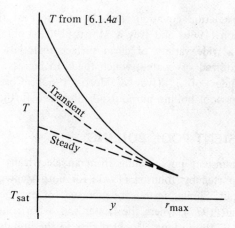

Figure 6.2.13 Nucleation cavity at $r = r_{max}$.

heating rate increases (t_0 decreases), the incipient temperature difference increases above this steady-state prediction. When the liquid temperature reaches the nucleating condition, shown in figure 6.2.13 for nucleation at r_{max}, the wall temperature in the transient case must be higher than in the steady state.

Figure 6.2.14 shows transient boiling curves for various rates of heating. In general, the curves start out at ΔT's higher than those for steady-state boiling and

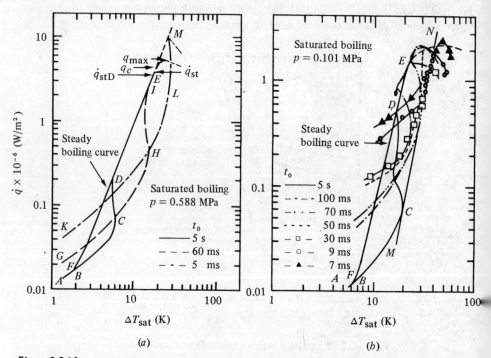

Figure 6.2.14 Transient boiling curves for various exponential periods: at 0.588 MPa (*a*) and at 0.101 MPa (*b*).

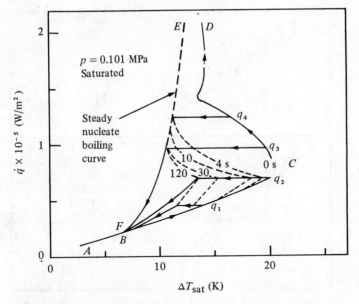

Figure 6.2.15 Thermal hysteresis loops for heat input first increased exponentially with period 5 s and then kept constant for 120 s at a certain level and decreased exponentially with the same period.

return to steady-state values. At higher heating rates (smaller t_0), the curves may not return to the steady state.

Figure 6.2.15, for $t_0 = 5$ s, shows the effect of stopping exponential heating and holding steady heat flux after the transient. For example, in heating in the transient from B to C and stopping at q_3, ΔT returns to the steady-state curve in about 20 s.

A $\dot{q}_c$ was observed where nucleate boiling ceased and a $\dot{q}_{max}$ at the maximum of the curve. Figure 6.2.16 shows the increase in both of these quantities as the rate of heating increases (t_0 decreases).

6.2.6 FILM BOILING

Film boiling as a cooling process has not had wide commercial application because of the accompanying high surface temperatures; it may find use in the future as better materials become available. It is, however, often encountered in chemical process equipment and in cryogenic systems.

In film boiling, vapor is generated at the liquid-vapor interface by conduction and radiation from the heating surface through the vapor film. Using the hydrodynamic instability of the liquid-vapor boundary, Zuber & Tribus (1958) arrived at the following equation representing the minimum heat flux for film boiling:

$$\dot{q}_{min} = 0.09 \, \rho_{Gf} h_{LG} \left[\frac{g(\rho_L - \rho_G)}{\rho_L + \rho_G} \right]^{1/2} \left[\frac{\sigma}{g(\rho_L - \rho_G)} \right]^{1/4} \qquad [6.2.25]$$

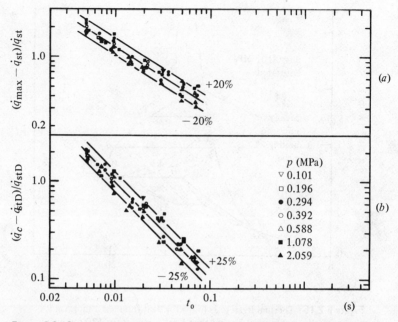

Figure 6.2.16 (a) Difference between transient and steady maximum heat fluxes divided by steady maximum value. (b) Difference between transient and steady burnout heat fluxes divided by steady burnout value, for regular and perfectly regular processes.

where ρ_{Gf} is the vapor density at film temperature and the other properties are evaluated at saturation temperature. The coefficient 0.09 was determined empirically by Berenson (1960). It is significant that the data for any surface finish converge on this point and in the film boiling region are independent of surface finish. In the transition boiling region the data are influenced by the same factors that influence nucleate boiling data, suggesting that the film does occasionally touch the heating surface.

The minimum heat flux in film boiling on horizontal cylinders is correlated (Brentari et al. 1965) by the Lienhard & Wong (1963) equation

$$\dot{q}_{\min\,\text{cond}} = 0.114 \frac{h_{LG}\rho_G}{D} \left[\frac{2g(\rho_L - \rho_G)}{\rho_L + \rho_G} + \frac{4\sigma}{D^2(\rho_L + \rho_G)}\right]^{1/2} \left[\frac{g(\rho_L - \rho_G)}{\sigma} + \frac{2.0}{D^2}\right]^{-3/4}$$

[6.2.26]

where D is diameter. Radiation for $T < 240$ K is usually $< 5\%$ of $\dot{q}$.

The stable film regime was studied experimentally and analytically by Bromley (1950, 1953) for horizontal tubes and vertical plates. By balancing the buoyant and frictional forces on the vapor flowing in the film on the outside of a horizontal tube, Bromley arrived at the following equation representing the heat transfer coefficient α_c associated with conduction alone

$$\alpha_c = 0.62 \left[\frac{\lambda_G^3 \rho_G(\rho_L - \rho_G)g(h_{LG} + 0.4\,c_{pG}\Delta T)}{D_0 \mu_G(T_W - T_{\text{sat}})}\right]^{1/4}$$

[6.2.27]

Radiation contributes to the heat transfer and increases the vapor film thickness. reducing the effective contribution of conduction. The total heat transfer coefficient is given by

$$\alpha = \alpha_c \left(\frac{\alpha_c}{\alpha} \right)^{1/3} + \alpha_r \qquad [6.2.28]$$

where α_r is calculated for radiation between two parallel planes.

For forced convection flow of the liquid across the tube, Bromley (1953) suggested the following equation when $V_\infty \geqslant 2\sqrt{gD_0}$:

$$\alpha_c = 2.7 \sqrt{\frac{V_\infty \lambda_G \rho_G (h_{LG} + 0.4\, c_{pG} \Delta T)}{D_0 \Delta T}} \qquad [6.2.29]$$

and

$$\alpha = \alpha_c + \tfrac{7}{8}\, \alpha_r \qquad [6.2.30]$$

Film boiling on a horizontal surface was analyzed by Berenson (1960) and compared with data for pentane, CCl_4, benzene, and ethyl alcohol. The following equation resulted:

$$\alpha_c = 0.425 \left[\frac{\lambda_G^3 \rho_{Gf} (\rho_L - \rho_G) g (h_{LG} + 0.4\, c_{pG} \Delta T)}{\mu_G \Delta T \sqrt{\sigma/g(\rho_L - \rho_G)}} \right]^{1/4} \qquad [6.2.31]$$

Note that this is identical in form with [6.2.27] with D_0 replaced by $\sqrt{\sigma/g(\rho_L - \rho_G)}$, which is proportional to bubble diameter [6.1.22].

Data for film boiling of cryogenic horizontal cylinders was correlated by Breen & Westwater (1962):

$$\alpha_c = 0.59 + 0.069 \frac{\lambda_c}{D} \left[\frac{k_G^3 \rho_G (\rho_L - \rho_G) h'_{LG}}{\mu_G (T_w - T_{\text{sat}}) \lambda_c} \right]^{1/4} \qquad [6.2.32]$$

where

$$h'_{LG} = h_{LG} \left[1 + 0.34 \frac{c_G (T_w - T_{\text{sat}})}{h_{LG}} \right]^2 \qquad \lambda_c = 2\pi \frac{\sigma}{g(\rho_L - \rho_G)}^{1/2}$$

For quenching of spheres (Frederking & Clark 1962):

$$\frac{\alpha D}{\lambda} = 0.15\, Ra^{1/3} \qquad [6.2.33]$$

for $Ra > 5 \times 10^7$, where

$$Ra \equiv \frac{D^3 g(\rho_L - \rho_G)}{v_G^2 \rho_G} \Pr_G \left[\frac{h_{LG}}{c_{pG}(T_w - T_{\text{sat}})} + 0.4 \right] \frac{a}{g} \qquad [6.2.34]$$

where a is local acceleration, equal to g for a stationary sphere on the earth.

6.3 Preburnout Convective Boiling

Y. Y. Hsu

6.3.1 INTRODUCTION

In a typical boiling two-phase flow, the fluid gains enthalpy and quality as it proceeds downstream. The evolution of the flow pattern is depicted in figure 6.3.1, and the typical void fraction profile as a function of distance from the entrance is shown in figure 6.3.2. As fluid enters the channel, if subcooling is high enough, there is a section of single-phase forced convection until incipient boiling sets in (at location z_{sub} and subcooling ΔT_{sub} of figure 6.3.2). But even after boiling incipience the subcooled boiling is still very high, so that bubbles collapse before leaving the heating surface. Thus the void (volume fraction occupied by vapor) is concentrated at the wall. This is called the wall-void region (region I). As the fluid proceeds farther downstream and loses more subcooling, the bubbles grow bigger and depart from the surface. New bubbles can then grow under the departing bubbles. The void fraction increases with distance at a steeper gradient. This is the net vapor generation region (region II)–from the bubble departure point (z_D and ΔT_D), to the saturation condition ($\Delta T = 0$). Beyond the equilibrium point, bulk void increases even more rapidly. Flow is in high-quality region, with a flow pattern of the slug or annular type.

The preburnout boiling flow regime terminates when burnout sets in, either in the form of DNB (departure from nucleate boiling) when the heat flux is high, or in the form of dryout when the void fraction approaches 1.

6.3.2 WALL-VOID SUBCOOLED BOILING

6.3.2.1 Incipience of Boiling

Incipient boiling criteria are discussed in sections 6.1 and 6.2. For forced convective flow, Bergles & Rohsenow (1964) developed a criterion based on analyses by Hsu (1962) and Han & Griffith (1965) for boiling incipience. Basically, the hydrodynamic boundary-layer thickness is the limiting thickness under which a bubble can be conceived. In general, when subcooling is high or the limiting thermal

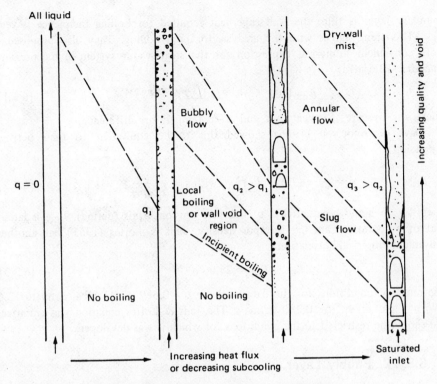

Figure 6.3.1   Development of flow patterns in boiling two-phase flow.

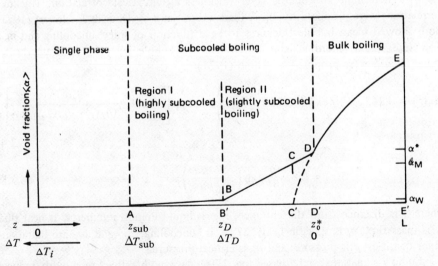

Figure 6.3.2   Bowring's (1962) model for subcooled boiling void distribution.

boundary layer is thin, the wall superheat required for boiling incipience is very high. This trend agrees with the analysis for pool boiling. They also proposed a more convenient numerical expression for the steam-water system in the pressure range 0.1–13.6 MPa:

$$\dot{q} = 0.0155 \, p^{1.156} (1.8\Delta T)^{0.718/p^{0.234}} \qquad [6.3.1]$$

where p is pressure, $\dot{q}$ is heat flux, and ΔT is temperature difference.

Davis & Anderson (1966) showed this to be equivalent to their derived expression

$$\dot{q} = \frac{\lambda_L}{8c_l^1 s} (T_W - T_b)^2 \quad \text{with } s = \frac{oT_{\text{sat}}}{h_{LG}\rho_G} c_l = 1 \qquad [6.3.2]$$

where λ_L is liquid conductivity, σ is surface tension, c_1 is (define), h_{LG} is latent heat of evaporation, and ρ_v is vapor density. Jens & Lottes (1951) had another convenient empirical correlation:

$$T_W - T_{\text{sat}} = 25.06 \, e^{-p/6.20} \dot{q}^{1/4} \qquad [6.3.3]$$

The range of conditions for the data used are $p = 0.689–17.23$ MPa, $\dot{q}$ up to 12.6 MW/m^2, and $\dot{m}$ up to 10,280 kg/m^2 s. The Jens & Lottes equation was empirical and should be restricted to the conditions for which it was developed.

6.3.2.2 Bubbly Layer

In the wall-void region, a thin layer of bubbles forms at the wall. Attempts were made to determine the bubble layer thickness by empirical correlation. Thickness correlations were proposed by Jiji & Clark (1964) and by Dougall & Lippert (1971). Both showed mean bubble thickness to be a function of inlet subcooling and mass flow rate. Later, more general correlations for bubble layer δ_b and superheated liquid layer δ were proposed by Cumo (1977):

$$\delta_b(z) = 0.245 \, z^{1/1.55} \exp\left(0.374 \, \Pr_{L,\text{sat}}^{7/8}\right) \left\{ 1 - \exp\left[-1.9 \, \frac{\dot{q}\rho_L}{\dot{m}(h_{LG} + c_l \Delta T_{\text{sub}})\rho_G} \right] \right\} \qquad [6.3.4]$$

$$\delta(z) = 0.85 \, \frac{p}{p_c} \exp\left(\frac{\dot{q}\rho_L}{h_{LG}\dot{m}\rho_G}\right) z^{0.95 - 0.7p/p_c} \qquad [6.3.5]$$

where z is distance from the entrance, $\Pr_L$ is liquid Prandtl number, $\dot{q}$ is heat flux; $\dot{m}$ is mass flux; c_l is specific heat; ΔT_{sub} is subcooling; ρ_L and ρ_G are liquid and vapor densities; p is pressure; and p_c is critical pressure.

Cumo's equations were based on 1200 data points for Freon with reduced pressure $p/p_c = 0.26$ and 0.53, subcooling 5–55°C, heat flux 6–28.5 W/cm^2, and mass flux 14–37 g/cm^2 s. Although these data were for Freon, the conditions were selected to simulate water under BWR (boiling-water reactor) and PWR (pressurized-water reactor) conditions. Since all the controlling parameters are dimensionless groups, there is a good possibility that [6.3.4] and [6.3.5] are applicable to water.

A semianalytical approach was taken by Larsen & Tong (1969), based on an analogy between heat and momentum transfer. Consider that the edge of the bubble layer is at radius r_2 and the heat flux from the bubble layer to the core is $\dot{q}_2$; then the difference between heat flow from the wall ($2\pi R\dot{q}_w\Delta z$) and heat flow from the bubble layer ($2\pi r_2\dot{q}_2\Delta z$) is the heat available for evaporation. One obtains $\dot{q}_2$ from the momentum-heat transfer analogy

$$\dot{q}_2 = \frac{\rho_L c_L}{\mathrm{Pr}_t}\frac{\tau_w r_2}{R\rho_L}\frac{T_{\mathrm{sat}} - T_{cl}}{u_{cl} - u_2} \qquad [6.3.6]$$

where the subscript cl denotes the centerline and τ_w is the shear stress. The velocity difference can be obtained from the turbulent velocity profile:

$$u_{cl} - u = -\sqrt{\frac{\tau_w}{\rho_w}}\frac{1}{K}\ln\left(1 - \frac{r}{R}\right) \qquad K = 0.4 \qquad [6.3.7]$$

The empirical shear stress is

$$f_{tp} = \frac{8\tau_w}{\rho_L[u_0/(1 - \langle\alpha\rangle)]^2} = 16.5\left[\frac{2\rho_L u_0 R}{(1 - \langle\alpha\rangle)\mu_L}\right]^{-0.6} \qquad [6.3.8]$$

The resulting expression for $\dot{q}_2$ is

$$\frac{\dot{q}_2}{\rho_L u_0} = -\sqrt{\frac{16.5}{8}}\frac{K}{\mathrm{Pr}_t}\frac{(r_2/R)c_L(T_{\mathrm{sat}} - T_{cl})}{\ln(1 - r/R)}\left(\frac{Du_0\rho_L}{\mu_L}\right)^{-0.3}\left(1 - \frac{\langle\alpha\rangle r_2^2}{R^2}\right)^{-0.7}$$

$$[6.3.9]$$

However, r_2 is not known without empirical input (such as from δ_b) or some assumption. Larsen & Tong assumed $r_2 = R - \delta_{\mathrm{lam}}$, with δ_{lam} the laminar sublayer thickness. Since $\dot{q}_2 r_2/\dot{q}_w R$ cannot be larger than unity for physical reasons, it is set equal to unity if the ratio is larger than 1. As soon as the liquid temperature is high enough that the heat flow ratio is less than 1, the residue heat is used for evaporation and the bubble layer grows rapidly and goes into the net vapor generation region (region II of figure 6.3.2).

The above model predicts steam-water data of Maurer (1960) for 8.27–13.78 MPa and of Bartolomei & Chanturiya (1967) for 1.49–4.48 MPa very well.

6.3.3 NET VAPOR GENERATION

The net vapor generation point is located where the subcooling is low enough that bubbles grow and depart into the stream. Two kinds of criteria were proposed. One is based on hydrodynamic criteria for bubble departure size; the other is based on heat balance to determine whether there is surplus heat for evaporation after heat is conducted away at the bubble boundary. Larsen & Tong's model, described in section 6.3.2, belongs in the heat balance category. It does not need a separate criterion since $\dot{q}_2 r_2/\dot{q}_w R$ accounts for the transition provided the initial r_2 is known. In this section, models proposed to determine the net vapor generation point are presented.

6.3.3.1 Hydrodynamic Criteria for Bubble Departure

In this category, two models are available. Both provide force balance at a bubble. Levy's (1967) model is based on the following assumptions:

1. The buoyancy force (assumed negligible) and shear force on a bubble, balanced against surface force, determine bubble size.
2. At the bubble tip, the liquid temperature equals or is higher than the vapor temperature inside the bubble, which obeys the Clausius-Clapeyron equation.
3. The temperature profile of the liquid is the universal profile for a turbulent boundary layer.
4. Shear stress is determined from the friction factor correlation for flow in a rough tube, with the roughness parameter ϵ/D_H assumed to be 10^{-4}.

Once the bubble departure point is determined, the bubble-layer thickness and quality at the departure point, x_s, are calculated. The quality downstream of the departure point is related to the equilibrium quality x_e through the exponential equation

$$x = x_e - x_D \exp\left(\frac{x_e}{x_D} - 1\right) \qquad [6.3.10]$$

Note that

$$\frac{dx}{dx_e} = 0 \quad \text{at } z = z_D \text{ and } x_e = x_D$$

$$x \to x_e \quad \text{when } x_e \gg x_D \text{ (note } x_D < 0\text{)} \qquad [6.3.11]$$

Levy's model has been used to calculate data for void fraction versus high mass flux with modest success.

Staub (1968) noted that Levy's model, by neglecting buoyancy force, did not apply to low flow. He proposed a model in which buoyancy force is included. Furthermore, the shear stress is based on the rough tube friction factor with roughness parameter $\epsilon/D_H = D_D/D_H$. Staub's model is adequate for the low flow case.

Both of the hydrodynamic departure criteria are complicated to use. Besides, they are based on the assumptions that bubbles attach to the wall and that liquid is superheated in the bubble layer. Both assumptions have been disputed by microscopic measurements (Dix 1971) of the bubble-layer void distribution and temperature distribution (figure 6.3.3). These measurements showed that the void fraction peaks at a short distance from the wall and significant subcooling exists even within the bubble layer.

6.3.3.2 Heat Transfer Models

Quite a few models in addition to Larsen & Tong's were proposed based on heat transfer criteria. The earliest was due to Bowring (1962), and various modifications were proposed by Rouhani & Axelsson (1970), Ahmad (1970), & Dix (1971).

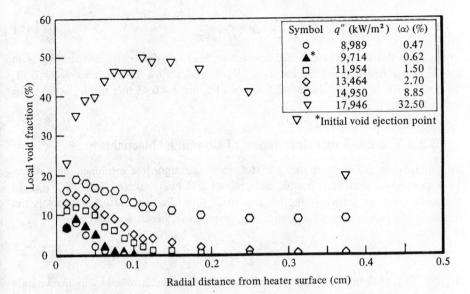

Figure 6.3.3 Subcooled boiling radial void fraction profiles (Dix 1971). Freon-114; $p = 0.314$ MPa, $G = 207.8$ kg/m^2 s, $T_i = 19°$C.

In Bowring's model, the criterion is a critical subcooling for the departure point, $\Delta T_D = T_D - T_{sat}$:

$$\Delta T_{sub} = T - T_{sat} \leqslant \Delta T_D = \frac{14 + p}{u_{Li}} \dot{q}_W \qquad [6.3.12]$$

In [6.3.12] $\dot{q}_W$ is wall heat flux (W/cm^2), p is pressure (MPa), and u_{Li} is inlet velocity (cm/s). If water temperature corresponding to this subcooling ΔT_D is lower than the temperature for incipience of boiling, then z_D moves to z_{sub} (figure 6.3.2). If the liquid temperature required for bubble departure is lower than the inlet temperature, then the departure point z_D moves to the inlet. Ahmad (1970) proposed the criterion

$$\Delta T_D = \frac{\dot{q}_W}{\alpha_L} \qquad [6.3.13]$$

where an empirical expression for the liquid heat transfer coefficient α_L is

$$\alpha_L = 2.44 \ Re_L^{1/2} \ Pr_L^{1/3} \left(\frac{h_L}{h_{L,sat}}\right)^{1/3} \left(\frac{h_{LG}}{h_{L,sat}}\right)^{1/3} \qquad [6.3.14]$$

This is based on the hypothesis that at the point of net vapor generation, the wall heat flux is balanced by heat removed by liquid subcooling. A similar criterion was proposed by Dix (1971) as

$$\Delta T_D = 0.00135 \frac{\dot{q}_W}{\alpha_L} \ Re_L^{1/2} \qquad [6.3.15]$$

Another criterion proposed by Unal (1975) is

$$\Delta T_D = K_u \frac{\dot{q}_w}{\alpha_L} \qquad [6.3.16]$$

where α_L is the single-phase forced convection heat transfer coefficient and K_u is an empirical coefficient such that, for water, $K_u = 0.24$, for $u \geqslant 0.45$ m/s and $K_u = 0.11$, for $u < 0.45$ m/s; for Refrigerant-22, $K_u = 0.18$, for $u \geqslant 0.45$ m/s and $K_u = 0.11$, for $u < 0.45$ m/s.

6.3.3.3 Saha-Zuber Correlation of Combined Mechanism

Saha and Zuber (1974) proposed a correlation based upon the combined mechanism. They postulated that both bubble detachment and heat transfer (i.e., $\dot{q}_w > \dot{q}_{cond}$) restraints must be satisfied. In the low mass flow the heat diffusion controls the condensation process; thus the controlling parameter is Nusselt number:

$$Nu = \frac{\dot{q}_w D_b}{\lambda_L (T_{sat} - T_D)} \qquad [6.3.17a]$$

In high flow, both bubble departure and heat transfer are controlled by hydrodynamic transport, and the Stanton number St is an appropriate scaling group:

$$St = \frac{\dot{q}_w}{\dot{m} c_{pL} (T_{sat} - T_D)} \qquad [6.3.17b]$$

A large body of data was used by Saha & Zuber (1970) to check this hypothesis. The data points were plotted (figure 6.3.4) in the form of St versus the Peclet number Pe, where

$$Pe = \frac{\dot{m} D_e c_{pL}}{\lambda_L} = \frac{Nu}{St} \qquad [6.3.18]$$

The plot readily indicates the existence of two regions:

$$Pe < 7 \times 10^4 \qquad St \propto Pe^{-1} \qquad or \quad Nu = 455 \qquad [6.3.19a]$$

$$Pe > 7 \times 10^4 \qquad St = 0.0065 \qquad [6.3.19b]$$

The corresponding subcooling ΔT_D and equilibrium quality $x_{De} (= c_{pL} \Delta T_D / h_{LG})$ at departure can be shown as

$$Pe < 7 \times 10^4 \qquad \Delta T_D = 0.0022 \frac{\dot{q}_w D_e}{\lambda_L} \qquad x_{De} = -0.0022 \frac{\dot{q}_w D_e c_{pL}}{\lambda_L h_{LG}} \qquad [6.3.20]$$

$$Pe > 7 \times 10^4 \quad \Delta T_D = 154 \frac{\dot{q}_w}{\rho_L h_{LG}} \qquad x_{De} = -154 \frac{\dot{q}_w}{\rho_L h_{LG} u_{Li}} \qquad [6.3.21]$$

The data base of the Saha-Zuber model includes water with

$$p = 0.1\text{-}13.8 \text{ MPa}$$

$$\dot{m} = 95\text{-}2760 \text{ kg/m}^2 \text{ s}$$

$$\dot{q} = 0.28\text{-}1.89 \text{ MW/m}^2$$

in rectangular channels and annular and circular tubes and Freon 114 with

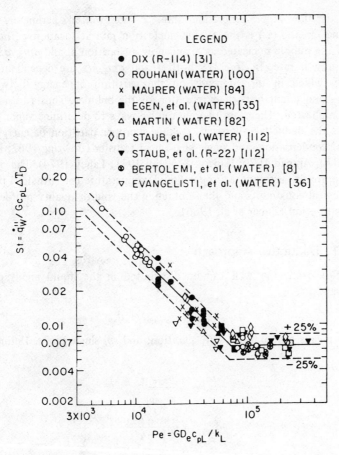

Figure 6.3.4 Stanton number versus Peclet number at the point of net vapor generation (Saha & Zuber 1970). Sources of data are listed in Saha & Zuber (1970).

$$p = 0.32\text{--}0.85 \text{ MPa}$$

$$\dot{m} = 101\text{--}2073 \text{ kg/m}^2 \text{ s}$$

$$\dot{q}_W = 0.0063\text{--}5.36 \text{ MW/m}^2$$

in an annular channel.

6.3.4 VAPOR GENERATION RATE IN A CONDUIT

The formal treatment for vapor generation rate is to integrate along the path the growth rate of all the bubbles:

$$\Gamma_G = \frac{P}{A} \int_{z_D}^{z} \frac{dm_G(z, z')}{dz} J(z') \, dz' \qquad [6.3.21]$$

where Γ_G is the vapor generation rate, P the wetted perimeter, A is the cross-sectional area, $J(z')$ is the bubble nucleation rate at location z', $m_G(z, z')$ is the mass of the bubble nucleated at z' and now at location z, and dm_G/dz is related to bubble growth rate. In [6.3.21] both J and dm_G/dz are dependent on liquid temperature, which in turn depends on the partition of energy between liquid sensible heat and latent heat of evaporation of the bubbles. Thus a formal solution is rather complicated. There are two alternative ways to determine vapor generation rate. One is the deductive approach, seeking a proper partition of energy between evaporation, condensation, and single-phase heat transfer (Bowring 1962; Rouhani & Axelsson 1970; Ahmad 1970; Hancox & Nicoll 1971; Lahey 1974). The other is the inductive approach, assuming a proper liquid temperature (or enthalpy) profile that fits a few logical constraints and then obtaining the void or quality profile from this assumed distribution (Zuber et al. 1966).

6.3.4.1 Deductive Approach

The heat flux from the wall can be distributed in the liquid and vapor in the following way:

$$\dot{q}_W = \dot{q}_{evap} + \dot{q}_{agit} + \dot{q}_{sp} \qquad [6.3.22]$$

where evap means evaporation, agit, agitation; and sp, single phase. Define a ratio c as

$$c = \frac{\dot{q}_{agit}}{\dot{q}_{evap}} \qquad [6.3.23]$$

Then
$$\dot{q}_{evap} = \frac{\dot{q}_W - q_{sp}}{1 + c} \qquad [6.3.24]$$

$$\frac{dx}{dz} = \frac{P(\dot{q}_{evap} - \dot{q}_{cond})}{\dot{m}Ah_{LG}} \qquad [6.3.25]$$

$$x = \frac{P}{\dot{m}Ah_{LG}} \int_{z_D}^{z} \left(\frac{\dot{q}_W - \dot{q}_{sp}}{(1 + c)} - \dot{q}_{cond} \right) dz \qquad [6.3.26]$$

Bowring (1962) assumed that $\dot{q}_{cond}$ is negligible, that

$$\left.\begin{array}{ll} c = 3.2\left(\dfrac{c_L\rho_L}{\rho_G h_{LG}}\right) & 0.1 < p < 0.95 \text{ MPa} \\[2ex] c = 1.3 & 0.95 < p < 5.0 \text{ MPa} \end{array}\right\} \qquad [6.3.27]$$

in general, and that $c = 1.6$ for $p > 5.0$ MPa for a rectangular channel with a 2.5-cm gap.

Note from [6.3.23] that as bulk boiling is approached, $\dot{q}_{agit}$ diminishes, and thus c is not independent of distance as given by Bowring. To account for the variation of c, Rouhani & Axelsson proposed

$$c = \frac{c_L \rho_L (T_{\text{sat}} - T_L)}{\rho_G h_{LG}} \tag{6.3.28}$$

Furthermore, they did not neglect $\dot{q}_{\text{cond}}$. The resulting equation is

$$\Gamma_G = \frac{P}{A h_{LG}} \left[\frac{\dot{q}_W}{1 + c_L \rho_L (T_{\text{sat}} - T_L)/\rho_G h_{LG}} - \dot{q}_{\text{cond}} \right] \tag{6.3.29}$$

with the condensation heat flux

$$\dot{q}_{\text{cond}} = \frac{K_c (T_{\text{sat}} - T_L)}{P}$$

$$K_c = a \frac{\lambda_L}{\text{Pr}_L} \left(\frac{\rho_G}{\rho_L} \right)^2 A^{2/3} \langle \alpha \rangle^{2/3} \left[\frac{\dot{m} D_e}{(1 - \langle \alpha \rangle) \mu_L} \right] N_q^{-0.5} \tag{6.3.30}$$

where $\langle \alpha \rangle$ is void fraction, a is a coefficient of value 30 m$^{-4/3}$, and

$$N_q = \frac{\dot{q}_W \mu_L}{(\rho_L - \rho_G) \sigma h_{LG}} \tag{6.3.31}$$

The Rouhani-Axelsson model was compared with high-pressure (1.9–13.8 MPa) water data in rod bundles, rectangular channels, and annular flow. Heat fluxes are up to 126 W/cm^2 and flow rates are 130–1600 kg/m^2 s. The error is usually less than 10%, sometimes up to 18%. Lahey (1974) proposed an equation similar to Rouhani & Axelsson's except that $\dot{q}_{\text{cond}}$ in [6.3.29] is replaced by

$$\dot{q}_{\text{cond}} = H_0 \frac{h_{LG} A}{V_{LG} P} (T_{\text{sat}} - T_L) \langle \alpha \rangle \tag{6.3.32}$$

where the constant H_0 is set at 0.075 (s °C)$^{-1}$. The resulting void profile is very close to that from the Rouhani-Axelsson model.

A similar approach was taken by Hancox & Nicoll (1970) but extended to cover both the steady-state and oscillating modes of void profile. Application to the oscillating mode gives the correct qualitative trend.

Ahmad (1970) presented an analysis with assumed expressions for liquid heat transfer and condensation coefficients. For heat balance, Ahmad obtained

$$\frac{dT}{dz} = \frac{P(T_{\text{sat}} - T_L)}{\dot{m} A c_L} (\alpha_L + K \sqrt{z - z_D}) \tag{6.3.33}$$

with α_L given by [6.3.14] and

$$K = 2.79 \, C \frac{B_k R_D P \dot{q}_W}{\sqrt{\dot{m} S}} \tag{6.3.34}$$

where B_k is a group of physical constants, R_D is the radius of the detaching bubble, C is a dimensional constant, and S is velocity ratio. The resulting temperature profile is

$$\frac{T_{\text{sat}} - T}{T_{\text{sat}} - T_D} = e - (C_1 z^* + C_2 z^{*3/2}) \tag{6.3.35}$$

$$C_1 = \frac{\alpha_L P(z_t - z_D)}{\dot{m} A c_L} \qquad C_2 = \frac{2}{3} \frac{K h_{LG}(z_t - z_D)^{3/2}}{\dot{m} A c_L}$$

$$z^* = \frac{z - z_D}{z_t - z_D}$$

where z_t is tube length.

6.3.4.2 Inductive Approach

In the deductive approach one has to assume the heat transfer coefficients, which are uncertain. In the inductive approach (Zuber et al. 1966) a temperature (or enthalpy) profile is assumed that satisfies the logical constraints

$$h_L = h_D \qquad \frac{dh_L}{dz} = \frac{h_L - h_D}{z_0 - z_D} \qquad \text{at } z = z_D \qquad [6.3.36]$$

$$h_L = h_{L,\text{sat}} \qquad \frac{dh_L}{dz} = 0 \qquad \text{at } z \to \infty \qquad [6.3.37]$$

where h_L is bulk enthalpy and z_0 is the location where $T = T_{\text{sat}}$. The equations that satisfy these constraints are

$$\frac{T(z) - T_D}{T_{\text{sat}} - T_D} = F$$

with

$$F = 1 - e^{-(z - z_D)/(z_0 - z_D)} \qquad [6.3.38]$$

or

$$F = \tanh\left(\frac{z - z_D}{z_0 - z_D}\right) \qquad [6.3.39]$$

From a comparison of experimental data for water at 1.0–5.0 MPa and $T_{\text{sat}} - T_D = 2.8\text{–}12°C$, Zuber et al. concluded that the exponential form [6.3.38] gives better results. It is interesting to note that [6.3.38] is the same as Ahmad's [6.3.35] with condensation neglected.

The quality profile, derived from the temperature profile of [6.3.38], is

$$x = \frac{\dot{q}_w P(z_0 - z_D)}{\dot{m} A h_{LG}}\left(\frac{z - z_D}{z_0 - z_D} - 1 + e^{-(z - z_D)/(z_0 - z_D)}\right) \qquad [6.3.40]$$

since at equilibrium

$$x_e = \frac{\dot{q}_w P(z_0 - z_D)}{\dot{m} A h_{LG}}\left(\frac{z - z_D}{z_0 - z_D} - 1\right) \qquad [6.3.41]$$

and at $z = z_D$

$$x_D = -\frac{\dot{q}_w P(z_0 - z_D)}{\dot{m} A h_{LG}} \qquad [6.3.42]$$

then

$$x = x_e - x_D\, e^{(x_e/x_D) - 1}$$

which is the same as that assumed by Levy in [6.3.10].

The inductive approach is easier to use. However, the verification is only from steady-state data with uniform heat flux. When one encounters nonuniform power distribution or a transient flow, the temperature profile will not be the same as assumed in [6.3.38]. Thus for uniform power [6.3.38] is recommended, but for other power profiles and equation analogous to [6.3.38] should be derived, following the basic approach of Ahmad.

6.3.5 HIGH–QUALITY FLOW

6.3.5.1 Slug Flow Heat Transfer

Slug flow with heat transfer differs from adiabatic flow in four ways:

1. Nucleation sites generate bubbles in the thin liquid film on the wall surrounding the cylindrical bubble. The bubbles not only enhance heat transfer but also help to spray liquid droplets into the interior of the cylindrical bubble. This effect has been observed in boiling from a thin falling film (Hsu et al. 1965) and in distillation columns (Nielsen et al. 1965).

2. The cylindrical bubble grows in length because of the evaporation into the bubble. The head of the bubble is thus subject to a body force due to both gravitational effects and the accelerating growth of the bubble head. Consequently, the bubble head is expected to be unstable and break up more easily than the cylindrical bubble in adiabatic flow (Hsu & Simon 1969). Furthermore, the void fraction increases with distance and quickly surpasses the limit for slug flow. Consequently, the slug flow regime cannot persist very long before the transition to annular dispersed flow.

3. According to many experimental observations (Gouse & Hwang 1965; Jeglic 1965) the slug flow regime occurs when the equilibrium enthalpy reaches the saturation point.

4. Probably the most important feature is the instability triggered by slug flow. When flow instability sets in, burnout can occur at a much lower heat flux than under steady-state conditions, as reported by Styrikovich & Nevstrueva (1966).

Concerning slug flow in a horizontal tube, Hughmark (1965) studied some experimental results for gas-liquid systems such as air-water, air-oil, and gas-oil and found that for turbulent flow $(26,000 < \mathrm{Re}_L < 4,500,000)$

$$\frac{\alpha_{tp}}{c_L \rho_L u_L} = \frac{f_L/2}{\dot{q}_W} \qquad [6.3.43]$$

where
$$u_L = \frac{\dot{m}_L}{\rho_L (1 - \langle \alpha \rangle)}$$

$$f_L = \left(\frac{\Delta p_{tp}}{\Delta z}\right)\frac{g_0 D}{2\,\rho_L u_L^2} = f(\mathrm{Re}_L) \qquad \mathrm{Re}_L = \frac{D u_L \rho_L}{\mu_L}$$

and for laminar flow $(1600 < \mathrm{Re}_L < 4600)$

$$\frac{\alpha_{tp} D \sqrt{1 - \langle \alpha \rangle}}{\lambda_L} = 1.75 \left[\frac{\dot{m}_L A c_L}{(1 - \langle \alpha \rangle)\lambda_L L}\right]^{1/2} \left(\frac{\mu}{\mu_W}\right)^{0.14} \qquad [6.3.44]$$

where L is length. Note that the viscosity ratio provides a differentiation between the cases of cooling and heating a fluid. The viscosity on the wall varies with temperature. This correlation for a two-component system can be applied to the single-component system by using the mean void fraction obtained from actual quality.

6.3.5.2 Annular Flow

There are two types of annular flow. In the early stage, the liquid film is in the nucleate boiling mode. As the film thins down, ebullition is suppressed and it becomes an evaporating film.

Nucleate Boiling Zone

The slug flow regime is usually very short, and the transition from a long cylindrical bubble to an annular flow is not clear. In early annular flow the flow core consists of alternating surges of flow with high and low voids, so it behaves as the alternating flow of slugs and bubbles. The only distinction between slug and annular flow with a highly variable void in the core is the absence of a liquid bridge across the channel in annular flow. Thus, from a heat transfer point of view, it is difficult to differentiate between slug flow and the early phase of annular flow. Both are characterized by nucleate boiling in the liquid film. In fact, as long as nucleate boiling is present, the heat transfer is dominated by this highly efficient process. Therefore, for the whole range from the incipience of boiling to the early phase of annular flow, an additive approach may be used in which the heat transfer is the sum of that attributed to boiling and that attributed to forced convection (Bergles & Rohsenow 1964).

Lavin & Young (1965) also found that McNelly's (1953) equation for nucleate boiling correlated well:

$$\text{Nu} = 0.225 \left(\frac{\dot{q}D_e}{\mu h_{LG}}\right)^{0.69} \left(\frac{c\mu}{\lambda}\right)^{0.67} \left(\frac{\rho_L}{\rho_G}\right)^{0.31} \left(\frac{D_e P}{\sigma}\right)^{0.31} \qquad [6.3.45]$$

The distribution of void in the early phase of annular flow is difficult to describe since it is space-varying and time-varying due to the periodic fluctuation of void in the core.

A great deal of data on droplet entrainment was accumulated for adiabatic gas-water flow (e.g., Lacey et al. 1962; Hutchinson & Whalley 1973; Whalley 1977). It was found that the core void distribution is highly dependent on previous history in the upstream. With the addition of heat, entrainment occurs due to bubble spray, redeposition occurs due to the large quantity of drops in the core, and a boundary layer develops due to flow acceleration. These tend to produce contradictory effects in the void distribution and to make analysis difficult. For lack of better information, the equilibrium quality and adiabatic void quality equation for the void profile are used.

Transition from Boiling to Evaporation at the Liquid Film

In annular flow, the liquid film is constantly being thinned due to evaporation or entrainment. The flow is also being accelerated, so that heat removal from the liquid film to the core is improved. Eventually, heat transfer across the liquid film due to conduction and evaporation is so efficient that nucleate boiling is suppressed. This begins a region of annular flow without boiling.

Collier & Pulling (1962) studied the boiling suppression phenomenon and found that they could use the criterion originally developed for boiling incipience if the liquid film thickness is used as the laminar sublayer (i.e., with $\delta^+ = 7$) in Hsu's equation. For the region where the film was thinner than the criterion value, they found that the heating surface was void of the circular marks characteristic of active nucleation sites. Hughmark (1966) used a similar procedure for design purposes.

Correlations for Annular Flow

Most empirical correlations use the Martinelli parameter χ_{tt} in the form

$$\frac{\alpha_{tp}}{\alpha_L} = a_1 \chi_{tt}^b + a_2 \frac{\dot{q}}{\dot{m} h_{LG}} \qquad [6.3.46]$$

where α_L is the heat transfer coefficient for the liquid portion of the total flow as if it were flowing in the pipe alone. The constants a_1, a_2, and b are as follows:

	a_1	a_2	b
Dengler & Addoms (1956)	$\dfrac{3.5 \, F_{DA}}{(1-x)^{0.8}}$	0	0.5
Guerrieri & Talty (1956)	$0.636 \left(\dfrac{r^*}{\delta}\right)^{-5/9}$	0	0.45
Bennett et al. (1959)	$0.64(317\dot{q})^{0.11}$	0	0.74
Schrock & Grossman (1962)	1.11	7400	0.66
Collier & Pulling (1962)	2.34	6700	0.66

where F_{DA} is a correction factor to account for nucleate boiling

$$r^* = \frac{2 \, R T_s^2 \sigma}{P h_{LG}(T_W - T_{\text{sat}})}$$

$$\delta = \left[\frac{10 \, \mu_L}{\rho_L} \frac{4 \, \rho_L}{(dp/dz)Dg}\right]^{1/2}$$

and $\dot{q}$ is in W/m^2.

6.3.6 CORRELATION FOR THE WHOLE RANGE OF NUCLEATE BOILING

Chen (1963) proposed an equation to cover a wide range of nucleate boiling. The data base is for water with:

$$p = 0.09\text{–}3.45 \text{ MPa}$$

$$\dot{m} = (0.054\text{–}4.07) \times 10^{-3} \text{ kg/m}^2 \text{ s}$$

$$\dot{q} \text{ up to } 2.4 \text{ MW/m}^2$$

$$x = 0\text{–}0.7$$

Recent data from General Electric extend the pressure range to 6.9 MPa.

In addition, other fluids are covered, including methanol-cyclohexane, pentane, heptane, and benzene under 0.1 MPa; velocity, 0.3–1 m/s; heat flux, 6–52 kW/m^2, x, 0–0.1. The Chen (1963) equation is in the form

$$\alpha = 0.00122 \frac{\lambda_L^{0.79} c_L^{0.45} \rho_L^{0.49}}{\sigma^{0.5} \mu_L^{0.29} h_{LG}^{0.24} \rho_G^{0.24}} (T_W - T_{\text{sat}})^{0.24} (\Delta p)^{0.75} S$$

$$+ 0.023 \left[\frac{D\dot{m}(1 - x)}{\mu_L} \right]^{0.8} \left(\frac{c_L \mu_L}{\lambda_L} \right)^{0.4} \frac{\lambda_L}{D} F \qquad [6.3.47]$$

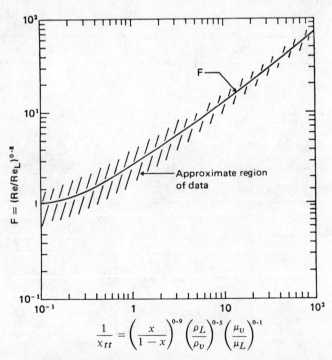

$$\frac{1}{X_{tt}} = \left(\frac{x}{1 - x} \right)^{0.9} \left(\frac{\rho_L}{\rho_v} \right)^{0.5} \left(\frac{\mu_v}{\mu_L} \right)^{0.1}$$

Figure 6.3.5 Reynolds number factor F used in Chen's (1963) correlation.

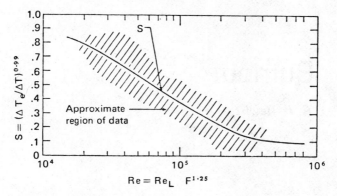

Figure 6.3.6 Suppression factor S used in Chen's (1963) correlation.

with

$$F = F \, \frac{1}{\chi_{tt}} \qquad\qquad [6.3.48]$$

$$S = S \, (\text{Re}_L \, F^{1.25}) \qquad\qquad [6.3.49]$$

The factors F and S are shown in figures 6.3.5 and 6.3.6. The error band was about 10%.

Equation [6.3.47] contains two parts. The first part is the contribution of microscopic agitation by bubbles and is based on the Forster-Zuber (1955) equation with a suppression factor S to account for reduction of bubble nucleation activities when flow is high. The second part is the contribution of macroscopic forced convection and is based on the Dittus & Boelter (1930) equation with a modifying factor F. One attractive feature is its automatic transition to forced convection of steam when quality becomes high and flow is in the form of annular flow with a thin evaporating liquid film on the wall. Equation [6.3.47] is recommended as the general equation for the saturated-flow nucleate boiling region.

6.4 Burnout

G. F. Hewitt

6.4.1 INTRODUCTION

Normally, boiling heat transfer processes are highly efficient. Indeed, the heat transfer coefficients are often so high that they do not represent the main resistance in the system, and an accurate knowledge of them is, therefore, often not required. However, if the surface temperature and/or heat flux is large enough, severe deterioration of the heat transfer process can take place. In this section, this deterioration phenomenon is termed *burnout*. A knowledge of the conditions leading to burnout is of considerable importance in the design of evaporative systems. The burnout transition is often accompanied by severe changes in the surface temperature or surface heat flux, but conditions also occur (e.g., at very high pressures) where the changes are relatively small. To include these latter cases, burnout is defined as follows:

1. For a system in which the surface heat flux is controlled (e.g., by electrical heating), burnout is defined as the condition in which there is an *inordinate* increase in surface temperature resulting from the change of one of the parameters of the system (e.g., the heat flux itself, the mass velocity, the fluid temperature).
2. For a system in which the surface temperature is controlled (e.g., by a heating fluid on the other side of the boundary wall), burnout is defined as the condition in which there is an inordinate decrease in surface heat flux at some point on the surface as a result of a small incremental change in one of the system parameters (e.g., wall temperature).

A number of terms other than burnout have been used to denote this phenomenon; these include boiling crisis, critical heat flux (CHF), departure from

The author acknowledges permission from the United Kingdom Atomic Energy Authority (UKAEA) to reproduce figures 6.4.9, 6.4.14, 6.4.15, 6.4.19, 6.4.24, 6.4.26, 6.4.27, 6.4.32, 6.4.37, 6.4.38, 6.4.39, 6.4.40, 6.4.47, 6.4.51, 6.4.52, 6.4.53, 6.4.54, 6.4.55, 6.4.56, 6.4.60, 6.4.61, 6.4.62, 6.4.63, 6.4.64, 6.4.65, and 6.4.66, which remain UKAEA copyright material.

nucleate boiling (DNB), and dryout. The choice of term is, to some extent, a matter of personal preference, since none of them is completely satisfactory. Boiling crisis is used extensively in the non-English language literature but becomes less acceptable on translation. Critical heat flux is the most widely accepted term in North America, although it tends to imply that there is a criticality in the heat flux level, whereas often the phenomenon is a hydrodynamic one not primarily concerned with the heat flux level itself. The term departure from nucleate boiling is unsatisfactory, since often the precritical mode of heat transfer is not actually nucleate boiling. Dryout would be a good general term were it not for the fact that it has become specifically associated with the film dryout mechanism of the critical phenomenon. In light of these factors, the term burnout has been retained for the present chapter; in the context of what is written here, the occurrence of burnout should definitely not be taken to imply the existence of physical damage to the heating surface.

Hundreds of papers, and many reviews, have been written on the burnout phenomenon. General introductions for the subject are given in the books of Tong (1965), Hewitt & Hall-Taylor (1970), Collier (1972), Butterworth & Hewitt (1977), and Ginoux (1978). Other detailed reviews of one or more aspects of burnout are given by Lahey (1975), Marinelli (1975), Bergles (1975, 1977), and Hewitt (1978). In the present chapter, the objective is to give general guidance on the nature and occurrence of burnout, together with selected recommendations for its calculation. Although this involves the citation of many sources, no attempt is made to give a comprehensive review and the review sources cited above should be consulted for further information.

6.4.2 PARAMETRIC EFFECTS ON BURNOUT

The objective of this section is to indicate the various situations under which burnout may occur in practical systems, to indicate the effect of system parameters on the occurrence of burnout, and to give a modest range of examples.

6.4.2.1 Burnout in Pool Boiling

Pool boiling is defined as boiling from a surface positioned in a static pool of liquid. In pool boiling, burnout occurs when the conditions are no longer such as to allow the vapor generated in nucleate boiling to be removed from the vicinity of the heated surface; the physics of this failure of the vapor removal mechanism is discussed further in sections 6.2 and 6.4.6. When burnout occurs, part or all of the heated surface is covered by a poorly conducting film of vapor and this leads to a deterioration in the heat transfer.

Since pool boiling experiments are inexpensive and easy to do, there are many hundreds of papers on pool boiling, and most of these deal to a greater or lesser extent with pool boiling burnout. A review of literature in this area is given by Bergles (1975). It may be useful here to summarize some of the effects of system parameters:

1. Heater geometry. Although most of the published work has been done with horizontal cylinders, a variety of other shapes have been investigated, notably by Lienhard & Dhir (1973a, b). The results for finite horizontal flat plates are very complex, depending on the vapor escape mechanism (section 6.4.6). For spheres, rectangular rods, and cylinders, the burnout heat flux value asymptotically approaches a constant (for given fluid properties) for large characteristic size. For smaller characteristic size, the flux increases as size decreases. For cylinders, this is illustrated by the example of burnout heat flux for water in figure 6.4.1.

2. System pressure. Burnout heat flux for pool boiling increases with system pressure and then decreases to zero at the critical pressure, as illustrated in figure 6.4.1.

3. Liquid viscosity. Burnout heat flux is independent of liquid viscosity for low viscosities, but for high viscosity it increases (Dhir & Lienhard 1974).

4. Liquid subcooling. The curves shown in figure 6.4.1 are for saturated boiling; if the liquid in the pool is subcooled, the burnout heat flux is higher, increasing linearly with increasing subcooling.

5. Surface finish. In contrast to nucleate boiling heat transfer coefficients, burnout heat flux is relatively insensitive to surface finish. However, if the surface is nonwetting, the burnout heat flux can be considerably reduced.

6. Multicomponent fluids. Multicomponent mixtures are the rule rather than the exception in many areas of application of boiling, particularly in the chemical and process industries. For mixtures of fluids, the burnout heat flux cannot be determined simply on the basis of average mixture properties. Figure 6.4.2 shows data for burnout heat flux obtained by van Stralen (1959) for a binary mixture. The burnout heat flux passes through a maximum that is greater than the flux for either of the pure components.

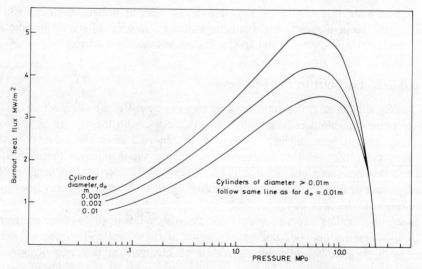

Figure 6.4.1 Effect of cylinder diameter and pressure on burnout heat flux for saturated pool boiling of water from horizontal cylinders.

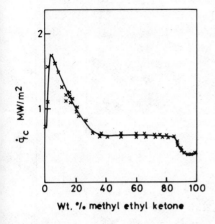

Figure 6.4.2 Burnout heat flux for the pool boiling of water-methyl ethyl ketone mixtures from a horizontal 0.02-cm diameter wire (results of van Stralen 1959).

In pool boiling from cylinders, natural circulation currents within the pool lead to an upward flow of liquid toward the cylinder. Thus, pool boiling is a low-velocity manifestation of cross-flow boiling. However, at low liquid velocities, the effect of cross flow is small; a further discussion of burnout in cross flow is given in section 6.4.2.4 and correlations for cross flow are discussed in section 6.4.3.1.

6.4.2.2 Burnout in Forced Convective Boiling: Vertical Channels

In the majority of boiling systems, evaporation occurs in the flow of fluid through vertical channels of one form or another. The practical importance of such systems is, perhaps, overreflected in the preponderance of work on vertical flows. Probably, this is due to the fact that such flows are important in nuclear reactor systems, in which context a considerable amount of funding has been available over the past 25 yr.

Round Tubes

The case of evaporation of water in vertical up flow in round tubes is the most commonly investigated one, with literally tens of thousands of data points available. However, even in this case, the available data have serious limitations in range of coverage of the important system variables of pressure, mass flux, tube diameter, and tube length. These limitations are a serious drawback in utilizing correlations for burnout for water in vertical up flow in round tubes (secion 6.4.3), since these correlations should not be extrapolated.

For vertical up flow of water in tubes, the simplest case is that where the water enters at a saturated or subcooled (i.e., single phase) condition. Figures 6.4.3–6.4.7 illustrate the various effects of the system parameters; the data given in these figures were calculated from the Bowring (1972) correlation (section 6.4.3) and the parameters covered are as follows:

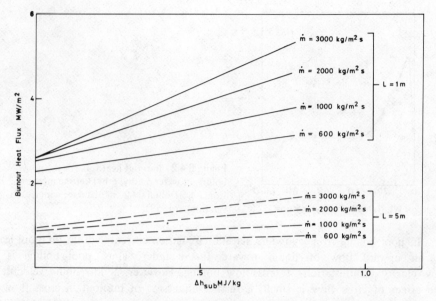

Figure 6.4.3 Relation between burnout heat flux and inlet subcooling, [calculated from the Bowring (1972) correlation for a system pressure of 6 MPa and a tube diameter of 0.01 m].

1. Subcooling. Burnout heat flux increases approximately linearly with increasing inlet subcooling over a wide range of subcooling. However, for very high subcoolings, deviations from the linear relation may sometimes occur, although these are not described by the correlation. Note that the fluxes shown in figure 6.4.3 can be higher or lower than the equivalent burnout heat fluxes shown in figure 6.4.1 for pool boiling. Since the mechanisms are quite different in the two cases, this is not surprising, and under no circumstances should pool boiling estimates be used for forced convective systems.
2. Tube length. Burnout flux decreases with tube length as shown in figure 6.4.4. However, total power input increases with length (as also shown in figure 6.4.4). Some data show an asymptotic value of power input over a wide range of tube lengths, corresponding to a constant outlet quality for burnout.
3. Pressure. Figure 6.4.5 shows the calculated effect of pressure on burnout heat flux; just as in the case of pool boiling (figure 6.4.1), there is a maximum in burnout heat flux as pressure increases. However, the mechanisms leading to this and the shape of the curve are different in the forced convective case.
4. Tube diameter. For fixed mass flux, length, pressure, and inlet subcooling, burnout heat flux increases with tube diameter, but eventually reaches an asymptotic value (and may even decrease slightly) with further increases in diameter, as illustrated in figure 6.4.6.
5. Mass flux. At low mass fluxes, burnout heat flux increases rapidly with mass flux and then tends to approach a constant value. Results calculated for various pressures at a fixed diameter, inlet subcooling, and tube length are illustrated in figure 6.4.7.

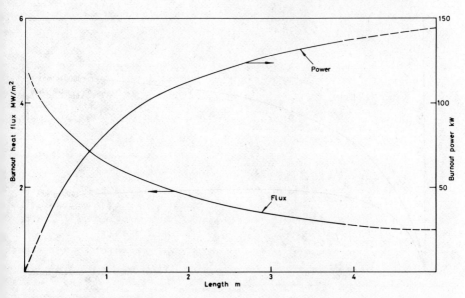

Figure 6.4.4 Relation between burnout heat flux and burnout power and tube length [calculated from the Bowring (1972) correlation for mass flux 3000 kg/m² s, tube diameter 0.01 m, pressure 6 MPa, and zero inlet subcooling].

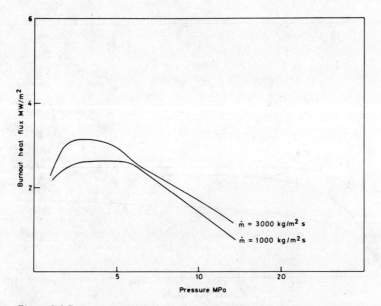

Figure 6.4.5 Relation between burnout heat flux and pressure for up flow of water in a uniformly heated round tube [calculated from the Bowring (1972) correlation for a tube diameter of 0.01 m and a tube length of 1 m with zero liquid subcooling at inlet].

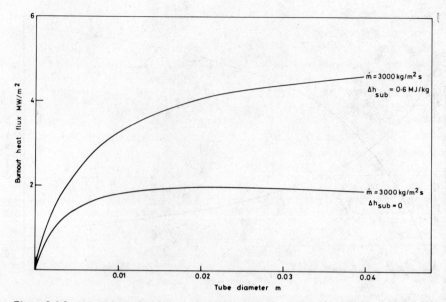

Figure 6.4.6   Relation between burnout heat flux and tube diameter for up flow of water in a round tube [calculated from the Bowring (1972) correlation for tube length 2 m and pressure 6 MPa].

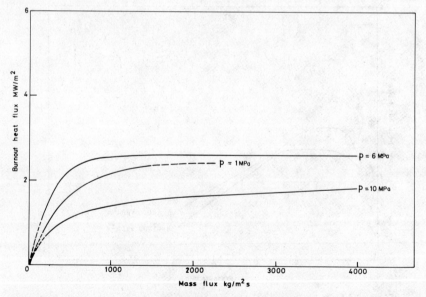

Figure 6.4.7   Relation between burnout heat flux and mass flux for up flow of water in a round tube [calculated from the Bowring (1972) for tube diameter 0.01 m, tube length 1m, and zero inlet subcooling].

6. Stability. It is particularly important to avoid the occurrence of instabilities in experiments on burnout. These can lead to oscillatory conditions and to premature burnout. Instabilities can often be minimized by throttling the flow upstream of the channel inlet, and well-throttled conditions of this type are often referred to as hard inlet conditions.

In many experimental studies of burnout in water up flow, a two-phase mixture is introduced at the tube inlet. This situation is much more complex and depends on the precise flow pattern and configuration of the inlet stream. However, some authors argue that the inlet effects are relatively unimportant (particularly for tubes of reasonable length). Extensive data for two-phase inlet conditions have been obtained (Doroshchuk 1970). More recently, the Scientific Committee of the Academy of Sciences in the U.S.S.R. (1975, 1977) published "standard" tables of burnout data giving the effect of mass flux, local quality, and pressure for a fixed tube diameter on 8 mm and length-to-diameter ratios in excess of 20 (see table 6.4.1).

Vertical down-flow systems with uniform heating have been investigated (e.g., Bertoni et al. 1976; Ganchev et al. 1976). Bertoni et al. made direct comparisons between burnout in up-flow and down-flow systems, using Refrigerant-12 as a scaling fluid for water (use of scaling fluids is discussed further in section 6.4.5). Their results are exemplified in figure 6.4.8; the data for down flow lie a little lower than those for up flow, although the differences are only of the order of 10%.

The discussion above refers to uniformly heated tubes; in many practical systems, the heat flux is highly nonuniform. The two main classes of nonuniformity (which sometimes occur together) are as follows:

1. Axial flux variations. These can take many forms (e.g., the cosine flux distribution found in nuclear reactor systems) and can lead to burnout upstream of the end of the test section. Figure 6.4.9 shows data obtained by Keeys et al. (1971) for the position of the first occurrence of burnout in the evaporation of water in a tube with a cosine axial heat flux distribution.
2. Circumferential variations. These occur, for instance, in water-tube boilers where the tubes are heated radiantly from one side only. The burnout heat flux at a given quality can be much higher than the equivalent value for uniform heating; this is exemplified by the results of Chojnowski & Wilson (1974) as illustrated in figure 6.4.10. Somewhat closer agreement is obtained when the results are compared on an average rather than a local flux basis.

A more detailed discussion of the effects of nonuniform heat flux is given in section 6.4.4 in the context of correlations.

Most of the available forced convection data for burnout are for water; data for other fluids are sparse. Fortunately, a fairly large data bank is available for fluorinated hydrocarbons in the context of their use as scaling fluids (section 6.4.5); this has made available data for fluids of different physical properties against which to test model hypotheses. In general, burnout fluxes for water are about an order of magnitude higher than those for organic fluids, due mainly to the high latent heat of water. The peculiar effects arising in burnout in pool boiling of multicomponent

Table 6.4.1 Tabulated Data for Burnout Heat Flux (MW/m²) for Boiling Water in a Round Tube 8 mm in Diameter[a]

Mass velocity (kg/m² s)	Subcooling (°C)					Mass steam content													
	75	50	25	10	0	0.05	0.1	0.15	0.2	0.25	0.3	0.35	0.4	0.45	0.5	0.55	0.6	0.65	0.7	0.75
p = 2.95 MPa																				
750						7.95	7.50	7.10	6.75	6.45	6.15	5.80	5.50	5.25	5.00	4.80	4.20	3.75	3.20	
1000		9.50	8.80	8.40	8.20	7.70	7.25	6.75	6.35	5.95	5.60	5.25	4.95	4.65	4.30	4.00	3.70	3.35		
1500		9.65	8.75	8.20	8.00	7.25	6.55	6.00	5.40	4.90	4.60	4.15	3.80	3.40	3.00	2.60				
2000	10.53	9.90	8.60	8.00	7.75	6.70	5.90	5.55	4.75	4.25	3.80	3.35	2.90	2.50						
2500	10.80	9.90	8.65	8.00	7.60	6.35	5.30	4.80	4.25	3.70	3.25	2.80	2.35							
3000	11.25	10.05	8.65	7.85	7.40	6.00	5.20	4.55	3.95	3.25	3.05	2.65								
4000	12.10	10.35	8.75	7.75	7.20	5.75	4.80	4.05	3.50	3.05	2.65									
5000	12.60	10.65	8.85	7.70	7.05	5.25	4.30	3.80	3.30	2.90	2.50									
p = 4.9 MPa																				
750					7.40	6.75	6.25	5.80	5.40	5.10	4.85	4.60	4.35	4.15	3.95	3.75	3.55	3.40	3.20	3.00
1000		8.55	8.00	7.60	7.40	6.50	5.95	5.55	5.20	4.90	4.60	4.30	4.05	3.85	3.60	3.40	3.20	2.95		
1500	9.40	8.75	8.10	7.60	7.25	6.25	5.50	5.00	4.60	4.30	4.05	3.80	3.55	3.30	3.05	2.85				
2000	9.75	9.00	8.15	7.60	7.10	5.90	5.10	4.50	4.05	3.70	3.40	3.15	2.90	2.65						
2500	10.05	9.20	8.20	7.45	7.00	5.70	4.75	4.15	3.70	3.35	3.05	2.75	2.35							
3000	10.40	9.40	8.25	7.35	6.90	5.55	4.60	3.95	3.50	3.10	2.75	2.45								
4000	11.20	9.75	8.30	7.20	6.60	5.30	4.30	3.65	3.15	2.50	2.10									
5000	11.65	10.15	8.40	7.10	6.35	5.05	4.05	3.35	2.85	2.30	1.75									
p = 6.9 MPa																				
750		7.40	6.85	6.45	6.20	5.45	4.90	4.50	4.20	3.95	3.75	3.55	3.35	3.20	3.00	2.85	2.65	2.45	2.25	
1000	8.15	7.60	6.85	6.45	6.15	5.30	4.70	4.30	4.00	3.75	3.50	3.30	3.05	2.80	2.60	2.35	2.10			
1500	8.50	7.80	6.95	6.45	5.95	5.10	4.35	3.95	3.60	3.25	2.95	2.75	2.55	2.35						
2000	8.85	8.00	7.00	6.40	5.80	4.80	4.05	3.55	3.20	2.85	2.55	2.30	2.05							
2500	9.20	8.25	7.00	6.35	5.70	4.50	3.75	3.25	2.90	2.55	2.25	1.95								

Table (continuation and sections for p = 9.8, 11.8, and 13.7 MPa). Column headers are not present on this page.

3000	9.75	8.45	7.15	6.25	5.55	4.30	3.60	3.10	2.65	2.25	1.90	2.40	2.25	2.10	1.95	1.75	1.55
4000	10.20	8.90	7.25	6.10	5.35	4.10	3.30	2.75	2.25	1.90		2.20	2.00	1.75	1.60		
5000	11.40	9.50	7.40	6.30	5.65	4.25	3.10	2.45	1.95	1.50		1.80	1.55				

p = 9.8 MPa

500	6.30	5.80	4.95	4.65	4.45	3.90	3.55	3.30	3.05	2.80	2.60	2.40	2.25	2.10	1.95	1.75	1.55
750	6.55	5.95	5.20	4.90	4.55	3.90	3.45	3.10	2.85	2.60	2.40	2.20	2.00	1.75	1.60		
1000	7.25	6.25	5.05	4.80	4.55	3.85	3.30	2.90	2.60	2.30	2.05	1.80	1.55				
1500	7.65	6.50	5.40	4.85	4.50	3.60	2.95	2.50	2.20	1.90	1.65						
2000	8.25	7.00	5.65	5.00	4.30	3.40	2.80	2.40	2.05	1.70	1.40						
2500	8.75	7.50	6.00	5.15	4.35	3.35	2.60	2.10	1.75	1.45	1.20						
3000																	
4000	10.00	8.25	6.40	5.25	4.50	3.25	2.40	1.95	1.55	1.25	0.95	0.75	0.55	0.45	0.85		
5000	11.40	9.40	6.90	5.80	4.55	3.30	2.25	1.70	1.35	1.10	0.90	0.75	0.60	0.50	0.40		

p = 11.8 MPa

500	4.90	4.40	3.90	3.70	3.40	2.95	2.60	2.40	2.25	2.05	1.90	1.75	1.60	1.45	1.30	1.20	
750	5.20	4.60	4.00	3.70	3.40	2.95	2.65	2.40	2.20	1.95	1.75	1.60	1.45	1.30			
1000	5.55	4.80	4.20	3.75	3.45	2.90	2.50	2.20	1.90	1.65	1.45	1.25					
1500	6.15	5.40	4.45	4.10	3.45	2.90	2.40	2.05	1.75	1.45	1.15						
2000	7.20	6.15	4.85	4.80	3.55	2.90	2.35	1.90	1.50	1.25	1.05						
2500	7.80	6.60	5.20	4.10	3.60	2.95	2.15	1.70	1.30	1.00							
3000	8.75	7.15	5.55	4.10	3.70												
4000	9.60	7.65	6.20	5.00	3.90	3.00	2.15	1.70	1.30	1.00	0.80	0.65	0.55	0.45	0.40		
5000	11.10	8.80	6.75	5.55	4.45	3.05	2.15	1.70	1.35	1.10	0.90	0.75	0.60	0.50	0.45		

p = 13.7 MPa

500	3.90	3.45	3.00	2.70	2.55	2.25	2.05	1.85	1.70	1.55	1.40	1.30	1.20	1.45	1.10
750	4.10	3.65	3.15	2.80	2.50	2.50	1.80	1.80	1.60	1.40	1.30	1.15	1.10	1.30	
1000	4.50	3.90	3.40	3.05	2.80	2.25	2.00								

[a] From Scientific Committee of the U.S.S.R. Academy of Sciences (1977).

Table 6.4.1 Tabulated Data for Burnout Heat Flux (MW/m^2) for Boiling Water in a Round Tube 8 mm in Diameter[a] (*Continued*)

Mass velocity (kg/m^2 s)	Subcooling (°C)					Mass steam content														
	75	50	25	10	0	0.05	0.1	0.15	0.2	0.25	0.3	0.35	0.4	0.45	0.5	0.55	0.6	0.65	0.7	0.75
$p = 13.7$ MPa																				
1500	5.30	4.50	3.80	3.25	2.95	2.30	1.95	1.70	1.45	1.20	0.90									
2000	6.15	5.15	4.15	3.50	3.10	2.40	1.95	1.60	1.30	1.00	0.80									
2500	6.75	5.70	4.50	3.75	3.25	2.50	1.95	1.45	1.10	0.90	0.75	0.60	0.50	0.40	0.30					
3000	7.55	6.30	5.00	4.00	3.40	2.55	1.90	1.45	1.15	0.90	0.80	0.60	0.55	0.40	0.35					
4000	9.20	7.40	5.70	4.65	3.80	2.75	2.05	1.55	1.30	1.05	0.90	0.75	0.65	0.55	0.45					
5000	10.60	8.45	6.40	5.30	4.00	3.05	2.20	1.80	1.50	1.25	1.05	0.90	0.75	0.60	0.50					
$p = 15.7$ MPa																				
500	2.95	2.55	2.20	2.00	1.85															
750	3.30	2.90	2.45	2.15	2.00	1.75	1.50	1.35	1.20	1.05	0.95	0.85								
1000	3.75	3.25	2.70	2.35	2.10	1.80	1.55	1.35	1.20	1.05	0.90									
1500	4.55	3.80	3.25	2.75	2.30	1.95	1.60	1.35	1.15	0.95	0.80	0.60								
2000	5.40	4.50	3.65	3.00	2.45	2.10	1.75	1.45	1.25	1.05	0.85	0.60	0.45	0.35	0.30					
2500	6.10	5.05	4.05	3.35	2.65	2.20	1.80	1.55	1.25	1.00	0.80	0.65	0.50	0.45	0.40					
3000	6.80	5.65	4.45	3.60	2.85	2.25	1.85	1.55	1.30	1.05	0.85	0.65	0.55	0.45	0.40					
4000	8.30	6.70	5.25	4.25	3.15	2.60	2.10	1.75	1.45	1.20	1.00	0.85	0.70	0.55	0.45					
5000	9.80	7.85	5.90	4.70	3.75	3.00	2.40	2.00	1.65	1.40	1.20	1.00	0.80	0.65	0.55					

p = 17.5 MPa

500	2.20	1.90	1.65	1.50	1.40										
750	2.95	2.50	2.10	1.75	1.50		1.10	0.95	0.80	0.70	0.60	0.50			0.20
1000	3.45	2.85	2.25	1.90	1.60	1.30	1.15	1.00	0.85	0.75	0.65	0.50	0.40	0.30	0.30
1500	3.70	3.20	2.55	2.25	1.80	1.35	1.30	1.10	0.90	0.80	0.65	0.55	0.45	0.35	0.30
2000	4.60	3.75	3.00	2.50	2.10	1.55	1.45	1.25	1.10	0.95	0.75	0.60	0.45	0.35	0.35
2500	5.05	4.35	3.30	2.80	2.15	1.90	1.65	1.45	1.20	1.00	0.80	0.65	0.55	0.45	0.35
3000	5.70	4.70	3.55	3.00	2.35	2.05	1.80	1.55	1.35	1.15	0.95	0.80	0.65	0.50	0.40
4000	7.25	5.75	4.40	3.55	2.85	2.45	2.05	1.85	1.55	1.35	1.15	1.00	0.80	0.65	0.50
5000	8.70	6.85	4.95	3.85	3.05	2.75	2.40	2.05	1.70	1.45	1.20	1.00	0.85	0.70	0.60

p = 19.6 MPa

500	1.70	1.55	1.45	1.35	1.30										
750	2.05	1.80	1.60	1.40	1.35	1.00	0.80	0.70	0.65	0.50	0.45	0.45			
1000	2.30	2.05	1.75	1.55	1.35	1.10	0.95	0.80	0.70	0.60	0.50	0.40	0.30		
1500	2.95	2.55	2.00	1.80	1.50	1.30	1.15	1.00	0.85	0.70	0.55	0.45	0.40	0.35	0.25
2000	3.55	2.85	2.40	2.00	1.65	1.45	1.30	1.15	1.00	0.85	0.70	0.55	0.45	0.35	0.30
2500	4.05	3.45	2.65	2.20	1.75	1.60	1.45	1.25	1.10	0.95	0.80	0.65	0.55	0.45	0.35
3000	4.95	3.75	3.00	2.35	1.90	1.75	1.55	1.35	1.20	1.05	0.90	0.75	0.65	0.50	0.40
4000	6.25	4.85	3.55	2.65	2.00	1.85	1.70	1.55	1.40	1.25	1.10	0.90	0.75	0.60	0.50
5000	7.55	5.80	4.05	3.00	2.30	2.30	2.10	1.90	1.70	1.45	1.25	1.05	0.90	0.75	0.60

[a] From Scientific Committee of the U.S.S.R. Academy of Sciences (1977).

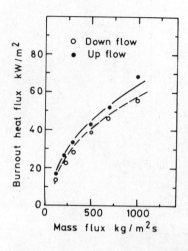

Figure 6.4.8 Comparison of burnout fluxes for up flow and down flow of water in a 0.780-cm-diameter tube at a pressure of 1.75 MPa and an inlet quality of -0.20 (Bertoni et al. 1976).

fluids were mentioned in section 6.4.2.1. Burnout data for multicomponent mixtures under forced convective conditions are sparse. However, results of Tolubinskiy & Matorin (1973) for binary mixtures (figure 6.4.11) show that similarly complex effects can be observed in forced convective subcooled boiling. Effects of dissolved solids on burnout have been investigated by Yusufova & Bronshtein (1976); burnout heat flux decreased with increasing dissolved solids concentration.

Rectangular Channels

Burnout in rectangular channels has been studied extensively as part of the nuclear reactor program. The parametric trends for such channels are similar to those

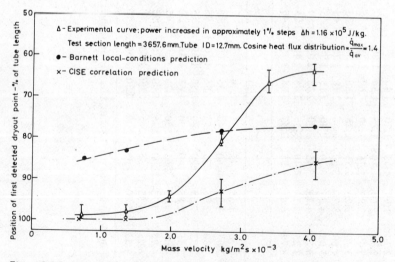

Figure 6.4.9 Effect of mass flux on position of burnout in evaporation of water at a pressure of 6.9 MPa in a 1.27-cm-diameter tube with a cosine heat flux distribution (Keeys et al. 1970).

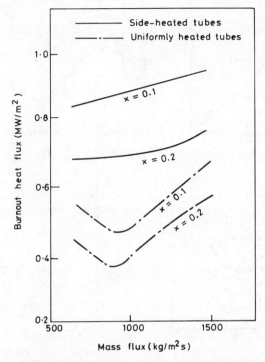

Figure 6.4.10 Comparison of data for burnout heat flux
for uniformly heated tubes and tubes heated from one
side only (3.2-cm-diameter tubes at 18.0 MPa (data of
Chojnowski & Wilson 1974).

encountered in round tubes, as described above; prime data sources for rectangular
channel burnout are the reports by de Bortoli et al. (1958) and by Maneri &
Schneider (1976).

Annuli

Annular channels have been extensively studied in the nuclear context. This is
because they are, essentially, a "one-rod bundle" and may therefore be deemed to
simulate more closely the rod bundle geometry than do round tubes. Most of the
data for annuli are therefore for the case of the center rod only being heated (e.g.,
Levitan & Lantsman 1977). Studies in which both the outer and inner surfaces are
heated are reported by Jensen & Mannov (1974) and Becker & Letzter (1975). Data
from the latter are illustrated in figure 6.4.12, where burnout steam quality is
plotted against the fraction of the total power that is on the outer cylinder. There
is a maximum steam quality corresponding to the point at which burnout occurs
simultaneously on both cylinders.

Burnout in eccentric annuli has been investigated by Tolubinski et al. (1971),
and the effect of nonuniform heat fluxes on burnout in annuli has been investigated
by Ornatskiy et al. (1975, 1976).

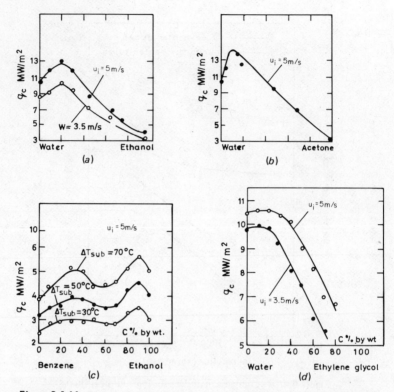

Figure 6.4.11 Burnout heat flux data for forced convective subcooled burnout in the evaporation of binary mixtures in a 0.4-mm-bore tube (pressure 0.66 MPa and 50 K subcooling except where otherwise stated) (results of Tolubinskiy & Matorin 1973).

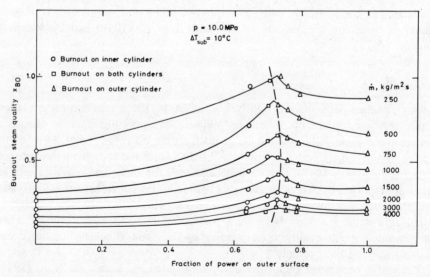

Figure 6.4.12 Burnout data for annuli with varying distribution of power between the inner and outer surfaces (results of Becker & Letzter 1975).

To maintain uniform spacing between the inner and outer cylinders, some form of support or spacer grid must usually be introduced in annuli (just as it is in rod bundles). The presence and configuration of spacers can have a significant effect on burnout, as demonstrated in the work of Ilic & Lawther (1973), Lee & Bowditch (1974), and Ilic (1975).

Rod Bundles

The importance of establishing burnout limits in nuclear reactor systems has led to extensive test work on bundles of rods. Useful reviews and compilations of data are given by Tolubinski et al. (1970) and Hughes (1974). Figure 6.4.13 illustrates the test section geometries that have been investigated. Table 6.4.2 is a list of data sources for rod bundle data.

The effects of system parameters on burnout in rod bundles are somewhat similar to those for burnout in tubes, as described above. Figure 6.4.14 shows data for a 36-rod bundle with uniform and nonuniform axial heat flux distribution. The flux distribution had little effect on burnout power at low mass velocities although it affects the burnout heat flux at the point of onset of burnout (see section 6.4.4). In rod bundles, the flux tends to continue to increase with mass velocity at high mass velocities, but at a reduced rate.

The effects of some of the main system parameters may be noted as follows:

1. Heat flux profile effects. Here, three different types of flux variation can be recognized, namely rod-to-rod variations, axial variations along the channel, and circumferential variations around each rod. In a pressure-tube nuclear reactor the outer ring of rods has a higher flux than the inner ring. Tests on 36-rod bundle with a factor of 2 difference in flux between the inner and outer rings of rods were reported by Bailey & Lee (1977); the dryout power for this case was about 7% less than that for uniformly distributed flux. For uniform flux distribution, burnout occurred first on the inner ring of pins, whereas with the flux variation experiment, burnout occurred first on the outer ring. Results of tests with uniform and cosine axial flux distributions are compared in figure 6.4.14 for a 36-rod bundle. At high mass velocities, there was a slight increase in burnout power for the cosine case. Also, the position of burnout moved upstream from the end of the test section with increasing mass velocity, much as was observed for the single tube as illustrated in figure 6.4.9.

2. Grid effects. In rod bundles, just as in annuli, the rods must be supported by some kind of grid arrangement. Katsaounis et al. (1977) showed that the grid tended to promote wetting of the surface and thus increase burnout heat flux. Burnout tends to occur immediately upstream of a grid for this reason. Grid effects may also explain the interesting observations of Macbeth (1974), which are illustrated in figure 6.4.15. Here, a uniformly spaced 30-rod cluster gave higher burnout powers than did a 36-rod cluster. Macbeth hypothesized that the unexpectedly high burnout powers for the 30-rod cluster were due to the fact that there was an odd number of rods on the periphery of the cluster; the experiment has thus become known as the "odds and evens" experiment. However, it may also be that

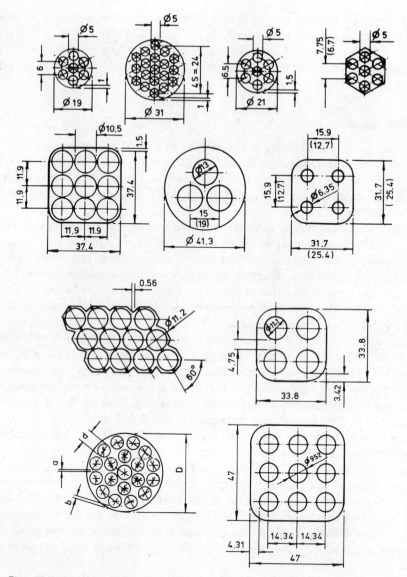

Figure 6.4.13 Bundle configurations used in tube bundle burnout tests (compiled by Tolubinskiy et al. 1970). Dimensions in millimeters.

the rod support grids exert a more significant influence in the case of the 30-rod cluster; more experiments are needed to clarify this matter.

3. Effects of bundle bowing and eccentricity. It is difficult to guarantee that rod bundles are supported in a precisely concentric position or that they do not bow. Experiments of Bailey & Lee (1977) and Nixon et al. (1975) indicate that the effects of bowing and eccentricity are small. However, Kobori et al. (1974) found a considerable effect, as illustrated in figure 6.4.16. Bowing toward an unheated wall would probably have little effect, whereas bowing toward a heated rod could

Table 6.4.2   Sources of Critical Heat Flux Data for Rod Bundles

Number of tubes in bundle	Data source	Rod diameter (cm)	Heated length (m)	Inlet pressure or pressure range (MPa)
3	Becker (1962)	1.30	0.97	0.3–1.0
3	Adorni et al. (1964)	0.50	0.80	6.9
3	Adorni et al. (1964)	0.50	0.82	5.0–9.0
3	Janssen & Kervinen (1963)	0.64	1.37	6.9
3	Becker (1967)	1.38	4.00	3.0–4.5
3	Becker (1967)	1.38	4.44	3.0
3	Becker et al. (1965)	1.00	0.83	1.0–4.6
3	Becker et al. (1965)	1.00	1.67	2.1–4.0
3	Kunsemiller (1966)	1.27	4.52	6.9
3	Smolin & Polyakov (1972)	1.20	1.50	
3	Smolin & Polyakov (1972)	1.35	7.0	
3	Smolin & Polyakov (1972)	1.20	2.2	
3	Becker et al. (1965)	1.00	0.83	1.6–3.5
3	Becker et al. (1965)	1.00	1.67	2.1–4.3
4	Hench (1963)	1.20	0.91	6.9
4	Hench (1963)	1.20	1.22	6.9
6	Becker (1967)	1.38	4.44	4.3
6	Becker (1967)	1.38	4.38	3.1–5.1
7	Becker (1967)	1.00	1.67	1.1–4.0
7	Matzner (1961)	1.40	0.94	6.9
7	Macbeth (1964)	1.27	1.83	6.9
7	Becker (1967)	1.00	3.00	3.0–7.0
7	Smolin & Polyakov (1967)	0.5	0.50	2.9–13.7
7	Smolin & Polyakov (1972)	1.20	1.50	
7	Adorni & Gaspari (1964)	1.02	0.41	5.0
7	Adorni & Gaspari (1964)	1.02	1.63	5.0–6.5
7	Smolin & Polyakov (1972)	1.20	2.2	
7	Besroukov et al. (1974)	0.90	1.75	
7	Besroukov et al. (1974)	0.90	2.5	
7	Besroukov et al. (1974)	0.90	3.5	
7	Doubrovsky et al. (1974)	0.90	1.0	
7	Doubrovsky et al. (1974)	0.90	1.8	
7	Doubrovsky et al. (1974)	0.91	2.5	
7	Doubrovsky et al. (1974)	0.90	2.5	
7	Kaputstin et al. (1974)	0.90	2.5	
7	Becker (1967b)	1.00	3.00	3.0–7.0
9	Wilson et al. (1969)	1.07	1.83	13.8–16.5
9	Janssen (1968)	1.45	1.83	6.9
9	Janssen (1965)	1.11	0.76	6.9
9	Polomik (1962)	0.95	0.46	6.9
9	Campanile et al. (1970)	1.02	1.18	3.9–14.7
9	Campanile et al. (1970)	1.02	1.18	4.4–15.7
9	Hench & Boehm (1966)	1.11	1.52	6.9
9	Janssen (1968)	1.11		9.6
9	Gellerstedt et al. (1969)	1.07	1.83	6.7–17.2
12	Matzner (1963b)	1.12	0.43	8.3
16	Lucchini & Marinelli (1975)	1.5	3.66	7.1
16	Israel et al. (1969)	1.43	1.83	6.0
16	Waters (1963)	1.49	1.93	8.4

Table 6.4.2 Sources of Critical Heat Flux Data for Rod Bundles (*Continued*)

Number of tubes in bundle	Data source	Rod diameter (cm)	Heated length (m)	Inlet pressure or pressure range (MPa)
16	Janssen et al. (1969)	1.43	1.83	6.9
16	Janssen et al. (1969)	1.43	1.83	4.1–8.6
19	Matzner & Casterline (1965)	1.98	0.46	6.9–8.3
19	Matzner & Casterline (1965)	1.98	0.89	3.4–8.3
19	Matzner & Casterline (1965)	1.98	1.83	3.4–8.3
19	Matzner & Casterline (1965)	1.98	2.74	3.4–8.3
19	Tong et al. (1967)	1.07	1.52	10.3
19	Waters (1963)	1.43	0.47	8.4
19	Matzner & Casterline (1965)	1.40	0.91	6.9
19	Matzner (1963a)	1.40	1.83	7.9
19	Macbeth (1964)	·1.59	1.22	6.9
19	Hessom et al. (1965)	1.55	1.93	6.9–8.3
19	Ceresa et al. (1974)	2.0	6.0	5.1
19	Edwards (1976)	1.59	1.22	6.9
19	Barnett (1968)	1.59	1.22	6.9
19	Kaputstin et al. (1974)	0.90	2.5	–
19	Waters (1963)	1.60	0.50	8.4
19	Waters (1963)	1.49	0.50	8.4
20	Letourneau et al. (1974)	1.9	2.39	8.3–13.8
20	Letourneau & Green (1971)	1.27	2.44	8.3–13.8
21	Cermak et al. (1970)	1.07	1.52	4.6–10.3
21	Tong et al. (1967)	1.07	1.52	10.3
25	Tong et al. (1967)	1.07	2.13	11.1–16.0
25	Lund (1975)	1.38	0.56	0.1
28	Kobori et al. (1974)	1.65	3.70	6.9
33	Smolin & Polyakov (1967)	0.50	0.50	2.9–13.8
36	Bailey & Lee (1977)	1.59	3.66	6.9
36	Lee & Bowditch (1977)	1.59	3.66	0.7–6.9
37	Becker (1967)	1.38	4.37	5.0
37	Becker (1967)	1.38	4.36	3.0–8.7
37	Barnett (1968)	1.59	3.66	6.9
37	Kaputstin et al. (1974)	0.90	2.5	–
64	Nixon et al. (1975)	1.9	3.75	6.9

decrease burnout heat flux. It seems that the existence of these effects depends very much on the design of the rod bundle.

Correlations for prediction of burnout in rod bundles are discussed in section 6.4.3.2, pp. 6-101 to 6-105.

Transients

Onset of burnout under transient conditions has become an important area of study in the context of nuclear reactor safety. Transients in mass flux, system pressure, and heat flux would all occur in the extremely unlikely event of a loss-of-coolant accident (LOCA). Typical of the many studies in this area are those of Leung (1977), who studied burnout heat flux during blowdown with flow reversal, and the

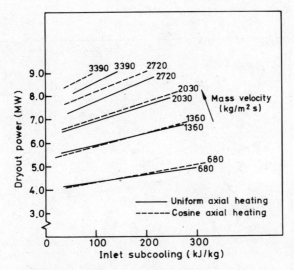

Figure 6.4.14 Burnout data for a 36-pin rod bundle at a pressure of 6.83 MPa (Bailey & Lee 1977).

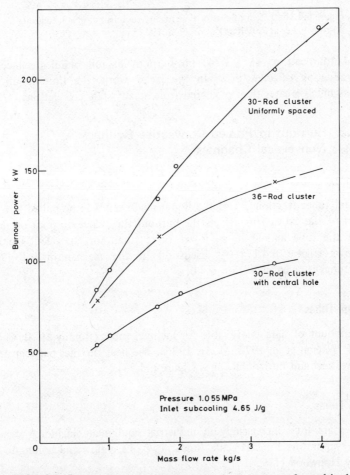

Figure 6.4.15 Effect of rod arrangements on burnout power for multirod clusters: odds and evens test of Macbeth (1974).

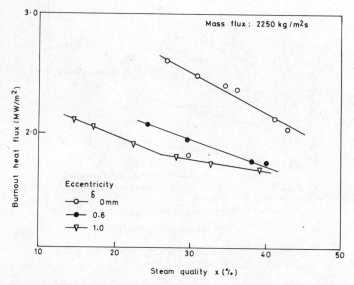

Figure 6.4.16 Effect of cluster eccentricity on burnout in a 3.7-m-long 28-rod cluster at 7.0 MPa (Kobori et al. 1974).

work or Letourneau et al. (1974) on burnout in rod bundles subjected to a transient reduction of inlet flow. In the latter work, the time required before burnout was much greater than predicted from steady-state correlations.

6.4.2.3 Burnout in Forced Convective Boiling: Nonvertical Channels

Horizontal Tubes

In horizontal tubes (section 2.1.4) the liquid phase tends to be pulled by gravity to the bottom of the tube. This affects the burnout flux, since burnout occurs first at the top of the tube and at much lower fluxes than for equivalent conditions in vertical flows (figure 6.4.17). A discussion of the mechanisms of burnout in horizontal tubes is given in section 6.4.6.

Inclined Tubes

A limited amount of data is available for inclined tubes (Roumy 1970; Chojnowski et al. 1974; Watson et al. 1974; Morris 1976). The heat flux lies between the values found for vertical and horizontal tubes (figure 6.4.18).

Coiled Tubes

Coiled tubes are used increasingly in industrial equipment, including steam-raising plants and evaporators for cryogenic fluids. Two-phase flow and boiling in coils are reviewed by Hopwood (1972).

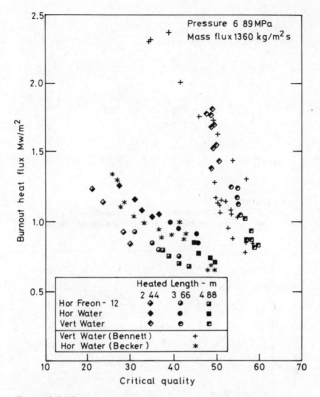

Figure 6.4.17 Comparison of burnout data for horizontal and vertical tubes (Merilo 1977).

Coils offer the advantage of having a large heat transfer surface area for a minimum of tube-to-header connections. Also, coils tend to have higher burnout fluxes than do straight tubes of the same length and with the same inlet conditions. Figure 6.4.19 shows a comparison of local burnout quality for straight tubes and

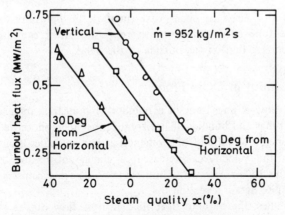

Figure 6.4.18 Effect of inclination on burnout heat flux in a tube at pressure 18.4 MPa (data of Watson et al. 1974).

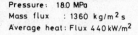

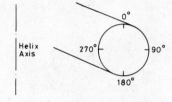

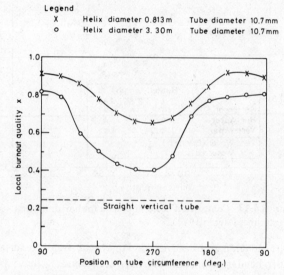

Figure 6.4.19 Local burnout quality for evaporation of water in helical coils (Hopwood 1972).

helical coils. Burnout tends to occur first (in these high-pressure experiments) on the inside of the tube curve. However, the opposite effect can also be observed, with burnout occurring first on the outside of the bend.

6.4.2.4 Burnout in Cross Flow

Burnout in cross flow is important in a number of industrial applications for both single horizontal tubes and bundles of horizontal tubes (e.g., in kettle reboilers).

For single tubes, the burnout phenomenon at low velocities is similar to that in pool boiling. As the velocity is increased, a change of regime occurs and the burnout flux begins to increase with fluid velocity. The mechanisms of this change are discussed in more detail in section 6.4.6.

For tube bundles, the burnout heat flux in cross flow can be lower or higher than the pool boiling value, depending on the flow conditions. A reduction in flux can occur when access of the liquid phase to the tubes in the heart of the bundle is limited because of limited circulation rate or flooding effects. Data for tube bundles are given, for instance, by Palen & Taborek (1962), Palen & Small (1964), and Palen et al. (1972). A further discussion of mechanisms in bundle cross flow is given in section 6.4.6.6, and correlations for this case are given in section 6.4.3.1.

6.4.2.5 Enhancement of Burnout Heat Flux

The importance of the burnout limitation has led to a search for methods of enhancing the burnout flux. For pool boiling, the methods of enhancement are reviewed by Bergles (1975); successful augmentation of the burnout heat flux in pool boiling has been obtained with volatile additives (this is related to the effects of multicomponent mixtures, illustrated in figure 6.4.2) by vibration of the heater, and by use of electric fields.

Methods of augmentation of burnout flux in forced convective systems are reviewed by Collier (1972) and Bergles (1977). Enhancement has been achieved mainly by use of swirl or mixing vanes and by use of tubes with internal ribbing.

The liquid phase can be induced to wet the heated surface (thus preventing burnout) by swirling the flow with twisted tapes. These tapes can be continuous along the test section or can consist of a number of short swirlers spaced along the channel. Figure 6.4.20 shows the influence of twisted tapes on burnout heat flux in a round tube (Moeck et al. 1964). Although the tape can increase the burnout flux at a given mass velocity, it is also possible to observe a decrease in flux due to capture of liquid by the tape itself. The action of rod support grids in enhancing burnout flux in rod bundles was mentioned above. By using short swirl sections or

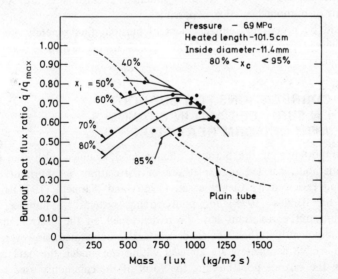

Figure 6.4.20 Fraction of inlet liquid evaporated as a function of mass velocity for a plain tube and a tube with helical tape inserts; $\dot{q}_{max}$ is the flux corresponding to evaporation of all the injected water (Moeck et al. 1964).

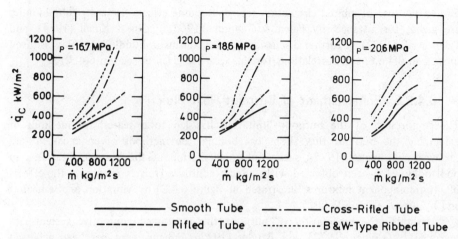

Smooth Tube —————— ———·———Cross-Rifled Tube

————————— Rifled Tube   ·············· B & W-Type Ribbed Tube

Figure 6.4.21   Burnout heat flux data for plain and modified-surface tubes (Nishikawa et al. 1974). (B & W = Babcock and Wilcox, Inc.)

other forms of mixing device within the grid, it is possible to obtain a further enhancement (Suchy et al. 1976).

The use of ordinary surface roughness elements tends to reduce the burnout flux. However, by introducing helical and fin-form deformations of the tube surface it is possible to induce swirl and turbulence in the flow, which promotes transfer from the liquid phase to the surface and thus gives enhancement (e.g., Nishikawa 1972; Nishikawa et al. 1974; Subbotin et al. 1975; Grachev et al. 1977). Figure 6.4.21 illustrates some of the results obtained at high pressure. Considerable enhancement of burnout heat flux is possible.

It should be noted that enhancement of burnout flux generally occurs at the cost of increased pressure drop, and this should be taken into account in overall system design.

6.4.3   CORRELATIONS FOR BURNOUT ON SURFACES AND IN CHANNELS WITH UNIFORM HEAT FLUX

The great importance of the burnout phenomenon, coupled with the absence of predictive methods, has led to a plethora of correlations for burnout. These are cataloged and reviewed by Clerici et al. (1966) and Marinelli (1977) for channel flows and by Bergles (1975) for pool boiling systems. A number of forced convective burnout correlations have been developed on the basis of mechanisms that have subsequently turned out to be physically unjustified. However, if enough arbitrary adjustable parameters are allowed within the model, the data can usually be fitted. In the case of pool boiling, the form of the commonly used correlations has a sounder physical basis, but even here a number of empirical factors have to be introduced. On the whole, therefore, it seems best to introduce correlations as straightforward methods, taken independently of a discussion of mechanisms.

Burnout mechanisms are discussed further in section 6.4.6. In section 6.4.7, predictive methods for forced convective systems are discussed.

To minimize confusion, only one correlation is stated for each of the cases referred to below. The selection is based on the following criteria:

1. The size of the data base from which the correlation has been derived, with particular reference to extent of coverage of the various system parameters.
2. The accuracy of the correlation as established by the originator and by subsequent test against further data.
3. Ease of use; thus, correlations having an algebraic form are preferred to those that are graphical.

It should be stressed that the choice between correlations is often marginal.

6.4.3.1 Correlations for Pool Boiling and Cross Flow

Pool Boiling

Large horizontal flat plate Zuber analytical form (Zuber 1958; Zuber et al. 1963) as modified by Lienhard & Dhir (1973a, b). The burnout heat flux $\dot{q}_c$ (W/m^2) is given by

$$\dot{q}_c = 0.149\, \rho_G^{1/2} h_{LG}\, [\sigma g(\rho_L - \rho_G)]^{1/4} \qquad [6.4.1]$$

where ρ_G and ρ_L are the vapor- and liquid-phase densities (kg/m^3), σ is the surface tension (N/m), g is the acceleration due to gravity (m/s^2), and h_{LG} is the latent heat of vaporization (J/kg).

Although not explicitly stated, examination of the results of Lienhard & Dhir (1973a) indicates that an accuracy of about $\pm 20\%$ is obtained with a wide range of fluids, for data within the range of limitations described below.

The correlation is subject to the following main limitations:

1. It is for saturated pool boiling only; if the liquid in the pool is subcooled (i.e., at a temperature less than the saturation temperature) the burnout heat flux is higher.
2. It is applicable only to large plates. Thus the characteristic dimension of the plate L (m) should obey:

$$L > \frac{32.6}{[g(\rho_L - \rho_G)/\sigma]^{1/2}} \qquad [6.4.2]$$

where L is given by the shortest side for a rectangular plate or by the diameter for a circular plate. For smaller plates the number of vapor escape jets is atypical, and this could give rise to either a higher or a lower burnout heat flux depending on the precise number of jets (Lienhard & Dhir 1973a, b).
3. Effects of liquid viscosity are not included in [6.4.1], although burnout heat flux for viscous liquids is higher than that for those with low viscosity. A more detailed correlation taking into account viscosity effects is given by Dhir &

Lienhard (1974). To use the low-viscosity correlation, the viscosity number Vi, as defined by

$$\text{Vi} = \frac{\rho_L \sigma^{3/4}}{\mu_L g^{1/4} (\rho_L - \rho_G)^{3/4}} \qquad [6.4.3]$$

should be greater than 400; in [6.4.3] μ_L is the liquid viscosity.

4. Edge effects: [6.4.1] applies only to the case where the horizontal flat plate is surrounded by vertical side walls. Many experiments have been conducted with plates suspended in a large pool of liquid; in this case, the circulation patterns are very complex and the burnout heat flux may be very different.

5. The correlation does not apply to liquid metals (see section 6.2 for a further discussion of this subject).

Horizontal cylinders Zuber-type correlation extended by Sun & Lienhard (1970) and Lienhard & Dhir (1973a, b). The burnout heat flux $\dot{q}_c$ is given by

$$\dot{q}_c = K \rho_G^{1/2} h_{LG} \left[\sigma g (\rho_L - \rho_G) \right]^{1/4} \qquad [6.4.4]$$

where the constant K is given by

$$K = 0.118 \qquad \text{for } R' > 1.17 \qquad [6.4.5]$$

$$K = \frac{0.123}{(R')^{1/4}} \qquad \text{for } 1.17 > R' > 0.12 \qquad [6.4.6]$$

where R' is a nondimensional radius defined by

$$R' = R \left[\frac{g(\rho_L - \rho_G)}{\sigma} \right]^{1/2} \qquad [6.4.7]$$

where R is the cylinder radius.

A comparison of the values of K estimated from experimental pool boiling burnout data with those calculated from [6.4.5] and [6.4.6] is illustrated in figure 6.4.22. As will be seen, the spread around the predictions is of the order of $\pm 20\%$.

The correlation given by [6.4.4]–[6.4.6] has the following main limitations:

1. It does not apply to very small cylinders (i.e., $R' < 0.12$). For smaller cylinders (e.g., small-diameter wires) the burnout flux is lower than predicted by these equations because the mechanism of burnout changes (Lienhard & Dhir 1973a, b).

2. It applies only for low-viscosity systems (i.e., $\text{Vi} > 400$). A correlation for viscous fluids is described by Dhir & Lienhard (1974).

3. The cylinder should be sufficiently long to ensure that the number of vapor escape jets (section 6.4.6) is close to the average for an infinitely long cylinder. Typically, the cylinder should be at least 20 diameters long to meet this criterion.

4. The correlation is for boiling of saturated fluids, and liquid subcooling increases the burnout heat flux. Ivey & Morris (1962) suggest the following expression for the effect of subcooling:

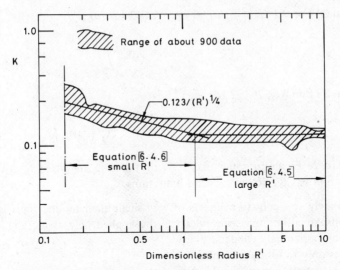

Figure 6.4.22 Comparison of K predicted from [6.4.5] and [6.4.6] with experimental data (Lienhard & Dhir 1973b).

$$\dot{q}_c = \dot{q}_{c,\text{sat}} \left[1 + 0.1 \left(\frac{\rho_L}{\rho_G} \right)^{3/4} \frac{C_{pL} \Delta T_{\text{sub}}}{h_{LG}} \right] \qquad [6.4.8]$$

where $\dot{q}_{c,\text{sat}}$ is the burnout heat flux for saturated conditions, C_{pL} is the liquid specific heat, and ΔT_{sub} is the difference between the saturation temperature and the bulk liquid temperature.

5. The correlation does not apply to liquid metals (see section 6.2).

   Other shapes A variety of other heater shapes have been investigated. Lienhard & Dhir (1973a, b) studied burnout on spheres and vertical ribbons. For spheres, [6.4.4] may be used with $K = 0.110$ for $R' > 4.26$ and $K = 0.227 / \sqrt{R'}$ for $R' < 4.26$, where R' is calculated from [6.4.7] with R equal to the sphere radius. Similar equations were proposed by Lienhard & Dhir for the ribbon case.

   Modifications of the heater surface have been proposed as a means of enhancing the burnout flux. This topic is reviewed by Bergles (1975).

Effect of Cross Flow on Single Cylinders

The correlation (Lienhard & Eichhorn 1976) is in three regions, whose boundaries are specified in terms of Weber number We_G defined as

$$\text{We}_G = \frac{2R\rho_G U_\infty^2}{\sigma} \qquad [6.4.9]$$

where U_∞ is the (vertical upward) approach velocity of the liquid flowing over the cylinder. The correlation is as follows.

   Region 1 For $\text{We}_G < 0.1 \, (R')^2 \rho_G / \rho_L$. In this region, the burnout flux is identical to that calculated for pool boiling.

Region 2 For $0.1\ (R')^2 \rho_G/\rho_L < \text{We}_G < 192\ (\rho_G/\rho_L)^{3/2}$

$$\frac{\pi \dot{q}_c}{\rho_G h_{GL} U_\infty} = 1 + \left(\frac{4}{\text{We}_G}\right)^{1/3} \qquad [6.4.10]$$

Region 3 For $\text{We}_G > 192\ (\rho_G/\rho_L)^{3/2}$

$$\frac{\pi \dot{q}_c}{\rho_G h_{LG} U_\infty} = \frac{(\rho_L/\rho_G)^{3/4}}{169} + \frac{(\rho_L/\rho_G)^{1/2}}{19.2\ \text{We}_G^{1/3}} \qquad [6.4.11]$$

Lienhard & Eichhorn show that 95% of the data are fitted to within ± 20%. The correlation has the following main limitations:

1. It is unlikely to apply to cylinders of very small diameter and short length. As a first approximation, the same rules may be applied here as are applied to pool boiling on horizontal cylinders.
2. It applies only to saturated boiling.
3. It is for vertical upward liquid flow over the cylinder only and should not be applied to other flow configurations.
4. The effect of viscosity is likely to be complex and the correlation should be used only for $\text{Vi} > 400$.

Horizontal Tube Bundles

The correlation (Palen & Small 1964) is for boiling from circular bundles of round tubes in a "static" pool of liquid (i.e., kettle reboiler configuration). Palen & Small suggest that, for a bundle of tubes, the burnout flux for a single tube in pool boiling (calculated as indicated above) should be multiplied by a factor related to a "tube density factor" defined as $D_b L/A$, where D_b is the bundle diameter, L the bundle length, and A the total heat transfer area of the tubes within the bundle. The relation is illustrated in figure 6.4.23.

The correlation is subject to large uncertainties and is given here only because of the lack of better published correlations. It is, by definition, subject to the same limitations as the pool boiling correlation. Also, the boiling process in tube bundles is highly complex; rapid recirculation of the liquid through the bundle is induced, and the flow may sometimes more closely resemble forced convective boiling (in the channels between the tubes) than pool boiling. The factors limiting the maximum heat flux depend on the way in which the liquid phase reaches the tubes, and it is unlikely that a simple correlation of the form shown in figure 6.4.23 can apply.

6.4.3.2 Correlations for Channel Flow

A very large number of correlations exist for channel flow, particularly for water. Wide ranges of pressures, geometries, and flow rates have been investigated. All of the general correlations are for vertical up flow. They may be applied approximately to vertical down flow, but they *must not be applied to inclined or horizontal channel situations*. The effect of tube inclination was discussed qualitatively in

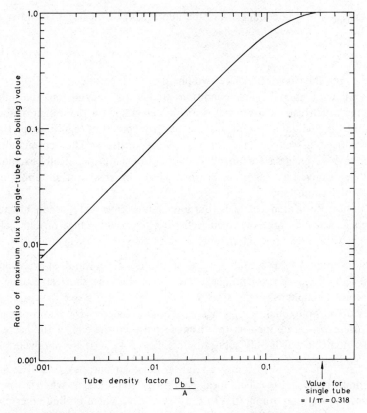

Figure 6.4.23 Correction factor of Palen & Small (1964) for burnout heat flux in horizontal bundles of tubes in a static pool of liquid.

section 6.4.2.3, and some tentative relations for horizontal flow are discussed in section 6.4.5.

The correlations in this section are for vertical up flow of water and are not applicable to nonaqueous fluids. It may be possible to estimate burnout in nonaqueous fluid systems by using scaling laws, which are introduced in section 6.4.5. Also, general methods for the prediction of burnout in annular flow can be used for any arbitrary fluid; these are discussed in section 6.4.7.

The first objective of most burnout correlations is to represent, by one relation, data for a given channel cross section, pressure, and mass flux arising from channels of differing length and with a range of inlet qualities. The inlet quality may be formally defined in terms of the local enthalpy h_{tp} of the fluid in the tube as follows:

$$x = \frac{h_{tp} - h_L}{h_G - h_L} = \frac{h_{tp} - h_L}{h_{LG}} \qquad [6.4.12]$$

where h_L and h_G are the saturated enthalpies for the liquid and vapor phases, respectively, with h_{LG} being the latent heat of vaporization. Thus if subcooled liquid is passed to the entrance of the test section, h_{tp} is less than h_L by an amount Δh_{sub}, the "subcooling," and the inlet quality x_i is negative and is given by

$$x_i = -\frac{\Delta h_{\text{sub}}}{h_{LG}} \qquad [6.4.13]$$

if $h_{tp} > h_L$, the inlet conditions are two-phase or "mixed inlet."

Burnout with mixed inlet conditions tends to depend on the inlet flow distribution, which can be arbitrarily variable depending on the design of the mixer. Furthermore, mixed inlet conditions are of little practical significance, the liquid being introduced in subcooled form in most applications. Thus correlations based wholly or in part on data for mixed inlet conditions are specifically excluded from this section. Conversely, the correlations given in this section apply only to subcooled inlet conditions.

For uniformly heated channels, burnout almost invariably occurs at the end of the heated length, and an experimental finding for a wide range of data is that, for a given mass flux, pressure, and channel cross section:

1. A plot of burnout heat flux $\dot{q}_c$ against quality at burnout at the end of the heated length x_{BO} gives a unique curve for all but the shortest channel lengths and for all subcoolings.
2. A plot of burnout quality x_{BO} against "boiling length" L_B also forms a unique curve. Here, L_B is defined as the distance between the end of the heated length and the point at which bulk saturation conditions ($x = 0$) are obtained.

The first plot seems to imply a relation between burnout heat flux and local quality conditions (the so-called local conditions hypothesis), whereas the second plot relates the fraction evaporated to the length over which boiling takes place (the so-called integral length hypothesis). In fact, it is not possible to deduce a mechanism from these plots, and furthermore they are completely interchangeable; thus if a $\dot{q}_c/x_{BO}$ relation is valid, it follows that, for uniformly heated channels, an x_{BO}/L_B relation is also valid. This is because the burnout quality is given by a heat balance as

$$x_{BO} = \frac{P_h L_B \dot{q}_c}{\dot{m} A h_{LG}} \qquad [6.4.14]$$

where P_h is the heated perimeter of the channel, A is the cross-sectional area, and $\dot{m}$ is the mass flux. Suppose that $\dot{q}_c = \text{fn}(x_{BO})$ (i.e., relation 1); it follows that

$$x_{BO} = \frac{P_h L_B \, \text{fn}(x_{BO})}{\dot{m} A h_{LG}} \qquad [6.4.15]$$

and, rearranging, relation 2 is obtained:

$$x_{BO} = \text{fn}(L_B) \qquad [6.4.16]$$

Even for subcooled inlet conditions, there may be deviations from the $\dot{q}_c/x_{BO}$ relation for short channel lengths; this is illustrated by the Refrigerant-12 data of Stevens et al. (1964) as shown in figure 6.4.24. Deviations occurred for length-to-diameter ratios less than about 80.

Most of the available correlations fall into either the $\dot{q}_c/x_{BO}$ or the x_{BO}/L_B

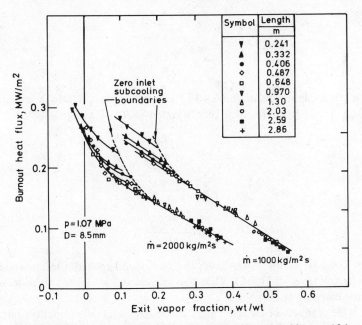

Figure 6.4.24 Burnout heat flux data for evaporation of Refrigerant-12 in a vertical round tube, showing deviations from flux/quality relation at short tube lengths (Stevens et al. 1964).

category. The most comprehensive correlations are often in the former category, whereas for practical application to nonuniform heating, it is probably best to use the x_{BO}/L_B form (section 6.4.4). However, since the forms can be readily transformed, this presents no great difficulty. Many of the heat flux/quality correlations take the linear form:

$$\dot{q}_c = a - b x_{BO} \qquad [6.4.17]$$

where a and b are functions of pressure, mass flux, and channel cross-sectional geometry. Since burnout quality is a dependent variable, it is more convenient to rewrite [6.4.17] to give an explicit relation involving inlet subcooling and channel length. This is achieved by writing the heat balance expression:

$$x_{BO} = \frac{\dot{q} P_h L}{\dot{m} A h_{LG}} - \frac{\Delta h_{\text{sub}}}{h_{LG}} \qquad [6.4.18]$$

where L is the channel length. Eliminating x_{BO} between [6.4.17] and [6.4.18] and rearranging, we have the common correlation form (e.g., Thompson & Macbeth 1964):

$$\dot{q}_c = \frac{A' + B' \, \Delta h_{\text{sub}}}{C' + L} \qquad [6.4.19]$$

where A', B', and C' are related to a and b, and to the system parameters, by

$$A' = \frac{a \dot{m} h_{LG} A}{b P_h} \qquad [6.4.20]$$

$$B' = \frac{A\dot{m}}{P_h} \qquad\qquad [6.4.21]$$

$$C' = \frac{\dot{m}h_{LG}A}{bP_h} \qquad\qquad [6.4.22]$$

The linear flux/quality relation [6.4.17] can be converted into a quality/boiling length relation by eliminating heat flux between [6.4.14] and [6.4.17]:

$$x_{BO} = \frac{cL_B}{d + L_B} \qquad\qquad [6.4.23]$$

where
$$c = \frac{a}{b} \qquad\qquad [6.4.24]$$

$$d = \frac{\dot{m}Ah_{LG}}{bP_h} \qquad\qquad [6.4.25]$$

Equation [6.4.23] is the form used in the widely applied CISE correlation for burnout (Bertoletti et al. 1965). Thus this correlation is close in form to the linear flux/quality correlations.

For wide ranges of length and subcooling, the flux/quality relation for uniformly heated channels is significantly nonlinear. A number of correlations attempt to represent this nonlinearity both in terms of flux/quality relations and by using quality/boiling length relations that are more complex than [6.4.23] (e.g., Hewitt & Kearsey 1969).

Finally, forced convective boiling correlations are gradually being overtaken by events; it is now becoming just as accurate to use predictive methods, and these are more readily extrapolated than correlations. Published burnout correlations should always be considered as interpolation devices covering the range of data on which they are based. Extrapolation of the correlations is always dangerous. A discussion of predictive methods is given in section 6.4.7.

Correlation for Burnout in the Evaporation of Water in Vertical Up Flow in Round Tubes

The correlation (Bowring 1972) is in the form devised by Macbeth (1963), Thompson & Macbeth (1964), and Barnett (1963). The form is that of a linear flux/quality relation rearranged into the form of [6.4.19], which for round tubes gives $\dot{q}_c$ (W/m^2) as follows:

$$\dot{q}_c = \frac{A' + 0.25\,D\dot{m}\Delta h_{sub}}{C' + L} \qquad\qquad [6.4.26]$$

where D is the tube diameter (m), $\dot{m}$ is the mass flux (kg/m^2 2), Δh_{sub} is the inlet subcooling (J/kg), and L is the tube length (m). A' and C' are functions of $\dot{m}$, D, pressure p (Pa), and latent heat h_{LG} (J/kg) as follows:

$$A' = \frac{2.317\,(0.25h_{LG}D\dot{m})F_1}{1.0 + 0.0143\,F_2 D^{1/2}\dot{m}} \qquad\qquad [6.4.27]$$

$$C' = \frac{0.077 \, F_3 D \dot{m}}{1.0 + 0.347 \, F_4 (\dot{m}/1356)^n} \qquad [6.4.28]$$

where n is given by

$$n = 2.0 - 0.5 \, p_R \qquad [6.4.29]$$

where p_R is the ratio of the system pressure to a pressure of 6.895 MPa (equivalent to a pressure of 1000 psia). Thus

$$p_R = \frac{p}{6.895 \times 10^6} \qquad [6.4.30]$$

The functions F_1-F_4 are also related to the value of p_R as follows:

For $p_R < 1$:

$$F_1 = \frac{p_R^{18.942} \exp [20.8 \, (1 - p_R)] + 0.917}{1.917} \qquad [6.4.31]$$

$$\frac{F_1}{F_2} = \frac{p_R^{1.316} \exp [2.444 \, (1 - p_R)] + 0.309}{1.309} \qquad [6.4.32]$$

$$F_3 = \frac{p_R^{17.023} \exp [16.658 \, (1 - p_R)] + 0.667}{1.667} \qquad [6.4.33]$$

$$\frac{F_4}{F_3} = p_R^{1.649} \qquad [6.4.34]$$

For $p_R > 1$:

$$F_1 = p_R^{-0.368} \exp [0.648 \, (1 - p_R)] \qquad [6.4.35]$$

$$\frac{F_1}{F_2} = p_R^{-0.448} \exp [0.245 \, (1 - p_R)] \qquad [6.4.36]$$

$$F_3 = p_R^{0.219} \qquad [6.4.37]$$

$$\frac{F_4}{F_3} = p_R^{1.649} \qquad [6.4.38]$$

Bowring reported that for the 3792 experimental points used, the root-mean-square (rms) error was 6.96% with an average error of -0.29%, and 95% of the points lay within an error band of $\pm 14\%$.

The Bowring correlation covers the following ranges of parameters:

Pressure: 0.2–19.0 MPa
Tube diameter: 2–45 mm
Tube length: 0.15–3.7 m
Mass flux: 136–18,600 kg/m^2 s

These figures refer to the extreme values of the variables included in the data set on which the correlation is based. This does not mean that the correlation is necessarily

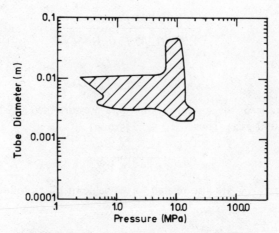

Figure 6.4.25   Range of tube diameters and pressures in
compilation and correlation of Bowring (1972).

accurate for any combination of variables within these ranges. It is instructive to
plot the positions of the data points in terms of the respective independent
variables, and an example of such a plot for the Bowring data set (figure 6.4.25)
shows that the larger tube diameter range was covered only in a limited pressure
range. It cannot be emphasized too strongly that empirical correlations of the above
type are strictly interpolation devices; they are likely to give very large errors
outside their range of data. When operating outside the range of data, it is always
worthwhile to check to make sure the calculated flux is such that:

1. In the quality region, not more than 100% evaporation of the liquid is predicted
   (i.e., x_{BO} should not be greater than unity!).
2. In the subcooled region, the wall temperature calculated from the single-phase
   heat transfer coefficient and the predicted burnout flux is above the saturation
   temperature. Otherwise, no boiling whatsoever is possible, let alone burnout.

Correlation for the Evaporation of Water
in Vertical Upflow in Rectangular Channels

The correlation is that of Macbeth (1963). The form of the correlation is similar to
that for round tubes, [6.4.26], as follows:

$$\dot{q}_c = \frac{A'' + 0.555C''\dot{m}\Delta h_{\mathrm{sub}}}{1 + C''L}$$ [6.4.39]

where $\dot{q}_c$ is the heat flux (W/m^2), $\dot{m}$ is the mass flux (kg/m^2 s), Δh_{sub} is the inlet
subcooling (J/kg), and L is the length of the channel (m). A'' and C'' are functions
of the gap S (m) between the heated major faces of the rectangular channel and of
$\dot{m}$ as follows:

$$A'' = y_0 S^{y_1} \dot{m}^{y_2}$$ [6.4.40]

$$C'' = y_3 S^{y_4} \dot{m}^{y_5} \tag{6.4.41}$$

where y_0-y_5 are constants defined for the individual pressure levels at which the data were available (table 6.4.3).

The rms error for each pressure level is indicated in table 6.4.3. The correlation was developed on the basis of data from rectangular channels of width 2.54 cm with a heated width on the major sides of 2.29 cm. Channels of this type are relevant to certain forms of pressurized-water nuclear reactor (hence the proponderance of data at 13.79 MPa). Since other data were not available, it was not clear how closely the correlation would represent channels that are wider than this, and great caution should be exercised in using the correlation outside the range of data covered.

Lumped Parameter Correlation for Annuli and Rod Bundles

The correlations of Bertoletti et al. (1965) and Becker (1967) are recommended for the calculation of annuli and rod bundles on a lumped parameter basis. They give an average value for the power input to burnout. There are severed limitations in lumped parameter models for rod bundles with a highly nonuniform distribution of rods and with complex power distributions, and subchannel analysis is preferable for these cases (section 6.4.3.2).

The CISE correlation for annuli and rod bundles is based on the form developed for water in round tubes, which, in turn, is of the linear form represented by [6.4.23]. The round tube correlation is

$$x_{BO} = \frac{W_B}{\dot{M} h_{LG}} = \frac{1 - p/p_c}{0.1 \, \dot{m}^{1/3}} \frac{L_B}{L_B + 0.1988 \, (p_c/p - 1) D^{1.4} \dot{m}} \tag{6.4.42}$$

where W_B is the power input (W) over the boiling length L_B (m), $\dot{M}$ is the mass rate of flow through the channel (kg/s), h_{LG} is the latent heat of vaporization (J/kg), $\dot{m}$ is the mass flux (kg/m² s), p is the inlet pressure (Pa), and p_c is the critical pressure (Pa). For annuli and rod bundles, Bertoletti et al. modified the round tube correlation:

$$\frac{W_{Bh}}{\dot{M} h_{LG}} = \frac{P_h}{P_{\text{tot}}} \frac{1 - p/p_c}{0.1 \, \dot{m}^{1/3}} \frac{L_B}{L_B + 0.1988 \, (p_c/p - 1) D_e^{1.4} \dot{m}} \tag{6.4.43}$$

where W_{Bh} is the power input through the heated surfaces over the boiling length

Table 6.4.3 Constants in Rectangular Channel Burnout Correlation[a]

Pressure (MPa)	y_0	y_1	y_2	y_3	y_4	y_5	rms error (%)	Number of experiments
4.14	2.63×10^{17}	−0.472	−3.29	5.77×10^{10}	−1.4	−3.93	6.1	22
5.52	2.15×10^3	−1.01	0.384	2.32×10^{-3}	−1.4	−0.007	12.9	28
8.27	1.96×10^8	−0.081	−0.526	8.84	−1.4	−1.29	4.9	42
13.79	8.11×10^5	−0.315	−0.056	0.116	−1.4	−0.725	9.4	349

[a]From Macbeth (1963).

L_B and the boiling length is defined as beginning at the point where the average conditions in the annulus or rod bundle reach saturation. P_h and P_{tot} are the heated and total channel perimeters (m), respectively, and D_e is the equivalent diameter of the channel, defined as

$$D_e = \frac{4A}{P_{tot}} \qquad [6.4.44]$$

where A is the channel cross-sectional area (m^2).

The Becker (1967) correlation is more accurate and has been tested against a wider range of data. However, it is more complicated than that of Bertoletti et al. and will not be stated in detail here.

Comparisons between [6.4.43] and a data bank consisting of 830 data points covering a fairly wide range of conditions are reported by Barnett (1968), who estimated an rms error of 14.8% with maximum errors ranging up to 40%. Comparisons reported by Bertoletti et al. (1965) indicated that the accuracy for rod bundle data was of about the same order of magnitude. For the Becker (1967) correlation, the accuracy is probably somewhat greater.

Notwithstanding the introduction of reduced pressure into the Bertoletti et al. correlation, it should not be used for nonaqueous fluids. As mentioned above, errors can occur in lumped parameter models, and they should be used with considerable reserve. However, they are useful in obtaining approximate first estimates.

Calculation of Burnout in Rod Bundles by Subchannel Analysis

It would be surprising if simple lumped parameter models could adequately describe the complex two-phase flow and heat transfer phenomena leading to burnout in rod bundles. However, there has been little systematic investigation of the efficacy of these models. A particularly interesting experiment in this context is that described by Heron et al. (1969), who made burnout power measurements on a seven-rod bundle with several rod dispositions as illustrated in figure 6.4.26. The experiments were carried out with Refrigerant-12 at a pressure simulating water at 7.0 MPa. If the lumped parameter correlations were valid the burnout power would be independent of the rod arrangement, whereas, in fact, there was a systematic change with configuration as illustrated in figure 6.4.27.

The failings of lumped parameter models have led to a great expenditure of time and effort on more detailed models, known as subchannel models. In this approach, the channel is divided into a number of separate channels and the flow and quality in each of these channels are calculated. Then one form or another of single-channel correlation is applied to test whether burnout is occurring. Usually, the single-channel correlation chosen is one for round tubes, although it is also possible to develop models specifically for subchannels (Bowring 1977).

In subchannel analysis, two different methods of dividing up the channel have been used, as illustrated in figure 6.4.28.

Channel-centered subchannels Here, the bundle cross-sectional flow area is divided up into channels whose boundaries are the rod surfaces and also lines

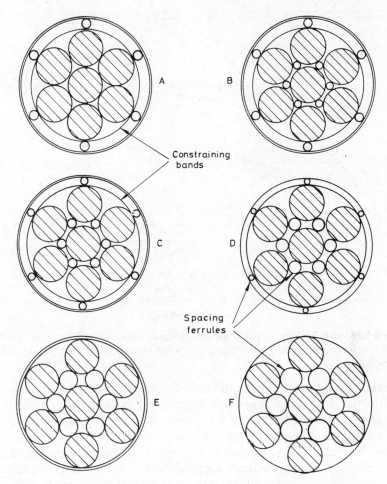

Figure 6.4.26 Arrangement of rods in seven-rod bundle (Heron et al. 1969). Total bundle length, 3 m; axial spacing of band-ferrule grids, 0.3 m. (See figure 6.4.27 for burnout data for A–F.)

passing through the rod centers. This form of subchannel has been used in most of the published analyses, and the application of such analyses is reviewed in detail by Weisman & Bowring (1975). Widely used codes based on this form of subchannel divisions are COBRA (Rowe 1967, 1970, 1972, 1973), FLICA (Fajeau 1969), HAMBO (Bowring 1962, 1968), MIXER (Lahey & Schraub 1969), and THINC (Chelemer et al. 1972). In these models there are usually two forms of mass transfer between adjacent subchannels:

1. Net flows due to differences in axial pressure gradient for the flow in one subchannel with respect to the flow in adjacent subchannels. The flow readjusts itself to give an approximately constant pressure gradient for each of the subchannels, although there may be small differences because a pressure gradient is required to drive flow from one subchannel to another.
2. Mixing between adjacent subchannels where the quality (and thus void fraction) is different.

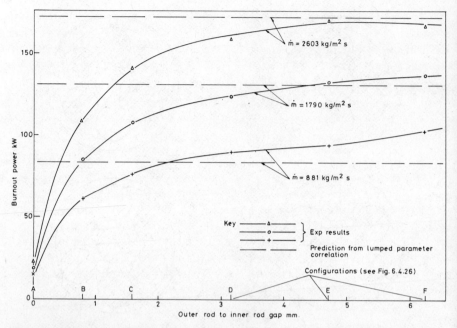

Figure 6.4.27 Data for burnout power for Refrigerant-12 evaporation in a seven-rod bundle utilizing rod arrangements illustrated in figure 6.4.26 (Heron et al. 1969). (See figure 6.4.26 for details of A–F.)

A specific difficulty in describing the first of these processes is that of ascribing a quality to the interchannel flow. Flow separation is likely to occur, and it is by no means certain that the quality of the transferred flow is identical to that in the donor subchannel. Two-phase mixing is highly complex and is poorly understood, although there have been a number of experiments to determine mixing characteristics in channels modeling adjacent subchannels (e.g., van der Roos 1970; Mayinger et al. 1977). The net result of trying to cope with these mixing processes is the introduction of a very large array of arbitrary constants, and this can lead to questioning the validity of this approach, especially since this form of subchannel modeling relies, in the end, on purely empirical single-channel burnout correlations.

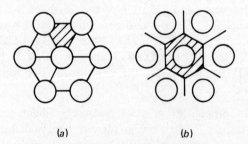

(a)   (b)

Figure 6.4.28 Types of subchannel division used in rod bundle burnout heat flux analysis. (a) Channel-centered subchannels. (b) Rod-centered subchannels.

Rod-centered subchannels Here, the subchannel is defined as a region surrounding the rod, as illustrated in figure 6.4.28(*b*). This form of subchannel modeling was employed by Gaspari et al. (1970, 1974), who selected the CISE round tube correlation for the single-channel calculations. Two extreme cases can be considered:

1. No mixing between subchannels, with each subchannel proceeding separately and not influencing adjacent subchannels
2. Complete interchange between subchannels to maintain constant two-phase enthalpy at any given cross section of the rod bundle

Results calculated by the two methods are compared in figure 6.4.29. The experimental data tend to lie between the two predictions with the assumption of no interchange being, on the whole, closest.

A set of comparisons between the various methods of prediction of rod bundle burnout data is presented by Guarino et al. (1973) and is summarized in table 6.4.4. The channel-centered subchannel predictions are not, on average, significantly better than those based on the much simpler rod-centered channel method. The latter is also much more suitable as a basis for predictive methods for annular flow burnout in rod bundles (section 6.4.7).

6.4.4 EFFECTS OF NONUNIFORM HEAT FLUX

The sources of nonuniform heat flux distribution and its influence on the occurrence of burnout were discussed briefly in section 6.4.2. Flux variations occur in most practical systems, and the designer of such systems has the considerable difficulty of estimating the power input at which burnout occurs in them. One

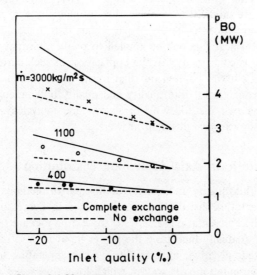

Figure 6.4.29 Effect of inclusion of enthalpy exchange on predictions of the rod-centered subchannel method (Gaspari et al. 1974).

Table 6.4.4 Errors (rms) between Calculated and Measured Burnout Heat Fluxes under Boiling-Water Reactor Conditions[a]

Analysis	Correlation	Uniform flux	Radial nonuniform flux	Long bundles
Lumped parameter	Barnett (1968)	9.86	9.36	21.33 12.79
Lumped parameter	Macbeth (1964)	12.48	16.73	12.96 10.5
COBRA (channel-centered subchannel)	Becker (1967)	7.67	13.34	4.7 5.2
CISE (rod-centered subchannel)	Bertoletti et al. (1965)	7.9	9.68	14.6 8.7
CISE (rod-centered subchannel)	Hewitt et al. (1969) (1969)	8.1	10.3	4.5 4.17

[a]Based on results of Guarino et al. (1973).

approach to the problem is to carry out experiments in which the practical flux profile is represented as closely as possible by, say, electrical heating. Such experiments are difficult and expensive, particularly for rod bundle geometries. Furthermore, the flux profile may change during the lifetime of a plant (e.g., it changes with burnup in nuclear reactor fuel elements). Thus, to have complete certainty, a whole series of experiments is needed. Although experimental data can be important, they are unlikely to provide the complete answer, and there must be some recourse to correlation methods. In particular, it is desirable that correlations developed for uniform heat flux can be applied to predict burnout with nonuniform heating. This section is concerned with the application of such correlations.

In section 6.4.3.2 it was pointed out that burnout correlations for channel flow fall mainly in the categories of flux/quality and quality/boiling length relations. For uniform heating, the two methods of correlation are equivalent. For nonuniform heating, however, they can give different answers.

6.4.4.1 Nonuniform Axial Heat Flux Distribution

Applications of the flux/quality and quality/boiling length methods to channels with nonuniform axial heat flux distribution are illustrated in figures 6.4.30 and 6.4.31, respectively. In each representation, a series of operating loci are shown corresponding to the effect of gradually increasing the power input with a fixed inlet flow and subcooling (i.e., fixed, negative, inlet quality). These operating loci represent, for the flux/quality representation, the way in which local flux varies with local quality along the channel. In the case of the quality/boiling length representation, the operating loci represent the variation of local quality with distance from the point

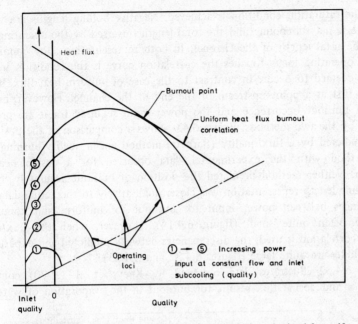

Figure 6.4.30 Application of flux/quality correlation obtained for uniform heat flux to prediction of burnout with a nonuniform (cosine) heat flux distribution.

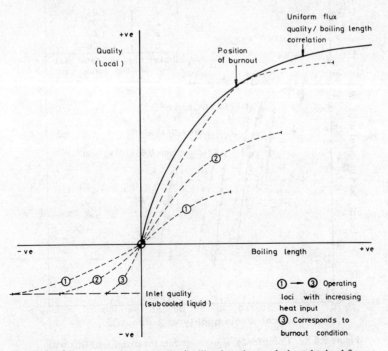

Figure 6.4.31 Application of quality/boiling length correlation obtained for uniform heat flux to prediction of burnout with nonuniform heat distribution.

at which the saturation condition is achieved. Negative boiling lengths are those in which there is net subcooling and the total length traversed by the operating line is equal to the total length of the channel. In both representations, the condition in which the operating locus touches the correlation curve is the condition in which burnout is deemed to occur. In contrast to the case of uniform heat flux, burnout may occur first at a point upstream of the end of the channel. However, both the location of burnout occurrence and the power input required for it are predicted differently by the two methods. Figure 6.4.9 shows a comparison of the position of burnout predicted by a flux/quality (Barnett) method and a quality/burning length (CISE) method with the experimental data observed for a cosine heat flux distribution. Neither method predicted the position of burnout accurately, but the quality/boiling length representation was closer qualitatively to the actual data.

Differences between power input for burnout for uniform and nonuniform heating are often quite small (figure 6.4.14). However, when the flux/quality method of correlation is used, the discrepancies between predicted and experimental local heat fluxes are quite large (figures 6.4.32 and 6.4.33).

Figure 6.4.32 illustrates data obtained by Keeys et al. (1970) comparing uniform flux and cosine flux results for burnout in the evaporation of water in a

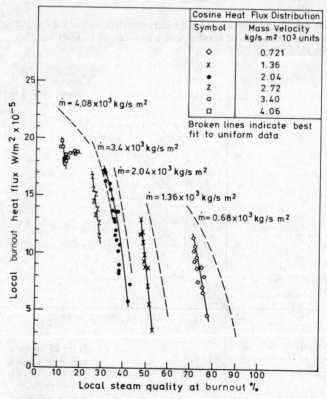

Figure 6.4.32 Comparison of burnout data for cosine heat flux with data for uniform heat flux: evaporation of water at 6.89 MPa in a 12.7-mm-bore tube (Keeys et al. 1970).

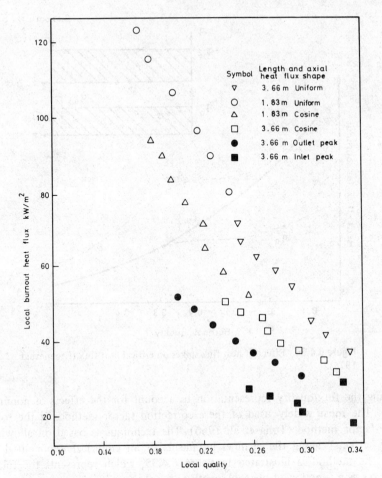

Figure 6.4.33 Flux/quality plots for Refrigerant-114 burnout data in an annulus with various axial heat flux distributions: pressure 0.86 MPa, mass flux 760 kg/m² s, inside diameter 14.3 mm, outside diameter 22.2 mm (data of Shiralkar 1972).

round tube at various mass velocities. Figure 6.4.33 shows data obtained by Shiralkar (1972) for Refrigerant-114 evaporation in an annulus at a fixed mass flux, but with different axial heat flux profiles. The local flux/quality relation is different for uniform and nonuniform heating. For extreme nonuniformity, this can lead to serious discrepancies in prediction, even on an average flux basis.

An example of an extreme nonuniformity in heat flux is that of a "flux spike" (e.g., Groeneveld 1975). Figure 6.4.34 shows the form of result obtained. At low and negative negative qualities, the flux for burnout in the spike approaches that for uniform heating, indicating the possibility of a true local-conditions effect. However, for higher qualities, the flux required for burnout in the spike is much higher than that for uniform heating. Moreover, the channel-average flux for burnout approaches that for uniform heat flux as the quality increases.

These well-recognized discrepancies have led to the search for methods of

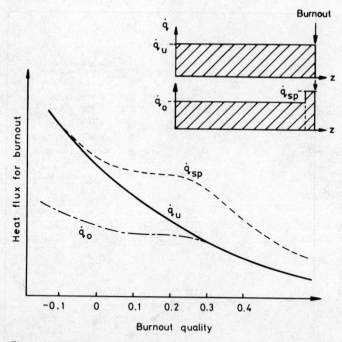

Figure 6.4.34 Effect of heat flux spikes on critical heat flux (Groeneveld 1975).

correcting the flux/quality representation to account for the effects of nonuniform heating. The most widely used of these correction factor methods is the so-called Tong F-factor method (Tong et al. 1966). The technique is based on allowing for "history effects" along the channel by means of an empirical exponential decay factor. The method is illustrated in figure 6.4.35, which represents the following heat fluxes as a function of channel length z:

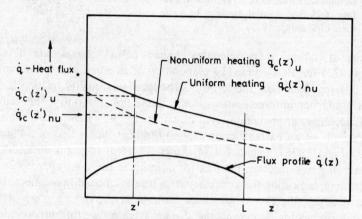

Figure 6.4.35 Basis of F-factor method for determination of burnout margins with nonuniform heat flux distribution.

1. The actual heat flux $\dot{q}(z)$, varying with position along the channel
2. A line representing $\dot{q}_c(z)_u$, the heat flux for burnout along the channel predicted from a uniform flux-burnout correlation
3. A line representing $\dot{q}_c(z)_{nu}$, the calculated burnout heat flux, as a function of position along the channel for the specific nonuniform heat flux distribution

A burnout margin may be defined for a position z' along the channel as

$$\text{Burnout margin} = \frac{\dot{q}_c(z')_{nu}}{\dot{q}(z')} = \frac{\dot{q}_c(z')_u}{F(z')\dot{q}(z')} \qquad [6.4.45]$$

where the F factor $F(z')$ is defined as

$$F(z') = \frac{\dot{q}_c(z')_u}{\dot{q}_c(z')_{nu}} \qquad [6.4.46]$$

Obviously, burnout occurs when the burnout margin at any given point along the channel becomes unity. Tong et al. (1966) derived a semiempirical expression for $F(z')$ of the form

$$F(z') = \frac{C}{1 - \exp(-Cz')} \int_0^{z'} \frac{\dot{q}(z)}{\dot{q}(z')} \exp[-C(z'-z)] \, dz \qquad [6.4.47]$$

where the distance along the channel z is given in meters and the factor C is given by the following empirical expression:

$$C = \frac{7.01 \times 10^6 \, [1 - x(z)]^{7.9}}{\dot{m}^{1.72}} \qquad [6.4.48]$$

where $x(z)$ is the quality at distance z along the channel and $\dot{m}$ is the mass flux (kg/m^2 s). Figure 6.4.36 shows typical values of F calculated for a "hot-patch" heat

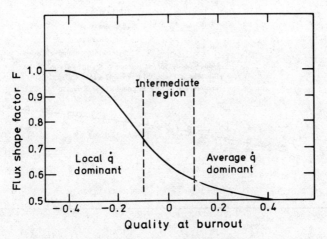

Figure 6.4.36 Variation of F factor with quality for hot patch or flux spike heat flux distribution (Tong 1972a).

flux distribution (compare figure 6.4.34). This method of calculation gives a physically reasonable picture with the local heat flux being dominant in the subcooled (negative quality) region and the average heat flux being dominant in the quality region. However, the calculation method is complex, since it requires repetitive calculation of the three curves shown in figure 6.4.35 until the condition of unit burnout margin is achieved somewhere along the channel. This is extremely tedious for hand calculation and it is usually necessary to use computer calculations.

If the quality/boiling length representation is used, data for uniform and a variety of nonuniform flux profiles can often be correlated by a single curve. This is illustrated by the data plotted by Keys et al. (1971b) as shown in figure 6.4.37. An appraisal of the F-factor and quality/boiling length methods is given by Lahey (1975). On the basis of this appraisal and other relevant information, the following recommendations are made for calculating the occurrence of burnout in channels with a nonuniform axial flux distribution:

1. Select an appropriate uniform heat flux correlation (section 6.4.3), plot the correlation in quality/boiling length form, and calculate the heat input level required for burnout, using the procedure illustrated in figure 6.4.31. If the burnout quality derived from this calculation is greater than 0.1, accept the values calculated.
2. If the burnout quality calculated in step 1 is less than 0.1, carry out a calculation by the F-factor method. If, by this method, the calculated quality at the burnout point is less than -0.1, accept the value calculated by this method.
3. If the calculated burnout quality is less than 0.1 by the quality/boiling length method and greater than -0.1 by the F-factor method, select the lower of the two calculated heat inputs as the safer basis for design.

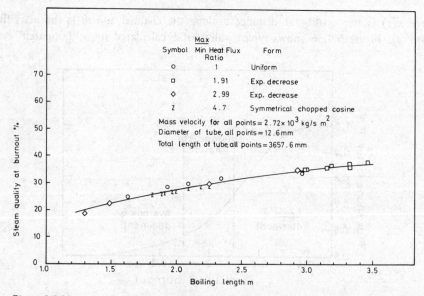

Figure 6.4.37 Data for burnout with various heat flux distributions plotted in the quality/boiling length form; system pressure 6.89 MPa (Keys et al. 1971).

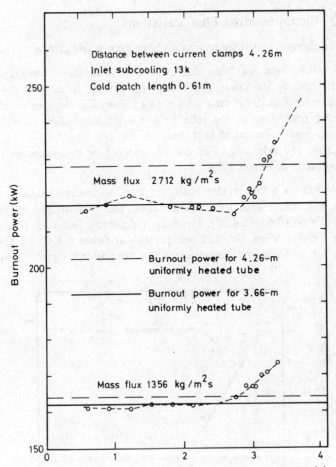

Figure 6.4.38 Burnout power in a tube with an unheated zone (cold patch): evaporation of water at a pressure of 6.89 MPa in a 12.6mm-diameter tube (data of Bennett et al. 1967b).

Neither method of handling axial nonuniformities can be applied completely generally, since both methods are empirical. As an illustration of the difficulties here, one might cite the "cold-patch" experiments described by Bennett et al. (1967b), typical results from which are illustrated in figure 6.4.38. A 61-cm unheated zone was present at various positions in a vertical tube test section of total length 4.27 m. With the unheated zone in certain positions, it was possible to obtain higher burnout powers than for the case where the tube was uniformly heated. This clearly vitiates (as might be expected) the flux/quality relation, but it is also contrary to the quality/boiling length representation. Clearly, such results are not readily predicted by empirical correlation methods, although they are calculable by the prediction methods described in section 6.4.7.

6.4.4.2 Circumferential Flux Variations

Two forms of circumferential flux variation have been investigated:

1. Those in which there is a "flux tilt," where the flux varies smoothly from one side of the tube to the other, the flux tilt ratio being the ratio of the maximum to the minimum flux. Such variations can be achieved in electrically heated tubes by eccentric machining of the tube to give a maldistribution of wall thickness with a consequent variation of heat flux.
2. Heating from one side only. This can be achieved by radiant heating from one side (Chojnowski & Wilson 1974).

When plotted on a flux quality basis, the data for maximum local heat flux for burnout fall well above data for uniform tubes. This is illustrated by the annulus data of Lee (1966) (figure 6.4.39). However, the average flux is quite close to that for uniform heating. Flux tilt data are plotted in figure 6.4.40 on the basis of average flux for uniform and circumferentially nonuniform distributions. Most of

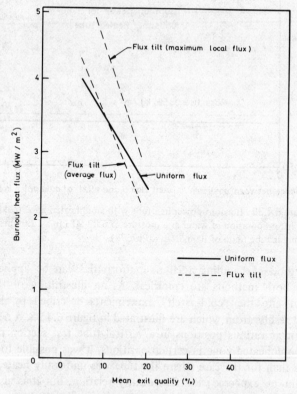

Figure 6.4.39 Data for burnout in an annulus with uniform heating and with a circumferential flux tilt ratio of 1.29 (data of Lee 1966). (Annulus heated only on inner surface; pressure 6.89 MPa, mass flux 2028 kg/m² s, internal diameter 15.9 mm, external diameter 21.3 mm, heated length 0.80 m).

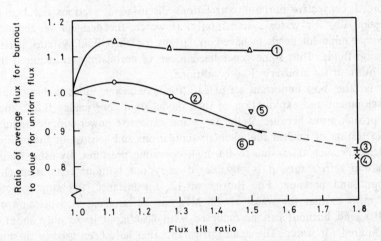

Key	Inlet Subcooling kJ/kg	Pressure MPa	L/D	Reference	All At $\dot{m} = 2000$ kg/m²s
1	0	5.9	40	Alekseev (1964)	
2	232	5.9	40	Alekseev (1964)	
3	0	10.0	26.5	Miropolskii (1958)	
4	232	10.0	26.5	Miropolskii (1958)	
5	0	9.8	40	Alekseev (1964)	
6	232	9.8	40	Alekseev (1964)	

— — — Predicted from film flow analysis of Butterworth (1971)

Figure 6.4.40 Effect of flux tilt on ratio of average heat flux for burnout to that for uniform heating (Lee 1966; Butterworth 1971).

the data give a small reduction in average flux in the circumferentially nonuniform case, although there are some data that give an increase.

The data of Chojnowski & Wilson (1974) for side-heated tubes give average heat fluxes that are typically 5–30% lower than those obtained for uniformly heated tubes at the same quality, although the local peak heat flux at burnout is much higher (some of their results are illustrated in figure 6.4.10).

The recommended procedure is as follows:

1. For modest flux tilts (< 1.3), the average flux may be assumed equal to the uniform flux within the accuracy of the uniform flux correlations and the data.
2. For more severe flux tilts, a reduction of 10–20% in average flux should be assumed, as indicated in figure 6.4.40.
3. For side-heated tubes, a deduction of 30% from the average flux value would appear to be conservative.

An empirical method for calculating the effect of circumferential flux variations was proposed by Styrikovich & Mostinskii (1959), and Chojnowski & Wilson (1974) found that this method predicted their data fairly well, although it was a little conservative. Butterworth (1971) attempted to model burnout with circumferential flux variations by using a simplified film flow model into which he introduced an empirical film spreading coefficient to take account of circumferential flow of the liquid film. His predictions are shown as a dashed line in figure 6.4.40. However, the assumption of a constant spreading coefficient is unlikely to be valid (Chojnowski & Wilson 1974).

6.4.5   USE OF SCALING FLUIDS AND PREDICTION FOR NONAQUEOUS SYSTEMS

The forced convective burnout correlations discussed in sections 6.4.3 and 6.4.4 were essentially for water systems only. However, the designer of chemical and petroleum equipment needs to have correlations for other fluid systems, particularly for organic fluids. Thus some generalized forms of correlation are required that can predict burnout for arbitrary fluid conditions.

By far the most important set of data for nonaqueous fluids is that obtained in the development and exploitation of the "model fluid" or "scaling fluid" approach. This approach arose because of the large and expensive power supplies required for full-scale testing of nuclear fuel element simulations and because of the high cost of equipment for such tests, due to the high operating pressures. By using fluorinated hydrocarbon refrigerants, it is possible to carry out burnout tests at much lower heat input and pressure. For Refrigerant-12, for instance, the same vapor/liquid density ratio as that for water at 7.0 MPa can be obtained at a pressure of only 1.04 MPa, and burnout can be achieved with heat input levels only about 6% of those required for water. The main refrigerants that have been used in these studies are listed in table 6.4.5.

Examples of the extensive work carried out on burnout with fluorinated hydrocarbons are as follows:

1. Round tubes. Data for burnout heat flux in vertical upward flow are reported by Stevens et al. (1964, 1965), Staniforth et al. (1965), Staniforth & Stevens (1965–1966), Ilic (1974), and Merilo (1977). Studies of burnout heat flux in horizontal tubes have been reported by Merilo (1977), in inclined tubes by Roumy (1970), and in serpentine tubes by Fisher & Yu (1975).
2. Annuli. Studies of burnout heat flux for Refrigerant-12 evaporation in annuli are reported by Stevens et al. (1968), Stevens & Macbeth (1968), and Riegel (1971).

Table 6.4.5   Refrigerants Commonly used in Heat Transfer Experiments

Refrigerant	Formula	Molecular weight	Boiling point (°C)	Critical pressure (MPa)	Critical temperature (°C)
Refrigerant-11	CCl_3F	137.4	23.8	4.41	198
Refrigerant-12	CCl_2F_2	120.9	− 29.8	4.12	112
Refrigerant-22	$CHClF_2$	86.5	− 40.8	4.98	96
Refrigerant-113	$CCl_2F\text{-}CClF_2$	187.4	47.6	3.7	216
Water	H_2O	18.02	100	22.12	374

3. Rod bundles. Data for burnout heat flux in rod bundles are presented by Stevens & Wood (1966), Heron et al. (1969), Stevens & Macbeth (1970, 1971), McPherson (1971), and Ilic (1974).

4. Transient (e.g., blowdown) conditions. This case is of importance in modeling LOCAs in water nuclear reactors. Data on transient burnout heat flux have been obtained by Leung (1976) and Henry & Leung (1977). In these experiments Refrigerant-11 was used in preference to Refrigerant-12 because of its higher boiling point and the possibility of operating the outlet at lower pressure. Data on blowdown were also obtained by Belda et al. (1974) with Refrigerant-12.

After data are obtained for the refrigerant system, the problem then arises of using these data to predict the behavior of the water system. Briefly, the methods available for scaling between refrigerant and water systems are as follows:

1. Use of empirical scaling factors
2. Use of dimensionless groups for scaling
3. Predictive methods

Although the use of empirical scaling factors is helpful in the refrigerant/water simulation technology, they are not generally applicable in predicting for other fluids. Scaling through dimensionless groups is particularly difficult in two-phase flow systems, especially with phase change. However, enough progress has been made to be able to make some tentative recommendations here. Predictive methods are discussed in section 6.4.7, and the existence of a large body of data for refrigerants allows more rigorous testing of these methods.

One of the most successful applications of dimensionless group scaling for burnout heat flux is that described by Ahmad (1973). For a fixed ratio of inlet subcooling to latent heat $\Delta h_{\text{sub}}/h_{LG}$, density ratio ρ_L/ρ_G, and length-to-diameter ratio L/D, Ahmad related the "boiling number" $\dot{q}_c/\dot{m}h_{LG}$ to the modeling parameter ψ, defined as

$$\psi = \frac{\dot{m}D}{\mu_L}\left(\frac{\mu_L}{\sigma D\rho_L}\right)^{2/3}\left(\frac{\mu_G}{\mu_L}\right)^{1/5} \qquad [6.4.49]$$

where $\dot{m}$ is the mass flux, μ_L and μ_G are the liquid- and vapor-phase viscosities, σ is the surface tension, D is the channel diameter, and ρ_L is the liquid-phase density.

An alternative definition for ψ is

$$\psi = \frac{\dot{m}D}{\mu_L}\left(\frac{\gamma^{1/2}\mu_L}{D\rho_L^{1/2}}\right)^{2/3}\left(\frac{\mu_L}{\mu_G}\right)^{1/8} \qquad [6.4.50]$$

where γ is defined by

$$\gamma = \frac{\partial(\rho_G/\rho_L)}{\partial p} \qquad [6.4.51]$$

where p is the system pressure. Equations [6.4.49] and [6.4.50] give somewhat similar results and can be selected depending on whether σ or γ is easiest to obtain from physical property data. A plot of boiling number against ψ gives the same curve for all fluids (figure 6.4.41).

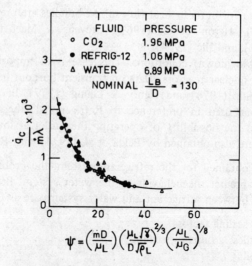

$$\psi = \left(\frac{\dot{m}D}{\mu_L}\right)\left(\frac{\mu_L\sqrt{\sigma}}{D\sqrt{\rho_L}}\right)^{2/3}\left(\frac{\mu_L}{\mu_G}\right)^{1/8}$$

Figure 6.4.41 Application of Ahmad (1973) scaling method to water, CO_2, and Refrigerant-12 data (Hauptmann et al. 1973).

Thus to calculate the burnout heat flux for forced convection burnout in a channel into which a subcooled nonaqueous fluid is flowing, the procedure is as follows:

1. Calculate the ratios (for the particular fluid) $\Delta h_{sub}/h_{LG}$ and ρ_L/ρ_G.
2. With the aid of steam tables, estimate the pressure that gives the equivalent value of ρ_L/ρ_G for water and estimate the subcooling required at the pressure to give the same value of $\Delta h_{sub}/h_{LG}$.
3. For the equivalent water conditions, *and with the same geometry* (it being by no means certain that the L/D scaling parameter is universal), calculate the burnout flux for water from the correlations given in section 6.4.3, for a range of mass flows.
4. Express and plot the data for water in terms of the boiling number $\dot{q}_c/\dot{m}h_{LG}$ versus the parameter ψ ([6.4.49] or [6.4.50]).
5. For the values of $\dot{m}$ of interest for the nonaqueous fluid, claculate ψ for this fluid and read off the appropriate values of boiling number from the boiling number versus ψ plot.
6. Calculate the burnout heat flux by multiplying the boiling number obtained in the previous step by $\dot{m}h_{LG}$.

Although the Ahmad method seems to work fairly well for vertical channels, it is less satisfactory for horizontal channels (figure 6.4.17). In these circumstances, further factors (representing the gravitational separation of the liquid phase) need to be introduced into the scaling laws, and Merilo (1979) suggested the following modified scaling parameter for horizontal flows:

$$\psi_H = \frac{\dot{m}D}{\mu_L}\left(\frac{\mu_L^2}{\sigma D\rho_L}\right)^{-1.57}\left(\frac{(\rho_L - \rho_G)gD^2}{\sigma}\right)^{-1.05}\left(\frac{\mu_L}{\mu_G}\right)^{6.41} \qquad [6.4.52]$$

where g is the acceleration due to gravity; ψ_H can be used in precisely the same way as described above for scaling water and refrigerant data for horizontal tubes. However, a correlation for burnout in water in horizontal tubes is needed, and Merilo (1979) suggested a relation that includes the scaling group within a general correlation for horizontal tubes as follows:

$$\frac{\dot{q}_c}{\dot{m}h_{LG}} = 6.18 \; \psi_H^{-0.340} \left(\frac{L}{D}\right)^{-0.511} \left(\frac{\rho_L - \rho_G}{\rho_G}\right)^{1.27} \left(1 + \frac{\Delta h_{\text{sub}}}{h_{LG}}\right)^{1.64} \qquad [6.4.53]$$

6.4.6 MECHANISM OF BURNOUT

Understanding the mechanisms of occurrence of burnout is important in two respects. First, an improved understanding of burnout mechanisms might reasonably be expected to lead to improved prediction methods. Second, an understanding of how burnout occurs may lead to the development of devices and systems to avoid its occurrence in practical plant.

This section begins with a discussion of burnout in pool boiling, and most of the classical understanding of burnout derives from this area. However, it has become increasingly clear that pool boiling mechanisms have little direct relevance to burnout mechanisms in forced convective systems.

6.4.6.1 Mechanism of Burnout in Pool Boiling

A number of mechanisms for burnout in pool boiling have been suggested, but the one that seems to have been most widely accepted, and that is consistent with recent detailed mechanistic studies, is that proposed by Zuber (1958; Zuber et al. 1963). The original Zuber hypothesis was for an infinite flat plate, and the situation is illustrated conceptually in figure 6.4.42. When boiling starts, the process is initially one of release of isolated bubbles from the surface. However, as the heat flux increases, there is a layer of closely packed bubbles adjacent to the surface. Provided vapor can escape from this layer, thus preventing it from becoming too

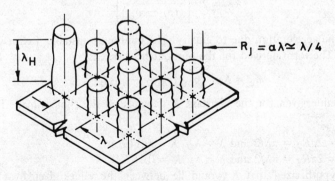

Figure 6.4.42 Vapor escape jets in boiling from a horizontal flat plate [representation by Lienhard & Dhir (1973b) of Zuber model].

thick, the liquid phase can penetrate the layer, wetting the surface and preventing burnout from occurring. The vapor escape mechanism is via the "vapor columns" illustrated in figure 6.4.42. These columns occur because the vapor-rich layer adjacent to the surface is fundamentally unstable; i.e., a small disturbance in the interface between the layer and the surrounding liquid is amplified at a rate that depends on the wavelength of the disturbance λ. This phenomenon is known as Taylor instability, and Zuber hypothesized that a rectangular square array of jets was formed with a pitch λ, as shown in figure 6.4.42.

Eventually, the velocity of vapor in the jets becomes so large that the jets themselves become unstable near the interface as a result of Helmholtz instability (of wavelength λ_H, as shown in figure 6.4.42). The breakup of the jets destroys the efficient vapor removal mechanism, increases vapor accumulation at the surface, and leads to the burnout phenomenon. If jet breakup occurs at a vapor velocity U_H within the jet, the critical heat flux $\dot{q}_c$ is given by

$$\dot{q}_c = \rho_G h_{LG} \frac{A_j}{A_h} U_H \qquad [6.4.54]$$

where ρ_G is the vapor density, h_{LG} is the latent heat of evaporation, A_j is the cross-sectional area of the jets, and A_h is the heated surface area. Zuber made the assumption that the jet radius R_j is equal to $\lambda/4$, giving A_j/A_h as $\pi/16$.

Helmholtz instability theory gives U_H as

$$U_H = \left(\frac{2\pi\sigma}{\rho_G \lambda_H}\right)^{1/2} \qquad [6.4.55]$$

where σ is the surface tension. Various assumptions can be made about λ_H; Zuber assumed that it was equal to the critical Rayleigh wavelength and thus to the circumference of the jet ($\lambda_H = \pi\lambda/2$). Lienhard & Dhir (1973a, b) suggested that it is closer to the real physical situation to take $\lambda_H = \lambda$, where λ is the selected value for the Taylor instability wavelength.

Taylor instability theory gives the following value for the wavelength of maximum rate of growth of a disturbance λ_D:

$$\lambda_D = 2\pi \left[\frac{3\sigma}{g(\rho_L - \rho_G)}\right]^{1/2} \qquad [6.4.56]$$

where g is the acceleration due to gravity. The minimum unstable Taylor wavelength λ_c is $\lambda_D/3$. The form derived for the burnout heat flux is:

$$\dot{q}_c = K\rho_G^{1/2} h_{LG} \left[\sigma g(\rho_L - \rho_G)\right]^{1/4} \qquad [6.4.57]$$

where the value given for the constant K depends on the choices made for λ_H and λ. Thus:

1. For $\lambda_H = 2\pi R_J = \pi\lambda/2$ and $\lambda = \lambda_D$, $K = 0.119$.
2. For $\lambda_H = 2\pi R_J = \pi\lambda/2$ and $\lambda = \lambda_c$, $K = 0.157$.
3. Zuber hypothesized that K would lie between the values given by (1) and (2) and suggested $K = \pi/24 = 0.131$.
4. For $\lambda_H = \lambda_D$ and $\lambda = \lambda_D$, $K = 0.149$.

The final value, due to Lienhard & Dhir, is probably closest to experimental data for flat plates and has been used in the recommended correlations in section 6.4.3.

For a small plate, then, the number of jets may not be representative of those for an infinite flat plate, and the experimental data appear to confirm this hypothesis. This effect can lead to both higher and lower burnout fluxes for small plates, depending on the relation between λ and the size of the plate (Lienhard & Dhir 1973a).

For the case of cylinders, a similar vapor jet formation phenomenon occurs, as illustrated in figure 6.4.43. The jets have a radius equal to the radius of the cylinder plus the thickness δ of the vapor blanket, as illustrated in figure 6.4.43c. The spacing of the jets depends on the cylinder size; the relations involved have been investigated by Sun & Lienhard (1970). For small cylinders (figure 6.4.43a), the spacing of the jets is approximately λ_D, and the critical Helmholtz wavelength λ_H may be taken as the circumference of the jet (i.e., $2\pi R_J$). For larger cylinders, the spacing increases to approximately two jet diameters (figure 6.4.43b) and λ_H is approximately equal to λ_D. The main difficulty in applying Zuber-type analysis to cylinders is the determination of δ, but Sun & Lienhard (1970) and Lienhard & Dhir (1973a, b) show that δ can be related to the cylinder radius, the relation being different for small and large cylinders. Introducing these relations leads to the recommended equations for cylinders given in section 6.4.3 ([6.4.4]–[6.4.7]).

For very small cylinders (where R' calculated from [6.4.7] < 0.01), the mechanism of burnout is quite different from the hydrodynamic instability-controlled mechanism described above. The mechanism for very small cylinders is illustrated in figure 6.4.44; when a bubble is nucleated on the wire it grows to surround the wire, and within the bubble there is a hot zone as illustrated. Oscillations in the boundary between the hot zone and the zone wetted by liquid

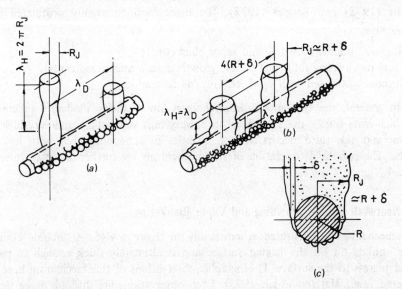

Figure 6.4.43 Vapor escape mechanisms in pool boiling from cylinders (Lienhard & Dhir 1973b). (a) Small cylinder. (b) Large cylinder. (c) Cross section.

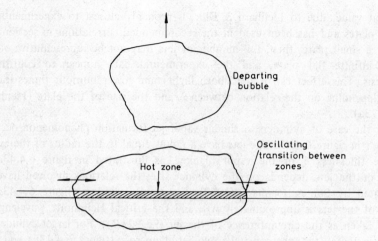

Figure 6.4.44 Mechanism of burnout for very small cylinders.

occur due to oscillations in current through the wire and due to bubble departures. The precise behavior depends very much on the nature of the fluid (Lienhard & Dhir 1973b). The region $0.01 < R' < 0.12$ can be regarded as a transition region between the hot-patch mechanism and the hydrodynamic mechanism.

6.4.6.2 Mechanism of Burnout in Forced Convective Channel Flow: Subcooled Boiling and Low-Quality Regions

Mechanisms in the subcooled and low-quality regions are reviewed by Tong & Hewitt (1972) and Bergles (1977). The three most commonly postulated mechanisms are

1. Near-wall bubble crowding and vapor blanketing
2. Local overheating following bubble growth from a nucleation center
3. Burnout associated with vapor clot or slug formation

In general, the first mechanism occurs at low qualities, moderate subcoolings, and high mass fluxes; the second occurs at very high subcoolings and very high mass fluxes; and the third occurs at low qualities or subcoolings but with low mass fluxes. The regions of operation of the mechanisms are further discussed in section 6.4.6.4.

Near-Wall Bubble Crowding and Vapor Blanketing

This mechanism is illustrated schematically in figure 6.4.45. A "bubble boundary layer" builds up on the heated surface and is ultimately thick enough to prevent liquid ingress to the surface. Photographic observations of this mechanism have been reported (e.g., Mattson et al. 1973). Such observations are difficult since the key phenomena occur so close to the interface. However, there does seem to be some

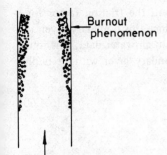

Burnout
phenomenon

Figure 6.4.45 Near-wall bubble crowding and vapor blanketing mechanism for burnout heat flux in subcooled and low-quality flows.

support for the idea that the burnout phenomenon is related to a boundary-layer separation effect (Tong 1972a). The boundary-layer separation concept for burnout was proposed by Kutateladze & Leontiev (1966) (figure 6.4.46).

The critical condition for boundary-layer separation from a flat plate with isothermal injection of the same fluid is given by Kutateladze & Leontiev as

$$\rho_{inj}v_{inj} = 2f_0\rho_0 U_0 \qquad [6.4.58]$$

where ρ_{inj} and v_{inj} are the density and velocity (normal to the main flow stream) of the injected fluid, f_0 is the friction factor in the absence of injection, and ρ_0 and U_0 are the density and velocity of the mainstream flow. In the case of boiling, the "injection" results from vapor formation at the wall, and in this case, if direct wall-to-liquid heat transfer is ignored, once can write

$$\rho_{inj}v_{inj} = \frac{\dot{q}}{h_{LG}} \qquad [6.4.59]$$

where $\dot{q}$ is the heat flux and h_{LG} the latent heat.

Kutateladze & Leontiev found that the burnout fluxes obtained by combining [6.4.59] and [6.4.58] were considerably lower than those observed, but that the sum of the fluxes so calculated and the flux for pool boiling was closer to the measured value. As pointed out by Tong (1968), addition of the pool boiling burnout heat flux is probably inconsistent since there is no reason to believe that the pool boiling mechanism is relevant in these circumstances. However, Tong was able to obtain reasonably accurate semiempirical predictions with a modification of

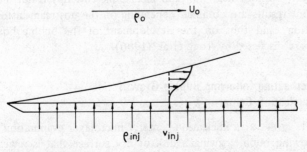

Figure 6.4.46 Parameters in boundary-layer separation with fluid injection (Tong 1972a).

the boundary-layer separation theory. As he pointed out, the friction factor for a channel with a bubble boundary layer is much higher, since this boundary layer acts as a rough surface over which the liquid is flowing. From air-water data, it is found that the two-phase friction factor f_{tp} for a bubble boundary layer without bubble departure is approximated by

$$f_{tp} \alpha \ Re^{-0.6} \tag{6.4.60}$$

where the Reynolds number is defined as

$$Re = \frac{\rho_L U_0 D_e}{\mu_L} \tag{6.4.61}$$

where D_e is the equivalent diameter of the channel, ρ_L the liquid-phase density, and μ_L the liquid-phase viscosity (taken at the saturation value). Introducing this into [6.4.58] and combining with [6.4.59], Tong obtained

$$\dot{q}_c = \frac{C_1 h_{LG} \rho_L U_0}{Re^{0.6}} = \frac{C_1 h_{LG} (\rho_L U_0)^{0.4} \mu_L^{0.6}}{D_e^{0.6}} \tag{6.4.62}$$

where C_1 is a constant that is a function of quality x. For the pressure range 7–14 MPa and the mass flux range 1000–4000 kg/m², Tong gives the following empirical correlation for C_1:

$$C_1 = 1.76 - 7.43x + 12.22x^2 \tag{6.4.63}$$

Alternative explanations of the occurrence of burnout as a result of near-wall bubble crowding are as follows:

1. Limitation of the rate of vapor removal by condensation and by axial transport of bubbles leads to accumulation of vapor at the surface at the onset of the burnout phenomenon (Hebel & Defevernier 1977).
2. When the rate of vapor injection from a single bubble generating center reaches its maximum (with successive bubbles touching), no further increase of vapor generation in the form of bubbles is possible and film boiling occurs (Maroti 1966).

It is one of the more important modes of burnout, and for this mode the relation between burnout heat flux and local bulk enthalpy is not unique. In other words, different results are obtained depending on the upstream history of the heat flux distribution (and thus on the development of the bubble boundary layer). These effects are discussed by Tong et al. (1966).

Local Overheating following Bubble Growth from a Nucleation Center

When a bubble grows at a nucleation center, "microlayer evaporation" often occurs under the growing bubble, giving a disk of dry surface that is rewetted when the bubble departs. Kirby et al. (1967) suggested that, at sufficiently high heat fluxes, this dry patch rises rapidly in temperature during the bubble growth phase, cannot

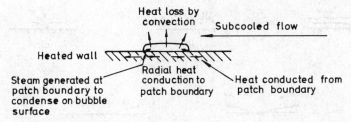

Figure 6.4.47 Heat flows in and around a bubble with a dry base (Kirby et al. 1967).

be rewetted subsequent to bubble departure, continues to rise in temperature, and spreads over the surface, giving rise to the burnout phenomenon. Kirby et al. were able to show that, for this form of burnout, the burnout flux depended only on local bulk enthalpy and there were no history effects. This was proved by coupling photographic observations with investigations of the effect of nonuniform heat flux. The various thermal transfers that occur at the bubble hot spot are illustrated in figure 6.4.47.

Burnout Associated with Vapor Clot or Slug Formation

In studying subcooled burnout in flow boiling, Fiori & Bergles (1970) observed that burnout was often associated with the formation of vapor slugs/clots. They postulated that burnout occurs as a result of the evaporation of a thin liquid layer under the vapor slugs or clots, the vapor volumes preventing access of subcooled fluid to the surface (figure 6.4.48a and b). Work by van der Molen & Galijee (1977) showed that the vapor slug is not, in itself, sufficient to cause burnout, which can occur only if bubble overcrowding takes place in the layer separating the vapor slug from the heated wall (figure 6.4.48c).

6.4.6.3 Mechanisms of Burnout in Forced Convective Flows: Annular Flow Regime

In the annular flow regime, a number of possible mechanisms have been postulated for burnout (figure 6.4.49):

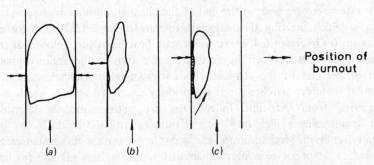

Figure 6.4.48 Burnout arising from vapor slug or clot formation in subcooled or low-quality flows.

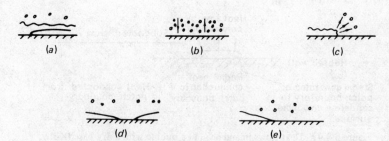

Figure 6.4.49   Mechanisms of burnout in the annular region. (*a*) Vapor film formation under liquid film. (*b*) Droplet mass transfer rate = rate of evaporation. (*c*) Sudden disruption of film. (*d*) Dry patch formation. (*e*) Film dryout.

1. Vapor film formation under the liquid film. The mechanism for forming this vapor film might be of the types described for subcooled and low-quality flows in section 6.4.6.2.
2. Burnout limited by droplet mass transfer rate. Burnout occurs when the rate of evaporation of droplets at the surface exceeds the rate at which they arrive at the surface by droplet mass transfer.
3. Sudden disruption of the liquid film. A hydrodynamic mechanism is postulated for the sudden disruption of the film beyond which the surface is dry and burnout occurs.
4. Dry patch formation. Dry patches form within the liquid film, causing a hot spot on the surface that cannot be rewetted.
5. Liquid film dryout. The film dries by progressive entrainment and evaporation and burnout occurs when all the film has gone.

The mechanism can be elucidated by direct visualization of burnout (Hewitt et al. 1965) and by measurement of the liquid flow rate in the film at the end of the heated channel by the suction method (section 10.2.2.1). Typical results obtained with the suction method are illustrated in figure 6.4.50. The mechanism that emerges from these studies is as follows. The liquid flow rate in the liquid film is decreased along the channel due to evaporation and droplet entrainment. This liquid removal is offset to some extent by droplet deposition onto the film (section 2.2.4). As the flow passes along the channel and/or as the heat flux is increased, the net film flow rate decreases and, at the end of the channel, burnout corresponds to the condition in which the film flow rate falls to zero (figure 6.4.50). This corresponds to mechanism (*e*) in figure 6.4.49. However, at a heat input just below that required for burnout, dry patches can be formed in the film in the region immediately upstream of the end of the channel; this corresponds to mechanism (*d*) but the formation of these dry patches is not the primary cause of burnout, which is due to liquid removal from the film. Indeed, the dry patches can be intermittently rewetted, maintaining a high rate of heat transfer until the liquid in the film has been totally removed. Mechanism (*b*) can occur under certain circumstances and can be regarded as a special case of mechanism (*e*). Mechanisms (*a*) and (*c*) have not been confirmed by direct experimental evidence.

Burnout occurs as a result of the integral effect of droplet mass transfer and

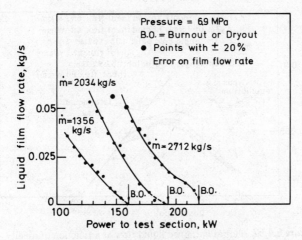

Figure 6.4.50 Variation of film flow rate with input power at the end of a uniformly heated round tube in which water is being evaporated at 6.9 MPa (Hewitt 1970).

evaporation along the channel. Experiments of the type illustrated in figure 6.4.50 give information only on the situation at the end of the channel, and to more fully understand the mechanism it is useful to make film flow measurements along the length of a channel in which burnout is occurring at the end (figure 6.4.51). The film flow rate is seen to go to zero at the end of the channel. However, a better understanding of the phenomena that occur is obtained if the data are plotted in

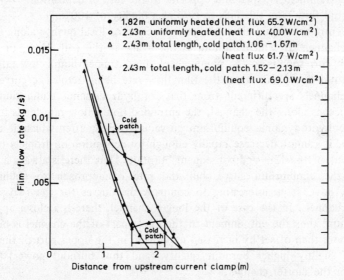

Figure 6.4.51 Variation of film flow rate with distance for uniformly heated tubes and tubes with unheated zones (cold patches). Evaporation of water at low pressure; burnout condition occurs at the end of the tube in each case (data of Bennett et al. 1966). Mass flux = 297 kg/m² s.

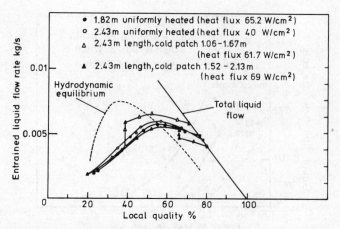

Figure 6.4.52 Plot of entrained liquid flow as a function of quality for evaporation of water in a tube at low pressure (Bennett et al. 1966). Mass flux = 297 kg/m² s.

terms of entrained liquid flow rate rather than film flow rate, as shown in figure 6.4.52. Figures 6.4.51 and 6.4.52 contain data for both uniform heat flux and tubes with an unheated zone (cold patch).

In figure 6.4.52, the following quantities are plotted in terms of local quality x:

1. Entrained liquid flow rate for a condition of "hydrodynamic equilibrium." This condition would be obtained in adiabatic flows in very long channels where the rate of entrainment is equal and opposite to the rate of deposition.
2. Total liquid flow rate; this falls to zero at a quality of 100%.
3. Loci of entrained liquid flow rate as a function of local quality along uniformly heated channels at which burnout is occurring at the end. Here, the burnout condition corresponds to the point where the entrained liquid flow rate is equal to the total liquid flow rate, the film flow rate being zero. The curves for the heated channels are different from that for hydrodynamic equilibrium. As the flow proceeds along the channel, the entrained liquid flow rate tends to increase until the hydrodynamic equilibrium curve is crossed, after which it decreases. However, it cannot decrease rapidly enough by deposition of droplets to prevent drying out of the film and consequent burnout. Thus there is always a tendency toward the equilibrium curve, but the rate of approach to equilibrium is relatively low. It is interesting to compare the curves for the two uniformly heated channels. In the case of the longer channel, there is a closer approach to equilibrium; thus the entrainment in the lower part of the channel is higher, but this is more than offset by increased deposition in the upper part of the channel, giving a slightly higher burnout quality (and thus burnout power) than that found for the shorter channel.
4. Data for two cases where there is an unheated zone. In this unheated zone, there is a tendency for the flow to approach the hydrodynamic equilibrium curve without any change in local quality. When the unheated zone is in the lower part of the channel this leads to an increase in entrainment and a lower quality for

burnout. When the unheated zone is in the upper part of the channel, there is a fall in the entrained liquid flow rate, giving an increased quality for burnout. These observations explain the cold-patch results in figure 6.4.38.

The mechanisms of entrainment and deposition (liquid mass transfer) in adiabatic annular flows are discussed in section 2.2.4. Where there is a heat flux, the rate of entrainment and/or deposition of droplets could be different because of the following possible mechanisms:

1. Nucleate boiling within the liquid film could give rise to bursting of bubbles at the film/vapor core interface with consequent release of droplets. The more intense the nucleate boiling, the more intense the entrainment by this mechanism.
2. The evaporation process leads to a flux of vapor away from the interface, and this may sweep away droplets that would otherwise have been deposited.

These local effects of heat flux are often difficult to distinguish from indirect integral effects of a heat flux resulting from the slow attainment of hydrodynamic equilibrium, as illustrated in figure 6.4.52. A method of determining the local effects is to make local film flow (and hence entrained flow) measurements along a channel, the first part of which is heated and the second part of which is unheated. Low-pressure experiments of this type are described by Hewitt (1970) and experiments at 6.9 MPa are described by Keeys et al. (1970). Typical results are illustrated in figure 6.4.53. If the rate of change of entrained liquid flow rate with length is the same on either side of the transition between the heated and unheated zones, then the heat flux effect on the rate of entrainment can be considered small. Both the low- and high-pressure data gave this result. It is for this reason that the direct heat flux effects are ignored in the Harwell annular flow prediction model for burnout (section 6.4.7). Alternative forms of experiment, carried out recently, are discussed by Hewitt (1978); the conclusion was that these experiments could not unequivocally demonstrate the direct heat flux effects.

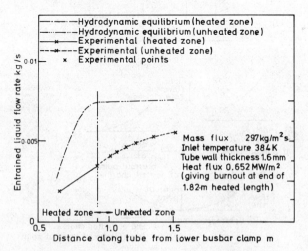

Figure 6.4.53 Effect of heat flux on rate of entrainment (Hewitt 1970).

It is interesting to consider, in the context of mechanism studies, a mass balance over a short zone immediately preceding the burnout point (figure 6.4.54a). In this short element, the film flow rate and film thickness are very small and one may expect entrainment to be negligible. Thus the supply of liquid to the element (by deposition and by flow along the film) is in balance with the evaporation of liquid from the element. The mass balance with the element of length δz is thus

$$- \delta z \frac{d\dot{M}_{LF}}{dz} + \dot{m}_D P \delta z = \frac{\dot{q}_c P \delta z}{h_{LG}} \qquad [6.4.64]$$

where $\dot{M}_{LF}$ is the liquid film flow rate, $\dot{m}_D$ is the rate of deposition of droplets per unit channel surface area, P is the channel periphery, $\dot{q}_c$ is the burnout, and h_{LG} is the latent heat. Rearranging, we have

$$\frac{\dot{q}_c}{h_{LG}} = \dot{m}_D - \frac{1}{P} \frac{d\dot{M}_{LF}}{dz} \qquad [6.4.65]$$

which states that the rate of evaporation at the burnout point is equal to the sum of the rate of deposition and the rate at which liquid approaches the burnout zone along the film. A condition in which the last term in [6.4.65] is negligible may be termed deposition-controlled. When burnout occurs at the end of a channel, it may or may not be deposition-controlled (figure 6.4.54b and 6.4.54c), but burnout upstream of the end of a channel must, by definition, always occur in the deposition-controlled mode with $d\dot{M}_{LF}/dz = 0$ (figure 6.4.54d).

It is interesting to discuss the occurrence of burnout in the quality region in terms of the deposition-control concept and in terms of the flux/quality diagram obtained for subcooled inlet conditions. Bennett et al. (1967b) classified the various regions of burnout as illustrated in figure 6.4.55.

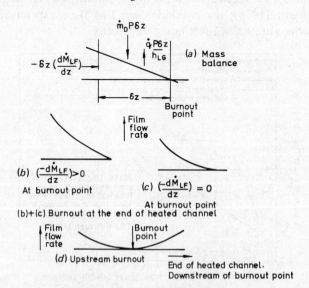

Figure 6.4.54 Mass balance over region immediately upstream of burnout point.

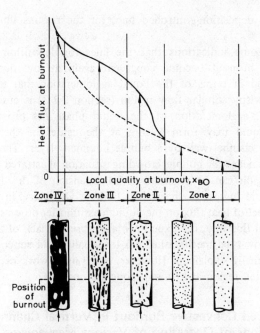

Figure 6.4.55   Zones of burnout (Bennett et al. 1967b).

1. Zone I corresponds to the highest-quality end of the flux/quality diagram; the burnout heat flux for uniformly heated tubes approaches that for deposition control. Very long tubes are required to enter this region if subcooled liquid is used at the tube inlet (Hewitt 1970).

2. Zone II is a region of rapidly increasing heat flux with decreasing quality. It corresponds to the region where the power required for burnout at any given inlet condition is more or less constant with increasing length. The effect of increasing the length is to increase the amount of entrainment in the lower part of the channel (since there is more time to approach the equilibrium value) and to increase the amount of deposition in the upper part of the channel; the net result is that there is little increase in burnout quality with increasing length. Thus the burnout quality may be approximately constant, although the flux will increase as the length is shortened since the power required to achieve the given outlet quality must be fed in over a shorter length.

3. As the length further decreases, the value of the entrained flow at the onset of annular flow becomes more important. If, as seems possible, a large amount of entrainment exists at the transition, then the effect of this on the burnout point becomes stronger as the tube length is decreased. Alternatively (and probably in addition) the influence of nucleate boiling on entrainment increases in this region. The net result is that, in zone III, the negative slope of the flux/quality curve may become less steep, as illustrated. In figure 6.4.55, the condition for deposition control is shown as a dashed line. The burnout flux for the uniformly heated tube in zones II and III is higher than that for deposition control. However, for upstream burnout in nonuniformly heated channels, the local burnout flux/quality relation

will fall along the deposition-controlled line, for the reasons illustrated in figure 6.4.54.

4. There are some indications that the lines for deposition control and for uniform heat flux burnout become congruent again at low quality. It may be tentatively explained in terms of the liquid agglomeration that takes place in the vapor core as the wispy annular flow region (section 2.1.3) is entered on reducing quality. Ultimately, agglomeration of the liquid phase has proceded to such an extent that the liquid may form a core at the center of the channel that is separated from the channel wall by a bubble boundary layer. The latter condition corresponds to the near-wall bubble crowding situation illustrated in figure 6.4.45. This (Zone IV) region can be regarded as an extension of the deposition-control situation where liquid ingress to the wall is limited. Of course, in the latter region, there is a strong effect of heat flux on the liquid mass transfer process.

When viewed in this way, the experimentally observed lack of a sharp transition between annular flow-type mechanisms and low-quality and subcooled boiling-type mechanisms is rationally explained. However, much more work needs to be done in studying the transition region at low and moderate qualities.

6.4.6.4   Forced Convective Burnout in Vertical Channels: Regions of Operation of Various Mechanisms

A tentative representation of the regions of operation of the burnout mechanisms discussed in section 6.4.6.2 and 6.4.6.3 was given by Semeria & Hewitt (1972) and is reproduced here as figure 6.4.56. Note enough is known to fix the transitions quantitatively, but the diagram may help to provide an overall qualitative picture.

6.4.6.5   Nonvertical Channels

In nonvertical channels, body forces (gravitational, centrifugal) act on the fluid in a direction that is not parallel to the fluid stream, causing flow separation. In these circumstances, the mechanisms of burnout are exceedingly complex.

For subcooled boiling, Merilo (1977) hypothesized that bubbles that are formed on a downward-facing surface are forced upward against the surface by buoyancy force. This force hinders bubble departure and burnout occurs at a lower heat flux than in vertical flow. This phenomenon affects both the single-bubble and bubble boundary-layer regions shown in figure 6.4.56.

Studies of mechanisms in the quality region in horizontal, serpentine, and helical channels are reviewed by Fisher et al. (1978). Three main regions are distinguished:

1. Very-low-quality region. At low qualities, a relatively stable stratification of the flow occurs with the formation of "ribbons" at the upper part of the channel. This type of result is obtained characteristically at very high pressures. Air-water simulation experiments do not exhibit the same form of behavior, and two-liquid systems (e.g., isoamyl alcohol and water) provide a better representation, as shown by Gardner & Kubie (1976) for inclined tubes and Kubie & Gardner (1977) for

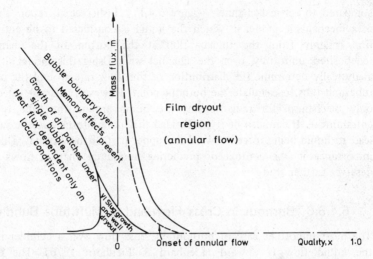

Figure 6.4.56 Tentative representation of regions of burnout (Semeria & Hewitt 1972).

helical coils. Kubie & Gardner showed that at a critical mass flux the ribbon was broken up, and this result could be related to the observed burnout data.

2. Low- and intermediate-quality region. Here, the mechanism is likely to be similar to that proposed by Coney (1974b), as illustrated in figure 6.4.57. A "frothy surge" passes along the channel and wets the upper surface of the tube. The film thus deposited drains away and, in the case of heated tubes, is also evaporated. If the drainage and evaporation are such that complete film removal (dryout) occurs before the arrival of the next frothy surge, then intermittent dryout and overheating can occur. Thus the susceptibility of the channel to intermittent dryout (or burnout) depends on the maximum possible interval between the surges. Measurements of these intervals for serpentine and helical tubes are reported by Fisher et al. (1978).

3. High-quality region. At high qualities, annular flow occurs; however, the liquid film at the upper part of the channel has a lower thickness (and a greater susceptibility to burnout) than the film at the lower part of the channel. This is the reason for the large reduction in burnout heat flux for horizontal channels

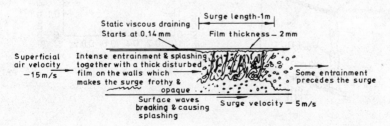

Figure 6.4.57 Splashing and draining mechanism in frothy surge flow (Coney 1974b).

compared to vertical channels (figure 6.4.17). Fisher et al. report the development of a mechanistic model in which the liquid is considered to be entrained from the film (mainly from the thicker film at the bottom of the channel) and then redeposited uniformly over the channel wall. Using this model, it is possible to analytically determine the distribution of film flow rate around the periphery of the tube and thus to calculate the burnout point. However, it is not yet certain that the only mechanism for redistributing the liquid around the tube is one of liquid entrainment. It can also be hypothesized that nonuniform waves around the channel lead to liquid being forced toward the upper part of the channel. This problem is of importance in the context of predicting horizontal channel flows in general and deserves further study.

6.4.6.6 Burnout in Cross Flow and in Multitube Bundles

The most important case of burnout in cross flow over a cylinder is that in which the liquid flow is upward (Lienhard & Eichhorn 1976). The observations of Lienhard and Eichhorn are illustrated in figure 6.4.58. At low liquid cross-flow velocities, the burnout heat flux is similar to that in pool boiling. However, there is a transition velocity at which the vapor escape pattern changes from a three-dimensional one (with separated jets) to a two-dimensional one, as illustrated in figure 6.4.58. After this transition, the burnout heat flux begins to increase with liquid velocity, and this effect is embodied in the correlations. The mechanism of burnout in horizontal tube bundles can be of a pool boiling type, but there is a tendency for the burnout flux to be depressed in such tube bundles.

Visualization experiments reveal that burnout can occur in such bundles as a result of restricted access of liquid to one or another part of the bundle.

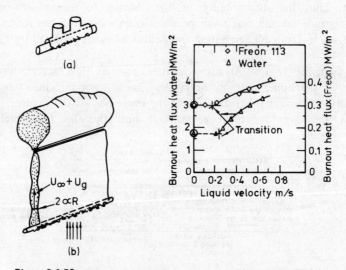

Figure 6.4.58 Burnout in cross flow over a cylinder (Lienhard & Eichhorn 1976). (a) Three-dimensional jets of vapor. (b) Two-dimensional jet.

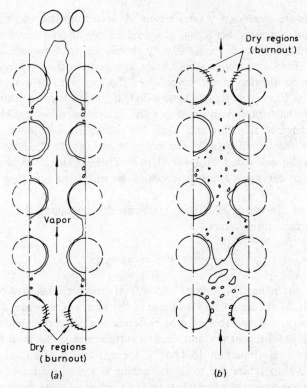

Figure 6.4.59 Mechanisms of burnout in tube bundles. (a)
(a) Flooding-limited burnout. (b) Circulation-limited burnout.

Restrictions in liquid access can take place by two mechanisms, as illustrated schematically in figure 6.4.59:

1. Flooding-limited burnout. Here, if the liquid access to the bundle is from the top, the vapor flow passing over the channels between the tubes inhibits the down flow of liquid and, ultimately, there exists a situation in which the lower tubes are dried out.

2. Circulation-limited burnout. This is similar to the pattern observed in straight channels where liquid becomes entrained and the liquid film becomes thinner in progressive rows, ultimately leading to dryout in the upper rows.

It is possible to obtain both types of burnout simultaneously, with liquid circulating to be evaporated on the lower rows of a bundle, and liquid passing down at a rate limited by flooding, to be evaporated on the upper part of the bundle. The precise mechanism in any given circumstance will depend on the overall system geometry.

6.4.7 PREDICTION OF BURNOUT IN ANNULAR FLOW

The mechanisms of burnout in annular flow were discussed in section 6.4.6.3. This form of burnout is the one most likely to occur in practical systems, where the channel lengths are commonly several meters. As seen from the discussion in section 6.4.6.3, burnout occurs in this region as a result of the effects, cumulative along the channel, of liquid removal from the film by entrainment and evaporation, leading to film dryout. These film removal processes are partly offset by redeposition of entrained droplets flowing in the vapor core. The local rate of evaporation can be calculated if the local heat flux is known and, if models can be postulated for the rate of entrainment and deposition of droplets, it then becomes feasible to calculate the rate of change of film flow rate along the channel. If some boundary condition is assumed (at the entrance or at the onset of annular flow), then the local film flow rate may be calculated as a function of distance along the channel and the onset of burnout estimated from the condition at which the film flow rate becomes zero.

The rate of change of film flow rate with distance along the channel can be obtained from the expression:

$$\frac{A}{P}\frac{d\dot{m}_{LF}}{dz} = \dot{m}_D - \dot{m}_E = \frac{\dot{q}}{h_{LG}}$$ [6.4.66]

where $\dot{m}_{LF}$ is the mass flux (related to the total cross-sectional area of the channel A) of that part of the liquid flow which is in the film, z is the axial distance, P the channel periphery, $\dot{m}_D$ the rate of droplet deposition per unit channel surface area, $\dot{m}_E$ the rate of entrainment per unit channel surface area, $\dot{q}$ the local heat flux, and h_{LG} the latent heat. Equation [6.4.66] is for a steady state and also ignores the contribution to evaporation due to liquid flashing as a result of the channel pressure gradient. More sophisticated expressions taking account of these factors are given by Whalley et al. (1978). For rod bundles, expressions analogous to [6.4.66] can be written for individual rods.

A number of predictive models have been proposed for the calculation of burnout in annular flow (Hewitt 1978). The models differ principally in their treatment of the entrainment and deposition processes and in the boundary conditions that the integration of [6.4.66] starts. The model that appears to have been applied to the widest range of situations is that developed at Harwell (Whalley et al. 1974, 1975, 1978; Hewitt & Hutchinson 1976). Predictive methods for annular flow were discussed in the context of models for pressure drop calculation in section 2.2.4. The main features of the Harwell model are, briefly, as follows:

1. The deposition rate $\dot{m}_D$ is given by

$$\dot{m}_D = kC$$ [6.4.67]

where k is a deposition mass transfer coefficient and C is the concentration of droplets in the vapor core (calculated on the basis of a homogeneous liquid/vapor mixture in the core). For the calculations described below, k was tentatively correlated in terms of surface tension (section 2.2.4).

2. The entrainment rate $\dot{m}_E$ was calculated from

$$\dot{m}_E = kC_E$$ [6.4.68]

where C_E is the droplet concentration under hydrodynamic equilibrium conditions (where entrainment rate and deposition rate are equal) for the appropriate local value of the group $(\tau_I \delta_F / \sigma)$. Here, τ_I is the interfacial shear stress, δ_F is the film thickness, and σ is the surface tension. In any given calculation τ_I and δ_F are dependent variables and have to be calculated, for the local value of $\dot{m}_{LF}$, by the simultaneous solution of the "triangular" and "interfacial roughness" relations described in section 2.2.4. Thus a by-product of the burnout calculation is the estimation of the interfacial shear and film thickness, from which the pressure gradient and the void fraction may be derived.

3. Only rarely are the boundary conditions at the tube inlet or the onset of annular flow known, but it is found that, for tubes of reasonable length, the effect of boundary conditions on the calculation is relatively small and it has been arbitrarily assumed that annular flow starts at a nominal quality of 0.01 with an entrained fraction of 0.99. Clearly, this would be invalid for very short channels.

4. The integration along the channel was carried out by a modification of the method of Gear (1968).

In spite of the very great simplifications in the entrainment and deposition relations, reasonable predictions are obtained. The search for better entrainment and deposition correlations is continuing (Whalley & Hewitt 1978). The following are typical applications of the methods for predicting burnout:

1. Known inlet conditions. Figure 6.4.60 shows predictions by Whalley et al. (1978) of the mixed inlet data of Bennett et al. (1965a). Here, the liquid film was injected smoothly at the entrance and zero entrainment could be assumed at that point. Excellent agreement is obtained between the predictions and the experiments.

2. Tubes with subcooled liquid inlet. Figure 6.4.61 compares the calculations of Whalley et al. (1974) with experimental data for water evaporation at 70 MPa obtained by Bennett et al. (1965a). The comparisons are made in the quality/boiling length representation. Calculated heat fluxes for given inlet conditions are within a few percent.

3. Annuli. Figure 6.4.62 shows a comparison of calculated and experimental

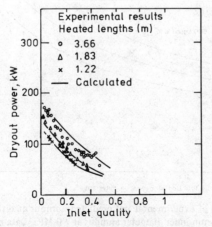

Figure 6.4.60 Comparison of mixed inlet burnout data of Bennett et al. (1965) with predictions from Harwell annular flow model (Whalley et al. 1978).

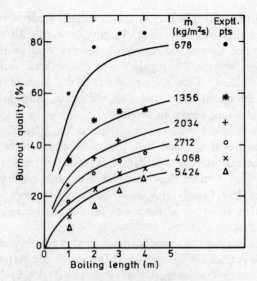

Figure 6.4.61 Comparison of experimental and predicted burnout qualities for evaporation of water in a 12.6-mm tube at a pressure of 6.89 MPa. Data of Bennett et al. (1965) (Whalley et al. 1974).

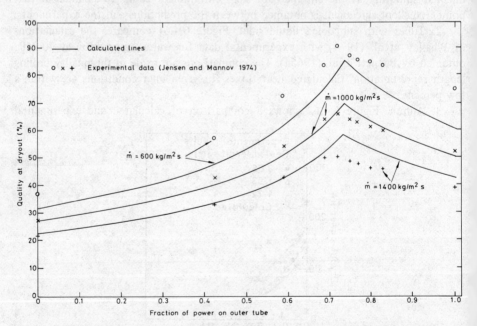

Figure 6.4.62 Comparison of experimental and predicted burnout qualities for evaporation in a 13-mm outer diameter, 8.5-mm inner diameter annulus at 7.0 MPa. Data of Jensen & Mannov (1974) (Whalley et al. 1974).

burnout quality as a function of the fraction of power on the outer tube of an annulus, compared with the experimental data of Jensen & Mannov (1974) (Whalley et al. 1975). The qualitative nature of the curves is predicted, as are the absolute values.

4. Transient conditions. Transient burnout is, of course, of considerable interest in reactor safety analysis. Typical of the experiments in this area is that of Moxon & Edwards (1967), who investigated the time required to reach burnout with a flow transient, as illustrated in figure 6.4.63. Using the known inlet flow transient, the film flow rate was calculated as a function of distance and time along the channel, and the boiling length to burnout was calculated as a function of time, as illustrated in figure 6.4.63. When the predicted boiling length becomes equal to the channel length (3.66 m), burnout begins to occur at the end of the channel. The time to burnout can be read from figure 6.4.64.

5. Rod bundles. Prediction of burnout in rod bundles is achieved by using the

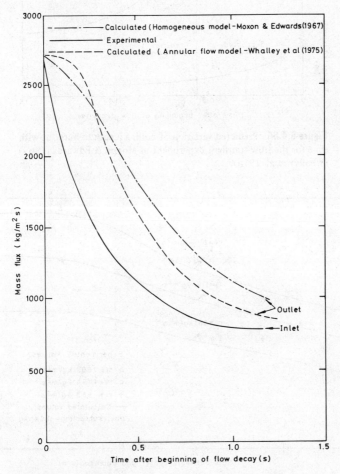

Figure 6.4.63 Mass velocity transients during flow decay in experiments of Moxon & Edwards (1967).

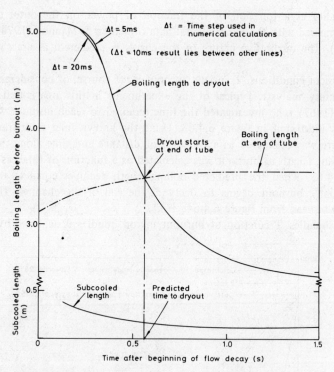

Figure 6.4.64 Predicted variation of boiling length to burnout with time for the flow transient experiment of Moxon & Edwards (1967) (Whalley et al. 1975).

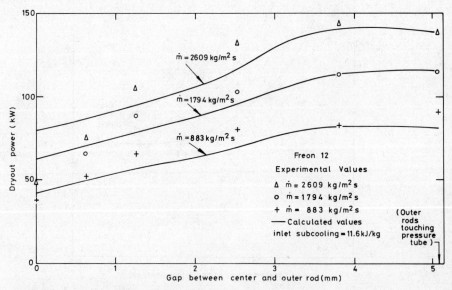

Figure 6.4.65 Calculation of burnout power for seven-rod-bundle experiments illustrated in figures 7.4.26 and 7.4.27 (Whalley 1976).

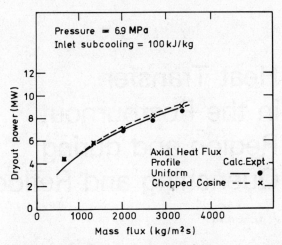

Figure 6.4.66 Comparison of measured dryout power for a 37-rod bundle with predicted values (Whalley 1978).

annular flow model coupled with the rod-centered subchannel concept discussed in section 6.4.3.2 and illustrated in figure 6.4.28. A good test of the validity of the modeling is to predict the variable spacing data illustrated in figures 6.4.26 and 6.4.27. Comparisons with these data are shown in figure 6.4.65. Both the quantitative values and the qualitative trend as a result of moving the rods are predicted. Predictions for a 37-rod bundle are illustrated in figure 6.4.66.

Thus, notwithstanding the rather crude component models used, predictions can be obtained that are of a general nature and are superior to those based on empirical correlations. More work needs to be done in advancing understanding of specific effects such as those associated with grids in rod bundles.

6.5 Heat Transfer in the Postburnout Region and during Quenching and Reflooding

J. G. Collier

6.5.1 POSTBURNOUT HEAT TRANSFER

6.5.1.1 Introduction

This section concerns the processes of heat transfer in regions where the burnout heat flux has been exceeded. The *burnout heat flux* represents a condition at which there is a more or less sudden decrease in the forced convective boiling heat transfer coefficient.

Knowledge of heat transfer rates in the postburnout region is required in many important applications. In a water-cooled reactor, a loss-of-coolant accident (LOCA; section 6.6) or an overpower transient may result in parts of the fuel element having to operate in the postburnout region for a limited time. Subcritical once-through steam generators, either fossil-fired or as currently designed for water-cooled, gas-cooled, and sodium-cooled nuclear power plants, require parts of the heat transfer surface to operate continuously in this region (Bailey & Collier 1970, Collier 1977). An understanding of the phenomena at and beyond the burnout location has a bearing on the water-side corrosion situation as well as the heat transfer performance. The use of cryogens, in particular liquefied natural gas (LNG) and liquefied petroleum gas (LPG), has meant that large-capacity once-through vaporizers are being built, and improved design methods are also required for this important application (Bailey et al. 1973, Durga Prasad et al. 1974).

The section starts with a physical description of the processes that occur and reviews the experimental information, which shows that the boiling curve in forced convection is basically similar in shape to that for pool boiling (sections 6.1 and 6.2). A brief section on the transition boiling region is followed by a discussion of the postburnout heat transfer correlations and physical models in current use. Finally, heat transfer in the low-vapor-quality and subcooled liquid states, corresponding to the inverted annular flow region, is considered.

The author thanks the United Kingdom Atomic Energy Authority (UKAEA) for permission to use figures 6.5.1, 6.5.2, 6.5.3, 6.5.7, 6.5.8, 6.5.10, 6.5.14, 6.5.16, 6.5.17, and 6.5.20, which remain UKAEA copyright material.

6.5.1.2 Physical Description of Postburnout Heat Transfer

The physical processes that occur in the postburnout region can best be discussed in terms of the experimental techniques used. The simplest experiment that can be undertaken involves establishing a particular condition of liquid flow to a long vertical tube heated uniformly (figure 6.5.1a). Burnout is initiated at the downstream end of the tube, either by increasing the heat flux or by reducing the flow rate (condition A). Increasing the heat flux drives the burnout point upstream, and the downstream section of the tube enters the postburnout region (condition B). Plotting the variation of surface temperature at a position z, one obtains the curve shown in figure 6.5.1b. Bennett et al. (1967a) carried out this experiment and showed that no hysteresis was associated with the curve in figure 6.5.1b when the heat flux was increased or decreased. This is in contrast to the situation in pool boiling, where the return from film boiling conditions to nucleate boiling occurs at a considerably lower heat flux than the burnout flux.

Further information about physical processes in the postburnout region can be obtained from a test with a two-section tube in which one section can be operated at a higher or lower heat flux from the rest of the tube. Consider a tube in which

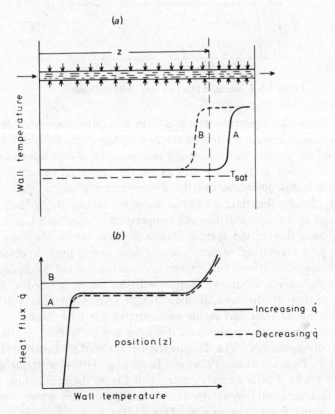

Figure 6.5.1 Burnout in a uniformly heated tube.

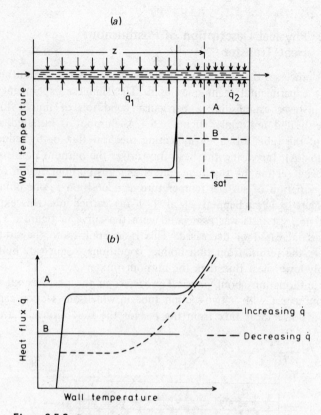

Figure 6.5.2 Burnout in a two-section heated tube.

the heat flux on the upstream section $\dot{q}_1$ can be adjusted separately from that on a short downstream section $\dot{q}_2$ (figure 6.5.2a). Initially, the two sections are operated at equal values of heat flux ($\dot{q}_1 = \dot{q}_2$) and burnout is established over the whole downstream section in the same way as for the uniformly heated tube (condition A). Burnout is now maintained at the downstream end of the upstream section by holding $\dot{q}_1$ fixed. The flux on the downstream section $\dot{q}_2$ is then progressively reduced, and it is found that the wall temperature at position z falls smoothly with decreasing heat flux in the manner shown in figure 6.5.2b. At some value of the heat flux ($\dot{q}_2$) "rewetting" occurs and the wall temperature drops sharply to the nucleate boiling condition. This experiment was carried out by Bailey (1972) and the above picture was confirmed. Similar behavior can be induced by having, in the upstream section of the tube, a short length over which the local heat flux is considerably higher than that in the remainder of the tube. Burnout is initiated at this heat flux spike, and postburnout behavior can be studied on the downstream sections at the lower heat flux. This technique was used by Groeneveld (1974) with Freon and by Plummer et al. (1974) and Iloeje et al. (1974) with nitrogen.

Figure 6.5.2b depicts a much greater similarity to the pool boiling situation and indicates that significant hysteresis can occur in situations where rewetting by an advancing liquid front is prevented. This finding is significant in relation to the conditions expected on a fuel pin during an LOCA. In particular, if parts of the fuel pin remain wetted during the transient, one expects rewetting of the areas where burnout previously occurred soon after the local surface heat flux falls below the burnout value. The time to rewet is, however, limited by the conduction-controlled velocity of the "quench" front (section 6.5.2). On the other hand, if the fuel pin has "dried out" completely during the transient, or if an upstream section persistently indicates burnout, then the pin surface heat flux must fall significantly below the burnout value (e.g., to 10–20% of the burnout heat flux) before rewetting can be initiated.

The existence of a transition boiling region is established by use of a test section consisting of two parts: a long, uniformly heated upstream section and a short, thick-walled, high-heat-capacity downstream section (figure 6.5.3a). Burnout is established at the downstream end of the long section and the short section is heated to a high initial temperature. A cooling or quench curve is then produced

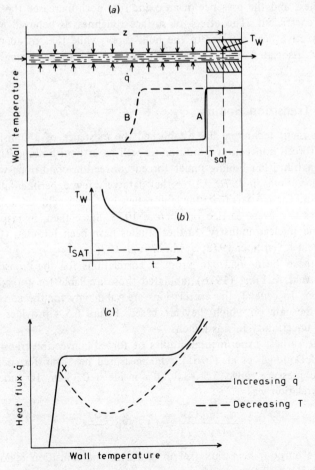

Figure 6.5.3 Burnout in a transient conduction downstream section.

(figure 6.5.3*b*) as the short section is cooled to the saturation temperature. Provided the thick-walled section can be treated as a lumped system (no axial or radial temperature profiles), the local heat flux can be established from the gradient of section temperature with time (figure 6.5.3*b*). The resulting curve of heat flux versus wall temperature is shown in figure 6.5.3*c*. Note that point *X* does not generally coincide with the burnout heat flux because, in general, both the flow in the liquid film and the droplet deposition flux contribute to the burnout heat flux. Measurements by Hewitt (1970) showed that *X* may normally be about 80% of the burnout value, rising on some occasions to as much as 100%, in which case *X* and the burnout value coincide.

Similar experiments may be carried out with burnout occurring at any location in the upstream heated section (condition B in figure 6.5.3*a*). Increasing the length of the dried-out section decreases the heat transfer coefficient at a given mass velocity and quality because of thermal nonequilibrium effects. No influence of heater material was noted between copper, Inconel 600, and aluminum. Increased surface roughness and the presence of an oxide film both increased the postburnout heat transfer coefficient. The effect of surface roughness is believed to be due to increased convective heat transfer to the bulk vapor while that of an oxide film is believed to be associated with better wettability of the oxide during droplet-wall contacts.

6.5.1.3 Transition Boiling

Use of the transient technique has established the existence of a transition boiling region in the forced convection condition as well as in pool boiling. The published information on transition boiling under forced convection conditions was reviewed by Groeneveld & Fung in 1976. Up to that date very few experimental studies had been carried out. Table 6.5.1, from the later review by Groeneveld & Gardiner (1977), lists the studies that were carried out before 1976. Since then, in response to the demands of the nuclear industry, further studies have been initiated (Cheng et al. 1978; Groeneveld & Gardiner 1978; Newbold et al. 1976).

Attempts have been made to produce correlations for the transition boiling region. Groeneveld & Fung (1976) tabulated those available for forced convective boiling of water. In general, the correlations are valid only for the narrow range of conditions of the data on which they are based. Figure 6.5.4 provides an example of the level of uncertainty in this region.

One of the earliest experimental studies of forced convection transition boiling was that by McDonough et al. (1961), who measured heat transfer coefficients for water over the pressure range 5.5–13.8 MPa inside a 0.38-cm ID tube heated by NaK. Their correlation was

$$\frac{\dot{q}_c - \dot{q}(z)}{T_W(z) - T_c} = 4.15 \exp \frac{3.97}{p} \qquad [6.5.1]$$

where $\dot{q}_c$ is the burnout heat flux (kW/m^2), $\dot{q}(z)$ is the transition region heat flux (kW/m^2), T_c is the wall temperature at burnout ($^\circ$C), $T_W(z)$ is the wall temperature in the transition region ($^\circ$C), and p is the system pressure (MPa).

Table 6.5.1 Transition Boiling Data for Water in Forced Convection[a]

Geometry	Reference	Range of data				Comments
		p (MPa)	$\dot{m}/10^3$ (kg/m² s)	$\dot{q}/10^3$ (kW/m²)	Subcooling (°C) or quality	
Annulus, 0.64 cm ID, 6.35 cm OD	Ellion (1954)	0.110–0.413	0.33–1.49	1.47–1.96	28–56°C	$\dot{q}$-controlled system with stabilizing fluid, z_h = 7.62 cm
Tube, D_e = 0.386 cm	McDonough et al. (1961)	5.51 8.27 13.78	0.27–2.04	0.32–3.78	Subcooled and low quality	NaK used as heating fluid; T_W inferred from heat-transfer correlation for NaK; data no longer available
Annulus, 0.013 cm ID, 1.21 cm OD	Peterson et al. (1973)	0.101	0.64–1.93	0.41–1.99	Saturated	Heat flux controlled by electronic feedback; z_H = 5.08 cm
Tube, D_e = 1.25 cm	Plummer et al. (1976)	6.89	0.07–0.34	0.06–0.27	x = 0.30–1.00	Transfer test; z_h = 10.16 cm
Annulus, 1.37 cm ID, 2.54 cm OD	Ramu & Weisman (1975)	0.172–0.206	0.02–0.05	0.03–0.26	x = 0–0.500	Hg used as heating fluid; x not reported; limited range in T_W
Rod bundles, D_e = 1.27 cm	Westinghouse (FLECHT), Cadeck et al. (1971)	0.103–0.620	0.05–0.25	0.01–0.27	0–78°C	Transient test; ΔT_{sub} or x unknown
Tube, D_e = 1.27 cm	Cheng & Ng (1976)	0.103	0.19	0.016–0.158	0–26°C	Transient and steady-state test; high intertia; copper block; z_h = 10.16 cm
Tube, D_e = 1.27 cm	Fung (1977)	0.101	0.068–1.35	0.008–1.89	0–76°C	Similar to Cheng & Ng tests
Tube, D_e = 1.27 cm	Newbold et al. (1976)	0.303	0.016–1.25	0.016–0.948	0–80°C	Similar to Cheng & Ng tests; however, guard heaters were employed to reduce axial conduction

[a]From Groeneveld & Gardiner (1977).

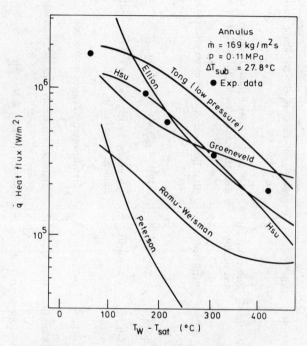

Figure 6.5.4 Comparison of various transition boiling correlations with Ellion's (1954) data (Groeneveld & Fung 1976).

Tong (1967) suggested the following equation for combined transition and stable film boiling at 13.8 MPa with wall temperatures less than 400°C $[T_W(z) - T_{sat} \leqslant 150°C]$:

$$\alpha_{tb} = 5.05 + 95.4 \exp \{-0.018 [T_W(z) - T_{sat}]\} \qquad [6.5.2]$$

where α_{tb} is the heat transfer coefficient for the transition region (kW/m² °C) and T_{sat} is the saturation temperature (°C). This was revised (Tong 1972b) to cover both transition and film boiling regions:

$$\alpha_{tb} = 39.75 \exp(-0.0144 \Delta T) + 2.3 \times 10^{-5} \frac{\lambda_G}{D_{eq}} \exp\left(-\frac{105}{\Delta T}\right) \mathrm{Re}_{G,f}^{0.8} \mathrm{Pr}_{G,f}^{0.4}$$

$$[6.5.3]$$

where λ_G is the thermal conductivity of the gas (W/m°C), D_{eq} is equivalent diameter (m), and $\mathrm{Re}_{G,f}$ and $\mathrm{Pr}_{G,f}$ are the Reynolds and Prandtl numbers. Equation [6.5.3] was derived from 1442 data points at a pressure of 6.89 MPa, mass flux $\dot{m}$ from 380 to 5230 kg/m² s, and ΔT $[T_W(z) - T_{sat}]$ from 36 to 550°C. A similar but separate equation was proposed for low-pressure reflooding situations.

More recently, Ramu & Weisman (1974) attempted to produce a single correlation for postburnout and reflood situations. They proposed the transition boiling heat transfer coefficient

$$\alpha_{tb} = 0.5\ S\ \alpha_c\ \{\exp\left[-0.140\ (\Delta T - \Delta T_c)\right] + \exp\left[-0.125\ (\Delta T - \Delta T_c)\right]\}$$

$$[6.5.4]$$

where α_c and ΔT_c are the heat transfer coefficient and wall superheat corresponding to the pool boiling burnout condition and S is the Chen nucleation suppression factor.

Tong & Young (1974) further revised the Westinghouse transition boiling correlation in terms of the surface heat flux in this region ($\dot{q}_{tb}$) (figure 6.5.5):

$$\dot{q}_{tb} = \dot{q}_{nb}\ \exp\left[-0.001\ \frac{x^{2/3}}{dx/dz}\left(\frac{\Delta T}{55.5}\right)^{1 + 0.0029\Delta T}\right]$$

$$[6.5.5]$$

where $\dot{q}_{nb}$ is the nucleate boiling heat flux (presumably equated with the burnout heat flux). They used the data of Bennett et al. (1967a) to develop this equation. They combined [6.5.5] with a stable film boiling heat transfer term and claimed a root-mean-square (rms) error of 29.2% when the correlation was compared with 507 data points from internally heated annuli and rod bundles. Despite some shortcomings in its derivation, this correlation is a most useful empirical equation.

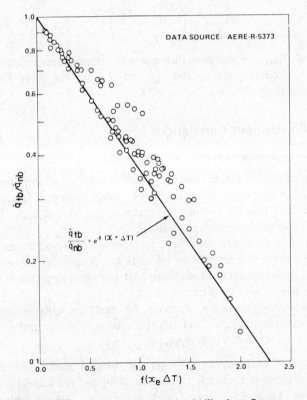

Figure 6.5.5 Correlation of transition boiling heat flux as a function of wall superheat and vapor quality (Tong & Young 1974).

A transition boiling correlation having a wider range of application may be developed if the heat flux and wall temperature difference at the points of maximum and minimum in the boiling curve can be predicted with confidence. The present state of the art allows an accurate prediction of $\dot{q}_c$ and ΔT_c, but the conditions at the minimum are still subject to a large degree of uncertainty. Section 6.5.2 discusses the present position regarding the rewetting temperature (T_{min}). The experimental data of Iloeje et al. (1975) show that this rewetting temperature is not a thermodynamic property but a complex function of the mass quality and flow rate in the channel.

S. C. Cheng et al. (1978) suggested that a simple correlation of the form

$$\frac{\dot{q}_{tb}}{\dot{q}_c} = \left(\frac{T_W - T_{sat}}{\Delta T_c}\right)^{-n}$$ [6.5.6]

has some promise, where ΔT_c is the wall superheat ($T_W - T_{sat}$) at burnout. Cheng et al. found that $n = 1.25$ fitted their low-pressure data acceptably well. A similar approach was adopted by Bjornard & Griffith (1977), who proposed

$$\dot{q}_{tb} = \delta \dot{q}_c + (1 - \delta)\dot{q}_{min}$$ [6.5.7]

$$\delta = \left(\frac{T_{min} - T_W}{T_{min} - T_c}\right)^2$$

where $\dot{q}_{min}$ and T_{min} are the heat flux and wall temperature corresponding to the minimum in the boiling curve, and $\dot{q}_c$ and T_c are the heat flux and wall temperature at burnout.

6.5.1.4 Postburnout Correlations

Three types of correlations have been adopted:

1. Correlations of an empirical nature, which make no assumptions about the mechanism of postburnout heat transfer, but solely attempt a functional relation between the heat transfer coefficient (assuming the coolant is at the saturation temperature) and the independent variables.
2. Correlations that recognize that departure from a thermodynamic equilibrium condition can occur and attempt to calculate the "true" vapor quality and vapor temperature. A conventional single-phase heat transfer correlation is then used to calculate the heated wall temperature.
3. Semitheoretical models, where attempts are made to write equations for the individual hydrodynamic and heat transfer processes in the heated channel and relate them to the heated wall temperature.

Groeneveld (1973) compiled a bank of selected data from a variety of experimental postburnout studies in tubular, annular, and rod bundle geometries for steam-water flows. Table 6.5.2, from Groeneveld's paper, lists the individual sources and the ranges of the independent variables examined.

Table 6.5.2 Postburnout Data[a]

Geometry	Reference	Range of data p (MPa)	$\dot{q}$ (kW/m²)	$\dot{m}$ (kg/m² s)	x	D_e (mm)	Comments
Tube	Parker & Grosh (1961)	0.2	10–60	50–100	0.89–1.00	25.4	500-mm heated length; rewetting of wall?
	Bennett et al. (1967a)	6.9	300–1900	400–5300	0.25–1.00	12.7	2.75-m heated length
	Bailey (1972)	16–18	80–800	670–2700	0.20–1.00	12.8	U tube
	Keeys et al. (1970)	6.9	800–1500	700–4100	0.15–0.90	12.7	Cosine heat flux distribution
	Bishop et al. (1964)	16.7–2.15	300–2000	700–3250	0.10–0.95	2.54, 5.08	
	Mueller (1967)	6.9	500–850	700–1000	0.62–1.00	15.7	Also measured vapor superheat
	Polomik (1967)	6.9	550–1100	700–1350	0.80–1.00	15.7	Also measured vapor superheat
	Brevi et al. (1969 a, b)	5.0	380–1500	470–3300	0.40–1.00	6.5, 9.3	Nonsteady temperature
	Bertoletti et al. (1974)	7.0	100–1600	1000–4000	0.40–0.90	5.0, 9.0	
	Era et al. (1967)	7.0	100–1300	1100–3000	0.20–1.00	16.	Data in graphic form
	Herkenrath et al. (1967)	13.8–25.0	100–2050	700–3250	0–1.00	10.0, 20.0	Data in graphic form; vertical and horizontal flow
	Swenson (1961)	20.7	280–570	950–1350	0.20–0.90	10.7	Indirectly heated (sodium-heated steam generator)
	Schmidt (1959)	21.5	320–850	420	0.10–0.90	8	Data must be derived from graphs
	Lee (1970)	14.0–18.0	300–1400	1000–4000	0.30–0.70	9, 13	
Annulus	Miropolskii (1963)	4–22	250–1100	1000–2000	0.20–1.00	8	
	Polomik et al. (1961)	5.5–9.7	600–2200	1000–2560	0.15–1.00	1.52, 3.05	Results affected by spacers
	Polomik et al. (1971)	6.9	750–2300	350–2700	0.15–0.65	3.38	
	Bennett et al. (1964)	3.5–6.9	600–1800	700–2700	0.20–1.00	3.3	
	Era et al. (1967)	7.0	130–1040	800–3800	0.30–1.00	2.5	Effect of spacers studied
	Era et al. (1971)	5.0	200–600	600–2200	0.20–0.90	3.0	Uniformly and nonuniformly heated
	Groeneveld (1969)	4.1–8.3	500–1400	1350–4100	0.10–0.50	4.05	Two heated sections separated by unheated section
Bundles	Hench (1964)	4.1–9.7	450–1900	390–2700	0.20–0.90	10.3	2-rod
	Kunsemiller (1965b)	4.1–9.7	550–1100	390–1350	0.30–0.70	11.2	3-rod
	Groeneveld et al. (1970)	6.3	330–1160	1100–2200	0.30–0.60	3.44	3-rod, effect of crud in-reactor experiment
	Adorni et al. (1966)	5.0–5.5	200–1500	800–3800	0.20–0.90		7-rod, mainly unsteady temperatures
	Matzner (1963a)	6.9	800–2350	700–2700	0.17–0.60	8.30	19-rod, mainly unsteady temperatures
	McPherson et al. (1971)	10.9–21.7	600–1450	700–4100	0.28–0.53	7.80	28-rod, mainly unsteady temperatures
	Matzner et al. (1968)	3.4–8.3	780–1150	700–1400	0.23–0.38	6.70	19-rod segmented bundle

[a] From Groeneveld (1973).

Empirical Correlations

A considerable number of empirical equations have been presented for the estimation of heat transfer rates in the postburnout region. Almost all of them are modifications of the well-known Dittus-Boelter relation for single-phase flow and take no account of the nonequilibrium effects discussed above. Various definitions of the "two-phase velocity" and physical properties are used in these modified forms. Table 6.5.3, also from Groeneveld's (1973) paper, lists 16 such correlations. Each of these correlations is based on a limited amount of experimental data, and Groeneveld therefore proposed a new correlation for each geometry optimized, using his bank of selected data.

The Groeneveld correlations for tubes and annuli have the form:

$$\mathrm{Nu}_G = a \left\{ \mathrm{Re}_G \left[x + \frac{\rho_G}{\rho_L} (1 - x) \right] \right\}^b \mathrm{Pr}_{G,w}^c Y^d \qquad [6.5.8]$$

where

$$Y = 1 - 0.1 \left(\frac{\rho_L}{\rho_G} - 1 \right)^{0.4} (1 - x)^{0.4} \qquad [6.5.9]$$

Nu_G is the Nusselt number; x is the quality; ρ_G and ρ_L are the densities of the gas and the liquid, respectively (kg/m^3); and the coefficients a, b, c, and d are given in table 6.5.4 together with the range of independent variables on which the correlations are based.

Slaughterbeck (1973a, b) examined the trends of Groeneveld's and other postburnout correlations and concluded that there were significant discrepancies between the correlations and between the correlations and experimental data. Figure 6.5.6 shows a comparison of the correlations with experimental data for one particular condition. This conclusion led Slaughterbeck to undertake a statistical regression of the Groeneveld data bank, which resulted in a modified form of the Groeneveld correlation that did not produce artificially high coefficients at low pressures:

$$\mathrm{Nu}_G = a \left\{ \mathrm{Re}_G \left[x + \frac{\rho_G}{\rho_L} (1 - x) \right] \right\}^b \mathrm{Pr}_{G,w}^c \dot{q}^e \left(\frac{\lambda_G}{\lambda_{\mathrm{crit}}} \right)^f \qquad [6.5.10]$$

where λ_{crit} is the thermal conductivity at the thermodynamic critical point.

Values of the coefficients for this modification are given in table 6.5.4. The revision makes a considerable difference at low pressure, as seen in figure 6.5.6.

Cumo and Urbani (1974) carried out postdryout experiments with identical test sections and instrumentation. They used a pressure of 7.0 MPa and a tube of 10 mm ID with a 4-m heated length. The scatter of the measured heat transfer coefficients was 10–25% with a mean of 17.9%. It was stated that agreement between these data and some published postburnout correlations was poor. However, the CNEN correlation gave good agreement:

$$\frac{\alpha(z)D}{\lambda_{G,f}} = 0.0089 \left(\frac{\dot{m}xD}{\alpha \mu_{G,f}} \right)^{0.84} \left(\frac{c_p \mu}{\lambda} \right)_{G,f}^{1/3} \left(\frac{1 - x_c}{x - x_c} \right)^{1/8} \qquad [6.5.11]$$

Table 6.5.3 Postburnout Correlations[a]

Equation and references	Range of applicability of equation				Equation agrees with data from references	Comments
	p (MPa)	$\dot{m}$ (kg/m² s)	x	Geometry		
$Nu_f = 0.00136\ Re_f^{0.853}\ Pr_f^{1/3} \left(\dfrac{x}{1-x}\right)^{0.147} \left(\dfrac{\rho_L}{\rho_G}\right)^{2/3}$ Polomik (1961)	5.5–10.0	1000–2450	0.40–0.70	Annulus	Polomik et al. (1961)	
$Nu_f = 0.416\ Re_f^{0.509}\ Pr_f^{1/3} \left(\dfrac{\rho_G}{\rho_L}\right)^{0.208} \left(\dfrac{1-x}{x}\right)^{0.616}$ Polomik (1961)	5.5–10.0	1000–2450	0.40–0.70		Polomik et al. (1961)	Exponents and coefficients for equations 1–3 obtained from least squares error analysis using data from Polomik et al. (1961)
$Nu_f = 0.0142\ Re_f^{0.292}\ Pr_f^{1/3} \left(\dfrac{1-x}{x}\right)^{0.01}$ $\cdot\ \dot{q}^{0.417} \left(\dfrac{\rho_L}{\rho_G}\right)^{0.091}$ $\dot{q}$ in W/m² Polomik (1961)	5.5–10.0	1000–2450	0.40–0.70		Polomik et al. (1961)	
$Nu_G = 0.00115\ Re_G^{0.9}\ Pr_G^{0.3} \left(\dfrac{T_W}{T_{sat}}-1\right)^{-0.15}$ T in °C Polomik (1967)	4–10	700–2700	0.20–1.00	2-rod	Hench (1964)	Has additional temperature parameter to allow for property variations at heater wall; $+20\%$ variation with data from Hench (1964)

Table 6.5.3 Postburnout Correlations[a] (Continued)

Equation and references	Range of applicability of equation				Equation agrees with data from references	Comments
	p (MPa)	$\dot{m}$ (kg/m² s)	x	Geometry		
$Nu_G = 0.0039 \left\{ Re_G \left[x + \dfrac{\rho_G}{\rho_L}(1-x) \right] \right\}^{0.9}$ Polomik (1967)	4–10	700–2700	0.20–1.00		Hench (1964)	± 10% variation with data from Hench (1964); better than equation above
$\dfrac{D_e^{0.2}}{\dot{q}(\dot{m}x)^{0.8}} = C(T_W - T_{sat})^m$ $\dot{q}$ in W/m² × 10⁻⁴ $\dot{m}$ in kg/m² s × 10⁻¹ D_e in m × 10⁻² T_W, T_{sat} in °C $m = 1.284 - 0.00312\,\dot{m}$ $C = \dfrac{1}{389}\, e^{0.01665\,\dot{m}}$ Collier (1962)	6.9	> 1000	0.15–1.00	Round tubes and annuli	Polomik et al. (1961) Bertoletti et al. (1961)	$T_W - T_{sat}$ must be below 200°C
$\dfrac{D_e^{0.2}}{\dot{q}(\dot{m}x)^{0.8}} = 0.018\,(T_W - T_{sat})^{0.921}$ Collier (1962)	6.9	See comments	0.15–1.00		Polomik et al. (1961) Bertoletti et al. (1961)	Correlations may be used if $\dot{m} < 1000$ kg/m² s or $T_W - T_{sat} > 200$°C
$Nu_f = 0.0193\, Re_f^{0.8}\, Pr_f^{1.23} \left(\dfrac{\rho_G}{\rho_L} \right)^{0.068} \left[x + \dfrac{\rho_G}{\rho_L}(1-x) \right]^{0.68}$ Bishop et al. (1965)	4–21.5	700–3400	0.07–1.00	Round tubes	Polomik et al. (1961) Bishop et al. (1965) Swenson et al. (1961)	

Bishop et al. (1965)

$$Nu_f = 0.033 \; Re_W^{0.8} \, Pr_W^{1.25} \left(\frac{\rho_G}{\rho_L}\right)^{0.197} \cdot \left[x + \frac{\rho_G}{\rho_L}(1-x)\right]^{0.738}$$

4–21.5	700–3400	0.07–1.00	Bishop et al. (1962) Bishop et al. (1964) Miropolskii (1963) — Based on high-pressure data

Bishop et al. (1964)

$$Nu_W = 0.098 \left\{ Re_W \frac{\rho_W}{\rho_G}\left[x + \frac{\rho_G}{\rho_L}(1-x)\right]\right\}^{0.8} \cdot Pr_W^{0.83}\left(\frac{\rho_G}{\rho_L}\right)^{0.50}$$

16.5–21.5	1350–3400	0.10–1.00	Swenson et al. (1961) Bishop et al. (1964) Miropolskii (1963)

Bishop et al. (1964)

$$Nu_W = 0.055 \left\{ Re_W \frac{\rho_W}{\rho_G}\left[x + \frac{\rho_G}{\rho_L}(1-x)\right]\right\}^{0.82} \cdot Pr_W^{0.96}\left(\frac{\rho_G}{\rho_L}\right)^{0.34}\left(1 + \frac{26.9}{L/D}\right)$$

16.5–21.5	1350–3400	0.10–1.00	Bishop et al. (1964)

Lee (1970)

$$T_W - T_{sat} = 1.975\left\{\frac{\dot{q}}{\dot{m}[x+(1-x)/4.15]}\right\}^2$$

14–18	1000–4000	0.30–0.75	Lee (1970) — Based on data obtained on 13-mm ID indirectly heated tube

Miropolskii (1963)

$$Nu_G = 0.023\left\{ Re_G\left[x + \frac{\rho_G}{\rho_L}(1-x)\right]\right\}^{0.8} Pr_W^{0.8} \, Y$$

$$Y = 1 - 0.1\left(\frac{\rho_L}{\rho_G}-1\right)^{0.4}(1-x)^{0.4}$$

4–22	700–2000	0.06–1.00	Swenson et al. (1961) Miropolskii (1963) Schmidt (1959) — Factor Y was determined empirically

Table 6.5.3 Postburnout Correlations[a] (*Continued*)

Equation and references	Range of applicability of equation				Equation agrees with data from references	Comments
	p (MPa)	$\dot{m}$ (kg/m² s)	x	Geometry		
$Nu_G = 0.0089 \left(Re_f \dfrac{x}{\alpha}\right)^{0.84} Pr_f^{1/3} \left(\dfrac{1-x_{BO}}{x-x_{BO}}\right)^{0.124}$ Brevi et al. (1969a, b)	5	500–3000	0.40–1.00		Brevi et al. 1969a, b)	
$Nu = 0.06 \left(\left\{Re_W\left[x+\dfrac{\rho_G}{\rho_L}(1-x)\right]\right\}\dfrac{\rho_W}{\rho_G}Pr_W\right)^{0.8}$ $\cdot \left(\dfrac{\dot{m}}{m_0}\right)^{0.4}\left(\dfrac{p}{p_c}\right)^{2.7}$ $m_0 = 1000$ kg/m² s Herkenrath et al. (1969, 1970)	14–22	750–4100	0.10–1.00		Herkenrath et al. (1967) Swenson et al. (1961) Bishop et al. (1964)	
$Nu_W = 0.005 \left(\dfrac{De\, u_m \rho_W}{\mu_W}\right)^{0.8} Pr_G^{0.5}$ Tong (1964)	> 13.8	> 700	< 0.10		Bishop et al. (1962, 1964)	Design equation; to be used only under low quality sub-cooled conditions

[a] From Groeneveld (1973).

e 6.5.4 Empirical Postburnout Correlations

eometry	a	b	c	d	e	f	Number of points	rms error (%)
				Groeneveld				
s	1.09×10^{-3}	0.989	1.41	-1.15			438	11.5
ıli	5.20×10^{-2}	0.688	1.26	-1.06			266	6.9
s and annuli	3.27×10^{-3}	0.901	1.32	-1.50			704	12.4
				Slaughterbeck				
s	1.16×10^{-4}	0.838	1.81		0.278	-0.508		12.0

Range of data on which correlations are based

netry	Tube	Annulus
direction	Vertical and horizontal	Vertical
ım	2.5–25	1.5–6.3
?a	6.8–21.5	3.4–10.0
ɡ/m² s	700–5300	800–4100
ction by weight	0.10–0.90	0.10–0.90
/m²	120–2100	450–2250
	95–1770	160–640
$[x + (1-x)\rho_G/\rho_L]$	$6.6 \times 10^4 – 1.3 \times 10^6$	$1.0 \times 10^5 – 3.9 \times 10^5$
	0.88–2.21	0.91–1.22
	0.706–0.976	0.610–0.963

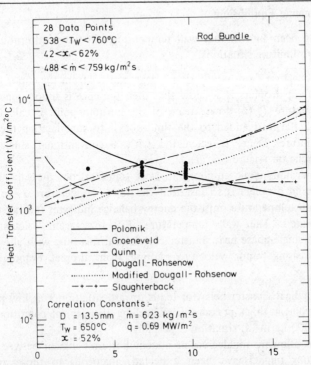

Figure 6.5.6 Heat transfer coefficient as a function of pressure (Slaughterbeck 1973a, b).

where α on the right-hand side of [6.5.11] is void fraction, μ is viscosity (Ns/m^2), and c_p is specific heat (J/kg K).

Mattson et al. (1974) extended the multiple linear regression analysis used by Slaughterbeck to cover the annulus and rod bundle geometries and the transition boiling region as well as the stable film boiling region. They recommended the following equations:

For film boiling in an internally heated annulus:

$$\alpha = 113.7 \ \text{Re}_G^{0.244} \ \text{Pr}_{G,w}^{2.54} \ D_{eq}^{-0.304} \ \lambda_G^{0.334} \qquad \text{(rms error 17.5\%)} \qquad [6.5.12]$$

For film and transition boiling in a tube or annular geometry:

$$\alpha = 5.16 \times 10^5 \ \exp{(-0.6708 \ \sqrt{\Delta T})}$$

$$+ \ 68.36 \ \text{Re}_G^{0.269} \ \text{Pr}_{G,w}^{3.67} \ D_{eq}^{-0.319} \ \lambda_G^{0.306} \ x^{-0.091} \qquad \text{(rms error 28.0\%)} \qquad [6.5.13]$$

For film and transition boiling in a rod bundle:

$$\alpha = 1.66 \times 10^5 \ \exp{(-0.6708 \ \sqrt{\Delta T})}$$

$$+ \ 5.164 \ \text{Re}_G^{0.505} \ \text{Pr}_{G,w}^{4.56} \ D_{eq}^{-0.160} \ \lambda_G^{0.189} \ x^{-0.113} \qquad \text{(rms error 25.8\%)} \qquad [6.5.14]$$

Use of these correlations outside the range of variables for the respective geometries given in table 6.5.2 is strongly discouraged.

Correlations Allowing for Departure from Thermodynamic Equilibrium

It has long been known that wall temperatures in the postburnout region are bounded by two limiting situations:

1. Complete departure from equilibrium. Heat transfer from the vapor phase to the entrained liquid droplets is so slow that their presence is simply ignored and the vapor temperature $T_G(z)$ downstream of the burnout point is calculated on the basis that all the heat added to the fluid goes into superheating the vapor. The wall temperature $T_W(z)$ is calculated with a conventional single-phase heat transfer correlation (figure 6.5.7a).

2. Complete thermodynamic equilibrium. Heat transfer from the vapor phase to be entrained liquid droplets is so fast that the vapor temperature $T_G(z)$ remains at the saturation temperature until the energy balance indicates that all the droplets have evaporated. The wall temperature $T_W(z)$ is again calculated with a conventional single-phase heat transfer correlation, this time with allowance made for the increasing vapor velocity resulting from droplet evaporation (figure 6.5.7b).

Postburnout heat transfer behavior tends toward situation 1 at low pressure and low velocity, while at high pressure (approaching the critical condition) and high flow rates (> 3000 kg/m^2 s) situation 2 pertains.

Correlations allowing for degrees of nonequilibrium behavior between these two limiting situations might have been expected, analogous to those available for

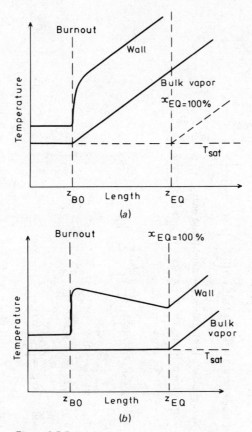

Figure 6.5.7 Limiting conditions for postburnout heat transfer,

subcooled void fraction. However, only in the past few years have such correlations appeared (table 6.5.5).

Consider figure 6.5.8, which represents the physical situation in the postburnout region for a vertical tube of diameter D heated uniformly with heat flux $\dot{q}$. Burnout occurs after length z_{BO}, and it is assumed that thermodynamic equilibrium exists at the burnout point. An energy balance indicates that all the liquid is evaporated by z_{EQ} if equilibrium is maintained. However, the actual situation depicted in figure 6.5.8. is one in which, following burnout, a fraction ϵ of the surface heat flux is used in evaporating liquid, while the remainder is used to superheat the bulk vapor. The liquid is completely evaporated a distance z^* from the tube entrance (downstream from z_{EQ}).

Let the surface heat flux $\dot{q}(z)$ be divided into two components, $\dot{q}_L(z)$, the heat flux associated with droplet evaporation, and $\dot{q}_G(z)$, the heat flux associated with vapor superheating:

$$\dot{q}(z) = \dot{q}_L(z) + \dot{q}_G(z) \qquad [6.5.15]$$

Table 6.5.5 Postburnout Correlations Allowing for Thermal Nonequilibrium

Reference	Fluid and range of conditions	Correlation
Plummer et al. (1974)	Water	Makes use of [6.5.15]–[6.5.22]
	Freon	Water: $\epsilon = 0.402 + 0.0674 \ln \left[\dot{m} \left(\dfrac{D}{\rho_G \sigma} \right)^{0.5} (1 - x_{BO})^5 \right]$
	Nitrogen	Freon: $\epsilon = 0.236 + 0.0811 \ln \left[\dot{m} \left(\dfrac{D}{\rho_G \sigma} \right)^{0.5} (1 - x_{BO})^5 \right]$
		Nitrogen: Data lies between water and Freon lines
Groeneveld & Delorme (1976)	Water	Correlation in terms of $x(z) - x^*(z) = (1 - \epsilon)\,[x(z) - x_{BO}]$
	$p = 4.1\text{–}20.5$ MPa	$x(z) - x^*(z) = \exp\left(-\tan \psi \right)$
	$\dot{m} = 270\text{–}5150$ kg/m^2 s	where $\psi = a_1 \, \mathrm{Pr}^{a_2} \, \mathrm{Re}_{tp}^{a_3} \left[\dfrac{\dot{q} D c_p}{\lambda_f f_G} \right]^{a_4} \displaystyle\sum_{i=0}^{i=2} b_i x_e(z)^i$
	$\dot{q} = 150\text{–}2700$ kW/m^2	if $\psi < 0 \quad \psi = 0$
	$x_E = 0.1\text{–}1.50$	$\psi > \pi/2 \quad \psi = \pi/2$
	$T_W = 400\text{–}845°$C	and $\mathrm{Re}_{tp} = \dfrac{GD}{\mu_G} \left\{ \dfrac{\mu_G}{\mu_G} \left[x(z) + \dfrac{\rho_G}{\rho_L} [1 - x(z)] \right] \right\}$
	1402 points	rms error on T_W: 6.7%
		$a_1 = 0.13864$
		$a_2 = 0.2031$
		$a_3 = 0.20006$
		$a_4 = -0.09232$
		$b_0 = 1.3072$
		$b_1 = -1.0833$
		$b_2 = 0.8455$

Jones & Zuber (1977)	Water Nitrogen	$\dfrac{d[x_E(z) - x^*(z)]}{dx_E(z)} + N_{SR} [x_E(z) - x^*(z)] = 1$

(where N_{SR} is the superheat relaxation number)

$P_r = 0.05–0.31$ MPa
$\dot{m} = 9.5–5200$ kg/m^2 s
$D = 5.8–12.4$ mm
$\dot{q} = 16–1836$ kW/m^2
$z = 1.21–5.53$ m
$z_{BO} = 0.05–5.53$ m
$x_E(z) = 0.13–3.2$
1755 points

$$\left[\text{implies that } N_{SR} = \frac{\epsilon}{x_E(z) - x^*(z)} \right]$$

$$N_{SR} = \frac{3}{2} \left(\frac{n\pi}{6} \right)^{2/3} \frac{\lambda_G Dif_G}{c_p G \dot{q} x^*(z)} \operatorname{Nu}_\delta (1 - \alpha)^{1/3}$$

$$N_{SR} = \begin{cases} 14.3 \, B_0 \left(\dfrac{S}{\sqrt{P_r}} \right)^2 & \dfrac{S}{\sqrt{P_r}} < 0.22 \\[3mm] 1.23 \, B_0 \left(\dfrac{S}{\sqrt{P_r}} \right)^{3/8} & \dfrac{S}{\sqrt{P_r}} > 0.22 \end{cases}$$

$$B_0 = \frac{\dot{m}}{\rho_L \sqrt{g\delta_0}} \qquad \frac{S}{\sqrt{P_r}} = \frac{3}{2} \left(\frac{n\pi}{6} \right)^{2/3} \frac{\lambda_G Dif_G}{c_p G \dot{q} x^*(z)\sqrt{P_r}} \operatorname{Nu}_\delta (1 - \alpha)^{1/3}$$

Chen et al. (1977)	Water 3641 points	Uses [6.5.15]; $\dot{q}(z) = \dot{q}_L(z) + \dot{q}_G(z)$

$\dot{q}_L(z) = \dot{q}_{LC}$ (droplet contact heat flux) $\times F_L$ (liquid contact area ratio)

$\dot{q}_{LC}$ given by three-step model similar to that of Iloeje et al. (1974)

$F_L = \exp \left[-A(\dot{m}) \sqrt{\Delta T_{sat}} \right]$

$\dot{q}_G(z) = \dot{q}_{GC}$ (convective heat flux to vapor) $\times (1 - F_L)$

$\dot{q}_{GC} = \alpha_G [T_W - T_G(z)]$ where $T_G(z)$ is the "true" vapor temperature

rms error 14.2% between measured and calculated heat fluxes

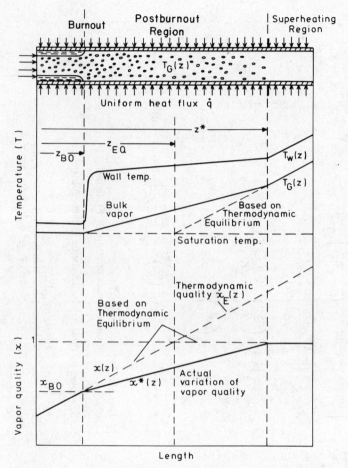

Figure 6.5.8 Departure from thermodynamic equilibrium in the postburnout region.

Let $\epsilon = \dot{q}_L(z)/\dot{q}(z)$; in general, ϵ can be considered a function of tube length z (or of local vapor quality x^*), but to keep the analysis simple we initially assume that ϵ is independent of tube length. This leads to the linear profiles of "actual" bulk vapor temperature and vapor quality with tube length shown in figure 6.5.8, rather than the smooth curves obtained experimentally (figure 6.5.9).

The "thermodynamic" vapor quality variation with length is given by

$$x(z) - x_{BO} = \frac{4\dot{q}}{D\dot{m}i_{fG}}(z - z_{BO}) \qquad [6.5.16]$$

for $z < z_{EQ}$, and z_{EQ} is given by

$$z_{EQ} = \frac{D\dot{m}i_{fG}}{4\dot{q}}(1 - x_{BO}) + z_{BO} \qquad [6.5.17]$$

where i_{fG} is the latent heat of vaporization (J/kg). The "actual" vapor quality variation with length is given by

$$x^*(z) - x_{BO} = \frac{4\dot{q}_L}{D\dot{m}i_{fG}}(z - z_{BO}) = \frac{4\epsilon\dot{q}}{D\dot{m}i_{fG}}(z - z_{BO}) \qquad [6.5.18]$$

for $z < z^*$, and z^* is given by

$$z^* = \frac{D\dot{m}i_{fG}}{4\epsilon\dot{q}}(1 - x_{BO}) + z_{BO} \qquad [6.5.19]$$

Thus from [6.5.16] and [6.5.17], ϵ is also given by

$$\epsilon = \frac{x^*(z) - x_{BO}}{x(z) - x_{BO}} = \frac{z^* - z_{BO}}{z_{EQ} - z_{BO}} \qquad [6.5.20]$$

Also, the actual bulk vapor temperature $T_G(z)$ is given by

$$T_G(z) = T_{sat} + \frac{4(1 - \epsilon)\dot{q}(z - z_{BO})}{\dot{m}c_{pG}D} \qquad [6.5.21]$$

for $z < z^*$ and

$$T_G(z) = T_{sat} + \frac{4\dot{q}(z - z_{EQ})}{\dot{m}c_{pG}D} \qquad [6.5.22]$$

for $z > z^*$. The two limiting conditions referred to above are recognized by setting ϵ equal to zero and unity, respectively.

Table 6.5.5 summarizes the correlations that allow for thermal nonequilibrium. In considering these correlations it is necessary to distinguish between the actual vapor quality $x^*(z)$, the thermodynamic vapor quality $x_E(z)$ (which can have a value greater than unity), and the equilibrium vapor quality $x(z)$ (which has a maximum value of unity and equals $x_E(z)$ for $z < z_{EQ}$) (figure 6.5.8).

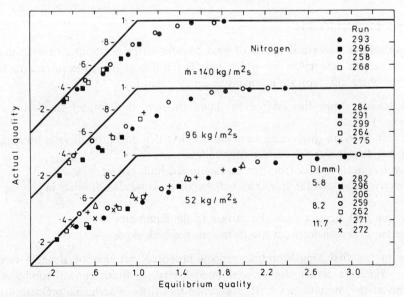

Figure 6.5.9 Actual versus equilibrium quality values for nitrogen at several mass fluxes (Forslund & Rohsenow 1966).

The Groeneveld & Delorme (1976) method is a significant improvement over the empircal correlations discussed earlier but appears to suffer from the disadvantage of having discontinuities in the slope of the $x^*(z)$ curve, both at the burnout point and at $x(z) = 1$.

The correlation by Jones & Zuber (1977) has the attraction that their first-order relaxation equation removes the restriction made earlier that ϵ is constant for any particular set of flow parameters. This assumption implies that the rate of return to equilibrium is constant, which is at variance with the facts (figure 6.5.9). The correlation of Chen et al. (1977) is probably the most comprehensive of this set of models but is consequently difficult to describe concisely. It is, however, strongly recommended.

Gardner (1974) considered in some detail the conditions under which a water droplet of a given size δ under equilibrium conditions is completely evaporated in a superheated steam flow. If the tube diameter is D and the wall heat flux is $\dot{q}$, then

$$\delta \left(\frac{\dot{q}}{D} \right)^{1/2} = \text{fn}(Z) \qquad [6.5.23]$$

where

$$Z = \Delta T_G \exp (0.209 p - 3.76) \qquad [6.5.24]$$

$$\text{fn}(Z) = 0.06 \, Z \, (1 - 0.509 \, Z^{0.109}) \qquad [6.5.25]$$

p is the system pressure (MPa), and ΔT_G is the vapor superheat corresponding to position z^*, i.e., $T_G(z^*) - T_{\text{sat}}$. The value of $T_G(z^*) - T_{\text{sat}}$ can therefore be conservatively calculated by estimating the maximum stable droplet size at the burnout condition and using [6.5.23]. This equation is valid for water only and is accurate for pressures from 4 to 18 MPa and superheats up to 50°C.

Semitheoretical Models

A comprehensive theoretical model of heat transfer in the postburnout region must take into account the paths by which heat is transferred from the surface to the bulk vapor phase. Six separate mechanisms can be identified:

1. Heat transfer from the surface to liquid droplets that impact the wall (wet collisions)
2. Heat transfer from the surface to liquid droplets that enter the thermal boundary layer but do not wet the surface (dry collisions)
3. Convective heat transfer from the surface to the bulk vapor
4. Convective heat transfer from the bulk vapor to suspended droplets in the vapor core
5. Radiation heat transfer from the surface to the liquid droplets
6. Radiation heat transfer from the surface to the bulk vapor

One of the first semitheoretical models proposed was that of Bennett et al. (1967a), which is a one-dimensional model starting from known equilibrium conditions at the burnout point. It is assumed that there is negligible pressure drop along the channel, that the wall surface temperature increases to such an extent that the droplets no longer wet the surface, and that the heat transfer coefficient between the wall and the fluid is given by one of the well-known single-phase relations. These assumptions mean that mechanisms 1 and 2 above were not considered.

The position of the burnout point must be known or calculated. At that point it is assumed that the liquid and vapor are in equilibrium and therefore the quality x_{BO} is known and the vapor is at the saturation temperature. To obtain the bulk vapor temperature downstream of the burnout point, four simultaneous differential equations are solved by the Runge-Kutta method. The first of these equations is a mass balance that gives the "true" vapor quality, assuming that the number N of droplets passing through a unit cross section per unit time does not change:

$$\frac{dx^*}{dz} = -\frac{N\pi\rho_L}{2\dot{m}}\delta^2\frac{d\delta}{dz} \qquad [6.5.26]$$

where

$$N = \frac{6\dot{m}(1-x_{BO})}{\pi\delta_{BO}^3\rho_L} \qquad [6.5.27]$$

The second equation is a heat balance that gives the "actual" bulk vapor temperature $T_G(z)$:

$$\frac{dT_G}{dz} = \frac{\dot{q}\pi D - A\dot{m}i_{fG}dx^*/dz}{A\dot{m}x^*c_{pG}} \qquad [6.5.28]$$

The third equation describes the acceleration of the droplets in the vapor stream, using Ingebo's (1956) drag coefficient:

$$\frac{du_\delta}{dz} = \frac{K_1(u_G-u_\delta)^{1.16}-g(1-\rho_G/\rho_L)}{u_\delta} \qquad [6.5.29]$$

where u_δ is the droplet velocity and u_G the vapor velocity, and

$$K_1 = 20.25\frac{\mu_G^{0.84}}{\rho_L}\frac{\rho_G^{0.16}}{\delta^{1.84}} \qquad [6.5.30]$$

The last equation describes the evaporation of the droplets by Ryley's (1961–1962) method:

$$\frac{d\delta}{dz} = \frac{2}{\delta}\frac{dr^2}{dt}\frac{1}{u_\delta} \qquad [6.5.31]$$

$$\frac{dr^2}{dt} = -\frac{2FMK_G(p_G-p_\infty)}{\rho_LRT_G} = -\frac{2\lambda_GF(T_G-T_{sat})}{\rho_Li_{fG}} \qquad [6.5.32]$$

where M is the molecular weight of the vapor, λ_G is the thermal conductivity of the vapor, δ is the ratio of the specific heat, ρ_G is the density of the vapor phase, p_G is the pressure in the droplet, T_{sat} is the saturation temperature at p_G, R is the universal gas constant, K_G is the self-diffusion coefficient in the vapor $[=M\lambda_G(\gamma-1)/\rho_GR]$, $r = \delta/2$, and

$$F = \text{"ventilation" factor} = 1 + 0.276\left[\frac{\rho_G(u_G-u_\delta)\delta}{\mu_G}\right]^{0.5}\left(\frac{\mu_G}{K_G\rho_G}\right)^{1/3}$$

Bennett et al. (1967a) compared estimates of surface temperature made by this method with experimental data taken in the liquid-deficient region for water evaporating at 6.9 MPa in a vertical tube 5.8 m long and 12.6 mm ID. Figure 6.5.10 shows this comparison for three different values of mass velocity. A reasonable fit was obtained with an assumed droplet size at the burnout point δ_{BO} of about 300 μm. It was originally assumed that there was negligible pressure drop along the channel, but Groeneveld (1972) revised the equations to allow for pressure gradient and flashing effects.

More recently, Iloeje et al. (1974) proposed a three-step model taking into account mechanisms 1–3. The physical picture they postulated is shown in figure 6.5.11. Liquid droplets of various sizes are entrained in the vapor core and have random motion due to interactions with eddies. Some droplets arrive at the edge of the boundary layer with sufficient momentum to contact the wall, even allowing for the fact that, as the droplet approaches the wall, differential evaporation coupled with the physical presence of the wall leads to a resultant force trying to repel the droplet (Gardner 1974). When the droplet touches the wall a contact boundary temperature is set up that depends on the initial droplet and wall temperatures and on $\sqrt{(\lambda \rho c)_L} / \sqrt{(\lambda \rho c)_W}$ (section 6.5.2). If this temperature is less than some limiting superheat for the liquid, then heat is transferred, first by conduction until a thermal boundary layer is built up that is sufficient to satisfy the conditions for bubble nucleation. Bubbles grow within the droplet, ejecting part of the liquid back into the vapor stream. The remaining liquid is not sufficiently thick to support

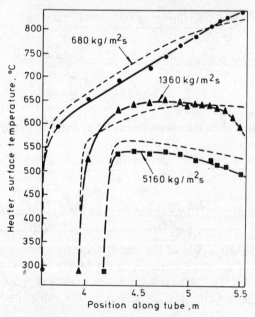

Figure 6.5.10 Experimental and calculated temperature profiles for heat transfer to steam-water mixtures in the liquid-deficient condition (Bennett et al. 1967a).

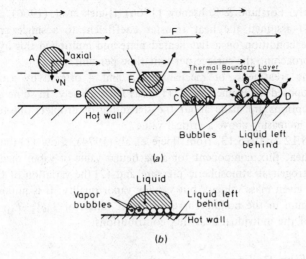

A   Liquid drop entering thermal boundary layer with velocity v_N normal to wall
B   Liquid drop of higher kinetic energy based on v_N, arriving on wall and beginning to absorb heat from wall via conduction
C   Nucleation and bubble growth from liquid drop on wall
D   End of bubble growth period, part of liquid drop is ejected into the mainstream by escaping vapor bubbles, part is left on wall to evaporate
E   Liquid drop of lower kinetic energy in thermal boundary layer and ageing reversed into the main flow without touching the wall
F   Bulk vapor flow

Figure 6.5.11 Dispersed-flow heat transfer model (Iloeje et al. 1974). (a) Dispersed-flow heat transfer process. (b) Idealized bubble geometry at end of bubble growth—square array.

nucleation and therefore remains until it is totally evaporated. The surface heat flux transferred by this mechanism can be arrived at by estimating the product of the heat transferred to a single drop and the number of droplets per unit time and per unit area that strike the wall. Iloeje et al. attempted to quantify the various mechanisms identified above and arrived at a somewhat complex expression for the droplet-wall contact heat flux $\dot{q}_{dc}$.

The droplet mass flux to the wall can be estimated from one of a number of turbulent deposition models (Hutchinson et al. 1971). It is important to appreciate that at very low values of $T_W - T_{sat}$ the heat flux $\dot{q}_{dc}$ predicted from the Iloeje model must coincide with the droplet deposition flux contribution of the Hewitt film flow model of dryout. The trends with vapor quality and mass velocity appear qualitatively correct, but a rigorous quantitative comparison with, for example, the prediction of Whalley et al. (1973) is needed for a range of working fluids.

Two basic approaches have been taken to estimate the heat flux $\dot{q}_{dow}$ to droplets that enter the thermal boundary layer but do not touch the wall. This heat flux can be estimated as the product of the heat flux that would occur across a vapor film separating the droplet from the heating surface and the fractional area covered by such droplets. This approach was adopted with slight modifications by Iloeje et al. (1974), Groeneveld (1972), Plummer et al. (1974), and Chen et al. (1977).

Alternatively, Forslund & Rohsenow (1966), Hynek et al. (1966), and Course & Roberts (1974) assumed the heat transfer coefficient to a single droplet in the spheroidal state condition on a flat heated plate and multiplied this by the number of droplets approaching the surface per unit time per unit area.

Finally, the treatments of mechanisms 3 and 4 offered by various workers follow that proposed by Bennett et al. (1967a) fairly closely. In some cases, slightly different assumptions are made about the shattering of droplets due to the droplet Weber number increasing above a critical value.

Figures 6.5.12 and 6.5.13, from Iloeje et al. (1974), show (1) the variation of each separate heat flux component for a particular value of vapor quality and mass velocity for nitrogen at atmospheric pressure and (2) the variation of the total heat flux curve at a given mass velocity but varying vapor quality. It is important to note that the minimum in the boiling curve occurs at values of $T_W - T_{sat}$ that depend on the values of the individual heat flux contributions.

6.5.1.5 Film Boiling

The conditions under consideration are illustrated in figure 6.5.14. The study of forced convective film boiling inside vertical tubes by Dougall & Rohsenow (1963) included visual observations of the flow structure. At low qualities and mass flow rates the flow regime appears to be an "inverted annular" one with liquid in the center and a thin vapor film adjacent to the heating surface. The vapor-liquid interface is not smooth, but irregular. These irregularities occur at random locations, but appear to retain their identity to some degree as they pass up the tube with velocities of the same order as that of the liquid core. The vapor in the film adjacent to the heating surface appears to travel at a higher velocity. The liquid core

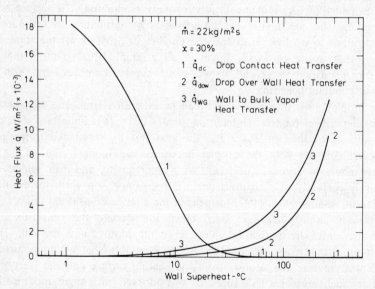

Figure 6.5.12 Behavior of components of total heat flux with quality at a mass velocity of 22 kg/m² s; the fluid is nitrogen (Iloeje et al. 1974).

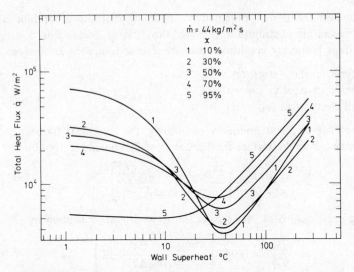

Figure 6.5.13 Theoretical boiling curves at a mass velocity of 44 kg/m²
s; the fluid is nitrogen (Iloeje et al. 1974).

may be in up flow, stationary, or in down flow. Vapor bubbles may be present in
the liquid core but have little influence except to modify the core velocity and
density, which determine the interfacial shear stress.

Simple Theories

Because the liquid is displaced from the heating surface by a vapor film and the
uncertainties associated with bubble nucleation are removed, film boiling is very
amenable to analytical solution. In general, the problem is treated as an analog of
filmwise condensation and solutions are available for horizontal and vertical flat
surfaces and also inside tubes under both laminar and turbulent conditions with and
without interfacial shear (Clements & Colver 1970; Hsu 1972; Bressler 1972;
Groeneveld & Gardiner 1977).

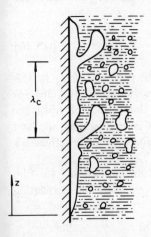

Figure 6.5.14 Schematic representation of low-quality
postburnout condition.

The simplest solution is obtained by assuming that the vapor film is laminar and the temperature distribution through the film is linear. For a vertical flat surface, various boundary conditions may be imposed on such an analysis, namely

1. Zero interfacial shear stress ($\tau_I = 0$)
2. Zero interfacial velocity ($u_I = 0$)
3. Zero wall shear stress ($\tau_W = 0$)

For the first of these boundary conditions, the local heat transfer coefficient $\alpha(z)$ at a distance z up the surface from the start of film boiling is given by

$$\frac{\alpha(z)z}{\lambda_G} = \left[\frac{z^3 g \rho_G(\rho_L - \rho_G)i'_{fG}}{4\lambda_G \mu_G \Delta T}\right]^{1/4} \qquad [6.5.33]$$

The average coefficient $\bar{\alpha}(z)$ over the region up to distance z is given by

$$\frac{\bar{\alpha}(z)z}{\lambda_G} = 0.943 \left[\frac{z^3 g \rho_G(\rho_L - \rho_G)i'_{fG}}{\lambda_G \mu_G \Delta T}\right]^{1/4} \qquad [6.5.34]$$

Define $\qquad \mathrm{Pr}^* = \dfrac{\mu_G i_{fG}}{\lambda_G \Delta T} \qquad \mathrm{Gr}^* = \dfrac{z^3 g \rho_G(\rho_L - \rho_G)}{\mu_G^2}$

$$\overline{\mathrm{Nu}_z} = \frac{\bar{\alpha}(z)z}{\lambda_G}$$

Then $\qquad\qquad\qquad \overline{\mathrm{Nu}_z} = C\,(\mathrm{Pr}^*\,\mathrm{Gr}^*)^{1/4} \qquad [6.5.35]$

Note the analogy with natural convection. The value of C for the first of these boundary conditions is 0.943 and for the second is 0.667. Typical values of heat transfer coefficient have been calculated from [6.5.33] for water over the pressure range 0.1–7.0 MPa for a distance z assumed to be 0.5 m (order of magnitude of grid spacing on a water reactor fuel element) and a temperature difference ΔT of 200 K (figure 6.5.15).

A similar analysis (Wallis & Collier 1968) may be carried out for the assumption of turbulent flow in the vapor film. In this case, for a vertical flat surface

$$\frac{\bar{\alpha}(z)z}{\lambda_G} = 0.056\,\mathrm{Re}_G^{0.2}\,(\mathrm{Pr}\,\mathrm{Gr}^*)^{1/3} \qquad [6.5.36]$$

Note that the coefficient is approximately constant, independent of z, in this equation. Typical values of heat transfer coefficient calculated from [6.5.36] for $\mathrm{Re}_G = 10^4$ are also shown in figure 6.5.15. Because of the neglect of resistance between the vapor film and the interface and the effect of interfacial drag, the heat transfer coefficients computed from [6.5.36] may be somewhat higher than the measured values.

In RELAP4 (Moore & Rettig 1973), the Berenson (1961) correlation for film boiling on a horizontal flat plate is used for a stagnation condition. This correlation is very similar in form to [6.5.33]:

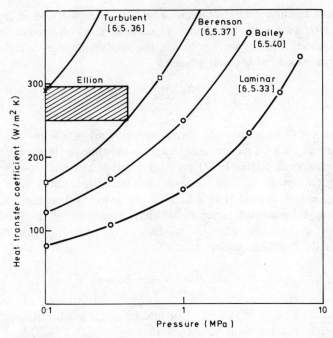

Figure 6.5.15 Film boiling heat transfer coefficients for water.

$$\alpha = 0.425 \left[\frac{\lambda_G^3 g \rho_G (\rho_L - \rho_G) i'_{fG}}{\mu_G \Delta T (\lambda_c / 2\pi)} \right]^{1/4} \qquad [6.5.37]$$

The thin vapor film over the horizontal surface is unstable and large bubbles form and break away. The characteristic spacing of these bubbles λ_c is determined by a balance of surface tension (σ) and gravitational (g) forces and is given by

$$\frac{\lambda_c}{2\pi} = \left[\frac{\sigma}{g(\rho_L - \rho_G)} \right]^{1/2} \qquad [6.5.38]$$

Values calculated for water from [6.5.37] are given in figure 6.5.15.

On vertical heated surfaces the vapor film also appears to break away from the wall in large globular voids and attempts have been made to produce an equation that is more consistent with this physical behavior than [6.5.33]. Bailey (1971) suggested that the globular voids are formed by "varicose" instability of a hollow gas cylinder within a denser liquid, as proposed by Chandrasekhar (1961). The wavelength for maximum growth for a surface tension-governed instability of this type is

$$\frac{\lambda_c}{2\pi} = \frac{r}{0.484} \qquad [6.5.39]$$

Substitution of λ_c from this equation for z in [6.5.33] leads to

$$\alpha = \left[\frac{\lambda_G^3 g \rho_G (\rho_L - \rho_G) i'_{fG}}{\mu_G \Delta T r} \right]^{1/4} \qquad [6.5.40]$$

where r is the fuel rod radius. Values of α calculated for water, assuming $r = 8$ mm, are given in figure 6.5.15. An alternative suggestion, which predicts heat transfer coefficients about 33% higher, is to use the original Bromley equation for film boiling on the outside of horizontal tubes:

$$\alpha = 0.62 \left[\frac{\lambda_G^3 g \rho_G (\rho_L - \rho_G) i_{fG}'}{\mu_G \Delta T D} \right]^{1/4} \qquad [6.5.41]$$

Some evidence that this gives the correct order of magnitude for the film boiling coefficient during reflood experiments was given by Amm & Ulrych (1974).

Suryanarayana & Merte (1972) provided a turbulent boundary-layer analysis of film boiling on vertical surfaces that assumes a zero vapor-liquid interface velocity ($u_I = 0$) and empirically takes into account the effect of interface oscillations by the use of an enhancement factor B, which is a measure of the increase in heat transfer over the smooth interface solution. B is related to the dimensionless amplitude of the interface oscillation $b(z)$ by

$$B = \frac{\alpha}{\alpha_{\text{smooth}}} = \frac{1}{\sqrt{1 - b(z)^2}} \qquad [6.5.42]$$

An empirical correlation of B with vapor film Reynolds number Re_G gave values of B around 2-2.5 for a Reynolds number of 10^3.

Another study of vertical film boiling that takes account of the time-varying vapor thickness as large vapor bubbles are released from the film is that of Greitzer & Abernathy (1972). This study also indicates that the smooth interface laminar flow solution [6.5.33] predicts a value that is too low by approximately 2. The effects of subcooling and liquid velocity are also established for methanol over a wide range of values. Typically, increasing the liquid velocity from 0 to 5 m/s or the subcooling from 0 to 20°C might double the heat transfer coefficient in each case.

The evidence at present is that laminar film boiling with a smooth interface occurs only over relatively short distances (~ 5 cm) downstream of the dryout or rewet front. At longer distances the coefficient becomes independent of distance and takes on a value considerably (approximately a factor of 2) higher than the laminar solution would indicate. The exact amount is a relatively weak function of the vapor film Reynolds number.

There is experimental evidence that film boiling heat transfer coefficients in down flow may be lower than those in up flow. This phenomenon was first observed by Papell (1970, 1971) with nitrogen and hydrogen and has been confirmed by Newbold et al. (1976) with water.

The maximum effect of buoyancy in reducing film boiling heat transfer coefficients is seen under conditions where the down-flow velocity is equal to the bubble drift flux velocity. This observation allowed Bjornard & Griffith (1977) to rewrite the recommended postburnout heat transfer correlations in terms of the drift flux model to account for the directional influence at low velocities.

6.5.2 HEAT TRANSFER DURING QUENCHING AND REFLOODING

6.5.2.1 Introduction

The need to guarantee the cooling of water-cooled reactor fuel elements during an LOCA has prompted considerable research into the quenching process. Quenching is a transient process that occurs when an initially very hot metal surface is exposed to a coolant. In the case of a tube, an annulus, or a rod bundle fuel element, the coolant may be admitted either from above—*top flooding*—or from the base of the channel—*bottom flooding*. Sometimes both methods are used simultaneously.

Figure 6.5.16 depicts the physical processes that occur in the case of top flooding. Initial cooling at the top of the channel allows a liquid film to form. This film begins to run down the surface. However, at some point the film is violently thrown off the surface. This ejection of the film from the rod has been termed sputtering. The sputtering point or the quench front divides the dry-wall, high-temperature region of the channel from the wet-wall, low-temperature region. It is observed that the quench front proceeds down the tube at a uniform velocity that is a function of the initial surface temperature T_W and other factors.

The vapor formed by the quenching process escapes upward out of the channel. However, if the channel is restricted and the vapor generation rate large, the rate of access of liquid to the channel may be limited by the flooding mechanism, as indicated in figure 6.5.16.

Figure 6.5.17 shows experimental measurements by Bennett et al. (1966) of the quench front velocity for a water film advancing down a vertical rod. The inverse quench velocity $(1/u)$ was found to vary with initial rod temperature and system pressure. The inverse extrapolated quench front velocity lines intersect the horizontal axis at a finite wall temperature. It was suggested that this temperature is

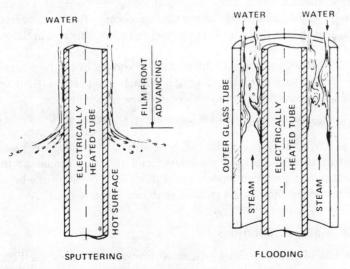

Figure 6.5.16 Physical processes during top flooding of a hot rod.

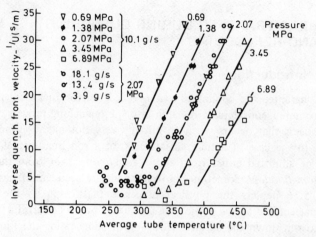

Figure 6.5.17 Experimental quench front velocity results of Bennett et al. (1966) for top flooding.

related to the so-called sputtering temperature just at the quench front. In fact, Bennett et al. extrapolated not to the horizontal axis but to the value 4 s/m, where the quench rate became independent of wall temperature.

The physical processes that occur with bottom flooding are different, depending on whether the rate of admission of coolant to the channel is high or low (figure 6.5.18). At low flooding rates an annular flow region is formed with the quench front being marked by the burnout transition between the hot-wall, liquid-deficient region and the climbing liquid film. Other nucleate boiling regimes occur upstream of the quench front. At high flooding rates the liquid level in the channel rises more rapidly than the quench front and a region of film boiling (inverted annular region) is formed. The quench front is marked in this instance by the point of collapse of the thin vapor film. At both low and high flooding rates a significant amount of entrainment of the coolant in the vapor stream occurs. This entrained coolant is ineffective in that it is carried out of the channel and takes little part in the quenching process.

At high flooding rates a significant amount of cooling of the tube occurs in the film boiling region just downstream of the quench front. Hsu (1975) correlated experimental heat transfer data during reflooding experiments by

$$\alpha = 1.33 \times 10^5 \, p^{0.558} \exp\left(-0.016 \, p^{0.1733} \Delta T_{sat}\right) \qquad [6.5.43]$$

where α is in kW/m^2 K, ΔT_{sat} in K, and p in MPa. This equation is based on the assumption that there is no axial conduction and therefore should be used only with one-dimensional rewetting models (see below). The equation can be combined with a fully developed film boiling relation as shown in figure 6.5.19.

6.5.2.2 Analytic Solutions

Analytic models of the quenching process all involve solution of the Fourier heat conduction equation for specified boundary conditions representative of the heat

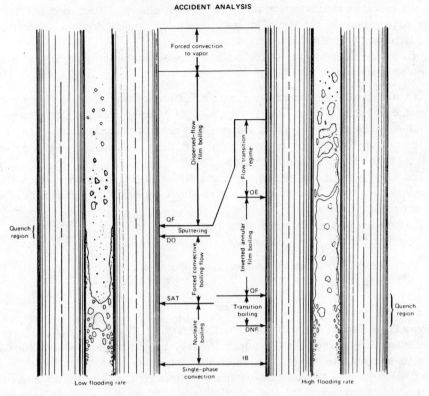

Figure 6.5.18 Physical processes during bottom flooding of a hot rod (Elias & Yadigaroglu 1978).

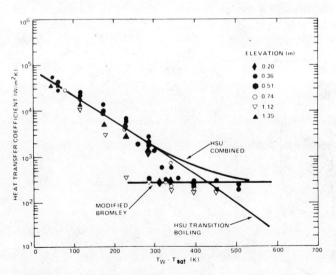

Figure 6.5.19 Correlation of transition and film boiling during bottom reflooding (Hsu 1975).

transfer processes at the surface of the solid. The validity of such models depends to a large extent on the choice of realistic boundary conditions and the methods used to solve the conduction equation.

To make the problem tractable simplifications are often introduced, such as the following assumptions:

1. The solid is a homogeneous slab (figure 6.5.20) of infinite height in the direction of the advancing quench front (z direction), of uniform thickness δ (y direction), and with constant (temperature-independent) physical properties.
2. The dry side of the slab is insulated ($y = 0$), the wet side is cooled ($y = \delta$), and there is no heat generation within the solid.
3. The liquid wets the surface up to the axial location ($z = 0$) where the surface temperature equals the sputtering temperature (T_0) which is a constant independent of time or position.
4. The position of the advancing quench front varies as a function of time only in the z direction; i.e., the problem is strictly two-dimensional.

With this simplification, the conduction equation reduces to

$$\frac{\partial^2 T}{\partial y^2} + \frac{\partial^2 T}{\partial z^2} = \frac{1}{\kappa} \frac{\partial T}{\partial t} \qquad [6.5.44]$$

where κ is the thermal diffusivity of the wall (m^2/s).

Duffey & Porthouse (1973) solved [6.5.44] by the method of separation of variables and obtained a set of eigenfunctions on either side of the quench front ($z = 0$). The form of the solution obtained implies that the velocity of the quench front u is constant provided the specified boundary conditions do not vary with time. Under these circumstances a further simplification can be made, namely the assumption that u is constant and the temperature distribution is invariant with respect to the advancing quench front:

$$\frac{\partial T}{\partial t} = - u \frac{\partial T}{\partial t} \qquad [6.5.45]$$

Hence

$$\frac{\partial^2 T}{\partial y^2} + \frac{\partial^2 T}{\partial z^2} = - \frac{u}{\kappa} \frac{\partial T}{\partial z} \qquad [6.5.46]$$

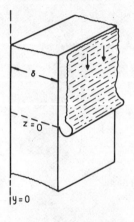

Figure 6.5.20 Coordinate system used in rewetting models.

The boundary conditions are

$$T = T_s \quad \text{the liquid coolant temperature at } z = -\infty$$

$$T = T_W \quad \text{the initial wall temperature at } z = +\infty$$

$$\left.\begin{array}{l} \dfrac{\partial T}{\partial y} = 0 \quad \text{at } y = 0 \\[4mm] -\lambda \dfrac{\partial T}{\partial y} = \alpha(z)\,(T - T_s) \quad \text{at } y = \delta \end{array}\right\} \qquad [6.5.47]$$

The sputtering temperature is the temperature at which a discontinuity in the value of $\alpha(z)$ occurs.

In nondimensional form [6.5.46] becomes

$$\frac{\partial^2 \theta}{\partial \eta^2} + \frac{\partial^2 \theta}{\partial \zeta^2} + \text{Pe}\,\frac{\partial \theta}{\partial \eta} = 0 \qquad [6.5.48]$$

where
$$\theta = \frac{T - T_s}{T_0 - T_s} \qquad \eta = \frac{z}{\delta} \qquad \zeta = \frac{y}{\delta}$$

$$\text{Bi} = \frac{\alpha(z)\delta}{\lambda} \qquad \text{Pe} = \frac{u\delta}{\kappa}$$

and the boundary conditions become

$$\theta = 0 \quad \text{at } \eta = -\infty$$

$$\theta = \theta_W \left(= \frac{T_W - T_s}{T_0 - T_s} \right) \quad \text{at } \eta = +\infty$$

$$\frac{\partial \theta}{\partial \zeta} = 0 \quad \text{at } \zeta = 0 \qquad [6.5.49]$$

$$\frac{\partial \theta}{\partial \zeta} = -\,\text{Bi}\,\theta \quad \text{at } \zeta = 1$$

This nondimensional analysis shows that, in general, the conduction solution depends on the Biot and Peclet numbers Bi and Pe and on the dimensionless temperature ratio θ.

One-dimensional Solutions

Assume that the boundary conditions are such that the temperature of the slab is uniform across its thickness at any value of z and a one-dimensional solution may be obtained. In this case

$$\frac{\partial^2 T}{\partial y^2} \cong -\frac{\alpha(z)}{\lambda \delta}\,(T - T_s) \qquad [6.5.50]$$

and [6.5.46] reduces to

$$\frac{d^2 T}{dz^2} + \frac{u}{\kappa}\frac{dT}{dz} - \frac{\alpha(z)}{\lambda \delta}\,(T - T_s) = 0 \qquad [6.5.51]$$

or in a nondimensional form:

$$\frac{d^2\theta}{d\eta^2} + \text{Pe}\,\frac{d\theta}{d\eta} - \text{Bi}\,\theta = 0 \qquad [6.5.52]$$

The general solution of this equation was given by Elias & Yadigaroglu (1977) as

$$\theta = a\,\exp\left(-\gamma\,\text{Pe}\,\frac{\eta}{2}\right) + b\,\exp\left(-\beta\,\text{Pe}\,\frac{\eta}{2}\right) \qquad [6.5.53]$$

where a and b are coefficients and

$$\gamma = 1 - \left(1 + 4\,\frac{\text{Bi}}{\text{Pe}^2}\right)^{1/2} < 0$$

$$\beta = 1 + \left(1 + 4\,\frac{\text{Bi}}{\text{Pe}^2}\right)^{1/2} > 0$$

Such a solution is valid for Pe < 1 and Bi < 1.

The various one-dimensional solutions differ only in the assumption made about the variation of $\alpha(z)$ in front of and behind the quench front. In general, the slab is divided into an arbitrary number of axial regions relative to the quench front and the value of $\alpha(z)$ for each region is specified. The separate conduction equations are solved and the solutions matched by requiring continuity of axial heat flux and temperature at the boundaries between the regions. The one-dimensional models are summarized in table 6.5.6, from Elias & Yadigaroglu (1978).

In the models of Semeria & Martinet (1966) and Yamanouchi (1968), only two axial regions are assumed: a dry region ahead of the quench front where $\alpha(z)$ equals zero and a wet region behind the quench front where $\alpha(z)$ is high but constant. For these assumptions the solution of [6.5.53] is

$$\sqrt{\frac{\text{Bi}}{\text{Pe}}} = [\theta_W(\theta_W - 1)]^{1/2} \qquad [6.5.54]$$

or in terms of the quench front velocity u:

$$\frac{1}{u} = \frac{\rho c_p}{2}\left[\frac{\delta}{\alpha(z)\lambda}\right]^{1/2}\left\{\left[\frac{2(T_W - T_0)}{T_0 - T_s} + 1\right]^2 - 1\right\}^{1/2} \qquad [6.5.55]$$

To fit [6.5.55] to measured quench front velocities, Yamanouchi (1968) had to introduce very high values for $\alpha(z)$ in the wet region, $\sim 10^6$ W/m^2 K. Such extreme values are not encountered in steady-state boiling siutations, although it is not inconceivable that they occur under transient conditions.

Later analyses introduced more complex variations of $\alpha(z)$ with position relative to the quench front. Sun et al. (1975) examined the effect of allowing for some cooling of the surface ahead of the quench front (so-called precursory cooling). In a separate paper, Sun et al. (1974) introduced a three-region model in which a high heat transfer coefficient, $\sim 2 \times 10^4$ W/m^2 K, was required over a short region, the sputtering region, immediately behind the quench front. The most recent model is that of Elias & Yadigaroglu (1977), which generalizes this approach and uses as

Table 6.5.6 One-dimensional Axial Conduction Models[a]

Reference	Experimental data correlated	Heat transfer coefficient $\alpha(z)$ (W/m² °C)	Sputtering temperature (T_0) (°C)	Comments and heat transfer coefficient profile
Yamanouchi (1968) Semeria & Martinet (1966)	Yamanouchi (1968)	$\alpha_2 = 2 \times 10^5 - 10^6$ $\alpha_3 = 0$	150	(α_2, α_3 profile)
Sun et al. (1975)	Yamanouchi (1968) Duffey & Porthouse (1973)	$\alpha_2 = 1.7 \times 10^4$ $\dfrac{\alpha_3}{N} = e^{-0.05z}$	260	Precursory cooling included (α_2, α_3 profile)
Sun et al. (1974)	Yamanouchi (1968) Duffey & Porthouse (1973) (only low-flow-rate data)	$\alpha_1 = 570$ (?) $\alpha_2 = 1.7 \times 10^4$ $\alpha_3 = 0$	260	Sputtering region between location of incipience of boiling and quench front (α_1, α_2, α_3 profile)
Chun & Chon (1975)	Case et al. (1973)	$\alpha_2 = 2.56 \times 10^4$ $\alpha_2 = 170$ $\alpha_4 = 0$	260	Calculated length of dispersed-flow region and mass carry-over to correlate α_3 (α_2, α_3, α_4 profile)
Ishii (1975)	Bennett et al. (1966)	$\alpha_1 = \alpha_c$ $\alpha_2 = 4 \times 10^5$ $\alpha_5 = 0$	260–390	1. Sputtering region between dryout and quench front 2. Correlated a pressure range 0.69–6.9 MPa 3. Defined thermal penetration length in sputtering region (α_1, α_2, α_3 profile)

Table 6.5.6 One-dimensional Axial Conduction Models[a] (*Continued*)

Reference	Experimental data correlated	Heat transfer coefficient $\alpha(z)$ (W/m² °C)	Sputtering temperature (T_0) (°C)	Comments and heat transfer coefficient profile
Thompson (1972)	Bennett et al. (1966)	$\alpha_1, \alpha_2, \approx 7 \times 10^6$ (peak values) $\alpha_3 = 0$	$T_s + 100$	High-pressure data 0.69–6.9 MPa $\alpha_2 = R\,\Delta T_s^3$
Elias & Yadigaroglu (1977)	Duffey & Porthouse (1973) (only low-flow-rate data)	$\alpha_1 = 170$ $\alpha_2, \alpha_3, \alpha_4, \ldots =$ boiling curve approximation	260	
Andréoni (1975)	Andréoni (1975)	α_1 from Jens-Lottes correlation α_2 extracted from rewetting data α_3 from experimental data	$T_s + 200$	
Yao (1976)	None			Constant internal heat generation included; assumes parabolic radial temperature profile

[a]From Elias & Yadigaroglu (1978).

many as 12 axial regions. Experimental quench front velocity data were well correlated with conventional boiling curve approximations for the heat transfer coefficient and a realistic value for the sputtering temperature. Figure 6.5.21 shows some typical results for Zircaloy 4, Inconel 600, and stainless steel. The Elias-Yadigaroglu model was also extended to allow for heat generation in the slab wall and heat transfer to the previously insulated internal wall ($y = 0$) to simulate decay heat being transferred from a fuel pellet across a gap between the pellet and the fuel cladding.

Two-dimensional Solutions

To apply one-dimensional solutions to correlate experimental data obtained at high Biot and Peclet numbers it is necessary to overestimate both the wet region heat transfer coefficient and the sputtering temperature. Two-dimensional solutions, where the slab temperature is considered a function of both z and y, are required for more realistic models.

Because of the complications involved in obtaining an accurate two-dimensional solution, the axial variation of $\alpha(z)$ is usually treated very simply, with a dry region ahead of the quench front where $\alpha(z)$ equals zero and a wet region behind the quench front where $\alpha(z)$ is high but constant. Table 6.5.7, from Elias & Yadigaroglu (1978), summarizes the various models.

Duffey & Porthouse (1973) solved [6.5.46] by the method of separation of variables and obtained the temperature distribution in the wet and dry regions in the form of infinite series. The first term of the series for the wet side was combined with a simple heat balance for this region. For small Biot numbers their solution reduces to the one-dimensional approximation [6.5.54]. For Bi $\gg$ 1:

$$\frac{\text{Bi}}{\text{Pe}} = \frac{\pi \theta_W}{2} \left(1 - \frac{4}{\pi^2} \frac{\text{Bi}}{\theta_W}\right)^{1/2} \qquad [6.5.56]$$

For the quench front velocity u to be real for typical values of θ_W, Bi $\leqslant$ 7, so that [6.5.56] is valid for $7 \gg$ Bi $\gg$ 1.

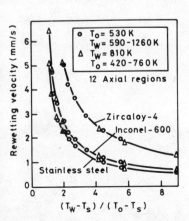

Figure 6.5.21 Rewetting velocity calculated by the model of Elias & Yadigaroglu (1977).

Table 6.5.7 Two-dimensional Rewetting Models[a]

Reference	Experimental data correlated	Heat transfer coefficient $\alpha(z)$ (W/m² °C)	Sputtering temperature (T_0) (°C)	Comments and heat transfer coefficient profile
Duffey & Porthouse (1973)	Yoshioka & Hasegawa (1970) Yamanouchi (1968) Duffey & Porthouse (1973) Andréoni (1975) Martini & Premoli (1972) Thompson (1972) Campanile & Pozzi (1972)	$\alpha_2 = 10^4 - 2 \times 10^6$ $\alpha_3 = 0$	190–250	α_2 α_3
Coney (1974a)	Bennett et al. (1966)	$\alpha_2 = 0.94 - 1.3 \times 10^6$ $\alpha_3 = 0$	$T_s + 68$	Pressure range 0.69–6.9 MPa α_2 α_3
Blair (1975)	Thompson (1974)	$\alpha_2 = 1.7 \times 10^4$ $\alpha_3 = 0$	260	Cylindrical geometry α_2 α_3
Yeh (1975)	None			Cylindrical geometry α_2 α_3

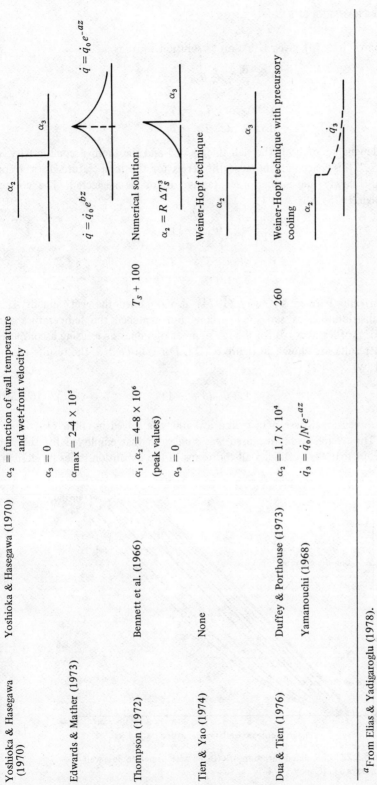

Yoshioka & Hasegawa (1970)   Yoshioka & Hasegawa (1970) α_2 = function of wall temperature and wet-front velocity

$\alpha_3 = 0$

Edwards & Mather (1973) $\alpha_{max} = 2\text{–}4 \times 10^5$ $\dot{q} = \dot{q}_0 e^{bz}$ $\dot{q} = \dot{q}_0 e^{-az}$

Thompson (1972) $T_s + 100$ $\alpha_1, \alpha_2 = 4\text{–}8 \times 10^6$ (peak values)   Numerical solution $\alpha_2 = R\,\Delta T_s^3$

Bennett et al. (1966) $\alpha_3 = 0$

Tien & Yao (1974)   None   Weiner-Hopf technique

Duffey & Porthouse (1973)   260 $\alpha_2 = 1.7 \times 10^4$ Weiner-Hopf technique with precursory cooling

Dua & Tien (1976)

Yamanouchi (1968) $\dot{q}_3 = \dot{q}_0/N\, e^{-az}$

[a]From Elias & Yadigaroglu (1978).

6-183

Expansion of [6.5.56] gives a first-order solution for u as

$$\frac{\text{Bi}}{\text{Pe}} = \frac{\pi}{2} \theta_W$$

[6.5.57]

or $\qquad \frac{1}{u} = \frac{\pi}{2} \frac{\rho c_p}{\alpha(z)} \frac{T_W - T_s}{T_0 - T_s}$

Thus u is independent of both the slab thickness δ and the thermal conductivity λ. Equation [6.5.57] is inaccurate because the series for the temperature distribution converges only slowly and higher-order terms cannot be neglected. The correct expression (Blair 1975) is

$$\frac{\text{Bi}}{\text{Pe}} = \frac{\pi}{2} (\theta_W - 1)$$

[6.5.58]

or $\qquad \frac{1}{u} = \frac{\pi}{2} \frac{\rho c_p}{\alpha(z)} \frac{T_W - T_0}{T_0 - T_s}$

Coney (1974a) and Farmer & Coney (1974) also obtained the wet- and dry-side temperature distributions as series expansions but matched the temperature and axial heat flux profiles at $z = 0$ for a large number of values of y, using a computer program. The results are shown in figure 6.5.22. For $\sqrt{\text{Bi}}/\text{Pe} > 3$, the results can be approximated by

$$\frac{\text{Bi}}{\text{Pe}} = 1.6 \, \theta_W(\theta_W - 1)$$

[6.5.59]

The two-dimensional case of a cylindrical rod was solved by Blair (1975) and Yeh (1975). The overall technique used was similar to that employed for the slab geometry, except that Blair retained all the terms in the expansion series by deriving

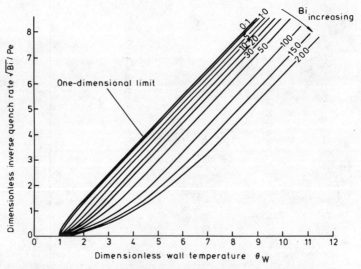

Figure 6.5.22 Calculated variation of $\sqrt{\text{Bi}}/\text{Pe}$ with dimensionless wall temperature θ_W (Coney 1974a).

an accurate asymptotic expression for the terms, which were then summed analytically. For Pe > 1 and Bi/Pe < 1, Blair obtained

$$\theta_W = 1 + \frac{Bi}{\pi \, Pe} \left(2 + \frac{\pi}{2 \, Pe} + \frac{2}{Pe^2} \right) + \frac{Bi^2}{2\pi^2 \, Pe^2} \left(\frac{8}{3} - \pi^2 - \frac{13\pi}{6 \, Pe} \right) \qquad [6.5.60]$$

For Pe ≫ 1 this reduces to [6.5.60]. For low values of Pe and Bi, Fairburn et al. (1977) established that [6.5.55] holds with $\delta = r/2$, where r is the rod radius, and that with this substitution [6.5.55] and [6.5.60] are asymptotes to Yeh's (1975) solution. The cylinder and slab solutions approach one another as Bi ≫ 1.

"Sputtering" or "Rewetting" Temperature

One outstanding item is the sputtering temperature itself, which must be specified as an input to these models. Theories relating this temperature to the Leidenfrost temperature, the minimum in the classical pool boiling curve, and the critical temperature have been put forward, but none is generally accepted. Moreover, it appears that the sputtering temperature depends to an extent on the condition of the heating surface (e.g., when there is an oxide film). Two different approaches to the sputtering or rewetting condition have been advanced, as described below.

1. There is a minimum rewetting surface temperature, which is a direct function of the surface material. For the short times involved in transient rewetting, heat conduction is the dominant transfer mechanism between wall and fluid. To a first approximation, the contacting phenomenon may be considered as the instantaneous contact between two semi-infinite slabs of material having constant physical properties $(\lambda\rho c)_W$ and $(\lambda\rho c)_L$ and different but uniform temperatures. At the time of contact the instantaneous interface temperature T_I is given by

$$\frac{T_W - T_I}{T_I - T_L} = \sqrt{\frac{(\lambda\rho c)_L}{(\lambda\rho c)_W}} \qquad [6.5.61]$$

Starting with [6.5.61], various theories have been developed to provide the minimum rewetting temperature, including those of Semeria (1973) and Henry (1973). These models result in a surface temperature at rewetting $(T_W = T_0)$ given by

Semeria:

$$T_0 \leqslant \frac{27}{32} T_c + \sqrt{\frac{(\lambda\rho c)_L}{(\lambda\rho c)_W}} \left(\frac{27}{32} T_c - T_L \right) \qquad [6.5.62]$$

Henry:

$$\frac{T_0 - T_I}{T_I - T_L} = 0.42 \left[\sqrt{\frac{(\lambda\rho c)_L}{(\lambda\rho c)_W}} \frac{i_{fG}}{c_{pL} (T_I - T_{sat})} \right]^{0.6} \qquad [6.5.63]$$

where $T_I - T_{sat} = \Delta T_{min}$ as predicted from the hydrodynamic model of Berenson (1961), and T_I is the interface contact temperature.

Experimentally, the rewetting temperature T_0 increases as $\sqrt{(\lambda\rho c)}_w$ decreases. Values of this property for various materials are given in table 6.5.8. The variation of rewetting temperature with this parameter is indicated in figure 6.5.23 and appears to have an asymptote somewhere between [6.5.62] and [6.5.63] for high values of $\sqrt{(\lambda\rho c)}_w$.

2. There is a minimum rewetting temperature, which is a function primarily of the flow parameters (rate, quality, and pressure) in the channel. Such an approach is exemplified by the theory of Iloeji et al. (1974), discussed in detail in section 6.5.1. A detailed mechanism is put forward for the interaction of droplets with hot surfaces. In particular, various mechanisms are identified, including heat transfer from the surface to liquid droplets that impact the wall, heat transfer from the surface to liquid droplets that enter the thermal boundary layer but do not wet the surface, and convective heat transfer from the surface to the bulk vapor. It is shown that a minimum is formed in the plot of heat flux versus wall temperature (figure 6.5.13) that is a function of mass velocity, vapor quality, and system pressure.

Observations from forced convective postburnout and reflooding experiments suggest that the rewetting temperature is not constant over a wide range of flow parameters. This tends to rule out the theories of Semeria and Henry and favor the Iloeji approach. However, the equations of Henry and Semeria are relatively simply applied and may be used to arrive at a simple criterion for estimating the sputtering temperature and testing whether rewetting occurs at points on the heat transfer surface well away from any preexisting quench front.

6.5.2.3 Experimental Rewetting Studies

The numerous experimental studies of quenching and reflooding have been reviewed by Elias & Yadigaroglu (1978) and by Hufschmidt (1977). The analytic models discussed in section 6.5.2.2 require as input the sputtering temperature and the wet-side heat transfer coefficient. The experimental data show a complex relation between quench front velocity and system variables such as initial wall temperature, material and surface condition, coolant flow rate and subcooling, and system pressure.

At atmospheric pressure, Yamanouchi (1968) and Duffey & Porthouse (1973) observed a direct influence of the flow rate per unit perimeter of surface. However, at high pressure, Bennett et al. (1966) and Elliott & Rose (1970, 1971) found no such dependence. This lack of agreement may indicate a pressure effect, or such

Table 6.5.8   Values of $\sqrt{(\lambda\rho c)}$

Fluid	$\sqrt{(\lambda\rho c)}$ (W s$^{1/2}$/m^2 K)
Water (0.1 MPa)	1,600
Stainless steel	8,170
Chromium	14,900
Silver	32,070
Copper	36,870

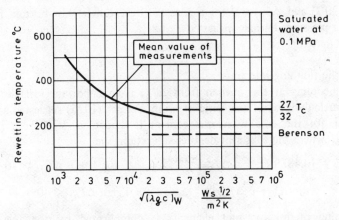

Figure 6.5.23 Influence of thermal surface properties on rewetting temperature.

variables as subcooling at the quench front and the presence of air or steam in the test section prior to reflooding may be important.

A number of workers suggested that the sputtering temperature and the wet-side heat transfer coefficient should be combined into a single parameter to correlate quench velocities during top flooding. Using Blair's analytic solution, [6.5.58], Thompson (1974) found that for pressures above 0.35 MPa

$$\alpha(z)(T_0 - T_s) = 21 \text{ MW/m}^2 \qquad [6.5.64]$$

The sputtering temperature T_0 was approximately equal to $T_s + 100°C$ for pressures above 0.69 MPa. For bottom flooding at pressures below 0.34 MPa the equivalent expression was

$$\alpha(z)(T_0 - T_s) = 3.4 \text{ MW/m}^2 \qquad [6.5.65]$$

with the sputtering temperature taken as $T_s - T_L + 600°C$.

Coney (1974a) and Farmer & Coney (1974) proposed as the correlating parameter

$$\phi = \alpha(z)(T_0 - T_L)^2 \qquad [6.5.66]$$

where for a saturated liquid $T_L = T_s$ and for a subcooled liquid $T_L = T_{qf}$, where T_{qf} is the local quench front coolant temperature. Their suggested procedure involves choosing a value of T_0, obtaining a value of $\alpha(z)$, using an analytic expression for the quench velocity, and finally correlating ϕ in terms of the flow rate per unit perimeter of heated surface Γ, the pressure, and the local subcooling at the quench front ΔT_{qf}. In a paper written by Farmer (1975), Yu proposed

$$\phi = (1 + 0.036 \, \Delta T_{qf} \Gamma)^2 \, (4.52 + 2.48 \log_{10} p) \, \Gamma^{0.0153/p} \times 10^9 \qquad [6.5.67]$$

with p in MPa, T in °C, and Γ in kg/m s. This correlation fits almost all the available data on rewetting by top flooding. To use [6.5.67] to calculate quench velocity, an assumption must be made about $\alpha(z)$ or T_0. Farmer (1975) proposed

$T_0 - T_s = 20°C$ and $\Delta T_{qf} = 0$ for a conservative estimate. For bottom flooding at atmospheric pressure, Farmer suggested

$$\phi = 1.8 \, v^{0.3} \times 10^9 \qquad [6.5.68]$$

where v is the flooding rate (m/s).

The subcooling at the quench front ΔT_{qf} is an important variable in bottom flooding, particularly at atmospheric pressure. Farmer (1975) suggested a correction to [6.5.68] for the case when the coolant is subcooled. If ϕ from [6.5.68] is denoted ϕ_{sat} where the subscript denotes saturation, then

$$\phi = [0.4839 \, (1 + v \, \Delta T_{qf}^2)^{0.346}]^2 \, \phi_{sat} \qquad \text{for } 1 + v \, \Delta T_{qf} \geqslant 40$$

$$\phi = (1 + v \, \Delta T_{qf}^2)^{0.26} \, \phi_{sat} \qquad \text{for } 1 + v \, \Delta T_{qf} < 40$$

$$[6.5.69]$$

Quenching of nuclear fuel elements is complicated by the presence of a heat-generating fuel pellet within the tubular cladding, which is separated from the cladding by a gas gap. The thickness of the gas gap is a function of the operating history of the fuel pin in the reactor, and during an accident sequence it may vary with time as a result of the clad straining under internal fission gas pressure. Details of such a complex analysis are outside the scope of this chapter, but Fairburn et al. (1977) and Blackburn & Pearson (1977) deal with this problem.

6.6 Accident Analysis

Stanislav Fabic

6.6.1 ACCIDENT SCENARIO

Appendix I to the Reactor Safety Study (WASH-1400) offers an in-depth listing of scenarios for various accidents and transients in pressurized-water reactors (PWRs) and boiling-water reactors (BWRs). The primary purpose of this section is to describe the types of thermohydraulic processes that need to be analyzed in loss-of-coolant accidents (LOCAs). Visualization of the complexities involved may help the reader to better appreciate the difficult task faced by the analysts.

Two types of LOCA were selected for this illustration, both pertaining to the PWR. The first type is the design basis accident (DBA), which involves a complete and instantaneous severance of the main coolant pipe between the pump and the reactor inlet nozzle. This so-called double-ended cold-leg break LOCA was judged for many years to result in the highest fuel cladding temperature in both PWR and BWR plants and therefore became the focus of an intensive reasearch program worldwide. The second type of accident selected for illustration actually occurred in the spring of 1979. The well-known accident in the Three Mile Island Unit 2 (TMI-2) plant featured the other extreme in the LOCA spectrum: the small-break LOCA.

6.6.1.1 Large-Break LOCA in PWR

The reactor coolant (water) is initially at about 15 MPa pressure and 560–594 K temperature upstream and downstream of the reactor core, respectively. An instantaneous, guillotine-type severance of the 0.7-m-diameter main coolant pipe, located somewhere between the pump and the reactor vessel inlet nozzle, causes a rarefaction wave to form. This wave propagates into the primary coolant system with a speed of 1060–1220 m/s, undergoing reflections and attenuations as it encounters changes in the flow area. Since different regions of the reactor vessel and coolant loops are depressurized at different times, sizable net pressure loads are produced on the core support barrel, core, steam generator internals, and primary system piping. Such blowdown-induced dynamic loads and their consequences must be analyzed to ascertain that (1) the stresses at various system supports and in the internal structures do not exceed allowable magnitudes and (2) no significant distortion of the reactor internals takes place that could impair flow of the emergency core coolant (ECC) and movement of the control rods.

This "subcooled blowdown" phase of a LOCA terminates when the system pressure drops below the cold-leg saturation pressure (about 7 MPa); when, due to flashing, sufficient vapor is generated throughout the system to drastically retard the wave propagation speed and amplitudes. For the DBA this occurs within 0.1 s after LOCA initiation.

A best-estimate (in contrast to a conservative) analysis of this phase of a LOCA requires (1) a thermal nonequilibrium model of the discharge process through the break, (2) multidimensional treatment of the field equations within the reactor vessel, and (3) consideration of hydroelastic effects. The last requirement stems from the fact that certain reactor internals, such as the core support barrel, deflect under the load and thereby significantly modify the instantaneous pressure fields within the down-comer gap. This feedback effect is considered through simultaneous solutions of the fluid dynamics and structural dynamics field equations. The pump model and heat transfer from the core and to the steam generators can be ignored because of the short time span of subcooled blowdown.

The saturated blowdown phase lasts approximately 20 s (for DBA), its end being arbitrarily defined by cessation of fluid outflow through the break as the system and containment pressures equalize. Now that some experience has been gained with best-estimate codes, it appears more meaningful to define saturated blowdown in terms of (1) the phase that ends with the start of ECC accumulator injection into the cold leg, followed by (2) the combined blowdown and refill stage, which ends when the lower plenum has been refilled and the water level has reached the lower core support plate.

For a DBA LOCA, sufficient void fraction is produced in the reactor core during the initial stage of saturated blowdown to stop the fission process before the reactor has been scrammed through the action of control rods. However, even though fission power production has ceased, the relatively slow radioactive decay of the fission products within the fuel pellets continues to generate heat. That heat would melt the fuel cladding—and the fuel itself—if not removed in timely fashion. For this reason, one of the objects of LOCA analysis is to calculate the peak cladding temperature (PCT). The search for the PCT involves all phases of a LOCA until the core has been quenched.

During the period before the system pressure drops to the level at which the accumulator check valve opens and ECC starts rushing into the system, the coolant flow in the core is determined by the competing effects of the break flow and the pumps. The break flow is greatest during the subcooled blowdown stage, causing the flow in the core to reverse direction. The flow stagnation location sweeps upward through the core and stabilizes, for some time, inside the upper plenum. This leads to coolant starvation and rapid buildup of void fraction (steam) throughout the core. As the flow begins to choke at the break, the pump-driven coolant in the intact loops could again resume up-flow through the core. This situation is short-lived, however; due to increased void fraction, pump head degrades to the point that the break flow again predominates and the down flow of fluid in the core continues until the end of the lower plenum refill stage.

High-power regions of the core are likely to experience burnout heat flux within the first second (or less) as the core voids. Coolant channels in the regions containing control rods or instrument guide thimbles (i.e., heat sinks) may experience temporal rewetting as the lower void fraction fluid is swept by during reversals. Low-power core regions may experience a significant delay in burnout heat flux.

During the period of saturated blowdown before the onset of ECC accumulator injection, the most important aspects of analysis involve modeling of break flow, pump behavior, two-phase pressure drops, and core heat transfer.

After the onset of subcooled ECC injection and until the beginning of reflood, core heat transfer plays a minor role as heat transfer coefficients are generally low. In contrast, the hydraulic behavior becomes much more complex and demands very sophisticated modeling techniques involving considerations of thermal and mechanical nonequilibrium. A best estimate description of the ECC mixing process in the cold leg requires treatment of mass, momentum, and energy exchange between superheated steam and subcooled liquid. This process can lead to significant flow oscillations (chugging). The subcooled liquid injected into the reactor inlet pipes is intended to flow through the reactor vessel downcomer into the lower plenum and eventually into the reactor core. However, during the period of depressurization, steam is rushing downward through the core and upward through the downcomer on its way to the broken inlet pipe. As long as the momentum of the up-flowing steam in the downcomer is high, it will prevent ECC liquid from flowing downward. The liquid is then held up in the upper section of the downcomer and directed toward the break. This is called the ECC bypass period. The source of the up-flowing steam is augmented by flashing of the residual liquid within the lower plenum as the system pressure decreases and by boiling of EEC liquid as it contacts hot walls within the downcomer.

As the system pressure drops to 0.6–1.5 MPa above the containment pressure, the momentum of up-flowing steam within the downcomer decreases to the point at which the ECC liquid can flow downward and eventually fill the lower plenum.

The thermohydraulics of ECC bypass and penetration is extremely complex, requiring, for best-estimate analyses, consideration of thermal and mechanical nonequilibrium in multidimensional flow configurations, as illustrated in figure 6.6.1. A great deal of research has been devoted to ECC bypass, including experiments with a variety of geometric scales and test conditions. In the licensing (evaluation model) calculations the conservative assumption is made that no ECC liquid can penetrate downward as long as the up-flowing steam can uplift (drag) small droplets.

The reflood period begins when the lower plenum has filled and the emergency coolant has reached the bottom of the reactor core. Progression of the coolant into the core, in this bottom reflood case, is determined by (1) the fluid pressure in the upper region of the downcomer, (2) the head of liquid contained between the liquid levels in the downcomer and the core, respectively, (3) the fluid pressure acting in the core above the rising liquid level, (4) liquid inertia in the downcomer and the

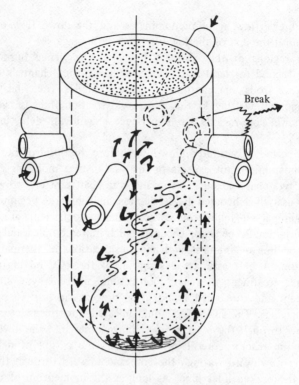

Figure 6.6.1   ECC flow in PWR downcomer. Light areas
represent liquid flow; gray areas, steam with entrained
liquid droplets.

core, and to a lesser extent (5) friction and other hydraulic losses experienced by
the liquid. Since the system pressure has dropped by this time sufficiently to
unchoke the break flow, the fluid pressure is only slightly higher than the
containment pressure. Actually, there may be a short period when the system
pressure drops below the containment pressure, due to inertia, and the containment
fluid (steam plus air) rushes through the break into the primary coolant system. The
liquid head in the downcomer is high initially, causing an upsurge of coolant into
the core. Flow of the liquid past very hot fuel surfaces generates steam, which
needs to be vented through the core, upper plenum, hot-leg piping, steam generator,
and pump belonging to the broken loop. This steam finally exits into the
containment through the pump side of the double-ended pipe break. It will be
shown below that this steam surge may entrain a certain amount of ECC liquid,
which may vaporize in its passage through the steam generator and augment the
volume of steam that needs to be vented. The pressure needed to expel this steam
acts on top of the liquid (or froth) level in the reactor core, opposing the
progression of the ECC. This phenomenon has been termed steam binding.

Considering the reactor downcomer and the core as two legs of a U-tube
manometer, it can be seen that there are forces that may cause the liquid flow to
oscillate: the liquid head pushing coolant into the core and the back pressure caused

by steam generation pushing it back out of the core. The oscillation frequency is determined predominantly by the inertia of the liquid.

During the reflood period the pumps in the unbroken loops either have coasted down to standstill if off-site power is not available—as assumed in the licensing calculations—or are being driven at synchronous (constant) speed (a most probable case for best-estimate analyses). In the broken loop the pump may accelerate to more than twice the rated speed if off-site power is absent, the fast-flowing steam driving the pump as a turbine. The maximum speed attained by that pump is of considerable interest in the licensing calculations in checks of whether structural disintegration could take place with consequent generation of "missiles." In either case, the pump offers the largest hydraulic resistance in the broken loop's steam venting path. That resistance can be calculated by means of the degraded homologous curves obtained from experiments.

Steam generators play a significant role during reflood, as contributors to the steam binding problem. Their role is preordained in the licensing calculations: (1) no liquid droplet deentrainment is assumed to take place anywhere in the path between the reactor core and the steam generator tubing, and (2) all the liquid carried over by the venting steam is assumed to completely vaporize in the steam generators. Both factors maximize steam binding, causing low reflood rates in the core.

In best-estimate analyses it is necessary to examine (1) liquid deentrainment within the steam generator inlet plenum and the curved inlet nozzle, (2) heat transfer from the hot secondary-side liquid through the tube wall and to either vapor or the impinging droplets, and (3) heat transfer between the vapor and entrained liquid droplets. These heat transfer processes determine the rate of evaporation of the entrained droplets within the steam generator tubing and thus their contribution to the steam binding problem.

The most interesting and most difficult processes to model, in best-estimate analysis of reflood, occur within the reactor core and the upper plenum. Since the cladding temperature is initially above the "sputtering" or Leidenfrost temperature, the liquid cannot contact hot surfaces. The initial surge of liquid produces a thin vapor blanket surrounding the fuel rods. Heat is transferred to the vapor blanket and the liquid core. Part of the latter serves to diminish the local subcooling; the remainder provides latent heat of evaporation, resulting in a high relative velocity between the liquid core and the surrounding vapor. The drag between the vapor and the rising liquid core causes the latter to break up into globules and eventually into small liquid droplets, which are then carried upward. In the zone of the reactor core characterized by the dispersed droplet flow regime, the heat transfer mode between fuel rods (cladding), vapor, and entrained droplets is similar to one described for the steam generator—i.e., cladding to vapor and to impinging droplets, vapor to droplets, and also thermal radiation from cladding to droplets, vapor, and adjacent solid surfaces if the latter are cooler. Entrained droplets in this region provide significant "precooling" of the fuel rods, especially in the immediate vicinity of the fuel rod spacers and at the top of the core where the fuel rods are cooler because of the locally lower rate of heat generation from decay.

When the local clad surface temperatures fall below the sputtering temperature, the liquid wets the surface, resulting in a very high (boiling) heat transfer mode.

This manner of cooling or quenching, of fuel rods normally starts from the bottom of the core. The quench front propagates upward due to the combined effects of axial heat conduction through the cladding and precooling in the "inverted annular" flow region. The latter extends between the quench front and the axial location at which the liquid core has shattered into dispersed droplets. When the back pressure, due to steam binding, is large enough to cause slow reflooding, the quench front propagation is primarily due to axial heat conduction in the cladding. A very steep surface temperature profile is located at the quench front in such cases, its axial extent being only a few millimeters. Farther upstream from the quench front, the boiling heat transfer mode eventually changes into the forced convection mode as the cladding cools below saturation temperature. Quench fronts could also be formed at the top of the reactor core once the entrained droplets have cooled the local clad surfaces below the sputtering temperature. Those quench fronts would propagate downward as the liquid film caused by accumulation of droplets falls along the surface, shattering at the quench front into droplets. Impingement of these high-kinetic-energy droplets aids in local precooling.

Complexities of this thermohydraulic process in the core are further increased by the oscillatory nature of the reflood process. The oscillating column of liquid in the core not only causes variations in the length of the inverted annular flow regime but may even cause its complete disappearance if the "foam" level drops below the upward-propagating quench front. In that case, a thin liquid film is left on the clad surface below the quench front and will evaporate and cause downward motion of the quench front if sufficient time is available before the next liquid (froth) level upsurge.

In licensing (evaluation model) analyses quench fronts are not tracked, nor is liquid entrainment calculated from first principles. Global, empirical correlations are used to determine both, based on the conservatively estimated steam binding effects. In best-estimate analyses heat conduction within the fuel pellets and cladding, thermal energy partitioning between liquid and vapor, relative velocity of vapor and liquid phases, and finally breakup of liquid columns and entrainment of liquid droplets are all considered on a local rather than a global basis. This calls for programming of extensive selection criteria for defining the local flow topology (flow regime map) and local heat transfer regimes. Consideration of liquid fallback into the core, from the upper plenum, calls for a multidimensional (at least two-dimensional axisymmetrical) representation of fluid dynamics, especially if, in the case of high-local-power regions, clad swellings may create local flow blockages.

The core steam and entrained liquid droplets reach the upper plenum through restricted flow passages within the fuel end box and the upper core support plate. At the start of reflood the upper plenum does not contain any liquid. Droplets reaching the plenum from below encounter a dense array of control rod guide tubes and support columns on their way toward the broken loop outlet nozzle. Only very minute droplets may be carried by steam through the tortuous flow passages all the way to the outlet nozzle(s). Most of the larger droplets impinge on the internal structures (guide tubes, support columns) and form falling liquid films. In some regions of the upper plenum the vapor velocity component perpendicular to the internal structures may be sufficiently high to displace the falling film toward the downwind side of structures. Trailing vortices will tear up the thick film at those locations, entraining fairly large droplets in the wake. This process is called reentrainment. In the more quiescent regions of the plenum the liquid films will propagate toward the upper core support plate, i.e., the bottom boundary of the upper plenum.

As long as the up flow of steam through the upper core support plate is large enough to prevent countercurrent flow of liquid, the deentrained liquid in the upper plenum will accumulate and form a frothy pool. It can be seen, therefore, that after a while the droplets originating in the reactor core will join the liquid stored in the upper plenum. The steam flowing upward through the pool will entrain some of the pool liquid. Consequently, the droplets now flowing through the internal structures—again experiencing deentrainment and reentrainment—are of the second generation, belonging to the pool liquid.

The steam generation rate in the reactor core, during reflood, is a function of local decay heat generation. Since the latter falls off rapidly near the core (radial) periphery, the steam up flow in the narrow peripheral zone *may* be low enough to allow countercurrent flow through the peripheral holes in the upper core support plate, perhaps after the pool height has become sufficiently large. A fraction of the pool liquid may therefore drain back into the core—a process called fallback, illustrated in figure 6.6.2.

Whether or not fallback actually takes place, it is clear that the upper plenum internal structures will act as a vapor/liquid separator and, at least temporarily, store a significant quantity of liquid within the upper plenum. The important consequence is that the amount of entrained liquid actually flowing through the outlet nozzle(s) toward the steam generator(s) will be significantly lower than that reaching the upper plenum from below. As less entrained liquid reaches the steam generators the steam binding effect is reduced and the core reflood rate increases.

It was mentioned above that some deentrainment of liquid may also occur in the steam generator inlet nozzle and associated inlet plenum. Liquid droplets would separate in those places by centrifugal action and accumulate in parts of the steam generator inlet plenum.

The period of liquid accumulation in the upper plenum and the steam generator inlet plenum, even without fallback, may be long enough to allow speedy quenching of the hottest regions of the core. These processes are purposely left out in licensing audit analyses. If best-estimate analyses are performed to quantify the margin of safety, such complex processes need to be considered. This is not to say, however, that each of these processes needs to be resolved from first principles. For example, empirical information could be used to define sources and sinks for the droplet (liquid) fraction within a typical computational cell when a given (calculated) vapor flow is crossing the cell boundaries. The computational cell size would, in general, be large enough to encompass a number of the control rod guide tubes and/or support columns. Liquid entrainment from the pool by the up-flowing steam would also be described by use of empirical correlations.

In these and other situations that are very complex or are highly localized in space, one must ensure that the empirical relations adopted are applicable to the

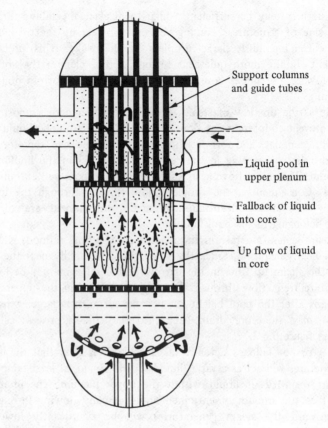

Figure 6.6.2 PWR reflood.

range of geometric scale sizes, all the way to full (plant) scale. Concerning the global motion of fluids, it is clear that best-estimate analyses require multidimensional models, with a flow topology recognition capability that differentiates liquid pools, films, or very large "globs" from the liquid droplets carried by vapor. The second-generation best-estimate, advanced LOCA code, COBRA-TF, developed for the U.S. Nuclear Regulatory Commission (NRC), has separate governing equations for these two liquid fields.

The search for the PCT ends by the time the calculated reactor hot spot (usually midplane) temperature has turned around, during reflood, and exhibited a steadily decreasing trend. In licensing audit calculations the PCT is found during reflood. Best-estimate calculations show that, under more realistic assumptions, the PCT is likely to occur during the early phase of blowdown.

The scenario above pertains to a double-ended cold-leg break in PWRs outfitted with a system that supplies emergency coolant to the cold legs only, without assuming simultaneous rupture of some steam generator tubes. More recently, both integral system tests (in the Semiscale-Mod 2 test facility) and analyses were performed to examine the consequences of a LOCA with simultaneous steam generator tube ruptures. The assumed number of ruptured tubes was parametrically varied to find the worst condition. Such studies revealed that a very narrow band of the ruptured tubes resulted in PCTs higher than those for a DBA LOCA without simultaneous tube ruptures. In other cases, especially when the number of broken steam generator tubes was relatively large, the enhanced reverse flow of steam through the core removed a significant amount of the stored energy in the fuel and diminished the magnitude of the PCT. Best-estimate analysis of such cases is, however, more demanding, showing a need for multidimensional modeling of flow within the upper plenum and the core, as a higher-density coolant is brought into the upper plenum from the loop containing the damaged steam generator.

More demanding analysis is also required for plants that feature not only the usual cold-leg ECC injection but also simultaneous injection into the upper plenum, e.g., in Westinghouse two-loop plants. In PWRs of German design, this additional ECC is injected into the hot legs. However, a specially provided duct transports this coolant close to the upper plenum in order to condense the steam generated in the core during the bottom quenching process and thereby decrease the steam binding problem. Since the upper plenum injection starts before bottom reflood, condensation in the upper plenum could also diminish the steam supply into the downcomer and shorten the ECC bypass period.

Reactors designed by Babcock & Wilcox Co. are provided with core barrel vent valves that open when the pressure inside the upper plenum exceeds the downcomer (upper annulus) pressure. This provides a venting path for the core steam generated during the bottom reflood process and thus eliminates the steam binding problem.

Finally, the Westinghouse upper head injection (UHI) design injects the (additional) emergency coolant into the upper plenum and on top of the reactor core early during blowdown, for the purpose of removing a significant amount of the stored energy in the core before the beginning of bottom reflood.

6.6.1.2 The Three Mile Island Accident

It will be assumed that the reader is familiar with the details of the TMI-2 accident scenario. This example is chosen to illustrate the thermohydraulic modeling requirements imposed by this particular kind of small-break LOCA.

The initial phase of this accident involved a loss of steam generator feedwater that led to depletion (boil-off) of the liquid inventory on the steam generator secondary side. The resulting loss of heat removal caused heat-up and expansion of the primary coolant. The attendant pressure increase led to reactor scram and actuation of the pressurizer relief valve, which failed to close as coolant pressure decreased. This initial stage of the incident does not call for sophisticated analysis, and the models employed in plant simulators used for operator training can address it adequately.

That, however, is not the case for the subsequent, small-break LOCA stage. The simulators available at that time for training of PWR plant operators did not include provisions to account for the presence of two-phase flow within the primary coolant system. Any void (steam) generated anywhere in the system was thought to end up, without delay, in the upper portion of the pressurizer. The simulators therefore taught the operators to concentrate on keeping the pressurizer liquid level within prescribed limits; a liquid-full pressurizer was regarded as an indication of a liquid-full primary coolant system.

Lack of heat removal (the auxiliary feedwater was inadvertently blocked off), combined with loss of pressure caued by discharge of coolant through the stuck-open relief valve, eventually caused liquid flashing in parts of the reactor vessel and accumulation of steam within its upper regions. The liquid displaced by steam was pushed into the pressurizer, through the pressurizer surge line, giving the high water level indication and causing the operator to terminate the injection of ECC. It took 140 min before the operators realized that uncontrolled loss of inventory occurred through the pressurizer relief valve. This process was terminated by closure of the block valve. It took much less time to realize that the auxiliary feedwater was blocked off, and this was immediately rectified. Subsequent calculations indicated that the relatively short period of steam generator coolant starvation did not significantly contribute to the course of the accident.

The net loss of liquid inventory during the first 140 min of the accident resulted in extensive flashing within the primary coolant system, causing the main coolant pumps to cavitate. The last two pumps were shut off about 100 min into the event to prevent their further deterioration. Cessation of forced flow allowed the steam to separate from the steam-water mixture, starting the core uncovery process. During the period 100–142 min, thermocouples above the core and self-powered neutron detectors began to indicate temperatures in the 810 K range and high radiation levels in coolant samples and in the containment building as the result of fission product release from the overheated core. The system pressure decreased to about 4.5 MPa at about the time the uncontrolled coolant leakage was terminated, followed by a sharp increase soon thereafter. ECC injection was significantly increased at about 200 min. Over the next 14 h, the primary system pressure varied between about 13.8 and 3.8 MPa in response to changes in the ECC injection rate and opening and closing of the block valve downstream of the open pressurizer relief valve. At about 10 h, the containment pressure briefly increased by 0.19 MPa, indicating a hydrogen burn. During most of the first 16 h of the accident, the pressurizer water level indicated a full pressurizer.

Based on this unfortunate experience and information gained from numerous in-depth analyses and small-break experiments in test facilities, the following requirements can be stated for best-estimate analyses of small-break events.

System hydraulics must account for two-phase forced and natural circulation flow. The models must allow for inhomogeneous flow of steam and liquid; the fluid phases must be allowed to flow with different velocities and in different directions. Checks for countercurrent flow limitation (CCFL) must be included. CCFL in the pressurizer surge line is thought to have been largely responsible for the liquid holdup inside the TMI-2 pressurizer. Phase separation by gravity and tracking of liquid or foam levels is necessary for all vertically oriented system components. Phase separation by gravity and gravity-induced flow of liquid in horizontal pipes—including the CCFL—must be modeled. Careful consideration of condensation-induced heat transfer in steam generators is mandatory. It is important to determine the type of fluid reaching the break, since it greatly affects the discharge rate. Discharge of pure steam causes the largest efflux of thermal energy, hence the fastest rate of depressurization; discharge of liquid causes the largest rate of loss of coolant mass inventory. Significant core damage (oxidation) results in release of hydrogen. Hydrogen transport and distribution within the primary coolant system must be calculated to determine if and when it could cause cessation of natural circulation, decreased steam generator heat removal, and hydrogen venting into the containment. The TMI-2 accident showed the need for multicomponent fluid modeling and for the ability to address damaged reactor cores. This is in sharp contrast with the pre-TMI philosophy, which precluded studies of reactor cores in which the PCT exceeded the regulatory limit. Finally, the long transient duration associated with small-break LOCA (14 h in TMI-2!) clearly established the need for very fast numerical solution techniques.

6.6.2 GENERAL CLASSIFICATION OF LOCA CODES

6.6.2.1 Licensing Audit Codes

The licensing audit calculations are performed with assemblies of various "self-standing" codes. For example, the major phases of a LOCA are calculated with their own codes, which are connected to a common fuel behavior or "hot channel" code. In the past, initialization of each code in the assembly and intercode data transfer were carried out manually. More recent practices, reflected in the WRAP/PWR and WRAP/BWR code packages developed for the NRC by the Savannah River Laboratory, utilize steady-state fuel codes such as GAPCON or FRAP-S to calculate the core stored energy, its spatial distribution, and the gap conductance just before initiation of a LOCA. That information is utilized during self-initialization of the blowdown code. Data transfer between codes is fully automatic. The sequences of codes interfaced in the WRAP packages are illustrated in figures 6.6.3 and 6.6.4. The containment pressure history is either supplied as a boundary condition or calculated with simple models adjusted on the basis of separate calculations

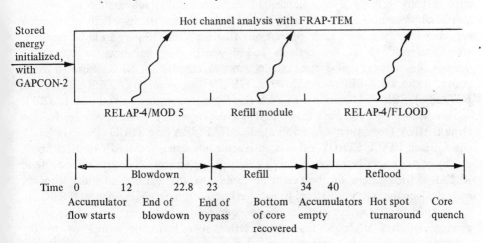

Figure 6.6.3 PWR LOCA audit analysis with WRAP code package.

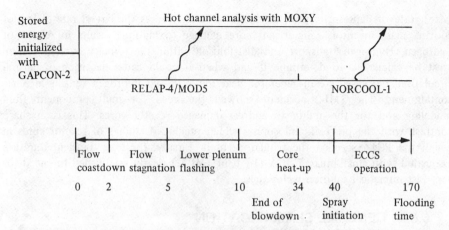

Figure 6.6.4   BWR LOCA audit analysis with WRAP code package.

performed with a containment code such as CONTEMPT. That procedure is iterated if necessary.

The so-called evaluation models employed in the licensing audit codes contain the conservatisms specified, e.g., by the NRC acceptance criteria described in appendix K to 10 CFR 100 (Nuclear Regulatory Commission 1974).

6.6.2.2 Best-Estimate Codes

These codes employ best-estimate models to calculate the expected evolution of thermohydraulic properties during a postulated accident or transient. Best-estimate codes are subdivided into two main categories: systems codes and component codes. The systems codes are further subdivided into reactor coolant systems codes and containment systems codes.

The main difference between systems codes and component codes is that the latter usually provide a very detailed description of thermohydraulic behavior in individual system components in order to examine the effects of all phenomena expected to play a part. Only phenomena that are found to play an important role are then included in the systems codes, which must account for synergistic interactions between all system components. Examples of NRC-sponsored component codes are K-FIX (break flow), K-TIF (PWR downcomer), COBRA-TF (PWR, BWR core), SOLA-FLX and K-FIX-FLX (loads on reactor internals), PELE-IC (BWR containment pool dynamics), and FRAP-T (fuel behavior). Other examples are the Danish TINA (core thermohydraulics), French FLIRA and PSHIT (core reflood), and German FLUX, STRUYA (loads on reactor internals), and DRIX (critical flow).

Systems codes evolved from a lumped parameter concept embodied in RELAP-4 (first-generation best-estimate code) to the current modular concept embodied in the advanced (third-generation) best-estimate codes such as TRAC. In the lumped parameter concept the control volumes (or lumps) are interconnected in a more or less arbitrary fashion to arrive at a hydraulic equivalent to the resistance-capacitance-inductance electrical network representing the primary coolant system. The control volumes do not distinguish the actual system components; they may represent sections of pipe or regions of the reactor vessel, steam generator, etc. While each control volume may contain a volumetric source or sink of thermal energy, special routines account for such terms for the control volumes representing the reactor core and steam generators.

Second-generation systems codes have originally been aimed at the description of a portion of a LOCA transient, such as the subcooled and saturated blowdown phases, or the reflood phase, of LOCAs. Most of them are based on one-dimensional models, utilizing tee junctions to form arbitrary networks of one-dimensional flow passages. Examples are the Westinghouse BLODWN-2 and MULTIFLEX, German DAPSY, Norwegian NORA, Japanese DEPCO-MULTI, Canadian RAMA, French CLYSTERE, and Danish NORCOOL.

BLODWN-2, MULTIFLEX, DAPSY, and DEPCO-MULTI are based on homogeneous equilibrium models and are solved by the method of characteristics. Fabic (1971) studied the application of such one-dimensional codes to analysis of multidimensional wave propagation during the early stage of a DBA LOCA. NORA, NORCOOL, and CLYSTERE employ thermal and mechanical nonequilibrium and are solved by the finite-difference method (explicit in NORA, implicit in CLYSTERE and NORCOOL).

Third-generation systems codes are designed to cover, continuously, all phases of LOCA, anticipated transients without scram (ATWS), and reactivity insertion accidents (RIA), utilizing the most advanced thermohydraulic models and their solution schemes. Examples of the currently operational third-generation codes are TRAC and RELAP-5, developed for the NRC by Los Alamos Scientific Laboratory and by Idaho National Engineering Laboratory (INEL), respectively.

About 1 yr before the TMI-2 accident, the NRC established the need for the development of fast-running advanced codes for scoping studies of a large number of accident scenarios and for application to small-break LOCA accidents. Achievement of high computation speeds dictates the ability to collapse the geometric representation to one-dimensional for all system components. Special annotation was introduced in the family of TRAC codes to distinguish between the detailed and fast-running versions and between the PWR and BWR versions. A suffix composed of two letters and a numeral was added, the first letter (P or B) denoting PWR or BWR version, the second letter (D or F) denoting detailed (three-dimensional) or fast-running version and the numeral indicating the vintage. For example, TRAC-PD2, which was released to the public in October 1980, supersedes TRAC-P1A as the detailed PWR version. The first detailed BWR version, TRAC-BD1, is currently under development at INEL and is slated for completion during 1981. The fast-running version TRAC-PF1 is under development at Los Alamos, while INEL has completed development of RELAP-5/MOD1. Both of these fast-running codes are based on a two-fluid model, with the ability to account also for the presence of noncondensable gas.

Some of the first-generation and second-generation codes have undergone extensive modification and improvements, extending their capabilities to address all phases of LOCA in a single calculation. An outstanding example is the RELAP-4/MOD7 code developed at INEL. This code was released to the public during the first half of 1980.

In TRAC-PD2 all regions within the reactor vessel are modeled with the full (six field equation) two-fluid model, solved three-dimensionally (r, θ, z coordinates) by a semi-implicit finite-difference method. System components outside the reactor vessel, such as pipes, steam generators, pressurizer, and accumulators, are modeled one-dimensionally with a five-equation, full thermal nonequilibrium drift flux model. Flow regime and heat transfer regime maps are employed to select the appropriate constitutive equations. The code is fully modular. However, because of the complexities it addresses, with 750 computational cells, the code runs over 10 h on the CDC 7600 computer to cover the entire, design basis PWR plant LOCA transient.

Further advances in the numerical solution technique are expected to reduce the running time considerably. This code also features improved modeling of core quenching during reflood and removal of various errors and deficiencies uncovered during the TRAC-P1A code assessment process.

Modeling of the upper head injection design in the more recent Westinghouse PWRs called for a highly flexible nodalization capability for the reactor vessel in which the multidimensional regions are penetrated by one-dimensional channels. The component code COBRA-TF, originally designed for addressing thermohydraulic transients in the reactor core, possessed this capability. Toward the end of 1979 this code was merged with TRAC-P1A, by replacing the original TRAC vessel module, resulting in yet another third-generation systems code named COBRA/TRAC.

CATHAR is a French equivalent of RELAP-5 (third-generation LOCA systems code) now under development. The interested reader should consult yearly issues of the *Nuclear Safety Research Index* (OECD/NEA) for further information on computer codes in existence or being developed in the United States and abroad. That index does not list the proprietary codes developed by reactor vendors, which can be found in Fabic (1977b).

Best estimate systems codes are needed for interpretation of integral system experiments. They can also be used to investigate ECC system performance and evaluate the margin of safety. More recently they have been used to determine the accident "signature" that could be perceived by the plant operator and for exploring consequences of operator actions.

Containment systems codes calculate thermohydraulic behavior of the containment atmosphere. During normal operation this atmosphere consists of air at nearly atmospheric pressure. Should a rupture occur in the primary coolant system, hot water and a steam are discharged into the containment, increasing its energy content and changing the composition of its atmosphere. PWR containments feature compartments interconnected with flow passages of irregular shape. The net volume of a PWR containment is designed to accept the added fluid mass and energy without exceeding the design pressure. During the early phase of a LOCA, violent expansion of the discharged flashing fluid can create sizable pressure differentials between various subcompartments, and within the break compartments, jet impingement loads on containment walls could locally create significant hydraulic and thermal loads. Once the containment sprays are activated, steam starts to condense on spray droplets and the containment atmosphere pressure starts to decrease. Should metal-water chemical reaction occur within the reactor core during a LOCA, hydrogen gas is generated, which is then vented through the break into the containment. It is necessary to analyze the diffusion of the hydrogen to determine whether local concentrations may form that could be ignited (by static charges) and detonated. In BWR containments the discharged steam is vented into subcooled liquid pools to achieve condensation and, thereby, pressure reduction.

Containment systems codes must model all the above processes to ascertain that the containment safeguards function as designed and that the containment, which presents the last barrier, is not breached.

CONTEMPT-LT, CONTEMPT-4 COMPARE, BEACON-3, and PELE-IC are examples of the containment codes developed for the NRC. The first three are of the lumped parameter variety, while BEACON-3 features multidimensional multifluid modeling with thermal and mechanical nonequilibrium, suitable for the analysis of the first few minutes of a LOCA involving hydraulic loads on intercompartment barriers and jet loads. PELE-IC addresses multidimensional processes within the wet wall of a BWR pressure suppression pool caused by air and steam venting through downcomers and including the hydroelastic effects caused by flexible walls.

6.6.3 THERMOHYDRAULIC MODELS

Details of the governing, or field, equations useful for description of transient multiphase flow are given elsewhere in this handbook. The simplest formulation involves three field equations, representing conservation of mass, momentum, and energy for a homogeneous mixture of liquid and vapor in thermodynamic and mechanical equilibrium. The first-generation LOCA codes, and even some second-generation ones, were based on such simple models, solved either in a lumped parameter form or one-dimensionally. Only two constitutive equations are needed in this case: one describing the source (or sink) of thermal energy, the other describing hydraulic losses.

Although useful, bounding-type calculations can be performed with such simple models, experience has indicated that they are inadequate for best-estimate analyses of LOCA. Subsequent evolutions sought to remove the restrictions concerning either mechanical or thermal equilibrium, or both. This led to a gradual increase in the number of field and constitutive equations, culminating in the multifield model, in which one to three field equations are employed for each fluid component and/or phase, and for each "node" of computational cell.*

In a one-dimensional two-fluid model the six field equations must be supplemented by three equations defining the interfacial transfer conditions (e.g., $\Gamma_L + \Gamma_G = 0$),† one equation defining the axiom of continuity (e.g., $\alpha_L + \alpha_G = 1$),‡ one thermal equation of state and one caloric equation of state for each phase, and a variety of constitutive equations. The latter define viscous stress; conduction heat transfer (within each phase); interfacial transfers of mass, momentum, and energy; interfacial temperature; relation between the phasic pressures; wall heat transfer to each phase; wall shear; etc.

All of the interfacial transport, wall shear, and wall heat transfer constitutive equations are furthermore dependent on the flow topology (or flow regime). Predictive capability for the evolution of flow topology is not yet at hand. The chances for obtaining that goal are improved the more one is able to track the

---

*It is understood that the number of momentum balance equations, for a given field, equals the number of dimensions considered.

†Γ is the rate of generation of ... per unit volume.

‡α is the fraction of ... per unit volume.

evolution of the individual components—bubbles, droplets, continuous liquid regions, and continuous vapor regions—through the individual field equations supplemented by additional constitutive equations defining coalescence, breakup, deposition, entrainment, turbulence level, etc.

Fabic (1977b, tables 1 and 2) attempted to illustrate the variety of models then in existence and assign shorthand notations for their characterization. Subsequent research indicated shortcomings of that approach, because of the need to go beyond the six-equation two-velocities-/two-temperatures ($2V2T$) model. For example, the liquid phase could appear in a variety of forms such as pools (with or without enclosed vapor bubbles), jets, films, or dispersed droplets. Characterization of mass, momentum, and energy exchange between liquid and vapor depends significantly on flow regime or topology; i.e., the geometric form and extent of the interfacial or contact area between liquid and vapor. In addition, in a given computational cell the continuous and dispersed-liquid regions may be moving in different directions with different velocities and may have different temperatures.

The COBRA/TRAC code, for example, assigns separate field equations to the dispersed droplets and the contiguous liquid (film or pool) entities. It could be argued that the droplets come in different sizes—the largest being determined by the critical Weber number—and may not have uniform velocities. However, a systems code cannot be overburdened with complexities that would make calculations totally impractical. Consideration of one droplet field may be adequate if calculations of the interfacial area included criteria for the droplet size distribution, to allow for evaluation of the effective interfacial transfers of mass, momentum, and energy. Modeling of the droplet field requires constitutive equations for droplet formation owing to entrainment (from films, jets, or pools) and for droplet disappearance owing to deposition. Breakup and coalescence are not handled directly; instead, the critical Weber number, in conjunction with the local vapor velocity, is used to determine the largest droplet diameter; the effective (mean) diameter is then found from the size distribution function. LOCA applications that could benefit from tracking of the droplet field involve countercurrent flow in which the vapor stream contains entrained droplets, flow in the PWR and BWR upper plenum during reflood, core dryout, simultaneous top and bottom core quenching, annular dispersed flow, and PWR downcomer ECC penetration.

As ECC accumulators empty of liquid, nitrogen gas is forced into the primary coolant system. The importance of the noncondensable gas during reflood has not yet been ascertained. It is known, however, that the rate of vapor condensation is greatly affected by it. Tracking the evolution and transport of noncondensable gas is even more important for analysis of small breaks. In situations where the main coolant pumps are tripped and core cooling must rely on natural circulation, accumulation of the noncondensable gas in the hot legs and/or steam generator can disrupt natural circulation. The effects of the noncondensable gas will be explored with TRAC and RELAP-5 by adding one more mass conservation equation and assuming that the gas comes quickly into thermal and mechanical equilibrium with the continuous phase.

With all these considerations, the number of field equations increases from 6 in TRAC-PD2 to perhaps 10 in TRAC-PD3 and none of the definitions listed in tables

1 and 2 of Fabic (1977b) apply. For this reason, it is more meaningful to characterize the existing thermohydraulic codes as shown in tables 6.6.1 and 6.6.2. Entries in the first column give the code name and the institution at which the code was (or is being) developed. The second column indicates the dimensionability: LP, lumped parameter; 1-D, one-dimensional; and 2-D or 3-D, two- or three-dimensional computational mesh, respectively. More than one notation indicates that the code is capable of operating in the mixed dimensions. The third column gives the shorthand notation for all the field equations: C, continuity (or mass balance); M, momentum balance; and E, energy balance. The arguments in parentheses indicate the nature of the field: m, mixture (of liquid and vapor), G, vapor; L, liquid; g, noncondensable gas; and d, dispersed liquid droplets. $G + L$ indicates a sum of the particular field equations for the vapor and liquid fields, $G - L$ indicates a difference. When a separate droplet field is not indicated, L stands for all forms of liquid; otherwise, L stands for the continuous liquid field within a computational cell, such as a pool or film, or both. The fourth and fifth columns list the important restrictions and features. The sixth column lists the intended application: The shorthand notation SYST indicates a systems code. LOCA indicates that the code is capable of describing the whole LOCA process; otherwise the individual, applicable LOCA phases are indicated. Absence of the word SYST indicates a component code, and a particular system component is indicated. All the codes listed in tables 6.6.1 and 6.6.2 were being developed for the NRC's Division of Reactor Safety Research as of July 1978 and most have been completed by now.

In the advanced systems and component codes all constitutive equations are specified as functions of the local flow regime. The latter employs selection criteria that are based on the magnitudes of the local void fraction and mass flux. This highly simplified flow regime map is expected to be satisfactory for zones of low and high void fraction in which the dispersed phases (bubbles and droplets, respectively) play dominant roles in the interfacial exchange of mass, momentum, and energy. The high-mass-flux zones ($G > 2700$ kg/m^2 s) and the zones for which the Froude number Fr $\leqslant 1$ are also expected to be adequately handled. In the former case the constitutive equations are based on churn-turbulent flow models; in the latter case buoyancy effects lead to vertical separation of liquid and vapor and establishment of liquid levels that can be identified in vertically oriented system components. However, separated flows in horizontal pipes are not yet adequately handled.

The flow regimes described above are considered largely independent of the geometric shape and scale of the system components. This is not the case, however, for flow regimes characterized by intermediate void fractions, $0.20 < \alpha < 0.80$. In such cases it is unlikely that the local flow regime can be properly defined by local values of void fraction and mass flux.* Instead, a series of global flow regime maps, dependent on both the geometric shape and scale (size) of the individual system (reactor vessel) components, would be more appropriate. Ongoing sensitivity studies are designed to yield information about the importance of scale- and shape-dependent flow regimes. If it is found, for example, that the time spent in the

---

*Unless special criteria are utilized to recognize rising or falling liquid or froth interfaces through computational cells belonging to vertically oriented components.

Table 6.6.1 Light-Water Reactor Systems Codes under Development for NRC, as of July 1978

Code name (developed at institution)[a]	Dimensions	Field equations	Restrictions	Special features	Applications[b]
RELAP-4/MOD7 (INEL)	LP	$C(m), M(m), E(m)$ Also, explicitly solved $E(L)$ for specified control volumes to account for nonequilibrium	$V_G = V_L = V_m$ $T_G = T_L = T_{sat}$	In energy equation phasic enthalpy flux considered via slip correlation	PWR SYST LOCA (BE)
RELAP-5 (INEL)	1-D	$C(G + L), C(G - L)$, $M(G + L), M(G - L)$, $E(G + L)$	$T_k = T_{sat}$ $k = L$ or G		LWR SYST LOCA (BE)
TRAC-P1A, TRAC-PD2 (LASL)	Loops: 1-D Vessel: 3-D (r, θ, z)	Loops: $C(m), C(G), M(m)$, $E(G), E(L)$ Vessel: $C(G), C(L), M(G)$, $M(L), E(G), E(L)$	$V_k = F_k(V_m, V_r)$ $k = L, G$	Form of liquid (droplet, film, pool, etc.) not distinguished	PWR SYST LOCA (BE)
TRAC-BD1 (INEL)	Same as TRAC-PD2, except for introduction of 1-D channels penetrating 3-D regions and two-fluid modeling, everywhere.				BWR SYST LOCA (BE)
TRAC-PD3 (LASL)	Loops: 1-D Vessel: 3-D	$C(G), C(L), C(g)$, $C(d), M(G), M(L)$, $E(G), E(L), E(d)$, $M(d)$	$V_d = V_G$ $V_g = V_G$ $T_g = T_G$	Droplet field (d), and noncondensable gas (g) considered multi-dimensional neutron kinetics	PWR SYST LOCA, and non-LOCA, including ATWS and RIA (BE)
TRAC-PF1 (LASL)	Ability to collapse to 1-D everywhere	$C(G), C(L), C(g)$, $M(G), M(L), E(G)$, $E(L)$	$T_g = T_G$ $V_g = V_G$	Considering noncondensable gas; fast running	PWR SYST LOCA and non-LOCA (BE)
COBRA/TRAC (PNL)	Loops: 1-D, modeled same as in TRAC-PD2 Reactor vessel Axial and lateral flow, irregular mesh, 3-D cartesian	$C(G), C(L), C(d)$, $M(G), M(L), M(d)$, $E(G), E(L)$	$T_d = T_L$	Turbulence model being incorporated	LWR SYST LOCA (BE)
BEACON/MOD3 (INEL)	2-D chambers inter-connected with 1-D passages	$C(G), C(L), C(g)$, $M(G), M(L), E(G)$, $E(L)$	$T_g = T_G$ $V_g = V_G$	Models creation of liquid films on walls, due to deentrainment of droplets	PWR containments, during first few minutes in LOCA. Also BWR containment drywell (BE)

[a] INEL, Idaho National Engineering Laboratory; BNL, Brookhaven National Laboratory; LASL, Los Alamos Scientific Laboratory; PNL, Pacific Northwest Laboratory.

[b] BE, best estimate; EM, evaluation model; SYST, systems code.

Table 6.6.2 Component Codes under Development for NRC, as of July 1978

Code name (developed at institution)[a]	Dimensions	Field equations	Restrictions	Special features	Applications
K-FIX (LASL)	3-D	$C(G), C(L), M(G), M(L), E(G), E(L)$			General component (break flow, upper plenum)
K-TIF (LASL)	2-D	$C(g), C(G), C(L), M(G), M(L), E(G), E(L)$		Liquid incompressible, spatial gradients of phasic density neglected; noncondensable gas and vapor at same temperature	PWR downcomer
SOLA-FLX (LASL)	2-D	$C(m), C(G), M(m), E(m)$, plus structural dynamics	$V_k = f_k(V_m, V_r)$ $k = L, G$ $T_v = T_{sat}$	Hydroelastic	Force on PWR core barrel
K-FIX/FLX (LASL)	3-D	Same as K-FIX except structural dynamics added		Hydroelastic	As above
SALE-SPRAY (LASL)	2-D 3-D	$C(G), C(L),$ $n \times C(d), M(G),$ $M(L), n \times M(d),$ $E(G), E(L), E(d)$	Different droplets (sizes) tracked with separate field equations computed explicitly $1 < n < 1500$		Droplet flow in upper plenum
COBRA-TF (PNL)	Axial and lateral flow, irregular mesh	$C(G), C(L), M(G),$ $M(L), E(G), E(L),$ $C(d), M(d)$	Droplet field assumed to be at same temperature as the continuous liquid field; detailed modeling of fuel behavior		LWR core or portion of core (hot bundle); flow blockage and core damage effects
PELE-IC (LLL)	2-D	$C(G), C(L), M(G),$ $M(L), E(G), E(L)$	Tracking of pool free surface and of vapor region boundary; feedback from flexible walls included		Pool dynamics in BWR pressure suppression containments

[a]LASL, Los Alamos Scientific Laboratory; PNL, Pacific Northwest Laboratory; LLL, Lawrence Livermore Laboratory.

intermediate void fraction zone, with $G < 2700$ and $Fr > 1$, is small compared to the time spent in the scale- and shape-independent flow regimes, the need to develop global flow regime maps will be greatly deemphasized. Both the code complexity and the research effort needed to establish the appropriate models or correlations will be greatly increased if it is found that a better characterization of the scale- and shape-dependent flow regimes is needed for best-estimate analyses to yield acceptable accuracy. The code sensitivity studies alone are insufficient to establish that fact; supplementary code validation work, designed to check the code's scale-up potential, is also required.

The primary reason for introducing multidimensional flow description in TRAC was to remove the need for global correlations. For example, computer codes based on lumped parameter or one-dimensional models employ correlations for the countercurrent flow limitations to describe ECC bypass and penetration in the PWR downcomer, and liquid penetration into the reactor core at its upper boundary, during reflood. Such global correlations are obtained from separate effects tests, which are nearly always limited in some way. Either the size or the shape or both are atypical or pertain only to a particular PWR design, or steady-state operation is emphasized; or the employed transients do not account for all synergistic effects or for all system feedback effects. When the code employs global correlations for overall thermohydraulic behavior of individual compoents of the system, its applicability to best-estimate analyses for geometries, scales, and transients against which it has not been validated is suspect. Other examples are the description of flow and void fraction distribution in the reactor core for all phases of LOCA, liquid-vapor separation in the upper plenum during PWR reflood, ECC spray coverage in the BWR upper plenum, flow redistribution among the BWR fuel bundles, etc.

Does the multidimensional treatment remove all of these deficiencies and is the scale-up capability guaranteed? The answer cannot be an unqualified "yes." The computational mesh required for an acceptable code running time is expected to resolve only the gross flow patterns; e.g., radial flow and fluid property distribution within the PWR downcomer is ignored (assumed to be unimportant), secondary flows in the vicinity of sudden flow area changes are not resolved, and thermal and hydraulic boundary layers along solid boundaries are not described. Empirically derived correlations or empirically adjusted constitutive equations are employed in such cases. Empiricism in describing the flow topology (or flow regimes) was already considered. A good deal of empiricism is also employed in the constitutive equations concerning interfacial mass, momentum, and energy transfers. Knowledge of the instantaneous flow regime in any given computational cell serves only to identify the forms or patterns of the individual phases. The next step is to calculate the extent of the interfacial area, the local driving potentials (such as velocity or temperature differentials), and the exchange coefficients for "drag" friction, mass, and heat transfer. Models for the momentum and energy exchange between the solid walls (or internal solid structures such as rods and columns) and the adjacent fluid also involve empiricism.

One could argue, however, that a significant difference exists between the empiricism employed in the multidimensional codes and that in the lumped parameter or one-dimensional codes—when the latter are employed to describe complex flows in reactor vessels. In the former case the empiricism is constrained to single and fundamental processes on a local basis. Such processes can be extensively studied in laboratory-type, basic tests to arrive at constitutive laws or correlations and appropriate scaling criteria, and the tests can, in principle, include scale effects without the need to go to full scale.

In summary, while the scale-up capability of the lumped parameter and one-dimensional codes and their applicability to different component shapes and flow situations in large-break LOCA are extremely limited, multidimensional codes offer a reasonable promise for success, if backed up by an extensive program of model development and basic tests. One-dimensional codes should be adequate for analysis of small-break LOCA and various non-LOCA transients.

The third-generation advanced systems codes are extensively modularized to allow for in-depth checkout and facilitate future model improvements or additions. [See Jackson et al. (1978) on the TRAC module structure.] Another important feature of third-generation codes is their emphasis on user convenience. Such codes are able to self-initialize—i.e., calculate the steady-state distribution of hydraulic and thermal properties—throughout the system before initiation of the postulated accident.

6.6.4 SOLUTION TECHNIQUES

Before describing the solution techniques that have been employed in analyses of two-phase flow transients, it may be useful to point out approximations that they all have in common. First, mathematical models only approximate actual physical processes. Second, numerical models only approximate mathematical models. Provided it can be shown that a numerical model is stable, convergent, and consistent, the error involved in the numerical model can be made arbitrarily small, at least theoretically. Two problems arise with this statement: (1) Stability, convergence, and consistency of the numerical model for a set of coupled nonlinear partial differential equations (PDEs) cannot yet be proved on purely theoretical grounds, and (2) higher-order finite-difference models are very cumbersome to program, requiring significantly larger amounts of computer core storage. Reduction of error in first-order finite-difference models can be achieved only by reducing the mesh spacing and the time increments. In either case, the smaller the finite-differencing error the longer the computation time. Most of the current finite-difference models are of first order. The third approximation results from the fact that digital computers use a finite number of digits to represent the result of any arithmetic operation. Because of this truncation error, the computer solution only approximates the solution of the numerical model.

Description of the numerical solution techniques employed in the first- and second-generation LOCA codes can be found in Fabic's survey of LOCA codes (1977a).

The third-generation advanced codes rely, in most cases, on finite-difference solution schemes. Such numerical models as ICE (implicit continuous-fluid Eulerian), IMF (implicit multi-fluid), and FIX (fully implicit exchange) are associated with Los Alamos Scientific Laboratory. None of these is fully implicit, and they are therefore restricted by the Courant criterion with respect to the maximum allowable time increment size. Increasing emphasis is being placed on mathematical and numerical models for the interfacial transport terms in the field equations. Mathematical formulations are being sought that would introduce history effects in the constitutive equations and thereby achieve a well-posed PDE set. Numerical models of existing interfacial transport mathematical models strive toward a greater degree of implicitness, as in K-FIX. Fully implicit schemes have been developed at Los Alamos for a one-dimensional, five-field-equation drift flux formulation of two-phase flow (Mahaffy & Liles 1979). Such schemes are being applied for the pipe segments adjacent to the break because very small spatial increments are needed for accuracy in a self-choking behavior. The numerical schemes employed in TRAC-P1A for the three-dimensional regions and other one-dimensional regions of the primary coolant system are described by Jackson et al. (1977). The subsequent modifications for TRAC-PD2 are described in Jackson et al. (1979).

Some researchers have investigated the consequences of introducing additional terms in the PDE to account for induced mass effects. Andersen et al. (1977) found that the latter result in shrinking but not eliminating the region of ill-posedness of the two-fluid model. Cheng et al. (1978) constructed the form of the induced mass term that is invariant with respect to coordinate system. They concluded that induced mass effects had an insignificant influence on the final results, even for situations that maximize those effects. However, the induced mass terms had a stabilizing influence, allowing for larger time steps and hence faster computations (Lahey et al. 1980).

Agee has noted that well-posedness could be obtained by removing the assumption of equal phasic pressures (Agee et al. 1978). However, a very arbitrary relation between the vapor- and liquid-phase pressures was employed.

Researchers at Los Alamos admit that the TRAC equations are not well posed (in the sense that all characteristics are real). However, they are made tractable by the artificial damping introduced through the finite-difference scheme. Presumably, only the uninteresting frequency components are damped in this procedure. In his survey of the two-fluid models, Wendroff (1979) points out that ill-posedness is a fine-scale concept since it concerns arbitrarily small wavelengths. However, at small wavelengths viscosity becomes important, yet it is not included in TRAC, COBRA, or RELAP-5. With the inclusion of viscosity the basic two-fluid model becomes well posed, no matter how small the (viscosity-related) coefficient. The growth rates of perturbations become bounded functions of the wave number, as the latter tends toward infinity. Wendroff remarks that it is improper to leave out viscosity when passing to the limit of infinite wave number. Besides, the averaging concept with which the differential equations (for two-phase flow) are formulated does not permit considerations of arbitrarily small wavelengths. Computational schemes developed, or being developed, at Los Alamos aim at accurate representation of the long-wavelength instability. The most recent example, particularly oriented toward fast-running codes, is Mahaffy's (1979) two-step method for one-dimensional two-phase flow.

Latrobe (1978) concluded that three finite-difference schemes that he examined applied to the same simple set of three PDEs, using the same constitutive equations and the same matrix inversion procedure, could yield different results for a two-phase flow problem, although they gave identical results in the case of single-phase transients. This indicates the need for evaluating the accuracy of the finite-difference solution methods, as applied to two-phase flow problems.

6.6.5 CURRENT STATUS OF LOCA CODES AND FUTURE PLANS

Most knowledgeable researchers and reviewers agree that very significant break-throughs were achieved, in both physical modeling and numerical solution tech-niques, with the emergence of the first version of TRAC. Nevertheless, neither the developers of that code nor its sponsors saw it as a tool capable of giving final answers. Many nagging problems remained; some of them have been touched on in section 6.6.3 and in Fabic's paper at the Manchester conference (Fabic 1977b).

Resolution of these problems has progressed slowly because they are difficult and because addition of more fields and more complex constitutive equations leads to very large and complex codes. The larger the code, the harder it becomes to trace and correct errors that occur, in spite of great care and attention to details. A large code is developed by a team of experts, each focusing on specific issues. Keeping track of experimental versions of various modules, consolidating them, integrating and maintaining the master code—in preparation of the next systems code version—is a monumental task. As a consequence, TRAC-P1A and TRAC-PD2 do not contain breakthroughs in modeling, but gradual improvements in running time and in some physical models. On the other hand, the newer versions remove errors that were found by various code users and in the course of code assessment. These are important accomplishments that are often ignored by specialists who focus on their specific areas of expertise.

Nevertheless, the question arises whether we are fast approaching the stage of diminishing returns. We have seen instances of improvements made in some particular areas that have had detrimental effects in other areas. The final version of TRAC for the detailed analysis of PWR LOCA (TRAC-PD3) will feature a much better description of fuel behavior by incorporating the essential modules of the latest version of FRAP-T. It will also include treatment of noncondensable gas and of multi-dimensional neutron kinetics. It may or may not include the droplet field, based on examination of its benefits in the COBRA/TRAC code. It will include modeling improvements for fluid flow in the upper plenum during reflood, for fallback of liquid into the core, and for stratified flow in horizontal pipes.

COBRA/TRAC developers are currently investigating means for addressing fluid turbulence, which, in their opinion, would significantly improve treatment of multidimensional flow, especially in the vicinity of local flow blockages in the reactor core. Both TRAC and COBRA/TRAC are being applied to analyses of current or planned experiments in the 2-D/3-D project. The hot-bundle version of COBRA (named COBRA-TF) is aimed at addressing regions of the reactor core in great detail, with axial and lateral boundary conditions specified by TRAC.

More basic research is under way to better define the local interfacial transports of mass, momentum, and energy and to improve flow regime recognition. Efforts are being made to guide this research so that it will be applicable to improving systems and component codes.

Development of fast-running, advanced codes is proceeding at an accelerated pace because of the current emphasis on studies of small-break accident scenarios. RELAP-5 is in use in support of LOFT and Semiscale small-break experiments, while TRAC-PF1 is expected to become operational in 1981. These codes will not be limited to LOCA analyses.

Yet LOCA code development is expected to reach its zenith during 1982, followed by a fairly fast phase-down. At the same time, code assessment activities and especially code application to the resolution of safety issues are gaining much more prominence.

6.6.6 LESSONS LEARNED FROM THE THREE MILE ISLAND ACCIDENT

The TMI-2 accident showed that (1) a single failure criterion is insufficient, (2) operator actions—which are difficult to predict—can significantly change the course of events, and (3) core damage needs to be considered in analyses of the consequences of an accident.

The question arises whether computer codes, as currently conceived and developed are the most appropriate tools for examining the consequences of an accident or whether they should be supplemented with plant simulators. Plant simulators look attractive because of their fast (real-time) execution, their ability to address both multiple failures and operator interaction, and their ability to consider the whole plant. Our review of PWR (training) simulators shows that they cannot handle two-phase flows within the primary coolant system and therefore cannot predict consequences of small breaks.

The NRC intends to investigate a great many accident scenarios involving multiple failures, the whole plant, and operator interactions. Should these investigations be performed with fast-running codes or with simulators?

If the former alternative is chosen, it will be necessary to model the balance of plant together with the complete set of controls and trips. Even then, it is questionable whether it will be possible to allow for arbitrary interactions by operators. The computer running time—with the whole plant modeled—is not likely to be shorter than twice the real time with computer codes designed to operate on multipurpose digital computers with sequential data processing. It should be pointed out that the small-break accidents could be two orders of magnitude longer (in real time) than those associated with a large break.

The second alternative—the use of plant simulators—becomes viable only if the existing simulators can be upgraded to make them predictive for small breaks. Upgrading the existing simulators would be the optimal solution because they (1) duplicate all features of the plant they are designed to simulate, (2) duplicate the control room and hence, allow for most realistic operator interactions, (3) run in real time, and (4) are used for operator training. Presumably, the regulatory staff would have access to such simulators for various existing plants.

If it is determined that the existing simulators cannot be upgraded to the degree necessary to meet the above objectives, it will become necessary to explore the feasibility of designing and building an engineering simulator. Current investigations show that the technology exists for simulating very complex processes with high accuracy and calculation speeds much faster than real time. Such techniques have not, however, been tried for simulation of LWR plants. The engineering simulator would utilize special-purpose computers optimized to address specific problems through parallel rather than sequential data processing. Simulation of the balance of plant presents a problem because of the large plant-to-plant variations. It is not clear whether a very flexible simulation of the balance of plant could be achieved that would allow for fast hookup of a certain number of general components, together with canned software, to represent various generic light-water reactor (LWR) designs reasonably well. The speed of computation (simulation) of the balance of plant should not be limiting. Hence, it may be possible to build an engineering simulator that could be useful in the Emergency Response Center, for example, to explore consequences of the alternate plant recovery procedures during an accident.

In summary, the detailed (slow-running) LOCA codes will be used for evaluation of the margin of safety, for large-break LOCA analyses, and for benchmarking fast-running codes and simulators. The fast-running advanced codes will be used to explore the consequences of various small-break and other transient scenarios, at least until the upgraded simulators become fully operational.

6.6.7 CODE VERIFICATION AND TEST DATA SOURCES

6.6.7.1 Terminology

The word verification has been featured in many papers and reports over the past 5 yr. Experts are uncomfortable with its use since it implies the act of proving the truth. They believe that truth cannot be claimed, either in the mathematical modeling of the immensely complex phenomena that LOCA codes need to address, or in their solution procedures. In this section the term code verification is synonymous with code assessment—determining how well the code can simulate the physical processes observed and measured in LOCA-related experiments, assessing the code's applicability to analysis of postulated accidents in full-scale LWR plants, and quantifying the error within which the code is capable of predicting certain key parameters—such as the PCT. The term verification will be retained for continuity.

It should be accepted that code developers wish to know how good the various models of the individual physical processes are, how accurate the numerical solution procedure is, how well the individual subroutines or modules simulate the behavior of system components, and, especially, how well the code performs in its totality. Nevertheless, it was felt in some quarters that it would be safer if the verification work were also audited by researchers who were not intimately involved in the development of a particular code; any vested interests would be removed and, presumably, the code assessment could be done more objectively. At the same time it was realized that the process of code development requires simultaneous performance of various stages of the verification process. This is the origin of the "developmental" and "independent" verification concepts.

The following illustrates the sequence of the developmental and independent verification activities:

1. Develop code version N and simultaneously conduct its developmental verification.
2. Repeat key cases of developmental verification, using the *frozen* version (N) of the code.
3. Document code (version N).
4. Document developmental verification.
5. Issue code and documents to public.

Repeat steps 1–5 above for code version N + 1.

1. Independently verify publically released code version N-1 (if version N-1 exists).
2. Document results of independent verification of version N-1 and issue documents to public.

Repeat steps 1 and 2 above for code version N.

6.6.7.2 Test Data Base

Before describing the verification process in detail, it will be useful to define three categories of test data sources.

1. Basic, or model, development tests are, essentially, small-scale tests for identifying and measuring basic thermohydraulic processes. Such observations and measurements are needed to formulate and check out constitutive equations describing the essential physics of interfacial transfers of mass, momentum, and energy, of wall shear and heat transfer, of liquid entrainment, droplet deposition, vapor-liquid separation, turbulent mixing, etc. Because of the increasing emphasis in advanced codes on understanding the details of the physics, it also became necessary to undertake intensive development of sophisticated measurement techniques. Basic tests are not used in code verification unless they combine simultaneous effects of more than one basic phenomenon.

2. Separate effects tests could be of small, intermediate, or large scale, emphasizing thermohydraulic processes in single system components. Examples are tests undertaken to understand fuel bundle heat transfer in all LOCA regimes; PWR downcomer and lower plenum behavior during the ECC bypass and penetration period; ECC distribution in the BWR upper plenum and penetration through the upper core support plate; phase separation in the PWR upper plenum during reflood; steam generator flow and heat transfer; behavior of centrifugal and jet pumps during off-design flow conditions; ECC mixing at the PWR cold-leg injection location; isolation valve, check valve, and pressure relief valve behavior; discharge flow through pipe ruptures; and so on. Full-height, electrically simulated fuel bundles are predominately used in the heat transfer tests, although tests featuring nuclear rods are also available.

Separate effects tests are also used to study the influence of component size and shape in order to assess the computer code's scale-up capability. Such tests are performed in both the steady-state and controlled transient modes. Various separate effects tests used or planned before 1976 are described by Fabic (1976).

3. Integral systems tests provide information about synergistic and feedback effects between system components configured to simulate a PWR or BWR and the associated coolant systems. Some examples follow. (a) Semiscale-Mod 1 features 40 electrically simulated, less than half-length fuel rods, one fully equipped "intact" loop (scaling the volumes etc. of three intact loops of a PWR), and one "broken" loop with inactive simulators for the steam generator and pump. (b) Semiscale-Mod 3 differs from Mod 1 in that the "core" contains 25 full-length fuel rod simulators and the broken loop contains an active steam generator and pump. (c) The LOBI test loop, built in Ispra, Italy, resembles Semiscale-Mod 3 except that its vessel contains 64 full-length fuel rod simulators. (d) LOFT resembles the Semiscale-Mod 1 loop except that its vessel contains 1500 nuclear rods of the same length as in Semiscale-Mod 1. However, the LOFT system size is much larger: the ratio of the LOFT volume to the Semiscale-Mod 1 volume is approximately equal to the corresponding ratio between a four-loop PWR and LOFT.

The four test facilities outlined above are capable of undergoing total (integral) LOCA transients, from full pressure and temperature conditions. (e) The Two Loop Test Apparatus (TLTA), for studies of BWR system blowdown, features one full-length, electrically heated bundle, jet pumps, and other system components. This facility has been modified to allow studies of ECC injection and system reflood. (f) The GOTA facility at Studsvik, Sweden, for BWR system reflood tests features one full-scale, electrically heated bundle. (g) The FLECHT-SET facility for PWR system reflood tests features a 100-rod, full-length electrically heated bundle and has one full-height steam generator in each of its two loops. (h) The Primären Kreislauf test facility for PWR system reflood features 340-rod, full-length electric simulators, three loops, and full-height steam generators. (i) The Japan Atomic Energy Research Institute test facility (also for PWR system reflood) features a 2000-rod, full-length electric simulator, four loops, and four full-height steam generator segments. Although this item properly belongs in the separate effects category, present FRG-Japan-U.S. plans call for performing PWR reflood tests in a 2000-rod slab vessel of full height, the slab width being equal to the full-scale vessel radius. This test will be an important milestone in checking out the TRAC code's multidimensional capability.

Tong (1980) provides an excellent summary of the existing and planned test data base, for all test categories.

6.6.7.3 Developmental Verification

Developmental verification includes, but is not constrained to, the following activities:

1. Comparisons of code results with test data selected from sources that give pertinent information to code developers. If comparisons are unsatisfactory, running time is too long, or other defects are uncovered, code improvements are attempted.
2. Check of accuracy of code numerics against either the closed form or the accurate solutions, for cases where they exist.

3. Sensitivity studies of the constitutive equations, especially those previously found to be important, to establish the best-estimate values of various coefficients, their uncertainty ranges, and probability distributions.
4. Studies of system component(s) and overall systems nodalization and time step sensitivity, utilizing best-estimate values for all coefficients in the constitutive equations, to obtain recommended nodalization for various important test facilities and for LWRs.
5. Study of code's scale-up capability. If the code yields acceptable results in comparisons with small-scale test data, what assurance exists that it will acceptably predict the full-scale behavior? Results from separate effects and integral tests are useful in this study, if different geometric sizes are present.
6. Rerun of all key comparisons with the "frozen" code version being released to the public, prior to documenting results of the developmental verification process.

6.6.7.4 Independent Verification

Independent verification emphasizes blind predictions of data obtained in integral test facilities, in addition to spot-checking (auditing) results of the developmental verification. In conducting blind runs, actual (measured) initial and boundary conditions are considered. Double-blind prediction—i.e., with nominal rather than actual run conditions employed in generating the code input—has no intrinsic value if the actual and nominal test conditions differ for important parameters.

Blind prediction is considerably more valuable if it involves a new test facility or a type of test, in an existing facility, that differs significantly from test conditions already utilized in the developmental verification process.

The code assessment matrix recommended by Fabic and Andersen (1981) for independent assessment of an advanced LWR systems code such as TRAC involves about 50% of all the available integral systems tests, about 30% of the available separate effects tests, and a small fraction of the available basic tests. Stated differently, this choice involves about 90 integral systems tests, about 170 separate effects tests, and about 60 basic tests, indicating that the total number of tests available in each category is smallest for the integral systems tests and largest for the basic tests.

The factors that influenced this selection were as follows:

1. Integral systems tests:
   a. Coverage of accident/transient scenarios. Scenarios associated with a greater risk to the public are given more prominence.
   b. Facility design (PWR, BWR). Facilities featuring nuclear cores are given more weight.
   c. Facility scale, including not only the volumetric scale but also the number of active loops, core length, and steam generator height. The larger the test scale, the more emphasis in the selection.
   d. Quality, quantity, and diversity of measurements.
   e. Virginity. Tests scheduled for a new facility, or new and significantly different tests for an existing facility, play a prominent part in the selected

test data base, as they offer the best opportunity to examine the predictive capability of the code.

2. Separate effects tests:
   a. Coverage of system components, except for those, such as a centrifugal pump, that the code describes purely empirically. Whether the empiricism adopted for such a component is adequate can be determined from the integral systems test data.
   b. Design. The more faithful the geometric simulation and the greater the ability to reproduce the processes expected in the particular LWR component, the stronger the candidacy.
   c. Scale. The larger the scale, the stronger the candidacy.
   d. Quality, quantity, and diversity of measurements.
   e. Virginity.
   f. Age. Newer tests featuring better controls and measurements take precedence; an example is FLECHT versus FLECHT-SEASET.
   g. Potential for studying the code's capability for serving as a scaling tool. This includes the potential to study the validity of physical models in the code.
   h. Diversity of initial and boundary conditions.

3. Basic tests:
   a. Exclusion of all tests used for the development of correlations utilized by the code, and other empiricism embedded in the constitutive relations. (This was one of the biggest contributors to reducing the number of candidate cases.)
   b. Elimination of tests with fluids other than air, water, and steam, because they would require development of specific equations of state, and the empiricism built into the code involving the fluids of interest in reactor safety may not be valid for other fluids (e.g., Freon).
   c. Emphasis on tests, in the same facility, where gradual introduction of complexities could help in assessing the "physics" of fluid flow and heat transfer built into the code. Tests featuring simple geometry and two-phase fluid transients are also useful for assessment of the numerical solution technique.
   d. Emphasis on tests sponsored by the NRC, because analytic support is, in most cases, required to ascertain that test results can be assimilated by the systems and component codes used in the reactor safety work.

6.6.7.5 Choice of Computed Results Used in Determination of Code Accuracy

The choice of results selected for code assessment could involve global and local, single-valued results; time histories of results; and statistical measure of fit of time histories. It is certainly necessary to select the key results that reflect the basic mission of the code and for which information on code accuracy needs to be obtained and compared with code acceptance criteria. In addition, results must be identified that provide information about the ability of the code to model the relevant physical processes.

Global and Local, Single-valued Results

For code comparisons against test data from the basic and separate effects tests, local, single-valued results need to be determined on a case-by-case basis, depending on the individual processes or system components. Examples are too numerous to be listed here.

The following global and local, single-valued results pertain to comparisons with integral systems test data: Results defining the reactor core clad temperature "signatures." These are described in detail further on and are applicable to all types of accidents and transients. Incidentally, they are also applicable to separate effects tests featuring single fuel bundles or bundle arrays.

Other results particularly applicable to small-break LOCAs may involve:

1. Minimum liquid or froth level (whichever measured) reached in the reactor vessel.
2. Amount of heat removed by a specified steam generator during a specified time period, $0 - t^*$. t^* may be the final core quench time or the time at which some operator action is initiated.
3. Amount of coolant mass lost through the break during the same time period.
4. Amount of coolant energy released through the break during the same time period.
5. Times (seconds) when coolant pressure in the upper plenum reaches 10 and 5 MPa, respectively. These quantities provide the pressure "signature" for certain types of small-break LOCAs. For types featuring very small break sizes the time and magnitude of the minimum pressure may be more relevant.

Other global results, pertaining to large-break LOCAs and to non-LOCA transients, may involve:

1. Times to start and end the discharge of ECC accumulators in the intact loop(s).
2. Time to start LPIS (Low Pressure Injection System).
3. Time of the minimum coolant inventory within the lower plenum.
4. Time when the lower plenum liquid inventory first exceeds 90% of maximum.
5. Time when the minimum liquid inventory is reached on the secondary side of a specified steam generator.
6. Time of first activation of the steam generator relief valve.
7. Time of first activation of the pressurizer safety valve.
8. Minimum coolant pressure reached, etc.

Examples of various plotting formats for the quantity ϕ representing any of the global results above are illustrated in figure 6.6.5.

Time Histories of Results

Plotted overlays of time histories of the predicted and measured results provide the most useful information regarding the code's capability and, in particular, the consistency of the calculated trends.

In the case of the basic and separate effects tests, it is important to plot all results for which measurements are made, as well as other results that shed light on the consistency of trends.

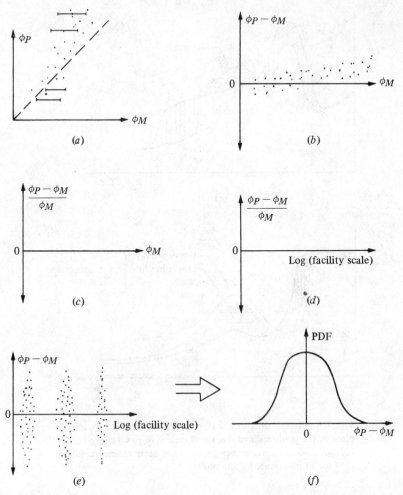

Figure 6.6.5 Alternative plots of global results. ϕ is a single-valued key result; subscript P indicates a predicted value, and M indicates a measured (best-estimate) value. Cases (c) and (d) are suitable for ϕ = time. Case (e) illustrates prediction uncertainty that is scale-independent. If scale effects exhibit clear trends, it may be possible to extrapolate to an LWR.

For comparison against data from integral systems tests, examples include the time histories of clad temperature, the mass of liquid within the lower and the upper plenum, the upper plenum pressure, the local void fractions within regions of the reactor vessel (where measured), the froth or liquid level positions within the vessel for small-break cases, and results for all the important measurements recorded in the loop spool pieces (local void fraction, coolant temperature, fluid velocity, pressure differentials, metal temperature) and other system components (steam generator, pressurizer, etc.).

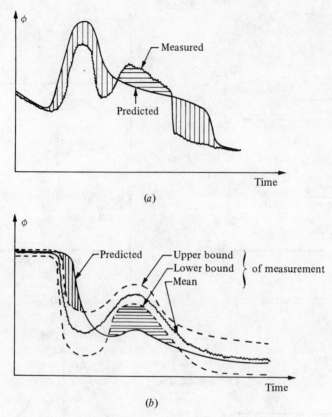

Figure 6.6.6 Information for statistical manipulation of overlay plots of the predicted and measured time histories. Hatched areas indicate zones of disagreement. (a) Case of accurate measurement. (b) Case of inaccurate measurement.

Statistical Measure of Fit of Time Histories

Overlays of time histories are not amenable to condensation of results and to application of the acceptance criteria. Therefore statistical means have been proposed by some researchers for quantifying the discrepancies between calculated and measured results. For example, the hatched areas in figure 6.6.6, indicating the amount of discrepancy, could be weighted differently for different time segments of the transient (e.g., blowdown, refill, reflood), for different results (e.g., flows, pressures, temperatures), and even for different regions of the system. The idea is to produce "statistics" of the code accuracy that can be expressed by a figure of merit related to the sum of all the weighted areas of discrepancies, perhaps normalized by the number of terms in the sum. Other statistical approaches can be concocted, with an endless variety of weighting factors and figures of merit.

The final aim would be to compare the figure of merit for each test case against some acceptable bound and count the percentage that remained within. The main disadvantage of this approach is that it obscures the information regarding the validity of physical models and the computed trends. In addition, it may be extremely difficult to specify weighting factors and other assumptions that would be widely acceptable.

Current Approach at NRC

The current approach being tried at NRC/RES is to utilize the global and local key results enumerated above for the case of integral systems tests and confront them with acceptance criteria, if and when they become available. In addition, the approach relies heavily on numerous overlays of time histories and subjective judgments of their validity for all test categories.

6.6.7.6 Quantification of Clad Temperature Signatures

The measured time behavior signature of fuel clad temperature T_{CL} reflects the local core hydraulics. For example, the time when the clad temperature commences its first excursion in the case of large cold-leg break LOCA (signature illustrated in figure 6.6.7) denotes the condition of an increase in the local void fraction and a decrease in the local mass velocity. The temperature decrease after its first peak is a consequence of an enhanced local cooling caused by a surge of coolant from above or below. The last local quench, at time t_{LQ}, is caused by the reflood process. A small-break LOCA clad temperature signature is illustrated in figure 6.6.8, where the onset of temperature excursion indicates the local increase in void fraction caused by the falling liquid or froth level or the depletion of the vessel coolant inventory.

Given the facts that (1) the majority of experiments are conducted with electric simulators of the nuclear fuel rods, (2) most tests feature fairly extensive measurement locations for the clad temperature, and (3) very few tests provide indication of the local void fraction in the core while measurements of the local fluid velocities in the core interior are extremely rare, the information provided by the clad temperature signatures presents the only feasible way of evaluating the code performance where it matters most.

A computer code calculates such signatures for each computational cell representing a given core region. There may be more than one measured signature

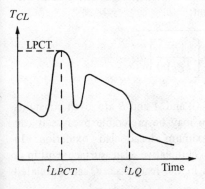

Figure 6.6.7 Sample T_{CL} signature for large-break LOCA.

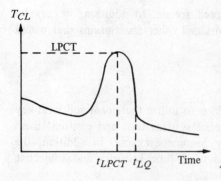

Figure 6.6.8 Sample T_{CL} signature for small-break LOCA.

within individual computational cells. Some weighted mean—to diminish the influence of thermocouples facing the unpowered rods or the control rods—must be employed in making comparisons with test data. In comparisons of computed and measured clad temperature histories, for qualitative assessment, the upper and lower bounds of the measured histories should also be shown.

The issues at hand are (1) how to represent a signature, (2) how to quantity the difference between the measured and the predicted signatures, and (3) how to specify and apply the acceptance criteria. Three single-valued parameters are indicated in figures 6.6.7 and 6.6.8 that collectively aid in identifying the signature: The local peak clad temperature LPCT, the local time of peak clad temperature t_{LPCT}, and the local final quench time t_{LQ}. If these three parameters are insufficient to identify the signature, one may also consider some forms of the weighted integral.

One such integral may be of the form

$$I_{\Delta T\text{sat}} = \int_0^{t_{LQ}} [T_{CL}(t) - T_{\text{sat}}(t)]^n \, dt$$

where $n > 1$ (say $n = 2$) emphasizes the peaks above T_{sat}. The quantities in the integral and the upper limit of integration would come either from the code (for $I_{\Delta T\text{sat,calc}}$) or from measurements (for $I_{\Delta T\text{sat,meas}}$), utilizing the weighted average mentioned above.

Another type of signature integral may assume the form used in the computation of the local amount of clad oxide penetration:

$$\Delta R_{\text{ox}} = \sqrt{2A \int_0^{t_{LQ}} \exp\left[\frac{B}{T_{CL}(t)}\right] dt}$$

where it is assumed that no oxide existed at $t = 0$, and A and B are given constants featured in the Cathcart-Pawel model. This form may be preferable because it can be related to the regulatory limit for maximum local clad oxidation. In addition, summation of all ΔR_{ox} (times the cumulative clad surface within a computational cell), over all computational cells in the reactor core, can be related to the global (corewide) amount of clad oxidation and, therefore, hydrogen genera-tion. Allowable upper bounds for both are currently specified in the Appendix K acceptance criteria in reactor licensing applications.

Admittedly, the oxidation thickness is not directly measured and the PCTs reached in experiments may not be high enough to give a significant contribution to ΔR_{ox}. Nevertheless, the difference $\log (\Delta R_{\text{ox}})_{\text{calc}} - \log (\Delta R_{\text{ox}})_{\text{meas}}$ is a meaningful representation of the code's ability to calculate the clad temperature signature.

Knowledge of how well the local signatures are predicted sheds light on the code's ability to calculate multidimensional behavior where it matters most. Even in one-dimensional calculations, it is important to know whether the code calculates well the axial distribution of signatures. If these comparisons are not adequate, then it is questionable whether the code has predictive capabilities, even if the corewide properties, such as the global peak clad temperature (GPCT) and the global t_{GPCT} and $(t_{LQ})_{\text{max}}$, are well predicted.

Should all the parameters above (LPCT, t_{LPCT}, t_{LQ}, $I_{\Delta T\text{sat}}$, or ΔR_{ox}) be used in quantifying the prediction accuracy, or only some of them? Some strategies may ignore the local signatures and only quantify the accuracy for the global parameters, such as GPCT (the largest PCT anywhere), and the summation of $I_{\Delta T\text{sat}}$ (or ΔR_{ox}) over all cells. One should bear in mind that the differences between the measured and predicted times, t_{LPCT} or t_{LQ} or t_{GPCT} or $(t_{LQ})_{\text{max}}$, may differ greatly for large- and small-break LOCAs, or for short- versus long-duration transients. For such situations it may therefore be more convenient to feature the differences in predicted and measured times, divided by the measured time, to fit many comparisons on the same scale. It appears that condensation of results of compari-sons with many test cases could be done only for the global parameters. The local parameters can be plotted as illustrated in figure 6.6.9.

The most informative way to display the calculated versus measured signatures is shown in figure 6.6.10, pertaining to a vertical stack of computational cells at a given azimuthal location illustrated in figure 6.6.11. Such a display is useful for a qualitative rather than a quantitative assessment of the code and is not amenable to confrontation with acceptance criteria.

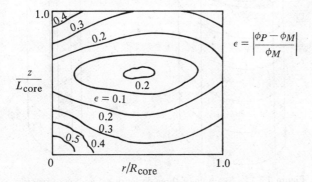

Figure 6.6.9 Contours of equal values of ϵ for local parameters.

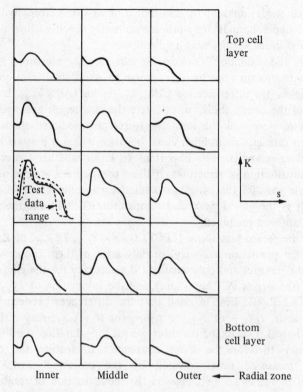

Figure 6.6.10 Clad temperature histories in the stack of cells pertaining to a specific circumferential zone (used for qualitative assessment).

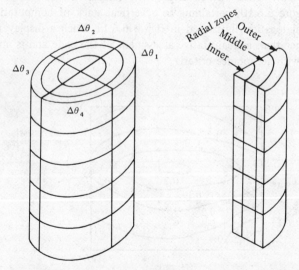

Figure 6.6.11 Example of three-dimensional noding of reactor core with illustration of a stack of cells for which the temperature histories are plotted, as in figure 6.6.10.

6.6.7.7 Characterization of Code Accuracy

Measurement of some physical property ϕ is reported in terms of its best-estimate (or mean or nominal) value and its uncertainty band, supplemented (in some cases) by information on the confidence level. Measurement uncertainty is caused by imperfections in the measuring instrument, in signal processing, and in the models through which certain indirect measurements are combined to define ϕ. The narrower the uncertainty band, the more accurate is the measurement. In other words, the measurement accuracy is characterized by the magnitude of the measurement uncertainty.

The best-estimate code predictions also contain uncertainties. In addition, the nominal or best-estimate value of the code prediction may differ from the nominal or best-estimate value of the measurement. The smaller that difference (or the offset) and the narrower the uncertainty band of the code prediction, the more accurate is the code.

In the following, the causes of prediction uncertainty will be described together with two methods for its quantification. The preferred method will be indicated.

Sources of Code Prediction Uncertainty

Uncertainty in the prediction of key single-valued results for an LWR can be viewed as the result of:

1. Uncertainty in the plant condition at the onset of a given accident scenario. The plant condition may include fuel burnup, peaking factors, core power, and water levels in ECC accumulators and in the steam generator secondary side. For obvious reasons, these uncertainties are not considered in the course of code assessment.

2. Uncertainties in modeling reactor fuel rod thermal and mechanical properties, such as the thermal conductivity of UO_2, gap conductance as affected by gap size, gap gas composition and pressure, pellet deformation, clad deformation, etc. Information about the nuclear fuel rod modeling uncertainty is obtained from a separate assessment program involving fuel behavior codes. That information is pertinent to systems codes, since the latter will eventually include all models and correlations that were found to be important.

    Even though most of the test data bases used for assessment of systems codes feature electric heaters for simulation of nuclear fuel rods, uncertainties related to their modeling are still present. For example, electric heaters may contain nonuniform materials properties, nonuniform centering of the heater coils or tubes, and uncertainties in heater coil spacing and installation of clad thermocouples. Effects of these nonuniformities and shadow and/or fin cooling effects of clad thermocouples are not accounted for in mathematical/physical models of fuel simulators. Their effects should, however, not be ignored in forming conclusions about code accuracy.

3. Uncertainties in modeling the reactor primary and secondary coolant systems thermohydraulics. The causes are:

a. Code input uncertainties related to physical properties or to coefficients whose specification is left to the discretion of the code user. The current trend in the design of advanced codes is to eliminate, as much as possible, input choices left to user discretion.
b. Coefficients embedded in the code that are related to physical models and/or correlations.
c. Degree of system geometry discretization used for numerical solution.
d. Upper limits on time steps and on convergence criteria.
e. Adequacy or inadequacy of the set of conservation (field) equations solved in the code.
f. Adequacy or inadequacy of the thermohydraulic models for interphasic and fluid/wall interactions and for the flow/heat transfer regime recognition criteria.
g. Truncation and numerical diffusion errors inherent in the numerical solution strategy.
h. Inability to address phenomena of a stochastic nature.
i. Coding (programming) errors.

Quantification of Code Uncertainty through Statistical Code Uncertainty Study

Such a study requires

Specification of a particular accident or transient scenario.

Specification of the key result, such as the PCT for which the probability distribution function is to be determined, as affected by the uncertainties in the selected input parameters.

Identification of the parameters to be varied, together with their individual uncertainty ranges and individual probability distribution functions.

Only the uncertainties listed above in 1, 2, and 3, a–d, can be examined by this method. This is an important limitation since it implies that the code formulation is perfect, the numerical solution flawless, and code errors nonexistent.

Only a limited number of parameters to be varied can be considered, since the method requires very significant expenditures of computing resources. Consequently, prior knowledge of the importance of each uncertain input parameter is needed to select only those that are judged to affect significantly the chosen key result.

Numerous computer runs are performed, each featuring different values of each variable input parameter x_i, sampled from within the individual uncertainty ranges. The most commonly used sampling procedures involve the "experimental design" and "Latin hypercube" methods (McKay & Conover 1976). The latter was specifically designed to minimize the number of computer runs. Results of all computer runs define the manner in which the computed key result Y (say the PCT) changes due to code input variations. These changes are represented by a response surface in the form of an algebraic expression $Y = F(x_1, x_2, \ldots, x_n)$.

The next step is to perform Monte Carlo calculations with the response surface to obtain the PCT probability distribution. This step requires knowledge of the probability distribution $p(x_i)$ for each variable parameter x_i defining the response surface. Many of these will be judgmental. However, since the Monte Carlo calculations with the response surface are fast and economical, a variety of forms of $p(x_i)$ can easily be explored.

Figure 6.6.12 illustrates the steps in the statistical code uncertainty study.

Code uncertainty studies are very expensive and their results are restricted to the selected accident scenario. In the past, when the main emphasis was placed on the large-break LOCA, it was reasonable to argue for the need for such studies to (1) get an idea of the probability distribution of the computed key result (PCT, etc.), (2) prioritize the efforts in code development, and (3) prioritize the experimental programs.

The new research direction, which does not focus on one particular accident scenario, may refrain from extensive use of code uncertainty studies—unless very fast-running and economical tools for analyses become available.

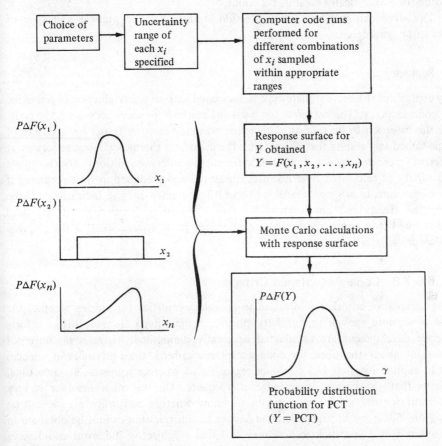

Figure 6.6.12 Illustration of procedure for statistical study of code uncertainty.

Information on Code Uncertainty from Scatter Plots

In the statistical code uncertainty study, input parameters are varied around their best-estimate or nominal values. If, on the other hand, code predictions are made of many test situations, using only the nominal or best-estimate input values, plots of predicted minus measured (nominal or best-estimate) values of key single-valued results will exhibit scatter, as illustrated in figure 6.6.5. That scatter not only will reflect the uncertainties associated with the nominal values of the code input and the embedded coefficients, but will account for *all* the effects listed under 3, a–i, above.

Through proper normalization of the ordinate in the scatter plot, the abscissa can account for a large variety of test conditions, at different geometric scales.

Scatter plots are amenable to quantification of the code uncertainty probability distribution function and of the offset, provided sufficient entries are present to provide for a statistically meaningful count.

This approach influences the selection strategy for the number and type of cases to be considered.

Summary

Any analysis of the best-estimate type is associated with an uncertainty band reflecting the code accuracy. The narrower the band (or scatter), the more accurate is the code. For this assertion to be valid the prediction accuracy must be tested for a variety of single-valued key results that characterize the important thermohydraulic processes, at different geometric scales and with different boundary conditions. Overlay plots of a variety of calculated time histories (measured and predicted, or just predicted if the measurements are not available) should be obtained to give indications of the computed trends and consistency. Plots of the spatial distribution of the local results (predicted minus measured) are also used to determine whether the physical models are adequate.

6.6.7.8   Code Acceptance Criteria

Code acceptance criteria are intended to provide a yardstick for judging whether the code is accurate enough to fulfill its mission. If the criteria are met, further efforts in code development are terminated or greatly diminished. There is no universal agreement about the need for code acceptance criteria, since advances in sciences and in applied research will continue regardless of whether someone, at some time, believes that the current knowledge is adequate. On the other hand, it is very important for the regulatory agencies to know whether and when a code can be relied on. Some might argue that the answer to this question cannot be obtained in the absence of a yardstick; others may feel that a subjective judgment could serve equally well.

Most people agree that predicted results that lie between the measurement uncertainty bounds are automatically acceptable. However, some measurements are poor enough to provide little challenge even for simple codes. In other instances, the computational mesh is made so coarse that many measurements are taken within a computational cell; their combined scatter is then used to define such a wide uncertainty band that most codes would pass the accuracy test. A typical example may be a very coarse nodalization of the reactor core and comparison of clad temperature signatures. This approach serves no useful purpose in code assessment, unless one is trying to prove that, because of special conservatisms used in the code, the computed results are upper bounds for the measured temperatures. Some measurements (temperatures, pressures, pressure differentials), however, are so accurate that code acceptance criteria based on their uncertainty bands are unnecessarily stringent.

Realizing that such easy acceptance criteria are not going to be helpful, let us see what could be done for the selected global results. It should again be pointed out that a global result is represented either by the difference between the predicted and measured values, or by that difference divided by the measured value. The former is more amenable for temperatures and certain other single-valued results. Global results involving time are better represented by the latter method, owing to wide ranges of transient durations.

The acceptance criteria may be connected to some regulatory requirements or may originate from an accuracy goal that is thought to be achievable.

Current regulatory requirements for conservative analyses of the design basis LOCA prohibit the PCT from exceeding 1478 K. Best-estimate analyses of the design basis LOCA yield much lower PCTs. How accurate should such best-estimate analyses be? Having concluded in the preceding section that the best-estimate analysis is associated with a probability distribution, which appears to be "normal" in the case of PCT, it may be possible to define an acceptable standard deviation as a function of the regulatory limit. For example, it could be required that the standard deviation σ_{tot} be of such magnitude that the probability of the PCT exceeding the regulatory limit is $\leqslant 5\%$. As illustrated in figure 6.6.13, such a

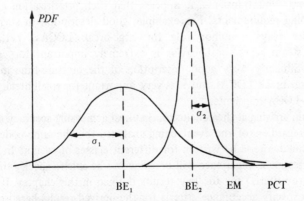

Figure 6.6.13 Illustration of two probability distribution functions for PCT, both of which obey the limitation on the probability of PCT exceeding some regulatory limit (EM). The case featuring the best-estimate (BE) value of PCT that is closer to the regulatory limit demands a more accurate code, i.e., smaller standard deviation.

criterion would tolerate a fairly large uncertainty (for the PCT) if the best-estimate (or mean) value were much lower than 1478 K. Conversely, if the best-estimate value of GPCT happened to be much closer to the regulatory limit, the required standard deviation would be so small as to be unattainable. Considerations of multiple failures and operator actions may, in some instances, lead to cases in which the regulatory limit is not only reached but even exceeded. It appears, therefore, that the prescription for code acceptance described above may not be very useful.

This leads us to acceptance criteria based on an accuracy goal that is thought to be achievable. However, the proof of code accuracy must come from an in-depth assessment of the code involving many comparisons with test data. The available, or achievable, test data base may in itself impose a limitation on the code accuracy that can be substantiated as pertinent to LWRs.

These considerations lead us to believe that a reasonable accuracy goal, reflecting the current state of the art in code development, can be posed only after a good deal of experience has been gained in assessment of the current generation of codes. From what is known today, and based on the experience gained thus far in assessment of the advanced systems code (TRAC), a reasonable accuracy goal for the PCT may amount to 80–100°C in $\sigma_{T\text{-}H}$ and 100–135°C in σ_{FB} (nuclear fuel), resulting in a σ_{tot} of about 125–170°C for calculating accidents and transients that do not involve significant core damage. $\sigma_{T\text{-}H}$ and σ_{FB} denote standard deviations associated with thermohydraulics and fuel behavior predictions, respectively.

An accuracy of 20% for times t_{PCT} and t_{LQ} may be achievable. No experience exists so far to forecast the achievable accuracy in $I_{\Delta T}$ or ΔR_{ox} (defined in section 6.6.7.6).

One may be tempted to invoke the code sensitivity studies for prioritization of various systems effects on the clad temperature signatures, since other key results measure the code's ability to describe these effects; more stringent accuracy would be required for systems effects that more strongly influence the core thermohydraulics. Bearing in mind, however, that the same code could be used to analyze different accidents and transients, it appears that such prioritization efforts could lead to conflicting requirements. For example, good description of steam generator thermohydraulics plays a minor role for large-break LOCAs. Yet, very good description of steam generator behavior is extremely important for certain small-break LOCAs. Similarly, very good description of the pressure-time history is not essential for large-break LOCAs, but it is very important for small-break LOCAs and for certain non-LOCA transients.

Are we again arriving at the conclusion that best achievable accuracy is needed for all key results regardless of the event being analyzed (by the same code), or should separate acceptance criteria be written for different classes of events? In a year or so enough code assessment experience will be gained to be able to specify the achievable goals (acceptance criteria) for the key results defined in this chapter. It would take much longer to specify acceptance criteria for the derived results based on statistical manipulation for predicted versus measured time histories, and this approach is not recommended. In the meantime, emphasis is being placed on displays (overlays) of measured and predicted time histories of all results listed in section 6.6.7.5, to ascertain whether correct trends are predicted and to make subjective judgments about the code adequacy.

6.6.7.9 Code Verification Results

During 1979 and 1980 the TRAC-P1A code underwent extensive verification. Illustration by a few comparisons with test data would not be informative and might, in fact, be misleading. Readers interested in learning about the code's capabilities should consult the references listed below:

1. Vigil, J. C. et al. 1979 TRAC-P1A Developmental Assessment, *Rept.* NUREG/CR-1059, LA-8059-MS.
2. Saha, P. et al. 1980 Annual Report on TRAC Independent Assessment at BNL, *Rept.* BNL-NUREG-27580.
3. Rohatgi, U. S. & Saha, P. 1980 Constitutive Relations in TRAC-P1A, *Rept.* BNL-NUREG-51258, NUREG/CR-1651.
4. Knight, T. 1980 TRAC-P1A Assessment-1979, *Rept.* LA-8477-MS.
5. Peterson, A. C. 1980 TRAC-P1A Independent Assessment Summary, *Rept.* EGG-CAAP-5147.
6. Lekach, S. V. 1980 Calculation of the CANON Experiment Using the TRAC Code, *Rept.* BNL-NUREG-28290.
7. Wheatley, P. D. 1979 Comparison of TRAC-P1A Calculation with LOFT L2-3 Experimental Results, *Rept.* EGG-CAAP-5072.
8. Demmie, P. N. 1980 An Analysis of Semiscale MOD-1 LOCE S-04-6 Using the TRAC-P1A Computer Program, *Rept.* EGG-CAAP-5181.
9. Larson, J. R. 1980 Calculation of a Large Cold Leg Break with Steam Generator Tube Ruptures in a PWR Using the TRAC-P1A Computer Program, *Rept.* EGG-CAAP-5189.
10. Wheatley, P. D., & Bolander, M. A. 1980 TRAC-P1A Calculations for a 200%, 0.25 m Diameter, and 0.1 m Diameter Cold Leg Break in a Pressurized Water Reactor, *Rept.* EGG-CAAP-5190.
11. Bolander, M. A. 1980 TRAC-P1A Calculations for a 200% Hot Leg Break and a 200% Hot Leg Break Simultaneous with a Rupture of 16 Steam Generator Tubes in a Pressurized Water Reactors, *Rept.* EGG-CAAP-5191.

Reference 1 deals with results of developmental verification performed, with a "frozen" code, by its developers. References 2–5 summarize the independent verification effort performed by the staffs of three national laboratories. References 6–8 give details of comparisons of TRAC-P1A predictions with data from particular tests. Finally, references 9–11 do not present comparisons with test data, but examine the code's capability to handle a variety of severe PWR accidents.

The current effort involves independent assessment of TRAC-PD2. Independent verification of the improved (or new) versions of the same code may require repetition of only a certain of the comparisons that were made with the preceding code version, one test from each integral system test facility (domestic and foreign), and repetition of previous tests that the preceding code version predicted poorly. Hence, the majority of test comparisons with the new code version may feature new cases from the overall code assessment "matrix," emphasizing new and, especially, "virgin" tests. Independent verification of the RELAP-5 code will be initiated during 1981.

6.7 Nomenclature for Chapter 6

ROMAN LETTERS

A	area, m^2
a	acceleration, m/s^2
a_1, a_2	constants
a, b, c, d, e, f	coefficients in power law expressions
B	enhancement factor [6.5.42]
B_k	property group
$b(z)$	dimensionless amplitude of interface oscillation
C	continuity balance
C	concentration of droplets in vapor core
C_{sf}	coefficient in [6.2.1]
C_E	concentration of droplets under hydrodynamic equilibrium conditions
C_{pL}	liquid specific heat
c	specific heat
c_0	velocity of sound in fluid
c_L	liquid specific heat
D	characteristic dimension
D	diameter
D_e	hydraulic diameter
D_e	equivalent diameter of channel
D_b	tube bundle diameter
D_b	bubble departure diameter
E	energy balance
F	function
$F'(z)$	F factor
f	friction factor
f	frequency
f_0	friction factor without injection
f_{tp}	two-phase friction factor

G	mass flux, kg/m^2 s
g	acceleration due to gravity, m/s^2
h	enthalpy, J/kg
h_{LG}	latent heat of vaporization,
h_G	saturated enthalpy for vapor
h_L	saturated enthalpy for liquid
h_{tp}	local enthalpy
Δh_{sub}	subcooling enthalpy
J	rate of formation of clusters
J	bubble nucleation site population distribution function
K	coefficient
k	Boltzmann constant
k	deposition mass transfer coefficient, m/s
L	characteristic dimension, m
L_B	boiling length, m
M	mass, kg
M	momentum balance
$\dot{M}$	mass rate of flow through channel, kg/s
$\dot{M}_{LF}$	liquid film flow rate
$\dot{m}$	mass flux, kg/m^2 s
$\dot{m}_D$	rate of deposition of droplets
$\dot{m}_E$	rate of entrainment
$\dot{m}_{LF}$	mass flux in liquid film
N	dimensionality of grid
P	wetted perimeter, m
P_h	heated perimeter, m
P_{tot}	total channel perimeter, m
p	pressure, Pa
p_c	critical pressure, Pa
p_G	vapor pressure
p_L	liquid pressure
p_g	partial pressure of gas
p_∞	saturation pressure
$\dot{q}$	heat flux, W/m^2
$\dot{q}_c$	burnout heat flux
$\dot{q}_{c,sat}$	burnout heat flux for saturated conditions
$\dot{q}_b$	heat transfer at bubble locations
$\dot{q}_0$	initial heat flux
$\dot{q}_{min}$	minimum heat flux
$\dot{q}(z)$	actual heat flux varying with position along channel
R	universal gas constant
R	radius, m
R'	nondimensional radius
R_G	gas constant
R_J	jet radius

R_{cav}	cavity radius
r	rod radius
r^*	dimensionless radius
r_c^*	critical bubble radius
r_{max}	maximum cavity size
r_s	radius of largest cavity present
S	Chen's nucleation suppression factor
s	entropy, J/kg K
T	temperature, K
T_{sat}	saturation temperature
ΔT_{sub}	difference between saturation temperature and bulk liquid temperature
t	time, s
t_c	bubble growth time
t_w	waiting time between bubbles
U	approach velocity of liquid, m/s
u	velocity
V_{inj}	velocity of injected fluid
v	flooding rate
v	volume, m³
v	latent specific volume change
W_B	power input over boiling length, W
w	mass, kg
x	quality
x_i	inlet quality
x_{BO}	quality at burnout
Y	correction factor given by [6.5.9]
y	height, m
z	distance along channel, m
z^*	distance along channel at which last droplets disappear, m

DIMENSIONLESS GROUPS

Bi	Biot number
Fr	Froude number
Gr*	Grashof number
N_q	dimensionless group [6.3.31]
Nu	Nusselt number
Pe	Peclet number
Pr	Prandtl number
Re	Reynolds number
St	Stanton number
Vi	viscosity number
We$_G$	Weber number

GREEK LETTERS

$\alpha, \alpha(z)$	heat transfer coefficient, W/m² K
$\alpha, \langle\alpha\rangle$	void fraction

α_c	heat transfer coefficient associated with conduction
α_r	heat transfer coefficient associated with radiation
β	cavity angle
Γ_G	vapor generation rate, kg/m^2 s
δ	bubble layer thickness, m
δ	thickness of vapor blanket
δ	droplet diameter
δ_F	film thickness
θ	contact angle
κ	thermal diffusivity
λ	thermal conductivity, (W/m^2)/(K/m)
λ	Taylor instability wavelength, m
λ_c	minimum wavelength for Taylor instability
λ_D	maximum wavelength for Taylor instability
λ_H	wavelength of Helmholtz instability
λ_L	liquid thermal conductivity, (W/m^2)/(K/m)
μ	viscosity, kg/m · s
μ	chemical potential
ν	Planck constant
ρ	density, kg/m^3
ρ_{Gf}	vapor density at film temperature
σ	surface tension N/m
τ	shear stress, N/m^2
τ_I	interfacial shear stress
χ_{tt}	Martinelli parameter
ψ	modeling parameter
ψ	parameter in Groeneveld-Delorme correlation
ψ_H	modeling parameter for horizontal flows

SUBSCRIPTS

agit	agitation
B	boiling
BO	burnout
b	bubble
b	bulk
c	critical
c	conduction
c	cross-sectional
c	value at burnout
cav	cavity
cl	centerline
cond	condensation
crit	value at thermodynamic critical point
D	departure
D	droplet
DO	dryout

d	dispersed liquid droplets
dc	direct contact
dow	absence of contact
E	entrainment, thermodynamic
EQ	equilibrium
e	equilibrium
e	equivalent
eq	equivalent
evap	evaporation
f	film
G	vapor
g	inert gas component of vapor
H	horizontal
H	Helmholtz
h	heated
h	hydraulic
I	interfacial
i	inlet
incip	incipient
inj	injection
J	jet
L	liquid
LF	liquid film
$LPCT$	local peak clad temperature
LQ	local quench
l	latent heat
l	evaporating
m	mixture
max	maximum
min	minimum
nb	nucleate boiling
nu	nonuniform
nucl	nucleation
ox	oxide
p	pressure
qf	quench front
r	radiation
S	solid
sat	saturation
sub	subcooling
sp	single-phase
smooth	smooth interface
t	turbulence
tb	transition boiling
tot	total
tp	two-phase

u	uniform
W	wall
w	waiting
z	edge of bubble layer
0	initial

6.8 References for Chapter 6

Abdelmessih, A. H., Fakhri, A., & Yin, S. T. 1974 Hysteresis Effects in Incipient Boiling Superheat of Freon-11, *Proc. 5th Int. Heat Transfer Conf., Tokyo* paper B45. 4:165.

Addoms, J. N. 1948 Heat Transfer at High Rates to Water Boiling outside Cylinders, Ph.D. thesis, Massachusetts Inst. of Technology, Cambridge.

Adorni, N., Gaspari, G. P., Germani, G., & Peterlongo, G. 1964 Heat Transfer Crisis with Steam-Water Mixtures in Complex Geometries: Experimental Data in Annuli and Clusters, *CISE Rept.* R-123.

Adorni, N., Gaspari, G. P., Germani, F., Hassid, A., Ravetta, R., & Rubiera, L. 1966 Heat Transfer Crisis and Pressure Drop with Steam-Water Mixtures: Experimental Data with Seven Rod Bundles at 50 and 70 kg/cm^2, *CISE Rept.* R-170.

Agee, L. J., Banerjee, S., Duffey, R. D., & Hughes, E. D. 1978 Some Aspects of Two-Fluid Models for Two-Phase Flow and Their Numerical Solution, *2d OECD/NEA Specialists Meet. Transient Two-Phase Flow, Paris,* paper T2.

Ahmad, S. Y. 1970 Axial Distribution of Bulk Temperature and Void Fraction in a Heated Channel with Inlet Subcooling, *J. Heat Transfer, Trans. ASME,* Ser. C 92:595–609.

Ahmad, S. Y. 1973 Fluid to Fluid Modelling of Critical Heat Flux: A Compensated Distortion Model, *Int. J. Heat Mass Transfer* 16:641–661.

Alekseev, G. V., Zenkevich, B. A., Peskov, O. L., Sergeev, N. D., & Subbotin, V. I. 1964 Burnout Heat Fluxes under Forced Water Flow, *3d U.N. Int. Conf. Peaceful Uses Atomic Energy,* A/Conf. 28/P/237a.

Amm, H. & Ulrych, G. 1974. Comparison of Measured Heat Transfer Coefficients during Reflooding a 340-Rod Bundle and Those Calculated from Current Heat Transfer Correlations, *European Two-Phase Flow Group Meet., Harwell,* paper E7.

Andersen, P. S., Astrup, P., Eget, L., & Rathmann, O. 1977 Numerical Experience with the Two-Fluid Model, RISQUE, *Proc. Topical Meet. Thermal Reactor Safety, Sun Valley, Idaho,* CONF-770708. 2:409–423.

Andréoni, D. 1975 Echanges Thermiques lors du Renoyage d'un Coeur de Réacteur à Eau dans le Cadre de l'Accident de Référence, D. Ing. Thesis, Univ. of Grenoble.

Austin, L. 1903 *Mitt. Forsch.* 7:75.

Averin, E. K. 1954 *Izv. Akad. Nauk SSSR Otd. Tekh. Nauk* 3:116; AERE Lib. transl. 562.

Bailey, N. A. 1971 Film Boiling on Submerged Vertical Cylinders, Rept. AEEW-M1051, UKAEA, Winfrith.

Bailey, N. A. 1972 The Interaction of Droplet Deposition and Forced Convection in Post-Dryout Heat Transfer at High Subcritical Pressure, *European Two-Phase Flow Group Meet., Rome; Rept.* AEEW-R807, UKAEA, Winfrith (1973).

Bailey, N. A. 1977. A Review of Dryout Data in SGHWR Fuel Bundle Simulation. *Conf. Heat Fluid Flow Water Reactor Safety, Manchester, Sept. 1977,* Inst. of Mechanical Engineers, London.

Bailey, N. A. & Collier, J. G. 1970 The Estimation of Tube Wall Temperatures in the Evaporator Region of Sub-critical Once-through Sodium Heated Steam Generators, *Rept.* AEEW-M1000, UKAEA, Winfrith.

Bailey, N. A. & Lee, D. H. 1977 A Review of Dryout Data in SGHWR Fuel Bundle Simulations, *Proc. Conf. Heat Fluid Flow Water Reactor Safety, Manchester,* pp. 203–207, Inst. of Mechanical Engineers, London.

Bailey, N. A., Collier, J. G., & Ralph, J. C. 1973 Post-Dryout Heat Transfer in Nuclear and Cryogenic Equipment, *Rept.* AERE-R7519, UKAEA, Harwell.

Balzheiser, R. E. & Colver, C. P. 1963 Investigation of Liquid Metal Boiling Heat Transfer, *Rept.* RTD-TDR-63-4130, Wright-Patterson Air Force Base, Ohio.

Bankoff, S. G. 1956 Ebullition from Solid Surface in Absence of Pre-existing Gas Phase, *Proc. Heat Transfer Fluid Mechanics Inst.,* pp. 1–14, Stanford Univ. Press, Stanford, Calif.

Barnett, P. G. 1963 An Investigation into the Validity of Certain Hypothesis Implied by Various Burnout Correlations, *Rept.* AEEW-R314, UKAEA, Winfrith.

Barnett, P. G. 1968 A Comparison of the Accuracy of Some Correlations for Burnout in Annuli and Rod Bundles, *Rept.* AEEW-R558, UKAEA, Winfrith.

Bartolemei, G. G. & Chanturiya, V. M. 1967 Experimental Study of Time Void Fraction when Boiling Subcooled Water in Vertical Tubes, *Teploenergetika* 14:80–83.

Becker, K. M. 1962 Burnout Conditions for Flow of Boiling Water in Vertical Rod Clusters, Aktiebolagel-Atomenergi, Sweden, *Rept.* AE-74.

Becker, K. M. 1964 Measurements of Burnout Conditions for Flow of Boiling Water in Vertical 3-Rod and 7-Rod Clusters, Aktiebolagel-Atomenergi, Sweden, *Rept.* AE-153.

Becker, K. M. 1967a A Burnout Correlation for Flow of Boiling Water in Vertical Rod Bundles, Aktiebolagel-Atomenergi, Sweden, *Rept.* AE-276.

Becker, K. M. 1967b Measurements and Predictions of Burnout Conditions in Rod Bundles, Aktiebolagel-Atomenergi, Sweden, *Rept.* S-366.

Becker, K. M. & Letzter, A. 1975 Burnout Measurements for Flow of Water in an Annulus with Two-sided Heating, *Rept.* KTH-NEL23, Royal Inst. of Technology, Stockholm.

Becker, K. M., Hernborg, G., Bode, M., & Eriksson, O. 1976 Burnout Data for Flow of Boiling Water in Vertical Round Ducts, Annuli and Rod Clusters, *Rept.* AE-177.

Becker, R. & Doring, W. 1935 *Ann. Phys.* 74:719.

Beer, H., Burrow, P., & Best, R. 1977 Bubble Growth, Bubble Dynamics, and Heat Transfer in Nucleate Boiling, Viewed with a Laser Interferometer, in *Heat Transfer in Boiling,* eds. E. Hahne & U. Grigull, pp. 21–52, Hemisphere, Washington, D.C.

Belda, W., Mayinger, F., & Viert, K. P. 1974 Blow Down Studies with Refrigerant R12, *Proc. Reaktortagung,* Berlin.

Bell, C. R., Oberle, N. P., Rohsenow, W. M., Todreas, N. E., & Tso, C. 1974 Radiation Induced Boiling in Water and Organic Liquids, *Nucl. Sci. Eng.* 53:458.

Bennett, A. W., Kearsey, H. A., & Keeys, R. K. F. 1964 Heat Transfer to Mixtures of High Pressure Steam and Water in an Annulus. Part VI. A Preliminary Study of Heat Transfer Coefficient and Heater Surface Temperature at High Steam Qualities, *Rept.* AERE-R4352, UKAEA, Harwell.

Bennett, A. W., Hewitt, G. F., Kearsey, H. A., & Keeys, R. K. F. 1965a Experiments on Burnout in a Uniformly Heated Round Tube at 1000 psia with Steam-Water Mixtures at the Tube Inlet, *Rept.* AERE-R5072, UKAEA, Harwell.

Bennett, A. W., Hewitt, G. F., Kearsey, H. A., Keeys, R. K. F., & Lacey, P. M. C. 1965b Flow Visualization Studies of Boiling at High Pressures, *Rept.* AERE-R4874, UKAEA, Harwell; *Proc. Inst. Mech. Eng. London* 180:3c, paper 5.

Bennett, A. W., Hewitt, G. F., Kearsey, H. A., & Keeys, R. K. F. 1966 The Wetting of Hot Surfaces by Water in a Steam Environment at High Pressure, *Rept.* AERE-R5146, UKAEA, Harwell.

Bennett, A. W., Hewitt, G. F., Kearsey, H. A., & Keeys, R. K. F. 1967a Heat Transfer to Steam-Water Mixtures Flowing in Uniformly Heated Tubes in Which the Critical Heat Flux Has Been Exceeded, *Rept.* AERE-R5373, UKAEA, Harwell; *Inst. Mechanical Engineers Thermodynamics Fluid Mechanics Convention, Bristol,* paper 27 (1968).

Bennett, A. W., Hewitt, G. F., Kearsey, H. A., Keeys, R. K. F., & Pulling, D. J. 1967b Studies of Burnout in Boiling Heat Transfer, *Trans. Inst. Chem. Eng.* 45:T319–T333.

Bennett, J. A. R., Collins, J. G., Pratt, H. R. C., & Thornton, J. D. 1959 Heat Transfer to Two-Phase Gas Liquid System, *Rept.* AERE-R3159, UKAEA, Harwell.

Berenson, P. J. 1960 Transition Boiling Heat Transfer from a Horizontal Surface, Ph.D. thesis & Heat Transfer Lab. Rept. 17, *Massachusetts Inst. of Technology, Cambridge; ASME-AIChE Heat Transfer Conf., Buffalo,* AIChE paper 18.

Berenson, P. J. 1961 Film Boiling Heat Transfer from a Horizontal Surface, *J. Heat Transfer, Trans. ASME* 83:351–358.

Bergles, A. E. 1975 Burnout in Boiling Heat Transfer. Part 1: Pool-Boiling Systems, *Nucl. Saf.* 16(1):29–42.

Bergles, A. E. 1977 Burnout in Boiling Heat Transfer. Part II: Subcooled and Low-Quality Forced-Convection Systems, *Nucl. Saf.* 18(2):154–167.

Bergles, A. E. & Rohsenow, W. M. 1964 The Determination of Forced Convection Surface-Boiling Heat Transfer, *J. Heat Transfer, Trans. ASME* 86:365–372.

Bergles, A. E., Bakkru, N., & Shires, J. W. 1968 Cooling of High-Power-Density Computer Components, *Rept.* 70712-60, Massachusetts Inst. of Technology, Cambridge.

Bernath, L. 1952 Theory of Bubble Formation in Liquids, *Ind. Eng. Chem.* 44:1310–1313.

Bernath, L. 1955 Prediction of Heat Transfer Burnout, *AIChE Heat Transfer Symp., Louisville, Ky.*

Bernath, L. 1960 A Theory of Local-Boiling Burnout and Its Application to Existing Data, *Chem. Eng. Prog. Symp. Ser.* 56:95–116.

Bertoletti, S., Lesage, J., Lombardi, C., Peterlongo, G., Silvestri, M., Soldaini, G., & Weckermann, F. 1961 Heat Transfer and Pressure Drop with Steam-Water Spray, *CISE Rept.* R-36.

Bertoletti, S., Lombardi, C., & Silvestri, M. 1964 Heat Transfer to Steam-Water Mixtures, *CISE Rept.* R-78.

Bertoletti, S., Gaspari, G. P., Lombardi, C., Peterlongo, G., Silvestri, M., & Tacconi, E. A. 1965 Heat Transfer Crisis with Steam-H_2O Mixtures, *Energ. Nucl. (Milan)* 12:121–172.

Bertoni, R., Cipriani, R., Cumo, M., et al. 1976 Up-Flow and Down-Flow Burnout, *Rept.* CNEN, Italy, Rept. RT/ING(76)24.

Besroukov, Yu. A., Astahov, V. I., Saly, L. A., Logvinov, S. A., Brantov, V. G., Testov, I. N., & Stekolnikov, V. V. 1974 *Collection: T-74 Seminar, Investigation into Critical Heat Fluxes in Rod Bundles,* Council for Mutual Economic Assistance, Moscow.

Bier, K., Gorenflo, D., & Wickenhäuser, G. 1977 Pool Boiling Heat Transfer at Saturation Pressures up to Critical, in *Heat Transfer in Boiling,* eds. E. Hahne and U. Grigull, pp. 137–158, Hemisphere, Washington, D.C.

Bishop, A. A., Efferding, L. E., & Tong, L. S. 1962 A Review of Heat Transfer and Fluid Flow of Water in the Supercritical Region and during 'Once-thru' Operation, *Rept.* WCAP-2040, Westinghouse Electric Co.

Bishop, A. A., Sandberg, R. O., & Tong, L. S. 1964 High Temperature Supercritical Pressure Water Loop. Part V. Forced Convection Heat Transfer to Water after the Critical Heat Flux at High Subcritical Pressures, *Rept.* WCAP-2056, part V, Westinghouse Electric Co.

Bishop, A. A., Sandberg, R. O., & Tong, L. S. 1964 High Temperature Supercritical Pressure Water Loop. Part V. Forced Convection Heat Transfer to Water after the Critical Heat Flux at High Subcritical Pressures, *Rept.* WCAP-2056, part V, Westinghouse Electric Co.

Bishop, A. A., Sandberg, R. O., & Tong, L. S. 1965 Forced Convection Heat Transfer at High Pressure after the Critical Heat Flux, *ASME-AIChE Heat Transfer Conf., Los Angeles*, Aug. 8-11, paper 65-HT-31.

Bjornard, T. A. & Griffith, P. 1977 PWR Blowdown Heat Transfer, in *Symposium on Thermal and Hydraulic Aspects of Nuclear Reactor Safety*, vol. 1, *Light Water Reactors*, eds. O. C. Jones & S. G. Bankoff, pp. 17-41, ASME, New York.

Blackburn, D. & Pearson, K. G. 1977 Analytical Approximations to the Rewetting Rate of Overheated Composite Fuel Pins under Low Pressure, High Temperature Conditions, *Proc. Conf. Heat Fluid Flow Water Reactor Safety, Manchester*, pp. 39-46, Inst. of Mechanical Engineers, London.

Blair, J. M. 1975 An Analytical Solution to a Two-dimensional Model of the Rewetting of a Hot Dry Rod, *Nucl. Eng. Des.* 32(2):159-170.

Bowring, R. W. 1962 Physical Model Based on Bubble Detachment and Calculation of Steam Voidage in the Subcooled Region of a Heated Channel, *Rept.* HPR10, Halden Reactor Project, Halden, Norway.

Bowring, R. W. 1968 HAMBO: A Computer Programme for the Subchannel Analysis of the Hydraulic and Burnout Characteristics of Rod Clusters. Part 1: General Description, *Rept.* AEEW-R524; Part 2: The Equations, *Rept.* AEEW-R582, UKAEA, Winfrith.

Bowring, R. W. 1972 A Simple but Accurate Round Tube, Uniform Heat Flux, Dryout Correlation over the Pressure Range 0.7-17 MN/m^2 to the Power 2 (100-2500 psia), *Rept.* AEEW-R789, UKAEA, Winfrith.

Bowring, R. W. 1977 A New Mixed Flow Cluster Dryout Correlation for Pressures in the Range 0.6-15.5 MN/m^2 (90-2250 psia)—for Use in a Transient Blowdown Code, *Proc. Conf. Heat Fluid Flow Water Reactor Safety, Manchester*, pp. 175-182, Inst. of Mechanical Engineers, London.

Breen, B. P. & Westwater, J. W. 1962 Effect of Diameter of Horizontal Tubes on Film Boiling, *Chem. Eng. Prog.* 58:67, *5th Natl. Heat Transfer Conf., Houston*, AIChE reprint 19.

Brentani, E. G., Gerratano, P. J., & Smith, R. V. 1965 Nucleate and Film Pool Boiling Design Correlations for O$_2$, N$_2$, H$_2$ and He, *Nat. Bur. Stand.* TN317.

Bressler, R. G. 1972 A Review of Physical Models and Heat-Transfer Correlations for Free-Convection Film Boiling, *Adv. Cryog. Eng.* 17:382-406.

Brevi, R., Cumo, M., Palmieri, A., & Pitimada, D. 1969a Heat Transfer Coefficient in Post Burn-out Two-Phase Mixtures, *European Two-Phase Flow Group Meet., Karlsruhe.*

Brevi, R., Cumo, M., Palmieri, A., & Pitimada, D. 1969b Post Dryout Heat Transfer with Steam/Water Mixtures. *Trans. Am. Nucl. Soc.* 12:809-811.

Briggs, L. T. 1950 *J. Appl. Phys.* 21:721.

Bromley, L. A. 1950 *Chem. Eng. Prog.* 46-221.

Bromley, L. A. 1953 Heat Transfer in Forced Convection Film Boiling, *Ind. Eng. Chem.* 45:2639-2646.

Brown, W. 1967 Study of Flow Surface Boiling, Ph.D. thesis, Massachusetts Inst. of Technology, Cambridge.

Butterworth, D. 1971 A Model for Predicting Dryout in a Tube with a Circumferential Variation in Heat Flux, *Rept.* AERE-M2436, UKAEA, Harwell.

Butterworth, D. & Hewitt, G. F. eds. 1977 *Two Phase Flow and Heat Transfer*, Oxford Univ. Press, Oxford.

Cadeck, F. F., Dominicis, O. P., & Leyse, R. H. 1971 PWR FLECHT Final Report WCAP-7665.

Campanile, A. & Pozzi, G. P. 1972 Low Rate Emergency Reflooding Heat Transfer Tests in Rod Bundles, *Proc. CREST Specialist Meeting ECC Light Water Reactors, Garching/Munich*, Oct. 18-20, vol. 1, *Rept.* MRR-115.

Campanile, A., Galimi, G., Goffi, M., & Passavanti, G. 1970 Forced Convection Burnout and Hydrodynamic Instability Experiments for Water at High Pressure, Part VI, *Euratom Rept.* EUR-4468e.

Case, P., Hein, D., Riedle, K., & Schneider, E. 1973 The Rewetting Process of Hot Surfaces by Bottom Flooding, *European Two-Phase Flow Group Meet., Brussels.*

Ceresa, I., Gaspari, G. P., & Lucchini, F. 1974 Heat Transfer Crisis and Pressure Drop Measurements with Steam-Water Mixtures in a 6-Meter-Long 19-Rod Cluster, *European Two-Phase Flow Group Meet., Harwell,* paper C5.

Cermak, J. O., Farman, R. F., Tong, L. S., Casterline, J. E., Kokolis, S., & Matzner, B. 1970 The Departure from Nucleate Boiling in Rod Bundles during Pressure Blowdown, *J. Heat Transfer, Trans. ASME* 92:621–627.

Chandrasekhar, S. 1961 Hydrodynamic and Hydromagnetic Stability, Oxford Univ. Press, pp. 434 & 484.

Chang, Y. P. & Snyder, N. W. 1960 Heat Transfer in Saturated Boiling, *Chem. Eng. Prog. Symp. Ser.* 56:25–38.

Chelemer, H., Weisman, J., & Tong, L. S. 1972 Subchannel Thermal Analysis of Rod Bundle Cores, *Nucl. Eng. Des.* 21:35–45.

Chen, J. 1963 A Correlation for Boiling Heat Transfer to Saturated Fluids in Convective Flow, ASME paper 63-HT-34.

Chen, J. C. 1968 Incipient Boiling Superheats in Liquid Metals, *J. Heat Transfer, Trans. ASME,* ser. C 90:303–312.

Chen, J. C., Sundaram, R. K., & Ozkayrak, F. T. 1977 A Phenomenological Correlation for Post CHF Heat Transfer, *Rept.* NUREG-0237, Lehigh Univ.

Cheng, L. Y., Drew, D. A., & Lahey, R. T., Jr. 1978 Virtual Mass Effects in Two-Phase Flow, *Rept.* NUREG/CR-0020, Nuclear Regulatory Commission.

Cheng, S. C. & Ng, W. 1976 Transition Boiling Heat Transfer in Forced Vertical Flow via a High Thermal Capacity Heating Process, *Lett. Heat Mass Transfer* 3:333–342.

Cheng, S. C., Ng, W. W. L., & Heng, K. T. 1978 Measurements of Boiling Curves of Subcooled Water under Forced Convective Conditions, *Int. J. Heat Mass Transfer* 21:1385–1392.

Chojnowski, B. & Wilson, P. W. 1962 Critical Heat Flux for Large Dorler Tubes, *Central Electric Generating Board Rept.* CEGB/R/M/N652.

Chojnowski, B. & Wilson, P. W. 1974 Critical Heat Flux for Large Diameter Steam Generating Tubes with Circumferentially Variable and Uniform Heating, *Proc. 5th Int. Heat Transfer Conf., Tokyo* 4:260–264.

Chojnowski, B., Wilson, P. W., & Whitcutt, R. D. B. 1974 Critical Heat Flux for Inclined Steam Generating Tubes, *Symp. Multi-Phase Flow Systems,* Univ. of Strathclyde, Apr. 2–4, 1964, paper E3.

Chun, M. H. & Chon, W. Y. 1975 Analyses of Rewetting in Water Reactor Emergency Core Cooling Inclusive of Heat Transfer in the Unwetted Region, *ASME Winter Annu. Meet., Houston,* paper 75-WA/HT-32.

Cichelli, M. T. & Bonilla, C. F. 1945 *Trans. AIChE* 41:744.

Clements, L. D. & Colver, C. P. 1970 Natural Convection Film Boiling Heat Transfer, *Ind. Eng. Chem.* 62:26–46.

Clerici, E. C., Garriba, S., Sala, R., & Tozzi, A. 1966 A Catalogue of Burnout Correlations for Forced Convection in the Quality Region, *Euratom Rept.* EUR 33003.

Cole, R. 1960 Photographic Study of Boiling in Region of Critical Heat Flux, *AIChE J.* 6:533–542.

Cole, R. 1967 Frequency and Departure Diameter at Sub-atmospheric Pressures, *AIChE J.* 13:779–783.

Cole, R. 1974 Boiling Nucleation, *Adv. Heat Transfer* 10:86–164.

Cole, R. & Rohsenow, W. M. 1969 Correlation of Bubble Departure Diameters for Boiling of Saturated Liquids, *Chem. Eng. Prog. Symp. Ser.* 65:92 & 211–213.

Cole, R. & Shulman, H. L. 1966 Bubble Growth Rates in High Jakob Numbers, *Int. J. Heat Mass Transfer* 9:1377.

Collier, J. G. 1962 Heat Transfer and Fluid Dynamic Research as Applied to Fog Cooled Power Reactors, *Rept.* AECL-1631, Atomic Energy of Canada Ltd.

Collier, J. G. 1972 *Forced Convective Boiling and Condensation,* McGraw-Hill, New York.

Collier, J. G. 1977 Post-Dryout Heat Transfer—A Review of the Current Position, in *Two-Phase*

Flows and Heat Transfer, eds. S. Kakaç & T. N. Veziroglu, vol. 2, pp. 769–813, Hemisphere, Washington, D. C.

Collier, J. G. & D. J. Pulling 1962 Heat Transfer in Two-Phase Gas-Liquid Systems. Part II: Further Data on Steam-Water Mixtures, *Rept.* AERE-R3809, UKAEA, Harwell.

Coney, M. W. E. 1974b The Analysis of a Mechanism of Liquid Replenishment and Draining in Horizontal Two-Phase Flow, *Int. J. Multiphase Flow* 1:647–670.

Coney, M. W. E. 1974a Calculations on the Rewetting of Hot Surfaces, *Nucl. Eng. Des.* 31:246–259.

Cooper, M. G. 1969 Microlayer and Bubble Growth in Nucleate Pool Boiling, *Int. J. Heat Mass Transfer* 12:895–913.

Cooper, M. G. & Lloyd, J. P. 1966 Transient Local Heat Flux in Nucleate Boiling, *Proc. 3d Int. Heat Transfer Conf. Chicago,* 3:193–203.

Corty, C. & Foust, A. S. 1955 Surface Variables in Nucleate Boiling, *Chem. Eng. Prog. Symp. Ser.* 17:51.

Costello, C. & Frea, W. J. 1963 A Salient Non-hydrodynamic Effect on Pool Boiling Burnout of Small Semi-cylindrical Heaters, *6th Natl. Heat Transfer Conf., Boston,* AIChE reprint 15.

Costello, C. P., Bock, C. O., & Nichols, C. C. 1964 A Study of Induced Convective Effects on Saturated Pool Boiling Burnout, *7th Natl. Heat Transfer Conf., Cleveland,* AIChE reprint no. 7.

Course, A. F. & Roberts, H. A. 1974 Progress with Heat Transfer to a Steam Film in the Presence of Water Drops—A First Evaluation of Winfrith SGHWR Cluster Loop Data, *European Two-Phase Flow Group Meet., Harwell,* paper B8.

Cumo, M. 1977 Two-Phase Boundary Layers in Subcooled Boiling, in *Two-Phase Flows and Heat Transfer,* eds. S. Kakaç & T. N. Veziroglu, vol. 2, pp. 623–645, Hemisphere, Washington, D.C.

Cumo, M. & Urbani, G. C. 1974 Post Burn-out Heat Transfer (Attainable Precision Limits of the Measured Coefficient), *CNEN Rept.* RT/ING(74)24.

Danilova, G. N. 1976 Enhancement of Heat Transfer of Boiling Refrigerants, *Heat Transfer Sov. Res.* 8(4):1–8.

Davis, E. J. & Anderson, G. H. 1966 The Incipience of Nucleate Boiling in Forced Convection Flow, *AIChE J.* 12:774–780.

Deane, C. W., IV & Rohsenow, W. M. 1970 Mechanism of Nucleate Boiling Heat Transfer to Alkali Liquid Metals, *Proc. ASME Symp. Liquid Metal Heat Transfer Dynamics,* p. 90–99.

de Bartoli, R. A., Green, S. J., Letoureau, B. W., Troy, M., & Weiss, A. 1958 Forced-Convection Heat Transfer Burnout Studies for Water in Rectangular Channels and Round Tubes at Pressures above 500 psia, *Rept.* WAPD-188, Westinghouse Electric Co.

Dengler, C. E. & J. N. Addoms 1956 Heat Transfer Mechanisms for Vaporization of Water in a Vertical Tube, *Chem. Eng. Prog. Symp. Ser.* 52:95–103.

Dhir, V. K. & Lienhard, J. H. 1973a Similar Solution for Film Condensation with Variable Gravity or Body Shape, *J. Heat Transfer, Trans. ASME,* ser. C, 95:483–486.

Dhir, V. K. & Lienhard, J. H. 1973b Taylor Stability of Viscous Fluids with Application to Film Boiling, *Int. J. Heat Mass Transfer* 16:2097–2109.

Dhir, V. K. & Lienhard, J. H. 1974 Peak Pool Boiling Heat Flux in Viscous Liquids, *J. Heat Transfer, Trans. ASME,* ser. C, 96:71–78.

Dittus, F. W., & Boelter, L. M. K. 1930 Heat Transfer in Automobile Radiators of Tubular Type, *Publications in Engineering,* University of California, Berkeley, p. 443.

Dix, G. E. 1971 Vapor Void Fractions for Forced Convection with Subcooled Boiling at Low Flow Rates, *Rept.* NEDO-10491, General Electric Co.

Doroshchuk, V. E. 1970 *The Boiling Heat Transfer Crisis of Water in Tubes,* Energiya, Moscow.

Doubrovsky, I. S., Yughaj, T., Ghashenko, M. P., & Chalukh, A. F. 1974 *Collection: T-74 Seminar, Investigation into Critical Heat Fluxes in Rod Bundles,* p. 67, Council for Mutual Economic Assistance, Moscow.

Dougall, R. S. & Lippert, T. E. 1971 Net Vapor Generation Point in Boiling Flow of Trichlorotrifluoroethane at High Pressures, *NASA Rept.* CR-2241.

Dougall, R. S. & Rohsenow, W. M. 1963 Film Boiling on the Inside of Vertical Tubes with Upward Flow of the Fluid at Low Qualities, *Dept. of Mechanical Engineering Rept.* 9079-26, Massachusetts Inst. of Technology, Cambridge.

Dua, S. S. & Tien, C. L. 1976 Two-dimensional Analysis of Conduction-controlled Rewetting with Precursory Cooling, *J. Heat Transfer, Trans. ASME* 98:407–413.

Dua, S. S. & Tien, C. L. 1977 A Generalized Two-Parameter Relation for Conduction-controlled Rewetting of a Hot Vertical Surface, *Int. J. Heat Mass Transfer* 20:174–176.

Duffey, R. B. & Porthouse, D. T. C. 1973 The Physics of Rewetting in Water Reactor Emergency Core Cooling, *Nucl. Eng. Des.* 25:379–394.

Duke, E. E. & Shrock, V. E. 1961 Void Volume, Site Density, and Bubble Size for Subcooled Nucleate Pool Boiling, *Fluid Mech. Heat Trans. Inst.* 130–145.

Durga Prasad, K. A., Srinivasan, K., & Krishna Murthy, M. V. 1974 Cooldown of Foam Insulated Cryogenic Transfer Lines, *Cryogenics* 14:615–617.

Dwyer, O. E. 1976 *Boiling Liquid Metal Heat Transfer,* Hinsdale, Ill., American Nuclear Society.

Eddington, R. I. & Kenning, D. B. R. 1978 The Prediction of Flow Boiling Bubble Populations from Gas Bubble Nucleation Experiments, *Proc. 6th Int. Heat Transfer Conf., Toronto* 1:275–279.

Edwards, A. R. & Mather, D. J. 1973 Some UK Studies Related to the Loss of Coolant Accident, *Water Reactor Safety Meet., Salt Lake City, Mar. 26–28, CONF-730304,* pp. 720–737.

Edwards, P. A. 1976 An Experimental Study of Burnout and Pressure Drop in 19-Rod Clusters, *Rept. AEEW-R371, UKAEA, Winfrith.*

Elias, E. & Yadigaroglu, G. 1977 A General One-dimensional Model for Conduction-controlled Rewetting of a Surface, *Nucl. Eng. Des.* 42:185–194.

Elias, E. & Yadigaroglu, G. 1978 The Reflooding Phase of the LOCA in PWRs. Part II. Rewetting and Liquid Entrainment, *Nucl. Saf.* 19:160–175.

Ellion, M. E. 1954 A Study of the Mechanism of Boiling Heat Transfer. *Rept.* JPL-Memo-20-88, California Inst. of Technology.

Elliott, D. F. & Rose, P. W. 1970 The Quenching of a Heated Surface by a Film of Water in a Steam Environment at Pressures up to 53 bar, *Rept.* AEEW-M976, UKAEA, Winfrith.

Elliott, D. F. & Rose, P. W. 1971 The Quenching of a Heated Zircalloy Surface by a Film of Water in a Steam Environment at Pressures up to 53 bar, *Rept.* AEEW-M1027, UKAEA, Winfrith.

Era, A., Gaspari, G. P., Hassid, A., Milani, A., & Zavattarelli, R. 1967 Heat Transfer Data in the Liquid Deficient Region for Steam-Water Mixtures at 70 kg/cm² Flowing in Tubular and Annular Conduits, *CISE Rept.* R-184.

Era, A., Gaspari, G. P., Protti, M., & Zavattarelli, R. 1971 Post Dryout Heat Transfer Measurements in an Annulus with Uniform and Non-uniform Axial Heat Flux Distribution, *European Two-Phase Flow Group Meet., Riso, Denmark,* paper B3.

Fabic, S. 1971 Two- and Three-dimensional Fluid Transients, *Trans. Am. Nucl. Soc.* 14:360.

Fabic, S. 1976 Data Sources for LOCA Code Verification, *Nucl. Saf.* 17:671–685.

Fabic, S. 1977a Computer Codes in Water Reactor Safety: Problems in Modeling of Loss-of-Coolant Accident, *Conf. Heat Fluid Flow Water Reactor Safety, Manchester,* paper C201/77, Inst. of Mechanical Engineers, London.

Fabic, S. 1977b Review of Existing Codes for Loss-of-Coolant Accident Analysis, *Adv. Nucl. Sci. Technol.* 10:365–404.

Fabic, S. & Anderson, P. S. 1981 Plan for Assessment of Best Estimate LWR Systems Codes, *Rept.* NUREG-0676, Nuclear Regulatory Commission.

Fairburn, S. A., Hall, P. C., Piggott, B. D. G., Healey, T., & Duffey, R. B. 1977 Basic Studies on the Cooling of LWRs by In-Core Sprays. *Heat Fluid Flow Water Reactor Safety, Manchester,* pp. 47–53, Inst. of Mechanical Engineers, London.

Fajeau, M. 1969 Programme FLICA: Etude Thermodynamique d'un Reacteur ou d'une Boucle d'Essai, *Rept.* CEA-R-3716.

Farmer, P. R. 1975 The Rewetting of Hot Surfaces by Bottom Flooding–The Effect of Water Flowrate and Temperature, *European Two-Phase Flow Group Meet., Haifa,* paper 6.4.

Farmer, P. R. & Coney, M. W. E. 1974 The Application of a Two-Dimensional Conduction Model to Falling Film Rewetting Data, *European Two-Phase Flow Group Meet., Harwell,* paper E4.

Fath, H. S. & Judd, R. L. 1978 Influence of System Pressure on Microlayer Evaporation Heat Transfer, *J. Heat Transfer, Trans. ASME,* Ser. C 100:49–55.

Fiori, M. P. & Bergles, A. E. 1970 Model of Critical Heat Flux in Sub-cooled Flow Boiling, *Proc. 4th Int. Heat Transfer Conf., Versailles,* paper B6.3.

Fisher, J. C. 1948 *J. Appl. Phys.* 19:1062.

Fisher, S. A. & Yu, S. K. W. 1975 Dryout in Serpentine Evaporations, *Int. J. Multiphase Flow* 1:771–791.

Fisher, S. A., Harrison, G. S., & Pearce, D. L. 1978 Premature Dryout in Conventional and Nuclear Power Station Evaporators. *Proc. 6th Int. Heat Transfer Conf., Toronto* 2:49–54.

Florscheutz, L. W. & Khan, A. R. 1970 Growth Rates of Free Vapor Bubbles in Binary Mixtures, *Proc. 4th Int. Heat Transfer Conf., Versailles* 6:B7.3.

Forslund, R. P. & Rohsenow, W. M. 1966 Thermal Non-Equilibrium in Dispersed Flow Film Boiling in a Vertical Tube, *Dept. of Mechanical Engineering, Rept.* 75312-44, Massachusetts Inst. of Technology, Cambridge.

Forster, K. & Greif, R. 1959 *J. Heat Transfer, Trans. ASME* 81:4353 *Dept. of Engineering, Prog. Rept.* 7, Univ. of California, Los Angeles.

Forster, K. & Zuber, N. 1955 Dynamics of Vapor Bubbles and Boiling Heat Transfer, *AIChE J.* 1:531–535.

Frederking, T. H. K. & Clark, J. A. 1962 Natural Convection Film Boiling on a Sphere, *Adv. Cryog. Eng.* 8:501–506.

Frenkel, J. 1946 *Kinetic Theory of Liquids,* chap. 8, Oxford Univ. Press, New York.

Fritz, W. 1935 Maximum Volume of Vapor Bubbles, *Phys. Z.* 36:379.

Fung, K. K. 1977 Forced Convection Transition Boiling, M.Sci. thesis, Univ. of Toronto.

Gaddis, E. S. & Hall, W. B. 1967 Equilibrium of Bubble Nucleus at a Solid Surface, *Proc. Inst. Mech. Eng., London* 182:1.

Ganchev, B. G., Borov, A. Ye., & Misvik, A. B. 1976 Heat Transfer and Crisis Conditions in Vertical Channels with a Falling Liquid Film and Downward Two-Phase Annular Flow, *Heat Transfer Sov. Res.* 8:9–19.

Gardner, G. C. 1974 Evaporation and Thermophertic Motion of Water Drops Containing Salt in a High Pressure Steam Environment, *European Two-Phase Flow Group Meet., Harwell,* paper B7.

Gardner, G. C. & Kubie, J. 1976 Flow of Two Liquids in Sloping Tubes: An Analogue of High Pressure Steam and Water, *Int. J. Multiphase Flow* 2:435–451.

Gaspari, G. P., Hassid, A., & Vanoli, G. 1970 Some Considerations on the Critical Heat Flux in Rod Clusters in Annular Dispersed Vertical Upwards Two-Phase Flow, *Proc. 4th Int. Heat Transfer Conf., Versailles,* paper 6.4.

Gaspari, G. P., Hassid, A., & Lucchini, F. 1974 A Rod-centered Subchannel Analysis with Turbulent (Enthalpy) Mixing for Critical Heat Flux Prediction in Rod Clusters Cooled by Boiling Water, *Proc. 5th. Int. Heat Transfer Conf., Tokyo* 4:295–299.

Gear, V. 1968 The Automatic Integration of Stiff Ordinary Differential Equation, *Proc. IFIP Conf.*

Gellerstedt, J. S., Lee, R. A., Oberjohn, W. J., Wilson, R. H., & Stanek, L. J. 1969 Correlation of Critical Heat Flux in a Bundle Cooled by Pressurized Water, *Symp. Two-Phase Flow Heat Transfer Rod Bundles,* pp. 66–71, ASME, New York.

Gilmour, C. H. 1958 Nucleate Boiling–A Correlation, *Chem. Eng. Prog.* 54:54–77.

Ginoux, J. J. (ed.) 1978 *Two-Phase Flows and Heat Transfer with Application to Nuclear Reactor Design Problems,* Hemisphere, Washington, D.C.

Giot, M. 1978 Nucleation, Two Phase Flow in Nuclear Reactors, lecture series, von Karman Inst. for Fluid Dynamics.

Gouse, S. W. 1966 An Index to Two-Phase Gas-Liquid Flow Literature, *Rept.* 9, Massachusetts Inst. of Technology, Cambridge.

Gouse, S. W. & Hwang, C. C. 1965 Visual Study of Two-Phase One-Component Flow in a Vertical Tube with Heat Transfer, *Rept.* 8973-1, Massachusetts Inst. of Technology, Cambridge; ASME paper 53-WA-165.

Grachev, N. S., Kirillov, P. L., & Prokhorova, V. A. 1977 Heat Exchange in a Steam-Generating Pipe with Internal Ribbing, *High Temp. (USSR)* 14:1105–1110.

Greitzer, E. M. & Abernathy, F. H. 1972 Film Boiling on Vertical Surfaces, *Int. J. Heat Mass Transfer* 15:475–491.

Griffith, P. 1965–1966 Nucleation and Bubble Formation in Boiling, *Proc. Inst. Mech. Eng. London* 180:parts 1 and 3C.

Griffith, P. & Wallis, J. D. 1960 Role of Surface Conditions in Nucleate Boiling, *Chem. Eng. Prog. Symp. Ser.* 30:49.

Groeneveld, D. C. 1969 An Investigation of Heat Transfer in the Liquid Deficient Regime, *Rept.* AECL-3281, Atomic Energy of Canada Ltd.

Groeneveld, D. C. 1972 The Thermal Behavior of a Heated Surface at and beyond Dryout, *Rept.* AECL-4309, Atomic Energy of Canada Ltd.

Groeneveld, D. C. 1973 Post-Dryout Heat Transfer at Reactor Operating Conditions, *Natl. Topical Meet. Water Reactor Safety, Salt Lake City, Utah*, Mar. 26–28; American Nuclear Society, *Conf.* 730304, *Rept.* AECL-4513, Atomic Energy of Canada Ltd.

Groeneveld, D. C. 1974 Effect of a Heat Flux Spike on the Downstream Dryout Behavior, *J. Heat Transfer, Trans. ASME* 96:121–125.

Groeneveld, D. C. 1975 The Effect of Short Flux Spikes on the Dryout Power, *Rept.* AECL-4927, Atomic Energy of Canada Ltd.

Groeneveld, D. C. & Delorme, G. G. J. 1976 Prediction of Thermal Non-Equilibrium in the Post-Dryout Regime, *Nucl. Eng. Des.* 36:17–26.

Groeneveld, D. C. & Fung, K. K. 1976 Forced Convective Transition Boiling: Review of Literature and Comparison of Prediction Methods, *Rept.* AECL-5543, Atomic Energy of Canada Ltd.

Groeneveld, D. C. & Fung, K. K. 1977 Heat Transfer Experiments in the Unstable Post-CHF Region, *5th Water Reactor Safety Information Meet., Gaithersburg, Md., Nov.* 7–11.

Groeneveld, D. C. & Gardiner, S. R. M. 1977 Post CHF Heat Transfer under Forced Convection Conditions, in *Symposium on Thermal and Hydraulic Aspects of Nuclear Reactor Safety*, vol. 1, *Light Water Reactors*, eds. O. C. Jones & S. G. Bankoff, pp. 43–73, ASME, New York.

Groeneveld, D. C. & Gardiner, S. R. M. 1978 A Method of Obtaining Flow Film Boiling Data for Subcooled Water, *Int. J. Heat Mass Transfer* 21:664–665.

Groeneveld, D. C., Thibodeau, M., & McPherson, G. D. 1970 Heat Transfer Measurements on Trefoil Fuel Bundles in the Post Dryout Regime—with Data Tabulation, *Rept.* AECL-3414, Atomic Energy of Canada Ltd.

Groeneveld, D. C., Cheng, S. C., Fung, K. K., & Ragheb, H. 1978 Post-CHF Heat Transfer at Low Pressure, *6th Water Reactor Safety Information Meet., Washington, D.C., Nov.*

Guarino, D., Marinelli, V., & Pastori, L. 1973 Status of Art in Burnout Predictions for BWR Rod Bundles, *Trans. Am. Nucl. Soc.* 17:427–428.

Guerrieri, S. A. & Talty, R. D. 1956 A Study of Heat Transfer to Organic Liquids in Single-Tube, Natural Circulation, Vertical Tube Boilers, *Chem. Eng. Prog. Symp. Ser.* 52:18 & 69–77.

Han, C. Y., & Griffith, P. 1962 Mechanism of Heat Transfer in Nucleate Pool Boiling, *Heat Transfer Lab. Rept.* 19, Massachusetts Inst. of Technology, Cambridge.

Han, C. Y. & Griffith, P. 1965 The Mechanism of Heat Transfer in Nucleate Pool Boiling. 1. Bubble Initiation Growth and Departure, *Int. J. Heat Mass Transfer* 8:887–904.

Hancox, W. T. & Nicoll, W. B. 1971 A General Technique for the Prediction of Void Distributions in Non-Steady Two-Phase Forced Convection, *Int. J. Heat Mass Transfer* 14:1377–1394.

Hauptmann, G., Lee, V., & McAdam, D. 1973 Two-Phase Fluid Modelling of the Critical Heat Flux, *Proc. Int. Meet. Reactor Heat Transfer, Karlsruhe*, pp. 557–576.

Heat Mass Transfer Section, Scientific Council of the Academy of Sciences of the U.S.S.R. 1977 Tabular Data for Calculating Burnout when Boiling Water in Uniformly Heated Round Tubes, *Therm. Eng. (USSR)* 23:77–79.

Hebel, W. & Defevernier, W. 1977 Critical Heat Transfer Rate to Flowing Cooling Water, *Kerntechnik* 19:228–232.

Hench, J. E. 1963 Multirod (Four-Rod) Critical Heat Flux at 1000 psia, *Rept. GEAP-4358, General Electric Co.*

Hench, J. E. 1964 Transition and Film Boiling Data at 600, 1100 and 1400 psi in Forced Convection Heat Transfer to Water, *Rept.* GEAP-4492, General Electric Co.

Hench, J. E. & Boehm, R. F. 1966 Nine-Rod Critical Heat Flux Investigation at 1000 psia, *Rept.* GEAP-4929, General Electric Co.

Henry, R. E. 1973 A Generalized Correlation for the Minimum Point in Film Boiling, *ASME-AIChE 14th Natl. Heat Transfer Conf., Atlanta.*

Henry, R. E. 1974 A Correlation for the Minimum Film Boiling Temperature, *AIChE Symp. Ser.* 70:81–90.

Henry, R. E. & Leung, J. C. M. 1977 Transient and Steady-State Critical Heat Flux Experiments in Freon, *5th Water Reactor Safety Information Meet., Gaithersburg, Md., Nov. 7-11,* Nuclear Regulatory Commission, Washington.

Herkenrath, H. & Mörk-Mörkenstein, P. 1969 Die Wärmeübergangskrise von Wasser bei erzqungener Strömung unter hohen Drucken. 2. Der Wärmeübergang im Bereich der Krise, *Atomkernenergie* 14:403–407; The Heat Transfer Crisis for Water with Forced Flow at High Pressures. 2. Heat Transfer in the Crisis Region, transl. AERE-trans. 1129, UKAEA, Harwell (1970).

Herkenrath, H., Mörk-Mörkenstein, P., Jung, U., & Weckermann, F.-J. 1967 Wärmeübergang an Wasser bei erzwungener Strömung im Druckbereich von 140 bis 250 bar, *Euratom Rept.* EUR 3658d; Heat Transfer in Water with Forced Circulation in the Pressure Range 140–250 bar, transl. WH-trans. 208, UKAEA, Winfrith.

Heron, R. A., Kimmeir, J. H., & Stevens, G. F. 1969 Burnout Power and Pressure Drop Measurements on 12 Foot 7-Rod Clusters Cooled by Freon-12 at 155 psia, *Rept.* AEEW-R655, UKAEA, Winfrith.

Hesson, G. M., Fitzsimmons, D. E. & Batch, J. M. 1965 Experimental Boiling Burnout Heat Fluxes with an Electrically Heated 19-Rod Bundle Test Section, *Rept.* BNWL-206, USA

Hewitt, G. F. 1970 Experimental Studies on the Mechanisms of Burnout in Heat Transfer to Steam-Water Mixtures, *Proc. 4th Int. Heat Transfer, Conf., Versailles,* paper B6.6.

Hewitt, G. F. 1978 Critical Heat Flux in Flow Boiling, *Proc. 6th Int. Heat Transfer Conf., Toronto* 6:143–171.

Hewitt, G. F. & Hall-Taylor, N. S. 1970 *Annular Two-Phase Flow,* Pergamon, New York.

Hewitt, G. F. & Hutchinson, P. 1976 A Mathematical Model of Two-Phase Annular Flow Heat and Mass Transfer, *5th All Union Conf., Minsk, May 17–20,* paper 3.79.

Hewitt, G. F. & Kearsey, H. A. 1969 The Correlation of Critical Heat Flux for the Vertical Flow of Water in Uniformly Heated Tubes, Annuli and Rod Bundles, *Rept.* AERE-R5590, UKAEA, Harwell.

Hewitt, G. F., Kearsey, H. A., Lacey, P. M. C., & Pulling, D. J. 1965 Burnout and Film Flow in the Evaporation of Water in Tubes, *Proc. Inst. Mech. Eng. London,* 180:part 3C, paper 2.

Hopwood, P. F. 1972 Pressure Drop, Heat Transfer and Flow Phenomena for Forced Convection Boiling in Helical Coils. A Literature Review, *Rept.* AEEW-R757, UKAEA, Winfrith.

Houchin, W. R. & Lienhard, J. H. 1966 Boiling Burnout in Low Thermal Capacity Heaters, ASME paper 66-WA/HT-40.

Hsu, Y. Y. 1962 On the Size Range of Active Nucleation Cavities on a Heating Surface, *J. Heat Transfer, Trans. ASME,* ser. C 84:207–216.

Hsu, Y. Y. 1972 A Review on Film Boiling, *Adv. Cryog. Eng.* 17:360–381.

Hsu, Y. Y. 1975 A Tentative Correlation for the Regime of Transition Boiling and Film Boiling during Reflood, *3d Water Reactor Safety Research Information Meet.,* Nuclear Regulatory Commission Washington, D.C.

Hsu, Y. Y. & Graham, R. W. 1961 Analytical and Experimental Study of Thermal Boundary Layer and Ebullition Cycle, *NASA Tech. Note* TNO-594.

Hsu, Y. Y. & Simon, F. F. 1969 Stability of Cylindrical Bubbles in a Vertical Pipe, ASME paper 69-HT-28.

Hsu, Y. Y., Simon, F. F., & Lad, J. F. 1965 Destruction of a Thin Liquid Film Flowing over a Heating Surface, *Chem. Eng. Prog. Symp. Ser. 61* 57:139-152.

Hufschmidt, W. 1977 Quenching and Rewetting Problems, lecture at Ispra JRC on LWR Related Thermohydraulic Safety Problems, Sept. 29-30.

Hughes, E. D. 1974 A Compilation of Rod Array Critical Heat Flux Data Sources and Information, *Nucl. Eng. Des.* 30:20-35.

Hughmark, G. A. 1965 Holdup and Heat Transfer in Horizontal Slug Gas-Liquid Flow, *Chem. Eng. Sci.* 20:1007-1010.

Hughmark, G. A. 1966 Designing Thermosiphon Reboilers, *Chem. Eng. Prog. Symp. Ser.* 66:102 & 209-213.

Hutchinson, P. & Whalley, P. B. 1973 A Possible Characterization of Entrainment in Annular Flow *Chem. Eng. Sci.* 28:974-975.

Hutchinson, P., Hewitt, G. F., & Dukler, A. E. 1970 Deposition of Liquid or Solid Dispersions from Turbulent Gas Streams: A Stochastic Model, *Rept.* AERE-R6637, UKAEA, Harwell; *Chem. Eng. Sci.* 26:419-439 (1971).

Hynek, S. J., Rohsenow, W. M., & Bergles, A. E. 1969 Forced-Convection Dispersed-Flow Film Boiling, *Dept. of Mechanical Engineering, Rept.* DSR 70586-63, Massachusetts Inst. of Technology, Cambridge.

Ilic, V. 1974 The Effect of Pressure on Burnout in a Round Tube Cooled by Freon-12, Australian Atomic Energy Commission *Rept.* AAEC/E325.

Ilic, V. 1975 An Examination of the Influence of Spacers on Burnout in an Annulus Cooled by Upflow of Freon-12, Australian Atomic Energy Commission *Rept.* AEEC/E349.

Ilic, V. & Lawther, K. R. 1973 The Effect of Spacers on Burnout in an Annulus with a Uniformly Heated Central Rod Cooled by Freon-12, *Proc. 1st Australasian Conf. Heat Transfer, Monash Univ.*, sect. 4.3, pp. 17-24.

Iloeje, O. C., Plummer, D. N., Rohsenow, W. M., & Griffith, P. 1974 A Study of Wall Rewet and Heat Transfer in Dispersed Vertical Flow, *Dept. of Mechanical Engineering, Rept.* 72718-92, Massachusetts Inst. of Technology, Cambridge.

Iloeje, O. C., Plummer, D. N., Rohsenow, W. M., & Griffith, P. 1975 An Investigation of the Collapse and Surface Rewet in Film Boiling in Forced Vertical Flow, *J. Heat Transfer, Trans. ASME* 97:166-172.

Ingebo, R. D. 1956 Drag Coefficients for Droplets and Solid Spheres in Clouds Accelerating in Air Streams, *NACA TN* 3762.

Ishii, M. 1975 Study on Emergency Core Cooling, *J. Br. Nucl. Energy Soc.* 14:237-242.

Israel, S., Casterline, J. E., & Matzner, B. 1969 Critical Heat Flux Measurements in a 16-Rod Simulation of a BWR Fuel Assembly, *J. Heat Transfer, Trans. ASME* 91:355-363.

Ivey, H. J. 1967 Relationships between Bubble Frequency, Departure Diameter and Rise Velocity in Nucleate Boiling, *Int. J. Heat Mass Transfer* 10:1023-1040.

Ivey, H. J. & Morris, D. J. 1962a On the Relevance of the Vapor-Liquid Exchange Mechanism for Subcooled Boiling Heat Transfer at High Pressure, *Rept.* AEEW-R137, UKAEA, Winfrith.

Ivey, H. J. & Morris, D. J. 1962b The Effect of Test Section Parameters on Saturation Pool Boiling Burnout at Atmospheric Pressure, Fourth National Heat Transfer Conference, Buffalo; AIChE reprint 160, Chicago.

Jackson, J. F. & Stevenson, M. G. 1978 *Los Alamos Scientific Lab. Nuclear Reactor Safety Quarterly Prog. Rept., Jan. 1-Mar. 31,* NUREG/CR-0062, LA-7278-PR, Nuclear Regulatory Commission.

Jackson, J. F. & Stevenson, M. G. 1979 *Los Alamos Scientific Lab., Nuclear Reactor Safety Quarterly Prog. Rept., Oct. 1-Dec. 31,* NUREG/CR-1516, LA-8299-PR, Nuclear Regulatory Commission.

Jackson, J. F. et al. 1978 TRAC-P1: An Advanced Best Estimate Computer Program for PWR

LOCA Analysis. I. Methods, Models and User Information, and Programming Details, *Rept.* NUREG/CR-0063, LA-7279-MS, Nuclear Regulatory Commission.

Jakob, M. & Fritz, W. 1931 *Forsch. Geb. Ingenieurwes.* 2:434.

Janssen, E. 1965 Two-Phase Flow and Heat Transfer in Multirod Geometries, *Rept.* GEAP-4798, General Electric Co.

Janssen, E. 1968 Nine-Rod Critical Heat Flux Investigation, Steam-Water at 600 to 1400 psia, *Final Summary Rept.*, GEAP-5616, General Electric Co.

Janssen, E. & Kervinen, J. A. 1963 Burnout Conditions for Single Rod in Annular Geometry, Water at 600 to 1400 psia, *Rept.* GEAP-3899, General Electric Co.

Janssen, E., Schraub, F. A., Nixon, R. B., Matzner, B., & Casterline, J. E. 1969 Sixteen-Rod Heat Flux Investigation, Steam-Water at 600 to 1250 psia, *Symp. Two-Phase Flow Heat Transfer Rod Bundles*, ASME, New York, pp. 81–88.

Jeglic, F. A. 1965 *The Incipience of Flow Oscillations on Forced Flow Subcooled Boiling*, pp. 330–344, Stanford Univ. Press, Stanford, Calif.

Jens, W. H. & Lottes, P. A. 1951 Analysis of Heat Transfer, Burnout, Pressure Drop, and Density Data for High Pressure Water, *Rept.* ANL-4627, Argonne Natl. Lab.

Jensen, A. & Mannov, G. 1974 Measurements of Burnout, Film Flow, Film Thickness, and Pressure Drop in a Concentric Annulus 3500 × 26 × 17 mm with Heated Rod and Tube, *European Two-Phase Flow Group Meet., Harwell*, paper A5.

Jiji, L. M. & Clark, J. A. 1964 Bubble Boundary Layer and Temperature Profiles for Forced Convection Boiling in Channel Flow, *J. Heat Transfer, Trans. ASME*, ser. C 86:50–58.

Johnson, H. A. 1971 Transient Boiling of Water, *Int. J. Heat Mass Transfer* 14:67–82.

Jones, O. C. 1977 Liquid Deficient Cooling in Dispersed Flows. A Non-equilibrium Relaxation Model, *Rept.* BNL-NUREG-50639, Brookhaven Natl. Lab.

Jones, O. C. & Zuber, N. 1977 Post-CHF Heat Transfer—a Non-Equilibrium Relaxation Model, *ASME 17th Natl. Heat Transfer Conf., Salt Lake City, Aug. 14–17*, paper 77-HT-79.

Judd, R. L. & Hwang, K. S. 1976 Comprehensive Model for Nucleate Pool Boiling Heat Transfer Including Microlayer Evaporation, *J. Heat Transfer, Trans. ASME*, ser C 98:623.

Kaputstin, V. A., Kozlov, A. K., Kudryavtsev, Yu. V., Osmachkin, V. S., Asmolov, V. S., Ermakov, S. V., Lustsova, N. N., Seleznev, V. S., & Dushal, N. N. 1974 *Collection: T-74 Seminar, Investigation into Critical Heat Fluxes in Rod Bundles*, Council for Mutual Economic Assistance, Moscow.

Katsaounis, A., Fulfs, H., & Stein, M. 1977 Effects of the Core Grids on the Burnout, *European Two-Phase Flow Group Meet., Grenoble*, paper E4.

Kearsey, H. A. 1965 Steam-Water Heat Transfer—Post-Burnout Conditions, *Chem. Process. Eng. (Bombay)* 46:455–459.

Keeys, R. K. F., Ralph, J. C., & Roberts, D. N. 1970 Post Burnout Heat Transfer in High Pressure Steam-Water Mixtures in a Tube with Cosine Heat Flux Distribution, *Rept.* AERE-R6411, UKAEA, Harwell.

Keeys, R. K. F., Ralph, J. C., & Roberts, D. N. 1971 The Effect of Heat Flux on Liquid Entrainment in Steam-Water Flow in a Vertical Tube at 1000 psia (6.894 × 10⁶ N/m²), *Rept.* AERE-R6294, UKAEA, Harwell.

Keeys, R. F. K., Ralph, J. C., & Roberts, D. N. 1972 Post Burnout Heat Transfer in High Pressure Steam-Water Mixtures in a Tube with Cosine Heat Flux Distribution, *Prog. Heat Mass Transfer* 6:99–118.

Kenning, D. B. R. & Cooper, M. G. 1965 Flow Patterns near Nuclei and the Initiation of Boiling during Forced Convection Heat Transfer, *Boiling Symp. Inst. Mech. Eng. London*, vol. C180, part 3C, paper 11.

Kinneir, J. H., Heron, R. A., Stevens, G. F., & Wood, R. W. 1969 Burnout Power and Pressure Drop Measurements on 12 ft. 7 Rod Clusters Coded by Freon-12 at 155 psia, *European Two-Phase Flow Group Meet.*, Karlsruhe, paper V2; *Rept.* AEEW-R655, UKAEA, Winfrith.

Kirby, G. J., Stainiforth, R., & Kinneir, L. H. 1967 A Visual Study of Forced Convection Boiling. 2. Flow Patterns and Burnout for a Round Test Section, *Rept.* AEEW-506, UKAEA, Winfrith.

Kobori, T., Matsuo, M., & Kikuchi, A. 1974 The Effect of Fuel Cluster Eccentricity on Critical Heat Flux in a Full Scale Fuel Assembly, *Proc. J.U.I.C.E. Meet., Japan,* Rept. 11.

Kottowski, H. W. 1973 Activation Energy of Nucleation, *Prog. Heat Mass Transfer* 7:299–324.

Koumoutsos, N., Moissis, R., & Spyridonosa, A. 1968 Study of Bubble Departure in Forced Convection Boiling, *J. Heat Transfer, Trans. ASME,* ser. C 90:223–230.

Kroeger, P. G. & Zuber, N. 1968 An Analysis of the Effects of Various Parameters on the Average Void Fractions in Subcooled Boiling, *Int. J. Heat Mass Transfer* 11:211–233.

Kubie, J. & Gardner, G. C. 1977 Flow of Two Liquids in a Helix: An Analogue of High Pressure Helical Boilers, *Int. J. Multiphase Flow* 3:353–366.

Kunsemiller, D. F. 1965 Multirod, Forced Flow, Transition and Film Boiling Measurements, *Rept.* GEAP-5073, General Electric Co.

Kutateladze, S. S. 1952 Heat Transfer in Condensation and Boiling, *USAEC Rept.* AEC-tr-3770.

Kutateladze, S. S. 1963 *Fundamentals of Heat Transfer,* Academic Press, New York.

Kutateladze, S. S. & Leontiev, A. I. 1966 Some Applications of the Asymptotic Theory of the Turbulent Boundary Layers, *Proc. 3d Int. Heat Transfer Conf., Chicago* 3:1–6.

Lacey, P. M. C., Hewitt, C. F., & Collier, J. G. 1962 Climbing Film Flow, *Rept.* AERE-R3962, UKAEA, Harwell.

Lahey, R. T. 1974 Two-Phase Flow in Boiling Water Nuclear Reactors, *Rept.* NEDO-13388, General Electric Co.

Lahey, R. T. 1975 Boiling Transition. Lecture Notes for Two-Phase Flow and Heat Transfer in Water-cooled Nuclear Reactors, Dartmouth College.

Lahey, R. T. & Schraub, F. A. 1969 Mixing Flow Regimes and Void Fraction for Two Phase Flow and Heat Transfer in Rod Bundles, in *Proceedings of a Symposium on Two-Phase Flow in Rod Bundles,* ed. V. E. Schrock, pp. 1–14, ASME, New York.

Lahey, R. T., Cheng, L. Y., Drew, D. A., & Flaherty, J. E. 1980 The Effect of Virtual Mass on the Numerical Stability of Accelerating Two-Phase Flows, *Int. J. Multiphase Flow* 6:281–294.

Larsen, P. S. & Tong, L. S. 1969 Void Fractions in Subcooled Flow Boiling, *J. Heat Transfer, Trans. ASME,* ser. C 91:471–476.

Latrobe, A. 1978 A Comparison of Some Implicit Finite Difference Schemes Used in Flow Boiling Analysis, *2d OECD/NEA Specialists Meet. Transient Two-Phase Flow, Paris,* paper N5.

Lavin, J. G. & Young, E. H. 1965 Heat Transfer to Evaporating Two-Phase Flow, *AIChE J.* 11:1124–1132.

Lee, D. H. 1966 Burnout in a Channel with Non-Uniform Circumferential Heat Flux, *Rept.* AEEW-R477, UKAEA, Winfrith.

Lee, D. H. 1970 Studies of Heat Transfer and Pressure Drop Relevant to Sub-Critical Once-through Evaporators, *IAEA Symp. Progress Sodium-Cooled Fast Reactor Engineering, Monaco,* paper IAEA-SM-130/56.

Lee, D. H. & Bowditch, F. H. 1974 The Effect of the Proximity of an Unheated Surface on Dryout, *European Two-Phase Flow Group Meet., Harwell,* paper C9.

Lee, D. H. & Bowditch, F. H. 1977 An Experimental Study of Dryout at Low Flow in an SGHWR 36-Pin Cluster, *European Two-Phase Flow Group Meet., Grenoble,* paper E3.

Letourneau, B. W. & Green, S. J. 1971 Critical Heat Flux and Pressure Drop Tests with Parallel Upflow of High Pressure Water in Bundles of 20 Half Inch Rods, *Nucl. Sci. Eng.* 43:90–104.

Letourneau, B. W., Gavin, M. E., & Green, S. J. 1974 Critical Heat Flux and Pressure Drop Tests with Parallel Upflow of High Pressure Water in Bundles of Twenty Three-Quarter Inch Rods, *Nucl. Sci. Eng.* 54:214–232.

Leung, J. C. M. 1976 Occurrence of Critical Heat Flux during Blowdown with Flow Reversal, Ph.D. thesis, *Rept.* ANL/RAS/LWR 76-1, Argonne Natl. Lab.

Leung, J. C. M. 1977 Occurrence of Critical Heat Flux during Blowdown with Flow Reversal, *Rept.* ANL-77-4, Argonne Natl. Lab.

Levitan, L. L. & Lantsman, F. P. 1977 Critical Heat Fluxes in Internally Heated Annular Channels, *Therm. Eng. (USSR)* 24:16–21.

Levy, S. 1959 Generalized Correlation of Boiling Heat Transfer, *J. Heat Transfer, Trans. ASME,* ser. C 81:37–42.

Levy, S. 1967 Forced Convection Subcooled Boiling–Prediction of Vapor Volumetric Fraction, *Int. J. Heat Mass Transfer* 10:951–965.

Lien, Y. & Griffith, P. 1969 Bubble Growth at Reduced Pressure, Ph.D. thesis, Massachusetts Inst. of Technology, Cambridge.

Lienhard, J. H. & Dhir, V. K. 1973a Extended Hydrodynamic Theory of the Peak and Minimum Pool Boiling Heat Fluxes, *NASA Rept.* CR-2270.

Lienhard, J. H. & Dhir, V. K. 1973b Peak Boiling Heat Flux from Finite Bodies, *J. Heat Transfer, Trans. ASME* 95:152–158.

Lienhard, J. H. & Dhir, V. K. 1973c Peak Boiling Heat Flux in Viscous Liquids, *J. Heat Transfer, Trans. ASME* 96:71–78.

Lienhard, J. H. & Dhir, V. K. 1973d Peak Boiling Heat Flux on Finite Horizontal Plates, *J. Heat Transfer, Trans. ASME* 95:477–482.

Lienhard, J. H. & Eichhorn, R. 1976 Peak Boiling Heat Flux on Cylinders in a Cross Flow, *Int. J. Heat Mass Transfer* 19:1135–1141.

Lienhard, J. H. & Keeling, K. B. 1970 Induced Convection Effect on Peak Boiling Heat Flux, *J. Heat Transfer, Trans. ASME* 92:1–5.

Lienhard, J. H. & Sun, K. 1970 Peak Boiling Heat Flux on Horizontal Cylinders, *Int. J. Heat Mass Transfer,* 13:1425–1440.

Lienhard, J. H. & Wong, P. T. Y. 1963 Dominant Unstable Wavelength and Minimum Heat Flux during Film Boiling on Horizontal Cylinder, ASME paper 63-HT-3.

Lorenz, J. J., Mikic, B. B., & Rohsenow, W. M. 1974 Effects of Surface Conditions on Boiling Characteristics, *Proc. 5th Int. Heat Transfer Conf., Tokyo,* paper B2.1 4:35.

Lucchini, F. & Marinelli, V. 1975 Experimental Data on Burnout in a Simulated BWR Fuel Bundle, *Nucl. Eng. Des.* 31:371–378.

Lund, K. O. 1975 Critical Heat Flux in a Subcooled, Low-Pressure Rod-Bundle with Various Rod Spacings, ASME paper 75-HT-49.

Macbeth, R. V. 1963 Burnout Analysis: Part 4, Application of a Local Conditions Hypothesis to Wall Data for Uniformly Heated Round Tubes and Rectangular Channels, *Rept.* AEEW-R267, UKAEA, Winfrith.

Macbeth, R. V. 1964 Burnout Analysis: Part 5, Examination of World Data for Rod Bundles, *Rept.* AEEW-R358, UKAEA, Winfrith.

Macbeth, R. V. 1974 Odds and Evens. A Formula for Enhancing the Dryout Power in Boiling Water Reactor Fuel Channels, *European Two-Phase Flow Group Meet., Harwell,* paper C10.

Mahaffy, J. H. 1979 A Stability-Enhancing Two-Step Method for One-Dimensional Two-Phase Flow, *Rept.* NUREG/CR-0971, Nuclear Regulatory Commission.

Mahaffy, J. H. & Liles, D. R. 1979 Application of Implicit Numerical Method to Problems in Two-Phase Flow, *Rept.* NUREG/CR-0763, Nuclear Regulatory Commission, Washington.

Maneri, C. C. & Schneider, R. E. 1976 A Correction to Noncircular Duct Hot Patch Data, *J. Heat Transfer, Trans. ASME,* ser. C 98:332–334.

Marchaterre, J. F., Petrick, M., Lottes, P. A., Weatherhead, R. J., & Flinn, W. S. 1960 Natural and Forced-Circulation Boiling Studies, *Rept.* ANL-5735, Argonne Natl. Lab.

Marinelli, V. 1975 Critical Heat Flux: A Review of Recent Publications, *European Two-Phase Flow Group Meet., Haifa,* paper 3.0.

Marinelli, V. 1977 Critical Heat Flux: A Review of Recent Publications, *Nucl. Technol.* 32:135–171.

Marinelli, V., Guarini, D. & Pastori, L. 1973 Status of Art in Burnout Predictions for BWR Rod Bundles, *Trans. Am. Nucl. Soc.* 17:427–428.

Maroti, L. 1976 Critical Heat Flux in Subcooled and Low Quality Boiling, *Rept.* KFKI-74-34.

Martini, R. & Premoli, A. 1972 A Simple Model for Predicting ECC Transients in Bottom Flooding Conditions, *Proc. CREST Specialist Meet. ECC Light Water Reactors, Garching/Munich, Oct. 18-20,* vol. 2, *Rept.* MRR-115.

Marto, P. J. & Rohsenow, W. M. 1966 Nucleate Boiling Instability of Alkali Metals, *J. Heat Transfer, Trans. ASME* 88:183.

Mattson, R. J., Hammitt, F. G., & Tong, L. S. 1973 A Photographic Study of the Subcooled Flow Boiling Crisis in Freon-113, ASME paper 73-HT-39.

Mattson, R. J., Condie, K. G., Bengston, S. J., & Obenchain, C. F. 1974 Regression Analysis of Post-CHF Flow Boiling Data, *Proc. 5th Int. Heat Transfer Conf., Tokyo*, paper B3.8 4:115–119.

Matzner, B. 1961 Basic Experimental Studies on Boiling Fluid Flow and Heat Transfer at Elevated Pressures, *Rept.* TID-12574.

Matzner, B. 1962 Basic Experimental Studies on Boiling Fluid Flow and Heat Transfer at Elevated Pressures, *Rept.* TID-15637.

Matzner, B. 1963a Basic Experimental Studies of Boiling Fluid Flow and Heat Transfer at Elevated Pressures, *Rept.* TID-18296; *Dept. of Chemical Engineering Rept.* MPR-XIII-2-63, Columbia Univ., New York.

Matzner, B. 1963b Heat Transfer and Hydraulic Studies for SNAP-4 Fuel Element Geometries, *Rept.* TID-19563.

Matzner, B. & Casterline, J. E. 1965 The Effect of Length and Pressure on the Critical Heat Flux for a Closely Spaced 19-Rod Bundle in Forced Convection Boiling, *Rept.* TID-22539.

Matzner, B. & Neill, J. S. 1963 Forced-Flow Boiling in Rod Bundles at High Pressure, *AEC R&D Rept.* DP-857, E. I. duPont de Nemours & Co.

Matzner, B., Casterline, J. E., & Kokolis, S. 1968 Critical Heat Flux and Flow Stability in a 9 ft 19-Rod Test Section Simulating a String of Short Discrete Rod Bundles, *Topical Rept.* 10, Columbia Univ., New York.

Maurer, G. W. 1960 A Method of Predicting Steady-State Boiling Vapor Fraction in Reactor Coolant Channels, *Rept.* WAPD-BT-19, Westinghouse Electric Co.

Mayinger, F. & Bucher, B. 1977 Subcooled Boiling, in *Two Phase Flows and Heat Transfer*, eds. S. Kakaç & T. N. Veziroglu, vol. 2, pp. 581–621, Hemisphere, Washington, D.C.

Mayinger, F., Langner, H., & Seiffert, V. 1977 Experimental and Theoretical Investigations in Reactor Fluid Behaviour, *European Two-Phase Flow Group Meet., Grenoble*, paper B7.

McAdams, W. H., Kennel, W. E., Minden, C. S., Rudolf, C., & Dow, J. E. 1949 Heat Transfer at High Rates to Water with Surface Boiling, *Ind. Eng. Chem.* 41:1945–1953.

McDonough, J. B., Milich, W., King, E. C. 1961 An Experimental Study of Partial Film Boiling Region with Water at Elevated Pressures in a Round Vertical Tube, *Chem. Eng. Prog. Symp. Ser.* 57:197–208.

McKay, M. D. & Conover, W. J. 1976 Report on the Application of Statistical Techniques to the Analysis of Computer Codes, *Rept.* LA-NUREG-6526-MS, Los Alamos.

McNelly, M. J. 1953 A Correlation of the Rates of Heat Transfer to Nucleate Boiling Liquids, *J. Imp. Coll. Chem. Eng. Soc.* 7:18–34.

McPherson, G. D. 1971 The Use of Freon to Model Dryout in a High Pressure Water System, *Rept.* AECL-3787, Atomic Energy of Canada Ltd.

McPherson, G. D., Matzner, B., Castellana, F., Casterline, J. E., & Wikhammer, G. A. 1971 Dryout and Post-Dryout Behaviour of a 28-Element Fuel Bundle, *American Nuclear Society Winter Meet., Miami Beach.*

Merilo, M. 1977 Critical Heat Flux Experiments in a Vertical and Horizontal Tube with Both Freon-12 and Water as Coolant, *Nucl. Eng.* 44:1–16.

Merilo, M. 1979 Fluid-to-Fluid Modelling and Correlation of Flow Boiling Crisis in Horizontal Tubes, *Int. J. Multiphase Flow* 5:313–325.

Merte, J., Jr. & Clark, J. A. 1959 Study of Pool Boiling in an Accelerating System, *Rept.* 2646-21-T, *Tech. Rept.* 3, Univ. of Michigan.

Mikic, B. B. & Rohsenow, W. M. 1969 New Correlation of Pool Boiling Data Including the Effect of Heating Surface Characteristics, *J. Heat Transfer, Trans. ASME* 91:245.

Mikic, B. B., Rohsenow, W. M., & Griffith, P. 1970 On Bubble Growth Rates, *Int. J. Heat Mass Transfer* 13:657–666.

Miropolskii, Z. L. 1963 Heat Transfer in Film Boiling of a Steam-Water Mixture in Steam Generating Tubes, *Teploenergetika* 10:49–52; transl. AEC-tr-6252 (1964).

Miropolskii, Z. L. & Mostinskii, I. L. 1958 Critical Heat Flux in Uniform and Non-Uniform Heating of the Circumference of Steam-generating Tubes, *Teploenergetica* 11:64–69.

Moeck, E. O., Wikhammer, G. A., Macdonald, I. P. L., & Collier, J. G. 1964 Two Methods of Improving the Dryout Heat Flux for High Pressure Steam/Water Flow, *Rept.* AECL-2109, Atomic Energy of Canada Ltd.

Moissis, R. & Berenson, P. J. 1963 Hydrodynamic Transition in Nucleate Boiling, *J. Heat Transfer, Trans. ASME,* ser. C 85:221–229.

Moore, K. V. & Rettig, W. H. 1973 RELAP4—A Computer Program for Transient Thermal-hydraulic Analysis, microfiche ANCR-1127, Aerojet Nuclear Co.

Morris, A. W. L. 1976 The Resolution of a Dryout Induced On-Load Corrosion Problem in the Sloping Furnace Tubes of an Operational Boiler, *Proc. Inst. Mech. Eng. London* 190:721–727.

Moxon, D. & Edwards, P. A. 1967 Dryout during Flow and Power Transients, *Rept.* AEEW-R553, UKAEA, Winfrith.

Mueller, R. E. 1967 Film Boiling Heat Transfer Measurements in a Tubular Test Section, *Rept.* EURAEC-1871/GEAP-5423, General Electric Co.

Newbold, F. J., Ralph, J. C., & Ward, J. A. 1976 Post-Dryout Heat Transfer under Low Flow and Low Quality Conditions, *European Two-Phase Flow Group Meet., Erlangen,* paper D5; *Rept.* AERE-R8390, UKAEA, Harwell.

Nielsen, R. D., Tek, M. R., & York, J. L. 1965 Mechanism of Entrainment Formation in Distillation Columns, *Symp. Two-Phase Flow, Rept.* F-201-215, Univ. of Exeter.

Nishikawa, K. 1972 A Study of Burnout in Grooved Metal Tubes; *J. Jpn. Soc. Mech. Eng.* 75:700–707; CEGB transl. 6407.

Nishikawa, K., Fujii, T., Yoshida, S., & Onno, M. 1974 Flow Boiling Crisis in Grooved Boiler-Tubes, *Heat Transfer Jpn. Res.* 4:270–274.

Nixon, R. B., Matzner, B., & Lahey, R. T., Jr. 1975 The Effect of Reduced Clearance and Rod Bow on Critical Power in Full-Scale Simulations of 8 × 8 BWR Fuel, ASME paper 75-HT-69.

Noyes, R. C. & Lurie, H. 1966 Boiling Sodium Heat Transfer, *Proc. 3d Int. Heat Transfer Conf., Chicago* 5:92–100.

Nuclear Regulatory Commission 1974 Acceptance Criteria for Emergency Core Cooling System for Light Water-cooled Nuclear Power Plants, No. 3, *Fed. Regist.* 39:10 CFR 50.

Nuclear Safety Research Index 1977 Vol. 4: *Computer Codes,* OECD/NEA/IEA/CSNI.

Ornatskiy, A. P., Chernobay, V. A., Vasilyev, A. F., et al. 1975 Heat Transfer Crisis in Annuli with Cosinusoidal Heat Release along the Length. *Heat Transfer Sov. Res.* 7:66–70.

Ornatskiy, A. P., Chernobay, V. A., & Vasil'yev, A. F. 1976 Heat Transfer Crisis in Annuli with Hot Spots, *Heat Transfer Sov. Res.* 8:19–22.

Palen, J. W. & Small, W. M. 1964 A New Way to Design Kettle and Internal Reboilers, *Hydrocarbon Process.* 43:199–208.

Palen, J. W. & Taborek, J. 1962 Refinery Kettle Reboilers—Proposed Method for Design and Optimisation, *Chem. Eng. Prog.* 58:37–46.

Palen, J. W., Yarden, A., & Taborek, J. 1972 Characteristics of Boiling outside Large-Scale Horizontal Multi-Tube Bundles, *AIChE Symp. Ser.* 68:50–61.

Papell, S. S. 1970 Buoyancy Effects on Liquid-Nitrogen Film Boiling in Vertical Flow, *Adv. Cryog. Eng.* 16:435–444.

Papell, S. S. 1971 Film Boiling of Cryogenic Hydrogen during Upward and Downward Flow, *NASA TM* X-67855, microfiche N71-27866.

Parker, J. D. & Grosh, R. J. 1961 Heat Transfer to a Mist Flow, *Rept.* ANL-6291, Argonne Natl. Lab.

Peebles, F. N. & Garber, H. J. 1953 Studies on Motion of Gas Bubbles in Liquids *Chem. Eng. Prog.* 49:88–97.

Peterson, W. C., Aboul Fetouh, M. M., & Zaalouk, M. G. 1973 Boiling Curve Measurements from a Controlled Forced Convection Process, *BNES Int. Conf. Boiler Dynamics Control Nuclear Power Stations, London.*

Pitts, C. C. & Leppert, G. 1966 Critical Heat Flux for Electrically Heated Wires, *Int. J. Heat Mass Transfer* 9:365–378.

Plesset, M. S. & Zwick, J. A. 1954 The Growth of Vapor Bubbles in Superheated Liquids, *J. Appl. Phys.* 25:493.

Plummer, D. N., Iloeje, O. C., Griffith, P., & Rohsenow, W. M. 1973 A Study of Post Critical Heat Flux Heat Transfer in a Forced Convection System, *Dept. of Mechanical Engineering Rept.* DSR 73645-80, Massachusetts Inst. of Technology, Cambridge.

Plummer, D. N., Iloeje, O. C., Rohsenow, W. M., Griffith, P., & Ganic, E. 1974 Post Critical Heat Transfer to Flowing Liquid in a Vertical Tube, MIT Dept. Mech. Engng., *Dept. of Mechanical Engineering Rept.* 72718-91, Massachusetts Inst. of Technology, Cambridge.

Plummer, D. N., Griffith, P., & Rohsenow, W. M. 1976 Post-Critical Heat Transfer to Flowing Liquid in a Vertical Tube, *Proc. 16th Natl. Heat Transfer Conf., St. Louis,* paper 76-ASME/AIChE-13.

Polomik, E. E. 1962 Multi-Rod Burnout at High Pressure, *Rept.* GEAP-3940, General Electric Co.

Polomik, E. E. 1967 Transition Boiling Heat Transfer Program, *Rept.* GEAP-5563, General Electric Co.

Polomik, E. E. 1971 Deficient Cooling-7th Quarterly Report, *Rept.* GEAP-10221-7, General Electric Co.

Polomik, E. E., Levy, S., & Sawochka, S. G. 1961 Heat Transfer Coefficients with Annular Flow during Once-Through Boiling of Water to 100 per cent Quality at 800, 1100 and 1400 psi, *Rept.* GEAP-3703, General Electric Co.

Pramuk, F. S. & Westwater, J. W. 1956 *Chem. Eng. Prog. Symp. Ser.,* 52:79-82.

Ralston, A. & Wilf, H. S. (eds.) 1964 *Mathematical Methods for Digital Computers,* p. 165, Wiley, New York.

Ramu, K. & Weisman, J. 1974 A Method for the Correlation of Transition Boiling Heat Transfer Data, *Proc. 5th Int. Heat Transfer Conf., Tokyo,* paper B4.4 4:160-164.

Ramu, K. & Weisman, J. 1975 Transition Flow Boiling Heat Transfer to Water in a Vertical Annulus, *ASME 15th Natl. Heat Transfer Conf., San Francisco,* paper 75-HT-3; *Nucl. Eng. Des.* 40:285-295 (1977).

Rao, P. S. V. K. & Sarma, P. K. 1974 Partial Evaporation Rates of Liquid Patches on a Hot Plate under Film-Boiling Conditions, *Can. J. Chem. Eng.* 52:415-417.

Riegel, B. 1971 The Effect of a Cold Wall and the Influence of a Diaphragm in an Annular Cold Channel with Freon-12, *CEN Grenoble Rept.* TT105.

Rohsenow, W. M. 1952 A Method of Correlating Heat Transfer Data for Surface Boiling Liquids, *Trans. ASME* 74:969-976.

Rohsenow, W. M. 1966 Nucleation with Boiling Heat Transfer, *Ind. Eng. Chem.* 58:1.

Rohsenow, W. M. & Griffith, P. 1956 Correlation of Maximum Heat Transfer Data for Boiling of Saturated Liquids, *Chem. Eng. Prog. Symp. Ser.* 52:47.

Rouhani, S. Z. & Axelsson, E. 1970 Calculation of Void Volume Fraction in the Subcooled and Quality Boiling Regions, *Int. J. Heat Mass Transfer* 13:383-393.

Roumy, R. 1970 Dry-Out with Boiling Freon-12 in Straight Tubes of Different Slopes, *European Two-Phase Flow Group Meet., Milan,* paper D13.

Rowe, D. S. 1967 Cross-Flow Mixing between Parallel Flow Channels during Boiling. Part 1. COBRA: Computer Program for Constant Boiling in Rod Arrays, *Rept.* BNWL-371, pt. 1.

Rowe, D. S. 1970 COBRA II: A Digital Computer Program for Thermal Hydraulic Subchannel Analysis of Rod Bundle Nuclear Fuel Elements, *Rept.* BNWL-1229.

Rowe, D. S. 1972 COBRA III: A Digital Computer Program for Steady State and Transient Thermal Hydraulic Analysis of Rod Bundle Nuclear Fuel Elements, *Rept.* BNWL-B-82.

Rowe, D. S. 1973 COBRA IIIC: A Digital Computer Program for Steady State and Transient Thermal Analysis of Rod Bundle Nuclear Fuel Elements, *Rept.* BNWL-1695.

Ryley, D. J. 1961-1962 The Evaporation of Small Liquid Drops with Special Reference to Water Drops in Steam, *J. Liverpool Eng. Soc.* 7:1.

Saha, P. & Zuber, N. 1974 Point of Net Vapor Generation and Vapor Void Fraction in Subcooled Boiling, *Proc. 5th Int. Heat Transfer Conf., Tokyo* 9:175-179.

Saha, P., Shiralkar, B. S., & Dix, G. E. 1977 A Post-Dryout Heat Transfer Model Based on Actual Vapour Generation Rate in Dispersed Droplet Regime, *ASME 17th Natl. Heat Transfer Conf., Salt Lake City,* paper 77-HT-80.

Sakurai, A. & Shoitsu, M. 1977 Transient Pool Boiling, *J. Heat Transfer, Trans. ASME* **99**:547–560.

Schmidt, K. R. 1959 Thermodynamic Investigations of Highly Loaded Boiler Heating Surfaces. *Mitt. Ver. Grosskesselbesitzer* **63**:391. transl. AEC-tr-1033, Argonne Natl. Lab. (1960).

Schrock, V. E. & Grossman, L. M. 1962 Forced Convection Boiling in Tubes, *Nucl. Sci. Eng.* **12**:474–481.

Scientific Committee of the Academy of Sciences of the U.S.S.R. 1975, 1977 Recommendations for Calculating the Boiling Heat Transfer Crisis of Water in Uniformly Heated Round Tubes (in Russian), Scientific Committee, Academy of Sciences, Heat and Mass Transfer Section, Moscow.

Scriven, L. E. 1959 On the Dynamics of Phase Growth, *Chem. Eng. Sci.* **10**:1–13.

Semeria, R. 1973 Thermique des Fluides Diphasiques Bouillants, *Rev. Gen. Therm.* **12**:211–218.

Semeria, R. & Hewitt, G. F. 1972 Aspects of Two-Phase Gas-Liquid Flow, International Centre for Heat and Mass Transfer, Seminar on recent developments in heat exchangers, Trogir, Yugoslavia, Sept., lecture session H.

Semeria, R. & Martinet, B. 1966 Calefaction Spots on a Heating Wall: Temperature Distribution and Resorption, *Proc. Inst. Mech. Eng. London* **180**:192–205.

Shai, I. 1967 Mechanism of Nucleate Pool Boiling to Sodium, *Heat Transfer Lab. Rept.* 76-303-45, Massachusetts Inst. of Technology, Cambridge.

Shai, I. & Rohsenow, W. M. 1969 Stability Criteria for Nucleate Pool Boiling of Sodium, *J. Heat Transfer, Trans. ASME,* ser. C, **91**:315–329.

Shiralkar, B. S. 1972 Analysis of Non-uniform Flux CHF Data in Simple Geometries, *Rept.* NEDM-13279.

Siegel, R. & Usiskin, C. 1959 Photographic Study of Boiling in Absence of Gravity, *J. Heat Transfer, Trans. ASME* **81**:230–236.

Singer, R. M. & Holtz, R. H. 1970 A Study of Incipient Nucleation of Liquid Sodium, *Proc. 4th Int. Heat Transfer Conf., Versailles* **1**:B8.6.

Singh, A., Mikic, B. B., & Rohsenow, W. M. 1976 Active Sites in Boiling. *J. Heat Transfer, Trans. ASME,* ser. C **98**:401–406.

Slaughterbeck, D. C., Vesely, W. E., Ybarrondo, L. J., Condie, K. G., & Mattson, R. J. 1973a Statistical Regression Analysis of Experimental Data for Flow Film Boiling Heat Transfer, *ASME-AIChE 14th Natl. Heat Transfer Conf., Atlanta,* microfiche CONF-730803-4.

Slaughterbeck, D. C., Ybarrondo, L. J., & Obenchain, C. F. 1973b Flow Film Boiling Heat Transfer Correlations—Parametric Study with Data Comparisons, *ASME-AIChE 14th Natl. Heat Transfer Conf., Atlanta,* paper 73-HT-50.

Smolin, V. N. & Polyakov, V. K. 1967 Critical Heat Flux with Longitudinal Flow round a Rod Bundle, *Therm. Eng. (USSR)* **14**:54–58.

Smolin, V. N. & Polyakov, V. K. 1972 *Collection: Problems of Nuclear Science and Engineering, Series Reactor Engineering,* issue 1(8), Central Scientific and Research Institute of Information and Technical and Economic Researches in Atomic Science and Engineering, Moscow.

Sparrow, E. M. & Jonsson, V. K. 1963 Radiant Emission Characteristics of Diffuse Conical Cavities, *J. Opt. Soc. Am.* **53**:816–821.

Srinivasan, K., Seshagiri Rao, V., & Krishna Murthy, M. V. 1974 Analytical and Experimental Investigation on Cool-Down of Short Cryogenic Transfer Lines, *Cryogenics,* **14**:489–494.

Staniforth, R. & Stevens, G. F. 1965–1966 Experimental Studies of Burn-Out using Freon-12 at Low Pressure, with Reference to Burn-Out in Water at High Pressure, *Proc. Inst. Mech. Eng. London* **180**:part 3C, paper 10.

Staniforth, R., Stevens, G. F., & Wood, R. W. 1965 An Experimental Investigation into the Relationship between Burn-Out and Film Flow Rate in a Uniformly Heated Tube, *Rept.* AEEW-R430, UKAEA, Winfrith.

Staniszewski, B. E. 1959 Nucleate Boiling Bubble Growth and Departure, *Tech. Rept.* 16, DRS 7673, ONR contract NONR-1841(39), Heat Transfer Lab., Massachusetts Inst. of Technology, Cambridge.

Staub, F. 1968 The Void Fraction in Subcooled Boiling—Prediction of the Initial Point of Net Vapor Generation, *J. Heat Transfer, Trans. ASME*, ser. C 90:151–157.

Stevens, G. F. & Macbeth, R. V. 1968 Further Experimental Confirmation of the Freon Technique for Scaling Burnout, *European Two-Phase Flow Group Meet., Oslo*, paper E3.

Stevens, G. F. & Macbeth, R. V. 1970 Use of Freon-12 to Model Forced Convection Burn-Out in Water: The Restriction on the Size of the Model, *J. Br. Nucl. Energy Soc.* 9:249–257.

Stevens, G. F. & Macbeth, R. V. 1971 Use of Freon-12 to Model Forced Convection Burn-Out in Water: The Restriction on the Size of the Model, *Rept.* AEEW-R683, UKAEA, Winfrith.

Stevens, G. F. & Wood, R. W. 1966 A Comparison between Burn-Out Data for 19-Rod Cluster Test-Sections Cooled by Freon-12 at 155 lb/in sq. (abs) and by Water at 1000 lb/in sq. in Vertical Upflow, *Rept.* AEEW-R468, UKAEA, Winfrith.

Stevens, G. F., Elliott, D. F., & Wood, R. W. 1964 An Experimental Investigation into Forced Convection Burn-Out in Freon, with Reference to Burn-Out in Water, *Rept.* AEEW-R321, UKAEA, Winfrith.

Stevens, G. F., Elliott, D. F., & Wood, R. W. 1965 An Experimental Comparison between Forced Convection Burn-Out in Freon-12 Flowing Vertically Upwards through Uniformly and Non-Uniformly Heated Round Tubes, *Rept.* AEEW-R426, UKAEA, Winfrith.

Stevens, G. F., Wood, R. W., & Pryzbylski, J. 1968 An Investigation into the Effects of a Cosine Axial Heat Flux Distribution on Burnout in a 12 ft Long Annulus using Freon-12, *Rept.* AEEW-R609, UKAEA, Winfrith.

Styrikovich, M. A. & Mostinskii, I. L. 1959 The Effect of Non-uniform Heat Distribution on Steam Generation in Tubes, *Dokl. Akad. Nauk SSSR* 127:316–319; transl.: P. G. Morgan, *Eng. Boiler House Rev.*, pp. 336–338.

Styrikovich, M. A. & Nevstrueva, E. I. 1966 An Approximate Estimation of Circulation and Temperature Characteristics of Two-Phase Pulsation Flow with Surface Boiling, *Proc. 3rd Int. Heat Trans. Conf.*, 4:207–215.

Subbotin, V. I., Sorokin, D. N., & Kudryavtsev, A. P. 1970 Generalized Relationship for Heat Transfer in Developed Boiling of Alkali Metals, *At. Energy* 29:45.

Subbotin, V. I., Ushakov, P. A., Levchenko, Yu. D., & Aleksandrov, A. M. 1971 Velocity Fields in Turbulent Flow past Rod Bundles, *Heat Transfer Sov. Res.* 3:9–35.

Subbotin, V. I., Kaznovskiy, S. P., & Sapankevich, A. P. 1975 An Experimental Study of Methods for Augmenting the Critical Capacity of Steam-generating Tubes, *Heat Transfer Sov. Res.* 7:85–95.

Suchy, P., Ulrych, G., & Casterline, J. 1976 Influence of KWU Mixing Vanes on Critical Heat Flux, *European Two-Phase Flow Group Meet., Erlangen*, paper A12.

Sun, K. H. & Lienhard, J. H. 1970 The Peak Pool Boiling Heat Flux on Horizontal Cylinders, *Int. J. Heat Mass Transfer* 13:1425–1439.

Sun, K. H., Dix, G. E., & Tien, C. L. 1974 Cooling of a Very Hot Vertical Surface by a Falling Liquid Film, *J. Heat Transfer, Trans. ASME* 96:126–131.

Sun, K. H., Dix, G. E., & Tien, C. L. 1975 Effect of Precursory Cooling on Falling-Film Rewetting, *J. Heat Transfer, Trans. ASME* 97:360–365.

Suryanarayana, N. V. & Merte, H. 1972 Film Boiling on Vertical Surfaces, *J. Heat Transfer, Trans. ASME* 94:377–384.

Swenson, H. S., Carver, J. R., & Szoeke, G. 1961 The Effects of Nucleate Boiling versus Film Boiling on Heat Transfer in Power Boiler Tubes, *ASME Winter Annu. Meet., New York*, paper 61-WA-201; *J. Eng. Power* 84:365–371 (1962).

Thompson, B. H. & Macbeth, R. V. 1964 Boiling Water Heat Transfer Burnout in Uniformly Heated Round Tubes. A Compilation of World Data with Accurate Correlations, *Rept.* AEEW-R356, UKAEA, Winfrith.

Thompson, T. S. 1972 An Analysis of the Wet-Side Heat-Transfer Coefficient during Rewetting of a Hot Dry Patch, *Nucl. Eng. Des.* 22:212–224.

Thompson, T. S. 1974 Rewetting of a Hot Surface, *Proc. 5th Int. Heat Transfer Conf., Tokyo* paper B3.13, 4:139–143.

Tien, C. L. 1962 Hydrodynamic Model for Nucleate Boiling, *Int. J. Heat Mass Transfer* 5:533–540.

Tien, C. L. & Yao, L. S. 1974 Analysis of Conduction-controlled Rewetting of a Vertical Surface, *ASME Winter Annu. Meet., New York,* paper 74-WA/NT-49; *J. Heat Transfer, Trans. ASME* 97:161–165.

Tolubinskiy, V. I. & Matorin, A. S. 1973 Forced Convection Boiling Heat Transfer Crisis with Binary Mixtures, *Heat Transfer Sov. Res.* 5:98–101.

Tolubinskiy, V. I., Mazka, S. A., & Vasil'yev, V. A. 1970 Boiling Crisis in Longitudinal Flow past Rod Bundles, *Heat Transfer Sov. Res.* 2:1–6.

Tolubinskiy, V. I., Litoshenko, A. K., & Domashev, E. D. 1971 Critical Heat Transfer in Eccentric Annuli, *Therm. Eng.* 18:93–95.

Tong, L. S. 1964 Film Boiling Heat Transfer at Low Quality of Subcooled Region, *2d Joint USAEC-Euratom Two-Phase Flow Meet., Germantown, Md.,* CONF-640507, pp. 63.

Tong, L. S. 1965 *Boiling Heat Transfer and Two Phase Flow,* Wiley, New York.

Tong, L. S. 1967 Heat Transfer in Water-cooled Nuclear Reactors, *Nucl. Eng. Des.* 6:301–324.

Tong, L. S. 1968 Boundary Layer Analysis of the Flow Boiling Crisis, *Int. J. Heat Mass Transfer* 2:1208–1211.

Tong, L. S. 1972a Boiling Crisis and Critical Heat Flux, USAEC Critical Review Series, *Rept.* TID-25887.

Tong, L. S. 1972b Heat-Transfer Mechanisms in Nucleate and Film Boiling, *Nucl. Eng. Des.* 21:1–25.

Tong, L. S. 1980 *Int. Conf. Current Nuclear Power Safety Issues, Stockholm,* USNRC Research Program paper IAEA-CN-39/99.

Tong, L. S. & Hewitt, G. F. 1972 Overall Viewpoint of Film Boiling CHF Mechanisms, ASME paper 72-HT-54.

Tong, L. S. & Young, J. D. 1974 A Phenomenological Transition and Film Boiling Heat Transfer Correlation, *Proc. 5th Int. Heat Transfer Conf., Tokyo,* paper B3.9 4:120–124.

Tong, L. S., Currin, H. B., & Larsen, P. S. 1966 Influence of Axially Nonuniform Heat Flux on DNB, *Rept.* WCAP-2767, Westinghouse Electric Co.

Tong, L. S., Cheremer, H., Casterline, J. E., & Matzner, B. 1967a Critical Heat Flux (DNB) in Square and Triangular Array Rod Bundles, *JSME Semi-International Symp., Tokyo.*

Tong, L. S., Weissman, J., & Wenzel, A. H. 1967b Experimental Determination of the Departure from Nucleate Boiling in Large Rod Bundles at High Pressure, *Natl. Heat Transfer Conf., Seattle; Chem. Eng. Prog. Symp. Ser.* 64:114–125 (1968).

Tourneau, Le B. W. & Green, S. J. 1971 Critical Heat Flux and Pressure Drop Tests with Parallel Upflow of High Pressure Water in Bundles of Twenty $\frac{1}{2}$ in Rods, *Nucl. Sci. Eng.* 43:90–104.

Unal, H. C. 1975 Determination of the Initial Point of Net Vapor Generation in Flow Boiling Systems, *Int. J. Heat Mass Transfer* 18:1095–1099.

van der Molen, S. B. & Galijee, F. W. B. M. 1977 Boundary Layer and Burnout Phenomena in a Subcooled Two-Phase Flow, *European Two-Phase Flow Group Meet., Grenoble,* paper E1.

van der Roos, T. 1970 On Two-Phase Flow Exchange between Interacting Hydraulic Channels, *Rept.* WW015-R160, Eindhoven Univ. of Technology, Eindhoven, Netherlands.

van Stralen, S. J. D. 1959 Heat Transfer to Boiling Binary Liquid Mixtures, Part I, *Br. Chem. Eng.* 4:8–17.

van Stralen, S. J. D. 1968 Growth Rate of Vapor Bubbles in Superheated Pure Liquids and Binary Mixtures, Parts I & II, *Int. J. Heat Mass Transfer* 11:1467–1512.

van Stralen, S. J. D. 1970 Boiling Paradox in Binary Liquid Mixtures, *Chem. Eng. Sci.* 25:149–171.

van Stralen, S. J. D. & Zijl, W. 1978 Fundamental Developments in Bubble Dynamics, *Proc. 6th Int. Heat Transfer Conf., Toronto* 6:429–449.

Volmer, M. 1939 *Kinetic der Phasenbildung,* Steinkopf, Dresden; Edwards, Ann Arbor, Mich. (1945).

Wallis, G. W. 1961 *Int. Heat Transfer Conf., Boulder. Colo.,* vol. 2.

Wallis, G. B. & Collier, J. G. 1968 Two-Phase Flow and Heat Transfer, Notes for a Summer Course, Thayer School of Engineering, Dartmouth College, Hanover, N.H., vol. 3, pp. 33–46.

Wark, J. W. 1933 The Physical Chemistry of Flotation, *Int. J. Phys. Chem.* 37:623.

WASH-1400 1975 Reactor Safety Study, *Rept.* Nureg-75/104, Nuclear Regulatory Commission.

Waters, E. D. 1963 Boiling Burnout Experiments with 19-Rod Bundles in Axial Flow, *Rept.* HW-77303.

Watson, G. B., Lee, R. A., & Wiener, M. 1974 Critical Heat Flux in Inclined and Vertical Smooth and Ribbed Tubes, *Heat Transfer* 4:275–279.

Weisman, J. & Bowring, R. W. 1975 Methods for Detailed Thermal and Hydraulic Analysis of Water-cooled Reactors, *Nucl. Sci. Eng.* 57:225–276.

Westwater, J. W. 1956 *Boiling of Liquids*, Academic, New York.

Westwater, J. W. & Strenge, P. H. 1959 *Chem. Eng. Prog. Symp. Ser.* 29:95.

Whalley, P. B. 1974 The Calculation of Dryout in a Heated Annulus, *Rept.* AERE-M2661, UKAEA, Harwell.

Whalley, P. B. 1976 The Calculation of Dryout in a Rod Bundle, *European Two-Phase Flow Group Meet., Erlangen,* paper A9; *Rept.* AERE-8319, UKAEA, Harwell.

Whalley, P. B. 1977 The Calculation of Dry-Out in Rod-Bundles, *Int. J. Multiphase Flow* 3:501–515.

Whalley, P. B. 1978 The Calculation of Dryout in a Rod Bundle–A Comparison of Experimental and Calculated Results, *Int. J. Multiphase Flow* 4:427–431.

Whalley, P. B. & Hewitt, G. F. 1978 The Correlation of Liquid Entrainment Fraction and Entrainment Rate in Annular Two-Phase Flow, *Rept.* AERE-R9187, UKAEA, Harwell.

Whalley, P. B., Hutchinson, P., & Hewitt, G. F. 1973 The Calculation of Critical Heat Flux in Forced Convection Boiling, *Rept.* AERE-R7520, UKAEA, Harwell.

Whalley, P. B., Hutchinson, P., & Hewitt, G. F. 1974 The Calculation of Critical Heat Flux in Forced Convection Boiling, *Heat Transfer* 4:290–294.

Whalley, P. B., Hutchinson, P., & Hewitt, G. F. 1975 Prediction of Annular Flow Parameters for Transient Conditions and for Complex Geometries, *European Two-Phase Flow Group Meet., Haifa,* paper 2.1.

Whalley, P. B., Hutchinson, P., & James, P. W. 1978 The Calculation of Critical Heat Flux in Complex Situations using an Annular Flow Model, *Proc. 6th Int. Heat Transfer Conf., Toronto* 5:65–70.

Wilson, R. H., Stanek, L. J., Gellerstedt, J. S., & Lee, R. A. 1969 Critical Heat Flux in a Nonuniformly Heated Rod Bundle, ASME, New York.

Wismer, K. L. 1922 *J. Phys. Chem.* 26:301.

Yadigaroglu, G. 1978 The Reflooding Phase of the LOCA in PWRs. Part I. Core Heat Transfer and Fluid Flow, *Nucl. Saf.* 19:20–36.

Yamanouchi, A. 1968 Effect of Core Spray Cooling in Transient State after Loss of Coolant Accident, *J. Nucl. Sci. Technol.* 5:547–558.

Yao, L. S. 1976 Rewetting of a Vertical Surface with Internal Heat Generation, *16th Natl. Heat Transfer Conf., St. Louis, Mo.,* AIChE paper 9.

Yeh, H.-C. 1975 An Analysis of Rewetting of a Nuclear Fuel Rod in Water Reactor Emergency Core Cooling, *Nucl. Eng. Des.* 34:317–322.

Yoshioka, K. & Hasegawa, S. 1970 A Correlation in Displacement Velocity of Liquid Film Boundary Formed on a Heated Vertical Surface in Emergency Cooling, *J. Nucl. Sci. Technol.* 7:418–425.

Young, R. K. & Hummel, R. L. 1964 Improved Nucleate Boiling Heat Transfer, *Chem. Eng. Prog.* 60:53–58.

Yusufova, V. D. & Bronshtein, A. I. 1976 The Effect of Foaming on Burnout when Boiling Water of Above-critical TDS. *Therm. Eng. (USSR)* 22:104–107.

Zuber, N. 1958 Hydrodynamic Aspects of Boiling Heat Transfer, *Rept.* AECU-4439.

Zuber, N. 1959 Hydrodynamic Aspects of Boiling Heat Transfer, Ph.D. thesis, Univ. of California, Los Angeles; *USAEC Rept.* AECU-4439.

Zuber, N. & Findlay, J. 1965 Average Volumetric Concentration in Two-Phase Flow Systems, *J. Heat Transfer, Trans. ASME,* ser. C 87:453.

Zuber, N. & Tribus, M. 1958 Further Remarks on the Stability of Boiling Heat Transfer, *Rept.* 58-5, Univ. of California, Los Angeles.

Zuber, N., Tribus, M., & Westwater, J. W. 1961 The Hydrodynamic Crisis in Pool Boiling of

Saturated and Subcooled Liquids, in *International Developments in Heat Transfer,* pt. 2, pp. 230–236, ASME, New York.

Zuber, N., Tribus, M., & Westwater, J. W. 1963 The Hydrodynamic Crisis in Pool Boiling of Saturated Liquids, in *International Developments in Heat Transfer,* pp. 230–236, ASME, New York.

Zuber, N. F., Staub, F., & Bijwaard, G. 1966 Vapor Void Fraction in Subcooled Boiling and in Saturated Boiling System, *Proc. 3d Int. Heat Transfer Conf., Chicago,* 5:24–38.

Simmons, G. and Salinas, L. (1982), hydrocarbon movement processes in the Gulf Coast region, Oil & Gas, Atlantic Publ. Co., Houston.

Walker, W. (1981), Some recent techniques. New Trends in Biology and Medicine of Deep-Sea Research, Ann., ed., New York.

Young, J. and Brown, T. (1974), Geological Survey of Petrol. Sciences and Engineering Resources, New York.

7 CONVEYING

7.1 Pneumatic Conveying

S. L. Soo

Pneumatic conveying has been useful in the transporting, distribution, and processing of particulate materials. The conveyed material takes the form of a gas-solid suspension; in the majority of cases "pneumatic" means the gas is air.

The basic elements of a pneumatic conveying system include a feeder for the solids or bulk material, a blower for the gas, a pipeline for transport, and a collector to recover the solids. This mode of handling bulk or particulate materials is limited to materials of high strength, immune to attrition or breakage by impact or to materials that suffer only tolerable degradation in passing through a given system.

Pneumatic pipelines up to 5000 m long (U.S. Department of the Interior 1962) have been built for transporting various solids, in pipes up to 360 mm in diameter. Most test data were obtained in pipes with diameters less than 200 mm. Handling capacities were up to hundreds of tons per hour.

The density ratio of solid to gas tends to be low (dilute suspension) for transport over short distances, for reliability. Economy is usually gained via labor saving. Long distances of several kilometers may call for transmission of a dense suspension for optimum economy of operation (Soo & Leung 1977).

There is no well-founded, precise, scientific theory that covers all problems in detail and that has been verified in practice. The variety of physical properties of the materials being conveyed and the multiplicity of design possibilities hamper calculation by specific formulas and make research expensive. The first installations were built mainly on an empirical basis, either utilizing the results of research performed by the Engineering Equipment Users Association (EEUA) (1963) or by extending and scaling up from current practice.

The details of such empirical methods are presented by Fischer (1958), Engineering Equipment Users Association (1963), Hudson (1944, 1954), Dalla Valle (1942), Bannister (1959), and Gluck (1968). These authors present approximate methods and formulas for calculating the overall pressure drop in the gas-solid system, starting from a recommended superficial air (carrier gas) velocity based on

Study supported in part by the National Science Foundation.

the type of material conveyed. Their data are, in fact, the air rate at which blockage occurs plus a practical margin established by practice and experience for the particular material. They can serve only as rough guidelines for new situations and are useful where subsequent adjustments can be readily made in operation and where efficiency is not of prime importance.

Pneumatic conveying is not a new field; experimental investigations on grains and other particulate materials were first reported by Gasterstadt (1924) and Cramp & Priestley (1924). Further investigations of the fundamental phenomenon and design were motivated by applications in transporting coal and grains in pipelines. Dukler et al. (1964) reported that, by 1964, over 20,000 experimental data from various sources had been employed in obtaining correlations and generalizations of pressure drop, holdup and friction factor. Furthermore, different approaches have been used by theoretical investigators in their correlations and analyses of results. Empirical correlations is the most commonly employed technique. Dimensional analysis was used by Boothroyd (1966), Hitchcock & Jones (1958), Chowdhury et al. (1967), and Rose & Duckworth (1969). The work by Rose & Duckworth provides the most detailed and convincing solution for this type of approach. The first trial of similarity analysis was suggested by Dukler et al. (1964).

Currently, the range of application has been broadened to include materials and particle sizes as summarized in figure 7.1.1. The figure is a juxtaposition of particle sizes, materials, and design concerns other than operating efficiency (Soo, 1980).

Pneumatic conveying systems cover the range of particle sizes from 1 μm in dust-handling systems up to 100 mm in coal-mine hoists. Above 100 mm it would be advisable to use chutes or belt conveyors. Pneumatic conveying has the advantage of handling bulk material in a closed system and providing for automation.

There is no standard design procedure. The special concerns outlined in figure 7.1.1 often have more weight in the design procedure than operating efficiency. However, the overall economy must still justify a given installation. For instance, in the design of a system for handling explosives, safety is the prime concern and perhaps the principal product; safety is achieved via reduction of the number of personnel in hazardous areas as well as by decreasing the chance of human error. In such an instance, labor saving alone pays back the investment rapidly. Further details will be given in later sections, after the primary design procedures are outlined.

It is not possible to provide all the available information pertaining to pneumatic conveying in one chapter; nor are there standard data. Conflicting information and trade secrets are rampant. What follows is, rather, an attempt at a logical presentation of the design procedures and discussion of other valid concerns. Readers are referred to treatises such as those of Govier & Aziz (1972) and Boothroyd (1971). Other information sources are several Pneumotransport Conference Proceedings of the British Hydromechanics Research Association (Cranfield, U. K.) and the *Proceedings of the International Powder Institute*. The principal journals covering gas-solid fluid mechanics are the *International Journal of Powder Technology, Powder and Bulk Solid Technology,* and the *International Journal of Multiphase Flow.*

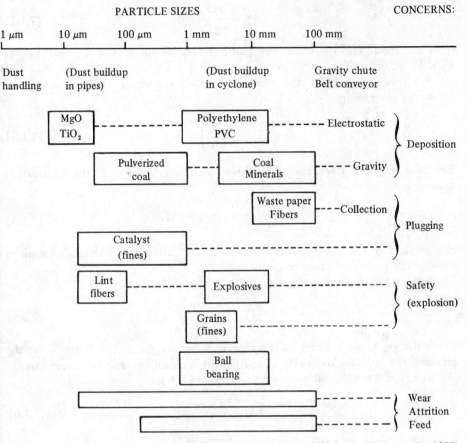

PARTICLE SIZES   CONCERNS:

Figure 7.1.1 Approximate size ranges and design concerns other than operating efficiency (Soo 1980).

7.1.1 STATE OF A GAS–SOLID SUSPENSION

Studies on the subject of gaseous suspensions often refer to a suspension as "dense phase" or "dilute phase." The extremes of each are obvious; however, there is no sharp division between the two. The idea of a dilute suspension is often invoked to simplify the analysis of a problem. Economy may call for a dense suspension, and safety may require a dilute suspension.

For the flow of a suspension of mean solid particle diameter d_p in a pipe of diameter D, the parameters of interest are the material densities of the solid and gas $\bar{\rho}_p$ and $\bar{\rho}_G$, the mean velocities of the phases V_p and V_G, the density of the particle cloud $\rho_p = \phi\bar{\rho}_p$, and the density of the gas in the mixture $\rho_G = \bar{\rho}_G\,(1 - \phi)$, ϕ being the volume fraction solid. The mass ratio of the phases is given by

$$m^* = \frac{\rho_p}{\rho_G} \qquad [7.1.1]$$

and the mass flow ratio of the phases is

$$\dot{m}^* = \frac{\rho_p V_p}{\rho_G V_G} \qquad [7.1.2]$$

since the mean velocity V_p of the particles lags behind that of the gas V_G, or $V_p < V_G$ in general, and $m^* > \dot{m}^*$.

For spherical particles, the mean interparticle spacing is given by the number density of particles n:

$$\frac{n^{-1/3}}{d_p} = \left(\frac{\pi}{6\phi}\right)^{1/3} \qquad [7.1.3]$$

The ratio of mean free path of particle-to-particle collision λ to the interparticle spacing, given by

$$\frac{\lambda}{n^{-1/3}} = \phi^{-2/3}(36\pi)^{-1/3} \qquad [7.1.4]$$

is a measure of the freedom of movement of the particles, and thus a measure of whether the phases are dense or dilute.

For solid particles in a gas, it is readily shown that

$$\frac{\phi}{1 - \phi} = \frac{\bar{\rho}_G}{\bar{\rho}_p} m^* = \frac{P}{RT \bar{\rho}_p} m^* \qquad [7.1.5]$$

where the gas phase is given by the state of a perfect gas, and P, T, and R are the pressure, the absolute temperature, and the gas constant per unit mass, respectively. For air below 2.0 MPa and near room temperature of 300 K, we get

$$\frac{\phi}{1 - \phi} = 11.77 \frac{P_{\text{MPa}}}{\bar{\rho}_p} m^* \qquad [7.1.6]$$

where P_{MPa} is in MPa and $\bar{\rho}_p$ is in kg/m^3. The flow rate of particles is given, for a circular pipe of diameter D, by

$$\dot{M}_p = \dot{m}^* \bar{\rho} \frac{\pi}{4} D^2 V_G = \frac{\phi}{1 - \phi} \bar{\rho}_p \frac{\pi}{4} D^2 V_G$$

and the mass of particles per unit volume is given by

$$\frac{\dot{M}_p}{(\pi/4) D^2 V_G} = \frac{P}{RT} m^* \frac{V_p}{V_G} \qquad [7.1.7]$$

For steady flow, $0.5 < V_p/V_G < 1$ (Govier & Aziz 1972).

For solid particles of coal in air, $\bar{\rho}_p = 1300$ kg/m^3 at pressure P_{MPa} and a temperature of 300 K, and we have

$$m^* P_{\text{MPa}} = 1.104 \times 10^2 \frac{\phi}{1 - \phi} \qquad [7.1.8]$$

Moreover, the total flow rate of the solid $\dot{M}_p$ is given by

$$\frac{\dot{M}_p}{(\pi/4) D^2 V_G} = 0.7355 \, m^* P_{\text{MPa}} \qquad [7.1.9]$$

Volume Fraction Solid, ϕ	m^* P_{MPa}	Interparticle Spacing/Size	Free Path/Size
0.8886	83060	0.838	0.2237 [1]
0.5230	12100	1.0	0.3186 [2]
0.2681	4044	1.25	0.4973
0.1551	2027	1.5	0.7163
0.09403	1146	---	1.00
0.06545	7.732	2.0	1.273
0.03351	38.28	2.5	1.989
0.01939	2183	3.0	2.865

(1)- Tetrahedral Piling   (2)- Cubic Piling

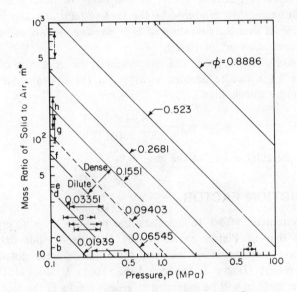

Figure 7.1.2 State of pneumatic suspension (25°C) air; specific gravity of coal = 1.3; $\dot{m}^*$ = kg solid/kg air; P = pressure, MPa (Soo et al. 1975). References in figure are as follows: a, U.S. Department of the Interior 1962; b, Konchesky & Craig 1973; c, Dogin & Lebedev 1962; d, Hariu 1949; e, Vogt & White 1948; f, Zenz 1949; g, Sandy et al. 1969; h, Albright et al. 1951; i, Wen & Simons 1959.

which shows that the product m^*P_{MPa} is directly proportional to the throughflow for a given pipe diameter and flow velocity.

The relations given by [7.1.3], [7.1.4], and [7.1.8] are shown in figure 7.1.2 for various volume fractions of solid ϕ with P_{MPa} from 0.1 to 10.0 MPa and $\dot{m}^*$ from 10 to 10^3. Ranges of data are shown for dilute-phase and dense-phase studies. Related to the lines of [7.1.8] for constant ϕ are interparticle spacing/particle size, m^*P_{MPa}. Since the main difference between dilute- and dense-phase suspensions is in the freedom of movement of the particles, we may assume the dividing line along the line of $\lambda/n^{-1/3} \cong 1$ or $\phi \cong 0.1$. This is an engineering definition; a definition based on multiphase mechanics is given in Soo (1976).

Figure 7.1.2 shows that, for a given state of suspension, increasing pressure will not always increase the solid flow capacity. Hence, there is an optimum between a vacuum and a high pressure. This is because a high gas density calls for a lower suspension velocity, a relation to be treated in section 7.1.3.

Also noted in figure 7.1.2 is the range of the design study in the 1962 report of coal-dust suspension in methane. In spite of its low mass flow ratio (because of the high pressure), this actually corresponds to the most dense suspension ever subjected to experiment. Since $V_p < V_G$, the actual m^* is expected to be much higher. The range of experiments on coal (U.S. Department of the Interior 1962) is also shown in figure 7.1.2. The actual m^* is likely to have been much higher because of the unsteady flow produced by the feed system.

It will be shown that the advantage of high pressure diminishes beyond 1.0-2.0 MPa of line pressure at an $\dot{m}^*$ of 10-20.

For other solid particles, gases, and temperatures, the mass ratio of solids to the gas m^* in figure 7.1.2, can be denoted as m_{AC}^* for the air-coal system, and figure 7.1.2 can be used by calculating

$$m^* = m_{AC}^* \frac{28.97}{300(1300)} \bar{\rho}_p \frac{T}{W} \qquad [7.1.10]$$

where W is the molecular weight of the gas.

7.1.2 FRICTION FACTOR

An extensive systematic effort to correlate the pressure drop in pipe flow with suspensions was that of Pfeffer et al. (1966). Because of wide data scatter, no general correlation was possible; however, some trends were noted. The study included other results (Dogin & Lebedev 1962; Hariu & Molstad 1949; Vogt & White 1948). The method will be extended to recent results in the following.

For isothermal pipe flow of a gaseous suspension in a system with pipe diameter D, length L, elevation H at one end, and total flow of solids and air $\dot{M}_p$ and $\dot{M}_a$, respectively, the pressure drop dP over a length dx is given by

$$dP = -4f_m \frac{dx}{D} \frac{\bar{\rho}_G V_G^2}{2} - d(\rho_m V^2) - \rho_m g\, dH \qquad [7.1.11]$$

where f_m is the friction factor of the mixture of gas and solid, V_G is the gas velocity, ρ_m is the density of the mixture ($\rho_m = \rho_G + \rho_p$), g is the gravitational acceleration, and dH is the rise in elevation over dx. In [7.1.11], the first term on the right-hand side is the pressure drop due to friction; the second term, the acceleration; and the third term, the gravity effect due to the change in elevation. Note that the mass flow G is given by

$$\rho_{G1}V_{G1} = \rho_{G2}V_{G2} = \rho_G V_G = \frac{\dot{M}_G}{(\pi/4)\,D^2} = G_G \qquad [7.1.12]$$

The subscripts 1 and 2 denote inlet and outlet, respectively.

The friction factor for turbulent flow of a fluid such as air in a smooth pipe is given by

$$f_G = \frac{0.046}{\text{Re}^{0.2}} \qquad [7.1.13]$$

where the Reynolds number Re is given by

$$\text{Re} = \frac{D\bar{\rho}_G V_G}{\mu_G} = \frac{D G_G}{\mu_G} \qquad [7.1.14]$$

where μ_G is the viscosity of the gas.

For small changes in the pressure or density of the gas phase, [7.1.11] can be integrated as for an incompressible fluid:

$$P_1 - P_2 = 4 f_m \frac{L}{D} \frac{G_G^2}{2\bar{\rho}_G} + (1 + \dot{m}^*) \rho_G (V_{G2}^2 - V_{G1}^2) + (1 + \dot{m}^*) \rho_G H g$$

$$[7.1.15]$$

For small ϕ, $p \cong \bar{P}$ for the gas. For large changes in the pressure of the gas P_1 to P_2, the effect of compressibility is accounted for via integration to

$$1 - \frac{P_2^2}{P_1^2} = 4 f_m \frac{L}{D} \rho_{G1}^2 V_{G1}^2 \frac{RT}{P_1^2} + (1 + \dot{m}^*) 2 G_G^2 \frac{R_G T}{P_1^2} \ln \frac{P_1}{P_2}$$

$$+ (1 + \dot{m}^*) 2 \bar{P}^2 \frac{gH}{R_G T P_1^2} \qquad [7.1.16]$$

for inlet pressure P_1 and velocity V_{G1}; $\bar{P} = (P_1 + P_2)/2$.

These relations were used to evaluate the data in tables of the study of the U.S. Department of the Interior (1962), and [7.1.15] was used to evaluate the data of Konchesky and Craig (1973) for coal-air mixtures in straight runs of pipes, because of the small change in pressure. Data for f_m/f_G versus Re are shown in figure 7.1.3 with ranges of $\dot{m}^*$ and pipe sizes indicated. Note that for similar $\dot{m}^*$ and Re, earlier tests at the Bureau of Mines (U.S. Department of the Interior 1962) give f_m/f_G values one to two orders of magnitude larger than those obtained from the Kinchesky tests, which were based on vacuum suction of coal 10 $\times$ 0 cm in size. This comparison confirms the suggestion that, because of unsteady flow, $\dot{m}^*$ had reached much higher values than the reported averages (U.S. Department of the Interior 1962). Konchesky and Craig also concluded that the size of the coal has an insignificant effect for $d_p < \frac{1}{3} D$. Experiments by Sproson et al. (1973) show ranges similar to those of Konchesky and Craig.

Many research results have been reported, but their usefulness is rather limited for industrial designers and users whose sole concern is a workable application. Furthermore, the phenomena that occur in pneumatic conveying are too varied and too complex to be expressed in an equation of general form; for example, the solid friction factor as presented in the Rose & Duckworth (1969) analysis, could be a function of 13 variables or 10 nondimensional groups. Symbolically,

$$f_m = F(\bar{\rho}_G, V_G, D, \mu_G, g, \dot{M}_p, \bar{\rho}_p, \phi_p, \epsilon, d, K, H, \beta, \theta)$$

$$= F\left(\frac{\bar{\rho}_G V_G D}{\mu_G}, \frac{V_G^2}{gD}, \dot{m}^*, \frac{\bar{\rho}_p}{\bar{\rho}_G}, \epsilon, \frac{d}{D}, \frac{K}{D}, z, \phi_p, \beta, \theta \right)$$

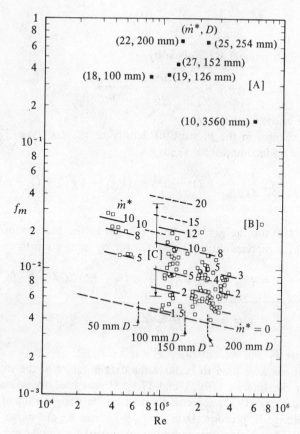

Figure 7.1.3   Friction factor f_m of pipe flow of coal suspension at various flow Reynolds numbers. m^* = kg/coal/kg air; D = pipe diameter, m. [A] U.S. Department of the Interior (1962); [B] Konchesky and Craig (1973); [C] Sproson et al. (1973).

Attempts to generalize the empirical art have not been successful. Nevertheless, theoretical analyses and correlations of friction-factor data for dilute gas-solid suspensions have been reviewed by Pfeffer et al. (1966). While there is no reliable generalized design equation for pneumatic transport, Duckworth (1971) has tabulated pressure gradient and velocity correlations of dilute-phase gas-solid flow, and discussed their pertinence to design.

Konchesky's results appear to be adequately correlated by the relation proposed by Dogin & Lebedev (1962) according to

$$f_m = f_G + A \left(\frac{d_p}{D}\right)^{0.1} \mathrm{Re}^{0.4} \mathrm{Fr}^{0.5} \frac{\bar{\rho}_p}{\bar{\rho}_G} \dot{m}^* \qquad [7.1.17]$$

where Fr is the Froude number

$$\mathrm{Fr} = \frac{V_G^2}{gD} \qquad [7.1.18]$$

which accounts for the gravity effect in horizontal pipe flow, and A is a parameter depending on the roughness of the pipe. For the Konchesky data,

$$A \cong 2 \times 10^{-7} \qquad [7.1.19]$$

instead of $10^{-6} < A < 2 \times 10^{-6}$ as proposed by Dogin & Lebedev; $A = 2 \times 10^{-6}$ seems to correlate data on coal dust (U.S. Department of the Interior 1962).

Another correlation of Rose et al. (1957) to account for the effect of mass flow of solid and density ratios of phases can be expressed in the form

$$f_m = f_G + \frac{\pi}{8} \dot{m}* \left(\frac{\bar{\rho}_p}{\bar{\rho}_G}\right)^{1/2} \psi \qquad [7.1.20]$$

ψ was given as a function of Re having a value below 10^{-5} for $\mathrm{Re} > 35{,}000$; however, calculations from Konchesky's data give $\psi \cong 10^{-4}$.

Pfeffer et al. (1966), coding various sources of data, suggested

$$f_m = f_G (1 + \dot{m}*)^{0.3} \qquad [7.1.21]$$

without regard for other factors. This correlation tends to give an optimistic estimate of pressure drop, and we shall treat it as the lower bound of f_m.

Extensive measurements were made on the transport of pulverized coal through pipes by Patterson (1958). Unfortunately, no data were taken on a straight run of pipe for comparison; the records on bends were archaic. His use of gamma-ray detection of sedimentation offers a useful method.

7.1.3 MINIMUM TRANSPORT VELOCITY

Of all the determinations to be made in designing a dilute gas-solid suspension system, the most fundamental one must be the minimum permissible gas flow rate for the system. This minimum must, however, be high enough to prevent settling of the solids, especially in a horizontal transport system, thus maintaining a steady flow condition. An air flow rate below this value leads to unstable operation and the possibility of solid flow stoppage. However, operation of a system at too high a velocity leads to unnecessarily high power requirements. In either of these two extreme cases, the system would be operating uneconomically, owing to frequent shutdown of the system in the former case, and excessive power consumption in the latter.

The importance of establishing the minimum air flow rate as a fundamental design parameter is emphasized by the following:

1. Power requirements for gas-solid transport systems might be higher than those of more conventional conveyors.
2. Blower power requirements increase approximately as the cube of the gas velocity.
3. Pipe erosion and particle attrition increase significantly as gas velocity increases.

Successful design depends, therefore, upon first establishing the minimum carrier gas velocity at which the material may be conveyed steadily. Successful prediction of the minimum gas velocity for any given system with a reasonable degree of certainty is, therefore, a prerequisite of economical design.

Most of the basic studies on the lift force on a particle in a gas-solid suspension treat cases of particle size smaller than the thickness of a laminar sublayer in the turbulent flow (Soo & Tung 1972; Graf 1971); these do not apply to the case of transport of large particles above millimeter size (Soo et al. 1975). Using particles of size greater than the laminar sublayer thickness, Thomas (1962) gave an equation intended to be applicable to all suspensions of particles which conform to the size criterion. However, the great complexity of his equation, coupled with the fact that it was developed from data obtained in rather small-scale model tests, might well discourage the use of this correlation for design purposes.

It is also interesting to note that there is considerable overlap in the variables used in the correlations developed by Doig & Roper (1963), ([7.1.22] below), Duckworth (1971) ([7.1.25] below), and Matsumoto et al. (1975) in a modified form, that the minimum transport velocity V_c is related to the mass flow ratio $\dot{m}^*$ and the settling velocity of solids in an infinite fluid V_∞:

$$\frac{V_c}{(gD)^{1/2}} = \mathrm{Fr}_c = \ln\left(\frac{V_\infty - 1}{8}\right)(\dot{m}^*)^{0.5} \qquad [7.1.22]$$

$$V_\infty = \left[\frac{4gd\,(\rho^* - 1)}{3C_D}\right]^{1/2} \qquad [7.1.23]$$

$$3 < V_\infty < 12 \quad \text{(m/s)} \qquad [7.1.24]$$

$$\mathrm{Fr}_c = \text{const} \times (\dot{m}^*)^{0.2}\left(\frac{D}{d_p}\right)^{0.6}\left[\frac{V_\infty}{(gD)^{1/2}}\right]^{0.5} \qquad [7.1.25]$$

where ρ^* is the material density ratio $\bar{\rho}_p/\bar{\rho}_G$ of particle to gas and C_D is the drag coefficient of the particle.

The equations of Matsumoto et al. (1975) include those that are being used extensively for designing pneumatic conveyors for wheat. However, these equations do not provide enough information for the general formulation for design.

Zenz (1969) suggested his correlation is applicable to large-scale coal-conveying installations with 200- and 300-mm pipe diameter and coal sizes ranging from 74 μm to less than 20 mm. His correlation is summarized as follows for $\beta > 10$:

$$\alpha = C_1\beta^s \qquad [7.1.26]$$

where $C_1 \cong 0.90$ for spherical particles and 0.5 for angular particles, $S \cong 0.45$, and

$$\beta = \frac{d}{\Delta} = 3(C_D\,\mathrm{Re}_p^2)^{1/2} \qquad [7.1.27]$$

where
$$\Delta = \left(\frac{3v^2/4g}{\rho^* - 1}\right)^{1/3}$$

and
$$\alpha = \frac{V_S}{6.27}\,\omega\,D_m^{0.5} \qquad [7.1.28]$$

where
$$\omega = \left[\frac{4g\nu}{3}(\rho^* - 1)\right]^{1/3} \qquad [7.1.29]$$

and D_m is the pipe diameter in meters; other groups are dimensionless, and V_S is the minimum suspension velocity of a single particle. For the mass flow ratio of particles $\rho_p V_p$ and for minimum transport velocity V_c in m/s, Zenz suggested the approximate relation (for d_p/Δ of order 10 or greater),

$$\frac{\dot{M}_p}{(\pi/4)\,D^2\,\bar{\rho}_p} = 0.7\,S^{1.5}\left(\frac{V_c}{V_S} - 1\right) \qquad [7.1.30]$$

By comparison to measurements of Konchesky (1973, 1975) and Radmark (1976), it was shown (Soo et al. 1975) to be useful to include a suspension parameter k so that

$$\frac{\dot{M}_p}{(\pi/4)\,D^2\,\bar{\rho}_p} = 0.7\,kS^{1.5}\left(\frac{V_c}{V_S} - 1\right) = \dot{m}^* V_c \frac{\bar{\rho}_G}{\bar{\rho}_p} \qquad [7.1.31]$$

Correlation of the Konchesky data, obtained from a large-scale experimental model, with the above relations on suspension velocity shows that the distribution of particle sizes of coal in his tests is represented by $d = 1.6$ mm, with flow velocity above the value of V_c obtained from [7.1.31].

In [7.1.31], the suspension parameter ranges from 1 to 10 and is consistent with the largest-capacity data of Konchesky et al. (1975). The calculated values of the parameters in their case are

$$\dot{M}_p = 55 \times 10^3 \text{ kg/h} \qquad \dot{m}^* = 7.32$$

$$f_a = 0.0031824 \qquad k \geqslant 0.81 \text{ for 1.6-mm coal}$$

$$f_m = 0.009385 \qquad k \geqslant 7.084 \text{ for 38-mm coal}$$

Based on data for the Radmark Pneumatic Conveying System (Radmark 1976) and Ball & Tweedy (1974), which should represent a current and workable system, further correlation results also fall into this range of suspension-parameter values. The calculated values of the parameters in this case are

$$\dot{Q}_a = 1\text{-}6 \text{ m}^3/\text{s at } 0.2 \text{ MPa}$$

$$\dot{m}^* = 6.0\text{-}6.61$$

$$f_m = 0.004\text{-}0.009181$$

$$k \geqslant 2.733\text{-}5.551 \text{ for 75-mm coal}$$

These results show the level of conservatism in Zenz's relations for a critical design. A k value of 10 appears useful for a critical economic design for long-distance transport.

For short distances of hundreds of meters, the minimum transport velocity is often not the controlling design parameter for an economic system.

The minimum transport velocity in vertical transport tends to be lower than in horizontal transport (Konchesky et al. 1975; Govier & Aziz 1972), but the risk of stoppage precludes utilization of such minor differences. When there is a size distribution, settling of the largest particles should be the principal concern. The predicament of overly critical design could be for a vertical section to start acting as a fluidized bed that gets dense with time, and for a horizontal pipe to develop dunes that grow in size. The fundamental relations for an inclined pipe were treated by Soo & Tung (1972).

In dealing with fines below 10 μm in size, the minimum transport velocity is often determined by the necessary magnitude of turbulent diffusion to overcome electrostatic deposition (Soo & Tung 1972). A governing parameter is

$$\alpha = \frac{\rho_{po}}{4\epsilon_0}\left(\frac{q}{M}\right)^2 \frac{D^2}{4D_p F} \qquad [7.1.32]$$

where ρ_{po} is the mean density of the particle cloud, ϵ_0 is the permittivity in free space, q is the charge, M is the mass of each particle, D is the pipe diameter, D_p is the particle diffusivity, and F is the inverse relaxation time for momentum transfer from gas to the particle:

$$F = \frac{18\mu}{d^2 \bar{\rho}_p} \qquad [7.1.33]$$

where μ is the viscosity of the gas. D_p is usually a fraction of the turbulent diffusivity of the gas in pipe flow (Soo 1978). Deposition will always occur (Soo 1973) when

$$\frac{\phi_1 \bar{\rho}_p}{\epsilon_0}\left(\frac{q}{M}\right)^2 \frac{R^2}{D_p F} > 8 \qquad [7.1.34]$$

When $\phi_1 < \phi_b$, electrostatic sedimentary flow will occur. ϕ_b is the volume fraction solid of packed bed of the same material. The magnitude of q/M depends on the materials (particles and pipe) and handling. Charging by surface contact (Cheng & Soo 1970; Soo 1971b) gives a q/M of magnitude 10^{-3}–10^{-5} C/kg, but detailed calculations are beyond the scope of this book. This type of buildup is a serious problem in the processing of titanium oxide in paint making.

7.1.4 CONVEYING SYSTEM AND TELESCOPING DESIGN

Figure 7.1.4 illustrates the high-pressure blow tank system. Its major parts include coal-feeding, air compression, transport pipeline, and separation and receiving facilities. Bulk material is transferred from a storage silo by a belt conveyor. This steel superstructure houses the feeding facilities, which include a screw feeder and two blow tanks with wye fitting and motor-driven rotary feeder. The tanks are connected such that while one is discharging the other is being filled, so that continuous feeding is possible. The operating cycle time is programmed and automatically controlled. The air source is supplied by a compressor package (motor driven) which also includes an intake filter and silencer.

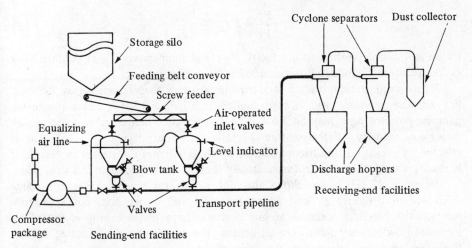

Figure 7.1.4 Schematic diagram showing pressure (blow-tank) pneumatic transport of coal (Leung 1976).

The solid-air suspension mixture is separated by using two cyclone separators (chapter 9) in series to ensure high recapture efficiency, and the coal-dust-laden air is cleaned by a dust filter before venting into the atmosphere.

Figure 7.1.5 illustrates the positive-negative (or push-pull) system. This system employs airflows created by the application of both pressure and vacuum principles. This flow operation is similar to that of the blow-tank system except that it has gravity feeding. Based on current technology, this system is limited to 0.24 MPa on the pressure side using a rotary feeder valve, and 0.03 MPa on the vacuum side with a suction blower. Selection of the type of pneumatic system is determined by the allowable solid size, energy requirement, and economic feasibility.

Equation [7.1.16] shows that for long pipelines and high operating pneumatic pressure, the pressure drops due to acceleration and elevation become minor, and the main pressure drop is that of friction:

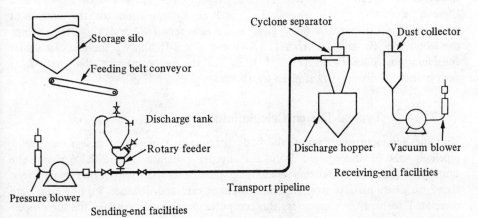

Figure 7.1.5 Schematic diagram showing pressure-vacuum (push-pull) transport of coal (Leung 1976).

$$1 - \frac{P_2^2}{P_1^2} = 4 f_m \frac{L}{D} \frac{V_{G1}^2}{RT_1} \qquad [7.1.35]$$

for an isothermal pipeline with velocity V_{G1} and temperature T_1 at the inlet. The gas temperature T tends to a constant value for a long pipeline.

When small station spacing is allowable, a rotary feeder system may be used. For air, the pressure ratio is then limited to $P_2/P_1 \geqslant 0.5457$, and a reasonable pumping-pressure ratio may be 1.6:1. For V_{G1} greater than or equal to minimum suspension velocity at temperature T_1, the only quantity in [7.1.35] that is affected by pressure is the friction factor, which determines the station spacing L. It is readily shown that such a design usually limits station spacing to less than 3 km.

Equation [7.1.35] also shows that for a uniform pipe diameter D, a large difference in pressures P_1 and P_2 at the inlet and outlet does not necessarily increase the length L because at low pressure, large pressure drop is caused by increased flow velocity due to low air density, thus causing greatly increased friction loss. This suggests telescoping the pipe diameters as the pressure is lowered, subject to the required suspension velocity. With such a design, a pressure ratio of 10:1 permits station spacing of approximately 100 km.

Since one must choose among standard pipe sizes, the design steps for given $\dot{m}^*$, $\dot{M}_p$, and T are worth mentioning. If we define

$$\gamma = \frac{4 \dot{M}_p}{\pi D^2 \bar{\rho}_p \omega} \qquad [7.1.36]$$

and

$$A^{-1} = 6.27 \dot{m}^* C_1 \beta^S \frac{\bar{\rho}_G}{\bar{\rho}_p} \left(\frac{4 \dot{M}_p}{\pi \bar{\rho}_p} \right)^{1/4} \qquad [7.1.37]$$

then [7.1.31] with [7.1.26] and [7.1.28] give

$$\gamma \left(A \gamma^{1/4} \omega^{1/4} - \frac{\omega}{0.7} k S^{1.5} \right) = 1 \qquad [7.1.38]$$

which is solved for γ, given in [7.1.36], and $V_{G1} = V_c$. For each P_1 (selected along a geometric scale), we get V_{G1} and D. Interpolation for the squares of standard pipe diameters D (IDs) gives one a new set of P_1 and V_{G1}, from which one computes Re and f_G from [7.1.13] and [7.1.14] and f_m for the case under consideration. Since P_2 in [7.1.35] is P_1 for the next pipe size, the length L of each branch of diameter D is given by [7.1.35].

7.1.4.1 Typical Design Calculations

With the design capacity input, the basic parameters required to design telescoping pipelines can be determined from a computer program. Figure 7.1.6 shows the simplified logic for calculating telescoping pneumatic transport-system parameters. Based on given particle size, transport tonnage rate and distance, loading ratio, and correlated suspension parameter, the computer program determines the air properties along the pipe, telescoping diameter, minimum suspension velocity, correlated friction factors, optimum pressure drop, and telescoping length. With these, the air and power requirements are then calculated.

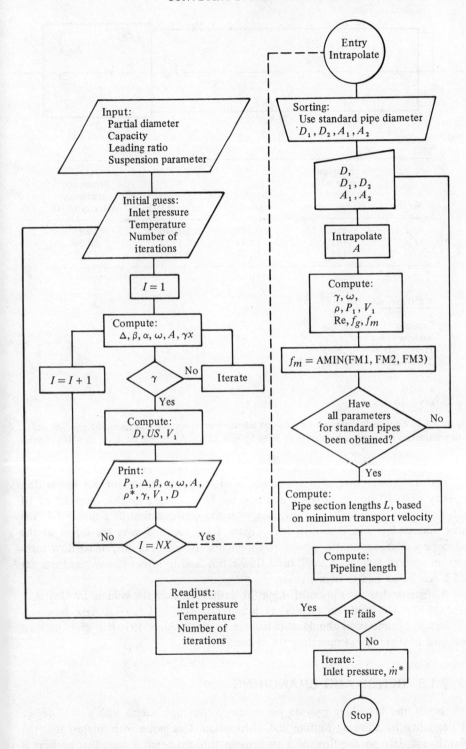

Figure 7.1.6 Simplified logic diagram for telescoping pneumatic coal transport system parameter calculations (Leung 1976).

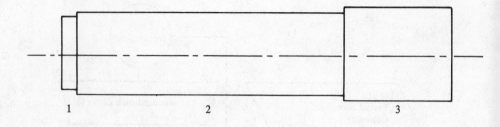

Section	Standard pipe #20: Inside diameter (mm)	Section length (km)	Inlet pressure (MPa)	Minimum transport velocity (m/s)
1	390.5	0.259	0.2040	15.85
2	441.4	3.691	0.1928	18.29
3	489.0	1.668	0.1261	20.12

6 X 0 mm size coal

Capacity = 3030 kg/min
Airflow = 4.13 m³/s
Pressure drop = 0.1 MPa
Theoretical power = 313.7 kW

$k = 10$
$\dot{m}^* = 10$

Figure 7.1.7 Schematic diagram of a 5.63-km telescoping pneumatic coal transport pipeline and flow parameters for transport capacity of 3030 kg/min of 6 X 0 mm coal per hour ($k = 10$) (Leung 1976).

For the design case of a pneumatic coal transport system of 5.8 km with a capacity of 3030 kg/min of 6 X 0 mm coal per hour, using a loading ratio $\dot{m}^*$ of 10 and suspension parameter k of 10, and with the configuration of figure 7.1.7, the power demand is less than 370 kW. Figure 7.1.7 also indicates the effect of the telescoping pipeline on the power requirements. Iteration on the mass flow ratio gives an optimal system, as small mass flow ratios lead to higher power requirements and bigger pipes lead to higher costs.

A designer has the option of using the design charts in the volume by Govier & Aziz (1972). The range of uncertainty is not discussed in Govier & Aziz, however.

Design optimization should also include costing (Leung 1976) to give the least unit cost of owning and operating the system.

7.1.5 BENDS AND BRANCHING

Pipe bends and branching provide pneumatic conveying systems with a large degree of flexibility by allowing routing and distribution. One notes with interest that the quantity of data on the flow of a suspension through bends is such that nothing is given on the topic in the volume by Govier & Aziz (1972). Recent results and correlation must be considered even more tentative than the friction factor in section 7.1.2. Limited experimental results of Mason & Smith (1973a, b) suggest a correlation of bend resistance number

$$\psi_{bp} = 0.027 \, \dot{m}* - 0.0025 \, \dot{m}*^2 \qquad [7.1.39]$$

for bends of curvature ratio D_b/D of 20; D_b is twice the radius of the bend for a Reynolds number of nearly 10^5, a D of 5 cm, and alumina particles of 15–70 μm. The loss on the air side is nearly constant, to give a total bend resistance number of

$$\psi_{bf} = 0.025 + 0.027 \, \dot{m}* - 0.0025 \, \dot{m}*^2 \qquad [7.1.40]$$

The pressure drop is given by

$$\Delta P_{bf} = \tfrac{1}{2} \, \psi_{bf} \bar{\rho}_G V_G^2 \qquad [7.1.41]$$

A correlation by Ikemori & Munakata (1973) includes further details, such that

$$\Delta P_{bf} = f_{zb} \frac{L_b}{D} \, \dot{m}* \, \frac{\bar{\rho}_G V_G^2}{2} \qquad [7.1.42]$$

where f_{zb} is the friction factor given by, for a horizontal band,

$$f_{zb} = f_{pb} \left(\frac{V_{pS}}{V_G} \right) + \frac{4(V_{pt}/V_G)(V_{pS}/V_G)}{D_b/D} \qquad [7.1.43]$$

f_{zb} is given approximately by

$$f_{pb} \cong 2 \frac{(1 - V_{pS}/V_G)^2}{(V_{pt}^2/gD)(V_{pS}/V_G)} \qquad [7.1.44]$$

where V_{pS} is the fully developed mean particle velocity in the straight section of pipe, and V_{pt} is the terminal velocity of the particles. The flow behavior was illustrated by Mason & Mills (1972) as shown in figure 7.1.8.

Branch pipe is used widely for distribution in pneumatic conveying systems. However, very little is quantified beyond a recent report of Harman et al. (1978). Applicable systems are shown in figure 7.1.9 in the forms of a tee and a manifold. In the case of a tee as in figure 7.1.9a, the pressure loss in branching from stations 1 to 3 is given by

$$\Delta P_{\mathrm{Br}} = \xi_L \frac{\bar{\rho}_G V_G^2}{2} \qquad [7.1.45]$$

where ξ_L is called Morikawa's (1976) branching coefficient. The trend is seen that for an air suspension (subscript a)

$$\xi_{ca} = -0.1 \quad (\text{for } 0 \leqslant n \leqslant 0.4)$$

$$\xi_{ca} = 0.8 \, n - 0.4 \quad (\text{for } 0.4 \leqslant n \leqslant 1)$$

where n is the ratio of lateral flow from the branch-point to header flow into the branch point. The total branching factor ξ_c is given by

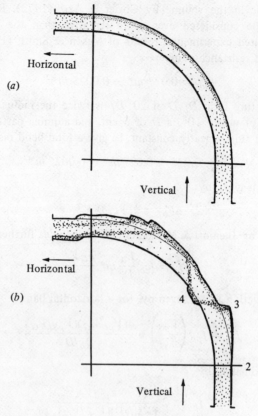

Figure 7.1.8 Bend flow pattern (Mason & Mills 1972). (*a*) Initial. (*b*) After some wear.

$$\xi_c = \alpha' + \xi_{ca} \qquad [7.1.46]$$

where α' is the solid component of Morikawa's correlation and is given by

$$\alpha' = 0.264 - 1.0825 \, n\dot{m}^* \qquad [7.1.47]$$

For a multilateral system, the pressure losses caused by flow turning into the first lateral of a multilateral system is given (figure 7.1.9*b*) by

$$\Delta P_{BT} = \xi_A \frac{\bar{\rho}_G V_G^2}{2} \qquad [7.1.48]$$

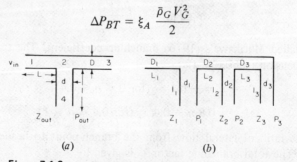

Figure 7.1.9 Applicable systems (Harman et al. 1978).

where
$$\xi_A = 1.0 - 0.436\, n \quad (\text{for } 0 \leqslant n < 0.45)$$
$$\xi_A = 0.48 + 0.72\, n \quad (\text{for } 0.45 < n < 1)$$

Another form of branching is for delivering into one branch at a time, such as by using rubberized pinch valves in packaging systems. In that case, the branches serve as turns from a tee. In general, branches should be made with smooth tees. Artistic forms of smooth curves add very little to the design other than cost.

7.1.6 HEAT TRANSFER CHARACTERISTICS

Heat transfer to pipes conveying a suspension is important, especially when the pipe is installed outdoors. Proper insulation and humidity control of the carrier gas might be needed to ensure satisfactory operation under various weather conditions (humidity control, frost prevention, and preservation of material properties). Pertinent data are plentiful but also anomalous (Pfeffer et al. 1966).

The data are referred to loading, i.e., the ratio of the rates of throughput of particles to gas, as a basic parameter. In the strict sense, loading is the mean mass flow ratio of particle to gas, or

$$\dot{m}^* = \frac{\rho_p \bar{V}_p}{\rho_G \bar{V}} = m^* \frac{\bar{V}_p}{\bar{V}_G} \qquad [7.1.49]$$

where $\bar{V}_p$ and $\bar{V}_G$ are mean velocities of pipe flow. This is one source of anomaly, since modification of the heat transfer rate of a gas by the added particles is influenced by the fluid-particle interaction and the electrostatic charge on the particles (Soo & Trezek 1966). Some authors, as a matter of logical choice, base their correlations on a weighted specific heat ratio

$$C^* = \frac{c_p \rho_p \bar{V}_p}{c_G \rho_G \bar{V}_G} = m^* \frac{c_p}{c_G} \frac{\bar{V}_p}{\bar{V}_G} \qquad [7.1.50]$$

With h_m denoting the heat transfer coefficient of the suspension, h that due to gas alone, $\mathrm{Re} = 2\,R_0 \bar{V}_G \bar{\rho}_G / \mu_G$ as the gas-phase Reynolds number, and $2\,R_0$ as the pipe diameter, various correlations were presented.

Farbar & Morley (1957), Farbar & Depew (1963), and Danziger (1963) all correlated with

$$\frac{h_m}{h} = f(\mathrm{Re}, \dot{m}^*) \qquad [7.1.51]$$

using silica-alumina catalyst (10–210 μm) and glass particles (30–200 μm) of $\dot{m}^* = 0$–41.6 with fluid temperature from 24 to 560°C. It was reported by Farbar & Depew that for similar $\dot{m}^*$, large particles contribute less to the increase in h_m. They also reported a decrease in h_m/h with increase in Re for given d and $\dot{m}^*$. Danziger's result is based on cooling the suspension for $2a = 50$ μm.

Schluderberg et al. (1961) gave

$$\frac{h_m}{h} = 0.78\,(1 + C^*)^{0.46} \qquad [7.1.52]$$

from experiments with graphite suspension (1-5 μm) in various gases at 32-600°C. The lack of reproducibility of their results was discussed by Wachtell et al. (1961), who suggested correlation with

$$\frac{h_m}{h} = 16.9 \, N_{Re}^{-0.3} \, (1 + C^*)^{0.45} \qquad [7.1.53]$$

Both studies used tube diameters of 8-22.2 mm and $\dot{m}^* = 0$-90. Equation [7.1.53] is recommended for general use.

Gorbis & Bakhtiozin (1962) also studied graphite particles and gave

$$\frac{h_m}{h} = 1 + 6.3 \, Re^{-0.3} \, Re_p^{-0.33} \, C^* \qquad [7.1.54]$$

where $Re_p = 2a\bar{V}_p\bar{\rho}_G/\mu_G$ for graphite dust only.

Tien & Quan (1962), with 30-200-μm glass and lead particles, showed that h_m/h actually decreased below 1 for $0 < \dot{m}^* < 4$. This was no accident, since a decrease in the friction factor below that of clean air in similar conditions is well known. Explanations were offered basing the damping effect of particles on turbulence (Soo & Trezek 1966), but the fact remains that such an effect must be accounted for in applications.

Investigations by Mickley & Trilling (1951) were made with a fluidized gas-solid mixture. Their results were in agreement with those of Farbar & Morley (1957), Danziger (1963), and Schluderberg et al. (1961) and reported an effect of particle size. A study by List (1958) also indicated such an effect, but there was no agreement with Mickley & Trilling.

7.1.7 ELECTROSTATIC EFFECTS AND SAFETY MEASURES

Electrostatic effects in a pneumatic conveying system, other than the deposition of fines in a pipe (section 7.1.3), often include the generation of charges by contact during conveyance and the deposition of charge in cyclones and bins (Soo 1973). The charging mechanism is well known (Soo 1971a, b; Cheng & Soo 1970), but accurate prediction is limited by the conditions of the contacting surfaces and the lack of accurate data on Fermi levels,* for instance, of various materials. It suffices to say that after passing over a length of pipe, particle charge may reach 10^{-3} C/kg for 40-μm particles and 2×10^{-6} C/kg for 2-mm particles (Soo 1971a, b, 1973). This is true for coal, polyethylene, and a number of explosives such as TNT chips and pellets of smokeless powder.

When charge of this magnitude is delivered to a cyclone for collection, and if the cyclone interior has become insulated from ground by a layer of deposited material, the cyclone will act as a Van de Graaff generator. A 1-m-diameter cyclone could achieve a surface charge density of 2×10^{-6} C/m^2 so that a potential of 21 kV would exist between the shell and the grounded outlet pipe across an 8-cm gap. Hence, for the same efficiency, a small cyclone is preferred (Soo 1973).

---

*A term in solid-state physics denoting the energy, in electronvolts, required to move an electron from the surface of the solid to infinity.

For safety and to prevent the deposition of material, every flange of the piping should be properly grounded, to reduce the charging and the chance of arc-over within the pipe.

In the handling of nonreactive materials such as polyethylene, deposition often occurs in cyclones and bins. This can be prevented by vibrators attached to the apparatus or by using nuclear static eliminators (Loeb 1958).

Nuclear static eliminators should not be used when handling combustible or explosive materials, because of the danger of nuclear contamination of a wide area if explosion occurs. The available means is humidity control. Even though the mechanism if static elimination by humidity is not clearly known, measurements made on borosilicate glass charged by contact with nickel showed the charge reduced by one-half at 15% relative humidity, and to zero at 60% relative humidity (Loeb 1958). In the use of humidity for charge elimination, condensation and frosting of water vapor must be taken into account. The heat transfer relation in section 7.1.6 should, therefore, be checked. In the case of explosives, the final collection of fines must be accomplished in a wet collector.

Humidity control is not suitable for hygroscopic materials such as flour, which is known to present an explosion hazard (Soo 1971a). In this case, grounding and dilution remain as the basic means of charge control. In such a case, a low mass flow ratio, far below 1, should be maintained in the dry sections, with ultimate collection of fines in a wet collector.

Control by dilution requires the use of a dilute suspension and greater pumping power, larger pipe, or high velocity. A high velocity above 30 m/s is desired for most materials of a few millimeters size, to prevent stoppage. This is often double the minimum suspension velocity. For handling explosives, 100% additional blower power is desirable to ensure that no plugging occurs. Positive-displacement-type blowers are preferred to the centrifugal type to avoid the surge characteristics of the latter.

To prevent fusing from one storage point to the other, alternate duration of operation of branches with storage in between can be used where extreme caution is justified. Intermittent feeding may be adopted to prevent fusing within the line.

In almost all cases, fines below 40 μm in size present an explosion hazard. This concern often justifies thorough washing of the whole system with water periodically. Hazard control may also include flame detectors and deluge systems.

When particles are received at ambient temperature, particle temperature control is essential. Otherwise, there is a chance of frosting, as cold particles are delivered for packaging in an air-conditioned space of comfortable humidity.

Coal dust used in power plants is normally conveyed with preheated air at a mass ratio of 1, which is usually far below the oxygen concentration needed to sustain burning.

Recent work (Strehlow 1974) has shown that when coal dust suspended in air with a 1:1 mass ratio was ignited in the tube, fines below 20 μm were ignited but the resulting flame was smothered by coarser coal particles. It has been demonstrated in practice that a pneumatic-type transport system for underground coal haulage is conducive to safer and more healthful mines than conventional transport means (Konchesky & Craig 1973).

In a pneumatic conveying system, safety, rather than optimum power consumption, often dictates the design.

7.1.8   EROSION AND ATTRITION

Erosion by impact of particles on the elements of the pneumatic piping system causes wear in the system and contamination of the conveyed solid by the eroded material. Erosion by moving dust is a special field of study (Tilly 1969). Yet there is as yet insufficient information for prediction in the design of pneumatic systems.

Figure 7.1.10 shows the erosion of several materials by a stream of sand dust, 60–125 μm in size, at 100 m/s. Contrary to what one might expect of a resilient material such as nylon, wear is affected by hardness; for example, nylon is more susceptible to ductile wear, whereas glass is more susceptible to brittle wear than steel. The correlation of ductile and brittle wear by a stream of dust particles impacting at various angles was treated by Soo (1977), whose results are in agreement with the test data of Arundel et al. (1973). The latter gave the wear rate, the volume removed per unit time of alumina on mild steel, as

$$W = 4 \times 10^{-8} \ (\dot{m}*)^{0.5} V^{3.3} \ \text{cm}^3/\text{mm} \qquad [7.1.55]$$

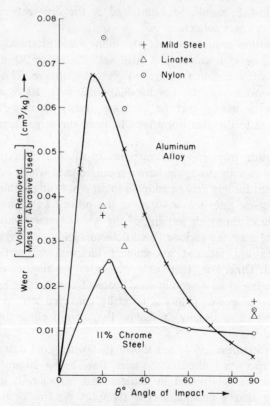

Figure 7.1.10   Variation of wear rate with angle of incidence for various materials (Arundel et al. 1973).

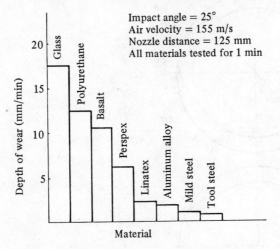

Figure 7.1.11 Comparison of wear rates of various materials (Arundel et al. 1973).

for V in m/s, an impact angle between 20 and 30°, and a 4.8-mm-diameter nozzle with 300 m/s flow.

A comparison of the wearing of various materials by alumina dust is shown in figure 7.1.11.

In a pneumatic system, significant wear occurs in bends (Mason & Smith 1973b) such as that shown in figure 7.1.8, with the greater amount of wear at point 3 and a wear pattern as described in figure 7.1.12. All the tests by Mills & Mason (1977a, b) were conducted with pipes of mild steel of 140-mm bend radius and 50-mm inside diameter. The patterns of wear are shown in figure 7.1.12. The eroded mass ranged from 20 g/ton conveyed at 26 m/s at $\dot{m}^* = 4$, to 3 g/ton at $\dot{m}^* = 2$ at 25 m/s, with 70-μm sand. Definitive conclusions on the effect of particle shape and concentration remain to be drawn.

For a dense suspension, a sliding bed is expected to form at a bend; the volumetric erosion rate per unit area W_D was given by Soo (1977) as

$$W_D \propto \frac{f\bar{\rho}_1\phi_1 V^3 h}{\epsilon_D R} F(\sigma_2, E_1, E, \nu_1, \nu_2, V^2, h, \bar{\rho}_p, \bar{\rho}_2) \qquad [7.1.56]$$

where F denotes a function, f is the coefficient of friction, h is the height of sliding bed, the subscript 1 pertains to the particles and 2 to the surface, σ_2 is the yield strength of the surface, E is the modulus of elasticity, ν is the Poisson ratio, and ϵ_D is the energy to remove a given volume of material. Although f and ϵ_D are not well known, the V^3 relation is in agreement with most experiments.

The attrition of material by impact is not well documented. The attrition of coal dust in a pulverized-coal firing system (Cheng et al. 1970) is of no great consequence, but wear of pipe bends is. Attrition in a grain-handling system degrades the grain and increases the waste, deposition of fines, and dust hazard. Mills & Mason (1978) reported degradation of quartz particles in various pipe materials (figure 7.1.13) and the degree of fragmentation of quartz particles on steel

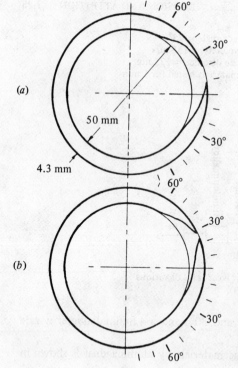

(a)

50 mm

4.3 mm

60°
30°
30°
60°

(b)

30°
60°

Figure 7.1.12 Bend pipe section wear profiles (Mills & Mason (1976). (a) 70-μm sand: fresh phase density = 2, velocity = 26 m/s, bend angle = 35°. (b) 70-μm sand: worn phase density = 2, velocity = 24 m/s, bend angle = 35°.

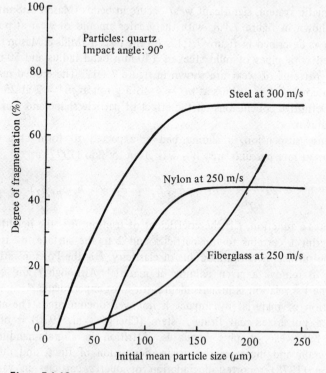

Particles: quartz
Impact angle: 90°

Steel at 300 m/s

Nylon at 250 m/s

Fiberglass at 250 m/s

Figure 7.1.13 Influence of initial particle size and target material on degree of fragmentation (Goodwin et al. 1969).

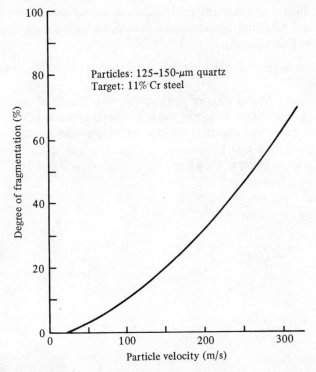

Figure 7.1.14 Effect of impact velocity on degree of fragmentation (Goodwin et al. 1969).

(figure 7.1.14). Although definitive relations cannot be drawn in a general sense, the results show what designers should be aware of and look into.

While the choice of a pressure or a vacuum system is often dictated by other design requirements, breakage is less likely at high air pressures than at atmospheric pressure because of the higher density of the gas, which results in a reduced velocity of impact of the particles on surfaces. It is readily shown that at 1.0 MPa the impact velocity of a particle for a given flow velocity and geometry is one-third that at atmospheric conditions. This is because the resistance to relative motion of solid particles is proportional to the product of the density of air and the square of the relative velocity. The resulting intensity of impact is $(\frac{1}{3})^{6/5}$, or 1.4 times that at atmospheric conditions (Soo 1967). Hence, at prevailing temperatures, wear and deposition due to fines are reduced; the amount of metal removed by impact is nearly one-ninth that at atmospheric conditions (Soo 1967; Smeltzer et al. 1969). Thus, it is postulated that pipe wear and cyclone wear, for instance, are lower at elevated pressures than at atmospheric pressure.

7.1.9 DISCUSSION

A design that is likely to be economical can be achieved by transporting a dense suspension at a velocity just above the minimum suspension velocity to achieve power saving. Such a design needs to be balanced against other factors considered above. Safety and reliability considerations dictate the final design. Special applications include the following:

1. Pneumatic conveying of thick pastes (Carleton et al. 1974), asbestos slurry (Cheng et al. 1971)
2. Extra-high-density (mass) ratio of solid to gas in a "fluidstat" system using the hydrostatic pressure of air to propel solids in several bypasses (Flatt 1971)
3. High-velocity pipe flow and high-velocity jet of gas-solid suspension (Trezek & Soo 1966; Hultberg & Soo 1965)
4. Capsulated systems (Simper 1973)

7.2 Three-Phase Flow

M. Giot

7.2.1 INTRODUCTION

A gas phase is sometimes injected into a liquid-solid mixture to provide either a pumping action or drag reduction. These two aspects are dealt with in the following.

According to Gibson (1961), the *air-lift pump* was invented by Carl Löscher at the end of the eighteenth century. Owing to its poor efficiency compared with other pumps, and its adaptability to many difficult cases of pumping, the gas-lift pump is encountered today only in particular applications, such as

Lifting of liquids: hydrocarbons in the oil industry; radioactive fluids in nuclear-fuel recycling plants; other kinds of aggressive liquids

Lifting of solids (Weber & Dedegil 1976): shaft and well drilling, the drillings being lifted together with the underground water; tunnel drilling and sinking of bridge piles into river or sea floors; vertical lifting of coal in shafts

Recently, the air-lift pump was utilized in a very unusual application, the pumping of manganese nodules from the bottom of the Pacific Ocean at depths reaching 4500 m. The first successful experiment of this type was conducted on July 30, 1970, by Deepsea Ventures Inc., in collecting nodules from about 850 m depth on the Blake Plateau (Atlantic Ocean).

Section 7.2.2 is devoted to the prediction of performance in the pumping of solids. To exemplify the calculations, the air-lift pumping of liquids is considered. Several authors have observed *drag reduction* occurring in the flow of pseudo-homogeneous suspensions, such as clay suspensions, aqueous polymer solutions, and asbestos slurry, when gas is injected into the flowing fluid. Section 7.2.3 reports data predictions given by Heywood & Richardson (1978).

7.2.2 VERTICAL THREE-PHASE FLOW AND THE AIR-LIFT PUMP

7.2.2.1 Description

Schematically (figure 7.2.1) the pumping system involves a vertical pipe consisting of three parts:

A suction pipe (height l_e) between the feeder (not represented in the figure) and the air injection port i

A submerged length l_s of upriser

A height l_d of discharge upriser above the liquid level

An air pipe located outside or inside the upriser supplies air from the air compressor C. In pumping from large depths (for example, $l_s + l_e > 20$ m), the upriser normally consists of a string of pipes with diameters increasing from injection port to discharge.

An important parameter for the operation of an air-lift pump is the submergence ratio $l*$, which is the fraction of upriser length below the liquid level:

$$l* = \frac{l_s}{L}$$

In the case of solid-liquid pumping, this ratio is close to unity.

7.2.2.2 Momentum Equation

Following Kato et al. (1975a, b), we consider a control volume bounded by the pipe wall and cross sections 1 and 2 of figure 7.2.1. If the cross-sectional area A of

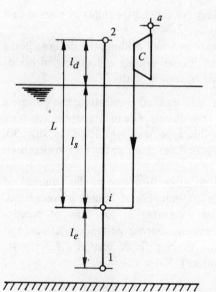

Figure 7.2.1 Schematic of vertical three-phase flow air-lift pumping system.

the pipe is uniform, the momentum equation may be written for steady flow:

$$p_1 + \frac{\dot{M}_L^2}{\alpha_L' \rho_L A^2} + \frac{\dot{M}_S^2}{\alpha_S' \rho_S A^2} = p_a + (\alpha_L' \rho_L + \alpha_S' \rho_S) g l_e$$

$$+ \int_i^2 (\alpha_G \rho_G + \alpha_L \rho_L + \alpha_S \rho_S) g \, dz + \frac{\dot{M}_G^2}{\alpha_{G,2} \rho_{G,2} A^2} + \frac{\dot{M}_L^2}{\alpha_{L,2} \rho_L A^2} + \frac{\dot{M}_S^2}{\alpha_{S,2} \rho_S A^2}$$

$$- \int_1^i \left(\frac{dp}{dz}\right)_{f,LS} dz - \int_i^2 \left(\frac{dp}{dz}\right)_{f,GLS} dz \qquad [7.2.1]$$

In this equation, which includes composite-averaged two-phase liquid-solid (LS) and three-phase gas-liquid-solid (GLS) quantities, $\alpha_K'(K = L, S)$ denotes the *in situ* volume concentration of phase K in the two-phase mixture flowing in the suction pipe ($\Sigma_K \alpha_K' = 1$), whereas $\alpha_K (K = G, L, S)$ stands for the *in situ* volume concentrations in the upriser ($\Sigma_K \alpha_k = 1$); $\dot{M}$ is the flow rate and ρ is the density. The wall friction terms in the suction pipe and upriser are expressed by means of the friction pressure gradients.

The pressure p_1 at the inlet is given by the expression

$$p_1 = p_a + \rho_L g (l_s + l_e) - \xi_{e,L} \frac{\dot{M}_L^2}{2\alpha_L' \rho_L A^2} - \xi_{e,S} \frac{\dot{M}_S^2}{2\alpha_S' \rho_S A^2} \qquad [7.2.2]$$

where the coefficients $\xi_{e,K}(K = L, S)$ of entrance loss for each phase in the suction pipe are dependent on inlet geometry and feeding conditions.

Eliminating p_1 between [7.2.1] and [7.2.2] gives

$$\rho_L g l_s - \alpha_S'(\rho_S - \rho_L) g l_e - \int_i^2 (\alpha_G \rho_G + \alpha_L \rho_L + \alpha_S \rho_S) g \, dz$$

$$= \left(\frac{dp}{dz}\right)_{f,LS} l_e - \int_i^2 \left(\frac{dp}{dz}\right)_{f,GLS} dz + \frac{\dot{M}_G^2}{\alpha_{G,2} \rho_{G,2} A^2}$$

$$+ \frac{\dot{M}_L^2}{\rho_L A^2} \left[\frac{1}{\alpha_{L,2}} + \left(\frac{\xi_{e,L}}{2} - 1\right) \frac{1}{\alpha_L'}\right] + \frac{\dot{M}_S^2}{\rho_S A^2} \left[\frac{1}{\alpha_{S,2}} + \left(\frac{\xi_{e,S}}{2} - 1\right) \frac{1}{\alpha_S'}\right]$$

$$[7.2.3]$$

The left side of this equation is the hydrostatic driving term of the pump, which may be written

$$\int_i^2 \alpha_G (\rho_L - \rho_G) g \, dz - \int_i^2 \alpha_S (\rho_S - \rho_L) g \, dz - \alpha_S'(\rho_S - \rho_L) g l_e - \rho_L g l_d$$

The physical meaning of each term of this expression is very clear. It is also obvious that relationships between the concentrations α_G, α_S, α'_S and the flow rates must be found if the characteristic curves of the pump are required, e.g., the relationships between the solid and gas flow rates $\dot{M}_S$ and $\dot{M}_G$ for given solid flow mass concentrations $[\dot{M}_S/(\dot{M}_S + \dot{M}_L)]$ in the suction pipe.

On the right side of [7.2.3], the friction gradients must also be expressed as functions of the mass flow rates.

7.2.2.3 Prediction of the *In Situ* Volumetric Concentrations

Vertical Solid-Liquid Flow

Govier & Aziz (1972) suggest using the analysis of Zuber & Findlay (1965) for predicting the holdup phenomenon in the vertical flow of fluid-solid mixtures:

$$\frac{\dot{V}_S}{\alpha'_S A} = C_{SL} \frac{\dot{V}_S + \dot{V}_L}{A} - w_{SL,j} \qquad [7.2.4]$$

where $\dot{V}$ is the volumetric flow rate, C_{SL} denotes a distribution coefficient whose value is close to unity, and $w_{SL,j}$, the volume fraction weighted average drift velocity of the solids relative to the mixture, can be estimated as the terminal settling velocity of the particles under turbulent flow conditions.

Vertical Three-Phase Flow

Proceeding with this method, one obtains the following equation for predicting the solid volumetric concentration in three-phase flow:

$$\frac{\dot{V}_S}{\alpha_S A} = C_{SGL} \frac{\dot{V}_G + \dot{V}_L + \dot{V}_S}{A} - w_{SGL,j} \qquad [7.2.5]$$

where C_{SGL} is a distribution parameter, and $w_{SGL,j}$, the terminal settling velocity of the particles in the gas-liquid mixture can be readily predicted.

Concerning the volumetric *in situ* concentration of the gas phase in the three-phase flow, the method of Zuber & Findlay (1965) gives

$$\frac{\dot{V}_G}{\alpha_G A} = C_{GLS} \frac{\dot{V}_G + \dot{V}_L + \dot{V}_S}{A} + w_{GLS,j} \qquad [7.2.6]$$

where C_{GLS} is a distribution parameter, and $w_{GLS,j}$ is the terminal rising velocity of the bubbles in the solid-liquid mixture. In the case of small solid concentrations ($\alpha_S \leqslant 0.10$) in large-diameter tubes, $w_{GLS,j}$ does not seem to be affected by the presence of the solid phase.

The void fraction α_G and concentration α_S of the three-phase flow are determined by superposition of a solid-liquid flow and a gas-liquid flow: an iteration is performed in which one alternately considers that the solid-liquid mixture flows through $(A - A_G)$, and that the gas-liquid mixture flows through $(A - A_S)$. For the solid-liquid mixture, the volumetric concentration α_S' is calculated by means of the following equation:

$$\frac{\dot{V}_L}{(1 - \alpha_S')A} - \frac{\dot{V}_S}{\alpha_S'A} = \left[\frac{4}{3}\frac{d_S}{C_D}\frac{\rho_S - \rho_L}{\rho_L}g(1 - \alpha_S')\right]^{1/2} \qquad [7.2.7]$$

where d_S is the average diameter of the particles, and C_D is their drag coefficient. For the gas-liquid mixture, the following expression for the void fraction is recommended by Weber and his co-workers:

$$\alpha_G' = \frac{1}{1/\alpha_{G,0}' + \dot{V}_L/\dot{V}_G} \qquad [7.2.8]$$

where $\alpha_{G,0}$ is the volume concentration of air in a stagnant column of liquid at the same air flow rate $\dot{V}_G$ as in the two-phase flow. This parameter can be determined by means of the curve given in figure 7.2.2, which results from experiments performed by researchers of the Technical University of Karlsruhe.

The validity of [7.2.8], using the curve of figure 7.2.2, has been tested. A comparison of experimental and calculated values of α_G' is presented in figure 7.2.3.

Kato et al. (1975a) assume for the three-phase flow that all solid particles are in the water and suggest the following extension of Akagawa's empirical formula:

$$\frac{1 - (\alpha_L + \alpha_S)}{\alpha_L + \alpha_S} = C\frac{(\dot{V}_G/A)^n}{(\dot{V}_L/A)^m} \qquad [7.2.9]$$

with values given as follows: for $\dot{V}_L/A$ (m/s) < 0.5, $C = 0.82$, $m = 0.69$, and $n = 0.96$; for $\dot{V}_L/A > 0.5$, $C = 0.67$, $m = 0.69$, and $n = 0.78$.

For given air and water volumetric flow rates, [7.2.9] is a linear relationship between α_L and α_S; in fact, with

$$\alpha_G + \alpha_L + \alpha_S = 1 \qquad [7.2.10]$$

it gives only the expression for α_G. Kato et al. (1975a) measured the volumetric

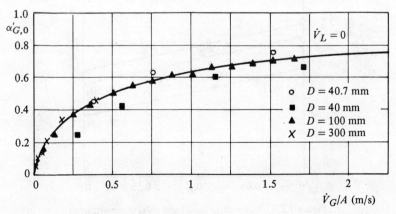

Figure 7.2.2 Volumetric concentration of air in a stagnant water column (Weber & Dedegil 1976).

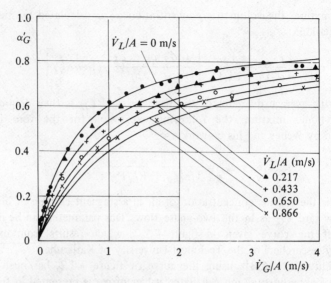

Figure 7.2.3 Void fraction of a gas-liquid flow ($D = 94$ mm) (Weber et al. 1978).

concentrations of air, water, and glass balls, by means of the quick-closing-valve technique, in a vertical tube whose internal diameter was 19 mm; they obtained the values reported in figure 7.2.4, where the straight lines are derived from [7.2.9]. The slug flow pattern was observed mainly in these small-scale experiments.

To compare the predictions obtained by means of the three methods, we consider the following conditions:

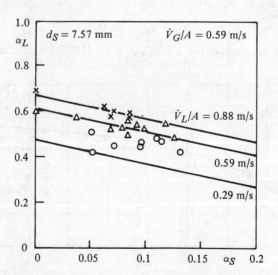

Figure 7.2.4 Volumetric liquid and solid concentrations in three-phase flow (Kato et al. 1975a).

Pipe diameter: 50 mm
Particle diameter: 10 mm
Densities: $\rho_G = 1.3$ kg/m³
$\qquad \rho_L = 1000$ kg/m³
$\qquad \rho_S = 2000$ kg/m³
Volumetric flow rates: $\dot{V}_G = 2 \times 10^{-3}$ m³/s
$\qquad\qquad\qquad \dot{V}_L = 2 \times 10^{-3}$ m³/s
$\qquad\qquad\qquad \dot{V}_S = 2 \times 10^{-4}$ m³/s

The *in situ* volumetric concentrations are

Method	α_G	α_L	α_S
Extension of Zuber & Findlay ([7.2.5] and [7.2.6])	0.418	0.500	0.082
Weber & Dedegil ([7.2.7] and [7.2.8])	0.363	0.559	0.078
Kato ([7.2.9])	0.402	–	–

For this comparison, we calculate

$$w_{SGL,j} = 0.89 \text{ m/s} \qquad w_{GLS,j} = 0.3 \text{ m/s}$$

and assume

$$C_{SL} = 1 \qquad C_{SGL} = 1 \qquad C_{GLS} = 1$$

7.2.2.4 Prediction of the Friction Pressure Drops

The friction pressure drops, which appear on the right in [7.2.3], are given by

$$-\left(\frac{dp}{dz}\right)_{f,LS} = f_{LS} \frac{4}{D} \frac{1}{2A^2} \left(\frac{\dot{M}_L^2}{\alpha_L' \rho_L} + \frac{\dot{M}_S^2}{\alpha_S' \rho_S}\right) \qquad [7.2.11]$$

$$-\left(\frac{dp}{dz}\right)_{f,GLS} = f_{GLS} \frac{4}{D} \frac{1}{2A^2} \left(\frac{\dot{M}_G^2}{\alpha_G \rho_G} + \frac{\dot{M}_L^2}{\alpha_L \rho_L} + \frac{\dot{M}_S^2}{\alpha_S \rho_S}\right) \qquad [7.2.12]$$

For the solid-liquid flow, the friction factor is the same as for water flowing at a velocity equal to that of the two-phase mixture. For the three-phase flow, the friction factor is calculated in the same way by Weber & Dedegil (1976).

Kato et al. (1975a, b) suggest that one writes in the same way as for two-phase gas-liquid flow,

$$\left(\frac{dp}{dz}\right)_{f,GLS} = \alpha_L^{-1.51} \left(\frac{dp}{dz}\right)_{f,L_0}$$

where $(dp/dz)_{L0}$ denotes the pressure drop of water whose flow rate is the same as for the three-phase flow.

Experimental evidence is still too scarce to point to a best design method. However, the friction pressure drops are usually not the most important resistance factor for three-phase flows, and inaccuracy in these terms entail no major consequences.

7.2.2.5 Solution of the Momentum Equation

In practice either the value of $\dot{V}_S/(\dot{V}_S + \dot{V}_L)$ or that of α'_S is imposed, based on the kind of solid-liquid mixer installed at the pipe inlet. For each case, [7.2.3] gives the relationship between the solid flow rate $\dot{V}_S$ that is delivered by the pump and the required gas flow rate $\dot{V}_G$.

For example, consider again the pumping of spherical particles ($d_S = 10$ mm, $\rho_S = 2000$ kg/m^3) by means of an air-lift pipe having the following characteristics:

$$D = 50 \text{ mm} \quad l_e = 10 \text{ m} \quad l_S = 10 \text{ m} \quad l_d = 0$$

As a first approximation, we assume that the friction and acceleration terms are negligible, i.e., that the right side of [7.2.3] vanishes. Then the momentum equation reduces to the hydrostatic balance:

$$\int_i^2 \alpha_G(\rho_G - \rho_L)g\,dz - \int_i^2 \alpha_S(\rho_S - \rho_L)g\,dz - \alpha'_S(\rho_S - \rho_L)g\,l_e = 0$$

Eliminating concentrations α_G, α_S, and α'_S by means of [7.2.6], [7.2.5], and [7.2.4], respectively, and neglecting ρ_G with respect to ρ_L lead to

$$\frac{\overline{\dot{V}}_G \rho_L g l_s}{\overline{\dot{V}}_G + \dot{V}_L + Aw_{GLS,j}} - \frac{\dot{V}_S(\rho_S - \rho_L)g l_s}{\overline{\dot{V}}_G + \dot{V}_L + \dot{V}_S - Aw_{SGL,j}} - \frac{\dot{V}_S(\rho_S - \rho_L)g l_e}{\dot{V}_S + \dot{V}_L - Aw_{SL,j}} = 0$$

$$[7.2.13]$$

where $\overline{\dot{V}}_G$ is the volumetric air flow rate at the mean upriser pressure. From this,

$$\frac{\overline{\dot{V}}_G}{\overline{\dot{V}}_G + (1/c_s - 1)\,\dot{V}_S + Aw_{GLS,j}} - \frac{\dot{V}_S}{\overline{\dot{V}}_G + \dot{V}_S/c_S - Aw_{SGL,j}} - \frac{\dot{V}_S}{\dot{V}_S/c_S - Aw_{SL,j}} = 0$$

$$[7.2.14]$$

Figure 7.2.5 shows the relationship between $\dot{V}_S$ and $\overline{\dot{V}}_G$ for three values of c_S; the calculations were performed with $w_{GLS,j} = 0.3$ m/s, $w_{SGL,j} = 0.89$ m/s, and $w_{SL,j} = 0.545$ m/s. For any given concentration c_S not all values of $\dot{V}_S$ are possible, since the liquid velocity must be sufficient to lift the solid particles. Constant liquid flow-rate curves are also presented in figure 7.2.5.

The mean volumetric gas flow rate $\overline{\dot{V}}_G$ can be related to the outlet volumetric gas flow rate $\dot{V}_{G,a}$ using the isothermal expansion relationships for an ideal gas (Gibson 1961):

$$\overline{\dot{V}}_G = \frac{\int_2^i \dot{V}_G\,dp}{\int_2^i dp} = \dot{M}_G RT \frac{\ln(p_i/p_a)}{p_i - p_a} = \dot{V}_{G,a} \frac{p_a}{p_i - p_a} \ln\frac{p_i}{p_a} \qquad [7.2.15]$$

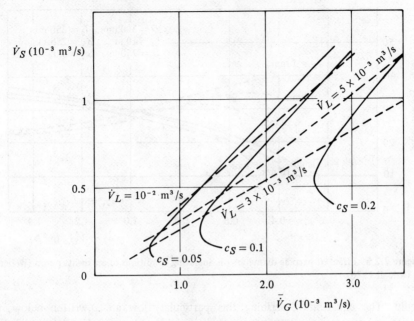

Figure 7.2.5 Approximate operating conditions for an air-lift pump.

In the case of pumping from large depths, [7.2.3] must be integrated by a step-by-step procedure. Examples of results of such calculations for several particle diameters are given in figure 7.2.6.

7.2.2.6 Efficiency

The efficiency η of the pumping device is defined by the ratio

$$\eta \equiv \frac{\text{power required for lifting the solids without friction at required flow rate}}{\text{compression power}}$$

This ratio can be divided into two factors, the isothermal efficiency η_C of the compressor and the so-called pumping efficiency η_p; this latter parameter is written

$$\eta_P = \frac{\dot{M}_{Sg}\{[(\rho_S - \rho_L)/\rho_S]\,(l_e + l_s) + l_d\}}{\dot{M}_G RT \ln (p_r/p_a)} \qquad [7.2.16]$$

where p_r is the injection pressure increased by the pressure difference due to the flow in the air supply pipe. Figure 7.2.6 shows typical values of η_P.

7.2.2.7 Air-Lift Pump for Liquids or Nonsettling Slurries

When the solid particles to be lifted consist of very fine material, e.g., particles with a maximum size of 44 μm, the liquid-solid mixture may be considered as homogeneous, and the air-lift pump operates in the same way as for the pumping of

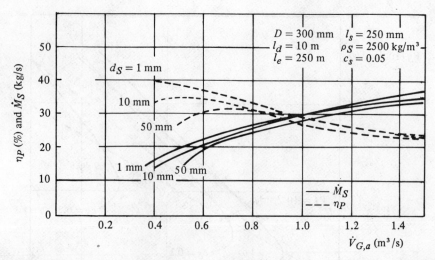

Figure 7.2.6 Effect of particle diameters on operating conditions of an air-lift pump (Weber & Dedegil 1976).

a liquid. The equations describing this particular flow are rewritten below; the subscript m denotes a mixture of a pure liquid and a fine solid material with homogeneous media properties such as density and viscosity. The momentum equation becomes

$$\int_i^2 \alpha_G(\rho_m - \rho_G)g\,dz - (\rho_m - \rho_L)g\,(l_s + l_e) - \rho_m g l_d = -\left(\frac{dp}{dz}\right)_{f,m} l_e$$

$$-\int_i^2 \left(\frac{dp}{dz}\right)_{f,mG}dz + \frac{\dot{M}_G^2}{\alpha_{G,2}\rho_{G,2}A^2} + \frac{\dot{M}_m^2}{\rho_m A^2}\left(\frac{1}{\alpha_{m,2}} + \frac{\xi_{e,m}}{2} - 1\right) \quad [7.2.17]$$

The left side of this equation is the hydrostatic driving term of the pump. Two possibilities exist: either the pipe is immersed in the pure liquid and lifts the mixture produced along the bottom, or the pipe is completely immersed in the mixture. In the latter case, the second term of the left side of [7.2.17] vanishes, and the problem is quite similar to that of the pumping of a liquid.

The void fraction α_G may be calculated by the Zuber & Findlay method:

$$\frac{\dot{V}_G}{\alpha_G A} = C_{mG}\frac{\dot{V}_G + \dot{V}_m}{A} w_{Gm,j} \quad [7.2.18]$$

where C_{mG} is a distribution parameter and $w_{Gm,j}$ is the terminal rising velocity of the bubbles in the mixture.

On the right side of [7.2.17], the friction pressure drops are given by

$$-\left(\frac{dp}{dz}\right)_{f,m} = f_{m,0}\frac{4}{D}\frac{\dot{M}_m^2}{2\,\rho_m A^2} \quad [7.2.19]$$

$$-\left(\frac{dp}{dz}\right)_{f,mG} = -(1-\alpha_G)^{-1.75}\left(\frac{dp}{dz}\right)_{f,mo}$$ [7.2.20]

where $(dp/dz)_{f,mo}$ denotes the pressure gradient due to the mixture flowing alone in the pipe with a flow rate equal to the total flow rate of the two-phase flow. But, as $\dot{M}_G$ is small compared with $\dot{M}_m$, [7.2.20] may be written

$$-\left(\frac{dp}{dz}\right)_{f,mG} = f_{m,0}\,\frac{4}{D}\,(1-\alpha_G)^{-1.75}\,\frac{\dot{M}_m^2}{2\,\rho_m A^2}$$ [7.2.21]

where $f_{m,0}$ is the friction factor of the mixture flowing alone in the pipe.

Neglecting the momentum flux term of the gas phase and dividing both sides of [7.2.17] by $\rho_m g(l_s + l_d)$, one obtains the nondimensional equation

$$\frac{1}{L}\int_i^2 \alpha_G\left(1-\frac{\rho_G}{\rho_m}\right)dz - \left(1-\frac{\rho_L}{\rho_m}\right)\frac{l_s+l_e}{l_s+l_d} - (1-l^*)$$

$$= \frac{\dot{M}_m^2}{2\,A^2\rho_m^2 gL}\left[\frac{4\,f_{m,0}}{D}\left(l_e + \int_i^2 \alpha_m^{-1.75}\,dz\right) + 2\left(\frac{1}{\alpha_{m,2}} + \frac{\xi_{e,m}}{2} - 1\right)\right]$$ [7.2.22]

For pumping at short depths, an average value of the void fraction may be considered, and, with the assumptions and approximations

$$\frac{\rho_G}{\rho_m}\ll 1 \qquad C_{mG}=1 \qquad \alpha_{m,2}=\bar{\alpha}_m=1-\bar{\alpha}_G \qquad \xi_{e,m}=\frac{1}{2}$$

[7.2.22] becomes

$$\frac{\dot{V}_m^2}{2\,A^2 gL} = \frac{\bar{\alpha}_G - (1-\rho_L/\rho_m)\,[(l_s+l_e)/(l_s+l_d)] - (1-l^*)}{(4\,f_{m,0}/D)\,[l_e + (l_s+l_d)(1-\bar{\alpha}_G)^{-1.75}] + 2\,[1/(1-\bar{\alpha}_G) - \frac{3}{4}]}$$ [7.2.23]

with

$$\bar{\alpha}_G \equiv \frac{\dot{V}_G}{\dot{V}_G + \dot{V}_L + Aw_{Gm,j}}$$

The relationship between the kinetic energy term $\dot{V}_m^2/2A^2 gL$ and $\bar{\alpha}_G$ is illustrated by figure 7.2.7, which presents the results of calculations performed with the following data: $\rho_m = \rho_L = 1000$ kg/m^3, $D=27$ mm, $l_e=11$ m, $L=7.255$ m. Similar curves are presented by Todoroki et al. (1973). These calculations suggest the existence of a void-fraction value leading to a maximum liquid flow rate. It is also obvious that this void fraction increases when the submergence ratio l^* decreases.

Figure 7.2.8 indicates the value of the air flow rate corresponding to the

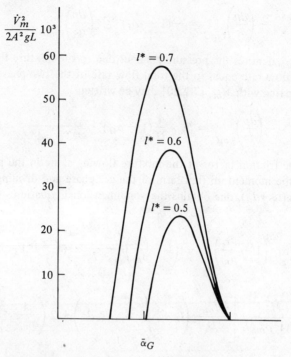

Figure 7.2.7 Relationship between kinetic energy term $\dot{V}_m^2/2A^2gL$ and $\bar{\alpha}_G$.

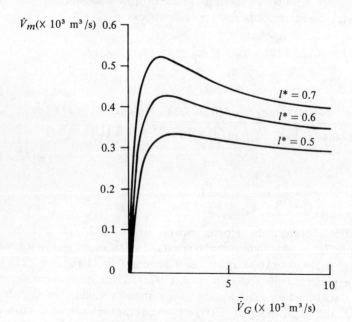

Figure 7.2.8 Operating conditions for an air-lift pump for the pumping of liquids.

maximum liquid flow rate. Larger air flow rates produce only increased friction pressure drops. It is clear that a minimum air flow rate is required for the operation of the pump.

Concerning the efficiency, two cases must be distinguished. In the first, the pump is to lift a nonsettling solid material or a liquid-solid mixture lying on a floor located at a depth $l_e + l_S$ below the liquid surface. The expression for the pumping efficiency is then given by [7.2.16], where $\dot{M}_S$ and ρ_S may be replaced by $\dot{M}_m$ and ρ_m if required.

In the second case, the pump is to produce the flow rate $\dot{M}_m$ in a mixture taken from the bulk of a liquid phase and discharged at a height l_d; the expression for the pumping efficiency is then given by

$$\eta_P = \frac{\rho_m g \dot{V}_m l_d}{\dot{M}_G RT \ln (p_r/p_a)} \qquad [7.2.24]$$

This expression may be split into two factors:

$$\eta_P = \eta_{P,\mathrm{id}} + \eta_{P,f}$$

with $\qquad \eta_{P,\mathrm{id}} = \dfrac{\rho_m g \dot{V}_m l_d}{\rho_m g \dot{V}_{m,\mathrm{id}} l_d} \qquad \eta_{P,f} = \dfrac{\dot{M}_G RT \ln (p_i/p_a)}{\dot{M}_G RT \ln (p_r/p_a)} \qquad [7.2.25]$

The factor $\eta_{P,\mathrm{id}}$, introduced by Todoroki et al. (1973), compares the effective power corresponding to the raising of the real mixture flow rate to the power input at the compressed-air injection port. In the absence of drift velocity and friction, the input power results in an ideal flow rate $\dot{V}_{m,\mathrm{id}}$:

$$\dot{M}_G RT \ln \frac{p_i}{p_a} = \rho_m g \dot{V}_{m,\mathrm{id}} l_d$$

In this ideal case, the right side of [7.2.22] vanishes, and one obtains

$$\bar{\alpha}_{L,\mathrm{id}} = \frac{\dot{V}_{m,\mathrm{id}}}{\bar{V}_G + \dot{V}_{m,\mathrm{id}}} = \sigma$$

The first factor of the pumping efficiency becomes

$$\eta_{P,\mathrm{id}} = \frac{\dot{V}_m}{\dot{V}_{m,\mathrm{id}}} = \frac{1 - l^*}{l^*} \frac{\dot{V}_m}{\dot{V}_G} \qquad [7.2.26]$$

For given values of the submergence ratio, this factor reaches its maximum value together with the ratio $\dot{V}_m/\bar{V}_G$. It is shown in figure 7.2.9 that the point of maximum efficiency $\eta_{P,\mathrm{id}}$ corresponds to flow rates $\dot{V}_m$ and $\bar{V}_G$ that are smaller than those at the point of maximum mixture flow rate. Usually, the maximum efficiency of an air-lift pump increases with the submergence ratio when this ratio is increased to 0.7–0.8 and subsequently decreases and vanishes for $l^* = 0.1$.

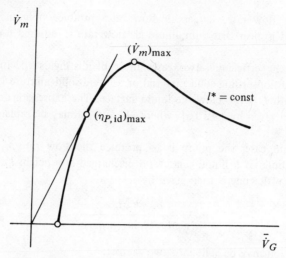

Figure 7.2.9 Points of maximum efficiency and maximum flow rate.

7.2.2.8 Recommendations for Air-Lift Pump Design

Choice of Submergence Ratio

It has been noted above that an optimum submergence ratio exists for air-lift pumps operating with liquids or nonsettling slurries at small depths; its value would lie in the range $l^* = 0.7$–0.8. This is confirmed by experiments and practice (Stenning & Martin 1968; Todoroki et al. 1973; Smith 1975). It is also well known that air-lift pumps cannot operate with insufficient values of the submergence ratio. The mechanism of instabilities appearing in the case of excessive discharge is studied in Hjalmars (1973).

According to Gibbs (1971) the optimum submergence ratio decreases to about 0.4 when the height at discharge level increases to 250 m.

For air-lift pumps operating with settling slurries, no general statement can be made. However, it has been calculated for pumps operating at great depths that increasing injection depths lead to increasing efficiencies, but that the rate of increase becomes smaller and smaller.

Choice of Pipe Diameter

Increasing the pipe diameter decreases the friction and acceleration pressure drops, and the efficiency is subsequently increased. When liquids or nonsettling slurries are to be lifted, it is recommended that the velocity in the suction pipe be restricted to values of the order of 3 m/s. It can also be economical to design the pipe string with diameters increasing with height, to limit the flow acceleration due to gas expansion.

For settling slurries, the liquid and/or liquid-gas mixture velocity must be sufficient to ensure proper dragging of the solids along the entire length of the pipe.

Choice of Gas Flow Rate

Air flow rates must be kept small to optimize efficiency. Moreover, at high air rates, at least for small-diameter tubes (e.g., less than 50 mm), bubble and slug flow patterns are replaced by froth and annular flow patterns, which are associated with poor solid-lifting efficiencies (Heywood & Charles 1978).

Choice of Injection Device

The design of the injection device has little influence on the efficiency of air-lift pumps operating at large depths. Any kind of injector producing small bubbles can be recommended from the efficiency point of view—e.g., a multihole annular chamber. However, in some applications efficiency has been improved by injecting gas by means of an ejector-type device located inside the pipe and forming a nozzle with it.

Effects of Concentration and Rheology of Suspensions

The *in situ* concentration of solid particles in the upriser greatly influences the efficiency. From the design point of view, when the solid flow rate is fixed, a small concentration implies a high liquid flow rate and consequently important friction losses, whereas a large concentration means large static-head losses, also resulting in a decrease in efficiency. It can be concluded that concentration must be optimized.

Heywood & Charles (1978) note a difference in behavior due to the rheological character of the suspension: For shear-thinning suspensions, which normally have high solid concentration, the shaft power required to compress air may be less than that required for a slurry mechanical pump; this is due to drag reduction in the slug flow regime for such suspensions, which, consequently, should have high solid concentrations (e.g., up to 30%).

Highly viscous suspensions like the sludges of sewage-treatment plants (Storck 1975) are extracted successfully by a pulsed-type air lift; the time required for the liquid in the pipe to recover its original level governs the pulse frequency.

7.2.3 DRAG REDUCTION BY GAS INJECTION FOR NON-NEWTONIAN SUSPENSIONS

It is known that air injection can be effective in reducing friction losses in the transport of concentrated pastes and slurries through pipelines. Recently, Heywood and Richardson (1978) produced extensive experimental data for pseudohomogeneous, highly flocculated kaolin suspensions and anthracite suspensions in 42-mm-ID pipelines, and results of some tests performed on a 158-mm-ID pipeline using kaolin suspensions only.

The pressure drops with and without air injection are compared by means of a drag ratio analogous to the Lockhart-Martinelli parameter:

$$\Phi_m^2 = \frac{\Delta p_{mG}/L}{\Delta p_m/L} \qquad [7.2.27]$$

Drag reduction is achieved when this parameter is smaller than unity. The authors found that the drag ratio can be correctly predicted for both kinds of suspensions at low air rates with the formula

$$\Phi_m^2 = \frac{1}{a}\,\alpha_m^b \qquad [7.2.28]$$

which is deduced from a simple plug flow model. Values of the constants a and b are given as follows:

Solid volume fraction	a	b	$1 - n$
	Kaolin suspensions		
0.122	0.87	0.758	0.822
0.142	1.10	1.04	0.836
0.183	0.97	0.850	0.847
0.220	0.93	0.888	0.861
0.234	0.93	0.895	0.872
	Anthracite suspensions		
0.489	1.06	0.60	
0.516	0.92	0.843	
0.540	0.94	0.839	

Equation [7.2.28] is based on the assumptions

$$\frac{\dot{V}_G}{A} < 1.0 \text{ m/s}$$

For the kaolin suspensions, which exhibit a power-law behavior,

$$\text{Re} \equiv \frac{D^n \rho_m}{\gamma}\left(\frac{\dot{V}_m + \dot{V}_G}{A}\right)^{2-n} < 500$$

where

$$\gamma = 8^{n-1} K \left(\frac{1 + 3n}{4n}\right)^n$$

K being the consistency coefficient. For anthracite suspensions, which exhibit a Bingham plastic behavior,

$$\text{Re} = \left\{\frac{\mu_p}{D\rho_m(\dot{V}_m + \dot{V}_G)/A} + \frac{\tau_y}{6\,\rho_m\,[(\dot{V}_m + \dot{V}_G)/A]^2}\right\}^{-1} < 500$$

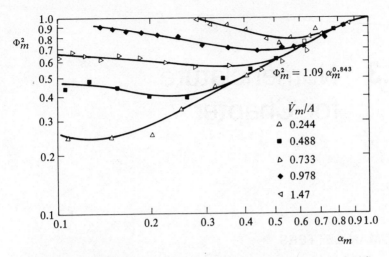

Figure 7.2.10 Drag ratio of anthracite slurry (concentration by weight, 0.516) (Heywood & Richardson 1978).

where μ_p is the plastic viscosity and τ_y is the yield stress. A comparison between experimental data for the anthracite slurry and calculations using [7.2.28] is presented in figure 7.2.10.

Maximum percentage drag reduction correlations are also given by Heywood and Richardson. For power-law slurries the maximum percentage drag reduction is a function only of Reynolds number and flow-behavior index. For Bingham plastic slurries, it depends only on Bingham plastic Reynolds number and Hedstrom number.

7.3 Nomenclature for Chapter 7

ROMAN LETTERS

A	cross-sectional area
c	specific heat
C	distribution coefficient
d	particle diameter
D	pipe diameter
D_p	diameter of pipe bend
D_p	particle diffusivity
g	gravitational constant
G	mass flow $(=\dot{m}/A)$
h	heat transfer coefficient
H	elevation
k	suspension parameter as defined in [7.1.31]
K	pipe roughness
K	consistency coefficient
l	length
l^*	submergence ratio
L	pipe length
M	mass per particle
$\dot{M}$	mass flow rate
n	number density of particles
p	pressure
P	static pressure
P_{MPa}	pressure in megapascals
ΔP	pressure drop
q	electrostatic charge per particle
$\dot{Q}$	volumetric flow rate
R	gas constant
T	temperature
V_s	saltation velocity for single particle
V	nominal velocity $(=\dot{m}/\rho A)$
$\dot{V}$	volumetric flow rate

V_∞ settling velocity of solids in an infinite fluid
w_j drift velocity
z axial coordinate

DIMENSIONLESS GROUPS

A correlation constant as defined in [7.1.17]
C_1 constant as defined in [7.1.26]
C_D drag coefficient [$= 4gd(\bar\rho_p - \bar\rho_f)/3\rho_f V^2$
C^* heat capacity ratio
f friction coefficient
Fr   Froude number ($= V^2/gD$)
l^* submergence ratio
m^* mass ratio of solid to gas ($= \rho_p/\rho_G$)
$\dot m^*$ mass flow ratio of solid to gas ($= \dot M_p/\dot M_G$)
Re   pipe Reynolds number
S exponential correlation constant as defined in [7.1.26]
ρ^* density ratio ($= \bar\rho_p/\bar\rho_f$)

GREEK LETTERS

α parameter as defined in [7.1.26]
α in situ volumetric concentration
β $d/\Delta = 3(C_D \text{Re}_p^2)^{1/2}$, parameter defines the spread of the sizes of particles
Δ $[3\nu^2/4g(\rho^* - 1)]^{1/3}$, m
ϵ shape factor
ϵ_0 permittivity of free space
η efficiency
θ pipe inclination
λ mean free path of particle-to-particle collision
μ dynamic viscosity, plastic viscosity
ν kinematic viscosity
ξ branching coefficient
ξ loss coefficient
ρ density
$\bar\rho$ density of material
τ stress
ϕ volume fraction solid
Φ drag ratio
ψ correlation constant as defined in [7.1.20]
ω $[\frac{4}{3} g\nu(\rho^* - 1)]^{1/3}$, m/s

SUBSCRIPTS

a atmosphere
a air
b packed or sliding bed, bend

C	minimum transport condition
d	discharge
D	drag
e	entrance
f	friction
G	gas
i	injection
L	liquid
m	mixture
o	stagnant condition, or phase flowing alone
p	particle
p	plastic
r	compressor discharge section
s	submerged
S	solid
y	yield
1	inlet
2	outlet

7.4 References for Chapter 7

Albright, C. W., Holden, J. H., Simons, H. P., & Schmidt, L. D. 1951 Pressure Drop in Flow of Dense Coal-Air Mixtures, *Ind. Eng. Chem.* 43:1837–1840.

Arundel, P. A., Taylor, I. A., & Dean, W. 1973 The Rapid Erosion of Various Pipe Wall Materials by a Stream of Abrasive Alumina Particles, *Pneumotransport* 2:paper E1, pp. 1–15.

Ball, D. G., & Tweedy, D. H. 1974 Redmark Engr., Portland, Oregon, Pneumatic Hoist, CIMM, Montreal.

Bannister, H. 1959 Theory and Design of Pneumatic Transport System I, *Chem. Process Eng.* 40:241–244, 320–322.

Boothroyd, R. G. 1966 Pressure Drop in Duct Flow of Gaseous Suspension of Fine Particles, *Trans. Inst. Chem. Eng.* 44:paper T3-6-13.

Boothroyd, R. G. 1971 *Flowing Gas-Solid Suspensions,* Chapman and Hall, London.

Carleton, A. J., Cheng, D. C. H., & French, R. J. 1973 Pneumatic Transport of Thick Pastes, *Pneumotransport* 2:paper F2, pp. 11–20.

Cheng, D. C., Jones, P. E., Keen, E. F., Laws, K. G., & French, R. J. 1971 The Design and Development of a Pneumatic Conveying System for an Asbestos Slurry, *Pneumotransport* 1:paper A1, pp. 1–16.

Cheng, L. & Soo, S. L. 1970 Charging of Dust Particles by Impact, *J. Appl. Phys.* 41:585–591.

Cheng, L., Soo, S. L., & Tung, S. K. 1970 Electrical Measurement of Flow Rate of Pulverized Coal Suspensions, *J. Eng. Power* 92:135–143.

Chowdhury, S. B., Banerjee, S., & Lahirr, A. 1967 Studies on Pneumatic Transport of Coal, *Ind. J. Tech.* 5:384–387.

Cramp, W. & Priestly, A. 1924 Pneumatic Grain Conveyors, *Engineer* 137:34, 64, 89, 112.

Dalla Valle, J. M. 1942 Theory and Practice of Pneumatic Conveying, *Heat Vent.* 39:28–32.

Danziger, W. J. 1963 Heat Transfer to Fluidized Gas Solids Mixtures in Vertical Transport, *Ind. Eng. Chem.* 2:269–276.

Dogin, M. E. & Lebedev, V. P. 1962 Dependence of the Resistance in Pneumatic Conveying Pipelines on the Fundamental Parameter of Two-Phase Flow, *Ind. Chem. Eng. (USSR)* 2:64–67.

Doig, I. D. & Roper, G. H. 1963 The Minimum Gas Rate for Dilute Phase Solids Transportation in a Gas Stream, *Aust. Chem. Eng.* 4:9–23.

Duckworth, R. A. 1971 Pressure Gradient and Velocity Correlation and Their Application to Design, *Pneumotransport* 1:paper R2, pp. 49–52.

Dukler, A. E., Wilkes, M., III, & Cleveland, R. G. 1964 Frictional Pressure Drop in Two-Phase Flow. Part A: A Comparison of Existing Correlations for Pressure Loss and Holdup; part B: An Approach through Similarity Analysis, *AIChE J.* **10**:38–51.

Engineering Equipment Users Association 1963 *Pneumatic Handling of Powdered Materials,* Handbook no. 15, Constable, London.

Farbar, L. & Morley, M. J. 1957 Heat Transfer to Flowing Gas-Solids Mixtures in a Circular Tube, *Ind. Eng. Chem.* **49**:1143–1150.

Farbar, L. & Depew, C. A. 1963 Heat Transfer Effects to Gas-Solids Mixtures Using Solid Spherical Particles of Uniform Size, *Ind. Eng. Chem. Fund.* **2**:130–135.

Fischer, J. 1958 Practical Pneumatic Conveyor Design, *Chem. Eng.* **65**:114–118.

Flatt, W. 1971 Capacity and Efficiency Increase of Pneumatic Conveying Systems through the Use of Buhler-Fluidstat Systems, *Pneumotransport* **1**:paper A2, pp. 17–22.

Gasterstadt, J. 1924 Die experimentalle Untersuchung des pneumatischen Fosderorgays, *Forsch. Arb. Ingenieur Wes.* **68**(265):1.

Gibbs, C. 1971 *Compressed Air and Gas Data,* 2d ed., Ingersoll-Rand Co.

Gibson, A. H. 1961 *Hydraulics and Its Applications,* 5th ed., Constable, London.

Gluck, S. E. 1968 Design Tips for Pneumatic Conveyors, *Hydrocarbon Process.* **47**:88–95.

Goodwin, J. E., Sage, W., & Tilly, G. P. 1969 Study of Erosion by Solid Particles, *Proc. Inst. Mech. Eng.* **184**(1):279–292.

Gorbis, Z. R. & Bakhtiozin, R. A. 1962 Investigation of Convection Heat Transfer to a Gas Graphite Suspension in Vertical Channels, *Sov. J. At. Energy* **12**:402–409.

Govier, G. W. & Aziz, K. 1972 *The Flow of Complex Mixtures in Pipes,* Van Nostrand-Reinhold, Princeton, N.J.

Graf, W. H. 1971 *Hydraulics of Sediment Transport,* p. 442, McGraw-Hill, New York.

Hariu, O. H. & Molstad, M. C. 1949 Pressure Drop in Vertical Tubes in Transport of Solids by Gases, *Ind. Eng. Chem.* **41**:1148–1160.

Harman, P. D., Bajura, R. A., & Kubo, T. 1978 Analytical Study of Manifold Flow Distribution Systems for the Pneumatic Transport of Pulverized Coal, *Rept.* PHH/RAB/TK-78-1, Dept. of Mech. Eng., West Virginia Univ., Morgantown.

Heywood, N. I. & Charles, M. E. 1978 The Pumping of Pseudo-homogeneous, Shear-thinning Suspensions Using the Air-Lift Principle, *5th Int. Conf. on the Hydraulic Transport of Solids in Pipes, BHRA Fluid Engineering, Cranfield, Bedford, U.K., May 1978,* pp. 59–80.

Heywood, N. I. & Richardson, J. F. 1978 Head Loss Reduction by Gas Injection for High Shear-thinning Suspensions in Horizontal Pipe Flow, *5th Int. Conf. on the Hydraulic Transport of Solids in Pipes, BHRA Fluid Engineering, Cranfield, Bedford, U.K., May 1978,* pp. 1–22.

Hitchcock, J. A. & Jones, C. 1958 The Pneumatic Conveying of Spheres through Straight Pipes, *Br. J. Appl. Phys.* **9**:218–222.

Hjalmars, S. 1973 The Origin of Instability in Airlift Pumps, *Trans. ASME, J. Appl. Mech.* **40**:399–404.

Hudson, W. G. 1944 Design of System for Conveying Pneumatically, *Chem. Met. Eng.* **51**:147–151.

Hudson, W. G. 1954 Why Use Pneumatic Conveyors?, *Chem. Eng.* **61**:191–194.

Hultberg, J. A. & Soo, S. L. 1965 Flow of a Gas-Solid Suspension through a Nozzle, *Astronaut. Acta* **11**:207–216.

Ikemori, K. & Munakata, H. 1973 A New Method of Expressing Pressure Drop in Horizontal Pipe Bends in Pneumatic Transport of Solids, *Pneumotransport* **2**:paper A3, pp. 33–43.

Kato, H., Tamiya, S., & Miyazawa, T. 1975a A Study of an Air-Lift Pump for Solid Particles and Its Application to Marine Engineering, *2d Symp. Jet Pumps & Ejectors and Gas Lift Techniques, Mar. 1975,* pp. 37–49.

Kato, H., Miyazawa, T., Timaya, S., & Iwasaki, T. 1975b A Study of an Air-Lift Pump for Solid Particles, *Bull. JSME* **18**:117, 286–294.

Konchesky, J. L. & Craig, T. G. 1973 Air and Power Requirements for the Vacuum Transport of Crushed Coal in Horizontal Pipelines, *Pneumotransport* **2**:paper B4, pp. 45–55.

Konchesky, J. L., George, T. J., & Craig, J. G. 1975 Air and Power Requirements for the Pneumatic Transport of Crushed Coal in Horizontal Pipelines, *Trans. ASME, J. Eng. Ind.*

94–100; Air and Power Requirements for the Pneumatic Transport of Crushed Coal in Vertical Pipes, 101–106.

Leung, S. T. 1976 A Study and Cost Evaluation of Pneumatic Coal Transport Pipelines, M.S. thesis, Dept. of Mech. and Ind. Eng., Univ. of Illinois at Urbana-Champaign.

List, H. L. 1958 Heat Transfer to Flowing Gas-Solids Mixture, Ph.D. thesis, Polytech. Inst. of Brooklyn, N.Y.

Loeb, L. B. 1958 *Static Electrification*, pp. 141, 211, Springer-Verlag, New York.

Mason, J. S. & Mills, D. 1977 Particle Size Effects in Bend Erosion, *Wear* 44:311–328.

Mason, J. S. & Smith, B. U. 1973a The Erosion of Bends by Pneumatic Conveyed Suspension of Abrasive Particles, *Powder Technol.* 6:323–335.

Mason, J. S. & Smith, B. U. 1973b Pressure Drop and Flow Behavior for the Pneumatic Transport of Fine Particles around 90 Degree Bends, *Pneumotransport* 2:paper A2, pp. 17–32.

Matsumoto, S., Harada, S., Saito, S., & Maeda, S. 1975 Saltation Velocity for Horizontal Pneumatic Conveying, *J. Chem. Eng. Jpn.* 8:331–333.

Mickley, H. S. & Trilling, C. A. 1951 Heat Transfer Characteristics of Air-Glass and Air-Lead Mixtures in Turbulent Pipe Flow, *Ind. Eng. Chem.* 43:1220.

Mills, D. & Mason, J. S. 1976 Conveying Velocity Effects in Bend Erosion, *Int. Symp. Freight Pipeline, U.S. Dept. Transportation, Washington, D.C.*

Mills, D. & Mason, J. S. 1977 Particle Concentrate Effects in Bend Erosion, *Powder Technol.* 17:35–73.

Mills, D. & Mason, J. S. 1978 The Effect of Pipe Bends and Conveying Length upon Particle Degradation in Pneumatic Conveying Systems, *Proc. 2d Int. Powder Bulk Solids Handling Processing, Rosemont, Ill.*, pp. 414–428.

Morikawa, T. 1976 Solid-Air Two-Phase Flow in Single and Double Branches, *Trans. JSME* 42:2787–2794.

Patterson, R. C. 1958 Pulverized Coal Transport through Pipes, *Combustion*, July:44–47.

Pfeffer, R., Rossetti, S., & Licklein, S. 1966 Analysis and Correlation of Heat Transfer Coefficient and Friction Factor Data for Dilute Gas-Solid Suspensions, *NASA TN* D-3603.

Radmark, Eng. Div. of Radar Pneumatics, Ltd. 1976 Data of the Radmark Pneumatic Conveying Systems, Victoria, British Columbia.

Rose, H. E. & Barnacle, H. E. 1957 Flow of Suspensions of Non-Cohesive Spherical Particles in Pipes, *Engineer*, June 14:898–901; June 21:939–941.

Rose, H. E. & Duckworth, R. A. 1969 Transport of Solid Particles in Liquid and Gases, *Engineer* 5703(Mar. 27, 1969):227, 392–396; 5904(Mar. 14, 1969):430–433; 5905(Mar. 21, 1969): 478–483.

Sandy, C. W., Daubert, T. E., & Jones, J. H. 1969 Vertical Dense Phase Gas-Solid Transport, paper presented at the Symp. on Fluidization, part IV, 64th National AIChE Meeting, New Orleans.

Schluderberg, D. C., Whitelaw, R. L., & Carlson, R. W. 1961 Gaseous Suspension–A New Reactor Coolant, *Nucleonics* 19:67–68, 70–72, 74, 76.

Simper, J. I. 1973 Pneumatic Pipeline Capsule Systems, *Pneumotransport* 2:paper F4.

Smeltzer, C. E., Guilden, M. E., & Compton, W. A. 1969 Mechanisms of Metal Removal by Impacting Dust Particles, ASME paper 69-WA/Met-8.

Smith, R. A. 1975 Experiments on a Gas-Lift Pump, *2d Symp. Jet Pumps & Ejectors and Gas Lift Techniques, BHRA Fluid Engineering, Cranfield, Bedford, U.K., Mar. 1975*, pp. 1–10.

Soo, S. L. 1967 *Fluid Dynamics of Multiphase Systems*, Blaisdell, Waltham, Mass.

Soo, S. L. 1971a Electrical Effects in Pneumatic Conveying, *Pneumotransport* 1:review paper R1, pp. 1–20.

Soo, S. L. 1971b Dynamics of a Charged Suspension, *Int. Rev. Aerosol Phys. Chem.* 2:81–149.

Soo, S. L. 1973 Some Basic Aspects of Cyclone Separators, *Part. Technol.* 9–16.

Soo, S. L. 1976 Net Effect of Pressure Gradient on a Sphere, *Phys. Fluids* 19:757.

Soo, S. L. 1977 A Note on Erosion by Moving Dust Particles, *Powder Technol.* 17:259–263.

Soo, S. L. 1978 Diffusivity of Spherical Particles in Dilute Suspensions, *AIChE Symp. Ser.* 174:184–185.

Soo, S. L. 1980 Design of Pneumatic Conveying Systems, *J. Powder Bulk Solids Technol.* 4(2/3):33–43.

Soo, S. L., Ferguson, J. A., & Pan, S. C. 1975 Feasibility of Pneumatic Pipeline Transport of Coal, ASME paper 75-1CT-22.

Soo, S. L. & Leung, S. T. 1977 Transportation and Distribution of Coal via Pneumatic Pipelines, *Proc. 2d Conf. Int. Powder Bulk Solids Handling Processing, Rosemont, Ill.*, pp. 28–34.

Soo, S. L. & Trezel, G. J. 1966 Turbulent Pipe Flow of Magnesia Particles in Air, *Ind. Eng. Chem. Fundam.* 5:388.

Soo, S. L. & Tung, S. K. 1972 Deposition and Entrainment in Pipe Flow of a Suspension, *J. Powder Technol.* 6:283–294.

Sproson, J. C., Gray, W. A., & Haynes, J. 1973 Pneumatic Conveying Coal, *Pneumotransport* 2:paper B2.

Stenning, A. H. & Martin, C. B. 1968 An Analytical and Experimental Study of Air-Lift Pump Performance, *J. Eng. Power,* 90:106–110.

Stork, B. 1975 Extraction of Sludges by Pneumatic Pumping, *2d Symp. Jet Pumps & Ejectors and Gas Lift Techniques, BHRA Fluid Engineering, Cranfield, Bedford, U.K., Mar. 1975,* pp. 51–60.

Strehlow, R. A. 1974 private communication.

Thomas, D. G. 1962 Transport Characteristics of Suspensions. part IV, Friction Loss of Concentrated-Flocculated Suspensions in Turbulent Flow, *AIChE J.* 8(2):266–271.

Tien, C. L., & Quan, V. 1962 Local Heat Transfer Characteristic of Air-Glass and Air-Lead Mixtures in Turbulent Pipe Flow, ASME paper 62-HT-15.

Tilly, B. P. 1969 Erosion caused by Airborne Particles, *Wear* 14:63.

Todoroki, I., Sato, Y., & Honda, T. 1973 Performance of Air-Lift Pump. *Bull. JSME,* 16:94, 733–741.

Trezek, G. J. & Soo, S. L. 1966 Gas Dynamics and Accelerating Particles Flow in Circular Pipes, *Proc. 1966 Heat Transfer Fluid Mech. Inst.,* pp. 148–166, Stanford Univ. Press, Stanford, Calif.

U.S. Department of the Interior 1962 Report on the Panel of Civilian Technology on Coal Slurry Pipelines.

Vogt, E. G. & White, R. R. 1948 Friction in the Flow of Suspensions-Granular Solids in Gaseous through Pipe, *Ind. Eng. Chem.* 40:1731–1738.

Wachtell, G. P., Waggener, J. P., & Steigelman, W. H. 1961 Evaluation of Gas-Graphite Suspensions as Nuclear Reactor Coolants, *Rept.* NYO-9672 AEC, Franklin Inst., Philadelphia, Pa.

Weber, M. & Dedegil, Y. 1976 Transport of Solids according to the Air-Lift Principle, *4th Int. Conf. Hydraulic Transport Solids Pipes, BHRA Fluid Engineering, Cranfield, Bedford, U.K., May 1976,* pp. 1–24.

Weber, M., Dedegil, Y., & Feldle, G. 1978 New Experimental Results regarding Extreme Operating Conditions in Air Lifting and Vertical Hydraulic Transport of Solids according to the Jet Lift Principle and Its Applicability to Deep-Sea Mining, *5th Int. Conf. Hydraulic Transport Solids Pipes, BHRA Fluid Engineering, Cranfield, Bedford, U.K., May 1978,* pp. 1–26.

Wen, C. Y. & Simons, H. P. 1959 Flow Characteristics in Horizontal Fluidized Solid Transport, *AIChE J.* 5:263–267.

Zenz, F. A. 1949 Two-Phase Fluid-Solid Flow, *Ind. Eng. Chem.* 41:2801–2806.

Zenz, F. A. 1969 Conveyability of Materials of Mixed Particle Size, *I&EC Fundam.* 3(1):65–75.

Zuber, N. & Findlay, J. A. 1965 Average Volumetric Concentration in Two-Phase Systems, *J. Heat Transfer* 87:453–468.

8 FLUIDIZATION

Subject coordinator: *John R. Grace*

8.1 Fluidized-Bed Hydrodynamics

John R. Grace

8.1.1 MINIMUM (OR INCIPIENT) FLUIDIZATION

When gas or liquid passes upward through a bed of solid particles at a very low flow rate, a porous plate or grid is required to support part of the weight of the solids. The particles are stationary and form a packed bed. If the flow rate is increased, a point is reached where the solid particles are supported or very nearly supported by the drag exerted by the fluid. The particles are then mobile. This is said to be the point of minimum or incipient fluidization.

The superficial fluid velocity at which minimum fluidization is achieved is denoted by u_{mf}. The preferred method for determining u_{mf} is to make a plot of pressure drop across the bed of solids versus superficial fluid velocity. As shown in figure 8.1.1, the resulting plot contains two nearly linear portions. The transitional region between them may show a peak (curve A) or may be smooth (curve B). It is common to have appreciable hysteresis in the transition zone, presumably because of particle segregation and orientation effects. The minimum fluidization velocity is defined as the superficial velocity at which the two linear portions intersect when extrapolated toward each other.

Other methods of measuring u_{mf} are sometimes used but are not generally recommended except for quick and approximate determinations. Visual observation of the point at which bed expansion or particle motion begins may be misleading, especially for wide particle size distributions, where small or light particles tend to segregate to the upper surface and move before the remaining solids. Use of the point at which a heavy object placed on the bed surface begins to sink tends to give estimates of u_{mf} that are too low because of higher than average local velocities around the test object. Observation of the point at which bubbles first appear or survive if injected works reasonably well for aggregative systems (see section 8.1.2) whose mean particle diameter is sufficiently large that the minimum fluidization and minimum bubbling velocities coincide (see section 8.1.5), but results are otherwise misleading.

Many correlations have been proposed for u_{mf}. The best are those derived by

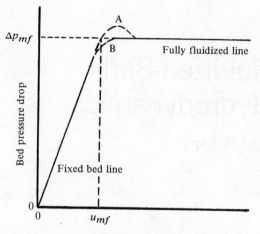

Figure 8.1.1 Illustration of bed pressure drop versus superficial velocity curve used to determine minimim fluidization velocity.

equating the pressure drop calculated from Ergun's equation (Ergun 1952) with that required to support the bed weight. With simplifications of the form suggested by Wen & Yu (1966a, b), these lead to equations of the form

$$\mathrm{Re}_{mf} = \sqrt{C_1^2 + C_2\,\mathrm{Ar}} - C_1 \qquad [8.1.1]$$

where

$$\mathrm{Re}_{mf} = \frac{\bar{d}_S u_{mf} \rho_F}{\mu_F} \qquad [8.1.2]$$

and

$$\mathrm{Ar} = \frac{\rho_F(\rho_S - \rho_F)g\bar{d}_S^3}{\mu_F^2} \qquad [8.1.3]$$

with ρ_S and ρ_F being the solid and fluid densities, μ_F the fluid shear viscosity, g the acceleration due to gravity, and $\bar{d}_S$ the mean particle diameter, discussed below. Values of the constants C_1 and C_2 for minimum fluidization correlation that have been ascribed in the literature are given below.

Reference	C_1	C_2
Wen & Yu (1966a, b)	33.7	0.0408
Richardson (1971)	25.7	0.0365
Inst. Gas Tech. (1978)	25.25	0.0651
Recommended	27.2	0.0408

Here we adopt and recommend compromise values, $C_1 = 27.2$ and $C_2 = 0.0408$. The former improves the fit for fine particles whereas the C_2 value is the same as that in the widely used Wen & Yu (1966a, b) correlation. Equation [8.1.1] with the recommended C_1 and C_2 values is plotted in figure 8.1.2 together with two limiting equations that apply to small and large particles, respectively; i.e.,

Ar $< 10^3$:

$$\text{Re}_{mf} = 7.5 \times 10^{-4}\ \text{Ar} \quad \text{or}\ u_{mf} = 0.00075\ \frac{(\rho_S - \rho_F)g\bar{d}_S^2}{\mu_F} \qquad [8.1.4]$$

Ar $> 10^7$:

$$\text{Re}_{mf} = 0.202\ \text{Ar}^{1/2} \quad \text{or}\ u_{mf} = 0.202\sqrt{\frac{(\rho_S - \rho_F)g\bar{d}_S}{\rho_F}} \qquad [8.1.5]$$

From figure 8.1.2 it is clear that correlations of the form [8.1.4] apply only for small particles. Note that at both small and large Ar, [8.1.4] and [8.1.5] give values of u_{mf} that are directly proportional to the corresponding terminal settling velocity v_T of a single sphere of diameter $\bar{d}_S$ in unbounded fluid. For small spheres, Stokes' law applies and v_T/u_{mf} approaches a value of 74. For large particles in the so-called Newton's law range, the coefficient for determining the terminal velocity is 1.73 (Clift et al. 1978) so that v_T/u_{mf} approaches 8.6. In the general case, v_T/u_{mf} lies within these limits:

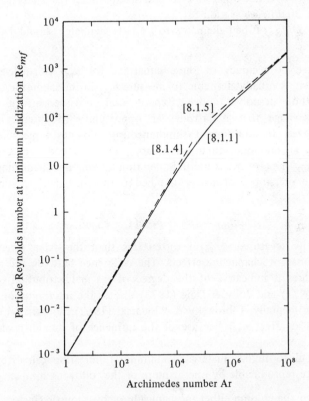

Figure 8.1.2 Graphic presentation of correlation used to find minimum fluidization together with limiting approximate equations.

$$8.6 \leqslant \frac{v_T}{u_{mf}} \leqslant 74 \qquad\qquad [8.1.6]$$

Richardson (1971) gives a graphic correlation of v_T/u_{mf} as a function of Ar and ϵ_{mf}.

The 284 data points used by Wen & Yu for their correlation were obtained from 14 different data sets, using water; gases including air, hydrogen, helium, and carbon dioxide; and particles varying widely in density, size, and shape. The average deviation was ± 25%. Subsequent work, including that at elevated pressures and temperatures and with other fluids, shows that their correlation, or the alternative form given by [8.1.1], works well over a broad range of conditions, but with the following restrictions:

1. The mean particle diameter should be defined as a surface-to-volume mean, commonly approximated from sieve analyses as

$$\bar{d}_S = \frac{1}{\Sigma(x_i/d_{Si})} \qquad\qquad [8.1.7]$$

where x_i is the weight fraction collected between sieves of mean aperture d_{Si}.
2. The correlation is not applicable to cohesive particles (generally particles smaller than about 30 μm; see section 8.1.3).
3. The radio $D/\bar{d}_S$ of bed diameter to particle diameter should be greater than about 20.

The degree of accuracy of these equations for u_{mf} is sufficient for many purposes, but it is usually desirable to measure u_{mf} in the laboratory, using the Δp versus u method described above. Experimental measurement of u_{mf} has the additional advantage that it provides an opportunity to observe how well the material fluidizes. In addition, it simultaneously provides a measurement of the pressure drop at minimum fluidization Δp_{mf} and the bed voidage at minimum fluidization ϵ_{mf}. The former is useful in determining whether channeling is occurring. In theory, the pressure drop across the bed is just sufficient to support the bed weight; i.e.,

$$\Delta p_{mf} = (\rho_S - \rho_F)g(1 - \epsilon_{mf})L_{mf} \qquad\qquad [8.1.8]$$

In practice, the measured Δp_{mf} is often less than the value given by [8.1.8], primarily because of channeling effects. The difference between the measured and theoretical values is indicative of the degree of gas maldistribution or channeling. Richardson (1971) and Jolly & Doig (1973) discuss the interpretation of Δp values obtained experimentally. Cibrowsky & Wlodarski (1962) show that the humidity of the gas can also affect u_{mf} because of the influence of humidity on electrostatic charges.

For difficult-to-fluidize materials, minimum fluidization can often be induced and made more reproducible by one or more of the following means:

1. Vibration of the column either mechanically or by acoustic (including ultrasonic) means.
2. Pulsation of the supply of fluidizing fluid.

3. Stirring or agitation of the contents of the vessel.
4. Addition of a "fluidization aid" to the powder, such as fine silica particles or dry inerts.

To aid in the application of [8.1.1], values of u_{mf} as a function of $\bar{d}_S$ and ρ_S are given in figure 8.1.3 for the most common fluidizing fluids, air and water, covering the ranges of particle diameter and density encountered most commonly. The effect of temperature and pressure on u_{mf} for fluidization by air is shown in figure 8.1.4 for particles of density 2500 kg/m³. Note that pressure has no effect on

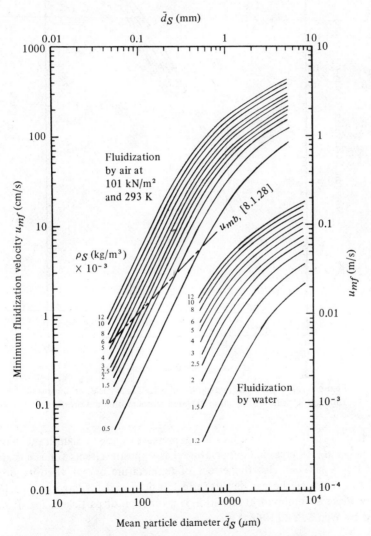

Figure 8.1.3 Minimum fluidization velocity of particles of different densities fluidized by air and water under standard conditions, 293 K and 101 kN/m². The line corresponding to the minimum bubbling velocity from [8.1.28] is also shown for air.

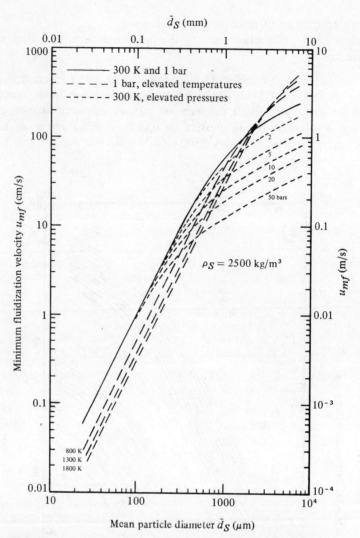

Figure 8.1.4 Minimum fluidization velocity for particles of density 2500 kg/m³ fluidized by air at elevated temperatures and pressures.

u_{mf} for fine particles, whereas increasing pressure causes a significant decrease in u_{mf} for larger $\bar{d}_S$. Increasing temperature has opposite effects for small and large particles. For small particles the effect of temperature on gas viscosity dominates (see [8.1.4]), whereas the gas density effect is dominant for large Ar (see [8.1.5]).

The voidage at minimum fluidization is a function of particle shape. It has been correlated by Wen & Yu (1966a) as

$$\epsilon_{mf} \approx (14\phi_s)^{-1/3} \tag{8.1.9}$$

where ϕ_s is a particle shape factor, often called *sphericity,* defined by

$$\phi_s = \frac{\text{surface area of sphere of equivalent volume}}{\text{actual surface area}} \qquad [8.1.10]$$

For most systems, $0.40 < \epsilon_{mf} < 0.55$, although higher values are sometimes encountered for fine irregular particles.

For binary mixtures consisting of particles of the same density but different sizes, the mixture minimum fluidization velocity has been correlated (Cheung et al. 1974) by

$$u_{mf} = (u_{mf})_2 \left[\frac{(u_{mf})_1}{(u_{mf})_2}\right]^{x_1^2} \qquad [8.1.11]$$

where $d_{S2} < d_{S1}$ and x_1 is the weight fraction of the finer material. Note that addition of a small quantity of finer to coarser material causes a marked reduction in u_{mf}, whereas addition of a similar quantity of coarse material alters the u_{mf} relatively little. Rowe & Nienow (1975) suggested a relationship for the minimum fluidization velocity of multicomponent mixtures. However, the equation requires knowledge of the change in voidage that occurs on changing the mixture composition. Because this information is difficult to obtain, it is easiest to measure u_{mf} for such mixtures.

8.1.2 REGIMES OF FLUIDIZATION

Past minimum fluidization, there are at least five different fluidization regimes. These regimes and their principal visual features are listed in table 8.1.1 and shown schematically in figure 8.1.5. The last four regimes in table 8.1.1 are often collectively referred to as *aggregative fluidization.*

Not all the regimes listed in table 8.1.1 are observed in every case. This is because the transition points between regimes depend not only on the gas-solid system, but on other features as well. Whereas u_{mf} and u_{mb} depend solely on properties of the gas and solids, u_{ms} also depends on the column diameter and bed depth, and u_{tr} depends on the rate at which solids are fed to the column. In addition, u_k depends on column diameter if the column is small enough for slugging to be possible (see section 8.1.8). For many systems u_{mf} and u_{mb} are essentially equal (section 8.1.5), and no particulate regime is observed. Conversely, for most liquid-fluidized beds only the particulate regime is observed under normal operating conditions. For shallow or large-diameter beds or for systems where a maximum stable bubble size is achieved, it is possible to pass directly from the bubbling to the turbulent regime without any slugging.

Whereas u_{mb} and u_k are sharply defined, the other transitions are commonly gradual. In columns equipped with internal baffles or tubes, two regimes may coexist in different parts of the same equipment (Staub & Canada 1978). The transition points and ensuing regimes are discussed below. First, however, it is useful to distinguish different classes of particles that tend to give different fluidization behavior.

Table 8.1.1 Regimes of Fluidization with Increasing Superficial Gas Velocity

Part in figure 8.1.5	Velocity range	Regime	Appearance and principal features
(a)	$0 \leqslant u < u_{mf}$	Fixed bed	Particles are quiescent; gas flows through interstices.
(b)	$u_{mf} \leqslant u < u_{mb}$	Particulate fluidization	Bed expands smoothly in a homogeneous manner; top surface is well defined; some small-scale particle motion; little tendency for particles to aggregate; very little pressure fluctuation.
(c)	$u_{mb} \leqslant u < u_{ms}$	Bubbling fluidization	Void regions form near the distributor, grow mostly by coalescence, and rise to the surface; top surface is well defined with bubbles breaking through periodically; irregular pressure fluctuations of appreciable amplitude.
(d)	$u_{ms} \leqslant u < u_k$	Slugging regime	Voids fill most of the column cross section; top surface rises and collapses with reasonably regular frequency; large and regular pressure fluctuations.
(e)	$u_k \leqslant u < u_{tr}$	Turbulent regime	Small voids and particle clusters dart to and fro; top surface difficult to distinguish; small-amplitude pressure fluctuations only.
(f)	$u_{tr} \leqslant u$	Fast fluidization	No upper surface to bed; particles are transported out the top and must be replaced by adding solids at or near the bottom. Clusters or strands of particles move downward, mostly near the wall, while gas, containing widely dispersed particles, moves upward; at fixed solid feed rate, increasingly dilute as u is increased.

8.1.3 POWDER PROPERTIES

Geldart (1972, 1973) introduced a useful classification scheme that distinguishes four broad groups of particles showing different characteristic fluidization behavior. Whether a powder belongs in group A, B, C, or D depends primarily on particle size and particle density, but also on the properties of the fluidizing gas and therefore

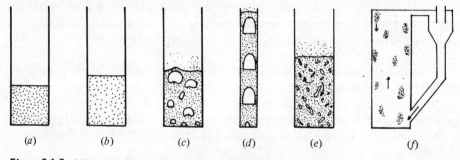

(a)   (b)   (c)   (d)   (e)   (f)

Figure 8.1.5 Schematic diagram showing the main visual features for each of six different regimes. Further details are given in table 8.1.1.

on temperature and pressure. The principal features of the four groups of solids are presented in table 8.1.2, and the approximate boundaries separating the regimes are given in figure 8.1.6 for fluidization by air under ambient conditions.

It is well to keep the distinctive features of these regimes in mind, for results obtained with powders in one group often totally fail to apply to a powder in a different group. Group A and group B powders are encountered most commonly. Group A powders include the cracking catalysts on which much of the early fluidization work was performed. These particles are most easily distinguished by their tendency to deaerate slowly after shutdown of the air supply. The boundary separating groups A and B can be taken as the condition under which there is an appreciable difference between the minimum bubbling and minimum fluidization velocities. From [8.1.4] and [8.1.28], the boundary is

$$\bar{d}_S = 44,000 \, \frac{\rho_F^{0.1} \, \mu_F^{0.9}}{g(\rho_S - \rho_F)} \qquad\qquad [8.1.12]$$

Very fine particles are difficult to fluidize and belong in the cohesive group, group C. They are especially prone to electrostatic effects and interparticle forces.

Table 8.1.2 Distinguishing Features of Four Groups of Particles[a]

Feature	Group C	Group A	Group B	Group D
Distinguishing word or phrase	Cohesive	Aeratable	Bubble readily	Spoutable
Example	Flour	Fluid cracking catalyst	Sand	Wheat
Particle size for $\rho_S = 2.5$ g/cm^3	$\leqslant 20 \, \mu m$	$20 < \bar{d}_S \leqslant 90 \, \mu m$	$90 < \bar{d}_S \leqslant 650 \, \mu m$	$> 650 \, \mu m$
Channeling	Severe	Little	Negligible	Negligible
Spouting	None	None	Shallow beds only	Readily
Collapse rate	–	Slow	Rapid	Rapid
Expansion	Low because of channeling	High; initially bubble-free	Medium	Medium
Bubble shape	Channels, no bubbles	Flat base, spherical cap	Rounded with small indentation	Rounded
Rheological character of dense phase	High yield stress	Apparent viscosity of order 1 poise	Apparent viscosity of order 5 poise	Apparent viscosity of order 10 poise
Solids mixing	Very low	High	Medium	Low
Gas back mixing	Very low	High	Medium	Low
Slugging mode	Flat raining plugs	Axisymmetric	Mostly axisymmetric	Mostly wall slugs
Effect of $\bar{d}_S$ (within group) on hydrodynamics	Unknown	Appreciable	Minor	Unknown
Effect of particle size distribution	Unknown	Appreciable	Negligible	Can cause segregation

[a]Drawn largely from Geldart (1972, 1973).

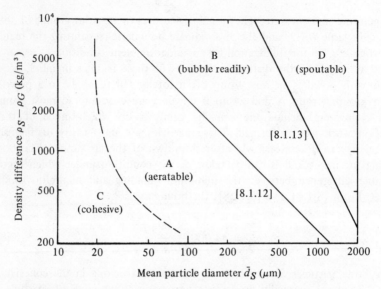

Figure 8.1.6 Boundaries for air under atmospheric conditions between different classes of powders identified by Geldart (1972).

Normal fluidization of these powders is difficult to achieve, and stirring or vibration may be required to initiate fluidization. The boundary between groups C and A is not very well defined and probably depends on the gas humidity and on the electrical properties (resistivity and dielectric constant) of the particles, as well as on ρ_S, $\bar{d}_S$, and gas properties.

Group B includes most sand and glass bead systems, which have been widely studied by fluidization researchers. Generally speaking, these systems bubble readily. Group D particles, on the other hand, tend to be large, often 1 mm or larger. Although they also bubble, they give relatively poor solids mixing and can be spouted readily. The boundary between groups B and D has been correlated (Geldart 1973) by

$$(\rho_S - \rho_F)\bar{d}_S^2 = 10^{-3} \, \text{kg/m} \qquad [8.1.13]$$

If the term on the left is greater than 10^{-3} kg/m for a powder, the powder belongs in group D.

Often the solid properties are fixed for a particular application. Where some choice does exist, properties that are generally desirable are as follows:

1. The powder should flow readily. This implies particles that are rounded or not too angular and dry enough and large enough not to cohere or form lumps because of interparticle forces. The surface-to-volume mean particle size, in the absence of sticky substances or extreme shapes, should be 50–500 μm (essentially groups A and B). Mean sizes outside this range can, however, often be tolerated. Controlled stickiness can sometimes be used to promote agglomeration of product or waste materials.

2. There should be a reasonably broad spectrum of particle sizes. As a rule, the ratio of the aperture openings on the largest and smallest sieves used to screen the particles should be in the range 10–25.
3. Particles should not be too readily attrited.

8.1.4 PARTICULATE REGIME

As noted in table 8.1.1, the particulate regime is characterized by smooth bed expansion. Additional flow of the fluidizing fluid is accommodated by the particles moving farther apart, with relatively little tendency to form aggregates or leave voids. The particulate regime is especially important for liquid-fluidized beds, because it is the only regime observed for most systems where the fluidizing fluid is a liquid.

For many practical purposes, particulately fluidized beds act like expanded packed beds. However, the details are much more complex. Nonuniformities in liquid or gas distribution at the base of the bed tend to give rise to gross circulation patterns. Particles differing in size or in density tend to segregate, with denser and larger particles collecting at the bottom. Small propagating void regions, sometimes called *parvoids,* can be observed on close inspection.

Expansion of liquid-fluidized beds is usually predicted by using the Richardson & Zaki correlation (Richardson & Zaki 1954; Richardson & Meikle 1961):

$$\epsilon^n = \frac{u}{u_i} \qquad \text{[8.1.14]}$$

This equation also applies for particle sedimentation. For spheres of narrow size distribution, the empirical exponent n is given by

$$n = 4.65 + 20\,\frac{\bar{d}_S}{D} \qquad (\text{Re}_T < 0.2) \qquad \text{[8.1.15]}$$

$$n = \left(4.4 + 18\,\frac{\bar{d}_S}{D}\right)\text{Re}_T^{-0.03} \qquad (0.2 < \text{Re}_T < 1) \qquad \text{[8.1.16]}$$

$$n = \left(4.4 + 18\,\frac{\bar{d}_S}{D}\right)\text{Re}_T^{-0.1} \qquad (1 < \text{Re}_T < 200) \qquad \text{[8.1.17]}$$

$$n = 4.4\,\text{Re}_T^{-0.1} \qquad (200 < \text{Re}_T < 500) \qquad \text{[8.1.18]}$$

$$n = 2.4 \qquad (\text{Re}_T > 500) \qquad \text{[8.1.19]}$$

while
$$\text{Re}_T = \frac{v_T \rho_F \bar{d}_S}{\mu_F} \qquad \text{[8.1.20]}$$

and for fluidization:

$$\log u_i = \log v_T - \frac{\bar{d}_S}{D} \qquad \text{[8.1.21]}$$

A correlation of n for nonspherical particles has been given by Fouda & Capes (1977). For wide size distributions of solids, and especially for gas-fluidized systems, values of n higher than given by [8.1.15]–[8.1.19] have commonly been reported; e.g., values as high as 20 (Crowther & Whitehead 1978). Once ϵ has been calculated, the expanded bed height is calculated from

$$L = \frac{M_S/\rho_S}{\pi/4} D^2 (1 - \epsilon) \qquad [8.1.22]$$

Particulate fluidized beds (as well as the dense phase for bubbling systems) can be described by means of continuum equations, with the scale of scrutiny chosen to be large with respect to the dimensions of a single particle but small with respect to the overall scale of the equipment. Local densities $\rho_S(1 - \epsilon)$ and $\rho_F \epsilon$ and local velocities $\mathbf{v}$ and $\mathbf{u}$ are assigned to the particulate and fluid phases, respectively. Continuity and momentum equations are written (assuming isothermal behavior) as if there were two interpenetrating continua, one composed of the fluidizing fluid and the other of the particles. For nonisothermal cases, corresponding energy equations have also been proposed. The relevant continuity equations for constant fluid and solids density are then:

Fluid:
$$\frac{\partial \epsilon}{\partial t} + \vec{\nabla} \cdot (\epsilon \mathbf{u}) = 0 \qquad [8.1.23]$$

Particles:
$$-\frac{\partial \epsilon}{\partial t} + \vec{\nabla} \cdot [(1 - \epsilon)\mathbf{v}] = 0 \qquad [8.1.24]$$

The corresponding linear momentum equations and accompanying constitutive and interaction relationships have been the subject of considerable controversy. Jackson (1971) reviewed the work in this area before 1970. With gravity the only body force, the equations are of the form

Fluid:
$$\rho_F \epsilon \frac{\mathfrak{D}\mathbf{u}}{\mathfrak{D}t} = -\rho_F \epsilon g \mathbf{k} + \vec{\nabla} \cdot \mathbf{T}^F + \mathbf{F}_I \qquad [8.1.25]$$

Particles:
$$\rho_S(1 - \epsilon) \frac{\mathfrak{D}\mathbf{v}}{\mathfrak{D}t} = -\rho_S(1 - \epsilon)g \mathbf{k} + \vec{\nabla} \cdot \mathbf{T}^S - \mathbf{F}_I \qquad [8.1.26]$$

where $\mathbf{T}^F$ and $\mathbf{T}^S$ are stress tensors for the fluid and solids, respectively, and $\mathbf{F}_I$ is the interaction term accounting for action and reaction between two phases. Although $\mathbf{T}^F$ can be represented by the usual constitutive equation for a Newtonian fluid, assuming that the fluidizing fluid is Newtonian, representation of $\mathbf{T}^S$ and $\mathbf{F}_I$ is difficult. Early workers tended to ignore $\mathbf{T}^S$ altogether or to treat the particulate phase as a Newtonian incompressible fluid. Later work has included further material constants, in some cases including allowance for yield stresses and elasticity. The interaction term $\mathbf{F}_I$ is commonly written to include virtual mass effects as well as drag. Clearly, the overall equations must be self-consistent and must be satisfied by the so-called *uniform fluidization solution,*

$$\left. \begin{array}{l} \epsilon = \text{const} \\[6pt] \mathbf{v} = 0 \\[6pt] \mathbf{u} = u_0 \mathbf{k} \end{array} \right\} \qquad [8.1.27]$$

This theoretical approach to fluidization is of interest with respect to two problems, the initiation of bubbling and the behavior of the dense phase around rising bubbles. These subjects are treated in sections 8.1.5 and 8.1.6.

Mixing of fluid and solids in particulately fluidized systems has been reviewed by Richardson (1971). Whereas diffusionlike models are inappropriate for describing mixing in aggregative systems, as discussed in sections 8.1.9 and 8.1.10, the motion of particles and fluid elements in particulate systems is more appropriately described by a diffusion-type equation. Carlos & Richardson (1967, 1968) showed that the distribution of particle speeds is of the same form as the distribution function for molecules in a gas predicted by molecular theory. However, there is considerable anisotropy, with axial (i.e., vertical) motions considerably more vigorous than radial ones. This is reflected in axial dispersion coefficients $\mathfrak{D}_a$ that are consistently higher than corresponding radial dispersion coefficients $\mathfrak{D}_r$. Typical axial Peclet numbers $u\bar{d}_s/\epsilon\mathfrak{D}_a$ are of order 0.01–10 for both liquid and solid dispersion over the Reynolds number range $1 < \rho_L \bar{d}_s u/\mu_L < 1000$. The values seem to depend strongly on the uniformity of distribution of the fluidizing liquid, nonuniformly fluidized beds giving rise to gross circulation patterns that significantly increase mixing and hence decrease the measured Peclet number range. Dispersion in particulately fluidized beds has been reviewed by Potter (1971).

8.1.5 ONSET OF BUBBLING

Some fluidized systems show bubbling as soon as the point of minimum fluidization is reached. Others show bubbling only at some superficial velocity greater than u_{mf}. Still others do not appear to give bubbles at any superficial velocity of the fluidizing fluid.

The onset of bubbling appears to be associated with inherent instability in the uniform state of fluidization discussed in the previous section. Linearized stability analyses have been carried out by a number of workers on the basis of equations of continuity and motion. Because these equations and the constitutive and interaction relationships used in these studies differ, the quantitative conclusions vary from study to study, although the qualitative conclusions are reasonably consistent. For systems that show immediate bubbling, the analyses predict that the uniform state of fluidization is unstable; small perturbations of voidage and/or velocity are shown to grow and propagate upward through the bed. On the other hand, systems that show no bubbling are predicted either to be unstable, with very slow rates of disturbance growth, or to be stable. Systems that show a gap between u_{mf} and the velocity u_{mb} at which bubbling occurs are predicted to have lower rates of disturbance growth than systems in which bubbling occurs immediately; i.e., where $u_{mb} = u_{mf}$. Experimental work on two-dimensional liquid-fluidized beds (El-Kaissy & Homsy 1976) has shown the formation and rise of planar waves. These waves may change their shape to convex, hug one wall, coalesce with other waves, or break up, depending on, among other factors, the fluid velocity. In some cases the breakup is into regions that strongly suggest the origin of bubbles. This seems to confirm that bubble formation is linked to growth and propagation of voidage waves.

For practical purposes, empirical or semiempirical parameters are useful for indicating whether bubbling occurs, and a number of such parameters have been proposed. These parameters are listed in table 8.1.3, together with limiting values beyond which bubbling is said to occur. The criteria in the table can be used for guidance, but caution should be exercised when the calculated parameter is close to the suggested transition value.

For gas-fluidized systems in which aggregative or heterogeneous fluidization occurs, the point at which bubbling is initiated may not coincide with minimum fluidization. Especially for small-particle systems ($\bar{d}_p < 80\ \mu m$ at atmospheric pressure) or for elevated system pressures, there is an interval $u_{mf} \leqslant u < u_{mb}$ in which particulate fluidization is observed. The superficial gas velocity at minimum bubbling can be estimated by a dimensional correlation according to Geldart & Abrahamsen (1978):

$$u_{mb} = 33\,\bar{d}_S\left(\frac{\mu_F}{\rho_F}\right)^{-0.1} \qquad\qquad [8.1.28]$$

Note that [8.1.28] applies only for $u_{mb} \geqslant u_{mf}$. When [8.1.28] predicts values of u_{mb} less than u_{mf}, it must be assumed that $u_{mb} = u_{mf}$. The line corresponding to [8.1.28] has been plotted in figure 8.1.3. Note the increasing gap between u_{mb} and u_{mf} with decreasing particle diameter and decreasing particle density.

8.1.6 BUBBLING REGIME

The bubbling regime of fluidization has received more attention than any other regime. Many industrial gas-fluidized beds operate in this regime. Bubbles are the void regions that form at or near the gas distributor and propagate upward. They give to a fluidized bed an appearance like that of pool-boiling liquid, and there are some analogies between the bubbles themselves and bubbles in liquids.

The bubbles and the solids motion induced by the bubbles give a fluidized bed many of its most important properties. Bed-to-wall and bed-to-internal-tube heat transfer tend to be favorable because of particle renewal induced by passing bubbles (section 8.2.3). Axial particle mixing is rapid because of particle motion associated with bubbles (section 8.1.9). The efficiency of many fluidized beds as chemical reactors is lowered by the tendency of gas in the bubbles to bypass contact with the solids (section 8.4). Entrainment of solids originates in the ejection of particles into the freeboard region by bubbles bursting at the bed surface. Hence, an understanding of bubble behavior is central to understanding and predicting the properties of fluidized beds operating in this regime.

8.1.6.1 Characteristics of Single Bubbles

To a first approximation, the dense phase surrounding a bubble rising in a fluidized bed acts like an incompressible Newtonian liquid with zero surface tension at the interface between the bubble phase and the dense phase. As a result, there is some similarity between the shapes and rise velocities of bubbles in fluidized beds and

Table 8.1.3 Alternative Criteria Defining the Transition between Particulate and Aggregative Fluidization

Source	Governing parameter	Particulate regime	Aggregative regime
Wilhelm & Kwauk (1948)	$\mathrm{Fr} = \dfrac{u_{mf}^2}{g d_S}$	$\mathrm{Fr} < 0.13$	$\mathrm{Fr} > 1.1$
Harrison et al. (1961)	$\dfrac{d_{b\max}}{\bar{d}_S}$ where $d_{b\max} = \dfrac{2v_T^2}{g}$	$\dfrac{d_{b\max}}{\bar{d}_S} < 30$	$\dfrac{d_{b\max}}{\bar{d}_S} > 30$
Rowe (1962)	u_{mf}	$u_{mf} < 0.2$ cm/s	$u_{mf} > 0.2$ cm/s
Romero & Johanson (1962)	$R = \dfrac{u_{mf}^3(\rho_S - \rho_F)L_{mf}}{g\mu_F D}$	$R < 100$	$R > 100$
Verloop & Heertjes (1974)	$(\rho_S - \rho_F)\dfrac{\sqrt{\bar{d}_S^3}}{\mu_F}$	Critical value said to depend on ϵ and ϵ_{mf} and on which of several criteria is limiting	
Doichev et al. (1975)	$\left[\dfrac{g\bar{d}_S^3 \rho_F(\rho_S - \rho_F)}{\mu_F^2}\right]^m \left[\dfrac{\rho_{mf}}{\rho_F}\right]^{0.5}$ where $\rho_{mf} = \rho_S(1 - \epsilon_{mf}) + \rho_F \epsilon_{mf}$	Critical value and m found to depend on range of operation	

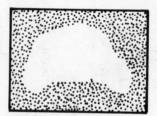

Figure 8.1.7 Sketch showing a
bubble as viewed by X-ray
photography by Rowe &
Partridge (1965) for 220 μm
glass Ballotini particles.

large bubbles (where surface tension effects are minor) in true liquids. This type of
bubble is loosely referred to as a *spherical cap,* although the true shape is often
closer to an ellipsoidal cap (Clift et al. 1978). The shape as traced from an X-ray
photograph of Rowe & Partridge (1965) is shown in figure 8.1.7. The included
angle is a function of the effective Reynolds number for the bubble, and hence it
can be used to infer an apparent viscosity μ_a of the dense phase (Grace 1970).
Typical values are in the range 4–14 poise (table 8.1.4), consistent with the most

Table 8.1.4 Apparent Viscosities for Systems Studied by Rowe & Partridge (1965)

Material	Mean diameter (μm)	Shape	Size range	μ_a (poise) From bubble shape[a]	From viscometry results[b]
Glass spheres	550	Spherical	Narrow	9.5	–
	460			–	12
	220			8.5	9
	170			7.5	8
	140			8	8
	120			8.5	8
	82			9	6
	60			7	4
Silver sand	500	Angular	Close	12	–
	460			10	14
	330			13	12
	230			7	10
	140			9	8
	82			8.5	7
	72			8	5
Synclyst catalyst	52	Rounded, irregular	Wide	4	–
Magnesite	240	Angular	Wide	9	10

[a]Grace (1970).
[b]Schugerl et al. (1961); Stewart (1968).

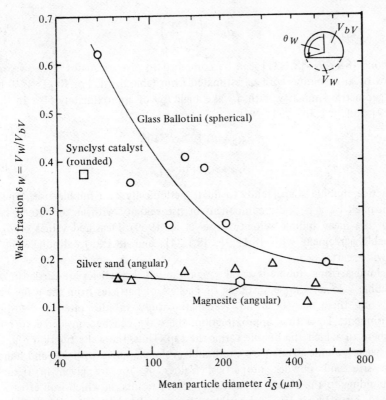

Figure 8.1.8 Wake volume fractions obtained from the X-ray photographs of Rowe & Partridge (1965) averaged from bubbles not appreciably subject to wall effects.

careful and satisfactory determinations of fluidized-bed apparent viscosity by standard viscometric techniques. The apparent viscosity tends to increase with increasing particle size, as shown in table 8.1.4.

The rise velocity of a single spherical-cap bubble is given by

$$u_b = \tfrac{2}{3} \sqrt{gr_b}$$ [8.1.29]

where r_b is the radius of curvature of the leading edge of the bubble. The relationship between the volume, radius, and wake angle θ_W (see figure 8.1.8) of a spherical cap is given by

$$V_{bV} = \frac{\pi}{3} r_b^3 \left(2 - 3 \cos \theta_W + \cos^3 \theta_W\right)$$ [8.1.30]

The angle θ_W in degrees has been correlated empirically (Clift et al. 1978) by means of

$$\theta_W = 50 + 190 \exp\left(-0.62 \, \mathrm{Re}_b^{0.4}\right)$$ [8.1.31]

where $$\mathrm{Re}_b = \rho_S \left(1 - \epsilon_{mf}\right) \frac{d_e u_b}{\mu_a}$$ [8.1.32]

and
$$d_e = \left(\frac{6V_{bV}}{\pi}\right)^{1/3}$$
[8.1.33]

Equations [8.1.29]–[8.1.31] can be combined to give estimates of rise velocity for bubbles of any volume with μ_a estimated from table 8.1.4. For $Re_b \gtrsim 150$, bubbles show geometric similarity with a wake angle θ_W of approximately 50°. In this case, [8.1.29] and [8.1.30] yield

$$u_b = 0.792\ g^{1/2}\ V_{bV}^{1/6}$$
[8.1.34]

or
$$u_b = 0.711\ \sqrt{gd_e}$$
[8.1.35]

In practice, bubble shape tends to dilate periodically as a bubble rises, and this is accompanied by a periodic component in rise velocity with an amplitude typically 20% of the mean bubble velocity (Toei et al. 1969). Measured values of u_b are in reasonable agreement with [8.1.29], [8.1.34], and [8.1.35], although the results show wide scatter.

Behind a rising bubble is a wake region in which particles are carried upward at the bubble velocity. Some shedding of packets of particles from the wake has been noted, but there has been no systematic study of the rate of shedding and replenishment. To a first approximation, the wake can be considered to complete the sphere of which the bubble forms the cap. Thus, the wake fraction δ_W, defined as the wake volume divided by the bubble volume, varies with θ_W and hence with bubble size and powder properties. Values of δ_W are given in figure 8.1.8 corresponding to the Rowe & Partridge (1965) results, in which wall effects can be neglected; i.e., $D/r_b \geqslant 10$. These values were calculated by assuming that the wakes complete the spheres of which the bubbles form the caps. Note that spherical or rounded particles and small particles give rise to larger wakes than angular or coarse particles. Wake volume fractions are expected to increase with increasing bubble size in the absence of wall effects (Grace 1970). When wall effects are appreciable, they give rise to smaller wakes. Particles in the wake undergo some circulation, as indicated in figure 8.1.9.

In addition to the transport of particles in their wakes, bubbles induce drift of solids. Drift profiles show that a spout of particles is drawn up behind a rising bubble, with the pattern shown in figure 8.1.9. To compensate for the upward movement of particles in the wake and in the central part of the drift profile, particles have a net downward movement away from the axis. In detail, the particles in the dense phase do not act exactly like a Newtonian fluid, and the common assumption that the dense phase acts like an inviscid fluid can lead to serious errors. The true rheological character of the dense phase has been the subject of some debate. Slip surfaces (Partridge et al. 1969, Gabor 1972b) indicate the possibility of an appreciable yield stress in many systems, whereas experiments by Mutsers and Rietema (1977) show that elastic properties also play an important role. The voidage of the dense phase is approximately uniform, but small increases in voidage occur adjacent to the bubble surface (Lockett & Harrison 1967).

The number of particles dispersed in rising bubbles is generally very small. A common estimate is that less than 0.1% of the bubble volume is occupied by

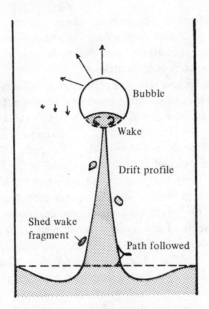

Figure 8.1.9 Particle motion caused by rise of a single bubble along the axis of a fluidized bed. Arrows represent particle velocities.

particles. Particles at the bubble roof are supported not by compressive "archlike" stresses but by a balance between gravity and drag (Rowe 1964). The resultant of these forces causes particles to move along the roof of the bubble away from the nose.

Some fingers of particles do form on the bubble roof, and these may lead to the splitting of bubbles. These fingers are believed to be associated with the Rayleigh-Taylor-type instability, in which a heavier overlying phase tends to penetrate a lighter underlying phase (Clift & Grace 1972b). A linearized stability analysis (Clift et al. 1974) shows that the effective dense phase viscosity plays a key role in determining whether fingers induce splitting. There has been some controversy over the maximum stable size of bubbles in fluidized beds. A common procedure for estimating this maximum is as follows. Calculate the terminal settling velocity v_T^* for a spherical particle of diameter $2.7\bar{d}_S$, where $\bar{d}_S$ is the surface-to-volume mean for the powder in question. Bubbles are said to be unstable if their rise velocities exceed v_T^*. From [8.1.35], the maximum bubble diameter is then approximately

$$(d_e)_{max} = 2.0\frac{(v_T^*)^2}{g} \qquad [8.1.36]$$

This procedure is modified from a postulate that bubbles split from the rear if the velocity of the circulating fluid is sufficient to entrain particles from the wake (Harrison et al. 1961). Although this postulated mechanism of bubble splitting appears to be false, the procedure above is said to give reasonable estimates of the maximum observable bubble diameter in many systems. Some predictions for particles fluidized by air under atmospheric conditions are given in figure 8.1.10. Matsen (1973) obtained experimental evidence for the existence of a maximum stable size for fine petroleum coke particles.

Gas motion tends to be more complex around bubbles in fluidized beds than around bubbles in liquids. The bubble boundary is permeable in fluidized beds, so gas enters a bubble at its base and leaves at the top. If the rate of entry and rate of exit are unbalanced, the bubble grows or shrinks. This causes considerable difficulty in studies of single bubbles in fluidized beds. It is common practice in such studies to inject a pulse of gas into an incipiently fluidized bed. However, it is generally necessary to keep the background superficial velocity about 10% above u_{mf} to minimize bubble growth or shrinkage, and even then, volume changes may interfere seriously with the phenomena under consideration.

Detailed measurements of gas motion in and near rising bubbles are difficult to obtain. Theoretical predictions tend to differ, and only certain features of the predictions have been testable. The three best-known theoretical treatments are compared in table 8.1.5. In each case a simplified rheological characterization of the particle properties was adopted, and solutions are given for an idealized spherical bubble rising at a steady velocity. Each of the theoretical approaches has advantages and disadvantages.

A key feature of each theoretical treatment is the prediction of the occurrence

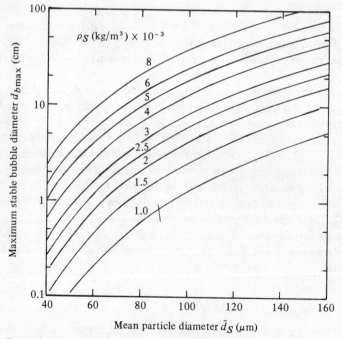

Figure 8.1.10   Predicted maximum stable bubble size for particles of different diameters and densities fluidized by air at 293 K and atmospheric pressure.

Table 8.1.5 Comparison of Principal Theoretical Approaches for Calculating Gas Motion in and around Rising Bubbles

Source	Key assumptions	Advantages	Disadvantages
Davidson (1961)	Particles in potential flow; gas motion relative to particles governed by Darcy's law; gas and particles incompressible	Simple; pressure distribution quite realistic	Predicted clouds too large; particle momentum equation not satisfied; variation in voidage not allowed
Murray (1965)	Constant voidage; linearized equation of particle momentum; viscous stresses, including particulate phase stresses, negligible; constant-pressure conditon on bubble surface satisfied only near nose	Cloud size and shape in reasonable agreement with experiment; gas motion follows directly from solids motion	Poor pressure distribution; unknown linearization constant; variation in voidage not allowed
Jackson (1963)	Voidage variation only in drag term; viscous stresses negligible; gas incompressible; constant-pressure condition on bubble surface satisfied only near nose	Voidage variation accounted for; cloud size and shape in reasonable agreement with experiment	Numerical difficulties; no analytical solution; poor pressure distribution

of "gas clouds" when the ratio of bubble velocity to remote interstitial gas velocity

$$u_b^+ = \frac{u_b \epsilon_{mf}}{u_{mf}} \qquad [8.1.37]$$

exceeds unity. The cloud is the dense phase region in which gas elements recirculate from a bubble. A cloud is bounded by a limiting gas path line (or streamline for steady flow), which is the limit of penetration (ignoring molecular diffusion) for gas elements that spend part of their time in a particular bubble. Flow visualization experiments in "two-dimensional" fluidized beds (Rowe et al. 1964) show that Murray's theoretical treatment gives a reasonable prediction of the cloud shape and size except at the rear of the bubble (see figure 8.1.11). For three-dimensional bubbles, the cloud boundary for a circular bubble of radius r_b with $u_b^+ > 1$ can be obtained from

$$(u_b^+ - 1)\left(\frac{r_c}{r_b}\right)^4 - u_b^+\left(\frac{r_c}{r_b}\right) - \cos\theta = 0 \qquad [8.1.38]$$

where θ is measured away from the vertical. An approximate relationship according to Partridge & Rowe (1966) giving the cloud volume/bubble volume ratio is

$$\frac{V_c}{V_{bV}} = \frac{1}{u_b^+ - 1} \qquad (u_b^+ > 1) \qquad [8.1.39]$$

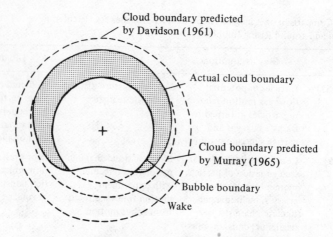

Figure 8.1.11 Comparison of predicted and experimental cloud boundaries in two-dimensional columns based on work by Rowe et al. (1964).

Values of V_c/V_{bV} calculated from [8.1.39] and values of r_c/r_b at $\theta = \pi/2$ evaluated from [8.1.38] are given in figure 8.1.12.

Pyle & Rose (1965) extended Davidson's treatment to predict gas streamlines within rising bubbles. They showed that in the absence of turbulence and molecular diffusion, there would be toroidal regions in which gas would recirculate entirely within the bubble, no matter how small u_b^+. In practice, turbulence and molecular diffusion are believed to keep the contents of bubbles well mixed. Although there are no reliable measurements of flow of gas through bubbles, the mean upward throughflow velocity (gas velocity relative to the bubble) is of order u_{mf} for isolated bubbles.

Local pressures tend to rise as a bubble approaches. The pressure falls below the mean value for the level as the bubble passes the probe and then recovers slowly in the wake. Davidson's treatment appears to give the best representation of pressure. For a three-dimensional bubble, the pressure change caused by the presence of a bubble is

$$p - p_0 = \rho_S(1 - \epsilon_{mf})\frac{gr_b^3}{r^2}\cos\theta \qquad (r \geqslant r_b) \qquad [8.1.40]$$

where r and θ are measured from the instantaneous bubble centroid and p_0 is the mean hydrostatic pressure at the measuring level in the absence of bubbles.

As the bubble dimension relative to the bed diameter D increases above a value of order 0.1, the bubble tends to elongate, the wake is smaller, and the rise velocity is retarded by the containing walls. An approximate expression according to Wallis (1969) for the rise velocity retardation is

$$\frac{u_b}{u_{b\infty}} = 1.13e^{-d_e/D} \qquad \left(0.125 \leqslant \frac{d_e}{D} \leqslant 0.6\right) \qquad [8.1.41]$$

where $u_{b\infty}$ refers to the rise velocity of a bubble in isolation as given by [8.1.29] and [8.1.35]. Once d_e/D exceeds about 0.5, the bubble is said to be a slug and its motion is dominated by wall effects. The slug flow regime is discussed in section 8.1.8.

8.1.6.2 Bubble Interactions

Bubble interactions are of key importance in determining such factors as bubble growth, interphase mass transfer, and lateral particle and gas motion. To a first approximation, the motion of two bubbles can be obtained by superposition, taking the vector sum of the rise velocity in isolation and the velocity at the position of

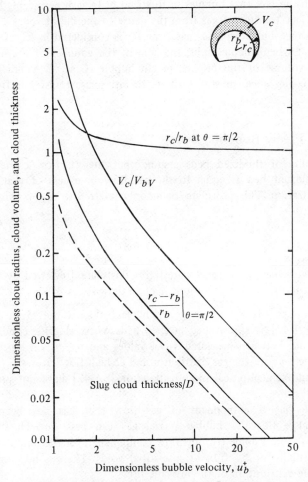

Figure 8.1.12 Cloud radius and volume in three dimensions as a function of the ratio of bubble velocity to interstitial fluidizing velocity.

the nose caused by the other bubble (Clift & Grace 1970, 1971). For relatively short-range interactions, the velocity field caused by each bubble, outside its own boundary and its wake, can be represented by a doublet. The wake is assumed to be stagnant relative to the bubble with which it is moving. These approximations lead to a reasonable description of the trajectories of coalescing bubbles and of the boundaries of the region within which a smaller following bubble overtakes a larger one (Clift & Grace 1971; Grace & Clift 1974b). This approach has been extended to bubble chains (Clift & Grace 1972a) and to freely bubbling beds (Johnsson et al. 1974; Nguyen et al. 1976) and can be used to simulate the development of bubble populations in fluidized beds, given the initial distribution at the grid.

When two bubbles interact and coalesce, the volume of the bubble formed is generally larger than the sum of the volumes of the original pair. This growth is associated with the fact that bubbles in fluidized beds have permeable boundaries. It also implies a net transfer of gas from the dense to the bubble phase. The effect of bubble coalescence on interphase mass transfer is considered in section 8.3.3. There is evidence that when bubbles split, the sum of the volumes of the new bubbles is less than the volume of the original parent bubble (Grace & Venta 1973). Hence splitting, like coalescence, must contribute to interphase transfer in freely bubbling beds.

8.1.6.3 Freely Bubbling Beds

Many treatments of fluidized beds assume that the gas flow carried as bubbles through a fluidized bed is equal to the gas flow in excess of that required for incipient fluidization. This postulate, commonly referred to as the two-phase theory of fluidization, is

$$\frac{\dot{V}_b}{A} = u - u_{mf} \qquad [8.1.42]$$

Considerable work has been done to test this postulate [reviewed by Grace & Clift (1974a)] and the following conclusions may be drawn:

1. Measured values of $\dot{V}_b/A$ are generally less than those given by [8.1.42], although [8.1.42] is approached in deep beds where slugging conditions prevail. The difference between measured $\dot{V}_b/A$ values and $u - u_{mf}$ is especially large at small distances above the gas distributor and at high flow rates.
2. Empirical and semiempirical modifications of [8.1.42] have not proved successful.
3. Each phase has a component of gas flow that has not been measurable experimentally. For the bubble phase, gas can pass through the permeable boundaries of the bubble (throughflow component); for the dense phase, gas can flow interstitially or by flux of interstitial voids. There is no conclusive proof regarding the distribution of the invisible flow.

Equation [8.1.42] can be used for approximation, but caution should be exercised wherever predictions depend critically on the assumed flow distribution.

Various correlations have been proposed for the mean bubble diameter as a function of height and operating conditions. The best are those of Mori & Wen (1975) and Darton et al. (1977). In the Mori & Wen correlation, one first calculates the maximum bubble diameter if total coalescence of bubbles occurred:

$$d_{bm} = 1.64[A(u - u_{mf})]^{0.4} \qquad [8.1.43]$$

The bubble size at height z above the distribution is then correlated by

$$d_b(z) = d_{bm} - (d_{bm} - d_{bo})e^{-0.3z/D} \qquad [8.1.44]$$

where d_{bo} is the initial bubble diameter formed at the grid, as discussed in the next section (see [8.1.55] and [8.1.56]). The ranges of key variables used to obtain this correlation are $5 \leqslant u_{mf} \leqslant 200$ mm/s, $60 \leqslant \bar{d}_s \leqslant 450$ µm, $u - u_{mf} \leqslant 0.48$ m/s, and $D \leqslant 1.30$ m. The correlation predicts an effect of bed scale on bubble size and in this sense represents an improvement over most previous correlations. In view of the transitions in flow regime discussed in section 8.1.2, this correlation should be applied only with caution outside the range of variables above.

The correlation of Darton et al. (1977) is based on a simple picture of lateral bubble coalescence. The resulting equation is

$$d_b(z) = 0.54(u - u_{mf})^{0.4}(z + 4\sqrt{A/N_{or}})^{0.8}g^{-0.2} \qquad [8.1.45]$$

where A/N_{or} is the area of distributor plate per orifice. Good agreement was obtained with experimental results of a number of workers, provided neither a maximum stable bubble size nor slugging conditions were achieved.

These correlations give a means of estimating mean bubble diameters in freely bubbling beds. The maximum stable bubble diameter should be calculated from [8.1.36], and this value should be used if it is less than the values predicted from [8.1.44] and [8.1.45]. In practice, there is a distribution of bubble sizes at any given height. Several workers have represented the bubble diameter distribution by means of log-normal or gamma distributions, but there are no general means of predicting the distribution parameters other than the mean. Certainly, the distribution tends to broaden with increasing height above the distributor. In practice, bubbles spend a large fraction of their time in coalescing and splitting (Rowe & Partridge 1965).

The characteristic bubble velocity at a particular height may be estimated from

$$u_b(z) = 0.711\sqrt{gd_b(z)} + (u - u_{mf}) \qquad [8.1.46]$$

The final term accounts approximately for bubble interaction and solids circulation effects, although it was originally included on the basis of an analogy with continuous slugs rising in liquids. The other term arises from [8.1.35].

The bed expansion and mean fraction of the bed occupied by bubbles $\bar{\epsilon}_b$ may be estimated by an iterative procedure. One first guesses a value of $\bar{\epsilon}_b$, from which the expanded bed height is given by

$$L = \frac{L_{mf}}{1 - \bar{\epsilon}_b} \qquad [8.1.47]$$

because the dense phase voidage remains essentially ϵ_{mf}. The bubble velocity at the midpoint of the bed $d_b(L/2)$ can then be calculated from [8.1.44] or [8.1.45] and the corresponding rise velocity $u_b(L/2)$ evaluated from [8.1.46]. If the original guess for $\bar{\epsilon}_b$ was correct, then $\bar{\epsilon}_b$ and $u_b(L/2)$ should satisfy

$$\frac{\dot{V}_b}{A} = \bar{\epsilon}_b u_b\left(\frac{L}{2}\right)$$

[8.1.48]

where $\dot{V}_b/A$ may be obtained from [8.1.42], bearing in mind the comments made thereon. If [8.1.48] is not satisfied, a new value of $\bar{\epsilon}_b$ is assumed and the procedure repeated until it is satisfied. At this point, the last values of $\bar{\epsilon}_b$ and L give estimates for the fraction of bed occupied by bubbles and the expanded bed height, respectively.

Staub & Canada (1978) give a simpler procedure for calculating bed expansion. The overall bed voidage may be estimated from

$$\bar{\epsilon} = \frac{u\epsilon_{mf}}{1.05u\epsilon_{mf} + (1 - \epsilon_{mf})u_{mf}}$$

[8.1.49]

The fraction of bed occupied by bubbles is then simply

$$\bar{\epsilon}_b = \frac{\bar{\epsilon} - \epsilon_{mf}}{1 - \epsilon_{mf}}$$

[8.1.50]

This procedure has the wrong limit at low u (i.e., as $u \to u_{mf}$), but appears to work well at high velocities approaching transition to the turbulent regime.

The coalescence pattern of bubbles in fluidized beds gives rise to nonuniform radial distributions of bubbles. Even if the spatial distribution is uniform at the gas distributor, a peak develops at about one to two mean bubble diameters from the wall. This maximum in bubble frequency as a function of radial position moves inward and intensifies higher in the bed, until the maximum bubble frequency and flow rate eventually coincide with the axis of the bed (Grace & Harrison 1968b; Werther 1974). For beds with a small number of gas inlet points, the maldistribution may manifest itself as a series of "bubble tracks" (Whitehead 1971) and dead zones may occur elsewhere. The mean bubble frequency at any level can be estimated from

$$f_b(z) = \frac{\dot{V}_b/A}{(\pi/6)d_b(z)^3}$$

[8.1.51]

where $\dot{V}_b/A$ and $d_b(z)$ are calculated from the preceding equations.

The nonuniform bubble patterns described above tend to give rise to established patterns of particle circulation. For shallow beds and low flow rates this may involve net solids up flow near the walls and down flow in the center of the bed. In deeper beds or at higher flow rates, one observes the more familiar pattern of "up the center, down the walls" solids motion. Motion at the walls is generally jerky, of a stick-slip variety, rather than smooth. Solids motion is treated in more detail in section 8.1.9.

8.1.7 GRID DESIGN

The distributor or grid must fulfill the following functions:

1. Distribute gas uniformly over the cross-sectional area
2. Prevent or minimize backflow of solid particles into the wind box below
3. Support the weight of the solids during periods when the bed is shut down
4. Resist thermal stresses, corrosion, erosion and blockage
5. Give minimum pressure drop consistent with 1–4

For most purposes, it is desirable that gas enter at a number of different points rather than at a single or a small number of orifices so that jets and bubbles that form will be small and heat and mass transfer processes rapid. With the many competing claims on distributors listed above, a large number of configurations have been devised. Some of the most common types are

Multiorifice plates: The plates may be horizontal or slightly dished. Orifices may be circular or slots. Pieces of angle may be welded on top or screens mounted on top to prevent backflow of solids.
Porous plates: These are common in laboratory-scale units but rarely practical for large-scale operations.
Grids: These are composed of grate bars or pipes.
Packed bed: This is a bed of much heavier or larger particles supported from below and sometimes sandwiched by an upper plate or screen.
Screens: On their own, screens tend to give pressure drops that are too low for uniform gas distribution. They are more successful in combination with other types of grid.
Nozzles, tuyeres, or bubble caps: These may be designed so that the gas emerges vertically upward, horizontally, or vertically downward. Horizontal injection helps to minimize erosion and attrition when there are heat transfer tubes or other internals in the bed. Downward injection aids in preventing solids backflow and plugging of orifices during shutdown periods.
Single central opening with conical section: This geometry used to be popular but is rarely used now, except for small-scale beds, spouted beds (section 8.1.16), or cases where the solids enter with the gas.
Proprietary and novel designs: Many of these have been patented or suggested in the literature; e.g., the segmental, solid-supported grid advocated by Davis (1977) or the perforated conical distributor for discharging sticky solids described by Young (1977).

Grid geometries are represented schematically in figure 8.1.13.

Little research has been done on the local effects of grids, except for upward-facing circular orifices. In this case, the penetration of isothermal jets has been correlated by Merry (1975) as

$$L_J = 5.2 \, d_{\text{or}} \left(\frac{\rho_F d_{\text{or}}}{\rho_S \bar{d}_S} \right)^{0.3} \left[1.3 \left(\frac{u_{\text{or}}^2}{g d_{\text{or}}} \right)^{0.2} - 1 \right] \qquad [8.1.52]$$

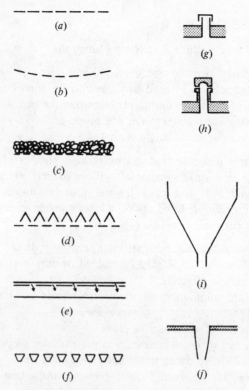

Figure 8.1.13 Common grid configurations for gas-fluidized beds: (*a*) flat perforated plate, (*b*) dished perforated plate, (*c*) packed bed of heavy solids, (*d*) angle deflectors, (*e*) downward-facing nozzles, (*f*) grate bars, (*g*) bubble caps, (*h*) tuyere or nozzle assembly, (*i*) single entry point, (*j*) shrouded jet entry.

where d_{or} is the orifice diameter and u_{or} the mean gas velocity through the orifice. Note that [8.1.52] predicts that jets form only for

$$u_{or} \geqslant 0.52 \sqrt{g d_{or}} \qquad [8.1.53]$$

At lower gas velocities, bubbles form right at the distributor plate. Merry (1971) also gave a semiempirical equation for the penetration of horizontal air jets, fitting 72 data points with a correlation coefficient of 0.94 by

$$L_J = d_{or} \left\{ 5.25 \left[\frac{\rho_G u_{or}^2}{(1 - \epsilon_{mf}) \rho_S g \bar{d}_S} \right]^{0.4} \left(\frac{\rho_G \bar{d}_S}{\rho_S d_{or}} \right)^{0.2} - 4.5 \right\} \qquad [8.1.54]$$

Again, there is a critical value of u_{or} below which no jet forms. Heat transfer tubes and other fixed internal surfaces should be located outside the paths of jets, vertical or horizontal, to reduce erosion and particle attrition.

Wen et al. (1978) showed that dead regions tend to form between vertical jets (figure 8.1.14). Particles in these regions are immobile and are supported by the distributor plate. There are regions of sluggish particle motion above the dead regions.

A number of different equations have been proposed to calculate the initial bubble size produced at an upward-facing orifice. Miwa et al. (1972) give

$$d_{bo} = \frac{1.38}{g^{0.2}} \left[\frac{A(u - u_{mf})}{N_{or}} \right]^{0.4}$$ [8.1.55]

where N_{or} is the number of orifices in the grid. For a porous plate distributor the same workers suggest

$$d_{bo} = 0.376(u - u_{mf})^2$$ [8.1.56]

Equation [8.1.56] is probably invalid for $u - u_{mf} > 0.2$ m/s. Geldart (1972) suggested that a porous plate acts like a perforated plate with 1000 holes/m^2, and this assumption can be combined with [8.1.55] to give an alternative procedure for estimating d_{bo}.

Fakhimi & Harrison (1970) and Davidson et al. (1977) proposed a criterion for the conditions under which all grid holes remain operative:

$$\frac{\rho_G}{2} \left(\frac{uD^2}{N_{or}d_{or}^2} \right)^2 \geq \frac{0.363 L_J \rho_S (1 - \epsilon_{mf})g}{1 - (u_{mf}/u)^2}$$ [8.1.57]

At values of u such that the left-hand side is lower than the right-hand side, some of the holes are blocked by particles and the superficial velocity must often be

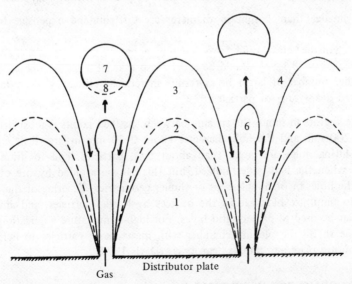

Figure 8.1.14 Zones of solids motion near grid jets identified by Wen et al. (1978): (1) dead zone, (2) quasi-dead zone, (3) intermittently mixed zone, (4) well-mixed zone, (5) grid jet, (6) forming bubble, (7) already formed bubble, (8) bubble wake.

made greater than the value of u at which the two sides are equal in order to clear the holes. Equation [8.1.57] gives one criterion that affects the design of the distributor. For practical purposes and uniformity of gas distribution it is usual to make the pressure drop across the distributor at least 10% of that across the bed, and a value of 30% is preferred for difficult operations; e.g., for difficult-to-fluidize materials, intermediate-rate catalytic reactions, or gas filtering and adsorption processes. The higher ratio is also preferred for shallow beds; i.e., where the aspect ratio L/D is less than about 0.5.

When the distributor pressure drop Δp_d has been specified in this manner, the next step is to calculate the corresponding gas velocity through each orifice:

$$u_{or} = C_d \sqrt{\frac{2\Delta p_d}{\rho_F}} \qquad [8.1.58]$$

For almost all cases of practical importance, the bed Reynolds number $\rho_F D u/\mu_F$ exceeds 2000 and the discharge coefficient C_d may then be taken as 0.6. Values of C_d for lower bed Reynolds numbers are given by Kunii & Levenspiel (1969). Knowing u_{or} and the superficial velocity u leads to specification of the free cross-sectional area of the plate through continuity; i.e.,

$$N_{or} d_{or}^2 = \frac{D^2 u}{u_{or}} \qquad [8.1.59]$$

Clearly, this equation can be satisfied by many different pairs of values of N_{or} and d_{or}; i.e., one can have a small number of large orifices or a large number of small ones. The choice is governed by a compromise between the following considerations:

1. Holes smaller than 1 mm in diameter are difficult and expensive to drill or punch.
2. The pitch of the holes should not be less than about 30 mm or greater than 300 mm.
3. The inequality [8.1.57] should be satisfied so that all holes are operative.
4. A smaller number of larger holes results in reduced efficiency of contacting and increased dead zones of particles.

With these factors in mind, the spacing between gas feed points is most often in the range 50-200 mm and the hole diameter about 2-30 mm in large-scale equipment. If the resulting holes are larger than about $5\bar{d}_s$, particles tend to drain into the wind box when the bed is defluidized, but this can be avoided by use of a screen covering the holes or of bubble caps or similar geometries. Tapering of the holes can be used to minimize blockage of the orifices by lodged particles, and antiabrasion washers can be used to protect grid holes. For high-temperature applications, it may be desirable to fill the plenum chamber with inert coarse particles to help support the distribution plate and reduce heat losses (Davis 1977).

8.1.8   SLUG FLOW REGIME

Slugs are bubbles or voids of diameter comparable to the inside diameter of the containing vessel. Slugging fluidized beds are analogous in many respects to gas-liquid systems operating in the slugging regime.

The necessary and sufficient conditions for an aggregative fluidized bed to be in the slug flow regime are

1. The superficial gas velocity must exceed the minimum slugging velocity, given (Stewart & Davidson 1967) by

$$u_{ms} = u_{mf} + 0.07 \sqrt{gD} \qquad [8.1.60]$$

2. The aspect ratio (height-to-diameter ratio) of the bed must be sufficiently large that slugs have an opportunity to form. This requires (Darton et al. 1977) that

$$L \geqslant 3.5 \, D \left(1 - \frac{1}{\sqrt{N_{or}}}\right) \qquad [8.1.61]$$

3. The maximum stable size of bubbles for the system must be of order D or greater (see section 8.1.6).
4. The superficial gas velocity must be lower than the value at which the turbulent regime is initiated (see section 8.1.14); i.e.,

$$u_{ms} \leqslant u < u_k \qquad [8.1.62]$$

These conditions are satisfied in a large proportion of laboratory-scale fluidized beds, including many units for which data have been reported in the literature. In addition, many pilot plant and industrial-scale columns are such that slugging is achieved. The slug flow regime is characterized by a more or less periodic rise and collapse of the entire upper bed surface. If the upper surface is obscured, slugging can generally be recognized by the bed pressure drop, which tends to rise and fall more or less periodically with a period of typically a few seconds. Because the voids are constrained to rise vertically by the containing walls and because they are similar in size and follow in a regular succession, it is somewhat easier to predict the properties of slugging beds than of normal bubbling beds. However, there are important differences between the slugging and other regimes, so that results obtained in small slugging columns should be applied with caution to larger columns operating in other regimes.

8.1.8.1 Properties of Single Slugs

Rising slugs in fluidized beds tend to be bullet-shaped with a rounded upper surface and a flat base as shown in figure 8.1.15a. For particles that can form bridges across the column, slugs tend to be diverted to one side of the column and rise along the wall with a shape as shown in figure 8.1.15b. These are called *wall slugs* or *half-slugs*. Factors that promote half-slugs are large $\bar{d}_S/D$ ratios, angular particle shapes, and roughened walls. Sometimes the term *slug* is also used to refer to square-nosed (flat on both top and bottom) voids that rise (rather slowly) because of the raining of particles from the lower surface of each plug of solids (figure 8.1.15c). This behavior is generally a sign of severe bridging and the solids cannot be considered truly fluidized. The tendency to form square-nosed slugs is most marked in columns of small diameter with coarse solids and is governed to a large extent by the internal angle of friction of the solid material (Kehoe & Davidson 1970; Thiel & Potter 1977).

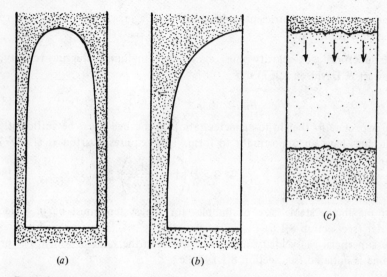

Figure 8.1.15 Shapes of gas slugs: (*a*) axisymmetric round-nosed slug, (*b*) wall slug, (*c*) square-nosed slug.

The rise velocity of an axisymmetric slug is given by

$$u_{si} = 0.35 \sqrt{gD} \tag{8.1.63}$$

Provided the void is large enough to be considered a true slug $[d_e = (6V_{bv}/\pi)^{1/3} > D/2]$, the rise velocity is independent of slug volume or length. Wall slugs have a rise velocity about 40% larger than that given by [8.1.63].

Just as for bubbles, clouds form for slugs if $u_b^+ = u_s \epsilon_{mf}/u_{mf} > 1$. The maximum cloud thickness is along the axis of symmetry. Davidson's and Murray's theoretical approaches give predictions that merge as the slug length approaches infinity (Collins 1969). There is excellent agreement between measured and predicted cloud thicknesses along the axis of symmetry (Stewart 1968). Predicted cloud penetration distances along the axis of symmetry (from slug nose to cloud nose) are given in figure 8.1.12.

8.1.8.2 Continuous Slugging

Like bubbles, slugs can overtake and coalesce, but the process is simpler in that oblique coalescences are precluded. It is generally assumed that a leading slug has no effect on a following one if the tail-to-nose separation exceeds a critical value. This critical value depends on particle properties and bed height. A mean value of $2D$ was assumed by Hovmand & Davidson (1968), but values as high as $8D$ have been observed by Thiel & Potter (1977).

Although [8.1.42] tends to overpredict the bubble flow rate in the bubbling regime, the theory appears to be valid in the slug flow regime. Continuity considerations (Nicklin et al. 1962) then require that the velocity of nonovertaking slugs be given by

$$u_s = u_{si} + (u - u_{mf}) \qquad [8.1.64]$$

where u_{si} is given by [8.1.63]. A coefficient of 1.2 is sometimes inserted before the $(u - u_{mf})$ term in [8.1.64] to account for nonuniform velocity profiles in the dense phase solids. Assuming an interslug spacing of $2D$, Hovmand & Davidson (1968) derived a quadratic expression from which the slug length can be calculated:

$$\frac{L_s}{D} - 0.495 \left(\frac{L_s}{D}\right)^{1/2} (1 + B) + 0.061 - 1.94B = 0 \qquad [8.1.65]$$

where
$$B = \frac{u - u_{mf}}{u_{si}} > 0.2 \qquad [8.1.66]$$

The slug frequency is then given by

$$f_s = \frac{u_s}{L_s + 2D} \qquad [8.1.67]$$

The upper surface of the bed rises at the velocity $u - u_{mf}$ during the approach of each leading slug and then collapses as the slug breaks the surface. The maximum height achieved by the bed surface is given by

$$L_{\max} = L_{mf}(1 + B) + B(2D - L_e) \qquad [8.1.68]$$

where L_e is an entry length (Grace et al. 1971). For most gas-solid systems $L_e \approx 2D$, so that the maximum expanded bed height is simply

$$L_{\max} \approx L_{mf}(1 + B) \qquad [8.1.69]$$

Except in the bottom region (from the grid to a height of about $1.5D$), where slugging is not yet fully established, the equations above give a method for predicting the behavior of both phases from first principles.

Thiel & Potter (1978) predicted and measured axial solids mixing characteristics for slugging beds. Generally, slugging systems give less axial and radial dispersion and back-mixing than comparable bubbling systems because of reduced wake volumes, reduced bubble coalescence, and more ordered motion.

8.1.9 SOLIDS MIXING AND SEGREGATION

The main features of bubble-induced solids motion for a single bubble were shown in figure 8.1.9. Each bubble carries with it a wake of particles, which to a first approximation can be assumed to complete the sphere of which the bubble forms the cap. Some shedding occurs from the wake en route. When the bubble reaches the bed surface, some wake particles are deposited at the surface while others are ejected into the freeboard. Inside the wake, particles circulate weakly, up at the center and down at the outside. In the dense phase outside the bubble and wake regions, particle motion results in a drift profile, with a spout of solids drawn up behind the rising bubble. To compensate for the particles carried upward by wake transport and the drift profile, particles descend outside the bubble path. For particles in groups B and D, this downward motion tends to be of a stick-slip variety.

The development of spatial nonuniformities in bubble distributions resulting from bubble coalescence patterns induces overall circulation of solids in the bed, as discussed in section 8.1.6. The most common patterns are illustrated in figure 8.1.16. Note that the grid geometry can play an important role in determining the extent and type of solids circulation.

This description of solids motion helps to explain the main features of solids mixing in freely bubbling fluidized beds. Because bubble motion is primarily in the vertical direction, the induced solids motion is also primarily vertical. Hence, mixing rates in the axial direction tend to be considerably higher than horizontal mixing rates. An individual particle's motion consists of brief periods of upward motion at velocities of the order of the bubble velocity and over distances of typically 0.1-1 m, followed by much longer periods of downward motion at considerably lower velocities. Because vertical motion does not occur by a series of small-scale random steps, efforts to correlate axial mixing in terms of longitudinal diffusion coefficients lead to inconsistent results and to coefficients that vary by more than four orders of magnitude (Potter 1971). A diffusional mixing model also fails to account for the cyclic response that occurs when a pulse of tagged solids is added to a fluidized bed of reasonable size (De Groot 1967).

The upward mass flux of particles caused by bubble motion at any cross section can be written as

$$\dot{M}_S = \rho_S \dot{V}_b \, (1 - \epsilon_{mf})(\delta_W + \delta_d) \qquad [8.1.70]$$

where the dense phase voidage is assumed to remain ϵ_{mf} and δ_W and δ_d are the volumes of solids carried by the wake and displaced because of drift per unit volume of bubble. A characteristic time or *turnover time* t_t may be defined as the total mass of particles in the bed divided by $\dot{M}_S$. Thus,

$$t_t = \frac{L_{mf}A}{\dot{V}_b(\delta_W + \delta_d)} \qquad [8.1.71]$$

Equation [8.1.42] is rewritten in modified form as

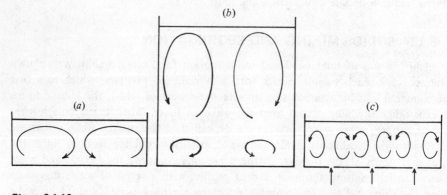

Figure 8.1.16 Solids circulation patterns observed in bubbling fluidized beds: (*a*) shallow bed: weak up-the-outside, down-the-center motion; (*b*) deeper bed: primary motion is up the center, down the walls; (*c*) bubble tracks caused by widely separated grid entry points.

$$\frac{\dot{V}_b}{A} = \delta_f (u - u_{mf}) \qquad [8.1.72]$$

where the coefficient $\delta_f \leqslant 1$, in view of the comments in section 8.1.6 regarding the distribution of gas between the two phases. Hence, [8.1.71] becomes

$$t_t = \frac{L_{mf}}{\delta_f (u - u_{mf})(\delta_w + \delta_d)} \qquad [8.1.73]$$

Experimental results indicate that homogeneity is achieved on addition of a pulse of tagged particles after two or three turnover times. Hence, t_t can be used as an indication of the effectiveness of vertical mixing. For the usual case where the mean residence time of particles in the equipment $\gg t_t$, perfect solids mixing is a good approximation (e.g., Wilson et al. 1976). Experimental values of δ_w are given in figure 8.1.8. The experimental range of δ_f is typically 0.35–1.0 (Werther 1974). Rowe (1973) suggested a value of δ_d of 0.35, whereas Baeyens & Geldart (1973) proposed a value of δ_d/δ_w in three dimensions of 1.6. Each of the three coefficients tends to decrease with increasing particle size (Baeyens & Geldart 1973), which explains why mixing is always more rapid for small particles. Equation [8.1.73] also shows that mixing becomes more effective for lower values of the aspect ratio L_{mf}/D and for higher superficial gas velocities.

Although it is inappropriate to consider a Fick's law type of diffusion process for vertical solids mixing, such a model can be useful in describing lateral mixing if the path under consideration is much longer than the lateral displacement induced during bubble coalescence (Whitehead et al. 1976; Reay 1978). The primary causes of horizontal solids motion are lateral bubble motion during coalescence and overall circulation patterns of solids. Reay (1978) measured lateral dispersion coefficients or order 10^{-4} m^2/s. Measured coefficients increased with increasing gas velocity and decreasing particle size. Highley & Merrick (1971) showed that lateral solids mixing is important with respect to the number of solids feed points in large-scale reactors.

In addition to the effect of the bubbling region on solids mixing, the grid jet region and freeboard region may play significant roles. As discussed in section 8.1.7, dead regions and regions of infrequent solids motion occur at the grid under normal jetting conditions, and this can lead to a long tail in measured residence time distributions.

Particle segregation is another aspect in which particle mixing can be an important consideration. Considerable work on two-species systems has been performed by Rowe and co-workers (Rowe & Nienow 1976), who showed that some segregation can occur, even in bubbling beds, especially in the top and bottom layers. Segregation is a complex function of gas velocity and particle characteristics. Differences in particle density are much more significant in promoting segregation than differences in particle size. For binary systems composed of two species that differ in size or density, the weight fraction of "jetsam" solids (i.e., the species that tends to sink to the bottom) in the upper part of the bed was found to be given (Rowe et al. 1972) by

$$x = \bar{x}f(u - u_{mf})\left(\frac{\rho_{S1}}{\rho_{S2}}\right)^{-2.5}\left(\frac{d_{S1}}{d_{S2}}\right)^{-0.2} \qquad [8.1.74]$$

where $\bar{x}$ is the overall weight fraction, $d_{S1} \geqslant d_{S2}$, and $\rho_{S1} \geqslant \rho_{S2}$. The function $f(u - u_{mf})$ was at first unspecified, but a complex form was suggested in a latter paper (Rowe & Nienow 1976). Note that the exponent of the density ratio is much greater than that of the diameter ratio. The form of relationship above works best when $\bar{x}$ is quite small.

In some applications it is desirable to promote segregation; e.g., to remove agglomerated and spent material from coal gasifiers. In this case, experiments (Chen & Keairns 1975, 1978) show that it is best to operate near the minimum fluidization velocity for the mixture. Separation rates are quite rapid, 30 s being sufficient under most operating conditions. Baffles that impede solids movement, such as fixed screen inserts or horizontal perforated plates, help to promote classification of particles. On the other hand, a central draft tube can give significantly enhanced mixing (Yang & Keairns 1976; LaNauze 1976).

8.1.10 GAS MIXING

Gas mixing is intimately related to solids mixing. As described above, solid elements remote from bubbles (e.g., in the wall region) move downward to compensate for upward solids motion caused by wake transport and drift. As a result, gas elements in this region tend to be dragged downward if the absolute downward solids velocity exceeds the relative velocity between the gas and the particles. By assuming that the latter is given by u_{mf}/ϵ_{mf} and that only wake transport of solids is important, Kunii & Levenspiel (1968) derived an equation for the superficial velocity $u\downarrow$ at which back mixing or incipient down flow occurs:

$$u\downarrow = u_{mf}\left(1 + \frac{1}{\epsilon_{mf}\delta_W}\right)[1 - \epsilon_b(1 + \delta_W)] \qquad [8.1.75]$$

where ϵ_b is the fraction of the bed occupied by bubbles. Downflow can be demonstrated experimentally by injecting tracer gas at the wall of a vigorously bubbling fluidized bed. Experimental results indicate that incipient down flow occurs for a u/u_{mf} value of 6–11.

Even when actual gas down flow or back mixing does not occur, different elements of gas spend quite different periods of time passing through a fluidized bed. This spread in residence times is caused by a number of factors, including: (1) gas elements associated with the bubble phase usually rise at a different velocity than interstitial gas; (2) grid jet gas rises much more rapidly than interstitial gas; (3) different bubbles have different velocities because of coalescence and variations in size; (4) net circulation patterns of solids cause bubbles and interstitial gas to move upward more rapidly in up flow regions than in down flow regions; and (5) gas is adsorbed on the particles. In general, measured residence time distributions correspond neither to plug flow nor to perfect mixing, although either of these limits may be approached in extreme cases. As in the case of solids mixing, attempts to correlate axial gas mixing in terms of a Fick's law model have been unsuccessful. A better approach is to consider the two-phase nature and the exchange of gas between the phases. This general approach is taken up in section 8.3.2.

There has been little work on radial dispersion of gas. As in the solids mixing case, radial mixing is primarily associated with lateral movement of bubbles during coalescence, and measured radial dispersion coefficients are typically an order of magnitude less than values that have been ascribed to axial dispersion coefficients. Kunii & Levenspiel (1969) related the gas phase radial dispersion coefficient to their bubbling bed model.

8.1.11 HYDRODYNAMIC EFFECTS OF INTERNAL TUBES AND BAFFLES

Fluidized beds commonly contain heat transfer tubes, diplegs, injection lances, baffles, or other fixed surfaces that affect the behavior of the bed. In some cases baffles are added in an effort to improve the quality of fluidization. The design of fluidized-bed processes in which there are internal surfaces requires knowledge of the influence of these surfaces. Some of the principal types of internals are illustrated in figure 8.1.17. As a general rule, the minimum gap between any fixed surfaces should be 20–30 particle diameters or more in order to allow solids to circulate freely.

8.1.11.1 Immersed Tubes

Heat transfer tubes are usually horizontal, but vertical tubes are also used. Inclined tubes should be avoided because they tend to induce gas channeling and bypassing on the downward-facing surface and sluggish solids motion on the upward-facing side. Tubes may be circular or noncircular in cross section and bare or finned.

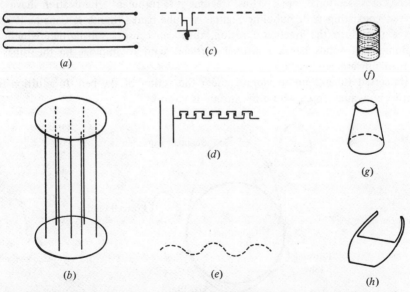

Figure 8.1.17 Principal types of internals in fluidized beds: (*a*) horizontal tubes or tube bundles, (*b*) vertical tubes, (*c*) horizontal perforated plate with downcomer, (*d*) bubble cap tray, (*e*) wavy-type baffle, (*f*) cylindrical open-ended screen insert, (*g*) inverted cone insert, (*h*) freeboard baffle plate.

Horizontal Tubes

Horizontal tubes can induce local fluidization and bubbling at their sides for $u < u_{mf}$ because of the higher local velocities at the sides. When u is somewhat in excess of u_{mf}, a film of gas forms on the underside of a tube, bubbles detach from the sides, and a dead or defluidized zone of particles forms on top (Glass & Harrison 1964). This situation is illustrated for a cylindrical tube in figure 8.1.18. The bubbles formed at the sides often alternate, one at one side, then another at the opposite side. These bubbles cause periodic sweeping of the particles at the sides of the tube, giving favorable heat transfer rates there, as discussed in section 8.2.

With increasing gas velocity, interactions between tubes and bubbles rising from below become more important. Bubbles that are much larger than a tube tend to split if they strike the tube directly. However, recombination of the resulting bubbles generally occurs above the tube unless there is an array of tubes preventing recombination. Hence, the influence of a single row of tubes on the bubble size distribution is small, whereas an array of tubes, filling a substantial fraction of the bed volume, can cause a marked reduction in the mean bubble size and standard deviation, while the radial pattern of bubbling becomes more uniform. The array is most effective if the tubes are placed on a 45° pitch and if the center-to-center spacing is 2–2.5 D_T, where D_T is the tube diameter. Closer spacings can impede solids circulation and cause gas channeling. Bubbles impinging on tubes tend to dislodge the dead zones of particles from their top surfaces.

At high gas velocities immersed tubes can trigger local changes from one fluidization regime to another because of the increased gas velocities in regions of reduced cross-sectional area. Thus, regions of turbulent fluidization have been observed coexisting with bubbling regions in tube banks (Staub & Canada 1978). If tubes extend into the freeboard region, they can cause a substantial reduction in entrainment of solids because ejected particles tend to impinge on the tubes and lose their upward momentum.

Immersed tubes tend to vibrate under the action of the bed. In addition to an effective buoyancy force whose magnitude is given by

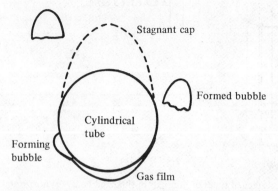

Figure 8.1.18 Zones of gas and solids motion around a horizontal tube in a bubbling fluidized bed at modest gas flow rates.

$$\mathbf{F}_b = \rho_S(1 - \epsilon_{mf})gV_T\mathbf{k} \qquad [8.1.76]$$

where V_T is the tube volume, there are periodic forces each time a bubble passes. During the approach of a bubble the resulting thrust is upward, while a downward thrust occurs as the bubble rises away from the tube (Nguyen & Grace 1978). Because the frequency of approaching bubbles is irregular, the tubes tend to vibrate at nearly their natural frequency, but with highly variable amplitude. Secure support is required to withstand the resulting stresses. To minimize tube erosion and particle attrition, grid jets should not be allowed to impinge directly on the tubes. When direct impingement does occur, experimental results of Vaux & Newby (1978) show that wear increases with the hardness of the particles and is more prominent for sharp, angular particles than for smooth, rounded ones. Erosion is said to depend on the square of particle velocity and to increase with increasing bed temperature.

The considerations above apply to finned tubes as well as bare ones. Heat transfer to horizontal tubes is treated in sections 8.2.3 and 8.2.4.

Vertical Tubes or Rods

Vertical tubes are sometimes employed for purely hydrodynamic reasons to improve the quality of fluidization and provide one simple method of scale-up. Volk et al. (1962) proposed that successful scale-up could be achieved if the hydraulic bed diameter

$$D_H = \frac{4 \times \text{free cross-sectional area of bed}}{\text{total wetted perimeter}} \qquad [8.1.77]$$

is maintained in the range 0.10–0.20 m. This criterion should be used with caution, however (Grace & Harrison 1968a; Botton 1970). The influence of the tubes or rods depends on the ratio $d_b(x)/D_T$. If the bubbles are small relative to the internals, the column is effectively divided into a number of smaller compartments in parallel, and a form of slugging may occur in these compartments. If the bubbles are much larger than the tubes, there is a tendency for the bubbles to enclose the tubes and travel along them with rise velocities typically 15% greater than in the absence of the tubes. Horizontal movement of gas and solids tends to be impeded in either case, with the result that radial mixing is lowered and there is greater radial uniformity of hydrodynamic properties.

8.1.11.2 Horizontal Plates

Horizontal plates may be used to divide a fluidized bed into a number of compartments in series. Various geometries have been tested, including drilled or punched flat plates, coarse mesh screens, slotted domes, sieve trays with downcomers, and proprietary designs. The holes should be 10 particle diameters or more in size if solids are to circulate freely between compartments. The fraction of plate consisting of free area should generally be in the range 10–45%. Therefore, the pressure drop caused by each plate is much lower than that caused by the grid, whose free area is typically of order 1%, but blockage of holes may lead to larger pressure drops than expected. Antiabrasion washers may be used to reduce erosion. Fines returned from the cyclones should be reintroduced near the gas distributor of the lowest compartment.

Varma (1975) suggested some further design criteria: a fractional free area of 30-50%, a plate spacing of $2D$, a ratio of orifice to particle diameter of 5-10, and a ratio of gas velocity through each orifice to terminal particle settling velocity in the range 0.3-1.7. There are two distinct regimes of solids flow down through the holes (Guignon et al. 1978). Relatively low solids fluxes are obtained if particles fall down around the periphery of a large number of holes. In another mode, promoted by having thick plates, solids pour downward through a few holes while the gas flows upward through the remaining holes. The solids efflux in the latter case is much higher. Patterson (1977) argued that a single large, centrally located hole should be used in preference to a large number of smaller orifices.

8.1.11.3 Other Fixed Internals

Considerable experimental work has been done on columns where small particles are fluidized in the interstices of much larger particles. This leads to smaller, more uniformly distributed bubbles and to reduced carry-over of solids. Of the many types of fixed packings that have been investigated, including spheres, Raschig rings, and Berl saddles, the best appear to be open-ended coarse screen cylinders, typically 10-20 mm in diameter and 10-20 mm tall (Sutherland et al. 1963). These occupy little volume and, when stacked vertically, do little to impede emptying of the bed.

Many other geometries of fixed baffles have been tested, but none have achieved the popularity of application of the horizontal and vertical tubes and horizontal plates discussed above. Rowe & Everett (1972) showed that inverted funnel shapes (see figure 8.1.17g) help to reduce the mean bubble size. A combination of vertical tubes and horizontal perforated plates was found to be effective in gas-making processes (Horsler & Thompson 1968). Harrison et al. (1974) proposed a freeboard baffle arrangement (see figure 8.1.17h) that is effective in reducing particle carry-over.

8.1.11.4 Mobile Packings

Mobile packings have received little attention, and there are no general design criteria. Objects that are very light tend to float at the bed surface and have been used to reduce particle carry-over and decrease fluctuations of the bed surface (Goikhman et al. 1969). In another study (Keillor & Bergougnou 1976), the mobile packings were heavy enough to spend most of the time immersed in the bed and it was intended that they should break up bubbles. There was evidence that some bubble splitting was induced in this manner.

8.1.11.5 Mechanical, Electrical, and Magnetic Aids to Fluidization

Many mechanical aids to fluidization have been proposed including impellers, vibration of the column, gas flow pulsation, grid rotation, and ultrasonic vibrations. These techniques are sometimes useful when one of the following applies:

1. Particles are too fine or too cohesive to be fluidized otherwise, or they channel badly.
2. There is severe danger of particle agglomeration or clinker formation.
3. It is desired to operate below the normal u_{mf} or u_{mb} value.
4. Higher heat or mass transfer rates are required than would otherwise be available.
5. Particles are extremely friable and gentle vibration permits continuous fluidized-bed processing with minimum attrition, as in vibratory driers.

Hence, these techniques extend the range of fluidization conditions under which normal operation can take place. There are no common design criteria on which incorporation of these aids can be based. Instead, pilot plant tests are normally required for the material in question.

Three further techniques have been applied recently to aid fluidization. Centrifugal (i.e., spinning) fluidized beds, with the gas flowing radially inward through a cylindrical gas distributor, give increased values of u_{mf}, reduced particle carry-over, and a larger "turndown" range (Levy et al. 1978; Demircan et al. 1978; Metcalfe & Howard 1978). Electrical pulsations can be used to induce bubble splitting in beds of low-conductivity solids (Johnson & Melcher 1975). An applied magnetic field can delay the onset of bubbling and give a more gentle mode of fluidization (Rosenweig 1979). These techniques are too recent to allow proper evaluation of their usefulness.

8.1.12 PARTICLE FEEDING AND PARTICLE EFFLUX

One of the principal advantages of fluidized systems is that particles can be continuously fed and removed. Solids can also be readily circulated from one system to another; e.g., from a reactor to a catalyst regenerator.

There are a number of methods of feeding solids, including:

1. Gravity feeding via hoppers
2. Table feeders
3. Feeding under pressure via lock hoppers
4. Rotary feeders
5. Screw feeders
6. Belt feeders including slinger belts
7. Pneumatic feeding from below or from the side

Two or more of the above may be used together. The type of feeding device depends on the pressure in the fluidized bed, the rheological character of the solids, the required number of feed points, the abrasiveness or erosion characteristics of the solids, whether or not the particles show a tendency to agglomerate, and the flow rate. In applications where incoming solids must be distributed uniformly across the column cross section, as in coal feeding, one feed point per square meter of bed area has proved to be a conservative basis for design. In some cases, as with the feed of caked materials into driers, it is desirable to premix with already processed solids. Special problems associated with feeding into pressurized fluidized beds have been considered by Chandrasekhar & Harding (1978).

Particles may also be withdrawn continuously be several methods. Weirs may be provided as for flow of liquids. Solids also flow through an orifice in accordance with the equation

$$\dot{m}_S = C_d \rho_S (1 - \epsilon_{mf}) \sqrt{2g\Delta L} \qquad [8.1.78]$$

where ΔL is the distance below a bed surface open to the atmosphere. For flow between two vessels or from a pressurized bed, ΔL must be replaced by the effective head difference across the orifice. The discharge coefficient C_d depends on the ratio $d_{or}/\bar{d}_S$. When this ratio exceeds about 20, C_d can be taken to be 0.5 (Massimilla 1971). Smaller values are obtained at lower ratios; e.g., $C_d < 0.4$ for $d_{or}/\bar{d}_S \lesssim 15$ (Chin 1979). The flow rate of solids is virtually independent of the fluidizing velocity u, provided $u > u_{mb}$. Jones & Davidson (1965) predicted the flow rate of gas leaving with the solids from an analysis in which voidage variations and interparticle stresses in the jet region were ignored and Darcy's law was assumed to apply. This method has been extended to non-Darcy flow by deJong & Hoelen (1975). Massimilla (1971) used experimental results to suggest a modified correlation for the mass density efflux of the fluidizing fluid:

$$\dot{m}_F = \rho_F \sqrt{2g\Delta L} \left(0.33 + 1.54 \frac{u_{mf}\Delta L}{d_H g^{1/2}}^{1/2} \right) \qquad [8.1.79]$$

where d_H is the hydraulic diameter of the opening. Equations [8.1.78] and [8.1.79] apply to slots and other geometries as well as to circular orifices. They can also be applied in cases where the fluidizing fluid is either a gas or a liquid.

Withdrawal of solids from fluidized beds may be through metering screws or through seal pots to minimize transfer of gas. Bends and valves should usually be purged to keep solids in motion and prevent plugging. Disk and slide valves are the most common type of valve in transfer lines.

In some processes, the solid product is taken from entrained solids carried over (see section 8.1.13). More commonly, entrained solids must be returned to the bed after being captured by cyclones. Standpipes are generally used for this purpose. Solids flow in standpipes has been reviewed by Leung & Jones (1978). Backflow of gas through the dipleg on start-up is minimized by providing a seal, generally via a trickle valve (see Zenz & Othmer 1960). Design of systems where fluidized solids are circulated from one bed to another is treated by Kunii & Levenspiel (1969).

8.1.13 PARTICLE ENTRAINMENT

Carry-over of particles represents one of the principal problems in the application of fluidized beds. Particle recovery devices must be added to return solids to the bed, to prevent air pollution, and, in some cases, to recover valuable products. For many processes where a lower limit of, say, 44 μm is imposed on particle size by screening, a single cyclone provides insufficient recovery. Where smaller particles are originally present or dust is produced by attrition, it is often necessary to add secondary cyclones, electrostatic precipitators, bag filters, or other such devices (see chapter 9).

Cyclones may be located within the freeboard of the bed or external to the bed. The *freeboard* is the region extending from the surface of the expanded bed to the top of the apparatus. Internal cyclones offer the advantages of a lower space requirement and reduced heat losses, but external cyclones are usually preferable because of their greater accessibility. Particles are usually returned to the bed proper by diplegs. The inside diameter of the dipleg should not be smaller than 10 cm, and the return should be as close as possible to the lowest gas distributor.

The mechanism by which entrainment occurs involves two principal steps: (1) transfer of solid material from the dense phase region into the freeboard, and (2) motion of particles within the freeboard. For bubbling fluidized beds the transfer step results from eruption of bubbles at the bed surface. Most evidence suggests that the majority of particles ejected by erupting bubbles come from the bubble wake. Typically, about half the wake particles are ejected by a 0.1-m-diameter bubble (George & Grace 1978). There is a range of initial velocities in the freeboard, with approximately 50% of the ejected particles having ejection velocities twice the velocity of the bubble as it approaches the bed surface. Ejection is primarily vertically upward, but splashing occurs in such a way that ejected particles also spread out radially in the freeboard.

Trajectories of particles within the freeboard are determined by a balance between gravity, inertia, and drag forces. If horizontal components of velocity are ignored, the force balance for a spherical particle gives (see chapter 3)

$$\frac{dv}{dt} = -\frac{3}{4}\frac{\xi(\text{Re}, \epsilon)\rho_F v_R |v_R|}{\rho_S d_S} - \frac{(\rho_S - \rho_F)g}{\rho_S} \qquad [8.1.80]$$

where v is the local value of the particle velocity directed vertically upward, v_R is the corresponding velocity relative to the local gas velocity, $\xi(\text{Re}, \epsilon)$ is the drag coefficient, and virtual mass and history effects have been neglected. Integrating [8.1.80] together with the relationship

$$v = \frac{dz}{dt} \qquad [8.1.81]$$

and the boundary conditions $z = 0$ and $v = v_0$ at $t = 0$ is straightforward by numerical techniques, but there are at least three problems. First, it is by no means clear what gas velocity should be used in the calculation of v_R. There is evidence that as bubbles burst, not only are particles ejected into the freeboard, but unsteady gas jets also occur (Zenz & Weil 1958). Second, the dependence of the drag coefficient ξ on particle concentration is complicated by the radial spreading of particles and the tendency of particles to form clusters. Previous work has tended to treat particles as if there were no particle-particle interaction effects, but recent work on entrainment of two-species systems (Geldart et al. 1979) shows that there are substantial interactions between particles. Finally, effects of free-stream turbulence on ξ are poorly understood at best (see section 8.1.14) and are not allowed for in existing theoretical treatments.

As a result of these limitations, mechanistic models for particle entrainment have so far had limited applicability, and empirical correlations are widely employed. Unfortunately, it is common for the predictions of these correlations to vary widely, variations of two orders of magnitude not being unusual. Accordingly, considerable caution must be excercised in using these correlations, especially for high-pressure systems, where entrainment increases significantly.

The mode of particle transport described above implies that there is a height over which large or heavy particles slow down and reverse direction, while smaller particles continue to be carried upward, no matter how tall the freeboard (assuming a freeboard of uniform cross-sectional area). This has led to the term *transport disengagement height* (TDH). In practical terms, this is the height over which an appreciable decrease in upward solids flux occurs due to gravity alone. It is often used in establishing the total height of the equipment, because there is little advantage in exceeding this height. Zenz & Weil (1958) and Zenz & Othmer (1960) gave a simple graphic correlation of the TDH that has been widely used (figure 8.1.19). The correlation is based primarily on fluid cracking catalyst particles and tends to be conservative when applied to other types of particles, although the authors recommended it for particles up to 400 μm in diameter. Note that gas properties and particle density do not appear in the correlation, although physical reasoning suggests that these are important variables in determining the TDH. Fournol et al. (1973) studied fluid cracking catalyst and obtained

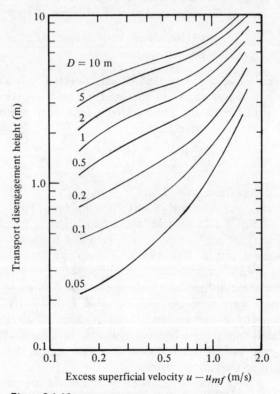

Figure 8.1.19 Simple graphic correlation based on Zenz & Weil (1958) for predicting transport disengagement heights with fine solids.

$$\text{TDH} = 1000\frac{u^2}{g} \tag{8.1.82}$$

for a 0.61-m-diameter column. However, their superficial velocity ranged only between 0.11 and 0.22 m/s and extrapolation appears to lead to excessively conservative results.

For large particles—e.g., $\bar{d}_S > 1$ mm—and u about 1 m/s or less, drag tends to play a relatively minor role in determining the height of rise of ejected particles, which can then be calculated from

$$H_{max} = \frac{v_0^2}{2g}\frac{\rho_S}{\rho_S - \rho_F} \tag{8.1.83}$$

where v_0 is the velocity of particle ejection from the bed surface. Based on the experimental finding that 99% of ejected particles have ejection velocities less than $6\,u_b$, where u_b is the velocity of the bubble causing the particle ejection (George & Grace 1978), the TDH for these large particles can be estimated from

$$\text{TDH} = \frac{27u_b(L)^2\rho_S}{g(\rho_S - \rho_F)} \tag{8.1.84}$$

where $u_b(L)$ can be calculated from [8.1.46] and [8.1.44] or [8.1.45]. An allowance of 50% has been made in [8.1.84] to account for the spread in velocities resulting from the distribution of bubble sizes at the bed surface and coalescence of bubbles right at the surface. If the conditions for slugging are satisfied, $u_b(L)$ should be replaced by u_s from [8.1.64].

For particles of intermediate size there are no reliable methods for calculating the TDH, although figure 8.1.19 and [8.1.84] are expected to give upper and lower bounds for most conditions.

Entrainment above the TDH is generally correlated in terms of a *specific rate constant* or *elutriation constant* $K^*(d)$, which is defined such that the flux of solids in a given narrow size range having mean diameter d_{Si} is assumed to be proportional to the mass fraction of particles x_i within that size range; i.e.,

$$\dot{m}_i = x_i K^*(d_{Si}) \tag{8.1.85}$$

The total entrainment flux is then obtained by summing the fluxes for all size fractions having terminal settling velocities less than the superficial gas velocity u.

Correlations for K^* differ widely. The correlation of Wen & Hashinger (1960) covers their own data and earlier data over the range of variables $40 < d_S < 150$ μm, $0.16 < \rho_F < 1.2$ kg/m^3, $1300 < \rho_S < 5000$ kg/m^3, and $0.22 < u < 1.32$ m/s:

$$\frac{K^*(d_{Si})}{\rho_G(u - v_T)} = 1.7 \times 10^{-5}\left[\frac{(u - v_T)^2}{gd_{Si}}\right]^{1/2}$$

$$\cdot \left(\frac{v_T d_{Si}\rho_G}{\mu_G}\right)^{0.725}\left(\frac{\rho_S - \rho_G}{\rho_G}\right)^{1.15}\left(\frac{u - v_T}{v_T}\right)^{0.10} \tag{8.1.86}$$

Equation [8.1.86] can be used to estimate the flux of each size fraction of solids

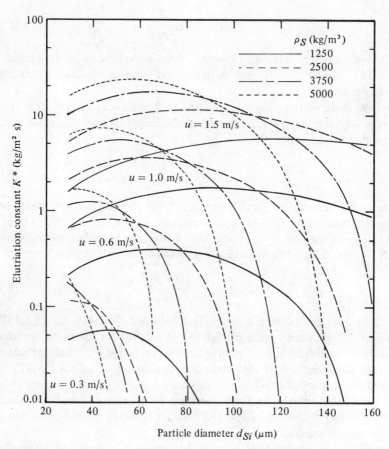

Figure 8.1.20 Values of elutriation constant K^* as a function of particle diameter and density and of gas velocity, where the fluidizing gas is air under normal atmospheric conditions.

above the TDH. Values of K^* obtained from [8.1.86] are plotted in figure 8.1.20 for different values of ρ_S and u, where the gas has the properties of air under standard conditions; i.e., 293 K and atmospheric pressure. Terminal velocities have been calculated by using the revised standard drag correlations for spheres proposed by Clift et al. (1978). Note that no carry-over of particles is predicted for the range of particle sizes where $v_T \geqslant u$. Note also that the equation cannot be extrapolated to particles much smaller than 40 μm because the wrong limit is given as $d_{Si} \to 0$.

A much more conservative prediction is given by the correlation of Merrick & Highley (1972), which is based on work with coal fluidized by air in pilot-scale units covering the superficial velocity range $0.61 \leqslant u \leqslant 2.44$ m/s. Their data were fitted by

$$K^*(d_{Si}) = 130 \, \rho_S u \, \exp \left[-10.4 \left(\frac{v_T}{u} \right)^{0.5} \left(\frac{u_{mf}}{u - u_{mf}} \right)^{0.25} \right] \qquad [8.1.87]$$

where v_T is evaluated for particles of size d_{Si}, whereas u_{mf} is evaluated for the bed as a whole.

There is a large range of conditions, especially in terms of particle sizes, over which there are no reliable correlations. A simple approach for setting an upper limit on the flux above the TDH is to take the flux of ejected particles at the bed surface with terminal velocities less than the superficial gas velocity; i.e.,

$$(\dot{m}_S)_{z > \text{TDH}} \leqslant \frac{1}{2} \delta_W x^* \frac{\rho_S \dot{V}_b}{A} \qquad [8.1.88]$$

where an upper limit on $\dot{V}_b$ is provided by [8.1.42], x^* is the mass fraction of particles having $v_T < u$, and half the wake particles are assumed to be ejected with each bubble. As discussed in section 8.1.9, δ_W is normally in the range 0.25–0.6. The actual flux is expected to be quite close to the limiting value given by [8.1.88] at low $u - u_{mf}$, where particle interactions are unimportant, but the flux is well below this limit with more vigorously fluidized beds because of particle clustering and streamers in the freeboard region. Where an expanded freeboard is used, x^* should be based on the fraction of particles having v_T less than the mean gas velocity in the expanded upper section.

Note that all these approaches imply that small particles are carried over in greater numbers than larger ones, because they are more readily conveyed by the gas stream. This leads to the term *elutriation,* which is the tendency for fine particles to be preferentially removed from a particle mixture. Because pollution control devices generally have lower collection efficiencies for fine particles than for coarse ones, there is also a tendency for fine particles to be lost altogether in the cyclones or other particle collection devices (see section 9.2.6). Hence there is a tendency in batch systems for the particle size distribution to shift toward larger particles over time, whereas in continuous systems the steady-state particle size distribution may differ from the feed distribution. Naturally, attrition and particle growth or shrinkage (if any) resulting from reaction or physical processes must also be taken into account in determining changes in particle size distributions.

Below the TDH the entrainment flux decreases approximately exponentially with height (Lewis et al. 1962; Fournol et al. 1973; Large et al. 1976), while the radial profiles of entrainment are quite uniform. Entrainment rates are reduced if fines returning from the cyclones are made to reenter the bed near the grid rather than at the bed surface.

8.1.14 TURBULENT REGIME OF FLUIDIZATION

As the gas flow rate through a fluidized bed is continuously increased, the violent bubbling action at first increases. Bubbles become larger while coalescence and splitting events are more and more frequent. Pressure fluctuations also grow in amplitude. However, beyond a certain superficial gas velocity, denoted by u_c (Yerushalmi & Cankurt 1979), the pressure fluctuations begin to decrease and large voids begin to disappear. Beyond a superficial velocity denoted by u_k, the amplitude of pressure fluctuations levels off at a value very much less than that corresponding to u_c, while the frequency of oscillation is much higher (Canada & McLaughlin 1977; Yerushalmi & Cankurt 1979). Usually, large voids are no longer observed.

Viewed from one perspective, voids in the turbulent regime are splitting as rapidly as they are coalescing, so that the mean void size is small and discrete bubbles or slugs in the usual sense cannot be distinguished. Viewed from another perspective, the turbulent regime is intermediate between the bubbling regime, where low-solids voids are dispersed in a solids-rich emulsion, and a fast fluidization regime, where solids-rich particle clusters are dispersed in a continuous phase consisting almost entirely of gas. The most notable visible features of a turbulent fluidized bed are tongues of gas, containing widely dispersed solids, darting in a zigzag manner up the column. Although there is an upper surface separating the turbulent bed from the freeboard, this surface is less clearly defined than for the bubbling regime. The top surface may fluctuate up and down, with a fairly regular periodicity, giving the deceptive appearance of slugging (Crescitelli et al. 1978). The overall bed voidage in the turbulent regime is typically in the range 0.7–0.8. Photographs of beds operating in the turbulent regime appear in figure 8.6 of Zenz & Othmer (1960) and in Kehoe & Davidson (1970).

The available data are insufficient to allow correlation of u_c and u_k for a wide range of conditions. For different particles fluidized by air under atmospheric conditions in a 0.152-m-diameter column and a 0.051 m by 0.51 m two-dimensional column, Yerushalmi & Cankurt (1979) obtained results that are correlated by

$$u_c = 3.0 \sqrt{\rho_S \bar{d}_S} - 0.17 \qquad [8.1.89]$$

$$u_k = 7.0 \sqrt{\rho_S \bar{d}_S} - 0.77 \qquad [8.1.90]$$

where u_c and u_k are in meters per second and $\rho_S \bar{d}_S$ is in kilograms per square meter. The range of $\rho_S \bar{d}_S$ values covered was 0.05–0.7 kg/m^2. The values of u_c/v_T and u_k/v_T, where v_T is the terminal velocity based on $\bar{d}_S$, exceeded 10 for fine particles, decreasing monotonically to order unity. Results of Staub & Canada (1978) show that $u_k/u_T \approx 0.65$ for 650-μm glass beads and ≈ 0.35 for 2.6-mm beads, these values being affected little by changes in system pressure. There are indications (Thiel & Potter 1977) that the transition velocity decreases with increasing bed diameter. When tube banks are present, local turbulent regions can occur in areas of high gas velocity (reduced cross-sectional area) even if bubbling is occurring throughout the major portion of the column.

Because many industrial fluidized beds run at high superficial gas velocities, there is no doubt that the turbulent regime is of great practical importance. However, there has been a predominance of work at low velocities in small columns, so that this regime has been studied only recently, and quantitative results are limited to measurements of bed voidage and heat transfer (Staub & Canada 1978) and gas back mixing (Cankurt & Yerushalmi 1978).

8.1.15 FAST FLUIDIZATION REGIME

If the superficial gas velocity is increased even further, there is a sharp increase in the amount of particle carry-over until a superficial velocity, designated the *transport velocity* u_{tr}, is achieved. At this velocity the column is quickly emptied of particles unless particles are recirculated or added continuously at a low level. The regime encountered for $u > u_{tr}$ depends on the rate of particle addition. For low rates, dilute pneumatic vertical conveying results. For high rates, a regime is encountered that is called *fast fluidization*.

A fast fluidized bed has been described (Yerushalmi et al. 1976) as a dense entrained suspension characterized by an aggregative state in which much of the solid is, at any given moment, segregated in relatively large, densely packed strands and clusters (figure 8.1.5). These clusters are essential to an understanding of the regime. Their formation has been explained (Grace & Tuot 1979) on the basis of stability considerations, analogous to those used to explain the origin of bubbles in low-voidage, low-velocity fluidized systems (see section 8.1.5). Most clusters tend to move downward, especially those near the walls of the column, while some single particles are dispersed in the continuous gas phase surrounding the clusters and are carried up rapidly. The overall bed voidage in this regime is generally in the range 0.75–0.95, with the actual value, as well as the pressure drop across the bed, depending both on net solids flux and on the superficial gas velocity.

Results obtained to date do not allow correlation of u_{tr}. They do indicate that u_{tr}, like u_c and u_k, increases with increasing ρ_S and $\bar{d}_S$. Typical values (Yerushalmi & Cankurt 1979) are 1.5 m/s for silica-alumina cracking catalyst ($\bar{d}_S = 49$ μm, $\rho_S = 1070$ kg/m^3) and 3.7–4 m/s for hydrated alumina particles ($\bar{d}_S = 103$ μm, $\rho_S = 2460$ kg/m^3). Although there appears to be no reason why a fast fluidization regime should not occur for coarse particles, practical difficulties in recirculating sufficient solids have restricted study of this regime to fine solids.

Few quantitative measurements are available for this regime. Yerushalmi et al. (1978a) made some estimates of typical cluster dimensions. Relative velocities between clusters and gas are typically an order of magnitude greater than the terminal settling velocity of individual particles. Solids back mixing is substantial, whereas very little gas back mixing occurs. Advantages claimed for high-velocity fluidized beds (Yerushalmi & Cankurt 1978) are intimate gas-solid contacting, high throughputs, and ability to handle cohesive solids.

8.1.16 SPOUTED BEDS

An alternative means of contacting a fluid with solid particles is the spouted bed (see section 8.5.6). The primary difference between a spouted bed and a fluidized bed is that the incoming fluid, gas or liquid, enters as a jet through a single, centrally located orifice in the former, whereas the incoming fluid is distributed more or less uniformly across the cross section of a fluidized bed. Other differences are likely to be as follows:

1. Particles used in spouted-bed applications tend to be larger. The mean particle size is almost always 1 mm or more, whereas in fluidized beds it is not uncommon to find mean particle sizes as small as 50 or 60 μm.
2. Fluidized beds are usually contained within nontapered containing vessels, although tapering is sometimes used in the freeboard or entry region. Spouted beds are almost always contained within vessels that are tapered over part or all of their height.

3. Fluidized-bed columns may have diameters of a few centimeters to tens of meters. The range of diameters used in practice for spouted beds is much narrower, approximately 0.1–1 m.
4. Fluidized beds commonly contain heat transfer tubes and/or other immersed surfaces. It is uncommon for spouted beds to contain tubes or other fixed immersed objects, although deflecting baffles may be placed in the freeboard.
5. The height-to-diameter ratio of fluidized beds can vary over a broad range from much less than 1 to much more than 1. For spouted beds, the height-to-diameter ratio is almost always in the range 1–5.

A schematic diagram of a spouted bed is given in figure 8.1.21. The three principal regions of the bed are the *spout*, a jet of fluid containing widely dispersed solids that penetrate the surface of the bed of particles; the *annulus*, the surrounding region containing the vast majority of the particles as well as interstitial fluid; and the *fountain*, the region above the bed proper in which particles entrained in the spout are disengaged and fall back onto the surface of the bed. The vessel geometry shown is the most common one. The cone angle should exceed the angle of repose for the material in order to keep all solids in motion and avoid dead regions. Other geometries that are sometimes used are shown in figure 8.1.22. For

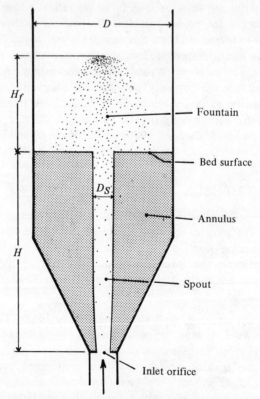

Figure 8.1.21 Principal regions and identification of dimensions for a spouted bed.

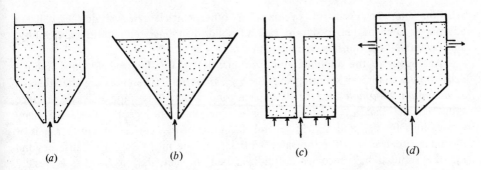

Figure 8.1.22 Column geometries for spouted beds: (*a*) conical lower section, cylindrical upper section; (*b*) conical vessel; (*c*) cylindrical vessel; (*d*) side-outlet column.

the cylindrical vessel shown in figure 8.1.22*c,* fluid may enter in smaller quantities distributed across the base plate in addition to the major flow through the central orifice. This case, somewhere between a fluidized and a spouted bed, is called a *spout-fluid bed.* The side-outlet spouted bed shown in figure 8.1.22*d* is a recent development pioneered by Hattori & Takeda (1976), which is said to give more favorable gas-solid contacting. With smaller particles, a central draft tube is then required to establish spouting (Hattori & Takeda 1978).

In addition to these axisymmetric geometries, experimental studies are often conducted in *half-columns,* where a vertical flat transparent plate forms one containing wall, giving a half-moon-shaped cross section, so that the spout can be viewed clearly. Comparative results between half-columns and corresponding full columns have shown that differences in behavior are relatively minor (Mathur & Epstein 1974).

Although spouted beds can operate with either a gas or a liquid as the spouting fluid, applications and studies with gases are much more common, and only this case is dealt with here. For an extensive review of spouted beds, see Mathur & Epstein (1974). Advantages and disadvantages of spouted beds, compared with fluidized beds, are as follows.

Advantages:
1. More predictable and reproducible solids and gas flow patterns
2. Good particle circulation at lower gas flow rates
3. Lower pressure drops for a given bed depth
4. Easier grid design

Disadvantages:
1. Lower bed-to-wall or bed-to-surface heat transfer rates
2. More limited throughput of gas
3. Generally not viable on as large a scale
4. Somewhat narrower particle size distribution usually required.

Both fluidized and spouted beds share the disadvantage, compared with packed beds, of having two phases with gas-solid contacting much more favorable in one than in the other. Both have the disadvantages, compared with packed beds, of attrition and the need for cyclones or other particle removal devices. Shared advantages over packed beds are ease of solids handling, temperature uniformity, and favorable heat transfer characteristics.

Analogous to the minimum fluidization velocity for fluidized systems, spouted beds show a minimum spouting velocity u_{ms}. Important differences are that there is a *maximum spoutable bed depth* L_m beyond which it is impossible to produce spouting, and that u_{ms}, unlike u_{mf}, is a function of bed depth. There are many correlations for u_{ms} and L_m. In general, the value of u_{ms} corresponding to L_m is of the same order as u_{mf} for the same particles, as one might expect because beyond L_m the spouted bed becomes a fluidized bed. In fact, u_{ms} at $L = L_m$ is usually somewhat greater than u_{mf}, with the ratio u_{ms}/u_{mf} at $L = L_m$ for columns 0.15–0.61 m in diameter falling in the range 1.0–1.5 (Mathur & Epstein 1974). For $L < L_m$ the most useful correlation for u_{ms} is that according to Mathur & Gishler (1955):

$$u_{ms} = \frac{\bar{d}_S}{D} \left(\frac{d_{or}}{D}\right)^{1/3} \left[\frac{2gL\left(\rho_S - \rho_F\right)}{\rho_F}\right]^{1/2} \qquad [8.1.91]$$

where $\bar{d}_S$ should be calculated from [8.1.7], as for fluidized systems.

The maximum spoutable bed depth increases with particle size for $\bar{d}_S \lesssim 1$ mm, where termination of the spout is caused by formation of a bubble, and then decreases with $\bar{d}_S$ for coarser solids. In the latter case, the mechanism of termination appears to be fluidization of the material in the annulus. Littman et al. (1978) correlated L_m for the more important coarse-particle case by means of

$$\frac{L_m}{D} = \frac{D}{d_{or}} \left[0.218 + \frac{0.005\left(\rho_S - \rho_F\right)gd_{or}}{\rho_F v_T u_{mf}}\right] \qquad [8.1.92]$$

where v_T is the terminal velocity corresponding to $\bar{d}_S$. A corresponding mean value of the spout diameter D_s can then be calculated from their equation

$$\frac{L_m D_s}{D^2 - D_s^2} = 0.345 \left(\frac{D}{D_s}\right)^{0.384} \qquad [8.1.93]$$

The pressure drop across a spouted bed is always less than the pressure drop across a fluidized bed of the same material and the same height. An expression for the pressure drop that takes into account the flow regime in the annulus (Epstein & Levine 1978) is

$$\Delta p = \left(\rho_S - \rho_F\right)gL_m\left(1 - \epsilon_{mf}\right)f\left(\Gamma, L^+\right) \qquad [8.1.94]$$

where

$$f\left(\Gamma, L^+\right) = \frac{1}{2\Gamma - 1}\left\{2(\Gamma - 2)L^+\left[1.5 - L^+ + \frac{1}{4}(L^+)^2\right]\right.$$

$$\left. + 3(L^+)^2\left[3 - 4.5L^+ + 3(L^+)^2 - (L^+)^3 + 0.143(L^+)^4\right]\right\} \qquad [8.1.95]$$

$$L^+ = \frac{L}{L_m}$$

and
$$\Gamma = 2 + 129 \frac{1 - \epsilon_{mf}}{Re_{mf}} \qquad [8.1.96]$$

The function $f(\Gamma, L^+)$ with $L^+ = 1$ goes to the limits 0.75 and 0.643 for small and large values of Re_{mf}, corresponding to the Darcy regime and the inviscid regime, respectively. Radial pressure gradients are small except near the gas inlet.

The division of gas between the spout and the annulus is given by a relationship modified from an equation derived by Mamuro & Hattori (1968):

$$u_a = u_{aLm} \left[1 - \left(1 - \frac{z}{L_m} \right)^3 \right] \qquad [8.1.97]$$

Here u_a is the superficial gas velocity in the annulus at any height z. For beds operating at about 10% in excess of u_{ms}, u_{aLm}/u_{mf} is approximately 0.9. This ratio appears to decrease as the superficial gas velocity u increases (Epstein et al. 1978), presumably because of increased downward movement of solids in the annulus to compensate for increased entrainment of solids in the spout. Note that [8.1.97] applies even when $L < L_m$. Although Darcy's law was used in the derivation leading to [8.1.97], the result is remarkably insensitive to an assumption of non-Darcy flow (Epstein & Levine 1978).

The voidage in the annulus remains constant at a value very close to the minimum fluidization voidage, typically 0.40-0.45. In the spout the voidage decreases from 1.0 at the inlet and may be as low as about 0.6 at $z = L_m$ (Lim 1975). The velocity profile of a particle in the spout is approximately parabolic. Particles are at first accelerated by the gas from the orifice, and then they decelerate in the upper regions. Lim & Mathur (1978) present a model that gives reasonable predictions of spout voidage and velocity in the upper regions. In the annulus, solids tend to move downward and inward along well-defined paths. The total fountain height is given (Grace & Mathur 1978) by

$$L_f = \epsilon_{sL}^{1.46} \frac{v_{soL}^2}{2g} \frac{\rho_S}{\rho_S - \rho_F} \qquad [8.1.98]$$

where ϵ_{sL} and v_{soL} are the spout voidage and the centerline particle velocity, respectively at $z = L$. Particles typically spend 95% of the time in the annulus and the remainder in the spout and fountain (Robinson & Waldie 1978).

Segregation of particles can occur for spouted beds as for fluidized beds (Piccinini et al. 1977). Segregation is less pronounced as the gas flow rate is increased. Larger and denser particles usually tend to congregate at the upper inside part of the annulus. Segregation can occur because of interparticle percolation in the annulus, aerodynamic segregation in the fountain, and rolling motion along the free surface (Cook & Bridgwater 1978). The residence time distribution of solids in continuous spouted-bed operations can deviate significantly from perfect mixing, especially if the geometry is such that there are dead regions.

Gas mixing in spouted beds can be explained bearing in mind the two-phase nature of these systems. Plug flow can be assumed in the spout, and greatest accuracy is achieved (Lim & Mathur 1976) if gas in the annulus is assumed to follow streamlines that fan outward from the spout boundary and terminate at the bed surface. Fitted streamwise dispersion coefficients are small enough that for most purposes it is reasonable to assume plug flow along these curved streamlines.

Mathur & Epstein (1974) give a number of practical hints regarding the design of spouted beds. The ratio d_{or}/D should not exceed about $\frac{1}{3}$. A screen mesh should cover the inlet orifice to prevent loss of solids. The minimum diameter suggested for pilot plant units is 0.15 m. As for fluidized beds, cyclones are generally required for solids recovery. Baffles may be used in the freeboard to deflect the fountain, but they should generally be avoided in the bed proper.

8.1.17 COCURRENT THREE-PHASE FLUIDIZATION

Three-phase fluidization refers to cases where a gas and a liquid are simultaneously brought into contact with solid particles. Contrary to three-phase slurry operation, three-phase fluidization is restricted to cases where there is both net flow of liquid and significant relative velocity between the liquid and the solids. Although three-phase fluidization could be applied where two immiscible liquids are contacted with solid particles, this case does not appear to have received attention.

When gas is introduced into a liquid-fluidized bed through an orifice or orifices, gas bubbles tend to form. The bubbles, their shape, and their rise velocity are very similar to what occurs when gas is bubbled into a viscous liquid (Ostergaard 1971; Darton & Harrison 1974b). The effective viscosity of the "continuous" (liquid-solid) phase is then of order 0.2–2 N s/m². However, the wake composition may differ considerably from the remainder of the continuous phase. In particular, the wake tends to contain relatively few solids and may even be free of solids. Shed vortices may also be composed entirely or largely of liquid (Rigby & Capes 1970). As discussed below, these wakes play a significant role in determining the expansion characteristics of three-phase fluidized beds.

Two fundamentally different approaches to three-phase fluidization have been followed. The first is in terms of purely empirical correlations; the second is to consider a system of equations relating velocities and voidages in the bubble, wake, and outer fluidized region, thereby restricting empirical parameters to a minimum. Neither approach has led to generally accepted results. The completely empirical approach is complicated by the large number of properties involved—physical properties of each of the three phases, particle properties, bed dimensions and geometry, and operating flow rates of both gas and liquid. Even the wettability of the solids by the liquid has been shown to have a significant effect (Bhatia et al. 1972; Armstrong et al. 1976).

Begovich & Watson (1978) have used a broader data base than other workers, so their correlations should have greater general validity. The minimum fluidization velocity for the liquid was correlated by

$$\text{Re}_{Lmf} = \frac{\rho_L \bar{d}_S u_{Lmf}}{\mu_L} = 0.00512 \left[\frac{\rho_L (\rho_S - \rho_L) g \bar{d}_S^3}{\mu_L^2} \right]^{0.66} \left(\frac{g \bar{d}_S}{u_G^2} \right)^{0.12} \qquad [8.1.99]$$

This equation is not valid as $u_G \to 0$, and the authors proposed an alternative form that was less satisfactory overall but had the correct limit as $u_G \to 0$. The overall void fraction was correlated, on the basis of 2381 data points, by a dimensional correlation

$$\epsilon = 3.93 \frac{u_L^{0.271} u_G^{0.041} \mu_L^{0.055}}{(\rho_S - \rho_L)^{0.316} D^{0.033} \bar{d}_S^{0.268}}$$ [8.1.100]

A corresponding correlation based on 913 points was given for the gas holdup:

$$\epsilon_G = 1.61 \frac{u_G^{0.72} \bar{d}_S^{0.168}}{D^{0.125}}$$ [8.1.101]

A good estimate for the pressure drop is obtained from

$$\Delta p = [\rho_S(1 - \epsilon) + \rho_L(\epsilon - \epsilon_G) + \rho_G \epsilon_G] gL$$ [8.1.102]

The expanded bed height is given by

$$L = \frac{M_S}{(\pi/4)D^2(1 - \epsilon)\rho_S}$$ [8.1.103]

where M_S is the mass of solid particles in the column.

In the theoretical approach, the bed is divided into three regions corresponding to bubbles, their wakes, and the remainder, which we may call the emulsion. These regions are shown schematically in figure 8.1.23. The volume fractions occupied by these three regions must obey

$$\epsilon_b + \epsilon_W + \epsilon_e = 1$$ [8.1.104]

The bubbles are assumed to consist solely of gas, whereas the wake and emulsion generally contain liquid and solids but no gas. Therefore, the volume fractions occupied by the three phases are such that

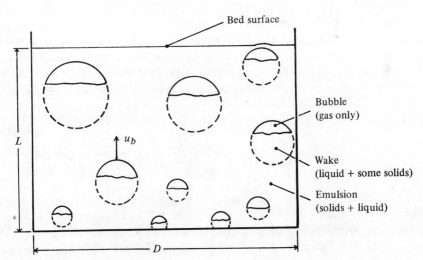

Figure 8.1.23 Principal regions of cocurrent three-phase fluidized beds.

$$\epsilon_G = \epsilon_b \tag{8.1.105}$$

$$\epsilon_L = \epsilon_W (1 - \epsilon_{SW}) + \epsilon_e (1 - \epsilon_{Se}) \tag{8.1.106}$$

$$1 - \epsilon_G - \epsilon_L = \epsilon_S = \frac{M_S}{\rho_S (\pi/4) D^2 L} = \epsilon_W \epsilon_{SW} + \epsilon_e \epsilon_{Se} \tag{8.1.107}$$

where ϵ_{SW} and ϵ_{Se} are the fractional volumes occupied by solids in the wake and emulsion regions, respectively. The mean bubble velocity is related to the superficial gas velocity by

$$\bar{u}_b = \frac{u_G}{\epsilon_G} \tag{8.1.108}$$

The wake regions are assumed to travel upward at the same velocity as the bubbles with vortex shedding neglected. Hence there is a net upward flux of solids in the wakes of $\epsilon_W \bar{u}_b \epsilon_{SW}$. To compensate for this, there must be an equal downward flux of solids in the emulsion region, so that the mean velocity of solids in the emulsion is

$$v_e = - \frac{\epsilon_W \bar{u}_b \epsilon_{SW}}{\epsilon_e \epsilon_{Se}} \tag{8.1.109}$$

The liquid is distributed between the wake, traveling upward at velocity $\bar{u}_b$, and the emulsion, where its velocity relative to the solids is designated u_{LS}. Hence

$$u_L = \epsilon_W \bar{u}_b (1 - \epsilon_{SW}) + (v_e + u_{LS}) \epsilon_e (1 - \epsilon_{Se}) \tag{8.1.110}$$

The relative velocity between liquid and solids in the emulsion region can be related to the volume fraction of liquid by using a Richardson & Zaki type relationship, as discussed in section 8.1.4; i.e.,

$$u_{LS} = u_i (1 - \epsilon_{Se})^{n-1} \tag{8.1.111}$$

where n and u_i are given by [8.1.15]-[8.1.21].

To complete the analysis, different assumptions are made by different workers assuming or correlating the ratios $\delta_W = \epsilon_W/\epsilon_b$ and $\epsilon_{SW}/\epsilon_{Se}$. In particular, a number of workers have assumed the latter ratio to be either 0 or 1. El-Temtamy & Epstein (1978) review the assumptions and suggest a procedure for estimating these two ratios. One begins by disregarding the gas and calculating the density and viscosity of the resulting liquid-solid fluidized bed:

$$\rho_0 = \rho_L \epsilon_0 + \rho_S (1 - \epsilon_0) \tag{8.1.112}$$

$$\mu_0 = 4540 \frac{\mu_L^{7/3} \rho_S^{1/2} u_L}{\rho_L^{4/3} \bar{d}_S \epsilon_0} e^{3.75/\epsilon_0} \tag{8.1.113}$$

where the subscript 0 denotes the absence of gas and the corresponding bed voidage ϵ_0 can be calculated as discussed in section 8.1.4. Equation [8.1.113] is a semiempirical correlation suggested by Hetzler & Williams (1969). One then calculates the effective kinematic viscosity μ_0/ρ_0. The ratio of $(\epsilon_W/\epsilon_b)'$ for single bubbles is then calculated, using two-dimensional experimental results obtained by

Table 8.1.6 Values of $(\epsilon_W/\epsilon_B)'$ Inferred from Shapes
of Single Gas Bubbles in Two-dimensional Liquid Columns[a]

Kinematic viscosity μ_L/ρ_L (m² /s)	Wake angle θ_W (deg)	$(\epsilon_W/\epsilon_B)'$ inferred from sphere completion
7.6×10^{-7}	51	10.1
1.0×10^{-6}	54	8.1
5.0×10^{-5}	64.5	4.1
1.4×10^{-4}	80	1.7

[a]Henriksen & Ostergaard (1974a).

Henriksen & Ostergaard (1974a), given in table 8.1.6. The wake is assumed to complete the sphere of which the bubble forms the cap. The wake fraction for the swarm of bubbles is then calculated from experimental results for liquid drops,

$$\frac{\epsilon_W}{\epsilon_b} = \left(\frac{\epsilon_W}{\epsilon_b}\right)' e^{-5.08\,\epsilon_b} \qquad [8.1.114]$$

Finally, experimental results lead to the following correlation (El-Temtamy & Epstein 1978) for the holdup of solids in the wakes:

$$\frac{\epsilon_{SW}}{\epsilon_{Se}} = 1 - 0.877 \frac{v_T}{\bar{u}_b - u_L/\epsilon_L} \qquad [8.1.115]$$

where v_T refers to the terminal velocity of particles in the liquid (in the absence of gas and other particles). The above correlation is consistent with the observation that wakes tend to be essentially free of particles when the particles are large, whereas there is a substantial holdup of solids in the wake for fine-particle systems.

Wakes also play a significant role in determining entrainment of solids into the freeboard above three-phase fluidized beds. Experimental results of Page & Harrison (1973) show that entrainment decreases with increasing particle size as well as with decreasing bubble volume and frequency. A horizontal coarse wire mesh placed across the freeboard was shown to be effective in disengaging entrained solids.

One of the interesting features of gas-liquid-solid fluidized systems is that the bed may either expand or contract when gas is introduced into an expanded liquid-solid fluidized bed. When contraction occurs, it is linked to the wake behavior in the sense that if the wake contains few particles, solids-free liquid is carried up quickly in the wake region, leaving less liquid to support the solids in the emulsion (Stewart & Davidson 1964). Epstein & Nicks (1976) showed that bed contraction occurs if

$$\psi_{3\phi} = \left(\frac{n}{n-1} + \frac{\epsilon_W}{\epsilon_b}\right)\frac{u_L}{\epsilon_L} - \left(1 + \frac{\epsilon_W}{\epsilon_b}\right)u_L - \frac{u_{LS}\epsilon_W}{\epsilon_b(n-1)} \qquad [8.1.116]$$

is negative, whereas expansion occurs if it is positive. Here n is the Richardson & Zaki (1954) exponent.

There are no correlations for bubble sizes in three-phase systems. Page & Harrison (1972) measured the size distribution of bubbles emerging from the surface of a three-phase system and showed that both bubble coalescence and splitting processes are important, as in two-phase systems. The gas distributor type seemed to have little effect after a short height. Bubble size decreased as the liquid flow rate increased, whereas there was little effect of gas flow rate beyond a certain level. Darton & Harrison (1974a) found bubble size distributions to be log-normal in a three-dimensional column, with mean bubble volumes ranging from 80 to 8000 mm^3 when u_G varied between 1.2 and 16.5 mm/s. Kim et al. (1977) also found bubble sizes to be normally distributed in a two-dimensional column. Bubble splitting in three-phase systems appears to depend on Rayleigh-Taylor instability as for two-phase systems (Henriksen & Ostergaard 1974b). Lee et al. (1974) proposed a critical Weber number as a criterion for bubble stability on impact by a particle. No breakup is said to occur for

$$\frac{\rho_S u_b^2 \bar{d}_S}{\sigma} \leqslant 3 \qquad [8.1.117]$$

This is consistent with the observation by a number of workers that bubbles tend to be smaller and more uniform in coarse-particle systems than in fine-particle systems. A result of this tendency is that gas holdup is higher for coarse-particle beds than for fine-particle systems (Ostergaard 1971).

Darton & Harrison (1974b) measured the rising velocity u_b for single bubbles in water-fluidized beds of 500-μm and 1-mm sand particles. The rising velocity relative to the fluidizing liquid was fitted to a relationship that gives u_b for bubbles in viscous liquids:

$$\text{Re}_b = \frac{\rho_0 d_e u_b}{\mu_0} = 3\left(\sqrt{1 + \frac{\text{Ar}_b}{18}} - 1\right) \qquad [8.1.118]$$

where $d_e = (6V_{bV}/\pi)^{1/3}$ is the bubble volume equivalent diameter, $\text{Ar}_b = g\rho_0^2 d_e^3/\mu_0^2$, and ρ_0 and μ_0 are the bed density and effective bed viscosity in the absence of gas, as discussed above. Values of μ_0 inferred in this manner ranged from 0.2 to 2.2 N s/m^2.

Gas and liquid mixing in three-phase systems has been reviewed by Ostergaard (1971). Because of the broader distribution of bubble sizes associated with fine-particle systems, axial gas dispersion tends to be more significant for fine particles than for coarse particles. Axial mixing of liquid is often represented well by an axially dispersed plug flow model, but probably not in cases where large solids-free wakes are carried upward by the bubbles.

8.1.18 COUNTERCURRENT THREE–PHASE FLUIDIZATION

A three-phase system that has had some application for scrubbing and absorption in the pulp and paper and metallurgical industries consists of a bed of light spheres, often hollow polyethylene or polypropylene spheres, on which gas in up flow contacts liquid in down flow. The particles themselves are inert and stay in the column, confined between lower and upper screens or perforated supports. Their sole purpose is to promote intimate contact between the gas and liquid phases. These devices have been variously labeled floating bed wet scrubbers, turbulent contact absorbers, and mobile bed contactors (see section 9.2.2).

Study of these systems is made difficult by the many equipment and property variables. There has been a limited amount of experimental work, virtually all of it confined to air, water, and spherical particles.

O'Neill et al. (1972) pointed out that there are two different modes of operation for beds of this type. If the particles are very light, $\rho_S \lesssim 300$ kg/m^3, a pressure gradient across the particles sufficient to support their weight is achieved without flooding. However, for $300 \lesssim \rho_S \lesssim 1300$ kg/m^3, fluidization occurs by incipient flooding, and an increase in gas flow causes the bed to expand further with incipient flooding maintained. Above a solids density of about 1300 kg/m^3, fluidization is impossible, flooding occurring while the particles remain fixed because the pressure drop at flooding is insufficient to support the weight of the packings.

Many experimental studies for countercurrent three-phase systems have employed large d_S/D ratios. Uysal (1978) used small d_S/D ratios and grid free cross-sectional areas more characteristic of industrial systems, so his correlations are generally preferred for the nonflooding case. The mass flow density of gas for minimum fluidization, defined as the point at which solids movement commences, was correlated by

$$\dot{m}_{Gmf} = 10.9 \ d_S^{0.49} 10^{-0.20\dot{m}_L} \qquad [8.1.119]$$

The mean bed expansion was found to follow

$$\bar{L} = L_0 + 0.147 \ (\dot{m}_G - \dot{m}_{Gmf}) \qquad [8.1.120]$$

over a considerable range. At a certain gas flow, depending on the liquid flow density, $\bar{L}$ began to increase more rapidly with gas flow than is given by [8.1.120] because of increased holdup of liquid. The amplitude of fluctuations of the upper bed surface also increased with increasing gas flow.

For $\dot{m}_L \leqslant 25$ kg/m^2 s, Uysal correlated the pressure drop by

$$\Delta p = 112 \ \dot{m}_L^{0.44} \frac{L_0}{d_S^{0.49}} \qquad [8.1.121]$$

whereas the mean liquid holdup was found to follow

$$\bar{\epsilon}_L = 1.15 \times 10^{-4} \ \frac{\dot{m}_L^{0.83}}{d_S^{1.29}} \qquad [8.1.122]$$

Note that liquid holdup is independent of gas flow, a result obtained earlier by Chen & Douglas (1968). The gas holdup may be calculated by difference from the relationships above, using

$$\bar{\epsilon}_G = 1 - \bar{\epsilon}_L - \frac{M_S}{\rho_S(\pi/4)D_L^2} \qquad [8.1.123]$$

where M_S is the mass of solid particles present. Axial mixing of both liquid and gas is intermediate between plug flow and perfect mixing conditions.

For fluidization in the incipient flooding regime, O'Neill et al. (1974) applied a correlation derived for flooding in packed towers to obtain a correlation for minimum fluidization. For spherical packings:

$$u_{Gmf} = \left(\frac{\rho_L}{\rho_G}\right)^{0.5} [0.35(gd_S)^{0.25} - u_L^{0.5}]^2 \qquad [8.1.124]$$

Procedures were also proposed for calculating the bed expansion and bed pressure drop.

Superficial gas velocities for countercurrent three-phase contacting are generally in the range 2–8 m/s, whereas the liquid flow rate is typically 5–15 kg/m² s. The height of the compartment in which the particles can expand should be about five times the settled bed height. In a typical industrial unit about 70% of the lower supporting grid is free area.

8.2 Fluidized-Bed Heat Transfer

John R. Grace

One of the most attractive features of a fluidized bed is the favorable rate of heat transfer to or from immersed heat transfer surfaces. Also attractive, for many processes, is the fact that temperature uniformity is generally excellent so that "hot spots" are avoided. Previous reviews of heat transfer in fluidized beds have been prepared by Barker (1965), Zabrodsky (1966), Kunii & Levenspiel (1969), Gelperin & Einstein (1971), Gutfinger & Abuaf (1974), Botterill (1975), and Saxena et al. (1978).

8.2.1 GAS-TO-PARTICLE HEAT TRANSFER

A number of workers have reported gas-to-particle heat transfer results in terms of heat transfer coefficients written as if the fluidized bed behaved as a single-phase system. If plug flow is assumed, a log mean temperature difference is appropriate and the heat transfer coefficient is based on the surface area of the particles:

$$\alpha_{GS} = \frac{\rho_G C_{pG} u}{L a_S} \ln \left[\frac{(T_G)_{\text{in}} - T_S}{(T_G)_{\text{out}} - T_S} \right] \qquad [8.2.1]$$

where L is the expanded bed height, a_S is the surface area of solids per unit volume, u is the superficial gas velocity, ρ_G and C_{pG} are the density and specific heat of the gas, T_S is the temperature of the solid particles, and $(T_G)_{\text{in}}$ and $(T_G)_{\text{out}}$ are the inlet and outlet gas temperatures. If the bed is assumed to be perfectly mixed, then

$$\alpha_{GS} = \frac{\rho_G C_{pG} u}{L a_S} \frac{(T_G)_{\text{in}} - (T_G)_{\text{out}}}{(T_G)_{\text{out}} - T_S} \qquad [8.2.2]$$

Results reported in this manner have been summarized by Kunii & Levenspiel (1969). The resulting values of the Nusselt number tend to be much less than 2, the limiting value for single spheres in an unbounded stagnant fluid. This results from two factors:

1. In a packed bed, the Nusselt number for individual particles can be much less than 2 at a low Reynolds number (Kunii & Levenspiel 1969) because of shielding, clustering, and channeling effects. Presumably the same must be true in the dense phase of a fluidized bed of fine particles.
2. The controlling heat transfer resistance, especially for small particles, is generally that between the two phases—i.e., between the bubble phase and the dense phase or between the jet phase and the dense phase—not that between particles and interstitial gas.

In view of the second factor, it is essential to consider the two-phase nature of the bed. The approach is then analogous to that for gas-to-particle mass transfer in section 8.3. The analysis can be presented in a simple manner if some reasonable assumptions are adopted. The interstitial gas and particles in the dense phase are assumed to have the same temperature, as confirmed experimentally by Baeyens & Goosens (1973), with all the resistance to interphase heat transfer residing within the bubble phase and perfect mixing of solids assumed to occur. Bubbles are assumed to be free of solids. A pseudo-steady-state approach is adopted in view of the considerably greater heat capacity of the solids than of the gas; i.e., temperature changes of the solids during the passage of a bubble up the bed are ignored. We may further assume constant properties and neglect contributions from radiation and from transfer between the distribution plate and the bed.

With these assumptions, an energy balance for the bubble phase yields

$$\delta_b u \rho_G C_{pG} \frac{dT_b}{dz} = \frac{6\epsilon_b}{\bar{d}_b} \alpha_{bd}(T_S - T_b) \qquad [8.2.3]$$

where δ_b, which is expected to lie between $(u - u_{mf})/u$ and 1, is the fraction of the incoming gas that flows in the bubble phase including both visible and invisible components, as discussed in section 8.1.6. The bubble area per unit bed volume is approximated by $6\epsilon_b/\bar{d}_b$, and α_{bd} is the heat transfer coefficient for transfer between the bubbles and the dense phase. Integrating [8.2.3] from the inlet to the outlet:

$$T_{bL} = T_S + [(T_G)_{\text{in}} - T_S] \exp\left[-\frac{6\epsilon_b \alpha_{bd} L}{\delta_b u \rho_G C_{pG} \bar{d}_b}\right] \qquad [8.2.4]$$

A heat balance at the bed surface gives

$$(T_G)_{\text{out}} = (1 - \delta_b) T_S + \delta_b T_{bL} \qquad [8.2.5]$$

With this substitution, it can readily be shown that

$$\frac{(T_G)_{\text{out}} - T_S}{(T_G)_{\text{in}} - T_S} = \delta_b e^{-N_H} \qquad [8.2.6]$$

where N_H is a dimensionless interphase heat transfer group,

$$N_H = \frac{6\epsilon_b \alpha_{bd} L}{\delta_b u \rho_G C_{pG} \bar{d}_b} \qquad [8.2.7]$$

The group $\alpha_{bd}/\rho_G C_{pG}$ may be estimated for isolated bubbles from the analogous mass transfer analysis of Davidson & Harrison (1963) (see also [8.3.27], giving

$$\frac{\alpha_{bd}}{\rho_G C_{pG}} = \frac{3}{4} u_{mf} + 0.975 \ \frac{\kappa_G^{1/2} g^{1/4}}{\bar{d}_b^{1/4}} \qquad [8.2.8]$$

where $\kappa_G = \lambda_G/\rho_G C_{pG}$ is the thermal diffusivity. Barile et al. (1970) found reasonable agreement with this analysis for isolated bubbles. However, application of the model to representative data for freely fluidized beds (Harriott & Barnstone 1967; Barile et al. 1970) leads to much higher values of α_{bd}, indicating augmented heat transfer rates when bubbles are interacting, splitting, and coalescing.

Equation [8.2.6] shows that the rate at which the gas temperature approaches the solids temperature depends on the fraction of gas flowing in the dense phase and on the exchange of heat between the phases. For small particles, where u_{mf} is low, this transfer tends to be small (see [8.2.8]) so that the overall heat transfer coefficient defined by [8.2.1] or [8.2.2] can be low. For particles approaching 1 mm or larger, interphase transfer becomes much more rapid, so that resistance to transfer within the dense phase between the particles and interstitial gas plays an appreciable role and should not be neglected.

This simple theory is similar to earlier treatments by Kunii & Levenspiel (1968, 1969) and Davidson (1973). These workers showed that it is possible to fit data from early studies, in which no account was taken of the two-phase nature of fluidized beds, by such a model, although the bubble sizes required to fit the data were smaller than might be expected in view of the finding of higher interphase heat transfer rates for interacting bubbles than for isolated bubbles.

For cases where grid jets form (see section 8.1.7), the relevant interphase transfer step over the lower portion of the bed is that between the jet and the dense phase. Behie et al. (1975) measured heat transfer coefficients between 1760 and 7300 W/m² K for jet-to-dense-phase transfer in beds of cracking catalyst. Heertjes et al. (1953) also showed that significant transfer can take place between the gas and the distribution plate itself. Hoebink (1977) analyzed transfer at the grid by treating the plate as a packed bed and showed that very rapid temperature equalization can occur, even for thin plates. The simple analysis of Rowe (1967) may be applied to show that any residual temperature difference between particles and gas entering the dense phase diminishes rapidly because of the large particle surface area per unit volume and modest interstitial gas velocities.

As a result of these considerations and rapid solids mixing, the temperature is so uniform in most gas-fluidized beds that gas-to-particle heat transfer is a minor consideration. After the first 1–2 cm, temperature gradients can usually be neglected. Important exceptions can occur, however, when solids circulation is severely impeded (e.g., when large particles are used in combination with closely spaced heat transfer tubes) or when heat is generated internally (e.g., in electro-thermal fluid beds or with highly exothermic reactions).

8.2.2 PARTICLE–TO–PARTICLE HEAT TRANSFER

Occasionally, hot particles are blended with cold particles or quenched in a bed of cold particles. Particle-to-particle heat transfer is then important. In feeding particles at one temperature to a bed operated at a different temperature, or where some particles are undergoing reaction while others are not (as in coal combustion), it may also be important to estimate the time required for temperature equalization. Wen & Chang (1967) showed that particle-to-particle transfer through points of contact is negligible. Radiative transfer is also small if the bed temperature is less than about 600°C. The important mode of transport is conduction or convection via the fluidizing fluid, just as in the case of transfer between the particles and a fixed heat transfer surface, as discussed in section 8.2.3. The relative importance of radiative transfer is considered by Hill & Wilhelm (1959). Generally, particles are small enough and λ_S large enough that temperature gradients inside individual particles can be neglected in fluidized systems, but this assumption should always be verified by calculating the Biot and Fourier numbers for the case in question.

8.2.3 BED-TO-SURFACE HEAT TRANSFER—MECHANISMS

The heat transfer coefficient between a gas-fluidized bed and an immersed tube or containing wall is generally of order 300–600 W/m² K. This is nearly an order of magnitude more than the heat transfer coefficient for packed beds under corresponding conditions, and nearly two orders of magnitude more than the best transfer coefficient for a corresponding flow of the same gas through an empty vessel.

The heat transfer coefficient between the bed and a wall is made up of three components:

$$\alpha_{bw} = \alpha_{cond} + \alpha_{conv} + \alpha_{rad} \qquad [8.2.9]$$

The term α_{cond} is that arising from conduction through stagnant gas and particles during the time when particles are stationary at the wall; some workers (e.g., Denloye & Botterill 1977; Xavier & Davidson 1978) call this the particle convective transfer because the time-averaged value relies on frequent particle replacement; i.e., on convection by the particles after the transfer has taken place by conduction. For modest bed temperatures (e.g., less than about 1000°C) the conductive component dominates for small particles, whereas the convective component α_{conv} is rate-controlling for large particles. The radiative component α_{rad} becomes important at high temperatures. It is a common simplification to assume that the three components can be predicted separately and then simply added. This procedure should be used with caution when two or more of the components are of comparable magnitude.

8.2.3.1 Conductive Transfer

The favorable heat transfer coefficients between fixed surfaces and fluidized beds of fine particles result from high values of α_{cond}. Although a dry packed bed of particles acts as a good thermal insulator because of the small area of contact between adjacent particles, instantaneous rates can be high when particles at one temperature are suddenly exposed to a wall at a different temperature because of the high temperature driving force. Favorable time-averaged values of α_{cond} are associated with frequent exposure of fresh particles from the bulk to the heat transfer surface. For a constant wall temperature, the instantaneous heat transfer coefficient due to conduction for an infinite "packet" of particles with voidage ϵ_{mf} exposed at $t = 0$ (see figure 8.2.1a) is given (Mickley & Fairbanks 1955) by

$$\alpha_{cond} = \left[\frac{\rho_S \,(1 - \epsilon_{mf}) \, C_{pS} \lambda_{eff}}{\pi t} \right]^{1/2} \qquad [8.2.10]$$

where λ_{eff} is the effective dense phase thermal conductivity. The instantaneous heat transfer coefficient therefore decreases with time, but before an equilibrium temperature profile can be established, the packet of particles is replaced by a new

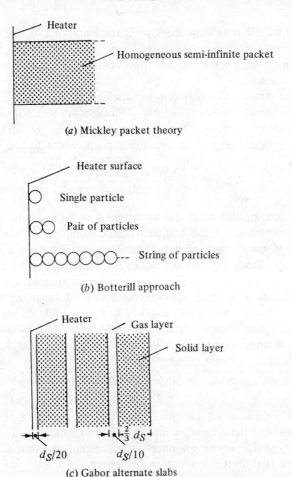

(a) Mickley packet theory

(b) Botterill approach

(c) Gabor alternate slabs

Figure 8.2.1 Schematic diagram showing basis for different bed-to-wall heat transfer models: (a) packet model proposed by Mickley & Fairbanks (1955), (b) single-particle and particle-string model employed by Botterill and co-workers, (c) alternate slabs of gas and solids used by Gabor (1970a).

one because of the passage of a bubble, and the process begins afresh. While a bubble is enveloping the heat transfer surface, the local instantaneous heat transfer rate falls off sharply. These changes in heat transfer associated with passing bubbles have been confirmed experimentally (Mickley et al. 1961; Tuot & Clift 1973; Baeyens & Goosens 1973; Kubie 1976; Bernis et al. 1977; Selzer & Thomson 1977).

The importance of the renewal frequency depends on the depth to which a significant change in the temperature profile penetrates during the residence of the packet at the wall. A characteristic thermal time for a single solid particle can be estimated (Glicksman & Decker 1980) as

$$t_S = \frac{\rho_S C_{pS} \bar{d}_S^2}{15\lambda_G}$$

[8.2.11]

If this time is much shorter than the typical residence time of packets at the wall (given approximately by the inverse of the local bubble frequency), then the packet renewal frequency plays an important role. This is generally the case for small particles, $\bar{d}_S \lesssim 1$ mm.

The original packet theory given by Mickley & Fairbanks (1955) leads to predictions of time-mean heat coefficients by integrating [8.2.10], including an age distribution function to account for different times spent by different packets of particles at the surface. For packets spending uniform time t_{packet} at the surface,

$$\bar{\alpha}_{\text{cond}} = 2 \left[\frac{\rho_S \left(1 - \epsilon_{mf}\right) C_{pS} \lambda_{\text{eff}}}{\pi t_{\text{packet}}} \right]^{1/2}$$

[8.2.12]

Other workers later modified the theory to account for constant heat flux rather than constant temperature at the wall, finite packet dimensions, contact resistances, and thin layers of gas in series with packets. Various packet age distributions have been assumed. See Gabor (1970a) and Selzer & Thomson (1977) for reviews of this work. Yoshida et al. (1969) compared the results for random and regular surface renewal of particles. The mean renewal frequency was assumed to be the local bubble frequency. Local transfer was assumed to be negligible during the fraction of the time when the heat transfer surface is covered by bubbles. Good agreement was obtained with the random renewal result

$$\bar{\alpha}_{\text{cond}} = (1 - \epsilon_b) \left[\frac{\rho_S \left(1 - \epsilon_{mf}\right) C_{pS} \lambda_{\text{eff}} \bar{f}_b}{1 - \epsilon_b} \right]^{1/2}$$

[8.2.13]

The mean bubble frequency $\bar{f}_b$ at the bubble volume fraction ϵ_b can be obtained from [8.1.51] and the iterative procedure described in section 8.1.6.

The packet model works reasonably well when the renewal frequency is sufficiently small that heat has a chance to penetrate a number of particle layers; i.e., when $t_S \ll 1/f_b$. Gabor (1970a) showed that the effective thermal conductivity of the dense phase moving past the heater should be taken as

$$\lambda_{\text{eff}} = \frac{0.9065}{0.13/\lambda_G + 0.667/\lambda_S}$$

[8.2.14]

Because $\lambda_G \ll \lambda_S$ for almost all gas-solid combinations, the thermal conductivity of the gas plays an important role, whereas the thermal conductivity of the solids is relatively unimportant. On the other hand, the volumetric heat capacity of the solids $\rho_S C_{pS}$ is an important property for the small particles under consideration.

An alternative theoretical approach, pursued primarily by Botterill and co-workers (Botterill et al. 1962, 1966, 1967; Botterill & Williams 1963), considers single particles, particle pairs, or strings of particles at one temperature exposed to a wall at another temperature at $t = 0$ (see figure 8.2.1b). The effective thermal conductivity in the packet model is replaced by a more precise geometric representation. Improved predictions are given when the residence time of particles at the wall is sufficiently short that penetration of heat involves only the first few layers of particles (i.e., t_S is of the same order as $1/\bar{f}_b$). However, it was necessary to add a thin gap of approximate thickness $d_S/10$ to reconcile the theory with experiments, which were carried out with a controlled renewal frequency by stirring. There is some experimental evidence for such gaps (Syromyatnikov 1974); they also compensate for failure of the model to account for noncontinuum effects in the thin gap separating particles and the wall near points of contact (Schlünder 1971). This approach shows the importance of particle size when renewal is rapid. Higher heat fluxes are obtained with smaller particles because of the reduction in path length through which heat must flow by conduction through the gas.

Gabor (1970a) showed that very similar results could be obtained with much less computational effort if a string of particles is replaced by alternate layers of gas and solids, with layer thicknesses as given in figure 8.2.1c. Experimental support for this simpler approach was obtained from a later study (Gabor 1972a). At large values of $t/\bar{d}_S^2$, this approach agrees closely with the packet theory if λ_{eff} is obtained from [8.2.14].

For large particles where $t_S \gg 1/\bar{f}_b$ (generally $\bar{d}_S > 1$ mm), a particle's temperature changes little during its residence at the wall. As a result, steady-state heat transfer can be assumed. From considerations of the gap and average conduction path length, Glicksman & Decker (1980) obtained a Nusselt number of 11.2 for this case. If it is assumed that transfer during coverage by bubbles is negligible, the corresponding conduction heat transfer coefficient for spherical particles is

$$\bar{\alpha}_{\text{cond}} = \frac{11.2\,(1 - \epsilon_b)\,\lambda_G}{\bar{d}_S} \qquad [8.2.15]$$

8.2.3.2 Convective Transfer

In addition to heat transferred by conduction through stagnant gas, transfer also occurs through mixing of gas percolating along the surface in the interstitial voids between the particles. Baskakov et al. (1974) correlated this component by

$$\frac{\bar{\alpha}_{\text{conv}}\bar{d}_S}{\lambda_G} = 0.009\ \text{Ar}^{0.5}\ \text{Pr}^{0.33} \qquad [8.2.16]$$

whereas Denloye & Botterill (1977) obtained a dimensional correlation:

$$\frac{\bar{\alpha}_{\text{conv}}\bar{d}_S^{0.5}}{\lambda_G} = 0.86\ \text{Ar}^{0.39} \qquad (10^3 < \text{Ar} < 2 \times 10^6) \qquad [8.2.17]$$

over an experimental range of operating conditions up to 1000 kPa. Both equations show that the convective component increases with particle size, in contrast to the conductive component.

Alternative approaches have been proposed by Xavier & Davidson (1978), based on the work of Gabor (1970b), who gave simple expressions for flat surfaces and cylindrical heaters, and by Glicksman & Decker (1980).

8.2.3.3 Radiative Transfer

Radiative transfer from fluidized beds is simplest for large particles, because their temperature does not vary appreciably during exposure to a hot or cold surface. Therefore, radiation can be predicted from the net flux between two isothermal planes. Because the bubbles can be considered transparent, no allowance needs to be made for the fraction of time during which bubbles are at the surface. By representing both the wall and the particle surface as gray bodies,

$$\bar{\alpha}_{rad} = \frac{\sigma(T_w^4 - T_S^4)}{[(1/\epsilon_w) + (1/\epsilon_{bed}) - 1]\,(T_w - T_S)} \qquad [8.2.18]$$

The effective bed emissivity ϵ_{bed} is greater than the particle emissivity ϵ_S because of multiple reflections. Results given by Botterill (1975), reproduced in table 8.2.1, suggest that

$$\epsilon_{bed} \approx 0.5(1 + \epsilon_S) \qquad [8.2.19]$$

For smaller particles the situation is more complex because the particle temperature changes during exposure, so that the frequency of renewal becomes important. Szekely & Fisher (1969) presented some calculations based on a simple model in which hot particles were exposed to a cold wall. They found that the importance of radiative transfer, relative to conductive transfer, increases with residence time at the wall as well as with increasing absolute temperature. Experimental results of Baskakov et al. (1973) are presented in figure 8.2.2, showing the fraction of heat transfer attributable to radiation. Note that the relative importance of radiation is greater for larger particles and at larger bed temperatures;

Table 8.2.1 Measured Emissivities of Typical Materials Used in High-Temperature Fluidized Beds[a]

Bed material	$\bar{d}_S$ (mm)	Particle shape	$\dfrac{u}{u_{mf}}$	Bed temperature (°C)	Particle emissivity ϵ_S	Bed emissivity ϵ_{bed}
Zirconium dioxide	0.25–1	Rounded	1.2–4.0	600–1150	0.23	0.59
Corundum	1.5–2	Rounded	1.2–3.0	800–1450	0.27	0.59
Chamotte	1–1.5	Irregular	1.2–3.0	450–1100	0.60	0.80
Sand	1–1.5	Rounded	1.2–3.0	500–1100	0.60	0.85
MgO-SiO$_2$ compound	1–1.5	Irregular	1.2–3.0	500–1200	–	0.95

[a]From tabulation of Botterill (1975).

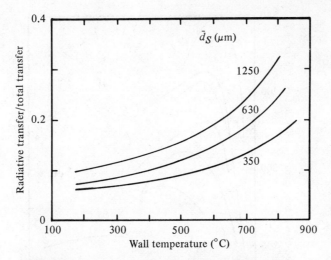

Figure 8.2.2 Fraction of total heat transfer resulting from radiation for three different sizes of chamotte particles as a function of wall temperature. Bed temperature was 850°C. Results are from Baskakov et al. (1973).

approximately 15-30% of the transfer is caused by radiation at a bed temperature of 800°C. Much lower ratios were found by Yoshida et al. (1974), using catalyst particles of mean size 180 μm.

8.2.3.4 Sensitivity to Different Variables

The dependence of bed-to-wall heat transfer on superficial gas flow rate and particle size is illustrated in figure 8.2.3. Note that as u increases, $\bar{\alpha}_{bw}$ tends to rise, pass through a maximum, and then fall. At low flow rates, the primary effect of increasing u is to improve the stirring action of bubbles so that the renewal frequency of fresh particles at the wall increases and heat transfer is improved. However, the fraction of time the heater surface is covered by bubbles also increases, and this eventually outweighs the renewal effect and leads to the decrease in $\bar{\alpha}_{bw}$. As particle size increases the effect of the renewal process becomes less important so that the maximum becomes less pronounced. The effect of particle size is shown further in figure 8.2.4, where the maximum bed-to-wall heat transfer coefficient α_{max} is plotted against particle size for two different types of particles. Over a broad range of particle sizes where conductive transfer is dominant, $\bar{\alpha}_{max}$ decreases with increasing $\bar{d}_S$. However, when $\bar{d}_S$ exceeds a certain value, typically in the range 1-3 mm, $\bar{\alpha}_{max}$ begins to increase again because the convective component has become dominant. The drop-off in heat transfer coefficient for very fine particles ($\sim$ 30 μm or smaller) is attributed to channeling and poor fluidization.

Because the dominant heat transfer mechanism differs for small and large particles, the significance of different physical properties and operating variables must also differ. For small particles, where conductive transfer is dominant, heat

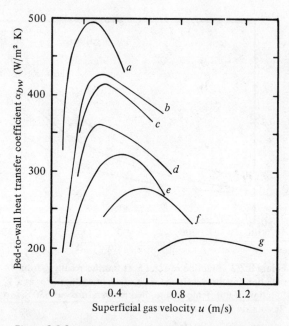

Figure 8.2.3   Bed-to-wall heat transfer coefficient plotted against superficial gas velocity for quartz sand particles of different mean size: (a) 140 μm, (b) 198 μm, (c) 216 μm, (d) 428 μm, (e) 515 μm, (f) 650 μm, (g) 1100 μm. Results are from Zabrodsky et al. (1978)

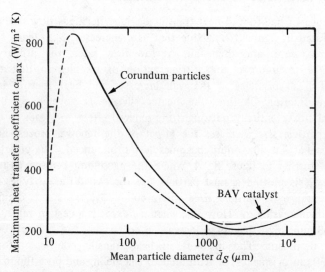

Figure 8.2.4   Effect of particle size on maximum bed-to-wall heat transfer coefficient for corundum and catalyst particles fluidized by air. Results are from Baskakov et al. (1973) and Zabrodsky et al. (1978).

transfer is strongly dependent on the thermal conductivity of the gas, so that improved fluxes can be achieved by using gases of high λ_G (e.g., hydrogen) or by increasing the operating temperature. Increasing the pressure has little effect, except insofar as alterations in bubbling patterns may alter the renewal frequency distribution. The volumetric heat capacity of the solids is also important for these particles. At high absolute temperatures, where radiation is important, bed emissivity also becomes a significant property.

For large particles, where the convective component is dominant, the situation is different. Pressure is an important variable, and increasing pressure improves heat transfer (see [8.2.16] and [8.2.17]). Radiation is more likely to be important for large particles, whereas the volumetric heat capacity of the solids ceases to play an important role.

8.2.3.5 Local Heat Transfer Variations around Immersed Tubes with Position and Time

Plots of local heat transfer coefficient versus angular position have been presented by a number of workers (e.g., Noack 1970; Gelperin & Einstein 1971; Berg & Baskakov 1974). At low gas velocities these traces show maxima near the equator, where bubbles tend to sweep past frequently. Minima occur on the underside, where a film of gas covers the surface, and at the top, where particles are seldom replaced and the tube supports a stagnant cap of particles. This is consistent with the local hydrodynamic conditions around a horizontal cylinder considered in section 8.1.11 and with the discussion of conductive transfer above. With increasing gas velocity, the position of the maximum moves around to the top of the cylinder (Baskakov et al. (1974) because of the regular dislodgement of particles there and the greater proportion of time the top surface is in contact with particles relative to the sides and bottom.

For vertical tubes, the local heat transfer coefficient tends to fall with increasing height (Selzer & Thomson 1977), but less rapidly than predicted by the Mickley packet theory if particle movement were purely parallel to the surface. This indicates that part of the solids motion is normal to the surface.

In addition to these spatial variations in heat transfer, there are temporal fluctuations associated with the arrival of bubbles and addition of fresh solids. The detailed fluctuations tend to be quite different for vertical tubes than for horizontal tubes (Selzer & Thomson 1977).

8.2.4 BED-TO-SURFACE HEAT TRANSFER— PREDICTIONS FOR SPECIFIC GEOMETRIES

The theories and mechanisms outlined in the previous section show the general features of bed-to-surface heat transfer in gas-fluidized beds and the importance of different variables. Despite the understanding that has been achieved, empirical and semiempirical correlations are still the most common means for predicting heat transfer rates. Gutfinger & Abuaf (1974) tabulate no fewer than 34 different correlations, and others have been added since their review. The predictions of different correlations commonly differ widely. It is important not to apply these correlations outside the ranges for which they were derived. Separate correlations are available for transfer to the external wall, to vertical tubes, and to horizontal tubes. Some correlations give the effect of superficial gas velocity, whereas others are for the maximum heat transfer coefficient only. The correlations presented below do not include the effect of radiation. Where radiation is important, it should be added as outlined in section 8.2.3. The correlations featured below are the best available at this time, but their accuracy should not be assumed to be better than ±50% within their ranges of application. Larger discrepancies must be expected when the correlations must be extrapolated to other conditions (Chen 1976). Since most correlations are based on data taken in small columns, application to large-scale equipment is risky.

8.2.4.1   Heat Transfer to the Containing Wall

The graphic correlation of Wender & Cooper (1958) for bed-to-external-wall transfer had the broadest data base, 429 points drawn from a number of investigations. The correlation is shown in figure 8.2.5 and the range of variables covered appears in table 8.2.2. Note the appearance of heater length in the correlation, consistent with movement of particles along the wall rather than simple renewal from the bulk by motion normal to the heater surface. In view of the comments in section 8.2.3, inclusion of ρ_G and C_{pG} in the correlation appears to be superfluous. Better results are commonly achieved by applying bed-to-vertical-tube transfer correlations given below, with a small downward correction (10–20%) in view of the observation that bed-to-external-wall transfer tends to be of the same order as, but somewhat lower than, bed-to-tube transfer. The same correlations may be used for vertical panel heaters as for external walls.

For particles much larger than those covered by these correlations, the predominant component of heat transfer becomes the convective component, so that the correlations given previously, e.g., [8.2.16], should be used.

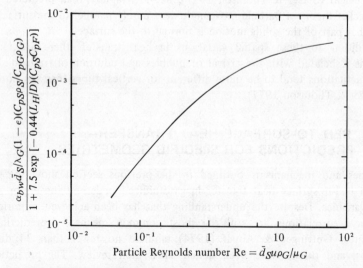

Figure 8.2.5   Correlation of bed-to-external-wall heat transfer given by Wender & Cooper (1958).

Table 8.2.2   Range of Variables Covered by the Correlations
of Wender & Cooper (1958)

Variable	Bed-to-external-surface correlation, (figure 8.2.5)	Bed-to-internal-surface correlation, [8.2.22]
$\bar{d}_S, \mu m$	50–850	40–880
ϵ (overall bed voidage)	0.43–0.95	0.40–0.96
D, m	0.025–0.13	0.08–1.9
L_H (heater length), m	0.04–1.0	0.10–5.5
C_{pS}, kJ/kg K	0.5–1.2	0.84–1.3
ρ_S, kg/m³	800–5300	800–2900
C_{pG}, kJ/kg K	0.96–5.2	0.5–5.2
ρ_G, kg/m³	0.1–3.0	0.18–7.8
λ_G, W/m K	0.028–0.19	0.010–0.066
μ_G, N s/m²	1.9×10^{-5}–2.9×10^{-5}	1.0×10^{-5}–3.8×10^{-5}

8.2.4.2 Vertical Tubes

The best-known correlation for heat transfer to vertical unfinned tubes is that
according to Vreedenburg (1960), who obtained

$$\frac{\bar{\alpha}_{bw} (D - d_T)}{\lambda_G} \left(\frac{d_T}{D}\right)^{1/3} \left(\frac{\lambda_G}{C_{pS}\mu_G}\right)^{1/2} = C \left[\frac{u(D - d_T)\rho_S}{\mu_G}\right]^n \qquad [8.2.20]$$

for fine, light particles; i.e., $\rho_S \bar{d}_S u/\mu_G < 2050$ where C and n are 2.7×10^{-16} and
3.4, respectively, for $\rho_S u(D - d_T)/\mu_G \leqslant 2.4 \times 10^5$, and 2.2 and 0.44, respectively,
for $\rho_S u(D - d_T)/\mu_G > 2.4 \times 10^5$. For coarse, heavy particles–i.e., $\rho_S \bar{d}_S u/\mu_G >$
2550–another equation was given:

$$\frac{\bar{\alpha}_{bw} (D - d_T)}{\lambda_G} \left[\frac{d_T \bar{d}_S \lambda_G}{D(D - d_T) C_{pS}\mu_G}\right]^{1/3} = C' \left[\frac{u(D - d_T)}{g^{1/2} \bar{d}_S^{3/2}}\right]^{n'} \qquad [8.2.21]$$

C' and n' were 1.05×10^{-4} and 2.0, respectively, for $u(D - d_T)/g^{1/2} \bar{d}_S^{3/2} < 1070$,
and 240 and 0.10, respectively, for $u(D - d_T)/g^{1/2} \bar{d}_S^{3/2} > 1070$. These two equations
strictly apply to a single tube positioned on the axis of a cylindrical column, but
they have been widely used for other cases, including banks of tubes. For single
tubes located at other radial positions, Vreedenburg (1952) found different heat
transfer results, presumably caused by nonuniform radial distributions of bubbles, as
discussed in section 8.1.6. Correction factors C_R may be applied to the above
correlations to account for nonaxial locations. Values of C_R are given in table 8.2.3.
Wender & Cooper (1958) drew a smooth curve through these few points.

A dimensional correlation obtained by Wender & Cooper (1958) has also been
widely used. This gives

$$\frac{\alpha_{bw} \bar{d}_S}{\lambda_G (1 - \epsilon)} \left(\frac{\lambda_G}{C_{pG}\rho_G}\right)^{0.43} = 3.5 \times 10^{-4} C_R \left(\frac{\rho_G \bar{d}_S u}{\mu_G}\right)^{0.23} \left(\frac{C_{pS}}{C_{pG}}\right)^{0.8} \left(\frac{\rho_S}{\rho_G}\right)^{0.66}$$

$$[8.2.22]$$

Table 8.2.3 Correction Factor C_R from the Work
of Vreedenburg (1952) for Different Radial
Locations of Vertical Tubes[a]

$2\dfrac{r}{D}$	C_R
0.0	1.0
0.35	1.76
0.71	1.57
→ 1	→ 0.9

[a]The value for tubes approaching the bed wall is
based on typical ratios of external wall to axial tube
heat transfer.

where all groups are dimensionless except one; the only dimensional term is the group on the left raised to the power of 0.43. The correlation was based on 323 experimental points covering a broad range of variables as shown in table 8.2.2. The constant C_R can be interpolated from table 8.2.3 for single tubes and should be taken as 1.0 when there is an assembly of tubes.

8.2.4.3 Horizontal Tubes

Although the details of particle renewal at the surface of horizontal tubes differ from those for vertical tubes (Selzer & Thomson 1977), the overall heat transfer coefficient usually does not differ greatly, typically being slightly lower for horizontal than for vertical tubes. One method for predicting average heat transfer coefficients for horizontal tubes is therefore to use the correlations for vertical tubes given above (e.g., [8.2.22]) with C_R taken as unity. Vreedenburg (1958) gave a separate correlation for horizontal cylindrical tubes:

$$\frac{\bar{\alpha}_{bw} d_T}{\lambda_G}\left(\frac{\lambda_G}{C_{pS}\mu_G}\right)^{0.3} = 0.66\left[\frac{\rho_S d_T u(1-\epsilon)}{\mu_G \epsilon}\right]^{0.44} \qquad [8.2.23]$$

for fine, light particles (i.e., $\rho_S \bar{d}_S u/\mu_G < 2050$), and

$$\frac{\bar{\alpha}_{bw} d_T}{\lambda_G}\left(\frac{\lambda_G}{C_{pS}\mu_G}\right)^{0.3} = 420\left(\frac{d_T u \mu_G}{\bar{d}_S^3 \rho_S g}\right)^{0.3} \qquad [8.2.24]$$

for coarse, dense particles ($\rho_S \bar{d}_S u/\mu_G > 2550$). For intermediate particles, both correlations should be used and the results averaged. Andeen & Glicksman (1976) have proposed a modification of this correlation that improves agreement for high gas flows. They replace 420 by $900(1-\epsilon)$ and the exponent 0.3 on the right-hand side by 0.326.

For particles larger than about 1 mm, where convective transfer becomes predominant, a correlation according to Glicksman & Decker (1980) should be used. This gives

$$\frac{\bar{\alpha}_{bw}\bar{d}_S}{\lambda_G} = (1 - \epsilon_b)\left(9.42 + 0.042\,\frac{\bar{d}_S u \rho_G C_{pG}}{\lambda_G}\right) \qquad [8.2.25]$$

This equation gave good agreement with large-particle results from a number of different studies, including some high-pressure data.

The effect of tube spacing is somewhat complex. As the tube spacing is decreased, some increase in $\bar{\alpha}_{bw}$ may be experienced because of smaller and more frequent bubbles (see section 8.1.11), at least for relatively small particles, where renewal frequency is important. This has been observed by Newby & Keairns (1978). However, if tubes are too close together, especially if the spacing is less than about $20\bar{d}_S$, solids motion is impeded and heat transfer decreases. Such an effect was observed by Lese & Kermode (1972).

Horizontal tubes may also be present in the freeboard region for waste heat recovery, quenching of reaction products, or because the bed depth varies. Transfer coefficients can be nearly as favorable in the splash zone as in the bed proper [e.g., within 80% in a study by Aulisio et al. (1976)], but coefficients tend to fall off with increasing distance from the bed surface. A correlation for transfer to tubes in the freeboard has recently been given by George (1980).

8.2.4.4 Maximum Heat Transfer Coefficient

A number of correlations have been given for the maximum heat transfer coefficient achieved when u is varied over a wide range (figure 8.2.3). The correlation of Zabrodsky et al. (1976) covers a relatively broad range of data, including beds operated at high temperature:

$$\frac{\bar{\alpha}_{max}\bar{d}_S}{\lambda_G} = 0.88\,\text{Ar}^{0.213} \qquad (10^2 < \text{Ar} < 1.4 \times 10^5) \qquad [8.2.26]$$

This equation may be applied for vertical or horizontal tubes or for transfer to the external wall. It is applicable to particles smaller than about 1 mm. The controlling mechanism of heat transfer is different for larger particles, as noted in section 8.2.3. For larger particles, Maskaev & Baskakov (1974) give

$$\frac{\bar{\alpha}_{max}\bar{d}_S}{\lambda_G} = 0.21\,\text{Ar}^{0.32} \qquad (1.4 \times 10^5 < \text{Ar} < 3 \times 10^8) \qquad [8.2.27]$$

and $\bar{\alpha}_{max}$ is then virtually independent of particle size.

8.2.4.5 Heat Transfer to Inclined Tubes

In general, tubes should be either horizontal or vertical and not obliquely inclined, as noted in section 8.1.11, because of gas bypassing and dead regions along the tube (Hager & Thomson 1973). Genetti et al. (1971) observed that the heat transfer coefficient passed through a minimum as tube orientation was changed. The minimum occurred at an orientation of $45°$ for a bare tube and at $60°$ to the horizontal for a finned tube.

8.2.4.6 Finned Tubes

Improved heat transfer rates on a bare tube basis can be obtained with externally finned tubes. Various types of fins have been tried. Hager & Thomson (1973) showed that fins have little effect on hydrodynamics for vertical tubes but play an important role for horizontal and inclined tubes. The defluidized region above tubes with radial spokes tends to be larger than for bare tubes. The region between transverse fins tends to be defluidized. There is less tendency for bubbles to adhere to finned than to bare tubes, whereas bubbles are distorted more as they pass finned tubes.

Rates of heat transfer increase as fins are added to bare tubes (Petrie et al. 1968; Bartel et al. 1971; Genetti et al. 1971; Bartel & Genetti 1973; Priebe & Genetti 1977; Staub & Canada 1978), but the increase levels off as the fin height is increased. Copper fins or spines give higher heat transfer rates than steel ones (Genetti et al. 1971; Priebe & Genetti 1977). In a typical case (Bartel et al. 1971), the maximum heat transfer coefficient on a bare tube basis was increased to 2340 W/m^2 K, compared with 256 W/m^2 K on a total area basis. The fins are much less effective if particles are unable to circulate freely between them. Deterioration in α_{bw} because of this effect was noted for $\bar{d}_S$ greater than about 0.1 fin spacing (Priebe & Genetti 1977).

Although correlations have been proposed for heat transfer from finned tubes (Bartel & Genetti 1973; Priebe & Genetti 1977), the range of experimental conditions covered is too narrow for reliable predictions to be expected under different conditions. The best procedure, if pilot plant data are unavailable, would appear to be to use bare tube correlations and apply correction factors to allow for the presence of fins, using the cited studies to suggest the degree of augmentation likely for a particular configuration and tube material.

8.2.4.7 Other Noncylindrical Tubes

Andeen et al. (1978) showed that it is possible to obtain one-third higher average heat transfer coefficients by flattening the sides of horizontal tubes in such a way that a smaller proportion of the surface area faces upward and downward. This improvement is associated with the fact that heat transfer tends to be inhibited at the top and bottom regions of a horizontal cylindrical tube, as noted previously. The data were obtained with sand particles of $\bar{d}_S = 360$, 510, and 710 μm at superficial velocities up to nearly 5 m/s.

8.2.4.8 Means of Augmenting Heat Transfer

For most purposes, heat transfer between fluidized beds and surfaces is rapid enough that no special means are required to augment the transfer rate. In addition to the two means of increasing the effectiveness of heat transfer surfaces (finned tubes and flattened tubes) discussed previously, some success has been achieved with:

1. Vibrated fluidized beds (vibrofluidized beds) or vibrated surfaces
2. Pulsations in the flow rate of fluidizing gas (pulsed fluidized beds)
3. Stirring by means of paddles or other impellers
4. Sonic or ultrasonic vibrations
5. Alternating electrical fields normal to a heat transfer surface
6. Baffles or jets designed to promote solids motion in the neighborhood of a heat transfer surface

Generally speaking, greater enhancement can be achieved near minimum fluidization than at higher gas velocities, and with small particles ($\bar{d}_S \stackrel{<}{\sim} 500 \ \mu m$) rather than larger ones, because heat transfer for smaller particles is more dependent on solids movement to and from the surface. Some of these techniques can also appreciably augment fluid-to-particle heat transfer rates.

8.2.5 LIQUID-FLUIDIZED BEDS

8.2.5.1 Liquid-to-Particle Transfer

Holman et al. (1965) correlated their data for steel and lead shot fluidized by water in a 50-mm-diameter column by

$$\frac{\alpha_{LS}\bar{d}_S}{\lambda_L} = 1.3 \times 10^{-3} \ (\text{Re} \ F_\epsilon)^{2.0} \ \text{Pr}^{0.67} \left(\frac{D}{\bar{d}_S}\right)^{0.5} \left(\frac{\rho_L}{\rho_S}\right)^2 \left(\frac{\mu}{\mu_0}\right)^{0.83} \quad [8.2.28]$$

where μ_0 is a reference value, taken as the viscosity of water at $27°C$, and

$$F_\epsilon = [1 - 1.21 \ (1 - \epsilon)^{2/3}]^{-1} \quad [8.2.29]$$

The results were said to be in general agreement with data of Sunkoori & Kaparthi (1960). In using [8.2.29], ϵ should be obtained from [8.1.14].

8.2.5.2 Bed-to-Surface Transfer

Heat transfer to surfaces in liquid-fluidized beds is also enhanced relative to heat transfer for packed beds or solids-free liquids, but the degree of enhancement and the mechanism differ from the gas-solid case. For a liquid-fluidized bed, the volumetric heat capacity of the fluidizing fluid is comparable to that of the solid particles (cf. gas-fluidized beds). Hence the primary role of the particles is to reduce the effective thickness of the thermal boundary layer. As the superficial liquid velocity is increased, the bed-to-wall heat transfer coefficient first increases because of the reduction in the boundary-layer thickness. With further increases in velocity a maximum is achieved (typically at $\epsilon \approx 0.7$) and heat transfer then decreases because of the reduction in the volumetric concentration of particles (Khan et al. 1978). With increasing particle size, heat transfer tends to rise because of the increased liquid velocities.

Various heat transfer correlations have been proposed. For transfer to the external wall, Hamilton (1970) gave

$$\frac{\alpha_{bw}\bar{d}_S}{\lambda_L} = 3.4 \left(\frac{\bar{d}_S}{D}\right)^{0.57} (\text{Pr}_L)^{0.33} \left(\frac{\rho_L \bar{d}_S u_i}{\mu_L}\right)^{0.565} [\epsilon^{0.565n} (1 - \epsilon)^{0.435}] \quad [8.2.30]$$

where n and u_i are obtained from [8.1.15]–[8.1.21]. A correlation of similar form was proposed for transfer to a concentric heater tube (Brea & Hamilton 1971):

$$\frac{\alpha_{bw}\bar{d}_S}{\lambda_L} = 0.93 \left(\frac{\bar{d}_S}{D_H}\right)^{0.15} (\text{Pr}_L)^{0.52} \left(\frac{\rho_L \bar{d}_S u_i}{\mu_L}\right)^{0.55} [\epsilon^{0.55n} (1 - \epsilon)^{0.45}][8.2.31]$$

where D_H is the hydraulic diameter of the column cross section. Although these appear to be the best correlations available, the range of certain variables covered, especially D (or D_H), was small. The correlations should not be applied when the particles are so heavy that aggregative fluidization occurs (Patel & Simpson 1977).

8.2.6 SPOUTED BEDS

8.2.6.1 Gas-to-Particle Transfer

Epstein & Mathur (1971) and Mathur & Epstein (1974) have given excellent discussions of heat transfer between gas and particles in spouted beds. As far as the annulus is concerned, equalization of gas temperature with the temperature of the particles occurs rapidly, generally within a few centimeters, as in the dense phase of fluidized beds (see section 8.2.1). In the spout, on the other hand, the gas velocity is much higher and the solids concentration is considerably lower, so that the height required to attain thermal equilibrium is one or two orders of magnitude greater. Consider the case where a bed is heated by hot gas. The annulus plays an important role as a heat source for cold feed particles and as a sink for particles heated above the mean bed temperature during entrainment in the spout. Under typical conditions the time required for the temperature of a feed particle to effectively reach the bed temperature was shown to be of the order of 1 min. Because spouted-bed particles tend to be much larger than particles used in most fluidized-bed processes, it is possible for significant temperature gradients to develop within individual particles.

For continuous heating or cooling of solids, a heat balance yields

$$\dot{M}_S C_{pS} [(T_S)_{\text{out}} - (T_S)_{\text{in}}] = u A \rho_G C_{pG} [(T_G)_{\text{in}} - (T_S)_{\text{out}}] \chi \quad [8.2.32]$$

whereas for batch heating, the corresponding result is

$$t = \frac{M_S C_{pS}}{u A \rho_G C_{pG} \chi} \ln \frac{(T_G)_{\text{in}} - (T_S)_{t=0}}{(T_G)_{\text{in}} - T_S} \quad [8.2.33]$$

where perfect mixing of the solids has been assumed and χ is the fractional approach to equilibrium,

$$\chi = \frac{(T_G)_{\text{in}} - (T_G)_{\text{out}}}{(T_G)_{\text{in}} - T_S} \quad [8.2.34]$$

For deep beds where thermal equilibrium can be assumed for the spout as well as the annulus, $\chi = 1$. For the more general case, Mathur & Epstein (1974) recommend that conservative estimates can be achieved by basing the gas-to-particle heat transfer on packed bed correlations, considering average annulus conditions.

Simultaneous heat and mass transfer data have been presented by Kmiec (1975). However, there are large differences between his correlations and the data of previous workers.

8.2.6.2 Bed-to-Surface Transfer

Transfer between the bed and the external wall tends to be somewhat less effective in spouted beds than in fluidized beds, with typical bed-to-surface heat transfer coefficients in the range 50–150 W/m^2 K (Malek & Lu 1964). The primary mode of transfer for particles used in typical spouted-bed operations is convective. Hence the heat transfer coefficient tends to increase with particle size, and [8.2.16] and [8.2.17] can be used to provide estimates for these coefficients. There is evidence of a decrease in heat transfer with increasing bed depth.

Somewhat higher heat transfer coefficients can be obtained with a heat transfer element within the bed itself, especially if it is located such that the spout impinges directly on the surface (Zabrodsky & Mikhailik 1967). The heat transfer coefficient for such an internal surface was found to increase with particle size and decrease with increasing height above the inlet. The data are insufficient to allow correlations of any generality.

8.2.7 THREE–PHASE FLUIDIZATION

There have been few studies of heat transfer in three-phase fluidized systems, and there are no general design correlations. Armstrong et al. (1976) studied transfer to a vertical axial heater tube in cocurrent air-water-glass bead systems. The presence of both particles and gas enhanced heat transfer relative to that with liquid alone, with the bed-to-surface coefficient increasing and then leveling off as the superficial gas velocity increased. Enhancement of heat transfer was more significant for larger particles.

The only study of heat transfer for countercurrent contacting is that of Dengler (1977), where simultaneous heat and mass transfer took place between the gas and liquid phases under cooling-tower conditions.

8.3 Fluidized-Bed Mass Transfer

C. Y. Wen and A. G. Fane

8.3.1 INTRODUCTION

Mass transfer in fluidized beds may occur in one of the following modes:

1. Mass transfer between the fluidizing medium and the solid particles (*fluid-to-solid*)
2. Mass transfer between lean and dense phases in an aggregatively fluidized bed (*bubble-to-emulsion* and *jet-to-emulsion*)
3. Mass transfer between the bed and an extended surface, such as the vessel wall or an immersed body (*bed-to-surface*)

Table 8.3.1 summarizes the significance of each of these modes of mass transfer for gas-fluidized and liquid-fluidized beds. Transfer between the fluidizing medium and the solids is the most important and directly applicable mode and is covered in section 8.3.2. Transfer between lean and dense phases is also important in the functioning of gas-fluidized beds through its role in many reaction situations. It is discussed in section 8.3.3, and its significance in fluidized-bed reactor operation is discussed in section 8.4. Bed-to-surface mass transfer is covered in section 8.3.4.

8.3.2 FLUID–TO–SOLID MASS TRANSFER

When a fluid is passed through a bed of fluidized solids in the presence of a transferable species, a concentration profile of that species develops through the bed. Prediction and/or analysis of the inlet and exit concentrations is the most common requirement.

8.3.2.1 Overall Mass Transfer Coefficients

The simplest approach is to assume plug flow of fluid, which is reasonable for fixed beds, liquid-fluidized beds, and gas-fluidized beds operating fairly close to the minimum fluidization velocity u_{mf}.

Table 8.3.1 Modes of Mass Transfer and Their Significance

Mode	Gas-fluidized beds	Liquid-fluidized beds
Fluid-to-solid	Basis of adsorption, sublimation, drying, gas-solid reactions	Basis of adsorption, ion exchange, dissolution (leaching), liquid-solid reactions
Bubble-to-emulsion	Possible controlling step in gas-solid reaction in a fluidized bed	Not applicable
Bed-to-surface	Drying, plating, fixed catalyst surface	Plating, dissolution

For the system depicted in figure 8.3.1 a mass balance over the incremental height dz gives

$$u \, \frac{dc}{dz} = K_f a_S (c^* - c) \qquad [8.3.1]$$

where c^* is the saturation concentration of solute, u is the superficial velocity of solvent-free fluid, K_f is the mass transfer coefficient, and a_S is the specific surface area of the solid particles. For particles of diameter d_S and sphericity ϕ_s the specific area is related to the voidage ϵ by

$$a_S = \frac{6(1 - \epsilon)}{d_S \phi_s} \qquad [8.3.2]$$

Assuming K_f to be independent of height

$$\bar{K}_f = \frac{u}{a_S} \ln \frac{c^* - c_{\text{in}}}{c^* - c_{\text{out}}} \qquad [8.3.3]$$

Equation [8.3.3] applies strictly to fixed-bed systems for which the use of the log mean driving force is justified on theoretical grounds. The equation has also been

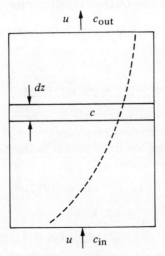

Figure 8.3.1 Concentration profile.

verified experimentally for fluidized beds by Wilkins & Thodos (1969) and Yoon & Thodos (1973). Equation [8.3.3] thus provides a simple way to analyze concentration data from a fluidized bed to give the overall mass transfer coefficient. A note of caution in the use of [8.3.3] is that as the exit concentration approaches the saturation value c^* the errors in either value become increasingly significant.

Rearrangement of [8.3.3] gives

$$c_{out} = c_{in}\, e^{-x} + c^*(1 - e^{-x}) \qquad [8.3.4]$$

where $x = \bar{K}_f a_S Z/u$. Equation [8.3.4] allows estimation of the outlet concentration if the overall mass transfer coefficient is known.

If the ratio of bed length to bed diameter is large (say 10 or larger) the plug flow assumption in [8.3.1] is accurate enough for most design calculations. However, if the length-to-diameter ratio is small, axial mixing should not be neglected (Wen & Fan 1975). Then

$$-E_z \frac{d^2c}{dz^2} + u \frac{dc}{dz} = K_f a_S (c^* - c)$$

where E_z is an axial dispersion coefficient that can be estimated from the following correlation (Chung & Wen 1968):

$$\frac{E_z}{\gamma} \frac{x}{\epsilon} = \frac{Re}{0.20 + 0.011\, Re^{0.48}} \qquad [8.3.5]$$

Here Re is $d_S u/\gamma$, γ is the kinematic viscosity, and $x = 1$ for fixed beds and $x = u_{mf}/u$ for fluidized beds. Equation [8.3.5] is valid for liquid-solids systems. For gas-solids systems operating at much higher than minimum fluidization velocity, bubbling phenomena must be taken into consideration. Gas-solids systems are discussed in a later section.

8.3.2.2 Correlations for Overall Coefficients

Mass transfer between a *single sphere* and a fluid (gas or liquid) is described by Froessling's equation (1938):

Single sphere:

$$Sh = 2.0 + 0.6\, Re^{0.5}\, Sc^{0.33} \qquad [8.3.6]$$

where $Sh = K_f d_S y/\delta$, $Re = d_S u/\gamma$, $Sc = \gamma/\delta$, δ is the molecular diffusivity, and y is the log mean fraction of nondiffusing component.

A similar equation applies for fixed beds at moderate Reynolds number (> 80) and for liquid-fluidized beds:

Fixed beds, Re > 80, gas or liquid, from Ranz (1952):

$$Sh = 2.0 + 1.8\, Re^{0.5}\, Sc^{0.33} \qquad [8.3.7]$$

Liquid-fluidized beds, $5 < Re < 120$, from Fan et al. (1960):

$$Sh = 2.0 + 1.5\, [(1 - \epsilon)\, Re]^{0.5}\, Sc^{0.33} \qquad [8.3.8]$$

where $\epsilon \leqslant 0.84$. Equations [8.3.7] and [8.3.8] may be combined with [8.3.3] to predict concentration profiles in the bed.

At low Reynolds numbers the data for fixed beds and fluidized beds deviate from the form of the Froessling equation with $Sh \ll 2.0$. Figure 8.3.2 shows the overall relationship between Sh and Re for single spheres, fixed beds, and fluidized beds.

The reasons for the inadequacy of a Froessling-type correlation for low Reynolds numbers are still a matter of controversy. Two approaches to the problem are presented here, one based on the work of Kato et al. (1970) for gas-fluidized beds, the other due to Nelson & Galloway (1975), who proposed a novel theoretical approach that may apply to gas- or liquid-fluidized systems. Both approaches lead to useful correlations for fluid-to-solid mass transfer.

Kato et al. (1970) explained the discrepancy by considering the order of magnitude of the boundary-layer thickness L_δ for mass transfer and showed that

$$L_\delta \propto d_S \, Re^{-0.5} \, Sc^{-0.33} \qquad [8.3.9]$$

For gas-solid systems in particular, the small value of Sc leads to relatively large values of L_δ at low Re. Consequently, the mass transfer boundary layers of closely adjacent particles overlap and the particles no longer behave as isolated spheres. In this situation the specific surface area a_S as defined by [8.3.2] is overestimated,

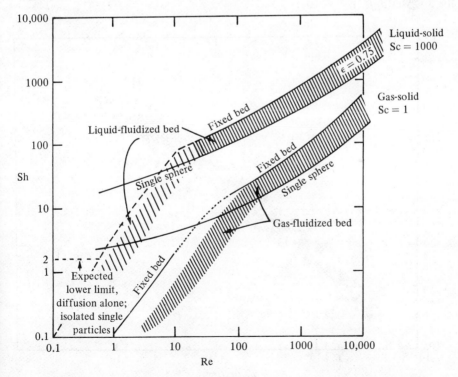

Figure 8.3.2 Fluid-to-solid mass transfer for single particles, fixed beds, and fluidized beds (adapted from Kunii & Levenspiel 1969).

leading to low values of $\bar{K}_f$ from [8.3.3]. The phenomena described above are accentuated as d_S becomes smaller and as the effective bed depth L' increases.

Figures 8.3.3 and 8.3.4 show data for gas-to-particle mass transfer in fixed and fluidized beds plotted as

$$\text{Sh} = f\left(\text{Re, Sc,}\frac{d_S}{L'}\right) \qquad\qquad [8.3.10]$$

where $L' = x_S L$ and x_S is the volume fraction of solids taking part in the mass transfer ($x_S = 1.0$ unless inert solids are present).

The following correlations describe the data in figures 8.3.3 and 8.3.4:

Fixed beds, gas-solid, from Kato et al. (1970):

$$\text{Sh} = 0.72 \left[\text{Re}\left(\frac{d_S}{L'}\right)^{0.6}\right]^{0.95} \text{Sc}^{0.33} \qquad\qquad [8.3.11]$$

for $0.1 \leqslant \text{Re } (d_S/L')^{0.6} \leqslant 5$, and

$$\text{Sh} = 1.25 \left[\text{Re}\left(\frac{d_S}{L'}\right)^{0.6}\right]^{0.63} \text{Sc}^{0.33} \qquad\qquad [8.3.12]$$

for $5 \leqslant \text{Re } (d_S/L')^{0.6} \leqslant 10^3$.

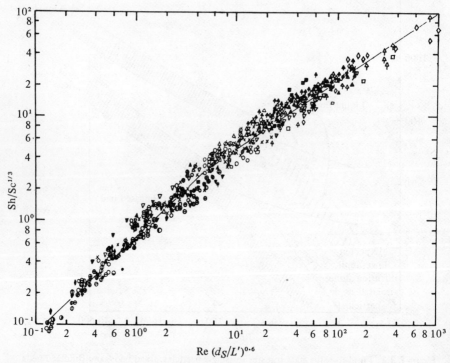

Figure 8.3.3 Gas-to-particle mass transfer in a fixed bed (Kato et al. 1970).

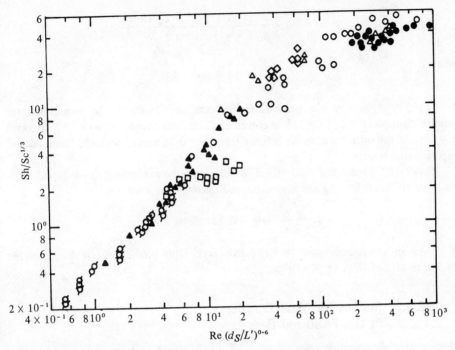

Figure 8.3.4 Gas-to-particle mass transfer in a fluidized bed (Kato et al. 1970).

Gas-fluidized beds:

$$Sh = 0.43 \left[Re \left(\frac{d_S}{L'} \right)^{0.6} \right]^{0.97} Sc^{0.33} \qquad [8.3.13]$$

for $0.5 \leqslant Re \, (d_S/L')^{0.6} \leqslant 80$, and

$$Sh = 12.5 \left[Re \left(\frac{d_S}{L'} \right)^{0.6} \right]^{0.2} Sc^{0.33} \qquad [8.3.14]$$

for $80 \leqslant Re \, (d_S/L')^{0.6} \leqslant 10^3$.

Equations [8.3.11]–[8.3.14] can be applied to those gas-to-solid mass transfer operations, such as drying, adsorption, and sublimation, for which the exit concentrations are required However, for catalytic reaction systems the use of L as the effective bed height L' frequently leads to underestimation of $\bar{K}_f$. The treatment of catalytic reaction systems is given in section 8.4.

Nelson & Galloway (1975) proposed a model to predict the anomalously low mass and heat transfer coefficients at low Reynolds numbers. The model simply treats the transfer process as one of stagnant molecular diffusion from a dispersion, with the boundary condition that the concentration gradient becomes zero at some point between particles. (Froessling's equation [8.3.6] arises from the assumption that the concentration gradient becomes zero at infinity, which is acceptable for an isolated sphere but unreasonable for a multiparticle system.) Nelson & Galloway's relationship is

$$\text{Sh} = \frac{2\beta + [2\beta^2\gamma_1/(1-\gamma_1)^2 - 2]\tanh\beta}{\beta/(1-\gamma_1) - \tanh\beta} \qquad [8.3.15]$$

where

$$\beta = \left(\frac{1}{\gamma_1} - 1\right)\frac{\alpha}{2}\,\text{Re}^{1/2}\,\text{Sc}^{1/3} \qquad [8.3.16]$$

$\gamma_1 = (1-\epsilon)^{1/3}$, and α is a proportionality constant. It should be noted that for infinite dilution, $\epsilon = 1$, [8.3.15] becomes equivalent to Froessling's [8.3.6] provided $\alpha = 0.6$. At the other limit as $\text{Re} \to 0$, we find $\text{Sh} \to 0$, in accord with the "anomalous" experimental results.

Rowe (1975) showed that [8.3.15] correlates the available data for liquid-fluidized beds if the following modifications and assumptions are made:

$$\gamma_1 \to \frac{\gamma_1}{\epsilon} \qquad \alpha = 0.7 \qquad \text{Sc} = 1400$$

Even in its original form, [8.3.15] gives acceptable predictions, as demonstrated by the results of Riba et al. (1978).

8.3.2.3 Models for Mass Transfer in Gas-Fluidized Beds

Models of fluid-to-solid mass transfer for gas-fluidized beds provide a means for better understanding the complex interactions that lead to the overall performance discussed above and for scale-up or extrapolation of existing data. The important features of gas-fluidized beds with respect to modeling fluid-to-solid mass transfer may be summarized as follows (also see section 8.1):

1. Gas (carrying its transferable species) travels through the bed in two phases, a bubble phase and an emulsion phase.
2. The bubble phase is assumed here to include the bubble voids as well as the bubble clouds.
3. Mass transfer occurs between the bubble phase gas and the solids in the cloud.
4. Mass transfer occurs between the emulsion phase gas and the solids in the emulsion.
5. Gas interchange occurs between the bubble void and the cloud.
6. Gas interchange occurs between the bubbles and the emulsion.
7. Gas interchange and relative phase velocities depend on the bubble size, which is a function of bed height.

Bubbling Bed Model

The bubbling bed model (BBM) (Kunii & Levenspiel 1969) assumes a constant bubble size d_b and relates the overall mass transfer coefficient $\bar{K}_f$ to the single-particle mass transfer coefficient given by [8.3.6]. For typical fluidized beds ($d_S < 0.1$ cm, $d_b > 0.5$ cm) the BBM predicts

$$\bar{K}_f \simeq \frac{\delta\epsilon_b}{yd_S(1-\epsilon)}\left(j_b\,\text{Sh}_t + \frac{y\phi_s d_S^2 F_{bc}}{6\delta}\right) \qquad [8.3.17]$$

where δ is the diffusivity, Sh_t is the Sherwood number calculated from [8.3.6] based on the terminal velocity of the solid particles, F_{bc} is the gas exchange coefficient between bubble and cloud (see [8.3.33]), j_b is the ratio of the volume of solids in bubble voids to the volume of bubble voids, ϵ_b is the ratio of the volume of bubble voids to the total bed volume, and ϵ is the ratio of the volume of voids (bubble and emulsion) to the total bed volume. Equation [8.3.17] is suitable for hand calculation of $\bar{K}_f$, although it relies on a judicious choice of d_b and j_b.

Bubble Assemblage Model

The bubble assemblage model (BAM) (Kato et al. 1970) provides for bubble growth in the fluidized bed and is therefore more realistic than the BBM, even though it is more complex. The BAM relates the overall mass transfer coefficient for the gas-fluidized bed to the fixed-bed coefficients given by [8.3.11] and [8.3.12]. The single-particle equation [8.3.6] is not used because of the discrepancy at low Re.

The basic assumptions for the BAM are:

1. The bed is divided into J compartments, with the height of a compartment set equal to the bubble size at that level.
2. The mass transfer coefficients in the bubble phase are obtained from the fixed-bed correlations (equations [8.3.11] and [8.3.12]) with the gas velocity equal to u_b, the bubble velocity.
3. The mass transfer coefficient in the emulsion phase is obtained from the fixed-bed correlation with the gas velocity equal to u_{mf}.

Figure 8.3.5 depicts the concentrations and flow rates in the bubble and emulsion phases. A mass balance for the bubble phase in compartment n gives

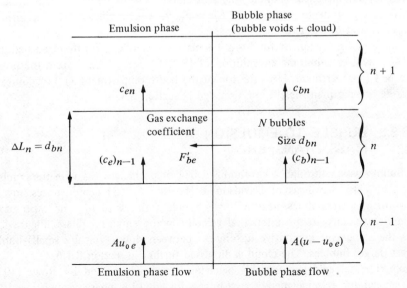

Figure 8.3.5 Representation of the BAM for mass transfer.

$$\frac{\text{Change in concentration}}{\text{X bubble phase flow rate}} = \frac{\text{material exchanged}}{\text{with emulsion}} + \frac{\text{material adsorbed on}}{\text{solids in cloud}}$$

$$A(u - u_{oe})[c_{bn} - (c_b)_{n-1}] = F'_{be}V_{bn}[c_{en} - c_{bn}] + K_{fn}a_{mf}V_{cn}[c^* - c_{bn}]$$

[8.3.18]

where $a_{mf} = 6(1 - \epsilon_{mf})/d_S\phi_s$ (see [8.3.2]), c^* is the saturation concentration of diffusing species, K_{fn} is the fluid-to-solid mass transfer coefficient based on the fixed-bed correlation and velocity u_b, and V_{bn} is the volume of bubble phase in compartment n, which is equal to Nx (volume of single bubble plus cloud) = N $(\pi d_{bn}^3/6) r$.

with
$$r = \left(\frac{d_c}{d_b}\right)^3 = \frac{u_{br} + 2 u_{mf}/\epsilon_{mf}}{u_{br} - u_{mf}/\epsilon_{mf}}$$
[8.3.19]

based on the theory of Davidson & Harrison (1963)

while
$$V_{cn} = \text{volume of cloud in } n = V_{bn} - N\left(\pi\frac{d_{bn}^3}{6}\right)$$
[8.3.20]

and
$$N = \text{number of bubbles in the compartment} = \frac{6A(L - L_{mf})}{\pi L d_{bn}^2}$$
[8.3.21]

A mass balance for the emulsion phase in compartment n gives

$$Au_{0e}[c_e - (c_e)_{n-1}] = F'_{be}V_{bn}[c_{bn} - c_{en}] + K_{fmf}a_{mf}[c^* - c_{bn}]$$ [8.3.22]

where K_{fmf} is the fluid-to-solid mass transfer coefficient based on the fixed-bed correlation and velocity u_{mf}. The parameter F'_{be} is the gas exchange coefficient between the bubble phase (bubble void plus cloud) and the emulsion. It is predicted from [8.3.32] with the correction $F'_{be} = F_{be}/r$, which allows for the different volumetric bases of the two coefficients.

Computer simulation of fluid-to-solid mass transfer in a gas-fluidized bed using the BAM involves simultaneous solution of [8.3.18] and [8.3.22] from the bottom of the bed (compartment 1) to the top of the bed (compartment J). Procedures for predicting compartment height are discussed in section 8.4.

8.3.3 BUBBLE-TO-EMULSION MASS TRANSFER

As a bubble passes through a gas-fluidized bed, it exchanges gas with the emulsion phase. The classic analysis of Davidson & Harrison (1963) demonstrates how the pattern of gas streamlines near a single bubble varies with $\tilde{u}_b^+$, the ratio of the bubble rise velocity to the interstitial velocity in the emulsion phase. Figure 8.3.6 shows the important qualitative differences between slow (typically small) bubbles and fast (large) bubbles. The cloud is discussed further in section 8.1.6.

Experimental evidence for this behavior has been provided by Rowe (1971). Slow, small bubbles serve merely as a bypass for emulsion phase gas, whereas larger

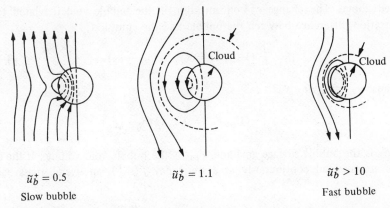

$\tilde{u}_b^+ = 0.5$ $\tilde{u}_b^+ = 1.1$ $\tilde{u}_b^+ > 10$

Slow bubble   Fast bubble

Figure 8.3.6 Differences between patterns of gas streamlines for slow and fast single bubbles (based on model from *Fluidized Particles*, by J. F. Davidson & D. Harrison, by permission of Cambridge University Press. Copyright © 1963 by Cambridge University Press.

bubbles carry with them a cloud of recirculating gas. The relative size of the cloud decreases as the bubble increases in velocity (diameter). Most bubbles are large enough to have an associated cloud phase, except in the grid region where embryonic bubbles or jets occur or for large particles. The grid region is dealt with separately in section 8.3.3.5.

As outlined in section 8.3.2.3, gas exchange between the bubble void and the cloud plays a significant role in fluid-to-solid mass transfer. Coupled with the convective exchange between the bubble void and the cloud is diffusive exchange at the cloud-emulsion interface. A further complicating factor in freely bubbling beds is that bubbles split, interact, and coalesce, and this inevitably disturbs the integrity of the cloud phase. It is shown in section 8.3.3.4 that coalescence inevitably leads to enhanced exchange between the cloud and emulsion.

8.3.3.1 Measurement of Overall Mass Transfer Coefficients

Two basic techniques are available for the measurement of overall bubble-to-emulsion transfer. The first technique involves direct measurement with single bubbles. The second involves a deductive approach in which a two-phase model is matched to a stimulus-response curve from a freely bubbling bed (Kobayashi & Arai 1967). The direct measurement technique has received the most attention and is described here.

Typically, single bubbles rich in a tracer component, such as ozone, helium, or ethylene, are injected into a bed fluidized by nontracer slightly above the minimum fluidization velocity. Tracer concentration and bubble size are measured at one or more levels within the bed. Chavarie & Grace (1976), Calderbank et al. (1976), and Rietema & Hoebink (1976) give details of suitable experimental techniques. The results of such tests may be interpreted in terms of an overall mass transfer coefficient K_{be} or an exchange coefficient F_{be}. These coefficients are essentially "lumped" parameters because they express the combined transfer mechanisms discussed above. The change of concentration in the bubble void is related to the concentration difference between the bubble and the emulsion; i.e.,

$$-\frac{d}{dt}(V_{bV}c_b) = K_{be}S_b(c_b - c_e) \qquad [8.3.23]$$

or, because $u_b = dz/dt$,

$$-u_b\frac{d}{dz}(V_{bV}c_b) = K_{be}S_b(c_b - c_e) \qquad [8.3.24]$$

where S_b is the bubble surface area and V_{bV} is the bubble void volume. If the single bubbles are injected continuously at a frequency $f\,(\mathrm{s}^{-1})$, an overall mass balance gives

$$-f\frac{d}{dz}(V_{bV}c_b) = Au_{0e}\frac{dc_e}{dz} \qquad [8.3.25]$$

where A is the bed cross-sectional area. Most analyses rely on [8.3.24] assuming $c_e \cong 0$, which is reasonable for isolated bubbles. Integrating [8.3.24], assuming that K_{be} and V_{bV} are independent of height, gives

$$\ln\frac{c_{b1}}{c_{b2}} = \frac{K_{be}}{u_b}\frac{S_b}{V_{bV}}(L_1 - L_2) \qquad [8.3.26]$$

where the subscripts 1 and 2 refer to different levels within the bed. Plotting $\ln(c_{b1}/c_{b2})$ versus level Z allows estimation of K_{be} from the slope (see figure 8.3.7a) where the ratio S_b/V_{bV} is $6/d_b$ for a three-dimensional bubble and $4/d_b$ for a two-dimensional bubble. Bubble velocity u_b may be measured directly or estimated from [8.1.34].

The mass transfer coefficient K_{be} obtained from this analysis has units $\mathrm{m\ s}^{-1}$. It is related to the gas exchange coefficient F_{be} by

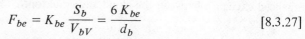

$$F_{be} = K_{be}\frac{S_b}{V_{bV}} = \frac{6\,K_{be}}{d_b} \qquad [8.3.27]$$

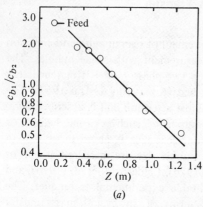

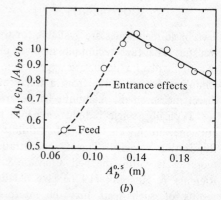

Figure 8.3.7 (a) Mass transfer analysis [8.3.26] (Reprinted with permission from *Chemical Engineering Science,* vol. 31, J. Chavarie & J. R. Grace, Interphase Mass Transfer in a Gas-fluidized Bed, Copyright 1976, Pergamon Press, Ltd.). (b) Analysis with bubble growth [8.3.28].

for a three-dimensional bubble; F_{be} has units s^{-1}. Both coefficients are found in the literature, and there is little standardization of symbols.

Two-dimensional Bed

For the case where bubble growth occurs in a two-dimensional bed (Chavarie & Grace 1976), [8.3.26] becomes

$$\ln \frac{A_{b1}c_{b1}}{A_{b2}c_{b2}} = - 4 \sqrt{\pi} \ K_{be} \frac{A_{b1}^{0.5} - A_{b2}^{0.5}}{u_b m} \qquad [8.3.28]$$

where A_{bi} is the visible frontal area of the two-dimensional bubble $= mZ + n$ (where m and n are coefficients found experimentally). Figure 8.3.7b shows data plotted on the basis of [8.3.28] and emphasizes the significance of entrance effects. More importantly, the value of K_{be} obtained from the slope of figure 8.3.7b is only 40% of the value obtained by neglecting bubble growth. This finding leads to uncertainty in the results reported by some other workers.

Three-dimensional Bed

If the extent of bubble growth for a three-dimensional bubble is known, it can be accounted for in the evaluation of bubble-to-emulsion mass transfer data. For example, the data of Kobayashi et al. (1965) suggest bubble growth in the form

$$d_b = mZ \qquad [8.3.29]$$

If this is used during integration of [8.3.23], the relationship obtained is

$$\ln \frac{V_{bV1}c_{b1}}{V_{bV2}c_{b2}} = - \frac{6 K_{be} \ln (d_{b1}/d_{b2})}{u_b m} \qquad [8.3.30]$$

To use [8.3.30] the concentration of tracer in the bubble and the size of the bubble must be measured simultaneously. The latter requires sophisticated probe techniques or X-ray ciné photography.

Calderbank et al. (1976) adopted a slightly different approach, simultaneously measuring bubble size and concentration difference $c_b - c_e$ for a stream of bubbles. By simultaneous solution of [8.3.24] and [8.3.25] we find

$$\frac{d}{dz} \ [\ln (c_b - c_e)] = K_{be} S_b \frac{A u_{0e} + f V_{bV}}{A u_{0e} V_{bV} u_b} \qquad [8.3.31]$$

The value of K_{be} is thus obtained from a semilogarithmic plot of $c_b - c_e$ versus Z.

8.3.3.2 Correlations for Overall Coefficients

Figure 8.3.8 presents measured values of the exchange coefficient F_{be} from [8.3.27] as a function of bubble size. Considering that this plot includes data from direct measurements with single bubbles and data deduced from stimulus-response curves of freely bubbling beds, the spread is not unreasonable. The clear trend in figure 8.3.8 is that the coefficient decreases as bubble size increases. From the data

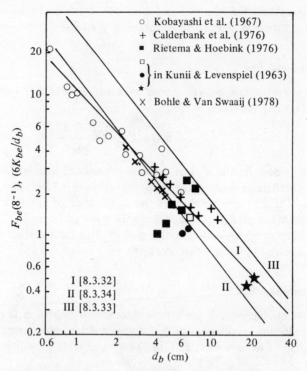

Figure 8.3.8 Gas exchange coefficient versus bubble size.

of Kobayashi & Arai (1967), Kato & Wen (1969) suggested the correlation for the gas exchange coefficient

$$F_{be} = \frac{11}{d_b} \; (s^{-1})$$

[8.3.32]

which is shown on line I on figure 8.3.8. This simple correlation can be seen to accommodate all the data except those of Rietema & Hoebink (1976). Although close to the correlation line, their data exhibit an increase in F_{be} rather than a decrease with d_b. This discrepancy may result from bubble growth, which Rietema & Hoebink observed but did not correct for (see section 8.3.3.1).

Lines II and III on figure 8.3.8 are obtained from alternative models of gas exchange discussed in section 8.3.3.3. Note that the simple empirical correlation (line I) and the model relationship (line II) give very similar results when incorporated into a fluidized-bed reaction model (see section 8.4).

The effect of adsorption of gas on the solids has been described by several workers (e.g., Nguyen & Potter 1974, 1976; Bohle & Van Swaaij 1978). Figure 8.3.9 from Bohle & Van Swaaij, shows the relative value of the exchange coefficient (per unit bed volume) for gases of different adsorptive property. (The adsorption parameter $m = c_s/c_e$ = ratio of the concentration at the solids surface to the concentration in the emulsion.) These results show that adsorptive capacity enhances the exchange coefficient, which increases by a factor of ~ 2 as m increases from 0 to 7.

8.3.3.3 Models of Gas Exchange

A number of models for bubble-to-emulsion mass transfer have been proposed and are summarized by Kato & Wen (1969), Drinkenburg & Rietema (1972), and Chavarie & Grace (1976). All of the models consider one or more of the following mechanisms of mass transfer: (1) diffusional and convective flux across the bubble boundary; (2) diffusion and convection within the cloud; (3) diffusive flux across the cloud-emulsion boundary; and (4) convective flux across the cloud-emulsion boundary if adsorbed onto solids released by shedding, etc. For example, Davidson & Harrison (1963) assume that all the resistance to mass transfer is concentrated inside the bubble; this is a reasonable assumption for very fast bubbles with negligible clouds. They also assume the diffusive and convective fluxes to be additive, obtaining

$$F_{be} = 5.85 \, \frac{\delta^{1/2} g^{1/4}}{d_b^{5/4}} + \frac{4.5 \, u_{mf}}{d_b} \qquad [8.3.33]$$

This is compared with experimental values in figure 8.3.8, where it can be seen that it overestimates the data.

Kunii & Levenspiel (1969) consider the resistance to mass transfer to reside at the bubble boundary and the cloud-emulsion boundary, obtaining

$$\frac{1}{F_{be}} = \frac{1}{F_{bc}} + \frac{1}{F_{ce}} \qquad [8.3.34]$$

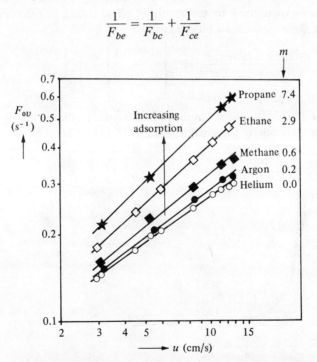

Figure 8.3.9 Exchange coefficient (per unit bed volume) F_{ov} with adsorption (Reprinted from W. Bohle & W. P. N. Van Swaaij in *Fluidization* edited by J. F. Davidson & D. L. Keairns by permission of Cambridge University Press. Copyright © 1978 by Cambridge University Press.). The parameter m = adsorptive capacity.

where F_{bc} is the bubble-to-cloud exchange coefficient = the value of F_{be} obtained from [8.3.33] and F_{ce} is the cloud-to-emulsion exchange coefficient:

$$F_{ce} = 6.8 \left(\frac{\epsilon_{mf} \delta u_b}{d_b^3} \right)^{1/2}$$ [8.3.35]

Equation [8.3.34] is compared with experimental data in figure 8.3.8; it slightly under-estimates the data at larger bubble sizes (note that for larger bubbles the cloud is very thin and should offer negligible resistance, whereas the model assumes a cloud resistance).

8.3.3.4 Effect of Bubble Coalescence

An effect not accounted for in the available models for bubble-to-emulsion mass transfer is that of bubble coalescence in freely bubbling beds. Coalescence typically involves capture of a following bubble by a leading bubble as the latter accelerates in the disturbed velocity field. As the bubbles coalesce the clouds lose their integrity and exchange of gas with the emulsion is enhanced. Indeed, on purely theoretical grounds it can be argued that the volume of the cloud phase of the resultant bubble will be less than the combined volumes of the cloud phases of the two original bubbles. From [8.3.19] and [8.3.20] and assuming $u_{br} \propto d_b^{1/2}$, the number of bubble volumes transferred to the emulsion phase during coalescence can be estimated (for a three-dimensional bubble) to be

$$J = \frac{\text{volume transferred}}{\text{bubble void volume}} = 2 \left[\frac{\tilde{u}_b^+ - 0.5}{\tilde{u}_b^+ - 1.0} \right] - 2^{6/7} \left[\frac{2^{1/7} \tilde{u}_b^+ - 0.5}{2^{1/7} \tilde{u}_b^+ - 1.0} \right]$$ [8.3.36]

where $\tilde{u}_b^+ = u_{br} \epsilon_{mf} / u_{mf}$.

Equation [8.3.36] is plotted in figure 8.3.10, which indicates that significant transfer can occur, particularly for small $\tilde{u}_b^+$ (i.e., small bubbles that are found in the grid

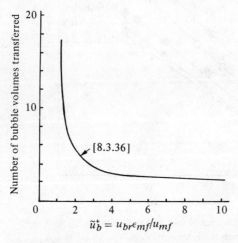

Chemical Reaction Engineering

Figure 8.3.10 Volume transferred on coalescence (Pyle, D. L. in *Chemical Reaction Engineering*, K. B. Bischoff, Ed., ADVANCES IN CHEMISTRY SERIES No. 109; American Chemical Society: Washington, D.C., 1972, p. 117).

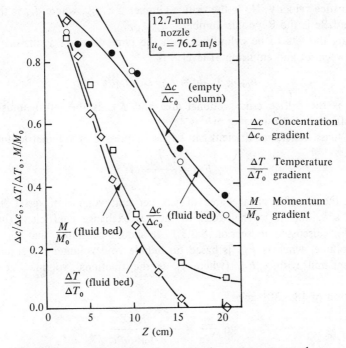

Figure 8.3.11 Axial profiles of concentration, temperature, and momentum for a high-velocity jet into a fluid bed (Behie et al. 1976).

region of the bed). Even for large bubbles (large $\tilde{u}_b^+$) a transfer of 20% can be expected. With these considerations in mind, the most practical approach to prediction of F_{be} or K_{be} is to use [8.3.32], which is derived from data obtained in a freely bubbling bed.

8.3.3.5 Bubbles and Jets in the Grid Region

Mass transfer at the bottom of a fluidized bed is directly related to the type of grid (gas distributor) used. Porous plate distributors lead to the formation of many small bubbles at the bottom of the bed, whereas perforated plate or tuyere (turret) distributors result in a jet formation zone before the bubbling zone.

Mass transfer between jets and the emulsion phase was studied by Behie et al. (1976), and figure 8.3.11 shows some of their concentration profile data obtained in a bed 61 cm in diameter and 122 cm deep. A bed of 60-μm cracking catalyst was used, and the analysis was based on CO_2 as a tracer in air. The exponential decay of axial concentration was significant, but less pronounced than the decay of either temperature or momentum. Behie et al. correlated their concentration profiles by

$$\ln \frac{\Delta c}{\Delta c_0} = -1.92 \ \text{Fr}^{-0.50} \ \text{No}^{0.91} \ \text{Re}^{0.07} \qquad [8.3.37]$$

where Δc and Δc_0 are differences in concentration between jet and emulsion at height Z and at the inlet, respectively; Fr is the Froude number $= (u_{\text{or}}^2/gZ)$; where

u_{or} is the orifice velocity; No is the orifice number $= Z/d_{or}$, where d_{or} is the orifice diameter; and Re is the Reynolds number $= d_{or} u_{or}/\gamma$.

Assuming the jets to be cylindrical with the same diameter as the orifice, mass transfer between jet and emulsion at level Z is

$$u_{or}\rho_G A_{or}dc = K_{Je} \, \Delta c \pi d_{or}dz \qquad [8.3.38]$$

where A_{or} is the orifice cross-sectional area and K_{Je} is the jet-to-emulsion mass transfer coefficient, with units kg m^{-2} s^{-1}.

The jet mass transfer coefficient can be also expressed in volumetric units as

$$F_{Je} = \frac{a_J K_{Je}}{\rho_G} \qquad [8.3.39]$$

where a_J is the transfer surface area of jets per unit volume of vessel. The units of F_{Je} are s^{-1}, and it is analogous to the gas exchange coefficient (bubble to emulsion) F_{be} discussed in section 8.3.3.1. It should be noted that F_{Je} is based on vessel volume, whereas F_{be} is based on bubble void volume; F_{Je} should therefore be compared with $\epsilon_b F_{be}$ (where ϵ_b is the fractional volume occupied by bubbles).

Integration of [8.3.38] gives

$$\ln \frac{\Delta c}{\Delta c_0} = - 4 \frac{K_{Je}Z}{d_{or}u_{or}\rho_G} \qquad [8.3.40]$$

Behie et al. (1976) presented numerical values of K_{Je} for $d_{or} = 6.4$, 12.7, and 19.1 mm. The data for the smallest orifice size for jet-emulsion are correlated within 10% by

$$K_{Je} = 2.08 \, (1 - e^{-xu_{or}}) \qquad [8.3.41]$$

where K_{Je} is the mass transfer coefficient (kg/m^2 s), u_{or} is the orifice velocity (m/s), and $x = 2.45 \times 10^{-2}$. Equation [8.3.41] also correlates the data for $d_{or} = 12.7$ mm within 25%.

The significance of the grid region for reaction situations is discussed in section 8.4.

8.3.4   BED-TO-SURFACE MASS TRANSFER

Transfer of material between the fluidizing medium and a surface in or bounding a fluidized bed is similar in many ways to transfer of heat between bed and surface. A detailed discussion of bed-to-surface heat transfer can be found in section 8.2.2 and in Botterill (1975). A critical review of bed-to-surface mass transfer has been given by Beek (1971).

Figure 8.3.12 from Coeuret et al. (1976) summarizes the relationship between the surface mass transfer coefficient K_s and fluid velocity for fixed, fluidized, transported, and empty beds. The coefficient for the fluidized system goes through a maximum, initially following the value for a fixed bed but then dropping to that for a transported bed at high velocities. Although figure 8.3.12 is for a liquid-

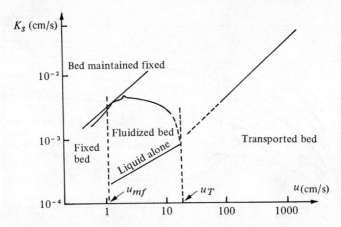

Figure 8.2.12 Variation of K_s with liquid velocity in different systems (Coeuret et al. 1976).

fluidized bed, similar behavior can be expected for gas-fluidized beds, judging from heat transfer data.

Conclusions to be drawn from figure 8.3.12 are

1. At velocities not much greater than u_{mf} the particles increase K_s by an order of magnitude compared with that for a particle-free system.
2. To obtain similar values of K_s in a particle-free system, the velocity has to be about 50 times the velocity in the fluidized system.

The fluidized particles enhance mass transfer by increasing the interstitial (local) fluid velocity and by physically disturbing the mass transfer boundary layer. (In the heat transfer situation the particles also act as carriers, because they can absorb and transport heat; in most cases the analogous phenomenon does not apply in mass transfer.)

Bed-to-surface mass transfer coefficients for liquid-fluidized beds can be correlated by

$$\text{Sh} = Cf_\epsilon \, \text{Re}^a \, \text{Sc}^{0.33} \qquad\qquad [8.3.42]$$

where Sh is the Sherwood number $= K_s d_S/\delta$; Re is the Reynolds number $= u d_S/\gamma$; u being the superficial fluid velocity; Sc is the Schmidt number $= \gamma/\delta$; f_ϵ is the voidage factor $= (1-\epsilon)^{(1-a)}/\epsilon$; a is a constant exponent of Re and is incorporated into f_ϵ; and C is a constant. For $6 < \text{Re}\,[1/(1-\epsilon)] < 200$ (Coeuret et al. 1967), $a = 0.48$, and $C = 1.21$, and for $200 < \text{Re}\,[1/(1-\epsilon)] < 23,800$ (Jagannadharaju & Rao 1965), $a = 0.62$ and $C = 0.43$.

The major unknown in [8.3.42] is the voidage ϵ, which may be estimated by the correlations of Richardson & Zaki (1954) (see section 8.1.4) or Wen & Yu (1966b). Based on the analysis of forces acting on the suspending particles, Wen & Yu (1966b) developed a relation between the drag coefficient C_D of a constituent

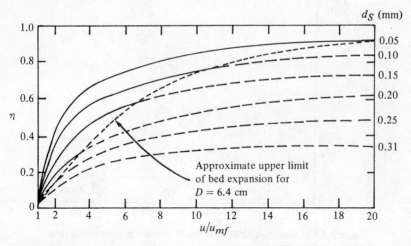

Figure 8.3.13   Efficiency factor used in [8.3.48] (Wen & Leva 1956).

particle in a multiparticle suspension and the drag coefficient C_{DS} of a single particle in an infinite expanse of fluid,

$$C_D = C_{DS}\epsilon^{-4.7} \qquad [8.3.43]$$

Unlike the correlation of Richardson & Zaki (1954), where the power of voidage varies as Re, [8.3.43] is applicable for Re from 0.001 to 500. Combination of this equation with the correlation for C_{DS} given by Schiller & Naumann (1935) leads to the following equation for estimating the bed expansion of particulate fluidization:

$$\epsilon = \left(\frac{\text{Ar}}{18\ \text{Re} + 2.7\ \text{Re}^{1.687}}\right)^{4.7} \qquad [8.3.44]$$

where

$$\text{Ar} = d_S^3 \frac{(\rho_S - \rho_F)\rho_F g}{\mu_F^2} \qquad [8.3.45]$$

Maximum values of K_s occur typically at $\epsilon \sim 0.6$ (Coeuret et al. 1976), and the superficial velocity giving the maximum is (Beek 1971)

$$\frac{u_{\max}}{u_{mf}} = (5.0 \pm 0.5)\, C_{DS}^{0.75} \qquad C_{DS} < 10 \qquad [8.3.46]$$

$$\frac{u_{\max}}{u_{mf}} = 36 \qquad C_{DS} > 10 \qquad [8.3.47]$$

where $u_{\max}$ is the superficial velocity corresponding to maximum K_s.

For gas-fluidized beds [8.3.46] may be applied, particularly at velocities close to u_{mf}. For vigorously gas-fluidized beds it is more appropriate to use the correlations for heat transfer with the following transformations: $\text{Sh} \to \text{Nu}$ and $\text{Sc} \to \text{Pr}\,(1 - \epsilon)\,(C_{pS}\rho_S/C_{pF}\rho_F)$, where Pr is the fluid Prandtl number and C_{pS} and C_{pF}

are the solid and fluid heat capacities. For example, the bed-to-wall heat transfer correlation of Wen & Leva (1956) can be transformed to give

$$Sh = 0.16\,(1 - \epsilon)^{-0.76}\,Re^{0.76}\,Sc^{0.4}\,Fr^{-0.2}\,\eta^{0.36}\,(1 - \epsilon_{mf})^{0.36} \quad [8.3.48]$$

where Fr is the Froude number $= u^2/gd_S$ and η is the efficiency factor, which can be estimated from figure 8.3.13. Equation [8.3.48] may be used as an approximate guide in estimating K_s for vigorously fluidized beds.

8.4 Fluidized-Bed Reactors

A. G. Fane and C. Y. Wen

8.4.1 INTRODUCTION

The most important application of fluidization is in the field of chemical reaction engineering. Within the last three decades fluidization has evolved to become one of the most useful reactor concepts available to industry. However, while there have been many successful applications, there have also been a number of misapplications and serious development problems. It is our purpose here to outline what is currently known about the use of the fluidized bed as a chemical reactor and to offer guidelines, methods, and practical advice for further successful application. A majority of cases where fluidization has been applied successfully to chemical reactions have involved gas fluidization. Consequently section 8.4 deals solely with gas-fluidized-bed reactors.

A convenient classification for gas-fluidized reactions is to consider them as either *gas-phase reactions* (which may be *catalytic* or *noncatalytic*) or *gas-solid reactions* (which are noncatalytic, with minor exceptions). The principal commercial applications of fluidized beds for catalytic gas-phase reactions are covered in section 8.5.2; applications of gas-solid reactions are treated in sections 8.5.3 and 8.5.4. Spouted-bed reactors have been treated by Mathur & Epstein (1974) and are not covered here.

The many applications of gas fluidization have been made because this method of gas-solid contacting offers several advantages over alternative techniques. The advantages for industrial operations are as follows:

1. Rapid circulation of the solids in the bed provides almost isothermal conditions and excellent heat transfer characteristics.
2. Continuous movement of solids also minimizes the formation of stagnant zones in the bed and ensures effective gas-solid contacting.
3. Solids in the fluidized state are relatively easy to handle, and this favors continuous flow and recirculation systems.
4. Fluidized beds are mechanically simple and suited to large-scale operations.

5. Fluidized beds tend to be more compact than alternative gas-solid contacting techniques.

Although the advantages listed above make gas fluidization a very attractive method, it has some disadvantages, as follows:

1. Inhomogeneities exist that can be important in special cases:
   a. There is frequently a sharp temperature gradient very close to the bottom of the bed (Kettenring et al. 1950).
   b. A portion of the gas passes up through the bed as bubbles, and this may lead to undersirable bypassing of reactant.
   c. The rapid circulation of solids leads to a significant spread of residence times for solid particles when continuous flow is adopted.
2. Not all solids fluidize well (see section 8.1.3). This disadvantage can be overcome by further preparation or special techniques such as spouting for large particles (see section 8.1.16 and Mathur & Epstein 1974) or stirring and pulsing for fine particles (see section 8.1.11.5).
3. Scale-up from laboratory- to commercial-sized reactors is not simple, because different regimes of fluidization tend to occur at different scales of operation; i.e., small-diameter beds tend to slug flow, moderate-sized beds are freely bubbling, and large-diameter beds exhibit large-scale circulation cells of solids and preferred bubble tracks. Scale-up is discussed in section 8.4.6.4

8.4.2 FLUID–BED HYDRODYNAMICS AND REACTION

The purpose of this section is to summarize the hydrodynamic features of gas-fluidized beds that are important in terms of reaction applications. Hydrodynamics are covered in detail in section 8.1.

8.4.2.1 Reaction Zones—The Idealized Fluid Bed

Figure 8.4.1 depicts the idealized fluid-bed reactor. This fluidized bed has three distinct reaction zones. At the bottom of the bed is the grid region, which contains vertical or horizontal gas jets and/or small formation-sized bubbles; the type of grid will determine the form of the gas voids (section 8.4.5.1).

Above the grid region is the bubbling zone. In this zone bubbles grow by coalescence and may even approach a diameter similar to the vessel width, forming slugs. The rising bubble voids have three important features:

1. A wake of solids is carried upward below the bubble void.
2. A shell or cloud of gas surrounds the bubble void.
3. A small fraction of solid particles enters the bubble void.

Different reaction conditions (local concentrations and possibly temperatures) can occur in the bubble cloud, the emulsion phase, and even the bubble void (Aoyogi & Kunii 1974).

The upward movement of solids in the wakes of bubbles will be compensated

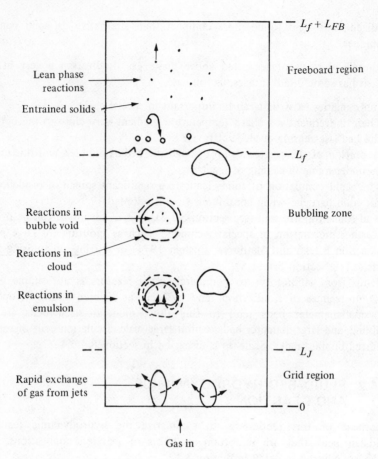

Figure 8.4.1 Reaction zones—the idealized fluid bed.

by a net downward flow of solids in the emulsion phase. This down flow of solids can lead to the surprising result that under certain conditions the gas in the emulsion phase also flows downward. Under typical conditions this occurs for $u/u_{mf} > 6-11$.

As bubbles break the surface of the bed, particles are entrained in the upward-flowing gas stream. Some are carried out, while others fall back to the bed. This is the freeboard region, and it affords an opportunity for lean phase reactions. Because solid particles are reacting in isolation, they heat up or cool down (because of exothermic or endothermic reactions) to a greater extent than particles in the dense phase of the bed. This may lead to adjustment of reaction equilibria or side reactions. Section 8.4.5.2 should be consulted for a more detailed discussion of the freeboard region.

8.4.2.2 Types of Reaction and Significance of Reaction Zones

Table 8.4.1 indicates the significance of the three reaction zones for conversion in the gas phase. This includes gas phase reactions and gas-solid reactions for which the course of the reaction is strongly dependent on the local gas phase concentrations; e.g., coal combustion and gasification. For moderate to fast reactions (first-order rate constants nominally 5 s^{-1} or greater) the bed hydrodynamics (bubble properties, etc.) are important, whereas for slow reactions the most important parameter is the gas residence time. This point is covered in more detail in section 8.4.3.

Reactions in which the conversion of solids is the major interest are principally affected by the conditions in the bubbling zone, although the freeboard may be important in special cases where particles shrink and become readily recirculated through cyclone/dipleg systems (sections 8.4.4.1 and 8.4.5.2). Provided there is no limitation of gaseous reactant or heat transfer in the bubbling zone, the most important hydrodynamic characteristic is the residence time distribution (RTD) of the solid particles. The RTD is strongly influenced by bubble flow; because solids are moved through the bed by bubbles; geometric factors such as bed cross section and internals also influence the RTD.

8.4.2.3 Regimes of Fluidization and Nonidealized Behavior

Most design techniques for gas-fluidized-bed reactors assume that all (or a large fraction) of the gas input in excess of minimum fluidization forms freely rising bubbles uniformly distributed across the bed cross section. Although this applies in many cases, there are as many cases in which it does not. Exceptions result from differences in particle properties, scale of operation, gas velocity, and non-atmospheric conditions (particularly operation at elevated pressures).

Particle groups (A–D) are discussed in section 8.1.3. Van Swaaij (1978) points out that although group A particles are of great practical significance, including many large-scale catalytic reactors, most published design methods and reactor

Table 8.4.1 Significance of Reaction Zones for Gas-Phase Conversion

Reaction zone	Fast reaction	Slow reaction
Grid region	Significant conversion is possible.	Insignificant conversion.
Bubbling zone	Conversion may become limited by bubble-to-emulsion gas exchange. Restricted bubble size will increase conversion and reduce gas bypassing. Knowledge of bubble size is important for design analysis. Solids present in bubble voids may have significant effect on conversion.	Conversion is limited by reaction rate. There is a need to increase gas residence time with deep beds and low gas velocities (fewer bubbles). Knowledge of bubble properties is not important. Solids in bubble voids voids are not likely to influence conversion.
Freeboard region	Conversion can be significant because there is no gas bypassing. Limitation may result from low solids population. Problems may occur because of secondary reactions and lack of temperature control.	Insignificant conversion.

models are more applicable to group B particles. He shows, however, that a simple model is appropriate to large-scale operation with group A particles (see section 8.4.3.2).

The interactions of particle size, gas velocity, and bed diameter are complex. The most important distinction is that between slug flow and freely bubbling beds. Criteria for the slug flow regime are presented in section 8.1.8. Conversion in the slug flow regime can be predicted by using the model presented in section 8.4.3.3.

At a high gas velocity the bubbling bed becomes "turbulent" and then "fast" (see sections 8.1.2, 8.1.14, and 8.1.15). Transitions from bubbling to turbulent and from turbulent to fast have been summarized by Van Swaaij (1978) for small particles, and by Staub & Canada (1978) for medium and large particles. The types of models that apply for each of these regimes are listed in table 8.4.2.

8.4.3 GAS–PHASE REACTIONS

This section deals with the effects of design and operating variables on the conversion of catalyzed gas-phase reactions in fluidized beds. Interest centers on the influence of the bubble zone; the effects of the grid and freeboard regions are treated separately in section 8.4.5.

It is commonly accepted that there is no a priori method for the accurate prediction of conversion of gas in a fluidized bed. On the other hand, a large number of mathematical models, varying in sophistication, have been proposed, and these in turn have been critically evaluated and compared by several authors (e.g., Rowe 1972; Pyle 1972; Calderbank & Toor 1971; Grace 1971; Horio & Wen 1977; Barreteau et al. 1978).

Seventeen models have been classified by Horio & Wen (1977) into three major groups (tables 8.4.3 and 8.4.4). Level I models are two-phase models, with several adjustable parameters not directly related to bubble behavior. Consequently these models are not well suited to scale-up and design, except in well-defined circumstances.

Level II models attempt to relate bed parameters to bubble size, which is treated either as constant or as an adjustable parameter. Extension of the level II bubbling model to include varying bubble size leads to the level III bubbling models, which are the most realistic from a mechanistic point of view, particularly

Table 8.4.2 Fluidization Regimes and Conversion Models

Regime	Conversion in gas phase
Slug flow	Two-phase, plug flow model applies (section 8.4.3.3)
Freely bubbling	Homogeneous models apply only for slow reactions, two-phase models for moderate to fast reactions (sections 8.4.3.2 and 8.4.3.4)
Turbulent flow and fast fluidized bed	Homogeneous plug flow model probably applicable (section 8.4.3.2)

Table 8.4.3 Classification of Fluidized-Bed Reactor Models[a]

Level	Description	Models	Code $(n_1 n_2 n_3 n_4 n_5 n_6)$[b]
I	Parameters constant along the bed	Shen & Johnstone (1955)	21 ×××1
		Van Deemter (1961)	25 ×××1
		Johnstone et al. (1955)	31 ×××1
	Parameters not related to bubble behavior ($n_3 \sim n_5$ cannot be specified)	May (1959)	21 ×××1
		Kobayashi & Arai (1965)	31 (or 5) ×××1
		Muchi (1965)	31 ×××1
II	Parameters constant along the bed	Orcutt et al. (1962)	21 × 211
		Kunii & Levenspiel (1969)	141111
		Fryer & Potter (1972)	131111
	Parameters related to bubble size, which is adjustable $n_5 = 1 \sim 3$		
III	Parameters related to bubble size	Mamuro & Muchi (1965)	21 × 541
		Toor & Calderbank (1967)	311241
		Partridge & Rowe (1966)	322341
	Bubble size varied along bed axis $n_5 = 4$	Kobayashi et al. (1969)	312541
		Kato & Wen (1969)	351441
		Mori & Muchi (1972)	21 × 541
		Fryer & Potter (1972)	21 × 241
		Mori & Wen (1976)	351442

[a]From Horio & Wen (1977).

[b]The code is defined in table 8.4.4. Example: 21 ×××1 means $n_1 = 2$ (i.e., the bed is divided into two phases, and the cloud phase is included in the emulsion phase); $n_2 = 1$ (i.e., the flow rate in bubble phase is $u - u_{mf}$); factors $n_3 \sim n_5$ are not specified (i.e., the parameters are not related to the bubble characteristics); and $n_6 = 1$ (i.e., the effect of jet is not considered).

if they can account for the special conditions of the grid region and the freeboard. Level III models should be used for scale-up and process evaluation, unless simple models (section 8.4.3.1) can be justified. However, level III models apply strictly only to class B particles and freely bubbling beds.

8.4.3.1 Simple Models—Homogeneous and Two-Phase

A number of simple models can be proposed (Horio & Wen 1977) to account for the general features of the gas-fluidized bed. Figure 8.4.2 depicts the models that are either homogeneous (P and M) or two-phase (P-P, P-M, and C). Used judiciously, these simple models can be reasonable predictors of performance.

Two dimensionless parameters may be defined to characterize gas-fluidized beds, the number of transfer units:

$$N_M = F_{be} \frac{\epsilon_b L}{u} \qquad [8.4.1]$$

Table 8.4.4 Code ($n_1 n_2 n_3 n_4 n_5 n_6$) for the Classification of Models[a]

Values of n_i	n_1, way of dividing the phase[b]	n_2, way of flow assignment	n_3, cloud volume	n_4, gas exchange coefficient	n_5, bubble diameter	n_6, effect of jet
1	Three phases B − C − E	$u_{ob} = u - u_{mf}$ $u_{oe} + u_{oc} = u_{mf}$ or $u_{oe} = u_{mf}$	Davidson model $r = \dfrac{\tilde{u}_b^+ + 2}{\tilde{u}_b^+ - 1}$ (three-dimensional)	Two interphases Kunii & Levenspiel (1969) model	Constant and adjustable	Not considered
2	Two phases B − (C + E)	$u_e = \dfrac{u_{mf}}{\epsilon_{mf}}$ $u_c = \dfrac{u_b}{\epsilon_{mf}}$	Murray model $r = \dfrac{\tilde{u}_b^+}{\tilde{u}_b^+ - 1}$	One interphase Orcutt et al. (1962) model	Constant $d_b = d_b$ at $\dfrac{L_f}{2}$ or $d_b = d_b$ at $\dfrac{L_{mf}}{2}$	Considered
3	Two phases (B + C) − E	$u_e = \dfrac{u_{mf}}{\epsilon_{mf}} - u_s$	$r = 1$	One interphase Partridge & Rowe (1966) model	Constant d_b from bed expansion data	
4		$u_{ob} = u - u_{mf}$ $u_{oc} = 0$ $u_{oe} = 0$		One interphase Empirical correlation by Kobayashi et al. (1969)	Varied along bed axis	
5		$u_{ob} = u_o$ $u_{oc} = 0$ $u_{oe} = 0$		The others		

[a] From Horio & Wen (1977).
[b] B, bubble phase; C, cloud phase; E, emulsion phase.

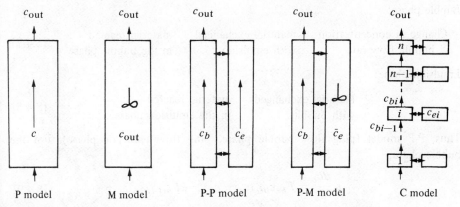

Figure 8.4.2 Simple homogeneous and two-phase models–gas-phase reaction.

and the number of reaction units:

$$N_R = \frac{kL_{mf}}{u} \tag{8.4.2}$$

where F_{be} is the (bubble-to-emulsion) gas exchange coefficient (see [8.4.36] in table 8.4.8); k is the first-order reaction rate constant (per unit volume of settled bed); L and L_{mf} are the expanded bed height and the height at minimum fluidization; u is the superficial gas velocity; and ϵ_b is the ratio of the volume of bubbles to the total bed volume $= (L - L_{mf})/L$ (see [8.4.26] in table 8.4.8).

The conversions for the simple models are as follows.

P model (plug flow): Over incremental bed height,

$$u \frac{dc}{dz} = - kc \tag{8.4.3}$$

Thus

$$c_{out} = 1 - \text{conversion} = \exp\left(\frac{-kL_{mf}}{u}\right) \tag{8.4.4}$$

$$= \exp(-N_R)$$

M model (complete mixing):

$$u(1 - c_{out}) = kL_{mf}c_{out} \tag{8.4.5}$$

Thus

$$1 - \text{conversion} = \frac{1}{1 + N_R} \tag{8.4.6}$$

Solution of the two-phase models assumes that the gas flow u_e in the emulsion phase is negligible (.i.e., the exit concentration of the bubble phase is a good approximation to the overall exit concentration from the bed). However, reaction occurs in both phases and gas exchange takes place between the phases. General relationships for the two-phase models are:

Bubble phase:

Change in concentration $=$ material exchanged $-$ material reacted
X bubble flow rate with emulsion in the bubble phase $\qquad$ [8.4.7]

Emulsion phase:

Material exchanged $=$ material reacted
with bubbles in the emulsion phase $\qquad$ [8.4.8]

Thus, P-P model (plug flow bubble phase, plug flow emulsion phase): For the bubble phase,

$$u \frac{dc_b}{d\zeta} = F_{be}\epsilon_b L (c_e - c_b) - kL_{mf}\gamma_S c_b \qquad [8.4.9]$$

where γ_S is the fraction of particles in the bubble phase (including cloud) based on total volume of particles (see [8.4.77]) and ζ is the dimensionless bed height $= Z/L$. Equation [8.4.9] becomes, for the bubble phase,

$$\frac{dc_b}{d\zeta} = N_M (c_e - c_b) - N_R \gamma_S c_b \qquad [8.4.10]$$

For the emulsion phase,

$$N_M (c_e - c_b) = - N_R (1 - \gamma_S) c_e \qquad [8.4.11]$$

The conversion obtained from [8.4.10] and [8.4.11] is given in table 8.4.5.

Table 8.4.5 Conversion from Simple Models (figure 8.4.2)

Model	$1 - $ conversion
Bubble-free	
P	$\exp(-N_R)$
M	$\dfrac{1}{1 + N_R}$
Two-phase	
P-P	$\exp\left(-N_R \left\{ \dfrac{N_M}{N_R} \left[\dfrac{1 - \gamma_S}{N_M/N_R + (1 - \gamma_S)} \right] + \gamma_S \right\}\right)$
M-M	$\left[1 + \gamma_S N_R + \dfrac{(1 - \gamma_S) N_M}{N_M/N_R + (1 - \gamma_S)} \right]^{-1}$
P-M	$\dfrac{1 + [\exp(-N_M)](N_R - 1)}{1 + N_R - \exp(-N_M)} \qquad \gamma_S = 0$
C	$\left\{ \dfrac{N_M/N_R + (1 - \gamma_S)}{(1 - \gamma_S)[1 + (N_R/n)\gamma_S + N_M/n] + (N_M/N_R)[1 + (N_R/n)\gamma_S]} \right\}^n$

M-M model (well-mixed bubble phase, well-mixed emulsion): For the bubble phase,

$$1 - c_b = N_M(c_b - c_e) + N_R \gamma_S c_b \qquad [8.4.12]$$

For the emulsion phase, [8.4.11] applies. The conversion is given in table 8.4.5.

P-M model (plug flow bubble phase, well-mixed emulsion): Assuming $\gamma_S \to 0$, the following equations apply. For the bubble phase,

$$\frac{dc_b}{d\zeta} = N_M(c_e - c_b) \qquad [8.4.13]$$

Overall balance:

$$1 - c_{out} = N_R c_e \qquad [8.4.14]$$

The conversion is given in table 8.4.5.

C model (compartments): The bed is split into n compartments and the general equations are, for the bubble phase,

$$c_{bi} - (c_b)_{i-1} = \frac{N_M}{n}(c_{ei} - c_{bi}) - \frac{N_R}{n}\gamma_S c_{bi} \qquad [8.4.15]$$

and for the emulsion phase,

$$\frac{N_M}{n}(c_{ei} - c_{bi}) = -\frac{N_R}{n}(1 - \gamma_S)c_{ei} \qquad [8.4.16]$$

The conversion is given in table 8.4.5.

Figure 8.4.3 shows the conversions from the various simple models for the case where $\gamma_S \to 0$; i.e., reaction occurs only in the emulsion phase (a reasonable first approximation). The compartment model (C) can be seen to approach the bubble-free plug flow model (P) when the number of compartments is appreciable $(n > 10)$. An estimate of n is obtained by assuming

$$n = \frac{L}{\bar{d}_b} \qquad [8.4.17]$$

where $\bar{d}_b$ is the estimated bubble size at mid-bed height. The value of F_{be} is itself related to $\bar{d}_b$ and recommended correlations for these two parameters are given in table 8.4.8. As noted above, level III bubbling models recognize the variation of d_b with height. They are, in effect, sophisticated versions of the C model. For example, the bubble assemblage model described in section 8.4.4 has a variable compartment size equal to the bubble size at a given level.

8.4.3.2 Application of Simple Models

Figure 8.4.3 or the relationships in table 8.4.5 may be used to estimate conversion in gas-fluidized beds. The most useful models are those designated M, P, P-P, and P-M, and the conditions appropriate to their application are outlined below.

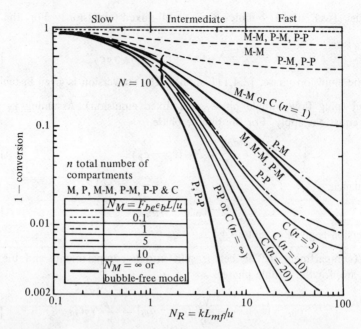

Figure 8.4.3 Conversions from simple models (see figure 8.4.2) (Horio & Wen 1977).

Slow Reactions ($k \leqslant 0.5$ s^{-1}, $N_R < 1.0$)

The predicted conversion is relatively insensitive to the value of N_M or the model used, because the system is limited by chemical reaction rather than mass transfer considerations. Almost any model may be used and the bubbleless P model is probably the most appropriate (the M model may be applied to estimate the lower limit of conversion). In this situation, emphasis should be placed on obtaining accurate kinetic data rather than assessing bed hydrodynamics.

Intermediate Reactions (nominally $0.5 < k < 5.0$ s^{-1}, $1 < N_R < 10$)

Conversion may be limited by chemical reaction or mass transfer between the bubble and the emulsion phase. The importance of the bed hydrodynamics requires the use of one of the bubble models, and the criteria should be (see section 8.1.10):

$$\text{P-P model applies if } \frac{u}{u_{mf}} < 6 \sim 11$$

$$\text{P-M model applies if } \frac{u}{u_{mf}} > 6 \sim 11$$

The parameter N_M becomes important and it can be either estimated from [8.4.1] and table 8.4.8, or determined experimentally. If the interaction between conversion and the dependent variables is to be evaluated with more confidence, it is necessary to apply a level III model (see section 8.4.3.4).

Fast Reactions (nominally $k > 5$ s^{-1}, $N_R > 10$)

For this type of reaction the conversion again becomes less sensitive to the bubble distribution and to mass transfer in the bubbling zone. Conversion is high in the grid region, where gas exchange is rapid, and in the freeboard, where dispersed phase contact occurs. The P-M model combined with a grid region model and a freeboard model is recommended and is considered in detail in section 8.4.5.

Turbulent and Fast Fluidized Reactors

The high superficial gas velocities and lack of conventional bubble structure suggest the use of a simple plug flow (P) model for these regimes. Table 8.4.6 compares the bed height requirements for fast reactors for a range of reaction rates for the P and P-M models.

Large-Scale Operation with Type A Powders

According to Van Swaaij (1978) and Van Swaaij & Zuiderweg (1973), the two-phase P-P model can be applied:

$$1 - \text{conversion} = \exp\left(-\frac{N_M N_R}{N_M + N_R}\right) \qquad [8.4.18]$$

or for large N_M the simple P model,

$$1 - \text{conversion} = \exp\left(-N_R\right) \qquad [8.4.19]$$

However, these simple models require adequate knowledge of N_M, which is presented in the form of L_M (the height of the gas mass transfer unit). Experimental data give the height of a mass transfer unit as

$$L_M = K^* \left(1.8 - \frac{1.06}{D^{0.25}}\right)\left(3.5 - \frac{2.5}{L^{0.25}}\right) \qquad [8.4.20]$$

Table 8.4.6   Length Required for Fast-Bed Reactors[a, b]

	L for 95% conversion (m)	
k for packed bed (s^{-1})	With no mass transfer limitation	With mass transfer limitation ($L_M = 2$ m)
0.1	500	500
1	50	56
3	17	23
10	5	11
30	1.7	9.8

[a]From Van Swaaij, W. P. M. in *Chemical Reaction Engineering Reviews— Houston,* D. Luss & V. W. Weekman, Jr., Eds., ACS SYMPOSIUM SERIES No. 72; American Chemical Society: Washington, D.C., 1978, p. 215.
[b]First-order reaction; $u = 5$ m/s; solids holdup = 18 vol %; plug flow model.

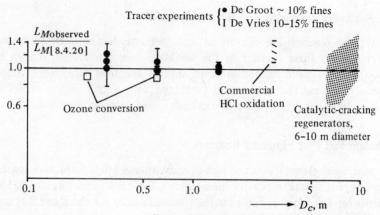

Chemical Reaction Engineering Reviews–Houston

Figure 8.4.4 Values of L_M, height of a mass transfer unit, for large-scale beds of type A powders compared with [8.4.20]. (Van Swaaij, W. P. M. in *Chemical Reaction Engineering Reviews–Houston*, D. Luss & V. W. Weekman, Jr., Eds., ACS SYMPOSIUM SERIES No. 72; American Chemical Society: Washington, D.C., 1978, p. 206.)

where K^* is a correction factor for varying fines ($<44\,\mu$m) content $= 1.2$ for 10% fines, 1.0 for 15% fines, and 0.8 for 20% fines. The height L_M is reported by Van Swaaij & Zuiderweg (1973) to be independent of reaction rate for $k < 2\ \text{s}^{-1}$ and to decrease for higher k. Figure 8.4.4 compares values from [8.4.20] with experimental data.

8.4.3.3 Model For Slug Flow Reactors

Slug flow tends to occur in small diameter fluidized beds typical of laboratory and pilot plant reactors. In addition, it can be deliberate policy to design larger commercial-scale reactors to operate in this regime to simplify scale-up (see section 8.4.6.3). The criteria for slug flow have been given in section 8.1.8.

A simple model for the case of a catalyzed gas phase reaction in a slugging bed has been presented by Hovmand & Davidson (1971). The development of the model is similar to that of the P-P model in section 8.4.3.1, except that reaction in the bubble phase is ignored and the flow through the emulsion phase is not neglected. Assuming the emulsion phase gas flow is u_{mf} (on a superficial area basis), write the following mass balances.

Mass balance over bed cross section:

$$u_{mf}\frac{dc_e}{d\zeta} + (u - u_{mf})\frac{dc_b}{d\zeta} + N_R c_e = 0 \qquad [8.4.21]$$

Mass balance on a rising slug:

$$\frac{dc_b}{d\zeta} + N_{Ms}(c_b - c_e) = 0 \qquad [8.4.22]$$

where N_R is given by [8.4.2] and N_{Ms} equals the number of gas exchange transfer units in the slugging bed (cf. [8.4.1]) = (gas exchange rate per slug volume) $\times$

(L/u_s). The gas exchange rate per slug volume is analogous to the gas exchange coefficient F_{be}, but it cannot be expected to have the same magnitude. A theoretical approximation of the gas exchange process by Hovmand & Davidson (1971) gives

$$N_{Ms} = \frac{L_{mf}}{0.35(gD)^{1/2} Dm} \left[u_{mf} + \frac{16\epsilon_{mf}I}{1 + \epsilon_{mf}} \left(\frac{\delta}{\pi}\right)^{1/2} \left(\frac{g}{D}\right)^{1/4} \right] \qquad [8.4.23]$$

where δ is the gas diffusivity and I is the surface integral over the slug surface. Table 8.4.7 gives an expression for the slug shape factor m and values of I for different values of L_s/D. The ratio L_s/D can be calculated from [8.1.65]. Solutions of [8.4.21] and [8.4.22] give

Slug flow reactor:

$$c_{\text{out}} = 1 - \text{conversion} = \frac{1}{m_1 - m_2}$$

$$\cdot \left[m_1 \exp\left(-m_2 L\right) \left(1 - \frac{m_2 L\alpha'}{N_{Ms}}\right) - m_2 \exp\left(-m_1 L\right) \left(1 - \frac{m_1 L\alpha'}{N_{Ms}}\right) \right] \qquad [8.4.24]$$

where m_1 and m_2 are the positive and negative roots from

$$2L\alpha' m_i = N_{Ms} + N_R \pm [(N_{Ms} + N_R)^2 - 4N_R N_{Ms}\alpha']^{1/2} \qquad [8.4.24a]$$

with $\alpha' = u_{mf}/u$.

Figure 8.4.5 compares [8.4.24] with experimental data for the decomposition of ozone. The agreement is reasonable, and certainly better than that with the simple well-mixed model (model M in table 8.4.5).

In summary, prediction of conversion in a slugging fluidized bed is as follows:

1. Check the slugging criteria in section 8.1.8; if slugging is not indicated, the need for a bubbling bed model should be assessed (section 8.4.3.2).

Table 8.4.7 Parameters to Use in Slug Flow Model [8.4.24][a]

$$\frac{L_s}{D} = 0.3 + \frac{3.9\,(u - u_{mf})}{0.35\,(gD)^{1/2}}$$

$$m = \frac{L_s}{D} - 0.495 \left(\frac{L_s}{D}\right)^{1/2} + 0.061$$

$\frac{L_s}{D} =$	0.3	0.5	1.0	2.0	3.0	4.0	5.0
$I =$	0.13	0.21	0.39	0.71	0.98	1.24	1.48

$$L = L_{mf} \left[1 + \frac{u - u_{mf}}{0.35\,(gD)^{1/2}} \right]$$

[a]Data from Hovmand & Davidson (1971).

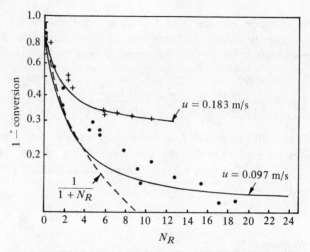

Figure 8.4.5 Slug flow model ([8.4.23] and [8.4.24]) compared with ozone decomposition in a 0.46-m-diameter reactor. With permission from Hovmand & Davidson (1971) in *Fluidization,* eds. J. F. Davidson & D. Harrison, p. 248. Copyright by Academic Press, Inc. (London) Ltd.

2. Calculate N_R for the specified bed depth and gas velocity [8.4.2].
3. Calculate N_{Ms} from [8.4.23] and the parameters in table 8.4.7.
4. Calculate the conversion from [8.4.24] and [8.4.24*a*].

8.4.3.4 Bubble Assemblage Model—Gas-Phase Reaction

Many models are available for predicting the performance of fluidized-bed reactors (table 8.4.3). Level III models are the most realistic, because they allow for variation of bubble size with bed height. One such model, the bubble assemblage model (BAM) (Kato & Wen 1969; Mori and Wen 1976), is described below.

An essential feature of the BAM is that the bed is divided into compartments whose heights are adjusted to the bubble sizes at that level. This greatly reduces computing time without loss of accuracy. For example, Shaw et al. (1974) compared the BAM with the level II model of Orcutt et al. (1962) and the level III model of Partridge & Rowe (1966) and found that it was more accurate and took 10–30% as much computing time. The BAM is depicted in figure 8.4.6. It relies on the following assumptions:

1. A fluidized bed may be represented by n compartments in series. The height of each compartment is equal to the size of each bubble at the corresponding bed height. A simple correlation for bubble growth is given by Kato & Wen (1969), as

$$d_b = 1.4\,\rho_S d_S \frac{u}{u_{mf}} Z + d_{b0} \qquad [8.4.25]$$

where d_{b0} is the initial bubble size ([8.1.55] and [8.1.56]).

Table 8.4.8 gives the compartment height ΔL_n based on [8.4.25]. A more comprehensive correlation for predicting d_b has been developed (Mori & Wen 1975) and [8.1.44]. Use of this in a modified BAM is discussed below.

2. Each compartment is considered to consist of a bubble phase and an emulsion phase; gas within each phase is considered completely mixed.

3. The void space within the emulsion phase is considered equal to that of the bed at incipient fluidization. The interstitial gas velocity is assumed to be negligibly small (i.e., $u_e \simeq 0$, which is reasonable for beds with $u/u_{mf} \simeq 6 \sim 11$).

4. The bubble phase is assumed to consist of spherical bubbles surrounded by spherical clouds. Table 8.4.8 gives the relationship between cloud diameter and bubble diameter as predicted by Davidson (1961). It should be noted that this relationship applies to large values of $\tilde{u}_b^+ (= u_{br}\epsilon_{mf}/u_{mf})$. For situations where this does not apply (e.g., with large particles) the BAM would need to be modified (e.g., Zabrodsky et al. 1972).

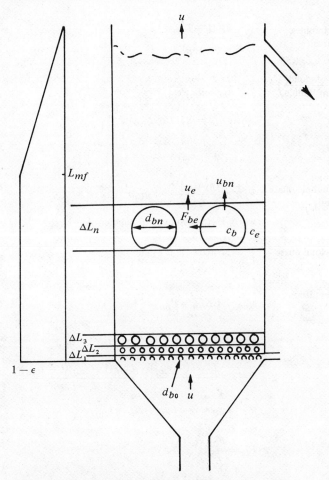

Figure 8.4.6 BAM of Kato & Wen (1969). See table 8.4.8 for parameter relationships.

Table 8.4.8 Relationships Used in the BAM

Parameter	Relationship	Equation
Average bubble size	$\bar{d}_b = 1.4\,\rho_S d_S \dfrac{u}{u_{mf}} \dfrac{L_{mf}}{2} + d_{b_0}$	[8.4.25a]^a
Bed expansion ratio	$\dfrac{L - L_{mf}}{L_{mf}} = \dfrac{\epsilon_b}{1 - \epsilon_b} = \dfrac{u - u_{mf}}{0.711\,(g\bar{d}_b)^{1/2}}$	[8.4.26]
Compartment height	$\Delta L_n = \dfrac{2d_{b_0}\,(2 + m)^{n-1}}{(2 - m)^n}$	[8.4.27]^a
	where $m = 1.4\,\rho_S d_S \dfrac{u}{u_{mf}}$	
	d_{b_0} see [8.1.55]	
Number of bubbles in compartment	$N = \dfrac{6A\,(L - L_{mf})}{\pi L (\Delta L_n)^2}$	[8.4.28]
$\left(\dfrac{\text{Diameter of cloud}}{\text{Diameter of bubble}}\right)^3$	$r = \dfrac{u_{br} + 2u_{mf}/\epsilon_{mf}}{u_{br} - u_{mf}/\epsilon_{mf}}$	[8.4.29]
	where $u_{br} = 0.711\,(g\,\Delta L_n)^{1/2}$	[8.4.30]
	$\geqslant \dfrac{u_{mf}}{\epsilon_{mf}}$	
Volume of bubble phase (void + cloud)	$V_{bn} = \dfrac{N\pi(\Delta L_n)^3 r}{6} = V_{bVn} r$	[8.4.31]
	where $V_{bVn} = $ volume of bubble void	
Volume of cloud phase	$V_{cn} = \dfrac{N\pi(\Delta L_n)^3\,(r - 1)}{6}$	[8.4.32]
Volume of emulsion phase	$V_{en} = A\,\Delta L_n - V_{bn}$	[8.4.33]
Voidage	$1 - \epsilon = \dfrac{L_{mf}\,(1 - \epsilon_{mf})}{L} \qquad Z \leqslant L_{mf}$	[8.4.34a]
	$1 - \epsilon = \dfrac{L_{mf}\,(1 - \epsilon_{mf})}{L} - \dfrac{L_{mf}\,(1 - \epsilon_{mf})(L - L_{mf})}{2L(L - L_{mf})}$	[8.4.34b]
	for $\quad L_{mf} \leqslant Z \leqslant L_{mf} + 2(L - L_{mf})$	
Gas exchange coefficient	$F'_{be} = \dfrac{F_{be}}{r}$	[8.4.35]
	and $F_{be} = \dfrac{11}{d_b}$	[8.4.36]

^{a}Alternative relationship in table 8.4.9.

5. The total volume of gas bubbles within the bed is $(L - L_{mf})A$.

6. Gas exchange occurs between the two phases. An empirical relationship between exchange coefficient F_{be} and bubble size is [8.4.36] in table 8.4.8. (Further details are given in section 8.3.3.) No allowance has been made for possible adsorption of gas onto solids.

7. Voidage is constant from the bottom of the bed to a bed height corresponding to L_{mf}. It then increases linearly to unity at a level corresponding to $L_{mf} + 2(L - L_{mf})$. Table 8.4.8 details the relationships for voidage computation.

The BAM relies on solving the mass balance equations around each compartment, from the bottom to the top of the bed. Mass balance for the bubble phase in the nth compartment gives

$$Au[(c_b)_{n-1} - (c_b)_n] = [F'_{be}V_b(c_b - c_e)]_n + (r_bV_c)_n \qquad [8.4.37]$$

where F'_{be} is the gas exchange coefficient per unit volume of bubbles (see table 8.4.8); r_b is the reaction rate in the cloud per unit volume (of solids at voidage $\epsilon_{mf}) = kc_b$ for first-order reaction with respect to gas composition; and V_b and V_c are, respectively, the total volume of the bubble phase (void and cloud) and the volume of the cloud phase in the compartment (see table 8.4.8). A mass balance for the emulsion phase gives

$$[F'_{be}V_b(c_b - c_e)]_n = (r_eV_e)_n \qquad [8.4.38]$$

where $r_e = kc_e$ for first-order reaction, and V_e is the volume of the emulsion phase (see table 8.4.8). Note that since the emulsion phase gas flow rate is assumed to be negligibly small, [8.4.37] and [8.4.38] are analogous in form to [8.4.10] and [8.4.11] for the simple P-P model.

The BAM as represented by [8.4.25]-[8.4.38] can be solved by computer simulation; the appropriate logic diagram is shown as figure 8.4.7. Examples of the output from the model are presented in figures 8.4.8–8.4.10 and may be summarized as follows:

1. Figure 8.4.8; slow reaction: the concentration of gas in the emulsion phase is not greatly different from that in the bubble phase.
2. Figure 8.4.9; fast reaction: the concentration of gas in the emulsion phase is considerably lower than that in the bubble phase, particularly close to the bottom of the bed (grid region).
3. Figure 8.4.10; comparison with P and M models: the BAM is clearly more effective than the simple homogeneous models, particularly for $N_R > 1.0$. (This agrees with the general trends discussed in section 8.4.3.2.)

The modified BAM (Mori & Wen 1976) makes use of a more comprehensive correlation for bubble size (Mori & Wen 1975), which allows for the effect of vessel diameter. In addition, the grid region is treated as a jetting region and is related to the predicted jet height. (More details of this are given in section 8.4.5.1.) Table 8.4.9 lists the relationships for d_b and compartment height ΔL_n used in the modified BAM. Figure 8.4.11 shows how the model accounts for the increased

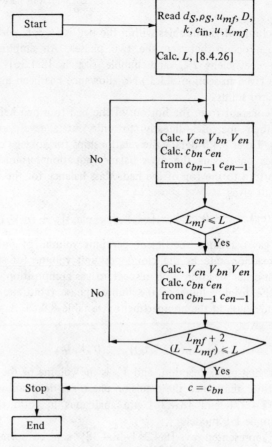

Figure 8.4.7 Logic diagram for computer simulation of BAM for gas-phase reactions (Kato & Wen 1969).

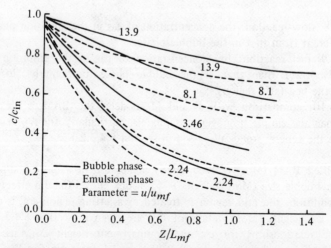

Figure 8.4.8 Relationship between concentration profile and bed height for slow reaction ($k = 0.07$ s^{-1}) from the BAM (Kato & Wen 1969).

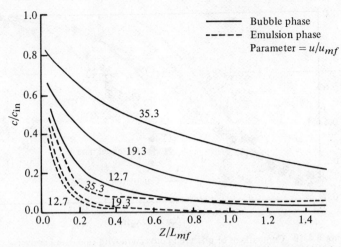

Figure 8.4.9 Relationship between concentration profile and bed height for fast reaction ($k = 9$ s^{-1}) from the BAM (Kato & Wen 1969).

conversion for a larger number of holes in a perforated plate distributor and figure 8.4.12 shows the effect of bed diameter on conversion (Mori & Wen 1976).

The BAM is amenable to further modification as new correlations or models become available for such parameters as bubble size, gas exchange coefficient, and jet height.

Table 8.4.9 Relationships in the Modified BAM

Parameter	Relationship	Equation
Bubble size at given level (L)	$d_b = d_{bm} - (d_{bm} - d_{b0}) \exp\left(-0.3 \dfrac{L'}{D}\right)$ where $L' = L - L_J$ L_J = jet height [8.1.54]	[8.1.44]
Maximum bubble size	$d_{bm} = 0.652\, [A(u - u_{mf})]^{2/5}$	[8.1.43]
Initial bubble size	$d_{b0} = 0.00376\, (u - u_{mf})^2$ (porous plate)	[8.1.56]
	$d_{b0} = 0.347 \left[\dfrac{A(u - u_{mf})}{N_{or}}\right]^{2/5}$ (perforated) where N_{or} = number of perforations	[8.1.55]
Compartment height	$\Delta L_n = \dfrac{d'_{bn}}{1 + 0.15\,(d'_{bn} - d_{bm})/D}$ where $d'_{bn} = d_b$ $\left(\text{at } L = \displaystyle\sum_{i=1}^{n-1} \Delta L_i\right)$	[8.4.39]

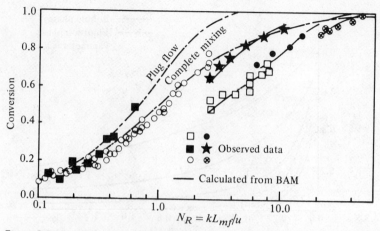

Figure 8.4.10 Comparison of observed conversion with calculated conversion based on plug flow and the complete mixing model and BAM (Mori & Wen 1976).

8.4.4 GAS-SOLID REACTIONS

This section deals with noncatalytic reactions represented in general form by

$$A \text{ (gas)} + b\text{B (solid)} \rightarrow \text{products (gas and/or solid)}$$

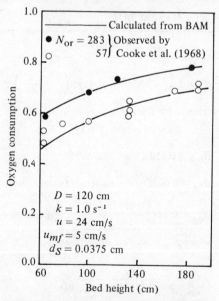

Figure 8.4.11 Effect of distributor design on conversion: experiment compared with the BAM (Mori & Wen 1976). (Note: N_{or} = number of holes in perforated plate.)

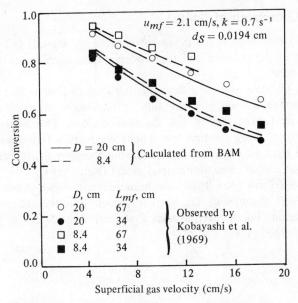

Figure 8.4.12 Effect of bed diameter on conversion: experiment compared with the BAM (Mori & Wen 1976).

The particles comprising the solid phase may remain unchanged in size, or they may shrink or grow as the reaction proceeds. Table 8.4.10 summarizes the particle size history for commercial and semicommercial gas-solid reactions of importance. In a number of cases the gas phase is either inert or in considerable excess, and attention is focused only on conversion of the solid phase (section 8.4.4.1). In other cases the conversion of both phases is of interest (section 8.4.4.2). Section 8.4.4 deals with reactions in the bed region only; reactions occurring above the bed (in the freeboard) are discussed in section 8.4.5.

Table 8.4.10 Particle Size History for Gas-Solid Reactions

	Particle history		
Gas-solid reaction	Size unchanged	Shrink	Grow
Coal combustion		X	
Coal carbonization	X		
Coal gasification	X		
Uranium processing	$(UO_2 \rightarrow UF_4)$	$(UF_4 \rightarrow UF_6)$	$(UO_3)^a$
	X	X	X
Roasting ores	X		
Calcining ores	X		
Iron ore reduction	X		
Spent liquor processing			X^a

[a]Solid phase formed from liquid sprayed in the bed.

8.4.4.1 Conversion of Solids

The two factors that control the degree of conversion of solids in a fluidized bed are the kinetics of the reaction and the residence time distribution of the particles in the reaction zone.

The extent of conversion of a single particle may be limited by (1) diffusion of species through the surrounding gas film, (2) diffusion of species through the product layer, or (3) the rate of the chemical reaction. Two models are usually considered, the first being reaction throughout the particle (homogeneous reaction model) and the second being reaction at a moving boundary (shrinking core model), although both are special cases of a general model (Wen 1968).

In its simplest form (Wen 1968) the homogeneous model assumes that gaseous reactant is present throughout the particle, which is isothermal and uniform in solids concentration. For a reaction with first-order dependence on gas concentration, the rate of reaction is

$$\frac{dc_S}{dt} = - k_V c_A c_S \qquad [8.4.40]$$

And because

$$c_S = c_{S0}(1 - X_B) \qquad [8.4.41]$$

$$\frac{dX_B}{dt} = k_V c_A (1 - X_B) \qquad [8.4.42]$$

where c_A, c_S, and c_{S0} are the molar concentrations of gaseous reactant, solid reactant, and initial solid reactant; k_V is the reaction rate constant per unit volume of solid; and X_B is the extent of conversion of solid phase. If c_A and k_V are constant

$$X_B = 1 - \exp\left(- k_V c_A t\right) \qquad [8.4.43]$$

Complete conversion is obtained only when $t \to \infty$. However, it is possible to define the time for almost complete conversion as

$$t^*_{0.999} = \frac{6.908}{k_V c_A} \qquad [8.4.44]$$

where $t^*_{0.999}$ is the time for 99.9% conversion for a reaction with homogeneous kinetics.

The shrinking core model is most conveniently expressed in terms of the rate-controlling step. Table 8.4.11 presents the kinetic relationship for fluid film control, chemical reaction control, and ash diffusion control. Levenspiel (1962) and Wen (1968) give detailed derivations and indicate how to distinguish among the various models. Equations [8.4.49] and [8.4.52] are useful approximations for the case where chemical reaction and ash diffusion are similar in magnitude.

For the case of a shrinking particle that is not surrounded by a product layer (either because of ablation of the ash or because the product is gaseous) [8.4.49] should be used. If diffusion through the gas film presents a resistance comparable to chemical reaction, [8.4.52] should be modified to

Table 8.4.11   Reaction Models for Conversion of Solids in Single Particles[a, b]

	A (gas) + b B (solid) → products	
Homogeneous model	$X_B = 1 - \exp(-k_V c_A t)$	[8.4.43]
	$t/t^*_{0.999} = \dfrac{\ln[1/(1-X_B)]}{6.908}$	[8.4.45]
	$t^*_{0.999} = \dfrac{6.908}{k_V c_A}$	[8.4.44]
Shrinking core: fluid film control	$t/t^* = X_B$ (equivalent to zero-order kinetics)	[8.4.46]
	$t^* = \dfrac{d_S \rho_{Sm}}{6 b K_f c_A}$	[8.4.47]
Shrinking core: chemical reaction control[c]	$t/t^* = 1 - (1-X_B)^{1/3}$	[8.4.48]
	$t^* = \dfrac{d_S \rho_{Sm}}{2 b k_c c_A}$	[8.4.49]
Shrinking core: ash diffusion control[c]	$t/t^* = 1 - 3(1-X_B)^{2/3} + 2(1-X_B)$	[8.4.50]
	$t^* = \dfrac{d_S^2 \rho_{Sm}}{24 b \delta_{fa} c_A}$	[8.4.51]

[a]X_B = extent of conversion; t^* = time for complete conversion.
[b]δ_{fa} is the diffusion coefficient of gas in ash layer (cm^2/s); K_f, the fluid-particle mass transfer coefficient (cm/s); k_c, the rate constant for chemical reaction based on particle surface (cm/s); k_V, the rate constant based on particle volume (cm^3/mol s); and ρ_{Sm}, the molar density of solid reactant (mol/cm^3).
[c]When chemical reaction and ash diffusion are similar in magnitude, [8.4.49] may be used with k_c replaced by $\bar{k}$, where

$$\frac{1}{\bar{k}} = \frac{1}{k_c} + \frac{d_S}{12\delta_{fa}}$$
[8.4.52]

$$\frac{1}{\bar{k}} = \frac{1}{k_c} + \frac{1}{K_f}$$
[8.4.53]

The mean conversion $\bar{X}_B$ of a group of particles passing through a fluidized-bed reactor is obtained by combining the kinetic equations [8.4.43]–[8.4.51] with the residence time distribution. Thus,

$$1 - \bar{X}_B = \int_{t=0}^{t=t^*} (1 - X_B) E(t)\, dt$$
[8.4.54]

where $E(t)$ is the exit age distribution function for the system, and t^* is the time for complete conversion of a single particle.

For single fluidized beds the solids can be assumed to be in back-mix flow (Yagi & Kunii 1961); i.e.,

$$E(t) = \frac{1}{\bar{t}} e^{-t/\bar{t}} \qquad [8.4.55]$$

where
$$\bar{t} = \frac{M_S}{\dot{M}_S} \qquad [8.4.56]$$

is the mean residence time, $\dot{M}_S$ is the solids mass flow rate (leaving the bed, unless the particle shrinks, in which case the solids feed rate may be used for rough estimation), and M_S is the mass of reacting solids in the system. For N beds in series the exit age distribution is

$$E(t) = \frac{1}{(N-1)!\bar{t}_i} \left(\frac{t}{\bar{t}_i}\right)^{N-1} e^{-t/\bar{t}_i} \qquad [8.4.57]$$

where $\bar{t}_i = \bar{t}/N$.

Solutions of [8.4.54] for single and multiple beds in series are given in table 8.4.12. The variation of conversion $\bar{X}_B$ with $1/\beta$ ($= \bar{t}/t^*$) is shown in figure 8.4.13 for selected conditions; this figure can be used as a quick guide to the required mean residence time for a specified conversion.

The development so far has neglected the effect of elutriation of fine particles on the residence time distribution. This refinement has been considered by Kunii & Levenspiel (1969). Thus, if a distribution of sizes exists,

$$\sum_{i=1}^{n} f_i = 1$$

where f_i is the fraction of particles of the characteristic size d_{Si}. Each size fraction passes through a single bed with an exit age distribution

$$E(d_{Si}, t) = \frac{1}{\bar{t}(d_{Si})} e^{-t/\bar{t}(d_{Si})} \qquad [8.4.67]$$

where
$$\bar{t}(d_{Si}) = \frac{M_S/\dot{M}_S}{1 + (M_S/\dot{M}_S)(1 - K_{1i})K_{2i}} \qquad [8.4.68]$$

with K_{1i} the collection efficiency of a cyclone system for particles of size d_{Si} and K_{2i} the elutriation constant for particles of size d_{Si}. (In the absence of experimental data, K_{2i} may be estimated from various correlations as outlined in section 8.1.13.) The mean conversion of solids passing through the system is then obtained from

$$1 - \bar{X}_B = \sum_{i=1}^{n} (1 - \bar{X}_{Bi}) f_i \qquad [8.4.69]$$

To use [8.4.69] the term $(1 - \bar{X}_{Bi})$ must be estimated from the appropriate equation in table 8.4.12, taking into account the effect of d_{Si} on extent of conversion and allowing for the differences in $\bar{t}(d_{Si})$ using [8.4.68].

Table 8.4.12 Conversion of Solids ($\bar{X}_B$) for Single- and N-Stage Fluidized Beds for Specified Kinetic Models[a]

Homogeneous model

Single stage

$$1 - \bar{X}_B = \frac{1}{1 + k_{VC_A}\bar{t}}$$ [8.4.58]

N stages in series

$$1 - \bar{X}_B = \left(\frac{1}{1 + k_{VC_A}\bar{t}/N}\right)^N$$ [8.4.59]

or, in terms of time for single particle to reach 99.9% conversion,

$$1 - \bar{X}_B = \left(\frac{1}{1 + 6.908\bar{t}/t^*_{0.999}}\right)^N$$ [8.4.60]

Shrinking core: fluid film control (or zero-order kinetics)

Single stage

$$1 - \bar{X}_B = 1 - \frac{1}{\beta}(1 - e^{-\beta})$$ [8.4.61]

N stages

$$1 - \bar{X}_B = 1 - \frac{1}{\beta} + e^{-\beta N}\left[\frac{1}{\beta} + \sum_{m=0}^{N-1}\frac{m(N\beta)^{N-m-1}}{(N-m)!}\right]$$ [8.4.62]

where

$$\beta = t^*/\bar{t} \quad \text{and} \quad \bar{t} = N\bar{t}_i$$

Shrinking core: chemical reaction control

Single stage

$$1 - \bar{X}_B = 1 - 3\left(\frac{1}{\beta}\right) + 6\left(\frac{1}{\beta}\right)^2 - 6\left(\frac{1}{\beta}\right)^3(1 - e^{-\beta})$$ [8.4.63]

or, for $1/\beta > 1$,[b]

$$1 - \bar{X}_B \simeq 0.25\,\beta - 0.05\,\beta^2 + 0.0083\,\beta^3$$ [8.4.64]

N stages

$$1 - \bar{X}_B = \sum_{m=0}^{N-1}\frac{(N-m+2)!}{(N-m-1)!m!}(\beta N)^{m-3}e^{-\beta N}$$

$$+ \sum_{m=0}^{3}\frac{(N+m-1)!\,3!}{(N-1)!m!(3-m)!}\left(-\frac{1}{\beta N}\right)^m$$ [8.4.65]

Shrinking core: ash diffusion control

Single stage[b]

$$1 - \bar{X}_B = 0.2\,\beta - 0.045\,\beta^2 + 0.0089\,\beta^3 - 0.0015\,\beta^4$$ [8.4.66]

---

[a]Table 8.4.11.
[b]For $(1/\beta) > 5$, the first terms in [8.4.64] and [8.4.66] give a good approximation.

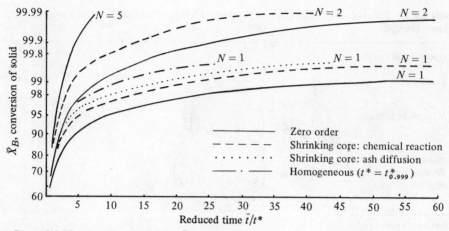

Figure 8.4.13 Conversion of solids ($\bar{X}_B$) for N stages in series for specified kinetic models (see tables 8.4.11 and 8.4.12).

8.4.4.2 Conversion of Gas and Solids

When conversion of both gas and solid is to be considered, the calculation procedure becomes more complex because reaction rates are assumed to be related to the compositions in both phases. In this case iterative calculations are inevitable. Two methods are presented here; one is amenable to hand calculation, the other is a development of the BAM and requires a computer.

P-P Model

A simple P-P model (plug flow in both bubble phase and emulsion phase) for conversion in the gas phase has been described in section 8.4.3.1. This model can be extended to account for conversion in the solid phase.

Assume a reaction

$$A \text{ (gas)} + b \text{ B (solid)} \rightarrow \text{products} \qquad [8.4.70]$$

and let $\bar{X}_A$ and $\bar{X}_B$ be conversion in the gas phase and the solid phase, respectively; $\bar{X}_A$ and $\bar{X}_B$ are related by mass balance and the appropriate kinetic equations.

An overall mass balance gives

$$(uA)c_{A\text{in}}\bar{X}_A b = w_S c_{SB\text{in}} \bar{X}_B \qquad [8.4.71]$$

where A is the bed cross-sectional area, b is the stoichiometric coefficient for [8.4.70], $c_{A\text{in}}$ and $c_{SB\text{in}}$ are the molar concentrations of gas and solid in feed streams, and w_S is the volumetric feed rate of solids. The conversion in the gas phase is (from table 8.4.5)

$$\bar{X}_A = 1 - \exp\left(-N_R\left\{\frac{N_M}{N_R}\left[\frac{1 - \gamma_S}{N_M/N_R + (1 - \gamma_S)}\right] + \gamma_S\right\}\right) \qquad [8.4.72]$$

Parameters N_M and N_R are defined by [8.4.1] and [8.4.2]. Application of [8.4.72] relies on [8.4.75] and [8.4.77]. The first-order rate constant k (incorporated into N_R) can no longer be assumed independent of solids concentration. For a shrinking core model with surface reaction, we can write

$$\frac{- dN_A}{dt} = 4\pi r_c^2 k_c c_A \quad \text{(per particle)} \qquad [8.4.73]$$

where k_c is the rate constant based on particle surface (see also table 8.4.11, footnote c), N_A is the number of moles of A, and r_c is the radius of unreacted core $= d_S (1 - X_B)^{1/3}/2$. Thus,

$$-\left(\frac{1 - \epsilon_{mf}}{V_p}\right)\frac{dN_A}{dt} = \left[\frac{6(1 - X_B)^{2/3}(1 - \epsilon_{mf})\, k_c}{d_S}\right] c_A \quad \begin{array}{l}\text{(per unit volume} \\ \text{of settled bed)}\end{array}$$

$$[8.4.74]$$

From [8.4.74], the first-order rate constant k (based on a unit volume of settled bed) is

$$k = \frac{6(1 - X_B)^{2/3}(1 - \epsilon_{mf})\, k_c}{d_S} \qquad [8.4.75]$$

The parameter γ_s (fraction of particles in the bubble phase based on total volume of particles) is the ratio of the volume of solids in the clouds and wakes of bubbles to the volume of the bubble-free bed; thus,

$$\gamma_S = \frac{\text{volume of bubbles}}{\text{volume of bed without bubbles}}\left(\frac{\text{volume of cloud}}{\text{volume of bubble}} + \frac{\text{volume of wake}}{\text{volume of bubble}}\right)$$

$$= \left(1 - r + \frac{V_W}{V_{bV}}\right)\left(\frac{\epsilon_b}{1 - \epsilon_b}\right) \qquad [8.4.76]$$

or
$$\gamma_S \cong \left(\frac{\epsilon_b}{1 - \epsilon_b}\right)\left(\frac{V_W}{V_{bV}}\right) = \frac{\delta_W \epsilon_b}{1 - \epsilon_b} \qquad [8.4.77]$$

where r is given by [8.4.29] and V_W is the wake volume. The wake fraction δ_W is plotted on figure 8.1.8.

Solid particles react in the bubble phase (i.e., the clouds and wakes) and in the emulsion phase. Because the gas concentrations in these phases differ, the effective mean gas composition is

$$\bar{c}_A = \gamma_S \bar{c}_b + (1 - \gamma_S)\,\bar{c}_e \qquad [8.4.78]$$

where $\bar{c}_b$ and $\bar{c}_e$ are the mean gas concentrations in the bubble and emulsion phases. The change of bubble concentration through the bed is typically exponential, which allows as a first approximation the use of a log mean bubble concentration:

$$\bar{c}_b = \frac{c_{A\,in}(\bar{X}_A)}{\ln{(1 - \bar{X}_A)}^{-1}} \qquad [8.4.79]$$

The mean emulsion-phase concentration can be obtained through [8.4.11]:

$$\bar{c}_e = \frac{\bar{c}_b}{1 + (N_R/N_M)(1 - \gamma_s)} \qquad [8.4.80]$$

The conversion in the solid phase, assuming a single back-mix stage and shrinking core kinetics with chemical reaction control, is (from table 8.4.12)

$$\bar{X}_B = 1 - 0.25\beta + 0.05\beta^2 - 0.0083\beta^3 \qquad (\beta < 1) \qquad [8.4.81]$$

where $\beta = t^*/\bar{t}$, $\bar{t}$ is the mean residence time for solids, and t^* is the time for complete reaction of solids in a gas of composition $\bar{c}_A$ (see [8.4.49] and table 8.4.11).

To use this P-P model, [8.4.71] –[8.4.81] must be solved simultaneously. The following steps are recommended:

1. Calculate N_M from [8.4.1] and γ_s from [8.4.77]; these parameters remain unchanged for a specified gas flow rate, bed diameter, and depth.
2. Guess a value of $\bar{X}_B{}^*$ and calculate k from [8.4.75].
3. Put k into N_R [8.4.2] and estimate $\bar{X}_A$ from [8.4.72].
4. Calculate $\bar{c}_b$ from [8.4.79], then $\bar{c}_e$ from [8.4.80] and then $\bar{c}_A$ from [8.4.77].
5. Calculate t^* and $\bar{X}_B$ from [8.4.81].
6. Check whether values of $\bar{X}_A$ and $\bar{X}_B$ comply with the mass balance, [8.4.71]. If they do not, return to step 2.

Before using this simple P-P model it is advisable to read sections 8.4.2.3, 8.4.3.1, and 8.4.3.2. There are other models that are amenable to hand calculation, notably that of Kunii & Levenspiel (1969).

Bubble Assemblage Model

A more detailed analysis of the conversion of gas and solids (e.g., evaluation of concentration profiles, complex reactions, effects of scale-up, etc.) requires computer simulation. The BAM described in section 8.4.3.4 for catalytic gas-phase reactions, can be readily adapted to handle noncatalytic gas-solid reactions (Yoshida & Wen 1970).

The assumptions in the model are as follows:

1-7. Identical to those given in section 8.4.3.4.

8. The solids are distributed between the two phases of the bed as

$$j_c = \frac{\text{volume of solids in clouds and wakes}}{\text{volume of bubbles}}$$

$$= \gamma_S (1 - \epsilon_{mf}) \left(\frac{1 - \epsilon_b}{\epsilon_b} \right) \qquad [8.4.82]$$

---

*To assist in the initial guess for $\bar{X}_B$ (which will usually approach unity) carry out the following: (1) assuming $\bar{X}_B = 1.0$, estimate $\bar{X}_A$ via [8.4.71], and (2) follow steps 4 and 5 above to give an initial guess for $\bar{X}_B$ for use in step 2.

where γ_S is the fraction of total particles in the bubble phase (see [8.4.77]) and $j_e =$ volume of solids in emulsion/volume of bubbles.

But solids mass balance (neglecting solids dispersed in the bubble voids) requires that

$$\epsilon_b\,(j_c + j_e) = (1 - \epsilon_{mf})\,(1 - \epsilon_b)$$

thus,

$$j_e = (1 - \epsilon_{mf}) \left(\frac{1 - \epsilon_b}{\epsilon_b}\right) - j_c \qquad [8.4.83]$$

9. Solids are carried upward in the wakes of rising bubbles, and this is compensated by a downward flow of solids in the emulsion phase. The net movement of solids depends on whether the bed is fed at the base (cocurrent feed) or the top (countercurrent feed). The total upward volumetric solids flow rate w_{bn} for compartment n is

$$w_{bn} = \left(\frac{w_S}{A} + \frac{\delta_w A_{bn} u_{bn}}{A_{bn}}\right) A_{bn} \qquad [8.4.84]$$

where A_{bn} is the cross-sectional area for bubble flow in compartment $n = N(\pi/4)$ $(\Delta L_n)^2$ (see table 8.4.8 for N and ΔL_n) and w_S is the volumetric feed rate (positive for cocurrent and negative for countercurrent feed). The total downward volumetric solids flow rate $w_{e(n+1)}$ into the compartment is

$$w_{e(n+1)} = \left(\frac{\delta_w A_{bn} u_{bn}}{A - A_{bn}} - \frac{w_S}{A}\right)(A - A_{bn}) \qquad [8.4.85]$$

10. Solids interchange occurs between the bubble and the emulsion. This mechanism can be represented by an interchange coefficient such as those proposed by Yoshida & Kunii (1968) and Chiba & Kobayashi (1977). For example, according to Yoshida and Kunii,

$$(K_{be})_{bS} \cong 3\,\frac{(1 - \epsilon_{mf})\,u_{mf} u_b}{\epsilon_{mf} u_{br} d_b} \qquad [8.4.86]$$

where $(K_{be})_{bS}$ is the coefficient of interchange (unit s^{-1}) of solids between the bubble and emulsion phases, based on the volume of a bubble, u_{br} is the rise velocity of an isolated bubble $= 0.711\,(g d_b)^{1/2}$, and u_b is the bubble velocity in the bubbling bed $= u_{br} + u - u_{mf}$. A simplifying assumption is that solids interchange is infinite in each compartment, which is equivalent to saying that the solids are completely mixed in each compartment. [An alternative approach, [8.4.92]-[8.4.94] below, shows how finite values of $(K_{be})_{bS}$ may be used.]

The development of the model is summarized below. A first-order reaction rate constant similar to that in [8.4.75] is defined as

$$K_r = \frac{6\,(1 - X_B)^{2/3} k_c}{d_S} \qquad [8.4.87]$$

where K_r is the reaction rate constant based on a unit volume of particles $[= k/(1 - \epsilon_{mf})]$.

The conversion of gas is described by mass balances around the nth compartment (analogous to [8.4.37] and [8.4.38]). Thus,

Bubble phase:

$$Au[(c_b)_{n-1} - (c_b)_n] = [F_{be}V_{bV}(c_b - c_e)]_n + [j_c V_{bV}K_r c_b]_n \quad [8.4.88]$$

(It should be noted that the gas exchange coefficient F_{be} and the parameter j_c [8.4.82] are based on the bubble void volume V_{bV}. Relationships for F_{be} and V_{bV} are given in table 8.4.8.)

Emulsion phase:

$$[F_{be}V_{bV}(c_b - c_e)]_n = [j_e V_{bV}K_r c_e]_n \quad [8.4.89]$$

Conversion of solids is treated in a fashion similar to that described for the P-P model above. Thus with complete mixing of solids in each compartment (assumption 10 above) the particles "see" an effective gas concentration given by

$$\bar{c}_{An} = \frac{(j_c c_b)_n + (j_e c_e)_n}{j_c + j_e} \quad [8.4.90]$$

This value of $\bar{c}_{An}$ can then be used to calculate t^* in [8.4.49] (table 8.4.11).

The mean residence time of particles in the nth compartment is

$$\bar{t}_n = \frac{[V_{bV}(j_c + j_e)]}{w_S} \quad [8.4.91]$$

With [8.4.49], [8.4.90], and [8.4.91], the mean conversion $\bar{X}_{Bn}$ of solids in the nth compartment may be calculated using [8.4.63] in table 8.4.12. Details of the procedure and worked examples are given in Yoshida & Wen (1970), and the model is extended to parallel and successive reactions in Yoshida & Wen (1971).

A further development of the BAM distinguishes between the solids in the emulsion and the solids in the bubble phase (Ishida & Wen 1973). In this modification the bed is divided into $2n$ compartments, n representing the bubble phase and n representing the emulsion phase. The relationship between compartments is depicted in figure 8.4.14, where each phase is represented by a compartment in series model and, at a given level, interchange of gas and solid may take place between phases.

The mass balance relationships for the solids become:

Emulsion phase (figure 8.4.14):

$$\begin{bmatrix} \text{Solids flowing out of } (2j-1) \text{ or} \\ \text{consumed in } (2j-1) \end{bmatrix} - \begin{bmatrix} \text{solids flowing into} \\ (2j-1) \end{bmatrix} = 0 \quad [8.4.92]$$

$$[F_e + K_{bS}L_j + k_V c_{A(2j-1)}V_{S(2j-1)}]\,Y_{(2j-1)} - K_{bS}L_jY_{2j} - F_eY_{(2j+1)} = 0 \quad [8.4.93]$$

where c_A is the molar gas concentration; F_e, the volumetric flux of solids in the emulsion phase (based on a unit cross section of bed) (m/s); K_{bS}, the coefficient of interchange of solids based on a unit volume of bed $= (K_{be})_{bS}\,\epsilon_b$, where $(K_{be})_{bS}$ is given by [8.4.86]; k_V, the reaction rate constant for the homogeneous reaction

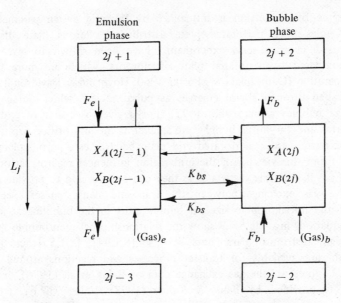

Figure 8.4.14 BAM for gas-solids reactions: relationship between compartments.

model [8.4.43]; V_S, the volume of solid particles in the compartment (per unit cross-sectional area); and Y, the fraction of unreacted solid $(= 1 - \bar{X}_B)$.

Bubble phase:

$$[F_b + K_{bs}L_j + k_V c_{A(2j)} V_{S(2j)}] Y_{2j} - K_{bs}L_j Y_{(2j-1)} - F_b Y_{(2j-2)} = 0 \qquad [8.4.94]$$

Reactor performance is calculated by simultaneously solving the $2n$ equations describing the $2n$ compartments and linking the calculated solids compositions to the gas compositions by mass balance. Further details of the procedure and worked examples are given by Ishida & Wen (1973).

8.4.5 END EFFECTS

The calculation procedures given in sections 8.4.3 and 8.4.4 deal only with the bubbling zone. However, the idealized fluidized bed (figure 8.4.1) distinguishes between the bubbling zone and the regions on either side of it, the grid region and the freeboard region. This section discusses the significance of these two important regions.

8.4.5.1 Grid Region

It is generally accepted that the design of the grid (or gas distributor) is crucial to the success of a fluidized-bed reactor. Grid design is discussed in section 8.1.6 and in Davidson et al. (1977). Experimental evidence (Cooke et al. 1968) indicates that with fast reactions most of the conversion occurs in the lower part of the bed and that the degree of conversion is influenced by the grid design parameters (e.g., number of holes in a perforated plate distributor). Porous plate distributors, commonly used in small-scale experiments, have been shown to give increased efficiency compared to perforated plate distributors, which are more typical of large-scale operation (Gomezplata & Shuster 1960; Hovmand & Davidson 1971). Gas entering the bed through a grid emerges as pulsating jets, which detach to yield formation-size bubbles (Zenz 1968, 1977). For a given free area of grid, the jets become shorter and the initial bubbles are smaller as the grid orifice size is reduced.

In the extreme case, a perforated grid plate behaves as a porous plate (Mori & Wen 1975). From this viewpoint, the grid region influences reactor performance in two ways. First, if pulsating gas jets exist they can be expected to provide a zone of very effective gas exchange between the lean and dense phases. Second, the influence of the initial bubble size on bubble sizes in the bubbling zone may be profound (equations in table 8.4.9 show the relationship between bubble size, initial bubble size, and distributor parameters; see also [8.1.44], [8.1.55], and [8.1.56]).

Few data are available for transfer processes and reactions around grid jets. Section 8.3.3.5 presents the gas exchange data of Behie et al. (1976), and further information is provided by Behie & Kehoe (1973). Values of F_{Je} (the jet-to-emulsion gas exchange coefficient per unit vessel volume; [8.3.39]) derived from the data of Behie & Kehoe range from about 18 to 4 s^{-1}, which can be compared with values of $\epsilon_b F_{be}$ (bubble-to-emulsion coefficient per unit vessel volume) typically from 2 to 0.2 s^{-1}, assuming $\epsilon_b = 0.5$ and taking values of F_{be} from figure 8.3.8. These limited data suggest that the gas transfer process in the grid region is roughly an order of magnitude faster than that in the bubbling region.

The extent of the grid region can be assumed to be equal to the jet height L_J, which can be predicted by the correlation of Basov et al. (1969):

$$L_J = \frac{d_S}{0.0007 + 0.556\,d_S} \left[\frac{A}{N_{or}} (u - u_{mf}) \right]^{0.35} \qquad [8.4.95]$$

where N_{or} is the number of holes in a perforated plate. Mori & Wen (1976) incorporated [8.4.95] into the modified BAM (section 8.4.3.4) to calculate the height of the first compartment ΔL_1, which is assumed to be well mixed. Thus

$$\Delta L_1 = L_J + L_c \qquad [8.4.96]$$

where L_c is the critical distance above the jets at which the bubble clouds overlap. Figure 8.4.11, from Mori & Wen, demonstrates the effect of N_{or} on conversion as a function of $N_R (= kL_{mf}/u)$ for a given gas flow and bed geometry. It shows that for small values of the reaction rate constant k the conversion is relatively insensitive to grid geometry. The opposite applies for moderate to fast reactions.

Behie & Kehoe (1973) proposed a simple extension of the P-M model (section 8.4.3.2) to account for the enhanced gas exchange in the grid region. The model, depicted in figure 8.4.15a, treats the jets as plug flow in series with the bubble phase, which is also in plug flow; the emulsion phase is well mixed throughout. This is called the $P_J\bar{M}/P_b\bar{M}$ model, and the relationship for conversion of gas is

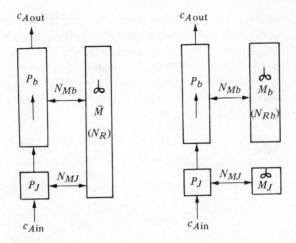

Figure 8.4.15 Simple P-M models with grid region. (*a*) The $P_J\bar{M}/P_b\bar{M}$ model ["grid model" of Behie & Kehoe (1973)]. (*b*) The P_JM_J/P_bM_b model.

$$1 - \text{conversion} = \frac{1 + e^{-\bar{N}_M}(N_R - 1)}{1 + N_R - e^{-\bar{N}_M}} = \frac{c_{A\,\text{out}}}{c_{A\,\text{in}}} \qquad [8.4.97]$$

This is identical to the equation for the **P-M** model in table 8.4.5, except for the definition of the number of mass transfer units; in this case,

$$\bar{N}_M = N_{Mb} + N_{MJ} \qquad [8.4.98]$$

where N_{Mb} is the number of mass transfer units in the bubble zone,

$$N_{Mb} = \frac{F_{be}\epsilon_b\,(L_f - L_J)}{u} \qquad [8.4.99]$$

and N_{MJ} is the mass transfer units in the jet zone,

$$N_{MJ} = \frac{F_{Je}L_J}{u} \qquad [8.4.100]$$

The definition of N_R is given by [8.4.2]. Behie & Kehoe (1973) applied the model to fast and slow reactions and showed how significant the conversion is in the grid region.

Applying [8.4.100] to the experimental data of Behie & Kehoe gives values of N_{MJ} from 4 to 3 transfer units, which may be considerably more than is achieved in the bubbling zone, particularly for shallow beds, high gas flows, and large bubble sizes. The extent of conversion in the bed may be limited by either gas exchange or reaction rate, and in the grid region the conversion can become reaction rate-limited for slow reactions. For fast reactions in the grid region the conversion should be balanced by the rapid exchange of gas, and should become gas exchange-limited only for exceptionally fast reactions. The $P_J\bar{M}/P_b\bar{M}$ model of Behie & Kehoe (1973) should be suitable for fast reactions, but it may be inadequate for slow reactions, because it assumes that gas transferred from the jets has access to the whole emulsion zone, and this will underestimate the effect of reaction rate limitation.

Figure 8.4.15b depicts a more appropriate model for both fast and slow reactions. This model, designated $P_J M_J / P_b M_b$, assumes that the jets are in plug flow and transfer gas to a well-mixed emulsion bounded by the grid region. The P-M grid model is then connected in series with a P-M bubble zone model, and the conversion of gas for the $P_J M_J / P_b M_b$ model is

$$1 - \text{conversion} = \prod_{i=J,b} \left[\frac{1 + e^{-N_{Mi}} (N_{Ri} - 1)}{1 + N_R - e^{-N_{Mi}}} \right] = \frac{c_{A\text{out}}}{c_{A\text{in}}} \qquad [8.4.101]$$

where N_{MJ} and N_{Mb} are given by [8.4.100] and [8.4.99], respectively, and

$$N_{RJ} = \frac{kL_J}{u} \qquad [8.4.102]$$

$$N_{Rb} = \frac{k (L_{mf} - L_J)}{u} \qquad [8.4.103]$$

Figure 8.4.16 shows concentration versus height profiles calculated from the $P_J \bar{M} / P_b \bar{M}$ model (lines a and b) and from the $P_J M_J / P_b M_b$ model [note that the freeboard profiles are calculated from the plug flow freeboard model (section 8.4.5.2)]. The value of $F_{Je} = 10$ was assumed from the data of Behie & Kehoe (1973) and F_{be} was estimated from figure 8.3.8. The calculations show the significance of the grid region, particularly for fast reactions. Differences between

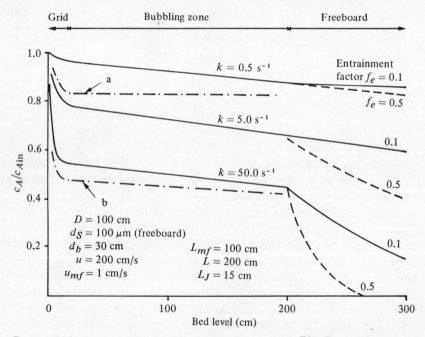

Figure 8.4.16 Concentration profiles in gas phase from the $P_J \bar{M} / P_b \bar{M}$ model (lines a and b) and the $P_J M_J / P_b M_b$ model with plug flow freeboard model [8.4.106].

the two grid models are slight for the fast reaction but considerable for the slow reaction. The $P_J M_J / P_b M_b$ model is recommended for use, although the two models converge for deep beds and low gas rates. Alternative extended grid models have been presented by Grace & de Lasa (1978).

In summary, the conversion in the grid region may be predicted by simple extensions of the P-M model, or by simple modifications to the BAM. A more precise analysis awaits suitable correlations for F_{Je} or K_{Je} ([8.3.41] may be useful as a rough guide). Consideration of the grid region is particularly important for fast reactions.

8.4.5.2 Freeboard Region

As gas bubbles erupt at the surface of a fluidized bed, particles are ejected upward. The precise mechanism by which ejection occurs is still controversial, although it is probably a combination of the following:

1. Some of the solids in the wakes of fast-rising bubbles are thrown upward as bubbles burst at the surface (Leva & Wen 1971; George & Grace 1978).
2. Solids at the surface become part of the erupting dome of a bubble and are thrown upward as the dome breaks (Do et al. 1972).

Solids that are ejected either return to the bed against the upward gas stream or are carried out of the bed. Larger particles that return to the bed describe trajectories that depend on their size, initial projection velocity, the background superficial velocity, etc. However, above a critical level the only particles found are those having a terminal velocity less than the superficial velocity. This critical level is termed the transport disengagement height (TDH). A detailed discussion of entrainment and elutriation can be found in section 8.1.13.

The space between the bed surface and the top of the reactor is known as the freeboard, and its main purpose is to provide disengagement of solids and gas. In many cases the freeboard has a larger cross section than the bed zone, so that the superficial gas velocity is lowered and fewer particles are elutriated. The freeboard height is usually above the TDH, but this is not mandatory if adequate particle collection is provided. Strictly speaking, the TDH depends on the properties of fines and gas in addition to the hydrodynamics.

If u_{io} is the initial velocity of the fine particles with diameter d_{Si} resulting from the eruption of bubbles at the surface of the bubbling bed, the TDH can be estimated (Leva & Wen 1971) by the following equation:

$$\text{TDH} = \frac{\rho_s d_{Si}^2}{18\mu} \left[u_{io} - (u_{Ti} - u) \ln\left(1 + \frac{u_{io}}{u_{Ti} - u} \right) \right] \qquad [8.4.104]$$

The initial ejection velocity of particle i, u_{io}, is difficult to estimate, and so far no general correlation of u_{io} is available, although most of the particles have velocities greater than twice the bubble velocity (George & Grace 1978).

The rate of entrainment in the freeboard below the TDH for fines with diameter d_{Si} can be estimated (Rengarajan 1978) from

$$(\text{Rate})_i = F_{i0} \exp\left(\frac{h}{\text{TDH}} \ln \frac{K_{zi} f_i}{F_{i0}}\right) \qquad [8.4.105]$$

where F_{i0} is the rate of entrainment of the fine fraction with diameter d_{Si} at the surface of the bed. F_{i0} is difficult to estimate but can be approximated by a certain fraction of wake solids in the bubble ejected.

Because information related to quantities such as u_{i0} and F_{i0} is not well established, a simplified version of the freeboard model is presented here. A more sophisticated model has been proposed (Rengarajan 1978).

Reactions occur in the freeboard in most practical situations where moderate to high gas flow rates are employed. These reactions are not subject to the thermal stability of the emulsion phase in the bubbling zone, and the temperature may be higher or lower depending on the heat of the reaction. For example, for the exothermic oxidation reactions occurring in the freeboard of a coal combustor Gibbs & Hedley (1978) reported gas temperatures 20°C above the bed temperature.

The two cases of catalyzed gas-phase reactions and noncatalytic gas-solid reactions will be treated separately.

Catalyzed Gas-Phase Reactions

The presence of catalyst particles in the freeboard offers an additional opportunity for gas conversion. A simple model of the freeboard region according to Yates & Rowe (1977) is considered here. It is assumed that the particles are well dispersed and traveling upward in the gas stream at velocity $u - u_T$ (where u_T is the average terminal velocity of the particles). The model does not account for particles that are entrained but subsequently fall back to the bed surface. This simplification is not unreasonable for moderate to high gas flow rates and for narrow-sized catalyst beds.

For a first-order reaction and plug flow of gas, the freeboard model predicts

$$\frac{c_{AF}}{c_{A\text{out}}} = 1 - \text{conversion in freeboard} = e^{-N_{RFB}} \qquad [8.4.106]$$

where the number of reaction units in the freeboard

$$N_{RFB} = \frac{(0.33 f_e) k' L_{FB}}{u - u_T} \qquad [8.4.107]$$

and $\qquad\qquad k' = \dfrac{1}{d_S/6 K_f (1 - \epsilon_{mf}) + 1/k} \qquad [8.4.108]$

with c_{AF} and $c_{A\text{out}}$, the gas concentrations at the top of the freeboard and the bed surface, f_e the fraction of wake solids ejected, k the first-order reaction rate constant, K_f the fluid-particle mass transfer coefficient (e.g., [8.3.6]), and L_{FB} the height of the freeboard zone.

Figure 8.4.16 shows calculations based on the plug flow freeboard model. In this case the model has been combined with the $P_J M_J/P_b M_b$ grid model described above. For a fast reaction the freeboard reactions are very significant, even at moderate entrainment.

Noncatalytic Gas-Solid Reactions

Solid reactant elutriated from the bed and returned through a cyclone system has a different residence time distribution than particles that remain in the bed. The effect of this on solids conversion in the bed can be accounted for ([8.4.67]–[8.4.69]), although no allowance is made for reactions that occur in the freeboard.

In many cases, including combustion, incineration, and fluidized-bed cracker (FBC) catalyst regeneration, the main concern is completion of conversion in the freeboard. Consequently, estimates of freeboard height based on burnout time are useful. Baeyens & Geldart (1978) presented a model of particle burnout based on the shrinking particle model for the reaction A (gas) + bB (solids) → products. The particle shrinks according to

$$\frac{dd_S}{dt} = -\frac{2\,bk_c\bar{c}_A}{\rho_{Sm}} \qquad [8.4.109]$$

and the time for complete conversion is given by [8.4.49] in table 8.4.11.

The minimum height of the freeboard should provide for complete burnout of particles initially of size d_{Si}, so that

$$L_{FB}\,(\text{min}) = \int_0^{t^*} (u_{FB} - u_T)\,dt = u_{FB}t^* - \int_0^{t^*} u_T\,dt \qquad [8.4.110]$$

where u_{FB} is the superficial gas velocity in the freeboard (usually less than u, the velocity in the bed).

Use of Stokes' law to calculate u_T gives a conservative design for $L_{FB}(\text{min})$. Equation [8.4.110] can be integrated by using [8.4.109] and [8.4.49]. However, for small burning particles the diffusion of oxygen is rate-controlling (Field et al. 1965), so that

$$k_c = K_f \simeq \frac{2\delta}{d_{Si}} \qquad [8.4.111]$$

and the minimum freeboard height is

$$L_{FB}\,(\text{min}) = \frac{u_{FB}\rho_{Sm}d_{Si}^2}{4b\delta\bar{c}_A} - \frac{g(\rho_S - \rho_G)\,\rho_{Sm}d_{Si}^4}{288\,\mu_G b\bar{c}_A\delta} \qquad [8.4.112]$$

Use of [8.4.112] requires selection of an appropriate value for d_{Si} and an estimate of $\bar{c}_A$, the mean gas composition in the freeboard.

8.4.6 DESIGN CONSIDERATIONS

The model equations presented above provide a means for predicting the interaction of the reactor geometry (bed diameter and depth, distributor characteristics, freeboard height, gas velocity, etc.) with conversion in the gas and/or the solid phase. Other considerations germane to the design of fluidized-bed reactors are briefly considered in this section.

8.4.6.1 Batch versus Continuous

Catalytic gas-phase and noncatalytic gas-solid reactors can be used for either batch or continuous operations with respect to the solid phase.

Catalytic Gas-Phase Reactions

For catalyzed reactions the criteria for batch or continuous operation are the extent of deactiviation or fouling of the catalyst. The mechanical advantages of (a long duration) batch operation are obvious and may justify using an initially more expensive catalyst or additional purification of the incoming gas streams.

Deactivation kinetics can usually be expressed as a first-order relationship,

$$k = k_0 a_0 e^{-K_a t} = k_0 a \qquad [8.4.113]$$

where a and a_0 are the catalyst activity, initial value (usually $= 1$); k_0 is the reaction rate constant for fresh catalyst (per unit volume); and K_a is the rate constant for deactivation. Small-scale fluidized-bed studies should be made to assess the rate of deactivation, and possible sensitivity to trace impurities. Gas-phase conversion is most conveniently expressed as a function of $k(t)$ through the number of reaction units N_R [8.4.2] and the two-phase model (P-P, P-M, etc. in table 8.4.5) most appropriate for the particular reactor system. If the minimum acceptable conversion is specified, N_R (min) can be calculated, and this gives, via [8.4.113], the catalyst life (or batch time). Note that loss of catalyst activity may be compensated by decreasing gas flow, increasing bed height, or increasing temperature. (Of course, other constraints may obviate these actions.)

For rapid deactivation or fouling of catalyst, as in the fluidized-bed catalytic cracker, there is no alternative but to continuously remove and reactivate the catalyst. With continuous feed and withdrawal of catalyst particles a mean activity $\bar{a}$ can be maintained, its value being dependent on the residence time distribution RTD of catalyst in the bed,

$$\bar{a} = \int_0^\infty a E(t) \, dt \qquad [8.4.114]$$

If the solids are perfectly mixed, $E(t)$ is given by [8.4.67] and thus,

$$\bar{a} = \frac{a_0}{1 + K_a \bar{t}} \qquad [8.4.115]$$

The mean residence time $\bar{t}$ is given by [8.4.56] or [8.4.68]. This allows calculation of the necessary catalyst recirculation flow rate. Techniques for the design of recirculation systems may be found in Zenz & Othmer (1960) and Kunii & Levenspiel (1969).

Noncatalytic Gas-Solid Reactions

The discussion in section 8.4.4.1 of conversion of solids in a fluidized-bed reactor assumes continuous operation. This is the usual mode of operation, because it simplifies control and materials handling.

However, if very high conversion of solids is mandatory, a single-stage continuous reactor may not be suitable. For example, consider a reaction with a time for completion t^* of 120 s and a requirement of 99.9% conversion. For shrinking core kinetics and chemical reaction control the mean residence time in a single stage is (from [8.4.64] about 8 h. In contrast, a batch treatment of this material may take as little as 30 min, allowing for feed and withdrawal periods and possible temperature adjustment. In this example the batch reactor has a much greater capacity than its continuous equivalent. The most likely limitation of the batch operation is the need to maintain thermal stability, which can be achieved only by matching the conversion rate to the available heat transfer capacity. For an exothermic reaction A (gas) + bB (solid) → products, the maximum bed temperature can be estimated from simple heat balance considerations,

$$\alpha_{bW} A_W \left(T_{\text{bed}} - T_W\right) + \sum \dot{M}_p h_p \left(T_{\text{bed}}\right) - \sum \dot{M}_r h_r \left(T_{G\text{in}}\right) = uA c_{A\text{in}} \bar{X}_A b \left(\Delta H_R\right)$$

[8.4.116]

where A_W is the available heat transfer area; $h_p(T)$ and $h_r(T)$ are the specific enthalpies of the gaseous product component and the gaseous inlet component; ΔH_R is the heat of reaction; $\dot{M}_p$ and $\dot{M}_r$ are the gas product mass flow rate and gas inlet mass flow rate; T_{bed}, $T_{G\text{in}}$, and T_W are the temperatures of the bed, gas inlet, and heat transfer surface; α_{bW} is the heat transfer coefficient; and $\bar{X}_A$ is the conversion of gaseous reactant [it can be assumed to be unity to estimate $T_{\text{bed}}(\text{max})$]. An example of commercial-scale production with batch operation is the production of uranium dioxide for nuclear fuels (Hawthorn et al. 1960). However, the high degree of conversion required can also be achieved by staging (as in figure 8.4.18a) (Smiley 1961).

8.4.6.2 Staging

Figure 8.4.3 indicates how gas conversion can be increased by increasing the bed depth; figure 8.4.13 and table 8.4.12 indicate how solids conversion can be increased by using a number of back-mix stages in series.

Four modes of staging are feasible, as shown in figure 8.4.17, cross flow (solids) and countercurrent flow being the two of practical significance. Cross flow (solids) is suitable when the cost of the gaseous reactant is not high and when maximum conversion of solids is required. Countercurrent flow maximizes gas conversion.

The example shown in figure 8.4.18a is the two-stage reduction of uranium trioxide (UO$_3$) to uranium dioxide (UO$_2$), using hydrogen. Emphasis in this process is on conversion of solids rather than usage of hydrogen. The example shown in figure 8.4.18b is the conversion of UO$_2$ to uranium tetrafluoride (UF$_4$) with hydrogen fluoride (HF) gas. Because the reaction is highly exothermic and the product sinters close to the desired reaction temperature, the first stage is maintained at a lower temperature than the second stage. An added complication is that the reaction is reversible; at low HF concentrations the UF$_4$ tends to revert to UO$_2$. Use of the countercurrent flow system minimizes the effects of reversibility because solid product is in contact with the highest concentrations of HF.

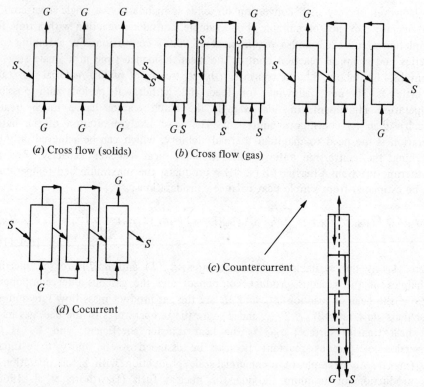

Figure 8.4.17 Modes of staging for fluidized-bed reactors.

Table 8.4.13 summarizes the advantages and disadvantages of countercurrent staging and cross-flow (solids) staging. Raghuraman & Varma (1972) reviewed countercurrent staging and cited a number of industrial applications. Further details of countercurrent and cocurrent operation are given by Varma (1975).

8.4.6.3 Internals

Bed internals may be in the form of heat transfer surface (vertical or horizontal tubes) or screens and baffles designed to modify the flow patterns of gas or solid. The hydrodynamic effects of these internals are discussed in section 8.1.11.

Vertical surfaces, such as those provided by the heat exchange arrangement in figure 8.4.19, can be designed to give the effect of multiple slug flow reactors operating in parallel. This offers a convenient approach to scale-up based on a small cross-sectional unit and modeling based on the slug flow model of section 8.4.3.3. Careful design is required to achieve uniform distribution of gas flow through each compartment.

Horizontal screens or baffles cause breakup of bubbles, as discussed in section 8.1.11. Bubble breakup improves the transfer of gas from bubble phase to emulsion through the effect of bubble diameter on the gas exchange coefficient F_{be} (see

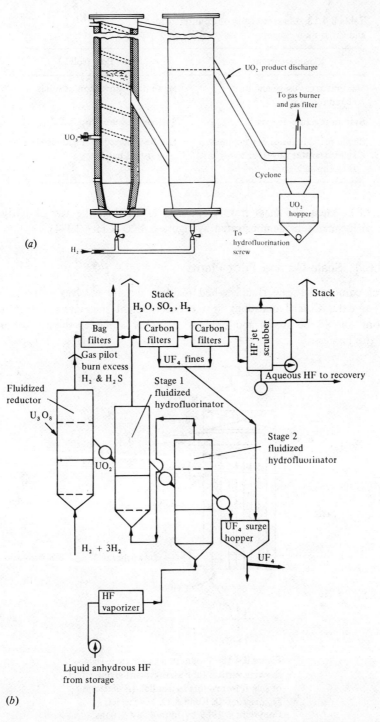

Figure 8.4.18 (a) Reduction of UO_3 to UO_2: two-stage cross flow (solids) (Smiley 1961). (b) Hydrofluorination of UO_2 to UF_4: countercurrent flow (Harrington & Ruehle 1959).

Table 8.4.13   Characteristics of Countercurrent
and Cross-Flow Staging

Countercurrent	Cross flow (solids)
Maximizes gas usage and heat economy	Maximizes conversion of solids
System pressure drop is $N \, \Delta P_{bed}$	System pressure drop is ΔP_{bed}
Single vessel requires downcomers, solids transfer valves, or two-phase flow through grids	Can be achieved in single vessel by use of baffles

figure 8.3.8). When the mass transfer process is limiting, the use of baffles will improve performance, as demonstrated by figure 8.4.20 (Grace 1974).

8.4.6.4   Scale-Up and Pilot Plants

Design of commercial-scale fluidized-bed reactors usually involves extrapolation or scale-up of data. Crucial questions at the development stage are (1) what tests or simulations should be made and (2) how complex a model should be used to evaluate the process.

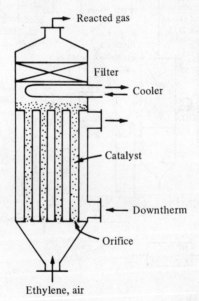

Figure 8.4.19   Production of ethylene oxide, showing vertical tube arrangement giving effect of slug flow reactors in parallel. (*Fluidization Engineering,* D. Kunii & O. Levenspiel, Copyright © 1969 by John Wiley & Sons. Reprinted by permission of John Wiley & Sons, Inc.)

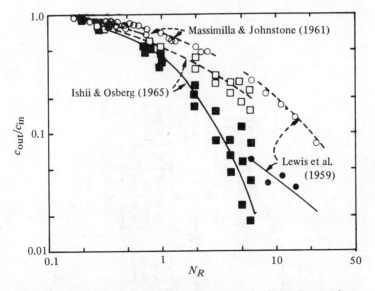

Figure 8.4.20 Experimental outlet concentrations for first-order gas-phase chemical reactions in fluidized beds with and without immersed baffles. Open symbols refer to unbaffled beds; filled symbols refer to baffled beds (Grace 1974).

Five levels of test are possible and are listed below in increasing order of probable cost.

1. *Laboratory-scale reactions* in fixed and/or fluidized systems (nominally D is 2-5 cm). The purpose of these tests is to obtain kinetic data (and information on catalyst deactivation if the reaction is catalyzed).
2. *Small-scale (cold) hydrodynamic* tests in fluidized systems (nominally $D \sim 15$ cm). The main purpose of these tests is to determine fluidization characteristics of the solids; i.e., u_{mf}, bed expansion, etc.
3. *Large-scale (cold) hydrodynamic tests* (nominally 20 cm $< D <$ 0.5 × diameter of commercial-scale unit). These tests may be used to determine RTD for solids, operability for staged systems, gas exchange and bubble behavior (using tracers), effect of internals on bed behavior, etc.
4. *Pilot-plant reactions* in moderate-size fluidized systems (nominally $D \sim$ 15-20 cm). These tests are most appropriate for reactions that are complex or are limited by the combined effect of interphase mass transfer and reaction rate. Conditions far removed from ambient (particularly high pressure) also call for this type of test.
5. *Semicommercial-scale* reactions (nominally 20 cm $< D <$ 0.5 × diameter of commercial-scale unit). This scale is appropriate if optimization of a complex system is required [e.g., coal gasification and combustion process demonstration units (PDUs)] or if significant quanties of product are required for market development.

Level 1 tests are always required and one or more additional levels may be appropriate, depending on the nature of the reaction. Figures 8.4.21 and 8.4.22

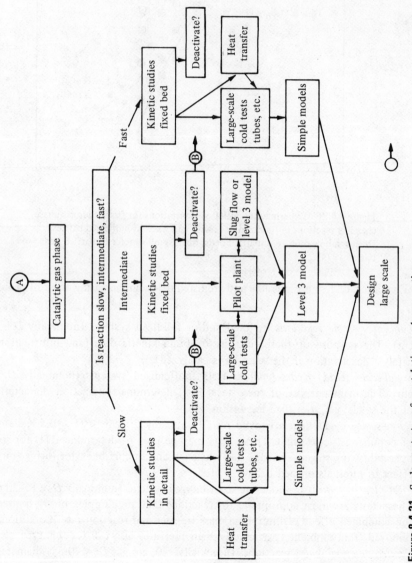

Figure 8.4.21 Scale-up strategy for catalytic gas-phase reactions.

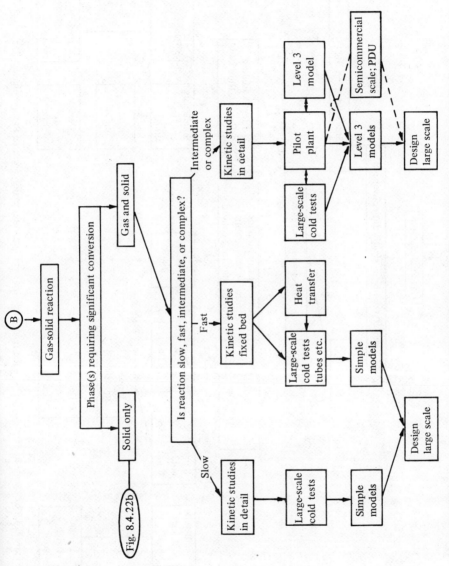

Figure 8.4.22a Scale-up strategy for gas-solid reactions with significant conversion required in both phases.

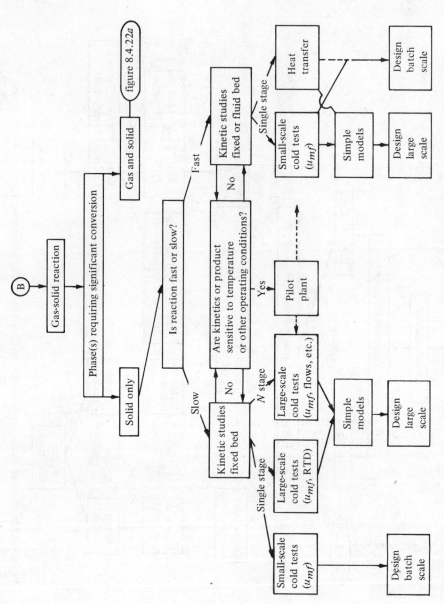

Figure 8.4.22b Scale-up strategy for gas-solid reactions with significant conversion required in solid phase only.

summarize the scale-up strategy for all types of chemical reactions. Details of the recommended models may be found in sections 8.4.3–8.4.5.

With respect to test levels 3–5, the following points should be noted (Grace 1974):

Aspect ratio (*L/D*) should be varied to give a bed depth similar to that anticipated in the commercial-scale unit. This is because the bubble structure is more closely related to *L* than to *L/D*.

Distributor design in the test facility should be similar to that proposed for the commercial-scale unit; the test distributor should not be a scale-down version.

The strategies recommended in figures 8.4.21 and 8.4.22 can be considered a minimum requirement. Proposals to use novel hydrodynamic features or extremes of temperature or pressure justify testing and simulation at higher levels than indicated.

8.5 Applications of Fluidized Beds

Section Editor: *J. Yerushalmi*

8.5.1 INTRODUCTION

J. Yerushalmi

Although scattered references to the use of fluidized beds appeared in the latter part of the nineteenth century, it is generally agreed that the Winkler gasifier (see section 8.5.4.1) represents the first significant large-scale application of the fluidization technique. Winkler's first patent, assigned to Badische Anilin und Soda-Fabrik (BASF), was awarded in 1922, and by 1926 the first gasifier went on stream. By 1929, a large plant was in operation in Leuna, Germany.

The Winkler technology remained ostensibly dormant until the dramatic appearance during World War II of the catalytic fluid cracking process in the United States (section 8.5.2.2). To be sure, ESSO (now EXXON) engineers did in the interim visit BASF in West Germany, but when the catalytic fluid process emerged years later, it appeared to have sprung from new roots. The extent to which the Winkler experience influenced and contributed to the new development is not clear.

The catalytic fluid process triggered interest in fluidization, and subsequent years saw widespread use of this versatile technique. Fluid beds have been used, are being developed, or are proposed for a wide range of applications: catalytic gas-solid reactions (section 8.5.2), noncatalytic gas-solid reactions (section 8.5.3), and physical operations (section 8.5.5). Fluid beds bring several advantages to the processing of coal and have accordingly been the subject of numerous developments in that area (section 8.5.4). Section 8.5.6 briefly describes applications of spouted beds.

Section 8.5 focuses almost exclusively on gas fluidization. Fluidized beds are primarily intended to bring gas into contact with a large inventory of solid surface per unit reactor volume. They offer a number of advantages: Intense mixing of solids results in temperature uniformity throughout the bed. A cold reactant, whether a gas, liquid, or solid, fed to the bed attains the temperature of the bed almost instantaneously. In addition, heat transfer rates between the bed and immersed surfaces are high (section 8.2), thereby providing means of introducing or withdrawing heat. The liquidlike character of the fluidized solids affords ease of solids handling, including easy circulation of solids between two fluidized beds. The latter can be used to transport large quantities of heat. Catalytic fluid processes (section 8.5.2.2) provide a classic example where these qualities come into play.

Section 8.5 surveys fluidized-bed applications in the general areas noted above. It is not exhaustive, and several applications that some may regard as important have been omitted.

8.5.2 CATALYTIC SOLID–GAS REACTIONS

8.5.2.1 Introduction

J. J. Graham and M. A. Bergougnou

The following considerations must be kept in mind in selecting a fluid-bed route to a high-performance catalytic chemical reactor:

1. The stability of products and intermediates must be evaluated at reaction conditions, but with extended residence time. Circulation of catalyst contributes to back mixing of reactants, which results in nonuniform residence time and a yield loss if the products are not stable. Mechanical devices have been tried for restricting catalyst back mixing, but generally these may create additional problems (see section 8.1.11).

2. The quality of fluidization should be evaluated because it affects the degree of contact between gas and solid. Theory and practical experience indicate that a multitude of small bubbles results in more complete conversion than fewer large bubbles.

3. Rapid circulation of solids in a fluidized system at commercial velocities results in isothermal conditions throughout the reactor. The catalyst inventory serves as a heat sink that absorbs temporary heat releases and damps temperature swings. Heat transfer from the catalyst to a coolant is usually very good, whether immersed cooling coils or a circulating catalyst system is used. The fluidized bed is therefore especially suited for temperature-sensitive reactions, highly exothermic or endothermic reactions, or where efficient heat transfer is required.

4. Fluid-bed reactors generally require greater residence times, compared with a plug flow fixed-bed reactor, to compensate for the reactant bypassing associated with bubbles. The general technique is to use more catalyst per unit of feed, but to use a less active catalyst than in a corresponding fixed bed to avoid excessive reaction severity.

5. Complete conversion of two or more reactants is generally not feasible because of bypassing of gas associated with the bubbling phenomena. In oxidation of hydrocarbons, excess oxygen is usually provided in order to bring the hydrocarbon conversion to practical completion. Where more than two reactants are

involved, it must be decided which reactant is to be essentially completely converted and which is to be in surplus in the effluent.

6. Cyclones and particle recovery devices must be designed with care because fluid beds of fine powders, which otherwise promote better performance, give rise to considerable particle carry-over. Two or more cyclone stages may prove necessary.

7. With complex reactions, scale-up may have to span several stages, including a semicommercial plant, because each size usually has different hydrodynamic characteristics.

8. Many of the drawbacks and uncertainties of conventional bubbling fluid beds may be obviated by employing high-velocity fluidized beds—fast or turbulent fluid beds (see section 8.1.2)—but experience in this area has been limited.

9. The ultimate success of a fluid-bed process depends on achieving a competitive advantage in production cost over alternative routes. Ingenious devices are often proposed to counter the deficiencies of a fluid-bed reaction system. Such devices tend to increase the capital cost of a plant and may result in an economically unattractive, even though technically feasible, process. Most of the fluid-bed chemical processes that exist under competitive market conditions are the simple single-vessel reactors without sophisticated appurtenances.

There are numerous examples of the application of fluid-bed technology to chemical reaction systems. A few of the commercially successful ones are presented in the following pages.

8.5.2.2 Fluid Catalytic Cracking

J. M. Matsen

Fluid catalytic cracking (FCC) is by far the most important fluid-bed process commercially and is also one of the oldest fluid-bed applications of current significance. Cracking converts a feedstock of virgin gas oil (a mixture of aromatic, paraffinic, and naphthenic hydrocarbons boiling between 270 and 570°C) into a product mixture consisting mainly of gasoline, kerosine, and diesel oil fractions. Butanes and lighter molecules are by-products, and a residue of carbon or coke is deposited on the catalyst. The earliest cracking process was thermal cracking, but this was superseded by the catalytic Houdry process, commercialized in 1936 by Sun Oil and Socony Vacuum Oil Co. (now Mobil). The Houdry process employed multiple fixed beds of catalyst in a cyclic operation consisting of 10 min cracking, 5 min purging, and 10 min regeneration to burn carbon deposits from the catalyst.

The fixed-bed process had numerous limitations, and development of a fluid-bed process began in the late 1930s. World War II greatly increased the demand for high-octane aviation gasoline and accelerated commercialization of fluid catalytic cracking. Under a wartime emergency agreement, "Recommendation 41," Standard Oil Development Co. (now EXXON Research and Engineering), M. W. Kellogg, Texaco Development Co., Universal Oil Products Co. (UOP), Standard Oil of Indiana (now American Oil), and the Royal Dutch Shell group pooled technical knowledge and development. A large pilot plant, with a feed capacity of 0.16 kg/s, went into operation in 1941, and the first commercial unit came on stream in 1942 with a design capacity of 24 kg/s.

Expansion of capacity has been rapid since that time, as shown in table 8.5.1. Today there are about 350 FCC units in operation, with oil feed rates ranging from 2 to 240 kg/s. The most active licensors are Kellogg-Amoco, UOP-Mobil, and EXXON. Other licensors have included Texaco, Gulf, and Shell.

Process Details

A survey of all the varieties of catalytic cracker designs is beyond the scope of this section. Currently available processes are basically the same, with some variations in mechanical details. A typical EXXON model IV of 0.11 m^3/s (60,000 bpd) capacity is shown in figure 8.5.1 and is described below and in table 8.5.2.

Oil feed is introduced into a transfer line and mixed with hot regenerated catalyst. Vaporization and some cracking take place in the transfer line, and gas velocity at the top of the line is typically 6–10 m/s. The oil-catalyst mixture passes upward through a perforated plate distributor into the main reactor vessel. Depending on the catalyst used and the desired conversion, a dense-phase fluid bed as deep as 1.6 m may be above the distributor, or the bed level may be below the distributor plate. Reactor product vapors are fractionated, and part of the fractionator bottoms containing the catalyst escaping from the reactor secondary cyclones may be combined with fresh feed for recycle to the process.

The cracking reaction is endothermic and deposits coke on the catalyst, causing rapid deactivation. The catalyst must be continuously regenerated and reheated by circulating it to the regeneration vessel and burning off the coke deposits. Catalyst leaves from the bottom of the reactor containing considerable amounts of hydrocarbons. These are partially removed in a stripping section, in which catalyst flows slowly downward, countercurrent to steam introduced at the bottom of the stripper. The stripper usually contains sheds or baffles to reduce catalyst back mixing.

In the regenerator, air is passed upward through a distributor and through a dense bed of catalyst, where it burns off the carbon deposits on the catalyst from perhaps 1.2% of the weight of catalyst exiting the stripper down to perhaps 0.2% of the weight of regenerated catalyst. The flue gas typically contains about 15% H_2O,

Table 8.5.1 Growth of Catalytic Cracking

	Capacity		
Year	m^3/s	bpd	kg/s
1945	1.8	1,000,000	1,580
1950	4.0	1,700,000	2,370
1960	9.6	5,200,000	8,210
1970	15	8,300,000	13,150
1980 (estimated)	20	10,900,000	17,260

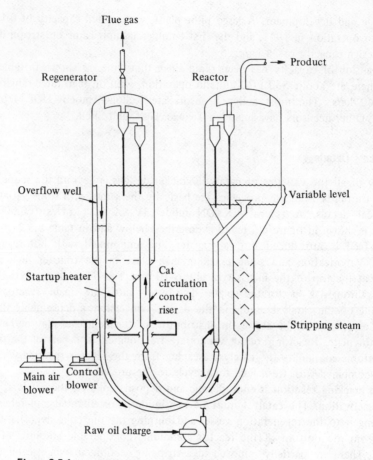

Figure 8.5.1 Model IV fluid catalytic cracking unit.

8.5% CO, 8.5% CO_2, and 67% N_2. Unconsumed O_2 is usually below 0.5%. The presence of CO and O_2 may lead to afterburning and a rise in flue gas temperature, particularly in and downstream of the cyclones. Regenerator cyclones are often fabricated from stainless steel to withstand afterburning temperatures, and water sprays may be used to prevent excessive temperatures.

Recently, high-stability catalysts have been developed that permit regeneration at temperatures above 700°C. The burning reaction is much accelerated by the higher temperatures, allowing 0.02–0.05% carbon on regenerated catalyst to be attained. Such low-carbon residues are of great benefit to modern, active catalysts and permit significant yield improvements in the cracking reaction. A concurrent benefit is reduction of the CO content of the flue gas from, e.g., 8 or 10% to below 500 ppm. This results in significant heat economy and in emissions that meet stringent pollution regulations without the need for CO combustion boilers.

Carbon steel becomes unsuitable for internals and valves on any vessel at high regeneration temperatures, and such components must be upgraded to stainless steel for long-term high-temperature operation. The recent availability of combustion promoters, which improve CO oxidation to CO_2, permits most process benefits of high-temperature oxidation to be obtained at intermediate temperatures of 650–700°C.

Fluidization Aspects

The catalyst fluidizes easily. Gas bubbles are small (of the order of 2–5 cm in diameter), with the result that gas-solid contacting is usually good. The chemical and kinetic nature of the reaction is such that catalyst back mixing is not a serious impediment to desired yield. Thus scale-up debits resulting from poor contacting and undesirable mixing were not a factor in large-scale development. Cracking catalyst defluidizes slowly, greatly facilitating handling and circulation through transfer lines. It is free-flowing, with none of the sticking or caking properties often detrimental to other types of fluid-bed operation. It is also fairly attrition-resistant, so that catalyst consumption is usually determined by deactivation rather than by high losses.

Composition, physical properties, and manufacturing techniques for cracking catalyst have changed considerably over the years. The most prevalent type now consists of 5–15% crystals of a synthetic zeolite embedded in a matrix of amorphous silica gel and clay, spray-dried to produce microspheroidal particles. Pore volume of fresh catalyst is quite high, but with use the pore volume and surface area decrease somewhat and bulk density increases. Some typical catalyst properties are given in table 8.5.3.

Fluid cracking catalyst is virtually a stoichiometric reactant because of rapid fouling by coke deposits and rapid cooling by the endothermic cracking reaction. Catalyst-to-oil ratios (i.e., weight of catalyst circulated to weight of oil fed) of 5–10

Table 8.5.2 Typical FCC Operating Parameters

Parameter	Value
Feed capacity, kg/s	60 fresh; 95 total
Reactor diameter, m	6.7
Bed depth of reactor, m	Variable 0–1.6
Reactor dilute-phase velocity, m/s	0.75
Reactor temperature, °C	520
Stripper diameter, m	3.3
Stripper height, m	11
U-bend diameter, m	0.86
Catalyst circulation rate, kg/s	450
Regenerator diameter, m	10.7
Regenerator bed depth, m	6.64
Regenerator gas velocity, m/s	0.64
Height of regenerator cyclones inlet above bed, m	10.3
Regenerator temperature, °C	670
Regenerator pressure, kN/m³ gauge	170
Catalyst inventory in regenerator, Mg	190
Entrainment to regenerator cyclones (estimated), kg/s	260
Catalyst losses in regenerator flue gas, g/s	15

Table 8.5.3 Typical Equilibrium Catalyst
Properties

Property	Value
Size, %	
Below 40 μm	15
40–80 μm	67
Above 80 μm	18
Mass median diameter, μm	59
Skeletal density, kg/m^3	1500
Loose bulk density, kg/m^3	750
(minimum fluidization density is about 95% of loose bulk density)	
Pore volume, cm^3/g	0.42
Surface area, m^2/g	110

are common. Catalyst mean residence time in the regenerator is only about 10 min. In the reaction zone of the reactor (i.e., excluding the stripper), residence time may vary from 10 s in a pure transfer line operation to 1 min when a dense bed is present. This high catalyst throughput distinguishes catalytic cracking from most other catalytic processes.

The driving force for circulation is provided by judicious control of hydrostatic pressure gradients within the process. In portions of the circuit where catalyst is flowing downward—reactor bed, regenerator bed, stripper, and standpipes—high density is maintained. Catalyst density in such down-flow zones is typically 400–640 kg/m^3. In up-flow or riser portions of the circulation loop, catalyst density and pressure gradient are kept much lower by addition of gas. In the reactor feed riser the gas is vaporized oil feed and steam, while in the spent catalyst riser entering the regenerator the lift gas is combustion air. Typical catalyst mass flow rates in standpipes and risers are 400–1200 kg/m^2 s. In most units catalyst flow control is effected by slide valves, but in the model IV design, circulation is regulated by differential pressure between reactor and regenerator and by the amount of air introduced to the spent catalyst riser.

Gas velocities in reactors and regenerators are well above the terminal velocity of the largest particle present. Typical entrainment rates are 5–25 kg catalyst per actual cubic meter of gas entering the primary cyclones. Two stages of cyclones are highly effective in removing particles, and the dust loading in a typical regenerator flue gas would be 475 mg/normal m^3. This is typically somewhat less than the rate at which catalyst suffers long-term deactivation (resulting from deposition of heavy metals and reduction of surface areas by sintering) and is thus acceptable from a process standpoint. Air pollution regulations, especially for new units, are becoming somewhat more strict. Tertiary cyclones operating at 70–80% efficiency can meet pollution limits in much of Europe, whereas electrostatic precipitators and venturi scrubbers with 90–95% efficiency may be necessary on new units in the United States.

Cracking catalyst at high velocity can be highly erosive, and erosion in cyclones, slide valves, transfer lines, and grids is a major cause of shutdowns. Modern technology to combat erosion includes (1) materials: high-density refractory linings in cyclones and transfer lines and Stellite hard surfacing in slide valves and grid holes; (2) operating conditions: avoidance of excessive velocity in cyclones, grids, lines, etc.; and (3) geometric detail: avoidance of impingement of high-velocity gas jets or catalyst streams on critical areas. Run lengths of 3 yr are now typical with good practice, but strong incentives exist for further improvement. An emergency shutdown for even minor repairs takes at least a week and may cost $0.5 to $1 million in lost profits for a 0.11 m^3/s (60,000 bpd) unit.

8.5.2.3 Fluid Catalytic Reforming

J. M. Matsen

Catalytic reforming is an isomerization process, converting straight-chain naphtha hydrocarbons into branched-chain compounds with higher octane numbers. The fluid-bed process, commercialized by Standard Oil Development Co., is similar to catalytic cracking in many respects (figure 8.5.2). Two vessels are used, a reactor in which the isomerization reaction occurs, and a regenerator in which carbon deposits are burned off the catalyst. The molybdenum-based catalyst is similar in physical properties to cracking catalyst. Circulation systems and cyclones are also of the type used in cracking. Cooling coils are necessary in the regenerator because more heat is liberated than is needed for the endothermic reforming reaction.

A high partial pressure of hydrogen in the reactor inhibits cracking, and fluid hydroformers typically operate at about 1500 kN/m^2 pressure. Early experiments showed that the quality of fluidization was much improved and entrainment much increased at high pressure. The isomerization reaction is adversely affected by back mixing of reactants, more severe in early commercial units than in pilot plants. Laboratory studies characterized mixing and led to the development of internal baffles for commercial reactors to prevent back mixing. Ten fluid hydroformers had been built by 1958, ranging in size from 3 to 40 kg/s. Some pertinent statistics for the largest of these are given in table 8.5.4.

The fluid-bed reforming process competed with fixed-bed processes for several years. Fixed-bed processes, such as Platforming and Powerforming, use pelleted, platinum-based catalysts and require cyclic operation to regenerate the catalyst. Platinum catalyst is too expensive for a fluid-bed process because of the attrition and cyclone losses, but it gives higher conversion and selectivity than the fluid hydroforming catalyst. The rate of catalyst fouling and the heat required for the endothermic reaction are much less for reforming than for cracking, so that the benefits of a continuous fluid-bed process are correspondingly reduced. Because modern fixed-bed reforming with precious-metal catalysts requires a lower investment and has better selectivity than fluid-bed reforming with nonprecious-metal catalysts, no fluid hydroformers have been built since 1959. Two of the 10 built, however, are still in operation.

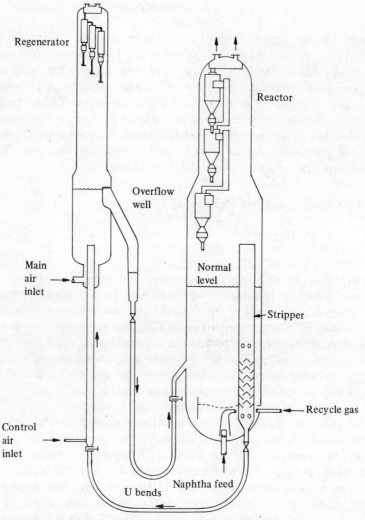

Figure 8.5.2 Fluid hydroformer.

Table 8.5.4 Fluid Hydroformer Operating
Parameters

Parameter	Value
Feed, kg/s	40
Bed diameter of reactor, m	6.6
Bed depth of reactor, m	9
Bed velocity of reactor, m/s	0.3
Reactor pressure, kN/m^2 gauge	1380
Reactor temperature, °C	575
Catalyst circulation rate, kg/s	35
Regenerator bed diameter, m	3.0
Regenerator bed depth, m	5.2
Regenerator temperature, °C	490
Total catalyst inventory, kg	300

8.5.2.4 Production of Phthalic Anhydride

J. J. Graham

Another early application of fluidized-bed technology was the oxidation of naphthalene to phthalic anhydride. Sherwin Williams pioneered the design and jointly with Davison Chemical Co. developed a catalyst; the process was later termed the Sherwin Williams/Badger process. The initial Sherwin Williams plant went on stream in 1945. Since then, 14 plants have been built utilizing this technology.

The reaction may be represented by the following expression:

$$C_{10}H_8 + 4\tfrac{1}{2}O_2 \rightarrow C_8H_4O_3 + 2H_2O + 2CO_2$$

Side reactions produce small quantities of naphthoquinone and maleic anhydride, in addition to CO_2 and CO arising from some combustion of naphthalene. Reaction theory indicates that naphthoquinone may be an intermediate oxidation product of naphthalene and that maleic anhydride may be an overoxidation product. The fluidized catalyst maintains a uniform temperature throughout the bed, usually within less than $1°C$ of the set temperature, which results in maleic anhydride yields of less than $\tfrac{1}{2}\%$. This compares with maleic anhydride yields of 5–10% in fixed-bed reactors, where temperature variations of 10–$38°C$ are noted. Because of bypassing of reactants through the fluidized bed, however, underoxidized products such as naphthoquinone may amount to as much as 2% of yield. Naphthalene, however, is practically undetectable in the reaction products, indicating complete conversion of feed.

The catalyst is principally vanadium oxide on a silica gel base and has a size range of 0–300 μm. Microspherical or irregular ground catalysts may be used.

Figure 8.5.3 is a schematic of a plant for the production of phthalic anhydride by the Sherwin Williams/Badger fluid-bed process.

Reactor temperatures are in the range 340–$385°C$ and the superficial velocity is 0.3–0.6 m/s. The reaction is highly exothermic and heat is removed by generation of steam with cooling coils immersed in the catalyst bed. The enormous circulation of catalyst provides a uniform bed temperature even though the coolant is several hundred degrees below the bed temperature.

A salient feature of the process is the injection of liquid naphthalene directly into the fluidized bed, thereby eliminating the need for a feed vaporizer. The liquid feed is vaporized and dispersed by the rapidly moving catalyst. Tar-forming components and other impurities in the naphthalene are oxidized to CO_2 without caking or coking on the catalyst. The grid plate design and feed nozzle configuration are reputed to be significant in maximizing conversion; however, nothing has been published.

Entrained catalyst in the gaseous reactants are removed by filters if total catalyst retention is desired. Alternatively, cyclones are used for dust recovery where a small catalyst loss is acceptable. Catalyst makeup of less than 1 kg per 100 kg feed is generally practiced to maintain a constant activity. Because catalyst losses by attrition are generally less than the makeup required for activity maintenance, total fines retention with filters is not absolutely essential.

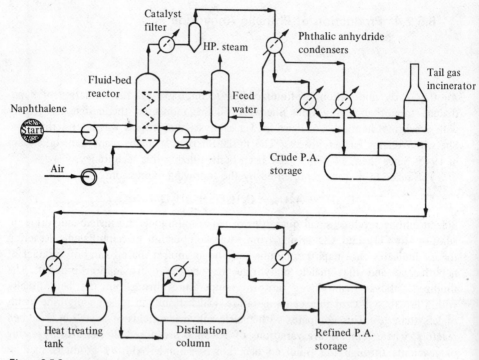

Figure 8.5.3 Phthalic anhydride production by the Sherwin Williams/Badger fluid-bed process.

Yields are on the order of 98 kg phthalic anhydride per 100 kg feed, which corresponds to 85% selectivity and is comparable to other fluid-bed reactions. Reactors more than 6 m in diameter with height-to-diameter ratios of 1–2 are in operation.

8.5.2.5 Production of Acrylonitrile

J. J. Graham

Nearly all the acrylonitrile used today is produced by the SOHIO process (Standard Oil Co., Cleveland, Ohio). The process is based on vapor-phase oxidation of propylene and ammonia, termed ammoxidation, in the presence of a fluidized catalyst. The reaction is strongly exothermic and extremely well suited to a fluid-bed design. The primary reaction takes place according to:

$$CH_2 = CH-CH_3 + NH_3 + \tfrac{3}{2} O_2 \rightarrow CH_2 = CH-CN + 3H_2O$$

The principal by-products are hydrogen cyanide, acetonitrile, and carbon oxides. Yields in excess of 0.85 kg acrylonitrile per kilogram of propylene feed have been reported—about 70% of the theoretical yield. The recovered yield of by-product HCN has been stated as over 0.10 kg per kilogram of acrylonitrile (Anon. 1977).

The first commercial catalyst used was a microspheroidal based principally on molybdenum and bismuth of high selectivity. Several improved catalysts have been introduced since then. More than 45 plants have been built throughout the world with capacities ranging from 1 to 10 kg/s acrylonitrile. Reactors more than 9 m in inside diameter are in operation. Essentially complete conversion of propylene is achieved, suggesting that the combination of a fine catalyst, vigorous fluidization, and reactor internals (cooling coils) provides good contact between gas and solid and minimal gas bypassing. Reactor pressure and temperature are reported in the ranges 35–210 kPa gauge and 400–500°C (Anon. 1977). Figure 8.5.4 is a schematic of the SOHIO process.

8.5.2.6 Production of Aniline

J. J. Graham

One of the commercial methods of producing aniline is by vapor-phase hydrogenation of nitrobenzene:

$$C_6H_5NO_2 + 3H_2 \rightarrow C_6H_5NH_2 + 2H_2O$$

The reaction is highly exothermic and accordingly well suited to fluid-bed operation. The process developed by American Cyanamid (figure 8.5.5) went on stream in 1958. Nitrobenzene is vaporized with hydrogen, and the mixture enters the base of the reactor. The amount of hydrogen used is nearly three times the stochiometric

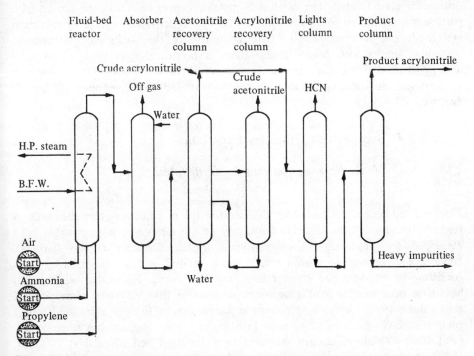

Figure 8.5.4 Acrylonitrile production by the Sohio process.

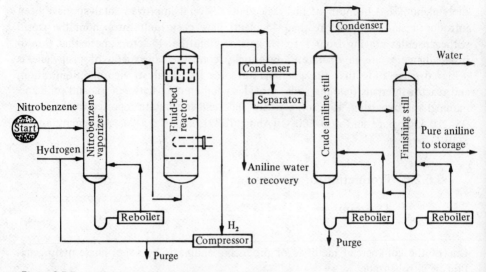

Figure 8.5.5 Aniline production by the American Cyanamid fluid-bed process.

amount to ensure practically complete conversion of nitrobenzene and to minimize side reactions. Operating conditions are around 270°C and 140 kPa gauge. The superficial gas velocity is around 30 cm/s.

Heat of reaction is removed by cooling bundles immersed in the bed. A porous distributor plate is used. The catalyst is metallic copper on a silica gel carrier, with particle size in the range 20–150 μm. The catalyst is activated in place by reduction with hydrogen at about 250°C. Careful control of the quality of nitrobenzene promotes long service before regeneration is needed. Regeneration is normally accomplished *in situ* by halting the flow of nitrobenzene, flushing the system with an inert gas, and passing air through the bed at 250–350°C to burn off organic deposits.

8.5.2.7 Synthesis of Other Hydrocarbons

M. A. Bergougnou and J. Yerushalmi

Fluidized-bed processing is used for the manufacture of a host of other chemicals. A few additional examples illustrate the utility of the technique. A process has been developed for production of polyethylene in the dry state (Union Carbide). Polyethylene is made to grow on very active catalyst particles fluidized by a gas consisting of ethylene and chain-termination compounds. Electrothermal fluidized beds have been used to synthesize hydrogen cyanide from methane, ammonia, and coke (Shine 1971). An electric current is passed directly through a fluidized bed of conductive coke particles to generate high temperatures. Methane has been synthesized from CO and hydrogen mixtures in a fluidized bed of catalyst (Streeter, 1977). Pressure is high (6700 kPa) and the heat release very large, on the order of 2

MJ/m^3. A 1% CO conversion produces an adiabatic temperature rise of $70°C$. Such conditions require excellent heat transfer between the bed and cooling coils immersed in the bed.

In the early 1940s, a major effort was launched in the United States to develop a fluid-bed process for the production of high-grade gasoline via Fischer-Tropsch synthesis. The synthesis gas, mainly hydrogen and CO, would be derived from reforming of natural gas. The design chosen for the process involved a bubbling fluidized bed of fine iron catalyst, with a cooling tube bank immersed in the bed to remove the heat of combustion (Zenz & Othmer, 1960). After extensive laboratory effort, a large plant (about 5 m ID), the so-called Carthage-Hydrocol, was built in Texas. The effort met with failure owing to, among other things, conversions well below those anticipated on the basis of the laboratory work. Fine iron can be classified in Geldart's group C (see section 8.1.3). It is cohesive and accordingly possesses poor fluidization characteristics. At low gas velocities typical of bubbling fluidized beds, such solids give rise to poor solid mixing, channeling, and attendant poor efficiency of contact between gas and solid.

In today's only Fischer-Tropsch plant, in Sasolburg, South Africa, the synthesis reaction is carried out in a circulating high-velocity fluid bed. The plant has seen successful operation since 1954 and a large expansion was recently announced. The so-called Synthol reactor (figure 8.5.6) operates at a pressure of about 2100 kPa. The temperature is about $315°C$ near the bottom of the reactor, after mixing of the

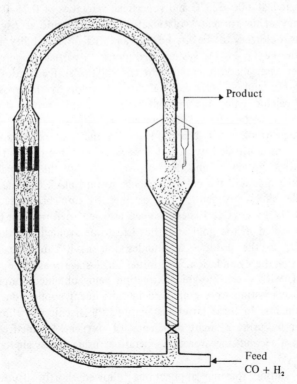

Figure 8.5.6 SASOL's Synthol reactor.

synthesis gas and the catalysts descending from the standpipe, and about 340°C in the settling hopper (Hoogendoorn 1973). Over the years, conversions have improved to nearly 85%. Otherwise, little has been published on the process. The success of the Synthol reactor demonstrates the potential of high-velocity fluidization for solids that display poor fluidization qualities in the low-velocity bubbling fluidized bed.

8.5.3 NONCATALYTIC GAS–SOLID REACTIONS

8.5.3.1 Fluid-Bed Roasting of Sulfide Ores

W. W. Jukkola

Roasting of sulfide ores has been carried out for many decades in various types of furnaces. The ability to accurately control both the roasting temperature and the gas composition within the fluid-bed reactors has led to almost universal adoption of the fluid-bed technique for many types of sulfide ores.

In 1946 a fluid-bed roaster of about 3 m ID was placed in operation for the treatment of gold-bearing arsenopyrite ores at the Cochenour Willans plant in Ontario, Canada. In this application, flotation concentrates of about 85% $-74\ \mu m$ in size were roasted at 600–625°C and superficial velocities of 0.25–0.30 m/s, using a slight deficiency of air to cause volatilization of the arsenic as As_2O_3 while the iron sulfide was oxidized to Fe_3O_4-Fe_2O_3 and SO_2. The ability of oxygen to transfer within the Fe_3O_4-Fe_2O_3 system in response to partial pressures of SO_2 and O_2 in the roaster gases made it possible to control the air-feed ratios. The relative amounts of Fe_3O_4 and Fe_2O_3 gave a distinct color to the roasted product. Employing this calcine color for air-feed ratio regulation proved to be a useful control technique in other fields of application such as roasting of pyrite and pyrrhotite for high-strength SO_2-bearing gases. In the gold roasting operation the bed temperature was controlled by injection of water into the bed and the feed rate was regulated to maintain a chocolate-brown color in the quenched calcines. Deficiency of oxygen caused the color to change toward black because of formation of Fe_3O_4, while excess oxygen caused calcines to turn bright red because of oxidation of Fe_3O_4 to Fe_2O_3. Excess oxygen also led to formation of nonvolatile arsenates, which sealed in the gold and thus had to be avoided. On the other hand, too much Fe_3O_4 in the product was undesirable as it caused excess chemical consumption during the cyanidation. The initial single-stage roasting operations were highly successful, with over 95% gold extraction being obtained. Improved designs involving two-stage roasting were employed in subsequent applications to minimize chemical requirements. In these latter installations the arsenic was eliminated in the first-stage roaster by using a slight deficiency of oxygen. Arsenic-free calcine was then retreated in a second-stage roasting operation, using excess air to fully oxidize the Fe_3O_4 to Fe_2O_3.

Many other sulfide roasting applications followed shortly afterward for uses such as

1. Dead roasting (complete oxidation) of iron and zinc sulfide ores and concentrates
2. Selective sulfate roasting of copper, zinc, cobalt, and nickel sulfide concentrates
3. Partial roasting of copper and nickel sulfide concentrates

A few typical examples of the fluid-bed sulfide roasting applications from hundreds of units operating worldwide are selected for illustration.

Roasting of Pyrites and Pyrrhotite

Large tonnages of pyrite and pyrrhotite ores, both massive and concentrates, are roasted in fluid-bed units to produce SO_2 gases, which are used mainly for the manufacture of sulfuric acid. The roasted ore or cinders are often converted to blast furnace feed if the levels of copper, lead, zinc, and arsenic are sufficiently low. By-product steam at 3100–4100 kPa is normally recovered by use of bed steam coils and waste heat boilers.

Massive pyrites and pyrrhotite are direct-mined ore crushed to about −10 mm in size before roasting, whereas the concentrates are finely ground ore, usually tailings from selective sulfide flotation operations. As a result the concentrates are very fine— often 100% − 0.250 mm in size—and are available as filter cake with 10–12% moisture. The two types of ores require different design parameters and give different results.

The major system components comprising a typical massive pyrite roasting installation for the manufacture of sulfuric acid are shown in figure 8.5.7. In addition to the fluid bed, unit component systems are required for feed and cinder handling, fluidizing and combustion air, waste heat recovery, stack gas cleaning and cooling, plus instrumentation and controls. Roasters of up to 14.0 m ID and units with capacities of more than 7.0 kg/s are in operation.

Table 8.5.5 shows a comparison of typical operating conditions and performance data from Dorr-Oliver FluoSolids roasters handling the two types of pyrite ores.

Oxidation rates for the pyrites are very rapid. Further, the feed material decrepitates because of the explosive release of labile atomic sulfur when feed is introduced into the hot fluid bed. Because of favorable kinetics, the pyrite roasters are designed for a high percentage of the cinders to be entrained by the product gases. In the case of flotation concentrates, up-flow operation, using inert materials for the fluidized bed, is often employed. In these operations all of the feed materials and reaction products are entrained by the fluidizing gases and are carried out of the unit.

Roasting of Zinc Sulfide

Zinc sulfide concentrates (zinc blends) for use in electrolytic zinc refining must first be oxidized by roasting to acid-soluble zinc oxide. The main roasting reaction is

$$ZnS + \tfrac{3}{2}O_2 \rightarrow ZnO + SO_2$$

Like most natural minerals, zinc minerals vary in chemical composition from one deposit to the next. Zinc sulfide roasting reactions are slower than those of pyrites and the roasted product is less porous, making it more difficult to obtain complete oxidation of the sulfides. These factors are taken into consideration in the

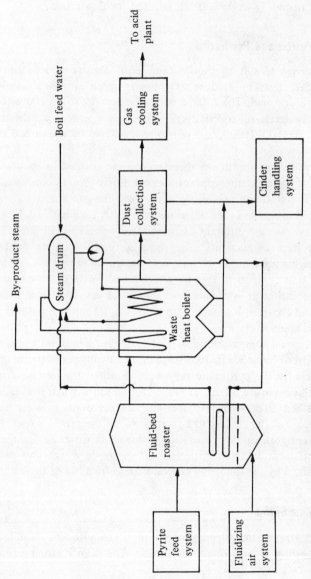

Figure 8.5.7 Fluid-bed pyrite roasting system.

Table 8.5.5 Operating Characteristics of Dorr-Oliver
Fluosolids Roasters.

Feed	Massive pyrite	Pyrite flotation concentrate
Type		
Size range	− 10 mm × 0	0.300 mm × 0
Chemical analysis		
Fe, %	38.0	42.0
S, %	40.0	46.2
Other metals, %	0.1	0.8
Inerts	15.0	13.0
Free moisture, %	5.0	12.0
Operating conditions		
Bed temperature, °C	950	900
Bed space rate, m/s	2.0	0.75[a]
Bed depths, m	1.5	1.5
Operating results		
Analysis gas to acid plant		
SO_2, mol % (dry basis)	11.5	13.0
O_2, mol % (dry basis)	4.0	2.0
Cinder analysis		
Sulfide sulfur, %	0.6–0.8	0.1
Total sulfur, %	2.0	0.4–0.8
Cinder distribution, %		
Roaster underflow	45	0
Waste heat boiler	35	50
Cyclones	16	45
Scrubber	4	5

[a]Inert sand bed used.

fluid-bed roaster design. Units are designed for higher roasting temperatures (925–1000°C), more excess air (20–30%), a lower space rate in freeboard (0.3–0.5 m/s), greater freeboard detention, and a bed depth of 1.75–2.0 m. Because roasting operations are carried out near the fusion temperature of the solid materials, the air distributor is carefully designed to provide pressure drops of 3.75–5.0 kPa to ensure that proper fluidization is maintained. Operations at or above the eutectic temperature of the components must be avoided.

Typical zinc sulfide concentrates have chemical and size analyses in the following ranges:

Chemical analysis		Size analysis	
Zn	49–54%	+ 0.300 mm	0
Fe	1–10%	+ 0.150 mm	5–10%
S	30–32%	+ 0.074 mm	20–30%
Pb	1.0–2.0%	+ 0.043 mm	40–50%
Cu	0.5–1.0%		
SiO_2	2.0–3.0%		
Free moisture	8–12%		

In northern climates, where frozen concentrates are often encountered, and in many other locations because of special considerations, repulping the concentrates and feeding the slurry into the roaster have been employed to simplify material handling problems. However, with 76–78% solid slurry the equilibrium roasting temperature is 925–950°C. With this operating temperature, product containing 0.2–0.5% sulfide sulfur and about 1.5% sulfate sulfur has been obtained. When possible, it is preferable to feed the moist zinc blend directly into the roaster as this permits operating at 950–1000°C, resulting in a product with 0.1–0.3% sulfide sulfur. By-product steam production is about 0.8 kg/kg solids with slurry feeding methods and 0.9–1.0 kg steam/kg feed solid with direct feeding of the 10% moist concentrate.

Sulfate Roasting

Currently, the roast, leach, electrowinning process is being used for the production of large tonnages of copper and cobalt, particularly in Zambia, Zaire, and Arizona. In the roasting step, fluid-bed roasters are used for selective sulfation of copper and cobalt while minimizing solubilization of the iron present in the feed concentrates. This is achieved by careful control of the roasting temperature and the air-to-feed ratio, which in turn determines the gas composition in the roaster. Numerous roasting reactions are possible depending on the temperature, the SO_2 concentration, and the SO_3/O_2 ratio. Substantial kinetic and equilibrium data on decomposition of sulfates have been presented by Stern & Weise (1966) and others. To achieve the desired air-feed control, all sulfate roasting plants, with one exception, use slurry feed systems, which permit accurate metering and good distribution of the feed.

The hot calcines from the roaster are quenched in the leach liquors while the roaster gases, after scrubbing, are usually sent to a sulfuric acid plant to meet environmental requirements and to supply acid for leaching of oxide ores. Waste heat boilers are not used because of the sticky nature of this dust and undesired reactions that occur as gases are cooled.

The copper and cobalt concentrates processed at the various plants have widely different chemical and mineral compositions. The most common copper and cobalt minerals encountered are chalcopyrite ($CuFeS_2$), chalcocite (Cu_2S), bornite (Cu_5FeS_4), and carrollite ($CuCo_2S_4$).

Some of the roasting reactions that can occur with the two most common copper minerals at the normal roasting temperature range of 650 to 750°C are

$$CuFeS_2 + \tfrac{15}{4}O_2 \rightarrow CuSO_4 + \tfrac{1}{2}Fe_2O_3 + SO_2$$

$$Cu_2S + \tfrac{5}{2}O_2 \rightarrow CuO \cdot CuSO_4$$

$$Cu_2S + \tfrac{5}{2}O_2 \rightarrow CuO + CuSO_4$$

$$Cu_2S + 2O_2 \rightarrow 2CuO + SO_2$$

$$CuFeS_2 + \tfrac{13}{4}O_2 \rightarrow \tfrac{1}{2}CuO \cdot Fe_2O_3 + \tfrac{1}{2}CuO + 2SO_2$$

Many other minerals are usually present, so these are only a few of the reactions that can occur and must be controlled for optimum roaster performance. The last reaction listed is detrimental as copper ferrite, $CuO \cdot Fe_2O_3$, is insoluble in dilute acid solutions. Nickel and zinc sulfide concentrates are also amenable to treatment by sulfate roasting techniques in fluidized beds.

Typical design and performance data for operating units of about 7.0 m ID handling copper-cobalt concentrates are as follows:

Operating temperature	$675 \pm 20\ °C$
Superficial space rate	0.5 m/s
Bed depth	1.5 m
Capacity	0.09–0.12 kg/m^2 s
Copper extraction	97–98%
Cobalt extraction	85–95%
Ratio Cu + Co/Fe in leach liquor	20:1

Partial Roasting of Copper Concentrates

One method being employed to lower sulfur dioxide emissions from copper smelters is partial roasting of the copper concentrates to remove approximately half of the sulfur content of the feed as a high-strength sulfur dioxide gas, 14–17% SO$_2$ (dry basis). This can be combined with the other smelter gases to obtain a mixed gas with 3–6% SO$_2$, which is sufficiently concentrated to be treated by a conventional acid plant. The fluid-bed partial roasting method is also employed for treatment of nickel sulfide concentrates at nickel smelters. Other benefits of the partial roasting of the concentrates and the introduction of the hot calcines directly into the reverberating or electric smelting furnaces are increased smelting capacity, substantially reduced volume of stack gases, and decreased fuel and power requirements.

Partial roasting is carried out at 565–625°C. The roasting reactions that occur are indicated by the following simplified equations:

$$FeS_2 + O_2 \rightarrow FeS + SO_2$$

$$CuFeS_2 + \tfrac{1}{2}O_2 \rightarrow \tfrac{1}{2}Cu_2S + FeS + \tfrac{1}{2}SO_2$$

$$FeS + \tfrac{5}{3}O_2 \rightarrow \tfrac{1}{3}Fe_3O_4 + SO_2$$

The latter reaction is carried out only to the extent necessary to obtain the desired degree of sulfur elimination from the feed.

Most smelting operations require addition of some silica and/or limestone flux to the smelter charge to obtain the desired slag composition and viscosity. Silica flux is added to the roaster to serve as an inert bed material and to be preheated before the smelter. Because the flux is usually − 6 mm while the concentrates are − 0.2 mm, the bed at any time contains only 1.0–2.0% of the sulfide concentrates, the remainder being the flux material. This enables the unit to be shut down and restarted with a minimum of problems.

A Dorr-Oliver fluid-bed copper partial roasting plant was started in 1973 at the Mount Isa smelter in Australia. Figure 8.5.8 shows schematically the major components. Performance has been discussed by Borgelt et al. (1974). The 7.6-m-diameter roaster at this plant handles 20.0 kg/s concentrates plus 0.69×10^{-3} to 2.0×10^{-3} kg/s flux. The concentrate is fed into the roaster in a slurry and

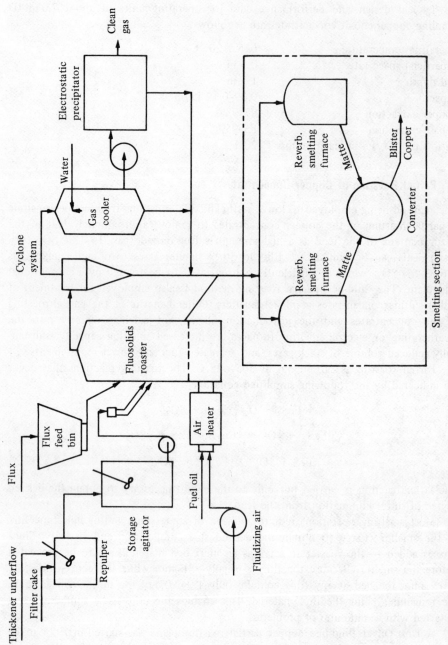

Figure 8.5.8 Schematic of Mount Isa copper concentrate partial roasting system.

contains 75-76% solids. The roasting operation is carried out at 575-625°C, with sufficient sulfur burned off to maintain autogenous operation while still producing a matte in the smelter with a 42% matte grade. The roaster is provided with a direct-fired air heater and refractory dome distributor plate. The air heater is used only during start-up, but it is also useful during the initial phase of the roasting in providing operating flexibility.

Twelve fluid-bed sulfide roasting systems for partial removal of sulfur from feed material for smelters have been installed worldwide. The units have an installed design capacity of more than 15,000 tons of concentrate per day.

8.5.3.2 Calcination of Limestone and Phosphate Rock

W. W. Jukkola

Calcination of limestones and phosphate rocks is a high-temperature, highly endothermic process. Multistage fluid beds are used and act as direct heat exchangers. In each stage the solids and gases reach an equilibrium temperature and leave the stage at bed temperature. In operation, the solids are introduced into the top fluidized bed and travel downward by gravity through a transfer pipe system countercurrent to the gas flow. One of the intermediate beds is the calcining bed, into which fuel is injected directly. Because of the properties of the fluidized beds—active mixing, high heat transfer rates, etc.—it is possible to burn the fuel with nearly stoichiometric air volumes without causing overheated zones. In operations at 900-1000°C excess air is used, primarily to maintain an oxidizing atmosphere. Units have been operated continuously for months with only 0.2-0.5% O_2 in the stack gases.

Another advantage of the multistage calciners is that reactions can be carried out at different temperature levels, thereby conserving heat. Drying takes place in the first stage, while dehydration occurs in an intermediate stage between drying and calcination. The lower or final stage is a cooling stage, where sensible heat from the calcined product is transferred to the combustion and fluidizing air.

Limestone Calcination

In 1948 a Dorr-Oliver FluoSolids five-compartment calciner was placed in operation at the New England Lime Co., Adams, Mass., for the production of 1.05 kg/s high-activity lime. This unit was designed to handle predried limestone sized to -2.5 mm X 0.2 mm feed. The design capacity was readily met with a fuel requirement of only 5.22×10^3 kJ/kg product. This unit plus three others, larger and with some refinements, are in operation at the plant.

In these calciners the heat transfer compartments are operated with shallow beds, 0.3-0.45 m deep, whereas the calcining bed is about 1.5 m deep. Low pressure drops, 1.5-2.0 kPa, occur across the refractory distributor plate of the preheating stages, whereas there is a slightly higher drop across the calcining compartment distributor. Scaling does occur in some of the distributor plates, requiring shutdown at intervals of 3–6 mo for cleanout. Limestone at other locations with higher impurity levels has shown even greater scaling. Prolonged pilot plant operation appears necessary to establish the suitability of a limestone source for treatment by the multistage calciners.

Many limestones decrepitate severely when subjected to fluid-bed treatment. Apparently because of the rapid heat transfer in the fluid beds, thermal stresses developed within the limestone crystals and rapid release of CO_2 cause the crystals to break apart, producing too fine a product for most commercial uses.

Phosphate Rock Calcination

Multistage fluid-bed calcination systems were developed by Dorr-Oliver in the 1950s as a step in the beneficiation of Idaho and Wyoming phosphate rock deposits to make them suitable as feed material for phosphoric acid manufacture by the wet process. Calcination of these rocks to remove carbon and hydrocarbon contaminants proved to have the following benefits in the wet phosphoric acid process:

1. Eliminated the need for defoamer during acidulation
2. Improved the filtration properties of the gypsum
3. Produced clear green acid
4. Minimized or eliminated precipitation during acid storage

Also, the grade of the ore was raised by calcination because of the stripping out of some of the clays, removal of the volatiles, and decomposition of calcium carbonate and hydrates. Calcination is also used to remove some toxic compounds from the ores. Fluid-bed calciners have an installed production capacity of about 20,000 tons per day in the United States and about 8000 tons per day in the rest of the world.

Most of the fluid-bed systems consist of three-compartment calciners followed by a fluid-bed direct water injection unit for cooling the product. The first stage of the calciner is a drying and preheat bed, the second or middle stage is the combustion and calcining stage, and the third or final stage is a calcine cooling and air preheat stage. Most phosphate ores in the western United States that are heat treated are crushed, prewashed, and dewatered before calcination. Feed to the calciners is usually of 3 mm or finer size with a moisture content of 10–15%. The carbon and hydrocarbon content of the feed supplies a large portion, and in exceptional cases all, of the fuel requirements for calcination operations carried out at 760–850°C. Auxiliary fuel, either bunker C oil or natural gas, is injected into the calcining bed. The gross fuel requirement ranges from 1150 to 1400 kJ/kg product. Units with 5.5-m ID calcining beds have a calcine production rate of 15–17 kg/s.

Many phosphate ores outside the United States have different mineralization and properties requiring different calcining treatment. Special modified designs have been employed in these cases.

8.5.3.3 Incineration of Waste Liquor and Solids Refuse

W. W. Jukkola

Incineration, which is a high-temperature oxidation and thermal decomposition process, is an important method for disposing of organic, biological, and toxic wastes. Fluid-bed incineration systems are widely used for heat treatment of liquid and solid wastes from municipal and industrial wastewater treatment plants. Waste solids recovered from the primary and secondary biological wastewater treatment plants are first dewatered by use of centrifuges, vacuum filters, or filter presses and then fed into the fluid bed for disposal. As the ash resulting from incineration of the wastes is normally 0.015 mm and smaller, an inert bed of sand, alumina, or magnesium oxide is used. The incineration units are operated at 750-1100°C, as required for the combustion and decomposition of the toxic material being treated. The inert bed material is generally in the size range 3-0.200 mm with bed space rates selected to be compatible with the bed sizing, but normally in the range 1.0-1.5 m/s. Many liquid wastes are injected directly into the inert bed of the incinerator for disposal. The incineration system often has waste heat boilers and/or heat exchangers for heat and energy recovery. Electrostatic precipitators and scrubbers are widely employed to clean gases from incinerators (see chapter 9).

Fluid-bed systems are also widely used for the combustion and incineration of waste liquors that contain sufficient inorganic chemicals that the ash from the combustion pelletizes and forms a chemical-fluidized bed in the combustion unit. Typical liquors having these properties are caustic wastes from oil refineries and waste liquor from the kraft, neutral sulfite semichemical, and nonsulfur-soda pulping processes for the manufacture of paper pulp. The fluid-bed combustion unit has become an important item in the chemical recovery system in these plants.

Operation of the chemical recovery system is complex but basically consists of the following steps:

1. Dilute waste liquor is preconcentrated in multiple-effect evaporators.
2. Waste liquor is further concentrated in a direct-contact venturi scrubber-evaporator using the combustion gases from the fluid-bed combustion system.
3. Concentrated liquor is fed into the fluid-bed combustor, where combustion and pelletization occur.
4. Ash product is withdrawn from the combustion unit and dissolved for reuse in the pulping process.

The major components of the ash from the combustion of waste pulping liquor are Na_2CO_3 and Na_2SO_4, depending on the pulping process and chemical being used. These chemicals have melting points of 854 and 883°C, respectively. However, many impurities lead to eutectics with drastically lower melting points. A small amount of liquid phase causes pelletization, but too much results in bed defluidization. Thus, careful control of impurity levels, operating temperatures, and pellet sizes is essential. Operating conditions vary from plant to plant, depending on the processes and chemicals employed and the wood or fiber materials used as feed, but the combustion units mostly operate in the range 700–750°C. Because of the low combustion temperature, the maximum bed space rate is about 1.0 m/s and 40–60% excess air is essential.

Municipal solid wastes can also be incinerated with fluid-bed systems but pretreatment is essential. The solid waste must be reduced to a small size. All glass, aluminum and other fusible noncombustible compounds should be removed from the feed material before incineration, or they will fuse in the unit and eventually cause defluidization of the bed. Successful pretreatment and resource recovery is being practiced in Franklin, Ohio, where solid waste is repulped and shredded in heavy-duty hydropulpers. An underflow heavy fraction is withdrawn from the repulper and sent to a trommel screen to remove larger metal pieces from the fibrous material. Iron is then magnetically separated from nonferrous metals. The undersize from the trommel screen is returned to the repulper. The overflow light fraction from the repulper is pumped through liquid cyclones to separate the fibers from the glass and other granular solids. The cyclone underflow is sent to the glass recovery system and the overflow to fiber recovery. Fibers are dewatered and nonmarketable fibers are fed into the fluid-bed incinerator by pneumatic means for disposal.

Wittman et al. (1975) described wet processing of solid wastes at the Franklin plant in a report prepared for the U.S. Environmental Protection Agency (EPA). No other large-scale fluid-bed unit is known to be in operation for this application, but several installations are in the planning stage. However, many small-scale experimental units are in operation. In a few instances where combustibles are separated from noncombustibles at the sources of the wastes, the resulting solid waste can be economically incinerated in the fluid-bed system with heat and energy recovery.

8.5.3.4 Production of Alumina from Aluminum Hydroxide by the Lurgi and Alcoa Processes

W. W. Jukkola

In the electrolytic production of aluminum, alumina trihydrate produced by the Bayer process must be completely dehydrated before being fed into the electrolytic cells. Dehydration of hydrated alumina to the anhydrous form requires a calcination temperature of 900–1200°C, depending on the detention time provided for the solids.

In 1950 a four-stage Dorr-Oliver fluid-bed pilot plant, similar to the multistage limestone calciner, was put in operation at Alcoa's Arvida, Quebec, plant (Zubrzycki 1963). The pilot plant operation indicated that high-quality gamma alumina could be made with substantial fuel savings compared with the rotary kilns operating at the plant. However, operating difficulties resulted from blockage of the inter-compartment distributor domes when catalytic agents were added to the unit to promote alpha alumina production. Other modified design concepts are necessary to overcome the scaling problems encountered with alpha alumina.

Alcoa Fluid-Flash Calciner

Around the same period, Alcoa was also investigating fluid-bed calcination. According to Fish (1974), the company went through several design modifications, starting with typical multibed units and ending with a "fluid-flash" calciner of 3.5 kg/s capacity at the Bauxite, Arkansas, plant. Further modification of the designs resulted in units with a reported product capacity of 17.4 kg/s, fuel savings of 30–40% compared with rotary kilns, and lower capital and maintenance costs. To achieve the high capacity in economically sized units the Alcoa calciners are designed to operate under pressure. Combustion and calcination are carried out in a dilute-phase flash calcination chamber at high temperature. The calcine suspension from the flash chamber is introduced into a cyclone for solids separation. A fluid bed is maintained in the bottom of the cyclone vessel and the degree of calcination is controlled by varying the solids detention at the calcining temperature in this bed. Gases leaving this chamber are used to dry, preheat, and partially calcine the incoming feed solids, which are then introduced into the flash calcining chamber. Calcined product transfers to a multistage fluid-bed calcine cooler, where the sensible heat of the solids is transferred to the combustion and fluidizing air by direct heat exchange.

Lurgi's Circulating (Fast)-Bed Calciner

Lurgi Chemie and Huttentechnik GmBh of Frankfurt, West Germany, was the first company to appreciate the broad commercial potential of the fast fluidized bed (Yerushalmi et al. 1976b). Lurgi realized this potential in a process developed jointly with Vereinigte Aluminum Werke AG for calcining aluminum hydroxide (Reh 1971). The heart of the process is the fast-fluidized-bed furnace (figure 8.5.9) or, as Lurgi sometimes refers to it, the highly expanded circulating-bed furnace. Calcination is normally provided at 1000–1100°C. Heat is provided by direct injection of fuel (usually oil) to the lower, denser portion of the bed; the primary air is substoichiometric and combustion is accordingly completed, following injection of secondary air, in the upper region of the furnace. The temperature, however, remains remarkably uniform throughout the fast-bed furnace (Reh et al. 1974). The superficial gas velocity near the top of the furnace is about 3–4 m/s. A large cyclone provides for circulation of the solids, which are smaller than 100 μm, at rates sufficiently high to establish the fast-bed condition. The product stream is withdrawn from the standpipe.

The Lurgi plant (figure 8.5.10) provides for efficient recovery of heat. Hot combustion gas from the fast-bed furnace is used to drive off surface and adsorbed moisture from the feed and preheat it in two-stage venturi fluid-bed preheaters. The venturi fluid bed is a highly expanded fluid bed in a conical grateless device. It exhibits the temperature uniformity of the conventional bubbling fluid bed, but is marked by higher gas velocities, lower pressure drops, and lower retention times.

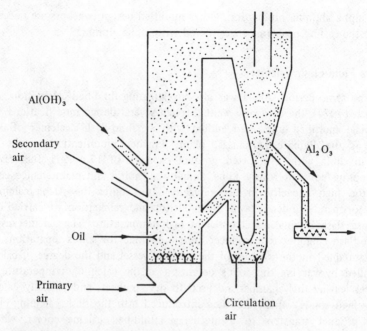

Figure 8.5.9 Lurgi's fast (circulating)-fluid-bed calciner.

Sensible heat of the product withdrawn from the standpipe is utilized in a multistage fluidized bed to heat the primary and secondary air. The former is introduced to the fast-bed furnace through the bottom grate and flows through the heating coils. The fluidizing gas in this heater is air, which serves as the secondary air to the furnace. Typical fuel requirements in a Lurgi plant are 3240–3370 kJ/kg Al_2O_3.

Since its introduction in 1970, the fast-bed calciner has proved highly successful. Several Lurgi plants now supply the bulk of alumina in West Germany, and plants are in operation or under construction in other countries in Europe and Asia. A Lurgi furnace with about 4 m ID has a capacity comparable to that of a conventional fluid-bed calciner nearly 7 m in diameter (Zubrzycki 1963). The Lurgi development suggests that fast beds could be scaled up readily for applications of this type. Lurgi's scale-up was in two steps: a 12.5-cm ID unit was followed by a pilot 90 cm in diameter and 8.5 m tall. Both the pilot and the first commercial plant (which was more than 3 m in diameter) achieved design operation within a few weeks after start-up.

8.5.3.5 Coking in Fluidized Beds

J. M. Matsen

Fluid Coking

Coking is a thermal cracking reaction for converting heavy residual petroleum stocks into lighter, more valuable products. Carbon, or coke, is deposited as a by-product

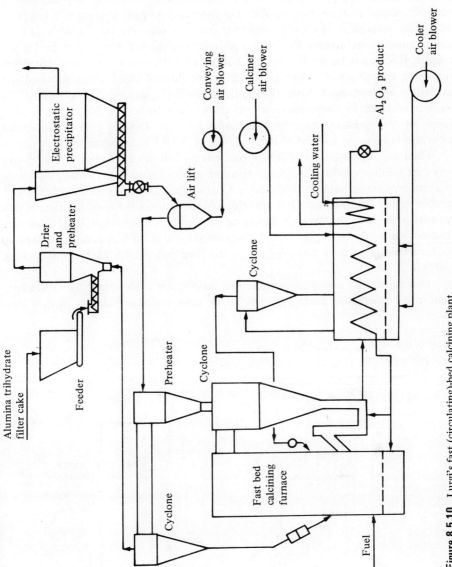

Figure 8.5.10 Lurgi's fast (circulating)-bed calcining plant.

of the reaction. Fluid-bed coking was developed by Standard Oil Development Co. and commercialized in 1954. Thirteen fluid cokers have been built since that time, ranging in feed capacity from 4 to 120 kg/s and having a total capacity of 480 kg/s.

In the coking process, heavy oil feed is sprayed into a hot fluidized bed of coke particles. Cracked products vaporize and pass overhead, while coke deposits on bed particles. Vapor products pass through a cyclone and into the bottom of a scrubber, where the residual coke dust is scrubbed out and heavy tars are condensed by a cooled pumparound stream. Part of the pumparound slurry is recycled as feed to the reactor. Coke particles leave from the bottom of the reaction zone and pass down through a stripping zone. Here a countercurrent flow of steam strips absorbed and interstitial hydrocarbons from the particles. Particles leaving the bottom of the stripper circulate to a separate burner vessel, where a portion of the coke is burned, supplying the necessary heat for the coking reaction. Product coke is withdrawn from the burner and used as boiler fuel. Figure 8.5.11 is a diagram of the process.

Fluid coke particles are relatively coarse (e.g., 200 μm average particle size) and very large bubbles can form. Although regarded as poor fluidization in many processes, large bubbles are desirable in fluid coking. Gas bubbles contain almost entirely cracked product rather than reactant. It is advantageous to minimize the residence time of this gas within the bed, and the large, fast-rising bubbles ensure this result. In addition, the reactor requires the very aggressive mixing caused by large bubbles in order to disperse coke particles that have been wetted by the feed and prevent them from sticking together.

Maintenance of a suitable particle size distribution is important for satisfactory fluid coker operation. Surface deposition of coke tends to increase particle size,

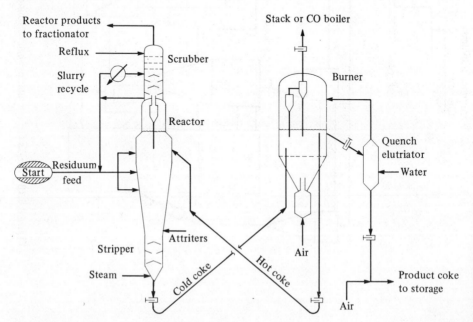

Figure 8.5.11 Fluid coker: schematic flow diagram.

while attrition and coke burning in the burner tend to reduce it. Additional attrition caused by high-velocity steam jets generates the fine seed coke needed to maintain a steady-state size distribution in the process. To minimize use of attrition steam, coke is withdrawn from the process through an elutriator, which returns fines to the process and yields a relatively dust-free product coke.

A phenomenon known as bogging sets the maximum rate at which feed can be injected into the fluid coker reactor. When the feed rate exceeds the cracking and vaporization rate in the bed, a tacky oil film accumulates on bed particles, allowing them to stick together and causing the bed to lose fluidity. This is similar to the defluidization that occurs in fluid-bed driers, incinerators, or calciners at excessive liquid feed rates. The permissible feed rate increases with temperature and with reactor holdup. Fluid coker reactors have very deep beds to provide the necessary holdup. The gradual increase in bed diameter from bottom to top produces a nearly constant superficial gas velocity, which is everywhere high enough to prevent bogging problems.

Although most cracking and carbon deposition occurs on the surface of bed particles, it is not possible to avoid formation and growth of coke deposits elsewhere in the reactor. A major part of the commercialization effort in fluid coking was devoted to minimizing the occurrence and effect of such deposits. Three approaches have been developed: (1) mechanical layout has minimized such factors as impingement of feed jets on vessel surfaces, amount of surface not bathed in hot coke particles, and vapor residence time above the bed; (2) techniques have been developed for on-stream cleaning or decoking in critical areas; and (3) provision has been made for periodic withdrawal of large coke chunks and agglomerates from low points in reactors and transfer lines. Fouling by coke deposits remains the most common limitation on run length, but 2 yr of operation between shutdowns is routinely achieved.

Flexicoking

During the late 1960s, environmental considerations indicated that in many areas it would no longer be possible to use high-sulfur fluid coke products as a boiler fuel. The Flexicoking process was therefore developed, in which a third vessel is added to fluid coking to gasify the coke. Sulfur in the low-heating-value synthetic gas is removed in a Stretford process, and the cleaned gas is a suitable refinery fuel. A large prototype Flexicoker was started up in 1974, and the first commercial plant went on stream in Kawasaki, Japan, in 1976. A diagram of the Kawasaki plant is shown in figure 8.5.12. Two more Flexicokers are currently under design and the 22-m-diameter gasifier for one of these will be the world's largest fluid-bed reactor.

The reactor for a Flexicoker is essentially the same as that for a fluid coker. The heater vessel is similar to the burner vessel in fluid coking, but heat is usually supplied by circulation of hot coke and gas from the gasifier rather than combustion. The heater permits heat recovery from product gas and allows reaction of COS to H_2S, which is the sulfur compound removed in the Stretford process. The heater also affords a variable bed level, in contrast to the reactor, which is operated at an essentially fixed bed level for process reasons, and the gasifier, in

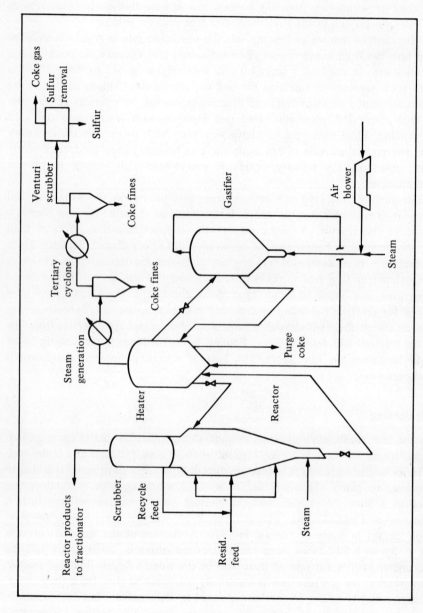

Figure 8.5.12 Simplified Flexicoking flow plan.

Table 8.5.6 Comparison of Particle Properties

Property	Fluid coke	Flexicoke
Bulk density, kg/m³	960	830
Particle density, kg/m³	1530	1360
Surface area, m²/g	<12	65
Mass median particle diameter, μm	220	135

which bed level is fixed by an overflow arrangement. The variable level allows for shifts in coke inventory resulting from changes in operating conditions.

The familiar steam-air reactions are used for coke gasification. Typical gas contains 20% CO, 8% CO_2, 9.4% H_2, 5.3% H_2O, 2.3% CH_4, and 55% N_2 and has a heating value of about 106 kJ/g mol. The high temperatures of the gasifier posed a major challenge in Flexicoker development. Slag formation is controlled by careful grid design and selection of operating conditions. Material problems are met by having only ceramics and refractories exposed to reaction temperature, with steel and alloy components partially insulated and at lower temperatures. The gasifier is designed without cyclones, and the gas velocity must therefore be low enough that the coke entrainment rate is less than the total desired coke circulation rate from gasifier to heater.

Because most of the coke deposited in a Flexocoker reactor is later gasified, the coke particles are much finer and more porous than conventional fluid coke particles (see table 8.5.6). As a direct result of the particle properties, Flexicokers have lower bed densities and higher entrainment rates than fluid cokers.

8.5.4 FLUID–BED PROCESSING OF COAL

8.5.4.1 Introduction

J. Yerushalmi

The projected decline in reserves of oil and gas will make coal assume an increasingly greater role as a source of energy and raw materials. Fluid-bed processing of coal is far from commercial maturity. The few processes that were active commercially in the past are generally not competitive in today's market. Of the many developments under way, only a handful may reach the commercial stage. For this reason, this section departs from the format expected of a handbook. One is hard put to offer design procedures and formulas for a technology that is so young and unformed. Almost without exception, available data are incomplete and were obtained from small-scale equipment over an insufficient period of operation. For design data, the engineer must await tests in larger pilot plants.

This section surveys some of the key developments, highlighting technical problems and possible solutions to these problems. Coal brings unique problems to fluid-bed operation. There is little experience related to operation of fluid beds of coarse particles at the elevated temperatures and pressures that often prevail in coal processing.

8.5.4.2 Fluid-Bed Combustion of Coal

A. M. Squires

Coal's chief use will no doubt continue to be as a fuel for conventional boilers in industry and the utilities. This technology has matured over much of this century, but must now be made compatible with environmental regulations.

Alternatively, coal can be burned in a fluidized bed of solid particles that are capable of capturing the SO_2 that evolves from the burning coal. A portion of the heat released from this coal combustion may be transferred to a medium (e.g., steam) flowing in a tube bank immersed in the bed, the remaining heat being extracted in convection sections or otherwise utilized downstream of the fluid bed. Fluidized-bed combustion of coal thus lends itself to different applications, and there can be a number of boiler configurations.

Origins

Research and development efforts in the field of fluidized-bed combustion of coal have grown rapidly in recent years, especially in the United States and Great Britain. The history of this technology has been described by Ehrlich (1976) and Nack et al. (1976). Development has branched in several directions. Fluid-bed combustion in relatively small-scale equipment (up to about 30 MWt) for industrial use now appears poised for widespread commercial service. In contrast, developments toward large-scale utility boilers have not reached any significant stage, either in scale or in overcoming the technical difficulties that are unique to large utility boilers.

The most securely established fluid-bed combustion system is the Ignifluid boiler (see section 8.5.4.3). Between 1955 and 1968, Fives-Cail Babcock of Paris placed more than 30 Ignifluids in commercial service, in sizes up to 100 MWt. The Ignifluid may be the most robust technique yet devised for burning coal: it needs simply crushed coal; it can process coals of high moisture and ash contents; it requires, even for the largest 100 MWt unit in operation, only one coal feed; it produces carry-over dust about 10 times larger in size and accordingly easier to collect than pulverized-coal fly ash; and it has excellent operating and maintenance records. Nevertheless, the Ignifluid has not seen wider sales and developement to larger scale because of a number of factors, including the entrenched position of pulverized-coal combustion and, in recent years, the inability of Ignifluid to use limestone to capture SO_2. Special roles for Ignifluid ought, however, to be considered: e.g., burning mines wastes, sulfur-rich tailings from coal beneficiation, and low-sulfur or high-ash coal.

The Ignifluid is a two-stage combustion device. Coal is fed to a fluid bed in which it is consumed by partial oxidation by air at substoichiometric proportions;

the gas arising from the bed, now containing combustibles, is burned by secondary air in the space above the fluid bed. The main thrust of development of fluid-bed combustion, however, took a different turn, toward complete combustion in a single stage. It is illustrated by figure 8.5.13.

Figure 8.5.13 is a schematic of a vertical fire-tube boiler for 3.5-MWt unit developed at the National Coal Board's laboratory at Leatherhead, England (Locke et al. 1976). Three rows of horizontal tubes remove heat directly from the 1.09-m-wide bed, and vertical tubes in a tank of water further recover heat from the combustion gases. The fluid bed consists almost entirely of inert particles of sand and a small proportion (about 1% by weight or less) of char particles arising from devolatilization of the coal feed. The inert solid has two major functions: it provides a reservoir of heat, which causes the coal particles fed to the bed to ignite almost instantaneously, and it serves to transfer heat to the water flowing in the heat exchange tubes. High heat transfer rates between a fluid bed and immersed surfaces

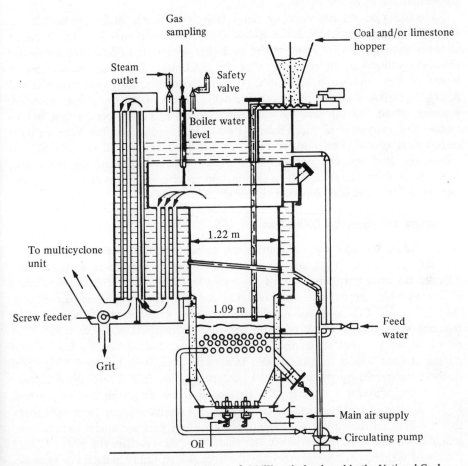

Figure 8.5.13 Vertical fire-tube boiler for about 3.5-MWt unit developed in the National Coal Board's laboratory at Leatherhead, England.

provide one of the outstanding advantages of fluid-bed combustors. The unit shown in figure 8.5.13 has been in operation for more than 6 yr.

In the United States, the main impetus for the development of fluid-bed boilers has been the potential of desulfurizing the combustion gases with a bed consisting of particles capable of reacting with SO_2—limestone and dolomite, for example. The first demonstration of this potential was provided by Bishop and Robison (Ehrlich 1976) of the firm of Pope, Evans, & Robbins, in a 1.4-MW fluid-bed boiler placed in operation in Alexandria, Va., in 1966.

Fluid-bed boilers can be designed for operation at atmospheric or elevated pressure. Development to date has focused on atmospheric operation. Boilers or experimental facilities that have emerged from the mainstream of development have beds about 1 m deep. Temperature is maintained around 800-950°C, because limestone sulfation rates peak within this range.

Of the theoretical heating value of the coal burned, about 50% is absorbed by water and steam flowing in the tubes immersed in the bed. Gases leaving the bed are further cooled in convection sections.

Fluidizing-gas velocities usually range from 1 to 5 m/s. Much of the work in Great Britain has been at the lower end of this range. The greater bed areas required at lower gas velocities are compensated by higher combustion efficiencies and better limestone utilization. In contrast, work in the United States has tended toward higher gas velocities, around 3-5 m/s. At higher velocities, carry-over from the bed is rich in carbon that cannot be consumed by recycle to the bed. Pope, Evans, & Robbins solved this problem by providing a separate, smaller combustion bed to receive the carry-over as fuel (Bishop 1968). This second bed has been called a *carbon burnup cell.* Fewer water tubes are provided in this cell per unit of heat release, so that the cell operates at a higher temperature than the main bed, generally at about 1100°C. With a carbon burnup cell, overall combustion efficiencies above 99% have been reported (Robison 1972).

Design and Operating Difficulties

Of the design and operating difficulties still to be overcome, coal feeding is one of the most formidable. Feed coal must be introduced to the bed in a manner that provides for even distribution across the entire bed area. Uneven distribution leads to considerable carbon loss from coal-rich zones in the form of unburned coal, char-rich dust, CO, and unburned hydrocarbons. Coal-rich zones also provide reducing atmospheres, which promote corrosion of the heat exchange tubes. Even dispersion of the coal across the bed is difficult to achieve because lateral solid mixing in fluid beds is in general poor (see section 8.1.9); in fluid-bed boilers it is further constrained by the presence of immersed tubes. It is accordingly necessary to feed coal through a number of ports spaced across the entire area of the bed. Highly & Merrick (1971) concluded on the basis of experimental and theoretical study that the designer should provide roughly one coal feed port per square meter of bed area. Subsequent work has borne out this guideline. This is perhaps the most awkward feature of mainstream designs, especially for large electric utility boilers. For example, a 500-MWe fluid-bed boiler would require about 500 coal feed ports.

The possibility of introducing coal in lump size to the top of a fluid bed has been considered and in several cases tested. It was recognized that if lump coal 2–3 cm in size could be burned in a fluid bed, loss of unburned carbon should be relatively small, permitting operation with reduced bed and freeboard height and with no need for a carbon burnup cell. Lump coal would also make it possible to use few feed ports, perhaps only one, even in beds of large area. The National Coal Board's Stoke Orchard Coal Research Establishment has successfully burned lump coal on a shallow fluid bed of sand (Highly 1976). Small-scale tests demonstrated combustion efficiencies of 96–97% in a bed only 0.15 m deep, without fines recycle or a carbon burnup cell. To demonstrate combustion of large coal on a larger scale, a conventional hot-water boiler, which previously fired gas and oil, was retrofitted with a shallow fluid bed of sand measuring 0.8 by 0.5 m. As figure 8.5.14 demonstrates, there were initially no tubes in the bed and the unit operated with a large excess of air in order to maintain the bed at the desired temperature. Later, water tubes were installed to remove 210 kWt, giving a total capacity of 600 kW. A combustion efficiency of 96% was routinely achieved without fines recycle.

Achieving turndown to follow load poses another operating difficulty. At the Pope, Evans, & Robbins 100-MWt unit at Rivesville, W.V. (Gamble 1976), there are four different fluid-bed cells, including a carbon burnup cell. Large changes in load can be accomplished by shutting down one or more of the three regular cells. Short-term reductions in load are achieved by lowering the bed level to uncover heat transfer tubes. The solid thus withdrawn is stored to be returned when increase in load is again required. Babcock & Wilcox's 13-MWt boiler at Renfrew, Scotland (Locke et al. 1976), has a compartmented air plenum, and turndown is accomplished by shutting off air to one or more compartments, causing the corresponding part of the bed to slump. The tapered design of the lower part of the fluid bed shown in figure 8.5.13 permits considerable reduction in bed level, uncovering heat exchange tubes through reduction in the fluidizing-gas velocity.

Start-up of fluid-bed combustors requires careful provisions. Some designers have followed the Ignifluid practice of firing an oil burner on top of the bed while passing air upward through it. Fluidization commences when the velocity of the air exceeds minimum fluidization on heating. At the Pope, Evans, & Robbins 100-MWt unit at Rivesville, start-up of the carbon burnup cell is achieved by drawing hot oil combustion products downward through the bed. After the carbon burnup cell is lit, hot solid is transferred to the adjacent cell; when that cell assumes normal operation, solid is transferred to the next cell, and so on.

The design of figure 8.5.13 provides a plenum for air and, between this plenum and the bottom of the fluidized bed, a smaller plenum for gas fuel. A large number of vertical pipes traverse the gas plenum and conduct air to the bottom of the fluidized bed. Each air pipe is pierced with an orifice communicating with the gas plenum so that gas can enter the pipe. Air and gas are well mixed in the pipes, and on start-up, premixed gas and air pass upward through the cold bed. The mixture can be lit above the bed, which gradually heats up by back-radiation from the fire in the freeboard. The fire penetrates the bed when the temperature reaches about 500°C.

Stone-Platt Fluidfire of England (Virr 1976) uses ceramic sparge plates to introduce air into combustion beds (see figure 8.5.15) and can introduce premixed

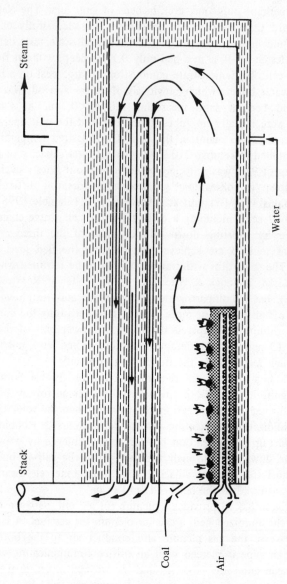

Figure 8.5.14 Retrofit of oil- or gas-fired horizontal fire-tube boiler for shallow fluidized-bed combustion of coal.

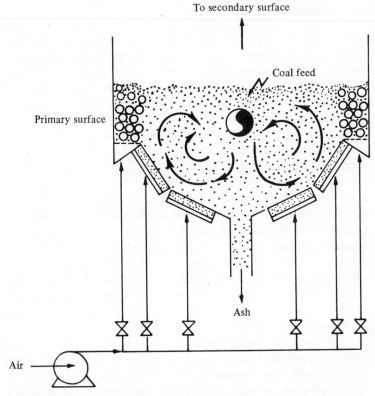

Figure 8.5.15 Fluidized-bed furnace developed by Stone-Platt Fluidfire Ltd. of Dudley, West Midlands, England.

air and gaseous fuel into a cold bed to effect start-up as described above for figure 8.5.13. Several designers have used sparging tubes, perforated along their bottom sides, for introducing air into their fluidized beds (e.g., see figure 8.5.14). Some of these designs provide external gas- or oil-fired burners to introduce hot combustion products via the sparging tubes into the bed from below, heating the bed. Some of the designs are flexible for shifting some or all of the heat duty to gas or oil. The furnace of figure 8.5.13 can burn oil that is supplied to the bed through several air pipes in which it is carried upward as a climbing film.

In a deep, bubbling bed, bubbles tend to move to the center, creating a strong upward current of solid in the middle and a sluggish downward return of solid at the walls (see section 8.1.6.3). Figure 8.5.15 is a furnace developed by Platt Fluidfire with a reverse pattern of solid circulation. There is a strong downward current of solid in the middle and a sluggish upflow in the wings. This reverse pattern leads to a long residence time for fuel particles in the bed. The furnace is claimed to be particularly effective in burning fuels that produce fine, light particles, which are otherwise difficult to burn. It has been tested successfully on paper wastes, fabric wastes, chopped rubber tires, wood and wood wastes, as well as coal. Turndown is excellent and is in part accomplished by turning down air flow to the wings.

Other Developments

Limestone utilization is one of the crucial issues determining the feasibility of using fluid-bed boilers as alternatives to pulverized-coal boilers with stack gas scrubbers. Typical designs for atmospheric fluid-bed boilers employ gas velocities in the range 1-5 m/s. Corresponding to these velocities, the limestone that makes up the bed is fairly coarse, typically 500 μm to 10 mm. Calcium sulfate, the product of sulfur capture, has a larger molecular volume than calcium carbonate or calcium oxide. As the sulfate forms it tends to block the pores near the outer surface of the particles effectively preventing further flow of SO_2 to the particles' interior. Sulfur absorption accordingly tends to slow down considerably at only 20-30% conversion of calcium to calcium sulfate. Beyond that, the stone becomes practically unreactive. This and the short residence time of the gas in the relatively shallow bed lead to limestone requirements that are well beyond stoichiometric proportions.

To reduce sulfur emissions to the levels mandated by the EPA (0.51 μg SO_2 per joule heating value of fuel), a coal containing 4% sulfur would require limestone corresponding to a calcium-to-sulfur molar ratio of 3-5. This translates to a quantity of limestone equal to 30-50% of the coal rate. Correspondingly large quantities of spent material must be disposed of, and every unit increase in the Ca/S molar ratio beyond theoretical requires an additional 0.75% increase in the quality of coal to fuel the calcination of the stone.

Several methods are being studied to reduce the limestone requirements. Precalcination, or controlled calcination of limestone in an atmosphere rich in CO_2, use of additive, and heat treatment aim at effecting changes in the physical structure of the stone toward wider pores, and accordingly greater reactivity. Alternatively, schemes for regenerating the sulfates back to oxides are being considered (Ruth 1976). Regenerative systems require significantly smaller quantities of limestone, but they entail additional hardware, including that needed to process the SO_2 in the regenerator off gas.

Westinghouse (O'Neill & Keairns 1977) has studied the effect of limestone particle size on its sulfation capacity. The results show that finer particles can afford significantly higher sulfation levels. They project that sulfation levels beyond 70% would be achieved with particles smaller than 100 μm at a Ca/S molar ratio approaching unity, if the system provides sufficient residence time for the solid. Fine particles could be maintained in the fluidized state at a low gas velocity, 30 cm/s, but the resulting boiler would have a very low coal processing capacity. High-velocity transport reactors operating in dilute-phase flow may not, however, afford the necessary residence time for the solid.

Battelle's Multi-Solids fluid-bed boiler (Nack et al. 1977) partly circumvents these difficulties. A bed of inert, closely sized coarse particles (Battelle has been using specular hematite 1.4-2.4 mm in size), maintained in turbulent fluidization at gas velocities around 9-12 m/s, serves as the mixing zone into which crushed coal and fine limestone (smaller than 70 μm) are fed. The dense inert bed acts as brake on the upward passage of the limestone and coal particles. The entrained sulfated lime and fly ash contact heat exchange tubes positioned in the freeboard. To increase and control heat transfer rates, additional fine solid (e.g., round sand) may be circulated. Alternatively, heat recovery from the circulating solid may be accomplished in an external bubbling fluid bed packed with heat exchange tubes. Battelle has tested the concept in a 15-cm round unit and a larger (0.22-m^2) rectangular rig and reported that a Ca/S ratio of only 2 was required to reduce sulfur emissions from a coal containing 4% sulfur to below the EPA standard noted above.

Yerushalmi et al. (1978) proposed a concept that employs a fast fluidized bed of fine limestone (figure 8.5.16). Coal is burned by air in a circulating fast bed of fine limestone (e.g., smaller than 100 μm) fluidized at gas velocities around 5–10 m/s. Solid is circulated via a bubbling fluid bed (running at 0.3–0.6 m/s) in which an array of heat exchange tubes is immersed. Turndown in both the fast-bed boiler and Battelle's Multi-Solids fluid-bed boiler is accomplished simply by reducing the rate of solid circulation.

Fluidized-bed combustion can be carried out at an elevated pressure. Whereas much of the earlier work focused on atmospheric combustion, pressurized fluidized-bed combustors have received considerable attention in the recent past. In this mode the bed temperature is maintained within the desired range (typically 800–1000°C) by either extracting heat from the bed to immersed heat exchange tubes or operating at high excess air. The hot pressurized flue gases, after removal of particulate matter, are expanded through a gas turbine to generate power. Removal of particulates from the hot flue gas to ensure a sufficient length of service for the turbine blades is perhaps the most serious obstacle to development of

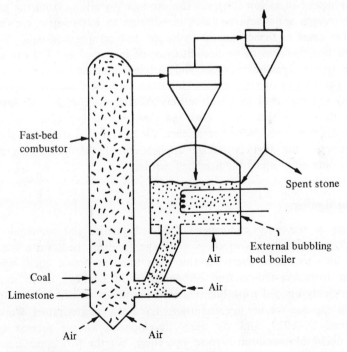

Figure 8.5.16 Schematic of the fast-bed boiler.

pressurized fluid-bed boilers. Otherwise, pressurized fluid-bed boilers offer a number of advantages compared with their atmospheric counterparts. Chiefly, they afford higher efficiencies of combustion and of limestone (or dolomite) utilization and give lower emissions of nitrogen oxides. Various cycle configurations offer the potential of comparatively higher coal-to-power efficiencies. On the other hand, they may require higher capital costs, detracting from the higher efficiencies as far as the cost of power is concerned. Pressurized fluid-bed boilers are also subject to the technical uncertainties that pressurized operation normally entails. Nevertheless, one approach appears promising, namely a pressurized fluid bed operating at high excess air without cooling tubes, and discharging hot gas, following suitable cleanup, to a gas turbine. Such a unit may be regarded as a *coal-fired turbine* an may be used for peak shaving service. Commercial design studies are well advanced, and such equipment may provide the first significant quantities of electricity from fluidized-bed combustion of coal.

8.5.4.3 Fluid-Bed Gasification of Coal

J. Yerushalmi

Gasification of coal gives rise to a gaseous product having carbon monoxide, hydrogen, and sometimes methane as its main combustible components. When coal is gasified by air, the resulting gas is diluted by the presence of nitrogen and is accordingly described as low-Btu gas. The product gas arising from the gasification of coal by oxygen and steam contains, in addition to water vapor, carbon dioxide, and in some cases methane, chiefly hydrogen and carbon monoxide. Such gas is often called intermediate- or medium-Btu gas, or industrial gas. The name synthesis gas is also applied because hydrogen and carbon monoxide are ingredients for the synthesis of a number of products, ranging from methane (high-Btu gas or synthetic natural gas) and methanol to a wide variety of chemicals. Fluid beds bring several advantages to the gasification of coal and have accordingly been the focus of a number of developments. None has reached the commercial stage, and the Winkler, which represents the first large-scale application of the fluidization technique, remains the only commercial fluidized-bed gasifier.

Winkler Gasifier

The Winkler is the only commercial fluid-bed gasifier and represents the first large-scale, commercially significant use of the fluidized bed. Fritz Winkler conceived the idea to utilize cheap reactive fuels, such as brown coals, lignites, and grude (char from low-temperature carbonization of lignites), which were readily available in finely divided form but remained unutilized or had to be briquetted at considerable expense for use in conventional fixed-bed gas generators. Winkler's first patent, issued in 1922, and the early development of the process apparently involved a cyclic blow-and-run type of operation, but the first commercial unit, at Leuna, Germany, in 1926, was blown simultaneously with air and steam. By 1929, there were five Winklers at Leuna, blown with air and steam and providing about 0.28 mm normal m^3/h of producer gas to power engines that ran compressors for an ammonia synthesis plant. The largest of these had an ID of 5.5 m and typically processed 7 kg/s of dried lignite.

In 1933 three of the units were modified and recommissioned to blow steam and oxygen for production of synthesis gas. The Leuna Winklers were shut down in 1971. Three Winkler plants are operating at present in Yugoslavia, Turkey, and Spain. The last Winkler plant constructed (now inactive) was built at the Union Rheinische Braunkholen in Wesseling, West Germany, in 1960. Altogether, 16 installations involving 38 gasifiers have been built. With the exception of the Leuna operation between 1926 and 1929, all commercial Winklers have been blown with steam and oxygen or enriched air to produce water or synthesis gas. The Winkler technology is now available from Bamag Verfahrenstechnik GmBh of West Germany. An air-blown Winkler is available from Davy-Power Gas, Inc., of Florida.

The Winkler gasifier operates at atmospheric pressure. The reactor is a mild steel, refractory-lined vertical shaft. Coal feed, crushed to a top size around 10 mm and dried of surface moisture, is fed to the gasifier by a variable screw conveyor. Solid mixing and high heat transfer rates in the fluid bed promote quick devolatilization of the coal. The bed of char is maintained rather shallow—the settled bed height is about 2 m—and the velocity of the gas near the top of the bed is typically around 3 m/s. In the early Winklers the bed was supported by a grate through which the gasifying medium was admitted, and a rotating scraper arm positioned on top of the grate provided for removal of the ash. In most of the postwar Winklers a conical base has been used, and steam and oxygen are blown through a number of tuyeres at the sides of the cone.

Figure 8.5.17 is a schematic of a typical postwar Winkler and the associated waste heat recovery train. The more recent of these Winklers are about 20 m tall, have about a 5-6 m ID, and may gasify around 10 kg/s of lignite.

The Winkler suffers from several disadvantages. Dust carry-over is high and typically includes about 70% of the coal's ash as well as considerable unreacted carbon. The ash purge (bottoms) contains the balance of the coal's ash and as a rule is also rich in carbon. To improve utilization of the carbon in the carry-over dust, additional gasification medium is blown to the space above the fluidized bed. Even so, the carbon utilization efficiency is only about 85-90%. Early attempts to increase the consumption of fines by expanding the upper section of the vessel and by providing for recycle proved on the whole unsuccessful, indicating that carry-over carbon fines have poor reactivities. In the plant in Turkey, overhead and bottoms char are burned in a steam boiler.

Oxygen introduced through the secondary ports often leads to temperatures high enough to cause clinkering (sintering) of the ash. To prevent accumulation of ash on the dome of the gasifier and in the gas outlet system, a radiant heat boiler has been installed in the upper part of the reactor. The temperature of the gas passing this boiler is typically reduced by 175-200°C.

The Winkler appears to be suited to reactive fuels only. This is particularly true when gasification by air and steam is intended. The bed temperature during processing of lignite is around 800°C. To compensate for the lower reactivity of

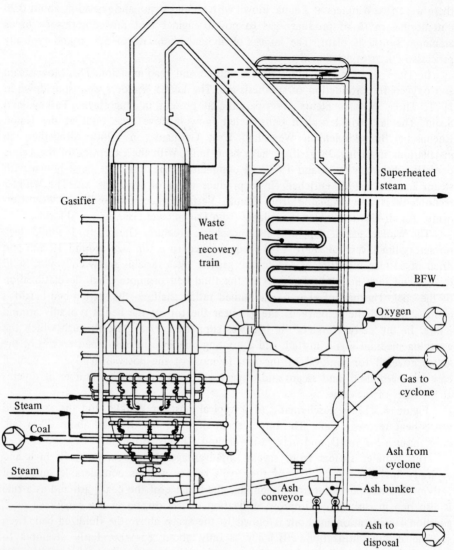

Figure 8.5.17 The Winkler gasifier.

hard coals, the temperature may be maintained as high as 1000°C. Higher temperatures pose the danger of ash clinker formation, especially in the vicinity of the oxygen inlet ports. The Winkler's poor performance probably results from not only its atmospheric operation but also the poor contacting between its shallow bed of coarse particles of char and the high-velocity gasification medium. At about 3 m/s, a shallow bed of coarse particles gives rise to channeling and to considerable bypassing of gas.

There are merits to the Winkler. The gas product is free of tars and oils, the gasifier is capable of operation at part load, and stops and restarts can be achieved quickly. Typical operating data from the Winklers at Union Rheinische Braun-kholen, Wesseling are available (Banchik 1973), and partial information is given as follows:

Feed: Lignite containing 8.6% moisture and 4–5% ash; 40% 1–8 mm, 60% 0–1 mm; 5210 kcal/kg.
Capacity: 8000–17,000 normal m^3/h of make gas of the following composition (dry basis):

$$
\begin{array}{ll}
CO_2 & 13.8 \\
CO & 48.2 \\
H_2 & 35.3 \\
CH_4 & 1.8 \\
N_2 & \underline{0.9} \\
& 100.0
\end{array}
$$

Higher Heating Value (HHV): 2554 kcal/normal m^3.
Gasifying medium: Steam and oxygen.
Carbon utilization efficiency = (carbon in gas)/(carbon in coal) = 0.90.

Postwar Developments

The impressive success of the U.S. petroleum industry in developing the fluid cracking process spurred new applications of the fluidization technique, including the gasification of coal. In contrast to the Winkler gasifier, postwar work on fluid-bed gasification has tended to center on the use of beds of relatively fine coals and chars (e.g., smaller than 1 mm) and gas velocities of the order of 30 cm/s. Good temperature control, easy solid handling, high heat transfer rates, and capability for quick stops and restarts are among the advantages of the fluidized bed for the gasification of coal. During the 1940s and 1950s at least nine research groups worked on development of fluid-bed gasifiers (Squires 1974). New discoveries of oil and gas in the 1950s and the early 1960s brought on a lull, but recent years have seen a resumption of old efforts and initiation of new efforts.

Fluid-bed gasification of coal has a number of inherent disadvantages:

1. The operating temperature is limited. The upper ceiling is the clinkering temperature (around 1040°C), and the lower temperature is dictated by the coal's reactivity and the need to avoid escape of tars.
2. Fluid-bed gasification of coal appears to give rise to formation of carbon fines in the micrometer size range. Buildup of fines in the system may pose a problem. Loss of this carbon from the entrained dust can be serious.
3. Because of the need to maintain a sufficient carbon inventory, a purge to extract ash would contain an appreciable amount of carbon.
4. Items 2 and 3 indicate that complete gasification cannot be achieved in a single-stage fluid-bed gasifier operating below 1040°C unless a burnup zone is provided. An external carbon burnup cell may provide utilization of the carbon in the carry-over and bottoms.
5. Feeding a caking coal directly to the bed without some pretreatment may lead to agglomeration and shutdown.

6. Low fluidizing velocities, around 30 cm/s, mean low coal processing capacities.
7. Fluid-bed gasifiers blown with oxygen may develop ash clinkers in the vicinity of the oxygen inlet points.

Each of the developments addressed below has features that are designed to obviate one or more of the difficulties noted above.

Three-Stage Gasifiers

A three-stage process provides, in addition to the gasifier itself, a first stage where fresh coal is devolatilized or pretreated or otherwise rendered nonagglomerating before introduction to the gasifier, and a carbon burnup cell for consumption of the carbon in carry-over dust and the ash purge.

Bituminous Coal Research is currently testing a pressurized, 45 kg/h, air-blown unit. The air-blown carbon burnup cell operates around 1040–1100°C and provides the gas for the first stage pretreater, which is maintained around 480–540°C. Effluents from the pretreater, together with some additional air and steam, provide the gasifying media for the second-stage bed, the gasifier. At this writing, individual components have been tested to varying degrees but integrated operation is yet to be attempted.

The concept has the potential of obviating most of the problems inherent in single-stage fluid-bed gasification, but the technical and economic feasibility of the integrated system is yet to be demonstrated.

Moving-Burden Processes

In a typical process, coal is gasified by steam and the requisite heat is supplied by a stream (moving burden) of hot solid. The solid in question is subsequently heated in an air-blown combustor fueled by unreacted char. Two types of burdens have been used: inert material and the gasifier's char itself. In either case, the gasifier's heat requirements are supplied by the burden's sensible heat. A circulating solid might also provide potential heat through a chemical reaction. The CO_2-Acceptor process (Fink et al. 1975), now inactive after several years of pilot operation, might accordingly be viewed as a moving-burden process.

Moving-burden processes have several advantages. An intermediate-Btu gas is produced without use of an oxygen plant. Devolatilization of coal takes place in an environment rich in steam; at a given pressure this enhances production of methane, and it gives rise to a char of high reactivity. The circulating burden might also be exploited to introduce a caking coal without pretreatment. There are disadvantages as well: circulation of the burden at the required rate may pose problems, and there is need for an additional gas treating train for the flue produced in the combustion unit, which may contain some combustibles and sulfur as H_2S or SO_2.

ICI moving-burden process Between 1949 and 1952 Imperial Chemical Industries operated an atmospheric, 500 kg/h, char-circulating pilot plant in Billingham, England. An excellent account has been published by Rayner (1952). A significant discovery was that fluid-bed gasification of coal gives rise to the formation of carbon fines in the micrometer size range. Even at low fluidizing velocities, loss of these fines in carry-over dust can be serious. Rayner reported careful experiments with several carbon feedstocks, including hard coke, in which carbon losses were typically in excess of 20%. These losses made the process uneconomical and led to shutdown. Rayner determined that the fines arose not from mechanical attrition but from the gasification process itself. He believed that a char particle undergoing gasification becomes vesicular; beyond a certain carbon conversion, it becomes fragile and tends to break into small bits. He did not believe that losses could be reduced significantly by recycling the fines back to the gasifier because of their very poor reactivity.

Consolidated Coal Co. and ESSO made the same discovery in 1949. The two companies jointly operated an atmospheric 3-m fluid-bed coal gasifier. The objective was to achieve nearly complete gasification in a single stage. The attempt failed because of, among other things, excessive formation of fines. Circulating the fines back to the gasifier did not reduce losses.

Cogas The Cogas Development Co., Inc., having recognized the problem that fines may pose, has incorporated a slagging cyclone burner in the gasifier receiving char from the pyrolysis section of their combined process for gas and oil (see section 8.5.4.4). The burner also solves the problem of utilizing the carbon in any bottoms withdrawn from the gasifier bed. Otherwise, the Cogas gasifier is similar to ICI's moving-burden process.

A gasifier pilot plant has been in operation since April 1974 at the laboratories of BCURA (British Coal Utilization Research Association) at Leatherhead, England. A schematic of the gasifier is shown in figure 8.5.18. The gasifier has an ID of 2.1 m and processes about 0.5 kg/s of char. Many hours of continuous operation have been logged. In a typical run, the temperature near the top of the lift tube is about 980°C and that in the gasifier is about 950°C. The gasifier pressure is around 120–130 kN/m^2. Make gas typically contains 50% H_2 and about 30% CO. The fluidizing velocity in the gasifier is 30–45 cm/s. The flue gas issuing from the lift tube normally contains sulfur as H_2S.

Battelle/Union Carbide ash agglomerating process This process involves gasification of coal by steam in a gasifier operating at an elevated pressure and a temperature around 900°C. Unreacted char is fed to an ash-accreting fluid-bed burner, which comprises dense, nearly spherical ash agglomerates of coarse size fluidized by air. Ash released from the burning char deposits on the particles in the bed, leading to their growth by an onion skin pattern. Hot ash agglomerates are continuously withdrawn from the burner, which operates around 1100°C, and are circulated through the gasifier to provide its heat requirements and returned to the burner. The burner also provides complete consumption of the coal's carbon. An original incentive for the burner was the hope of realizing high collection efficiencies for ash in the burner bed, thus giving a gas sufficiently clean to be suitable for direct discharge in a gas turbine.

Battelle has conducted limited tests in a 1 ton/h pilot plant. The plant is now inactive and the future of the process is uncertain. Serious potential problems are related to operation of the ash-accreting burner and circulation of the coarse burden around the process loop.

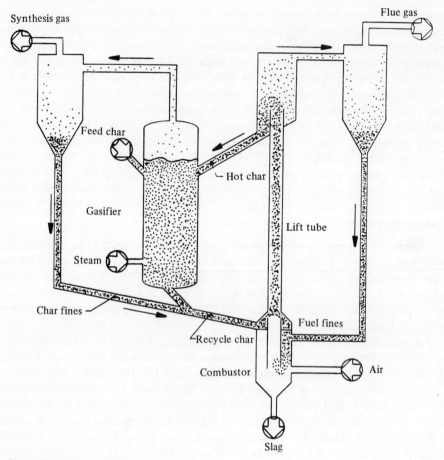

Figure 8.5.18 The Cogas gasifier.

Ash Agglomerating Processes

Fluid-bed processes belonging to this group exploit the tendency of ash to agglomerate at high temperatures to achieve selective extraction from the bed of ash low in carbon. This mode of operation has the potential of providing for complete utilization of the coal's carbon.

Westinghouse coal gasification process The concept is illustrated in figure 8.5.19. Fresh coal is introduced to the devolatilizer operating around 870°C. To overcome the agglomerating propensity of caking coals, the coal is injected into an internal draft tube, where it mixes and blends with dry char that continually circulates up the draft tube and down the annular region surrounding it. The char circulation rate may be typically 20–30 times the rate of coal feed. The devolatilizer is supplied with hot gas arising from the gasifier.

Overflow char from the devolatilizer is transferred to the gasifier. Overhead char fines from the devolatilizer are injected through the air tube into the combustion zone, which provides heat and the gasifying media (carbon oxides and steam) for the gasification. Gasification takes place in the bulk of the fluid bed occupying the upper portion of the reactor. Ash released from the burning char in the combustion zone forms agglomerates low in carbon, which gravitate down the annulus surrounding the air tube and are withdrawn from the bottom of the gasifier.

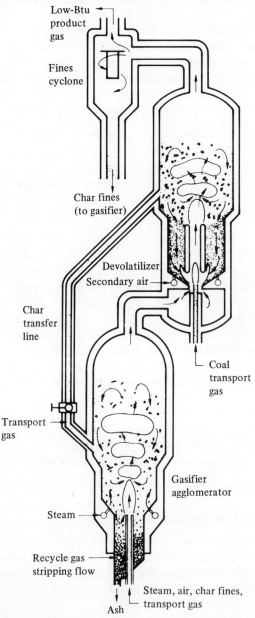

Figure 8.5.19 Westinghouse two-stage fluidized-bed gasification process.

Westinghouse has been conducting tests at 1200 kN/m² in a 0.13 kg/s process development unit at Waltz Mill, Pa. A Pittsburgh seam coal, a highly caking coal, has been processed in the devolatilizer without agglomeration, and several successful gasifier runs have been conducted with various feedstocks including caking bituminous coals (Archer et al. 1978). When a caking coal is processed directly in the gasifier, it is fed through the air tube, and carry-over fines are injected radially to the bed itself.

Operation of the integrated devolatilizer/gasifier system was scheduled for early 1979. Escape of tars from the devolatilizer, which operates at a relatively low temperature, may be a problem. The recent gasifier runs, however, have demonstrated the feasibility of processing coal directly in the gasifier, and the merit of the devolatilizer is being reexamined. Scale-up of the process may be the most challenging task lying ahead because of the use of internal tubes.

Institute of Gas Technology U-Gas A concept similar in outline to that of Westinghouse is being tested by the Institute of Gas Technology in a small atmospheric unit. A caking coal is rendered nonagglomerating in an external fluid-bed pretreater, and the combustion-agglomeration zone in the gasifier is fashioned after an earlier French arrangement studied briefly on a pilot scale by Jequier and co-workers (1960) at CERCHAR in the middle 1950s.

Ignifluid The atmospheric Ignifluid boiler has been described by Godel & Cosar (1967) and by Yerushalmi et al. (1975). The underlying phenomenon is similar to that in the ash agglomerating zone of the Westinghouse and Institute of Gas Technology gasifiers. Coarse coal (average size about 3 mm) is gasified by air in a bed fluidized at high velocity (e.g., 6 m/s near the top of the bed) at around 1200–1400°C, conditions that exploit to advantage the agglomerating tendency of coal's ash. Low-carbon ash agglomerates of various sizes and shapes form throughout the otherwise carbon-rich bed and are readily discharged into an ash pit after being collected on a moving grate that serves to support the bed. The gasifier is capable of handling a wide range of fuels at extremely high carbon utilization. Feedstocks to commercial Ignifluid boilers have included anthracite, low-grade coals of high ash content, various chars, and caking bituminous coals. Fuel gas from the gasifier streams upward and burns by secondary air above the fluidized bed, supplying heat to a boiler. The two 30-MW boilers at Casablanca, Morocco, are the largest Ignifluids built. Fives Cail Babcock has modified a small Ignifluid to run as a gasifier per se.

EXXON Catalytic Fluid-Bed Gasification Process

In EXXON's catalytic process, coal is impregnated by an alkali metal carbonate. The alkali catalyst speeds the gasification of coal by steam and promotes gas-phase methanation equilibrium. In addition, the alkali destroys the agglomerating tendency of caking coals and ensures a product free of tars. In a scheme for production of synthetic natural gas (SNG), carbon monoxide and hydrogen would be separated cryogenically from methane and recycled to the gasifier. A temperature of 650–750°C and a pressure of about 3000 kN/m² are considered nearly optimum for achieving a balanced operation combining high gasification rates and a feasible recycle ratio (1.5.). Operation of the gasifier is autothermal, but a reheat furnace is used to bring the temperature of the recycle gas to 65°C. Compared with other SNG processes, the catalytic approach requires very little high-level heat input (and no oxygen) and does not require shift conversion and extra methanation of the synthesis gas. As a result, it has a potential for thermal efficiencies higher than those of thermal coal gasification processes.

Char/ash residue containing catalyst is removed from the fluid-bed gasifier. About 50–75% of the carbonate may be recovered by water wash. Some catalyst reacts with the coal's ash to form an insoluble aluminosilicate, with an estimated 5% by weight of coal feed lost in the insoluble form. Recovery of this remaining catalyst by methods such as acid wash is currently being studied.

The concept has been studied on the bench scale and in a small process development unit. A 40 kg/h integrated, continuous pilot plant is being constructed.

Chemical Active Fluid Bed (CAFB) Gasification

The concept calls for gasification of coal at near atmospheric pressure and 870°C in a fluid bed of lime. The purpose of the lime is to retain the sulfur species that evolve as the coal is consumed. A stream of unreacted char and lime, now containing an appreciable quantity of calcium sulfide, is circulated to an air-blown fluid-bed regenerator. Sulfur dioxide from the regenerator off gas is removed by a Foster Wheeler Resox unit. Regenerated lime is returned to the gasifier along with makeup material.

The basis for the process is a small unit operating as described above but without the SO_2 removal system, developed by British ESSO to process oil (Moss 1976). Limited tests with coal have been conducted. The incentive for the CAFB process is supplying a hot fuel gas, with sulfur levels reduced below standards, to retrofit boilers now firing oil or gas. At this writing, construction of a CAFB plant is nearing completion in Texas. The plant will retrofit a 15-MW gas-fired boiler.

Some Operating Aspects of Fluid-Bed Gasifiers

Operation of a fluid-bed gasifier, as indicated earlier, is not without serious potential difficulties. Escape of tars in the product gas, the agglomerating propensity of caking coals, and ash clinker formation in the vicinity of the distributor in oxygen-blown reactors are some of the serious problems. This section addresses methods that may obviate these difficulties.

Tars The amounts and types of species formed when coal is introduced to a gasification zone depend, for a given particle size, on the coal type, the rate of heating of the coal to process temperature, the temperature level itself, the pressure, and the gas environment into which the coal is introduced. Subsequent transformation of these species again depends on temperature and pressure, gas and solid environments, transport conditions of the gas and solid, and residence time of the gas in the reactor.

It is not possible at present to differentiate the separate contributions of formation and subsequent transformation to the final output of tars from the gasifier.

However, an increasing amount of information is beginning to fill in the picture:

1. Tarry material formed on primary decomposition (devolatilization) may either escape with the product gas, decompose or react to light species, or polymerize to semicoke (often after depositing on char).
2. Decomposition of tars to lighter gaseous species is favored by higher temperatures, apparently with a marked temperature effect beginning around 900-950°C.
3. An environment rich in steam is also instrumental in directing primary carbonization products to gaseous species.
4. Long gas residence time promotes decomposition of the tars. In an environment rich in steam, above 900°C, the minimum residence time to prevent escape of tars is 10-20 s.
5. If the feed coal is fed to the bottom of the bed, the tars that evolve may be captured on the char that lies in the path of the gas. Subsequent condensation and cracking reactions, which are often catalyzed by the coal's ash, contribute to reduction or complete absence of tars in the product gas.

The last factor is important and has been confirmed by recent experiments at the Pittsburgh Energy Research Center of the U.S. Department of Energy (Nakles et al. 1975). Jolley et al. (1954) of the British Fuel Research Station also reported that direct injection of coal into the bottom of a bed fluidized by steam at 900°C gave a product free of tars.

Feeding a caking coal directly to a fluid-bed gasifier Attempts to process a caking coal in fluid beds have frequently been hampered by uncontrolled formation of large coke agglomerates. Operation at elevated pressures compounds the difficulty. Indeed, the normally noncaking low-rank coals (e.g., from the western United States) may display a tendency to cake under pressure and in an atmosphere rich in hydrogen. The method most commonly proposed or used to prevent agglomeration has been to subject the coal to oxidative pretreatment. This approach, however, exacts penalties in product yield and process efficiency, as well as in the cost of additional hardware. A pretreatment stage also adds complexity to the process, making it less amenable to power applications (especially combined-cycle generation of electricity), where close control of load variations may be mandatory.

The key to successfully feeding a caking coal directly to a fluid bed lies in achieving dispersal of the raw particles of coal in the dry char that comprises the bed. Effective dispersal depends on three factors:

1. The agglomerating tendency of the coal. This depends on the duration of the resolidification reaction and accordingly on the time it takes the molten coal to dry under the processing conditions, as well as on the fluidity and stickiness of the molten matter itself.
2. Fluidization characteristics of the char within the bed. Of particular importance is the extent of solid mixing in the vicinity of the coal inlet ports.
3. Coal injection. The number, location, and orientation of coal feed nozzles and the gas-solid transport conditions in the feed lines.

Once the operating conditions have been selected, the agglomerating tendency of a coal is essentially fixed; effective dispersal must accordingly be achieved by proper design of the coal injection scheme and the zone in the gasifier into which the coal is fed. Dispersal of feed coal can be promoted in several ways (Yerushalmi 1977):

1. A large number of coal feed nozzles spaced suitably apart. The greater the number of feed nozzles and distance between them, the smaller the local concentration of molten coal near the feed inlet points. However, the greater the number of nozzles used, the more complex the system required for evenly splitting the coal and conveying it through the corresponding number of lines. Technology for splitting a solid uniformly and conveying it through multiple lines is not well established.
2. High-velocity pneumatic injection. This would presumably effect deeper penetration in the char bed and allow for more interaction between the feed coal and the char, thus promoting dispersal.
3. Special feed nozzle designs. A simple approach is to provide a high-velocity dispersing gas through an annulus surrounding the coal feed line. The gas would be drawn from the gasifying medium.
4. High turbulence of the char in the vicinity of the coal inlet ports; e.g., by using high-velocity fluidized beds (i.e., turbulent and fast fluid beds).

High-velocity fluid beds could afford high production rates per unit volume of reactor space. The extensive solid mixing and relatively high solid concentrations promote the capacity to receive and disperse a caking coal without agglomeration. The same conditions minimize the chance of clinker formation in the vicinity of the oxygen inlet ports in a gasifier blown with steam and oxygen. The potential of the fast fluidized bed for gasification of coal by air and its ability to process a caking coal directly is to be investigated by Hydrocarbon Research, Inc., for the U.S. Department of Energy. At this writing, construction of a small pilot plant has been completed and trials will commence shortly.

Yerushalmi (1977) proposed the configuration shown schematically in figure 8.5.20. The gasifier contains two zones: an upper bubbling fluid bed maintained at a relatively low fluidizing velocity and comprising the bulk of the char, and a lower turbulent fluidized bed. The upper zone would afford a greater char inventory and greater gas residence time, two conditions that promote higher conversions. The turbulent fluid bed would provide the mixing zone into which the caking coal and much of the gasifying media are introduced. Some gas may be added at the expanding section connecting the two zones to ensure smooth fluidization in the bubbling bed. Solids mixing between the two zones should be extensive, but it might prove necessary or advantageous to permit transfer of char from the upper to the lower zone as shown in figure 8.5.20. For consumption of overhead fines and unreacted char, a carbon burnup cell or zone would have to be incorporated. In air-blown operation a cyclone burner could be installed at the bottom of the turbulent fluid bed; the gas arising from it would provide the gasifying medium for the reactor proper.

Section 8.5.6 describes the processing of a caking coal in a spouted bed.

Formation of ash clinkers near oxygen inlet ports Local overheating in the vicinity of the oxygen inlet ports may lead to formation of ash clinkers in a bed

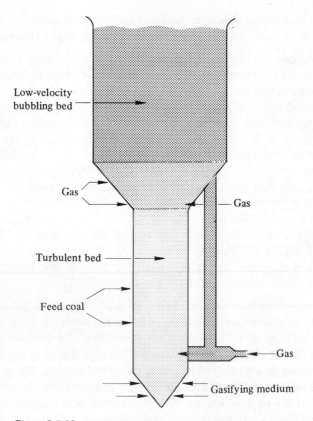

Figure 8.5.20 Fluid-bed gasifier with a turbulent mixing zone.

that otherwise operates well below the clinkering temperature, around 1000–1100°C for most coal ashes (Kolodney et al. 1976). This has occurred in a number of experimental units, most recently in the Synthane pilot plant of the Pittsburgh Energy Research Center. In the latter case, the extent of solid mixing in the gasifier, which operates in the bubbling mode and at rather low fluidizing velocities, was apparently not sufficient to disperse the heat arising from combustion of the char near the oxygen ports.

The conditions that promote dissipation of heat and minimize the chance of clinker formation parallel those that promote dispersal of a caking coal:

1. Feeding the oxygen through a large number of nozzles, or using a distributor plate with a large number of holes per unit area. In the case of coarse coal feed (1 mm mean size, say) a distributor with a minimum of 500 holes/m² is recommended if the superficial gas velocity is around or below 30 cm/s. A large number of holes or nozzles minimizes local concentration of oxygen at a given point and hence the intensity of combustion at that point. A large number of holes also promotes solid mixing in the distributor zone.
2. Feeding the oxygen to a zone in which the degree of solid (char) mixing is high. Such zones would as a rule involve higher gas velocities relative to the rest of the bed. The reactor shown in figure 8.5.20 provides an example.

8.5.4.4   Fluid-Bed Carbonization of Coal

J. Yerushalmi

Carbonization of coal involves its decomposition essentially in the absence of oxygen. Three products inevitably arise: liquid (tars), gas, and char (or coke). Each of these has provided sufficient incentive for research and development in the area. Of many developments launched in the past 20–30 yr, few have seen commercial service.

Interest in tar products and char (the latter mostly for metallurgy) led to a few commercial carbonization plants during the 1950s and 1960s. At least two used a fluidized bed for the main carbonization reaction.

The Carbofluid process (Ionescu & Paun 1975) in Calan, Romania, provides nine reactors, each consuming about 1.6 kg/s of high-volatile bituminous coal. The chief product is char for coke ovens and iron ore sintering. The reactors were first provided with a conical bottom of sharp angle, and a fuel gas was burned by air externally. The hot combustion gas was then admitted centrally to the bottom of the reactor to maintain the bed at the desired temperature ($550°C$). Because of difficulties in controlling the temperature at the reactor bottom, the cone was subsequently replaced with a straight distributor grate. Fuel gas and air are charged separately, and combustion accordingly takes place within the bed.

The British National Coal Board (Jones & Owens 1962) developed a carbonization process aimed at converting high-volatile coals to char for hot briquetting. Development stages included pilot plants of 200 and 4500 kg/h, and in the 1960s two large plants were installed at Markham and Coventry to provide open-fire smokeless fuel. The Conventry plant includes three fluid-bed reactors, each 4.25 m in diameter and close to 19 m tall. Each reactor is provided with a conical bottom through which an air-steam mixture is injected. Coal smaller than 2 mm is processed and the product char, still containing a substantial portion of volatiles, is withdrawn from the conical base. Five parallel primary and secondary cyclones, installed internally, keep dust carry-over to a minimum.

Fluid-bed carbonization of coal has been the subject of a number of other investigations. Of the processes in current development, two may be mentioned.

The COED process Like most carbonization processes, and as its name suggests, the COED (Char Oil Energy Development) process gives rise to three products: char, oil, and gas. The concept, developed by FMC Corporation, involves pyrolysis of coal in three or four fluid-bed stages, maintained at progressively higher temperatures to avoid agglomeration of a caking coal. A pilot plant consuming 50 kg/h of coal went into operation in 1966 at Princeton, N.J. In 1970 a 1400 kg/h plant with four fluid beds (the largest 2 m in diameter) was constructed and subsequently served to test a number of coals. The pilot also provided for hydrotreating of the oil product. To provide for consumption of the unreacted char, it is proposed to link the COED process to a moving-burden gasifier (as discussed earlier), the combination assuming the title of its development company, Cogas.

For most coals, three pyrolysis stages are required. In the first stage, coal is dried and undergoes partial devolatilization by a portion of the gas from the third stage. The char from the first stage flows to the next, where it is fluidized and further pyrolyzed by the remaining gas from the third stage. In the third stage, char is contacted by a portion of the hot synthesis or make gas produced in the gasifier. Gas from the first two stages is scrubbed and quenched to condense out the liquid products. The pyrolysis gas and the make gas from the gasifier may be converted to SNG, following the usual intermediate steps. Typical temperatures in the three pyrolysis vessels are 315, 425, and 540°C.

The clean coke process The U.S. Steel Corporation is developing a process that combines low-temperature carbonization and solvent hydrogenation. High-sulfur bituminous coal is beneficiated to yield two fractions: a low-sulfur, low-ash fraction from which much of the inorganic sulfur has been removed, and a corresponding high-sulfur, high-ash fraction. The former is fed to a fluid-bed carbonizer, maintained at 650–750°C and around 600 kN/m^2, where it reacts with hydrogen to yield gas, tars, and low-sulfur char. The latter is the starting material for a "clean" metallurgical coke. The second fraction is slurried in process-derived oil and subjected to high-pressure noncatalytic hydrogenation. The concept was first tested in a small unit in which the carbonizer measured 7.5 cm ID. A larger test facility with a coal throughput of 200 kg/h was built in 1974.

Some operating aspects In addition to the usual array of problems attending the operation of any fluid bed, carbonization poses two problems: processing of caking coals and prevention of tar condensation in the reactor exit lines. Condensation of tars, and inevitable pluggage, are compounded by the presence in the product stream of fine dust carried over from the bed. Condensation can be prevented by maintaining exit ducts above the dew point of the tars.

Processing a caking coal is more difficult. A method used commonly to overcome this problem is to subject the coal to oxidative pretreatment. This approach, however, leads to a drastically reduced yield of liquid products and should be avoided if liquids are the key to the economics of the process. General approaches to feeding a caking coal directly to a fluid-bed reactor have been discussed in section 8.5.4.3; the subject is discussed in greater detail by Yerushalmi (1977).

8.5.5 PHYSICAL OPERATIONS

8.5.5.1 Fluid-Bed Drying of Solids

S. Hovmand

Stationary Fluid-Bed Driers

The use of fluid-bed drying for granular products has increased considerably during the past 10 yr. Reviews of fluid-bed drying have been published by Vanecek et al. (1966), Romankov (1971), and Kroll (1978). The advantages offered by this technology, compared with other continuous drying methods are:

1. The fluidized bed permits continuous, automatically controlled, large-scale operation with easy handling of feed and product.
2. Heat and mass can be exchanged effectively between particles and the fluidizing gas because of the large surface area of the particles; thus gas-to-particle heat and mass transfer are not limiting factors in a fluidized-bed drying operation and overheating of particles is avoided.
3. Rapid mixing of solids leads to nearly isothermal conditions throughout the fluidized bed; i.e., easy and reliable control of the drying process.

Figure 8.5.21 shows a typical flow sheet for a totally mixed fluid-bed drier in which the wet feed is allowed to mix freely with the dried and partially dried product. Above the flow sheet in figure 8.5.21 is a drying curve for the product, showing the relationship between product moisture and time for a given set of drying conditions. It can be seen that drying of the surface moisture of the particles is very rapid until a transition point is reached. Beyond this point, the drying rate is controlled by diffusion of the volatiles inside the particles and is decreased considerably.

The height of the fluidized layer is controlled by a weir over which the dried material flows feely. The fluidizing air is heated before entering the plenum chamber of the fluid bed. Exhaust air is cleaned by a cyclone and fines recovered by the cyclone are returned to the dried product stream.

Wet lumps of feed dry rapidly when mixed with the hot and dry particles in the fluidized bed. For many products the lumps, below a certain moisture content, disintegrate into fluidizable particles. In certain cases it is not possible to disintegrate the lumps by this technique, and predrying of the feed (e.g., in a flash drier) may be necessary to avoid lumps in the dried product.

Figure 8.5.21 indicates the savings in heat input obtainable when heating panels are applied in a drying project for two different inlet air temperatures. The high inlet air temperature and the application of heating panels offer a significant savings in specific heat consumption.

Back-mixed fluid-bed driers are used in many industrial drying applications, especially for inorganic and organic materials, food products, and mining products. Driers with capacities up to nearly 100 kg/s have been installed for drying rock phosphates, coal, and sand.

The totally mixed fluid bed is not suitable when a product moisture content much lower than that at the critical point is desired, particularly if the required dyring time is long. The product from a totally mixed fluid bed is near equilibrium with the exhaust air. This means that the air may have to be kept at low humidity, resulting in a large drying air requirement with accompanying increased drying costs. Furthermore, the dried particles from a totally mixed fluid bed have a broad range of residence times and a large portion of the material is either overdried or underdried. Thus the risk of product damage is high when drying a heat-sensitive material at near-critical temperatures.

To overcome these limitations of the totally mixed fluid-bed drier, baffle plate arrangements are built into the fluid bed to ensure a particle residence time distribution approaching plug flow conditions. The product at discharge is then near

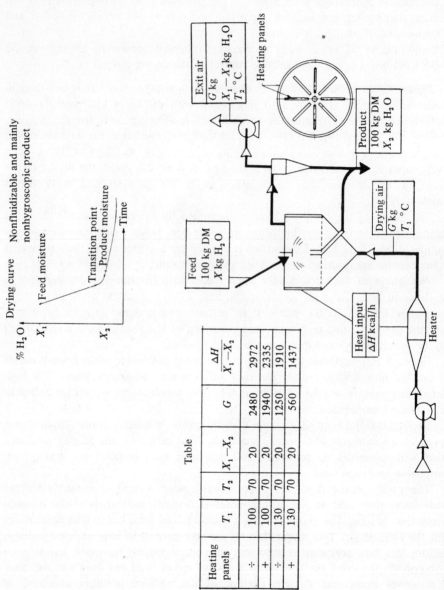

Figure 8.5.21 Totally mixed fluid-bed drier with heating panels.

Table

Heating panels	T_1	T_2	$X_1 - X_2$	G	$\dfrac{\Delta H}{X_1 - X_2}$
÷	100	70	20	2480	2972
+	100	70	20	1940	2335
÷	130	70	20	1250	1910
+	130	70	20	560	1437

Exit air

G kg

$X_1 - X_2$ kg H_2O

T_2 °C

Heating panels

Product

100 kg DM

X_2 kg H_2O

Feed

100 kg DM

X kg H_2O

Drying air

G kg

T_1 °C

Heat input

ΔH kcal/h

Heater

Drying curve   Nonfluidizable and mainly nonhygroscopic product

% H_2O

X_1 Feed moisture

Transition point

Product moisture

X_2

Time

equilibrium with the hot drying gas, and very low residual moisture contents can be achieved without overheating the material. Such driers may be used for drying polymers such as polypropylene and suspension PVC.

Vibrated Fluid-Bed Dryers

Some granular products are difficult to dry in a stationary fluid bed because of one or more of the following physical properties:

1. Wide particle size distribution
2. Low strength of wet or dry particles
3. Stickiness or thermoplasticity of particles
4. Pasty properties of wet feed

In the vibrated fluid bed, the material is easily transported through the drier by the combined effect of fluidization and vibration. The air rate for fluidization and drying can be chosen over a wide range without affecting the conveying rate and the residence time of the product, which is controlled mainly by adjusting the amplitude and direction of the vibration. A relatively low drying air rate can be selected such that the larger particles are only partially fluidized. In this way, entrainment of smaller particles is reduced and good control over the particle residence time is obtained.

The vibrated fluid bed provides very gentle transportation of material through the drier. Since a low gas rate can be chosen, gas bubbling in the fluidized bed is avoided, and this greatly reduces particle attrition. Consequently, the vibrated fluid-bed drier can be used for products having low mechanical strength in the wet or dry state. For example, vibrated fluid-bed driers are used extensively as after-driers for spray-dried dairy products.

Spray Granulation in Fluid Bed

Spray granulation involves simultaneous use of a fluid bed as a drier and a granulator. The process has been used for some time, particularly for batch granulation in the pharmaceutical industry. Continuous spray granulation, however, is a relatively new process and includes technology from spray drying and fluidized-bed drying. The flow sheet for this process is shown in figure 8.5.22.

Liquid feed is atomized and sprayed into the fluidized layer of already dried or partially dried particles. The fluidization medium is the drying air, and the fluid bed is normally in a state of vigorous fluidization. Particles leaving the bed are classified. Granules of the desired particle size are discharged from the unit, while the oversize fraction is milled and recycled together with the undersize fraction and fines recovered in the exhaust cyclone. The most characteristic and essential part of the spray granulation process is the formation of new particles and their growth in the fluidized bed.

The system can be used for organic and inorganic salts, sulfite wastes, ceramics,

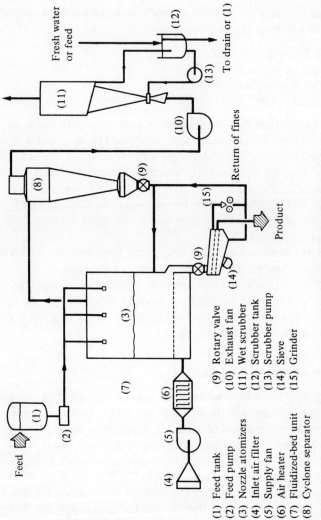

Figure 8.5.22 Flow sheet of a typical continuous spray granulation process.

(1) Feed tank
(2) Feed pump
(3) Nozzle atomizers
(4) Inlet air filter
(5) Supply fan
(6) Air heater
(7) Fluidized-bed unit
(8) Cyclone separator
(9) Rotary valve
(10) Exhaust fan
(11) Wet scrubber
(12) Scrubber tank
(13) Scrubber pump
(14) Sieve
(15) Grinder

single-cell proteins, and most other solutions or suspensions of materials acting as binders. The process in the spray granulator can also involve agglomeration, coating, encapsulation, and wetting. Typically, particles 0.5–2 mm in diameter are produced in the spray granulation process.

8.5.5.2 Sizing of Solids

W. W. Jukkola and J. M. Beeckmans

Sizing in the Freeboard Zone

In all dense-phase, noncirculating fluid-bed applications, some classification occurs to a certain degree of efficiency. Several commercial combination drying and sizing fluid-bed installations for handling limestone, dolomite, and iron ores are in operation. They have demonstrated that it is practical and economical to make sizing separations between 150 and 600 μm in a combination drying and sizing unit. To obtain effective sizing the solids must be essentially bone-dry, as moist fines have a great tendency to flocculate and agglomerate in the dilute phase, resulting in poor stripping and classification efficiency.

The actual sizing occurs in the freeboard zone. If the free-settling velocity is less than the velocity of the upward-flowing gases, particles are entrained and carried out with the gases. The gases, however, have a limited loading capacity, which depends on superficial velocity and the particle size, density, and shape factor. In drying and sizing crushed limestone, dust loadings of 0.25–0.50 kg per cubic meter of stack gas have been obtained when making size separations in the 150–600 μm range. Stripping efficiencies of 65–70% of the solids finer than the mesh of separation are obtained in commercial fluid-bed units treating -10 mm limestone at rates of 25–60 kg/s (Wall & Ash 1949).

Segregation in the Fluidized Layer

A number of devices have been developed that use segregation in a fluidized bed to achieve separation of the desired component. A dry pneumatic float-sink separator for sorting materials of different specific gravities was developed by Douglas & Walsh (1966). The unit employs fluidized particles with a specific gravity intermediate between those of the feed components. The feed particles must be substantially larger than the fluidizing particles, because the latter are separated by screening and recycled to the separator. The device is essentially a dry analog of the well-known liquid heavy medium separator employed in the beneficiation of coal and other minerals. Feed is introduced into a fluidized bed with a sloping, vibrating base. Dense particles sink in the fluidized medium and are carried upward along the bottom of the bed by the vibrating plate, which is located just below the surface opposite the sinks removal end.

The pneumatic pinched sluice, described by Douglas & Sayles (1971), is a device in which fluidized powder is made to flow along a sloping channel of decreasing cross section. The material therefore accelerates horizontally and the upper and lower strata of material are separated by a splitter plate at the sluice outlet. Vertical segregation of material in the fluidized channel causes compositional differences in the product streams.

8.5.5.3 Fluidized-Bed Coating

C. Gutfinger

When a hot object is dipped into a fluidized bed of plastic particles, the sticky particles melt and form a coating on its surface. This operation, known as fluidized-bed coating, is one of the modern solventless powder coating processes. Fluidized-bed applied coatings are thick, robust, and durable. Only one coat is needed. Because of its thickness, the coating has good abrasion and corrosion resistance and improved electrical insulating properties.

The coating ability of the fluidized bed is affected by two main features. High contacting fluidity is essential for obtaining a coating, because without fluidization the object cannot be immersed in the powder. On the other hand, the high heat transfer coefficient typical of a fluidized bed is a drawback for the coating process, as it results in increased heat losses from the object to the bed and thinner coating layers. The coating technologist is therefore interested in working under conditions of minimum heat transfer losses while still retaining complete fluidity. Thus it is advantageous to operate the fluidized bed close to its minimum fluidization velocity.

One of the main uses of fluidized-bed coating is in applying a polymeric protective layer on a metallic object (Pettigrew 1966). The main process parameters affecting the quality, uniformity, and thickness of the coating are the object temperature and immersion time; the size, shape, and size distribution of the particles; the fluidizing gas velocity; and the physical properties of the object, powder, and carrier gas. In addition, the surface properties and treatment of the object affect the adherence and general quality of the coating, but not its thickness.

Both thermoplastic and thermosetting resins, including polyamides, PVC, polyolefins, cellulosics, fluorocarbons, chlorinated polyethers, acrylics, and thermoplastic polyesters, may be used for fluidized-bed coating. When the objects to be coated are small in size and numerous, one may consider using them as the fluidized particles in a bed. The coating agent may be either a gas that reacts with the fluidized particles or a liquid solution sprayed into the bed. The latter technique is similar to the spray granulation process described above. Applications include coating pills and granular food products.

The coating process in a fluid bed has been analyzed by Abuaf & Gutfinger (1973). It may be viewed as a variation of the well-known Stephan problem. A hot object immersed in a fluidized bed loses part of its internal energy as heat to the bed, while another part is being used to melt the plastic powder forming the coating layer. Abuaf & Gutfinger (1974) studied the coating of a flat plate in a fluid bed maintained at a constant temperature. The object is initially at a temperature higher

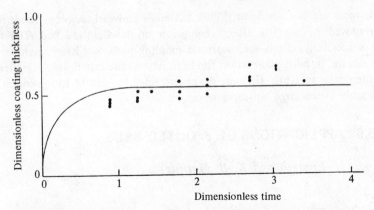

Figure 8.5.23 Dimensionless coating thickness as a function of dimensionless time. Comparison between theory and experimental data. Initial object temperature, 327°C; dimensionless melting temperature, 0.651; coating parameter, 0.428.

than the softening temperature of the coating material. As it is dipped into the bed, a coating begins to build up on it. Abuaf & Gutfinger described the heat transfer within the coating by a one-dimensional heat conduction equation, solved it numerically, and presented the results in the form of a dimensionless coating thickness as a function of dimensionless time. Figure 8.5.23 shows a typical solution together with some experimental results.

8.5.5.4 High-Temperature Baths

M. A. Bergougnou

A wide variety of fluidized high-temperature baths are used in laboratory and pilot plant work where a uniform, precisely controlled, highly thermally conductive environment is required around reactors, tubing assemblies, thermocouple calibration assemblies, etc. (Staffin & Choongham 1972). Depending on the application, these baths can be in the form of shallow rectangular troughs or deep cylindrical beds. They have the interesting property of being nearly isothermal throughout the fluidized mass, if properly designed. When used for thermocouple calibration, obtainable accuracies are better than ±0.05°C in the range −70 to 700°C and ±0.5°C at 1200°C. Utilization of fluidized solids eliminates fire and explosion hazards, odors, toxic fumes, corrosion, personnel hazards resulting from splatter with wet or oily specimens, long heat-up and cool-down times, messy cleanups of treated pieces, and the need for different media for temperatures ranging from about −100 to 2000°C. These baths can also be used to clean various combustible deposits from mechanical pieces. Typically, plastic residues can be quickly burned off extruder and molding machine hardware in a bed of fine particles fluidized by a gas having a controlled amount of oxygen at temperatures compatible with the metallurgy of the piece to be cleaned. Because of the near-isothermal condition of the bed, parts are not distorted. Fillter materials and carbonaceous residues can be easily removed by air jets after combustion in the fluidized bed. The fluidized furnace successfully cleans such intricate molding parts as filters, spinnerettes, and feeding screws. In pilot plant work, fluidized heaters are rapidly replacing lead baths and molten salts systems. They are easier and safer to operate and maintain and are more flexible over a large temperature range.

8.5.6 APPLICATIONS OF SPOUTED BEDS

N. Epstein and K. B. Mathur

The jet-induced agitation of coarse (e.g., 1–5 mm) solid particles in a spouted bed, as against the bubble-induced mixing of fine solids in a gas-fluidized bed, makes the two systems hydrodynamically quite different. Although both techniques provide good solids mixing and intimate fluid-particle contact, the spouted bed has certain unique features that contribute to its wide-ranging applications. These features and many applications are described by Mathur & Epstein (1974). For the present brief review, it is convenient to successively catalog applications of gas-solid spouting according to the main feature of the spouted bed that the particular application seeks to exploit.

Good solids mixing and effective gas-particle contact are the basis for spouted-bed drying of noncaking granular solids. The process was invented at the National Research Council of Canada in 1954 for wheat drying. It is particularly suitable for heat-sensitive materials such as agricultural products (e.g., peas, lentils, flax) or polymer granules, because the good agitation of the solids permits use of a higher-temperature contacting gas than in nonagitated driers without risk of thermal damage to the particles. Commercial driers of 0.6 m diameter with a bed depth of about 2 m are capable of safely drying up to 2 Mg/h peas through an 8% moisture range (dry basis), using about 3 Mg/h air at temperatures up to 284°C. Application has remained confined to small-capacity driers (1–2 Mg/h), and the potential for large-scale operation through use of multispout beds has not yet been exploited.

Sensible heating or cooling of coarse solids in spouted beds also makes use of the intimate gas-solid contacting. In the use of a spouted bed for blending of solids, however, the intimate gas-particle contacting is incidental and only good solids mixing is of importance. Multistage spouted-bed preheating of coal feed to coke ovens has been successfully piloted, and commercial-scale rectangular (4.9 by 1.8 m) two-stage multiple-spout fertilizer coolers with capacities up to 30 Mg/h and thermal efficiencies exceeding 85% have been developed by Fisons Ltd. Equally large single-spout circular units for blending polyester chips have been operated by ICI Fibres Ltd. for polymer batch sizes greater than 57 m³.

The relatively high gas velocities and correspondingly low gas residence times associated with spouting of coarse particles are the basis for the bench-scale development at Hokkaido University of a dual-spouted reactor-regenerator combination for thermal cracking of petroleum feedstocks. A similar combination has recently been developed by the same investigators for the catalytic desulfurization of residual fuel oil, using $650°C$ steam plus the fuel oil as the spouting fluid in the reactor and air in the regenerator (Uemaki et al. 1977). The potential for catalytic gas-phase reaction by spouting large porous catalyst particles (Piccinini et al. 1978) shows considerable promise, especially if a side outlet is used (Hattori & Takeda 1978).

High gas throughput per unit cross section also makes spouted beds attractive for gas cleaning. High efficiencies at minimum spouting velocities have been measured for the bench-scale collection of liquid and electrified-solid aerosols from a gas in spouted beds of inert solids (Balasubramanian et al. 1978), as well as for the chemical reduction of dilute SO_2 gas by a spouted bed of activated charcoal (Foong et al. 1976). For both of these gas cleaning processes, operation at velocities above minimum spouting sharply reduces the respective efficiencies because of gas bypassing through the spout. Gas capacities can be increased without loss of efficiency by use of larger column cross sections and multiple spouts, but additional control and bed stability problems (Foong et al. 1975) must then be dealt with.

The highly systematic cyclic movement of solids in a spouted bed is a key advantage in such processes as granulation and particle coating. In granulation, a melt or solution is atomized into a bed containing seed granules spouted by hot gas. These granules build up layer by layer as they cycle in the bed, yielding a final product that is well rounded and uniform in structure. Continuous operation requires that oversize product be crushed and recycled to the spouted bed along with undersize product. Spouted granulation of fertilizers (Uemaki & Mathur 1976; Berquin 1977), pigments, and dyes has been carried out on an industrial scale, and a number of 15 Mg/h sulfur granulators (Perlomatic system) have been built by PEC Engineering of France. In these units spouting occurs in the $60°$ conical base, which expands up to and is topped by a 2-m-diameter cylindrical disengaging section (A. Meisen, personal communication). The units have not been free of operating difficulties.

Coating of pharmaceutical tablets in a spouted bed is a well-established commercial operation, a typical batch being 100 kg. A newer thermal coating development, still on a pilot scale but with promising larger-scale economics, is spouted-bed coating of urea granules with sulfur to produce a slow-release fertilizer (Meisen & Mathur 1978). Thermochemical coating of pyrolytic carbon and/or silicon carbide onto submillimeter nuclear fuel kernels of uranium oxide or carbide has been standardized in spouted-bed furnaces of 75–125 mm ID, with kernel loads of about 1 kg for each coating operation (Piccinini 1975). Essentially the same technique is now being applied in pyrolytic coating of prosthetic devices (Voice 1974) by the Sorin Co. of Italy.

Solids attrition caused by high-velocity interparticle collisions in the spout is a liability for some spouted-bed operations (e.g., granulation and tablet coating), but is an asset for several others. The most successful of these, developed at the Leningrad Institute of Technology, is the drying of suspensions and solutions by atomizing them into the lower region of a hot gas-spouted bed of inert particles. The suspension or solution coats the particles, dries during the particle cycling, and the fine product is knocked off by the interparticle collisions and collected in the overhead gas. Materials that lend themselves to this method of drying include organic dyes, dye intermediates, lacquers, salt and sugar solutions, and several chemical reagents. More conventional spouted-bed drying of granular materials with caking tendencies—e.g., ammonium nitrate—has also been industrially successful (where fluidized-bed drying has failed), because of the breakdown of embryonic agglomerates in the high-velocity spout. Bench-scale spouted-bed developments for which this property has been important include comminution of particulate solids, iron ore reduction, shale pyrolysis, and carbonization at temperatures up to 650°C for Australian coal and up to 540°C for Indian coal (Ray & Sarkar 1976), which are coals of various caking tendencies. Indian noncaking coals have been similarly gasified with air and steam (Ingle & Sarkar 1976). An impressive recent development is the gasification at about 900°C and atmospheric pressure of 1.2–3.4 mm highly caking coals from western Canada in a 0.15-m diameter spouted bed containing a proportion of silica particles in the same size range (Foong et al. 1978).

The absence of a distributor plate in a spouted bed is a definite advantage in many of the above operations—especially in granulation and coating; drying of solutions, suspensions, and sticky solids; and carbonization or gasification of caking coals. It is also an important consideration in a high-temperature (1000–1500°C) industrial process for making granular activated carbon, as well as in bench-scale spouted-bed kiln operations for calcination of limestone (Golubkovich 1976) and for production of cement clinker from decarbonated cement granules. The decarbonation itself has been successfully accomplished in a system designated KSV (for Kawasaki spouted bed and vortex chamber) (Iammartino 1974). At least five cement plants with capacities of 40 kg/s and one with 100 kg/s, using KSV calcining furnaces, were in satisfactory operation as of 1975 (Vucović et al. 1975).

More than 40 different patents on spouted beds or their modifications were granted in various countries between 1957 and 1973 (Vucović et al 1975). A few of these were on liquid-solid or even three-phase spouting. For practical purposes, however, liquid- and gas-liquid spouted beds of solids are still in early stages of development.

8.6 Nomenclature for Chapter 8

ROMAN LETTERS

A	cross-sectional area of column
A	cross-sectional area of bed
A_b	cross-sectional area for bubble flow
A_{bi}	visible frontal area of two-dimensional bubble
A_{or}	orifice cross-sectional area
A_W	surface area for heat transfer
a	catalyst activity
a_J	transfer surface area of jets per unit volume of vessel
a_S	surface area of solids per unit volume
B	dimensionless excess gas velocity [8.1.66]
C, C'	constants in [8.2.20] and [8.2.21]
C_D	drag coefficient of particle in suspension
C_{DS}	drag coefficient of isolated particle
C_d	discharge coefficient
C_{pF}	heat capacity of fluid
C_{pS}	heat capacity of solid
C_{pG}	heat capacity of gas
C_R	ratio of heat transfer coefficient for vertical tube to that for tube located on bed axis
c	molar concentration in gas phase
c^*	molar concentration in gas phase at saturation
c_A	molar concentration of reactant A in gas phase
c_{AF}	gas concentration at top of freeboard region
c_b	gas concentration in bubble
c_e	gas concentration in emulsion
c_J	gas concentration in jet
c_S	gas concentration at solid surface
c_S	molar concentration in solid phase
c_{SB}	molar concentration of reactant B in solid phase

D	bed diameter
D	column inside diameter
D_H	hydraulic diameter of column cross section
D_s	spout diameter
D_T	tube diameter
$\mathfrak{D}_a$	axial dispersion coefficient
$\mathfrak{D}_r$	radial dispersion coefficient
d_b	bubble diameter
$\bar{d}_b$	mean bubble diameter
d_{b0}	initial bubble diameter
d_{b0}	diameter of bubble formed at orifice or at distributor plate
d_{bm}	maximum bubble diameter
d_{bm}	maximum bubble diameter if all bubbles coalesce [8.1.43]
d_{bmax}	maximum stable bubble diameter
d_c	cloud diameter
d_e	volume equivalent diameter of bubble
d_H	hydraulic diameter of orifice
d_{or}	orifice diameter
d_S	particle diameter
$\bar{d}_S$	mean particle diameter
d_{Si}	mean diameter in ith sieve interval or ith size fraction interval
d_T	tube diameter
E_z	axial dispersion coefficient
F_{bc}	gas exchange coefficient (bubble to cloud) based on bubble void volume
F_{be}	gas exchange coefficient (bubble to emulsion) based on bubble void volume
F'_{be}	gas exchange coefficient based on bubble phase (void plus cloud) volume
F_e	volume of flux of solids in emulsion based on unit bed cross-sectional area
$\mathbf{F}_I$	interaction force per unit volume between fluid and particles, section 8.1.4
F_{io}	rate of entrainment of fine fraction with diameter d_{Si} at surface of bed
F_{Je}	gas exchange coefficient (jet to emulsion)
F_{oV}	gas exchange coefficient based on unit bed volume
F_ϵ	voidage function [8.2.29]
f_b	bubble frequency
$\bar{f}_b$	mean local bubble frequency
f_e	fraction of wake solids ejected
f_i	fraction of particles of characteristic size d_{Si}
f_s	slug frequency
f_ϵ	voidage factor [8.3.42]
g	acceleration due to gravity
ΔH_R	heat of reaction
h_p	specific enthalpy of gaseous product component
h_r	specific enthalpy of gaseous inlet component
I	surface integral in [8.4.23]
j_b	ratio of volume of solids in bubble void to volume of bubbles
j_c	ratio of volume of solids in bubble phase to volume of bubbles
j_e	ratio of volume of solids in emulsion to volume of bubbles

K^*	elutriation constant [8.1.85]
K^*	correction factor in [8.4.20]
K_a	rate constant for catalyst deactivation
K_{be}	overall mass transfer coefficient (bubble to emulsion)
$(K_{be})_{bS}$	interchange coefficient of solids between bubble and emulsion phases, based on bubble volume
K_{bS}	interchange coefficient of solids, based on unit bed volume
K_f	fluid-to-solid mass transfer coefficient
K_{Je}	overall mass transfer coefficient (jet to emulsion), kg/m^2 s
K_r	first-order (gas) reaction rate constant per unit volume of particles
K_s	surface-to-bed mass transfer coefficient
K_1	collection efficiency of cyclone system
K_2	elutriation constant
k	unit vector in upward vertical direction
$\cdot k$	first-order (gas) reaction rate constant per unit volume of settled bed
k_c	rate constant for chemical reaction based on particle surface
k_V	rate constant based on particle volume
L	expanded bed height
L_0	static bed height
L'	effective bed height
L'	height from top of jets
L^+	L/L_m
ΔL	distance between orifice and free surface
L_δ	boundary-layer thickness
L_c	critical height above jets at which bubble clouds overlap
L_f	fountain height in spouted bed measured from bed surface
L_{FB}	height of freeboard region
L_H	length of heat transfer surface
L_J	height of jets
L_M	height of (gas phase) mass transfer unit
L_m	maximum spoutable bed depth
L_{max}	maximum height achieved by slugging bed or by particles ejected into freeboard
L_{mf}	height of fluidized bed at minimum fluidization
ΔL_n	compartment height in bubble assemblage model
L_s	slug length
$\dot{M}_r$	mass flow rate of inlet gas
$\dot{M}_p$	mass flow rate of outlet gas
M_S	mass of solids in system
$\dot{M}_S$	solids mass flow rate
m	adsorption parameter (c_s/c_e)
m	exponent
m	slug shape factor in [8.4.23]
$\dot{m}_f$	mass flow density of fluidizing fluid
$\dot{m}_G$	mass flow density of gas
$\dot{m}_{Gmf}$	mass flow density of gas at minimum fluidization

$\dot{m}_L$	mass flow density of liquid
$\dot{m}_S$	mass flow density of solids
m_1, m_2	roots of [8.4.25]
N	number of stages
N_A	moles of A
N_M	number of gas mass transfer units
N_{Mb}	number of transfer units in bubbling zone
N_{MJ}	number of transfer units in grid (jet) region
N_{Ms}	number of transfer units in slugging bed
N_{or}	number of orifices in grid
N_{or}	number of holes in perforated plate
N_R	number of reaction units
N_{Rb}	number of reaction units in bubbling zone
N_{RFB}	number of reaction units in freeboard region
N_{RJ}	number of reaction units in grid (jet) region
n	number of compartments
n, n'	exponents in [8.2.20] and [8.2.21]
p	local pressure
p_0	local pressure in the absence of bubbles
Δp	pressure drop
Δp_d	pressure drop across distributor
r	ratio of cloud sphere volume to bubble volume
r_b	radius of curvature of leading edge of bubble
r_b	reaction rate in cloud per unit volume ($= kc_b$)
r_c	cloud radius
r_c	radius of unreacted core
r_e	reaction rate in emulsion per unit volume ($= kc_e$)
S_b	bubble surface area
$\mathbf{T}^F$	fluid phase stress tensor
$\mathbf{T}^S$	solid phase stress tensor
T_b	temperature of gas in bubble phase
T_{bL}	value of T_b at $z = L$
T_{bed}	temperature of bed
T_{Gin}	gas temperature at inlet
T_{Gout}	gas temperature at outlet
T_S	temperature of solid particles
T_W	wall temperature
t	time
t^*	time for complete conversion
$t_{0.999}^*$	time for conversion of 99.9%
$\bar{t}$	mean residence time in system
$\bar{t}_i$	mean residence time in stage i
t_S	characteristic thermal time for solid particle [8.2.10]
t_t	turnover time or characteristic time for solids mixing
U_W	overall heat transfer coefficient, bed to transfer surface
u	superficial gas or liquid fluidizing velocity

$\mathbf{u}$	fluid velocity vector
$u\downarrow$	value of superficial velocity at which gas down flow commences
u_a	superficial velocity of fluid in annulus of spouted bed
u_{aLm}	value of u_a evaluated at maximum spoutable bed height
u_b	bubble velocity
u_b^+	dimensionless bubble velocity ($u_b \epsilon_{mf}/u_{mf}$ or $u_s \epsilon_{mf}/u_{mf}$)
$\tilde{u}_b^+$	ratio of bubble rise velocity to interstitial gas velocity
u_{br}	rise velocity of isolated bubble
$u_{b\infty}$	bubble velocity in the absence of wall and interaction effects
u_c	superficial velocity at which pressure fluctuations reach maximum
u_{cr}	critical gas velocity for gas back-mixing
u_e	gas velocity in emulsion phase
u_{FB}	gas velocity in freeboard
u_G	superficial velocity of gas in three-phase system
u_{Gmf}	minimum fluidization velocity for gas in three-phase system
u_{i0}	initial ejection velocity of particle i
u_k	superficial velocity at which transition to turbulent regime occurs
u_L	superficial velocity of liquid in three-phase system
u_{LS}	linear relative velocity between liquid and solids in emulsion region of three-phase system
$u_{\max}$	superficial gas velocity to give maximum K_s
u_{mb}	superficial velocity at onset of bubbling
u_{mf}	superficial velocity at minimum fluidization
u_{ms}	superficial velocity at onset of slugging
u_{0b}	superficial velocity through bubbles
u_{0c}	superficial velocity through clouds
u_{0e}	superficial velocity through emulsion
u_{or}	orifice velocity, m/s
u_S	absolute velocity of solids in emulsion phase
u_s	slug velocity
u_{si}	rise velocity of single slug
u_T	terminal velocity of particle
u_{tr}	superficial velocity for vertical transport
V_b	volume of bubble phase (void plus cloud)
$\dot{V}_b$	volumetric flow rate due to bubble displacement
V_{bV}	volume of bubble void
V_c	volume of cloud phase
V_e	volume of emulsion phase
V_p	particle volume
V_S	volume of solids in compartment per unit cross-sectional area [8.4.93]
V_T	tube volume
V_W	volume of bubble wake
$\mathbf{v}$	particle velocity vector
v_e	velocity of solids in emulsion
v_R	relative velocity of solids

v_{soL}	centerline velocity of particles in spout at bed surface
v_T	terminal settling velocity of particles
w_b	volumetric flow rate of solids in bubble phase
w_e	volumetric flow rate of solids in emulsion phase
w_S	volumetric feed rate of solids
X_A	conversion of gaseous reactant A
X_B	conversion of solid reactant B
x	weight fraction
x_S	volume fraction of solids taking part in mass transfer
y	log mean fraction of nondiffusing component
Z	height from bottom of fluidized bed
z	vertical position coordinate

DIMENSIONLESS GROUPS

Ar	Archimedes number $[g\rho_G(\rho_S - \rho_G)\bar{d}_S^3/\mu_G^2]$
Ar_b	bubble Archimedes number $(g\rho_0^2 d_e^3/\mu_0^2)$
Fr	Froude number $(u_{mf}^2/g\bar{d}_S)$
N_H	dimensionless interphase heat transfer group [8.2.7]
Pr	Prandtl number $(C_{pG}\mu_G/\lambda_G$ or $C_{pL}\mu_L/\lambda_L)$
R	dimensionless group defined in table 8.1.3
Re_b	bubble Reynolds number $(\rho_0 d_e u_b/\mu_0$ or [8.1.32])
Re_{mf}	Reynolds number at minimum fluidization $(\rho_F \bar{d}_S u_{mf}/\mu_F)$
Re_{Lmf}	Reynolds number at minimum fluidization based on liquid superficial velocity and properties $(\rho_L \bar{d}_S u_{mf}/\mu_L)$
Re_T	Reynolds number for particle at its terminal velocity $(\rho_F d_S v_T/\mu_F)$

GREEK LETTERS

α_{bd}	bubble-to-dense-phase heat transfer coefficient
α_{bW}	bed-to-wall or bed-to-surface heat transfer coefficient
α_{cond}	heat transfer coefficient corresponding to conductive component of bed-to-wall transfer
α_{conv}	heat transfer coefficient corresponding to convective component of bed-to-wall transfer
α_{GS}	gas-to-solid-particle heat transfer coefficient
α_{max}	maximum value of α_{bW} achieved on varying u for a given system
α_{rad}	heat transfer coefficient corresponding to radiative component of bed-to-wall transfer
β	ratio of time for complete conversion of particle to mean residence time
Γ	dimensionless parameter defined by [8.1.96]
γ	kinematic viscosity
γ_S	fraction of particles in bubble phase
δ	diffusivity
δ_b	fraction of incoming gas that flows in the bubble phase
δ_d	ratio of volume of particles transported due to drift to bubble volume

δ_f	actual bubble flow $\dot{V}_b$ divided by value predicted by two-phase theory
δ_w	wake fraction (wake volume/bubble volume)
ϵ	total void fraction (gas and/or liquid)
ϵ_0	voidage of corresponding liquid-solid fluidized bed in the absence of gas bubbles
ϵ_b	volume fraction of bed occupied by bubbles
ϵ_{bed}	bed emissivity
ϵ_e	volume fraction of bed occupied by liquid-solids emulsion
ϵ_G	volume fraction of bed occupied by gas
ϵ_L	volume fraction of bed occupied by liquid
ϵ_{mf}	voidage at minimum fluidization
ϵ_S	emissivity of a solid particle
ϵ_{sL}	voidage in spout at bed surface
ϵ_{Se}	volume fraction of solids in emulsion region
ϵ_{SW}	volume fraction of solids in wake regions
ϵ_W	volume fraction of bed occupied by wakes
ϵ_W	emissivity of a wall or heat transfer surface
ζ	dimensionless bed height
η	efficiency factor in [8.3.48]
θ	angle
θ_W	wake angle
κ_G	thermal diffusivity of gas ($\lambda_G/\rho_G C_{pG}$)
λ_{eff}	effective thermal conductivity of dense phase
λ_G	thermal conductivity of gas
μ_a	apparent dynamic viscosity
μ_F	fluid dynamic viscosity
μ_G	dynamic viscosity of gas
μ_L	liquid dynamic viscosity
μ_0	liquid-solid suspension viscosity in the absence of gas bubbles
ξ	drag coefficient
ρ_0	liquid-solid suspension density in the absence of gas bubbles
ρ_F	density of fluidizing fluid
ρ_G	gas density
ρ_L	liquid density
ρ_{mf}	bed density at minimum fluidization
ρ_S	solids density
ρ_{Sm}	molar density of solid reactant
σ	surface tension
σ	Stefan-Boltzmann constant, 5.67×10^{-8} W/m^2 K^4
ϕ_s	particle sphericity [8.1.10]
χ	fractional approach to thermal equilibrium [8.2.32]
$\psi_{3\phi}$	bed expansion parameter [8.1.116]

SUBSCRIPTS

| b | bubble |
| b | bed |

c	cloud
F	fluid
J_{max}	jet maximum
mf	minimum fluidization
or	orifice
L	liquid
G	gas
S	solid
s	slug
W	wake or wall
w	wall
$-$	time-mean value

8.7 References
for Chapter 8

Abuaf, N. & Gutfinger, C. 1973 Heat Transfer with a Moving Boundary–Application to Fluidized Bed Coating of Thin Plates, *Int. J. Heat Mass Transfer* 16:213–216.

Abuaf, N. & Gutfinger, C. 1974 Experimental Coating and Heat Transfer Studies in a Vibrating Fluidized Bed, *Int. J. Multiphase Flow* 1:683–695.

Andeen, B. R. & Glicksman, L. R. 1976 Heat Transfer to Horizontal Tubes in Shallow Fluidized Beds, ASME paper 76-HT-67.

Andeen, B. R., Glicksman, L. R., & Bowman, R. 1978 Heat Transfer from Flattened Horizontal Tubes, in *Fluidization,* eds. J. F. Davidson & D. L. Keairns, pp. 345–350, Cambridge Univ. Press, Cambridge, England.

Anon. 1977 Acrylonitrile (SOHIO Process), *Hydrocarbon Process.* 11:124.

Aoyogi, M. & Kunii, D. 1974 Importance of Dispersed Solids in Bubbles for Exothermic Reactions in Fluidized Beds, *Chem. Eng. Commun.* 1:191–197.

Archer, D. H., Salvador, L. A., & Vidt, E. J. 1978 The Westinghouse Fluidized Bed Process, paper presented at the 10th Synthetic Pipeline Gas Symposium, Chicago.

Armstrong, E. R., Baker, C. G. J., & Bergougnou, M. A. 1976 Heat Transfer and Hydrodynamic Studies on Three Phase Fluidized Beds, in *Fluidization Technology,* ed. D. L. Keairns, vol. 1, pp., 453–457, Hemisphere, Washington, D.C.

Armstrong, E. R., Baker, C. G. J., & Bergougnou, M. A. 1976 The Effects of Solids Wettability on the Characteristics of Three Phase Fluidization, in *Fluidization Technology,* ed. D. L. Keairns, vol. 1, pp. 405–409, Hemisphere, Washington, D.C.

Aulisio, C. J., Ehrlich, S., Bryers, R. W., & Bazan, J. 1976 Fluidized-Bed Performance with Internals; Heat Exchanger above the Slumped Bed, in *Fluidization Technology,* ed. D. L. Keairns, vol. 2, pp. 485–489, Hemisphere, Washington, D.C.

Baeyens, J. & Geldart, D. 1973 Particle Mixing in a Gas Fluidized Bed, in *La Fluidisation et ses Applications,* pp. 182–195, Société Chimie Industrielle, Toulouse.

Baeyens, J. & Geldart, D. 1978 Fluidized Bed Incineration–A Design Approach for Complete Combustion of Hydrocarbons, in *Fluidization,* eds. J. F. Davidson & D. L. Keairns, p. 264, Cambridge Univ. Press, Cambridge, England.

Baeyens, J. & Goosens, W. R. A. 1973 Some Aspects of Heat Transfer between a Vertical Wall and a Gas Fluidized Bed, *Powder Technol.* 8:91–96.

Balasubramanian, M., Meisen, A., & Mathur, K. B. 1978 Spouted Bed Collection of Solid. Aerosols in the Presence of Electrical Effects, *Can. J. Chem. Eng.* 56:297–303.

Banchik, I. N. 1973 The Winkler Process for the Production of Low-Btu Gas from Coal, in *Clean Fuels from Coal,* p. 163, Institute of Gas Technology, Chicago.

Barile, R. G., Seth, H. K., & Williams, K. A. 1970 Transfer of Heat from Bubbles in Fluidized Beds, *Chem. Eng. J.* 1:263–271.

Barker, J. J. 1965 Heat Transfer Coefficients in Fluidized Beds, *Ind. Eng. Chem.* 57(5):33–39.

Barreteau, D., Lauerie, C., & Angelino, H. 1978 An Evaluation of Some Fluidized Bed Reactor Models for SO₂ Sorption on Copper Oxide Particles, in *Fluidization,* eds. J. F. Davidson & D. L. Keairns, p. 297, Cambridge Univ. Press, Cambridge, England.

Bartel, W. J. & Genetti, W. E. 1973 Heat Transfer from a Horizontal Bundle of Bare and Finned Tubes in an Air Fluidized Bed, *AIChE Symp. Ser.* 69(128):85–93.

Bartel, W. J., Genetti, W. E., & Grimett, E. S. 1971 Heat Transfer from a Horizontal Discontinuous Finned Tube in a Fluidized Bed, *AIChE Symp. Ser.* 67(116):85–89.

Baskakov, A. P., Berg, B. V., Vitt, O. K., Filippovsky, N. F., Kirakosyan, V. A., Goldobin, J. M., & Maskaev, V. K. 1973 Heat Transfer to Objects Immersed in Fluidized Beds, *Powder Technol.* 8:273–282.

Baskakov, A. P., Vitt, O. K., Kirakosyan, V. A., Maskaev, V. K., & Filippovsky, N. F. 1974 Investigation of Heat Transfer Coefficient Pulsations and of the Mechanism of Heat Transfer from a Surface Immersed in a Fluidized Bed, in *La Fluidisation et ses Applications,* pp. 293–302, Société Chimie Industrielle, Toulouse.

Basov, V. A., Markhevka, V. I., Melik-Akhnazanov, T. Kh., & Orachko, D. I. 1969 Investigation of the Structure of a Non-uniform Fluidized Bed, *Int. Chem. Eng.* 9:263–266.

Beek, W. J. 1971 Mass Transfer in Fluidized Beds, in *Fluidization,* eds. J. F. Davidson & D. Harrison, pp. 431–470, Academic, New York.

Begovich, J. M. & Watson, J. S. 1978 Hydrodynamic Characteristics of Three-Phase Fluidized Beds, in *Fluidization,* eds. J. F. Davidson & D. L. Keairns, pp. 190–195, Cambridge Univ. Press, Cambridge, England.

Behie, L. A. & Kehoe, P. 1973 The Grid Region in a Fluidized Bed Reactor, *AIChE J.* 19:1070–1072.

Behie, L. A., Bergougnou, M. A., & Baker, C. G. J. 1975 Heat Transfer from a Grid Jet in a Large Fluidized Bed, *Can. J. Chem. Eng.* 53:25–30.

Behie, L. A., Bergougnou, M. A., & Baker, C. G. J. 1976 Mass Transfer from a Grid Jet in a Large Gas Fluidized Bed, in *Fluidization Technology,* ed. D. L. Keairns, vol. 1, pp. 261–278, Hemisphere, Washington, D.C.

Berg, B. V. & Baskakov, A. P. 1974 Investigation of Local Heat Transfer between a Fixed Horizontal Cylinder and a Fluidized Bed, *Int. Chem. Eng.* 14:440–443.

Bernis, A., Vergnes, F., & LeGoff, P. 1977 Influence du passage d'une bulle sur le coefficient instantané de transfert de chaleur à une paroi immergée dans un lit fluidisé, *Powder Technol.* 18:267–276.

Berquin, Y. F. 1977 Prospects for Full-scale Development of Spouting Beds in Fertilizer Granulation, paper 23, presented at the 1st International Conference on Fertilizers, London.

Bhatia, V. K., Evans, K. A., & Epstein, N. 1972 Effect of Solids Wettability on Expansion of Gas-Liquid Fluidized Beds, *Ind. Eng. Chem. Process Des. Dev.* 11:151–152.

Bishop, J. W. 1968 Process and Apparatus for Reduction of Unburned Combustible in Fly Ash, U.S. Patent 3,508,506.

Bohle, W. & Van Swaaij, W. P. N. 1978 The Influence of Gas Adsorption on Mass Transfer and Gas Mixing in a Fluidized Bed, in *Fluidization,* eds. J. F. Davidson & D. L. Keairns, pp. 167–172, Cambridge Univ. Press, Cambridge, England.

Borgelt, B. V., Casley, G. E., & Pritchard, J. 1974 Fluid Bed Roasting at Mount Isa, England. *Regional Meet. North West Queensland Branch Australia Inst. Mining Metallurgy, Aug. 1974,* Australian Inst. of Mining and Metallurgy, Parkville, Victoria.

Botterill, J. S. M. 1975 *Fluid Bed Heat Transfer,* Academic, New York.

Botterill, J. S. M. & Williams, J. R. 1963 The Mechanism of Heat Transfer to Gas-fluidized Beds, *Trans. Inst. Chem. Eng.* 41:217–230.

Botterill, J. S. M., Redish, K. A., Ross, D. K., & Williams, J. R. 1962 The Mechanism of Heat Transfer to Fluidized Beds, *Proc. Symp. Interact. Fluids Particles,* pp. 183–189, Institution of Chemical Engineers, London.

Botterill, J. S. M., Brundrett, G. W., Cain, G. L., & Elliott, D. E. 1966 Heat Transfer to Gas Fluidized Beds, *Chem. Eng. Prog. Symp. Ser.* 62:1–6.

Botterill, J. S. M., Butt, M. H. D., Cain, G. L., & Redish, K. A. 1967 The Effect of Gas and Solids

Thermal Properties on the Rate of Heat Transfer to Gas-fluidized Beds, *Proc. Int. Symp. Fluidization,* ed. A. A. H. Drinkenburg, pp. 442–453, Netherlands Univ. Press, Amsterdam.

Botton, R. J. 1970 Gas-Solid Contacting in Fluidized Beds, *Chem. Eng. Prog. Symp. Ser.* 66:8–18.

Brea, F. M. & Hamilton, W. 1971 Heat Transfer in Liquid Fluidized Beds with a Concentric Heater, *Trans. Inst. Chem. Eng.* 49:196–203.

Calderbank, P. H. & Toor, F. D. 1971 Fluidized Beds as Catalytic Reactors, in *Fluidization,* eds. J. F. Davidson & D. Harrison, pp. 383–429, Academic, New York.

Calderbank, P. H., Pereira, J., & Burgess, J. M. 1976 The Physical and Mass Transfer Properties of Bubbles in Fluidized Beds of Electrically Conducting Particles, in *Fluidization Technology,* ed. D. L. Keairns, vol. 1, pp. 115–167, Hemisphere, Washington, D.C.

Canada, G. S. & McLaughlin, M. H. 1977 Large Particle Fluidization and Heat Transfer at High Pressures, *AIChE Symp. Ser.* 74(176):27–37.

Cankurt, N. T. & Yerushalmi, J. 1978 Gas Backmixing in High Velocity Fluidized Beds, in *Fluidization,* eds. J. F. Davidson & D. L. Keairns, pp. 387–393, Cambridge Univ. Press, Cambridge, England.

Carlos, C. R. & Richardson, J. F. 1967 Particle Speed Distribution in a Fluidized System, *Chem. Eng. Sci.* 22:705–706.

Carlos, C. R. & Richardson, J. R. 1968 Solids Movement in Liquid Fluidized Beds, *Chem. Eng. Sci.* 23:813–831.

Chandrasekhar, R. & Harding, J. C. 1978 Development of Feed Systems for Pressurized Coal Conversion Processes, *Chem. Eng. Prog. Symp. Ser.* 74(176):237–242.

Chavarie, J. & Grace, J. R. 1976 Interphase Mass Transfer in a Gas-fluidized Bed, *Chem. Eng. Sci.* 31:741–749.

Chen, B. H. & Douglas, W. J. M. 1968 Liquid Hold-up and Minimum Fluidization Velocity in a Turbulent Contactor, *Can. J. Chem. Eng.* 46:245–249.

Chen, J. C. 1976 Heat Transfer to Tubes in Fluidized Beds, ASME paper 76-HT-75.

Chen, J. L. P. & Keairns, D. L. 1975 Particle Segregation in a Fluidized Bed, *Can. J. Chem. Eng.* 53:395–402.

Chen, J. L. P. & Keairns, D. L. 1978 Particle Separation from a Fluidized Mixture–Simulation of Westinghouse Coal-Gasification Combustor-Gasifier Operation, *Ind. Eng. Chem. Process Des. Dev.* 17:135–141.

Cheung, L., Nienow, A. W., & Rowe, P. N. 1974 Minimum Fluidization Velocity of a Binary Mixture of Different Sized Particles, *Chem. Eng. Sci.* 29:1301–1303.

Chiba, T. & Kobayashi, H. 1977 Solid Exchange between the Bubble Wake and the Emulsion Phase in a Gas-fluidized Bed, *J. Chem. Eng. Jpn.* 10:206–210.

Chin, E. J. 1979 A Fluidized Bed Particle Feeder, M. Eng. thesis, McGill Univ., Montreal.

Chung, S. F. & Wen, C. Y. 1968 Longitudinal Dispersion of Fluids Flow Through Fixed and Fluidized Beds, *AIChE J.* 14:857–866.

Ciborowski, J. & Wlodarski, A. 1962 On Electrostatic Effects in Fluidized Beds, *Chem. Eng. Sci.* 17:23–32.

Clift, R. & Grace, J. R. 1970 Bubble Interaction in Fluidized Beds, *Chem. Eng. Prog. Symp. Ser.* 66(105):14–27.

Clift, R. & Grace, J. R. 1971 Coalescence of Bubbles in Fluidized Beds, *AIChE Symp. Ser.* 67(116):23–33.

Clift, R. & Grace, J. R. 1972a Coalescence of Bubble Chains in Fluidized Beds, *Trans. Inst. Chem. Eng.* 50:364–371.

Clift, R. & Grace, J. R. 1972b The Mechanism of Bubble Breakup in Fluidized Beds, *Chem. Eng. Sci.* 27:2309–2310.

Clift, R., Grace, J. R., & Weber, M. E. 1974 Stability of Bubbles in Fluidized Beds, *Ind. Eng. Chem. Fundam.* 13:45–51.

Clift, R., Grace, J. R., & Weber, M. E. 1978 *Bubbles, Drops and Particles,* Academic, New York.

Coeuret, F., Le Goff, P., & Vergnes, F. 1967 Porosity Fluctuations and Mass Transfer in Liquid-fluidized Beds, *Proc. Int. Symp. Fluidization,* ed. A. A. H. Drinkenburg, pp. 537–552, Netherlands Univ. Press, Amsterdam.

Coeuret, F., Le Goff, P., Storck, A., Valentin, G., & Vergnes, F. 1976 Liquid Fluidization: Mass

Transfer between the Liquid and an Immersed Surface, in *Fluidization Technology*, ed. D. L. Keairns, vol. 1, pp. 369–371, Hemisphere, Washington, D.C.

Collins, R. 1969 The Effect of a Bubble on Gas Flow in a Plane Fluidized Bed of Finite Width: Two Theories Compared, *Chem. Eng. Sci.* 24:1291–1307.

Cook, H. H. & Bridgwater, J. 1978 Segregation in Spouted Beds, *Can. J. Chem. Eng.* 56:636–638.

Cooke, M. J., Harris, W., Highley, J., & Williams, D. F. 1968 Kinetics of Oxygen Consumption in Fluidized Bed Carbonizers, *Tripartite Chem. Eng. Conf. Symp. Fluidization* 1:14–20.

Crescitelli, S., Donsi, G., Russo, G., & Clift, R. 1978 High Velocity Behaviour of Fluidized Beds: Slugs and Turbulent Flow, *CHISA '78*, Prague.

Crowther, M. E. & Whitehead, J. C. 1978 Fluidization of Fine Particles at Elevated Pressure, in *Fluidization*, eds. J. F. Davidson & D. L. Keairns, pp. 65–70, Cambridge Univ. Press, Cambridge, England.

Darton, R. C. & Harrison, D. 1974a Some Properties of Gas Bubbles in Three-Phase Fluidized Beds, *Inst. Chem. Eng. Symp. Ser.* 38:1–28.

Darton, R. C. & Harrison, D. 1974b The Rise of Single Gas Bubbles in Liquid Fluidized Beds, *Trans. Inst. Chem. Eng.* 52:301–306.

Darton, R. C., Lanauze, R. D., Davidson, J. F., & Harrison, D. 1977 Bubble Growth due to Coalescence in Fluidized Beds, *Trans. Inst. Chem. Eng.* 55:274–280.

Davidson, J. F. 1961 Symposium on Fluidization–Discussion, *Trans. Inst. Chem. Eng.* 39:230–232.

Davidson, J. F. 1973 Fluidization: The Two-Phase Theory and Its Applications, paper presented at the Joint AIChE-CSChE Meet., Vancouver.

Davidson, J. F. & Harrison, D. 1963 *Fluidized Particles*, Cambridge Univ. Press, Cambridge, England.

Davidson, J. F., Harrison, D., Darton, R. C., & LaNauze, R. D. 1977 The Two-Phase Theory and Its Application to Chemical Reactors, in *Chemical Reactor Theory, A Review*, eds. L. Lapidus & N. R. Amundson, pp. 583–685, Prentice-Hall, Englewood Cliffs, N.J.

Davis, W. L. 1977 High-Capacity Scaleup of High-Temperature Fluidized Bed Reactors, *Proc. 2d Pacific Chem. Eng. Cong.* 2:1163–1170.

DeGroot, J. H. 1967 Scaling-up of Gas-fluidized Bed Reactors, *Proc. Int. Symp. Fluidization*, ed. A. A. H. Drinkenburg, pp. 348–361, Netherlands Univ. Press, Amsterdam.

DeJong, J. A. H. & Hoelen, Q. E. J. J. M. 1975 Cocurrent Gas and Particle Flow during Pneumatic Discharge from a Bunker through an Orifice, *Powder Technol.* 12:201–208.

Demircan, N., Gibbs, B. M., Swithenbank, J., & Taylor, D. S. 1978 Rotating Fluidized Bed Combustor, in *Fluidization*, eds. J. F. Davidson & D. L. Keairns, pp. 270–275, Cambridge Univ. Press, Cambridge, England.

Dengler, J. L. 1977 A Study of a Fluidized Turbulent Bed Contactor with Application to Cooling Towers, Ph.D. thesis, Purdue Univ., West Lafayette, Ind.

Denloye, A. E. & Botterill, J. S. M. 1977 Bed to Surface Heat Transfer in a Fluidized Bed of Large Particles, *Powder Technol.* 19:197–203.

DeVries, R. J., Van Swaaij, W. P. M., Mantovani, C., & Heykoop, A. 1972 *Proc. 5th European Symp. Chemical Reaction Eng.*, paper B9-59, Elsevier, Amsterdam.

Do, H. T., Grace, J. R., & Clift, R. 1972 Particle Ejection and Entrainment from Fluidized Beds, *Powder Technol.* 6:195–200.

Doichev, K., Todorov, S., & Dimitrov, V. 1975 Transition between Particulate and Aggregative Fluidization at Different State-of-Flow of Solids, *Chem. Eng. Sci.* 30:419–424.

Douglas, E. & Sayles, C. D. 1971 *Chem. Eng. Prog. Symp. Ser.* 67(116):201.

Douglas, E. & Walsh, T. 1966 *Trans. Inst. Min. Metall. Sect. C.* 75:226–232.

Douglas, W. J. M. 1964 Heat and Mass Transfer in a Turbulent Bed Contactor, *Chem. Eng. Prog.* 60(7):66–71.

Drinkenburg, A. A. H. & Rietema, K. 1972 Gas Transfer from Bubbles in a Fluidized Bed to the Dense Phase. I. Theory, *Chem. Eng. Sci.* 27:1765–1774.

Ehrlich, S. 1976 History of the Development of the Fluidized-Bed Boiler, *Proc. 4th Int. Conf. Fluidized-Bed Combustion*, pp. 15–20, Mitre Corp., McLean, Va.

El-Kaissy, M. M. & Homsy, G. M. 1976 Instability Waves and the Origin of Bubbles in Fluidized Beds, *Int. J. Multiphase Flow* 2:379–395.

El-Temtamy, S. A. & Epstein, N. 1978 Bubble Wake Solids Content in Three-Phase Fluidized Beds, *Int. J. Multiphase Flow,* 4:19–31.

Epstein, N. & Levine, S. 1978 Non-Darcy Flow and Pressure Distribution in a Spouted Bed, in *Fluidization,* eds. J. F. Davidson & D. L. Keairns, pp. 98–103, Cambridge Univ. Press, Cambridge, England.

Epstein, N. & Mathur, K. B. 1971 Heat and Mass Transfer in Spouted Beds–A Review, *Can. J. Chem. Eng.* 49:467–476.

Epstein, N. & Nicks, D. 1976 Contraction or Expansion of Three-Phase Fluidized Beds, in *Fluidization Technology,* ed. D. L. Keairns, vol. 1, pp. 389–397, Hemisphere, Washington, D.C.

Epstein, N., Lim, C. J., & Mathur, K. B. 1978 Data and Models for Flow Distribution and Pressure Drop in Spouted Beds, *Can. J. Chem. Eng.* 56:436–447.

Ergun, S. 1952 Fluid Flow through Packed Columns, *Chem. Eng. Prog.* 48:89–94.

Fakhimi, S. & Harrison, D. 1970 Multi-Orifice Distributors in Fluidized Beds: A Guide to Design, in *Chemeca Proceedings,* pp. 29–46, Butterworths, Melbourne, Australia.

Fan, L. T., Yang, Y. C., & Wen, C. Y. 1960 Mass Transfer in Semi-Fluidized Beds for Solid-Liquid System, *AIChE J.* 6:482–487.

Fane, A. G. 1974 A Review of Gas/Solid Contactors, *Australian Atomic Energy Commission Rept.* E282.

Field, M. A., Gill, D. W., Morgan, B. B., & Hawksley, P. G. W. 1965 Combustion of Pulverised Coal, British Coal Utilization Research Association, Leatherhead, U.K.

Fink, C. E., Curran, G. P., & Sudbury, J. D. 1975 CO_2 Acceptor Process Pilot Plant–1975, paper presented at the 7th Synthetic Pipeline Gas Symposium, Chicago.

Fish, W. M. 1974 Alumina Calcination in Fluid-Flash Calciner, *AIME Light Metals in 1974, Alumina & Bauxite and Carbon,* 3:673–682.

Foong, S.-K., Barton, R. K., & Ratcliffe, J. S. 1975 Characteristics of Multiple Spouted Beds, *Mech. Chem. Eng. Trans.* MCII(1,2):7–12.

Foong, S.-K., Barton, R. K., & Ratcliffe, J. S. 1976 Reduction of Sulphur Dioxide with Carbon in a Spouted Bed, *Chem. Eng. Aust.* pp. 1–8.

Foong, S.-K., Lim, C. J., Watkinson, A. P., & Mathur, K. B. 1978 Gasification of Caking Coals in a Spouted Bed, Year End Rept. Univ. of British Columbia.

Fouda, A. E. & Capes, C. E. 1977 Hydrodynamic Particle Volume and Fluidized Bed Expansion, *Can. J. Chem. Eng.* 55:386–391.

Fournol, A. B., Bergougnou, M. A., & Baker, C. G. J. 1973 Solids Entrainment in a Large Gas Fluidized Bed, *Can. J. Chem. Eng.* 51:401–404.

Froessling, N. 1938 The Evaporation of Falling Drops, *Gerlands Beitr. Geophys.* 52:170.

Fryer, C. & Potter, O. E. 1972 Countercurrent Backmixing Model for Fluidized Bed Catalytic Reactors. Applicability of Simplified Solutions, *Ind. Eng. Chem. Fundam.* 11:338–344.

Gabor, J. D. 1970a Wall-to-Bed Heat Transfer in Fluidized and Packed Beds, *Chem. Eng. Prog. Symp. Ser.* 66(105):76–86.

Gabor, J. D. 1970b Heat Transfer to Particle Beds with Gas Flows Less Than or Equal to That Required for Incipient Fluidization, *Chem. Eng. Sci.* 25:979–984.

Gabor, J. D. 1972a Wall-to-Bed Heat Transfer in Fluidized Beds, *AIChE J.* 18:249–250.

Gabor, J. D. 1972b On the Mechanics of Fluidized Particle Movement, *Chem. Eng. J.* 4:118–126.

Gamble, R. L. 1976 Design of the Rivesville Multicell Fluidized-Bed Steam Generator, *Proc. 4th Int. Conf. Fluidized-Bed Combustion,* pp. 133–152, Mitre Corp. McLean, Va.

Geldart, D. 1972 The Effect of Particle Size and Size Distribution on the Behaviour of Gas-fluidized Beds, *Powder Technol.* 6:201–205.

Geldart, D. 1973 Types of Gas Fluidization, *Powder Technol.* 7:285–292.

Geldart, D. & Abrahamsen, A. R. 1978 Homogeneous Fluidization of Fine Powders Using Various Gases and Pressures, *Powder Technol.* 19:133–136.

Geldart, D., Cullinan, J., Georghiades, S., Gilvray, D., & Pope, D. J. 1979 The Effect of Fines on Entrainment from Gas Fluidized Beds, *Trans. Inst. Chem. Eng.* 57:269–275.

Gelperin, N. I. & Einstein, V. G. 1971 Heat Transfer in Fluidized Beds, in *Fluidization*, eds. J. F. Davidson & D. Harrison, pp. 471–540, Academic, New York.

Genetti, W. E., Schmall, R. A. & Grimett, E. S. 1971 The Effect of Tube Orientation on Heat Transfer with Bare and Finned Tubes in a Fluidized Bed, *AIChE Symp. Ser.* 67(116):90–96.

George, S. E. 1980 Heat Transfer to Tubes in the Freeboard Region of a Fluidized Bed, Ph.D. thesis, McGill Univ., Montreal.

George, S. E. & Grace, J. R. 1978 Entrainment of Particles from Aggregative Fluidized Beds, *AIChE Symp. Ser.* 74(176):67–74.

Gibbs, B. M. & Hedley, A. B. 1978 Combustion of Large Coal Particles in a Fluidized Bed, in *Fluidization*, eds. J. F. Davidson & D. L. Keairns, p. 235, Cambridge Univ. Press, Cambridge, England.

Glass, D. H. & Harrison, D. 1964 Flow Patterns Near a Solid Obstacle in a Fluidized Bed, *Chem. Eng. Sci.* 19:1001–1002.

Glicksman, L. R. & Decker, N. 1980 Heat Transfer in Fluidized Beds with Large Particles, to be published.

Godel, A. & Cosar, P. 1967 *AIChE Symp. Ser.* 67:210–218.

Goikhman, I. D., Oigenblik, A. A., Genin, L. S., & Filippov, L. A. 1969 The Effect of Floating Spherical Packing on the Distribution of the Gas Residence Time in a Fluidized Bed, *Int. Chem. Eng.* 9:239–241.

Golubkovich, A. V. 1976 Study of the Limestone Calcination Régimes in Spouted-Bed Kilns, *Khim. Neft. Mashinostr.* 4:19–21.

Gomezplata, A. & Shuster, W. W. 1960 Effects of Uniformity of Fluidization on Catalytic Cracking of Cumene, *AIChE J.* 6:454–459.

Grace, J. R. 1970 The Viscosity of Fluidized Beds, *Can. J. Chem. Eng.* 48:30–33.

Grace, J. R. 1971 Evaluation of Models for Fluidized Bed Reactors, *AIChE Symp. Ser.* 67(116):159–167.

Grace, J. R. 1974 Fluidization and Its Application to Coal Treatment and Allied Processes, *AIChE Symp. Ser.* 70(141):21–26.

Grace, J. R. & Clift, R. 1974a On the Two-Phase Theory of Fluidization, *Chem. Eng. Sci.* 29:327–334.

Grace, J. R. & Clift, R. 1974b Coalescence of Bubble Pairs in a Three-dimensional Fluidized Bed, *Can. J. Chem. Eng.* 52:417–419.

Grace, J. R. & de Lasa, H. I. 1978 Reaction near the Grid in Fluidized Beds, *AIChE J.* 24:364–366.

Grace, J. R. & Harrison, D. 1968a The Effect of Internal Baffles in Fluidized Beds: A Guide to Design, *Inst. Chem. Eng. Symp. Ser.* 27:93–100.

Grace, J. R. & Harrison, D. 1968b The Distribution of Bubbles within a Gas-Fluidized Bed, *Inst. Chem. Eng. Symp. Ser.* 30:105–113.

Grace, J. R. & Mathur, K. B. 1978 Height and Structure of the Fountain Region above Spouted Beds, *Can. J. Chem. Eng.* 56:533–537.

Grace, J. R. & Tuot, J. 1979 Cluster Formation in Vertically Conveyed Suspensions of Intermediate Density, *Trans. Inst. Chem. Engr.* 57:49–54.

Grace, J. R. & Venta, J. 1973 Volume Changes Accompanying Bubble Splitting in Fluidized Beds, *Can. J. Chem. Eng.,* 51:110–111.

Grace, J. R., Krochmalnek, L. S., Clift, R., & Farkas, E. J. 1971 Expansion of Liquids and Fluidized Beds in Slug Flow, *Chem. Eng. Sci.* 26:617–628.

Guignon, P., Large, J. F., Bergougnou, M. A., & Baker, C. G. J. 1978 Particle Interchange through Thin and Thick Baffle Plates in Multistage Gas Fluidized Beds, in *Fluidization*, eds. J. F. Davidson & D. L. Keairns, pp. 134–139, Cambridge Univ. Press, Cambridge, England.

Gutfinger, C. & Abuaf, N. 1974 Heat Transfer in Fluidized Beds, *Adv. Heat Transfer* 10:167–218.

Gutfinger, C. & Chen, W. H. 1969 *Int. J. Heat Mass Transfer* 12:1097.

Hager, W. R. & Thomson, W. J. 1973 Bubble Behaviour around Immersed Tubes in a Fluidized Bed, *AIChE Symp. Ser.* 69(128):68–77.

Hamilton, W. 1970 A Correlation for Heat Transfer in Liquid Fluidized Beds, *Can. J. Chem. Eng.* 48:52–55.

Harrington, C. D. & Ruehle, A. E. 1959 *Uranium Production Technology,* Van Nostrand, Princeton, N.J.

Harriott, P. & Barnstone, L. A. 1967 Heat Transfer in Fluidized Beds, *Ind. Eng. Chem.* 59(4):55–58.

Harrison, D., Davidson, J. F., & de Kock, J. W. 1961 On the Nature of Aggregative and Particulate Fluidization, *Trans. Inst. Chem. Eng.* 39:202–211.

Harrison, D., Aspinall, P. N., & Elder, J. 1974 Suppression of Particle Elutriation from a Fluidized Bed, *Trans. Inst. Chem. Eng.* 52:213–216.

Hattori, H. & Takeda, H. 1976 Modified Spouted Beds with the Gas Outlet Located in the Side Wall Surrounding the Annular Dense Phase, *J. Fac. Text. Sci. Technol. Shinshu Univ. Ser. B* 12:1–13.

Hattori, H. & Takeda, K. 1978 Side-Outlet Spouted Bed with Inner Draft Tube for Small-sized Solid Particles, *J. Chem. Eng. Jpn.* 11:125–129.

Hawthorn, E., Shortis, L. P., & Lloyd, J. E. 1960 The Fluidized Solids Dryway Process for the Production of Uranium Tetrafluoride at Springfields, *Trans. Inst. Chem. Eng.* 38:197–207.

Heertjes, P. M., de Boer, H. G. J., & van Dorsser, A. H. H. 1953 Temperature and Humidity Measurements in a Drying Fluidized Bed, *Chem. Eng. Sci.* 2:97–107.

Henriksen, H. K. & Ostergaard, K. 1974a Characteristics of Large Two-dimensional Air Bubbles in Liquids and Three-Phase Fluidized Beds, *Chem. Eng. J.* 7:141–146.

Henriksen, H. K. & Ostergaard, K. 1974b On the Mechanism of Breakup of Large Bubbles in Liquids and Three-Phase Fluidized Beds, *Chem. Eng. Sci.* 29:626–629.

Hetzler, R. & Williams, M. C. 1969 Fluidized Bed Viscosity and Expansion Correlated with Glass-forming Liquid Model, *Ind. Eng. Chem. Fundam.* 8:668–677.

Highley, J. & Merrick, D. 1971 The Effect of Spacing between Solid Feed Points on the Performance of a Large Fluidized Bed Reactor, *AIChE Symp. Ser.* 67(116):219–227.

Highly, J. 1976 Report on Progress at the NCB Coal Research Establishment (CRE), *Proc. 4th Int. Conf. Fluidized-Bed Combustion,* pp. 199–212, Mitre Corp., McLean, Va.

Hill, F. B. & Wilhelm, R. H. 1959 Radiative and Conductive Heat Transfer in a Quiescent Gas-Solid Bed of Particles: Theory and Experiment, *AIChE J.* 5:486–496.

Hoebink, J. H. B. J. 1977 Drying Granular Solids in a Fluidized Bed, Ph.D. thesis, Eindhoven Univ., Eindhoven, Netherlands.

Holman, J. P., Moore, T. W., & Wong, V. M. 1965 Particle-to-Fluid Heat Transfer in Water-fluidized systems, *Ind. Eng. Chem. Fundam.* 4:21–31.

Hoogendoorn, J. C. 1973 Experience with Fischer-Tropsch Synthesis at Sasol, in *Clean Fuels from Coal,* p. 353, Inst. of Gas Technology, Chicago.

Horio, M. & Wen, C. Y. 1977 An Assessment of Fluidized-Bed Modeling, *AIChE Symp. Ser.* 73(161):9–21.

Horsler, A. G. & Thompson, B. H. 1968 Fluidization in the Development of Gas Making Processes, *Inst. Chem. Eng. Symp. Ser.* 30:58–66.

Hovmand, S. & Davidson, J. F. 1968 Chemical Conversion in a Slugging Fluidized Bed, *Trans. Inst. Chem. Eng.* 46:190–203.

Hovmand, S. & Davidson, J. F. 1971 Pilot Plant and Laboratory Scale Fluidized Reactors at High Gas Velocities: The Relevance of Slug Flow, in *Fluidization,* eds. J. F. Davidson & D. Harrison, p. 193, Academic, New York.

Iammartino, N. R. 1974 Cement's Changing Scene, *Chem. Eng. (N.Y.)* 81(13):102–104.

Ingle, A. N. & Sarkar, S. 1976 Gasification of Coal in Spouted Bed, *Indian J. Technol.* 14:515–516.

Inst. Gas Tech. 1978 Coal Conversions Systems. Technical Data Book Chicago sec. IVB.

Ionescu, D. & Paun, A. 1975 *Freiberg. Forschungsh. A* 541:63–68.

Ishida, M. & Wen, C. Y. 1973 Effect of Solid Mixing on Noncatalytic Solid-Gas Reactions in a Fluidized Bed, *AIChE Symp. Ser.* 69(128):1–7.

Ishii, T. & Osberg, G. L. 1965 Effect of Packing on the Catalytic Isomerization of Cyclopropane in Fixed and Fluidized Beds, *AIChE J.* 11:279–287.

Jackson, R. 1963 The Mechanics of Fluidized Beds: The Motion of Fully Developed Bubbles, *Trans. Inst. Chem. Eng.* 41:22–28.

Jackson, R. 1971 Fluid Mechanical Theory, in *Fluidization*, eds. J. F. Davidson & D. Harrison, pp. 65–119, Academic, New York.

Jagannadharaju, G. J. V. & Rao, C. V. 1965 Ionic Mass Transfer in the Presence of Fluidized Solids, *Indian J. Technol.* 3:201–205.

Jequier, L., Longchambon, L., & Van de Putte, G. 1960 The Gasification of Coal Fines, *J. Inst. Fuel* 33:584–591.

Johnson, T. W. & Melcher, J. R. 1975 Electromechanics of Electrofluidized Beds, *Ind. Eng. Chem. Fundam.* 14:146–153.

Johnsson, J. E., Clift, R., & Grace, J. R. 1974 Prediction of Bubble Distributions in Freely-bubbling Two-dimensional Fluidized Beds, *Inst. Chem. Eng. Symp. Ser.* 38:1–19.

Johnstone, H. F., Batchelor, J. D., & Shen, W. Y. 1955 Low Temperature Oxidation of Ammonia in Fixed and Fluidized Beds, *AIChE J.* 1:318–323.

Jolley, L. J., Poll, A., Noaks, C. C., & Stantan, J. E. 1954 Production of Water-Gas in Fluidized Beds, paper presented at the International Conference on Complete Gasification of Mined Coal, Liège.

Jolly, R. D. & Doig, I. D. 1973 Examination of Net Pressure Drop in Fluidized Beds, *Chem. Eng. Sci.* 28:971–973.

Jones, D. R. M. & Davidson, J. F. 1965 The Flow of Particles from a Fluidized Bed through an Orifice, *Rheol. Acta* 4:180–192.

Jones, W. I. & Owens, J. 1962 *J. Inst. Fuel* 38:404.

Kato, K. & Wen, C. Y. 1969 Bubble Assemblage Model for Fluidized Bed Catalytic Reactors, *Chem. Eng. Sci.* 24:1351–1369.

Kato, K., Kubota, H., & Wen, C. Y. 1970 Mass Transfer in Fixed and Fluidized Beds, *Inst. Chem. Eng. Symp. Ser.* 66(105):86–99.

Kehoe, P. W. K. & Davidson, J. F. 1970 Continuously Slugging Fluidized Beds, *Proc. Chemeca Conf.*, pp. 97–116, Butterworths, Melbourne, Australia.

Keillor, S. A. & Bergougnou, M. A. 1976 A Study of the Action of Floating Bubble Breakers in Fluidized Beds by Interactive Computer Graphics, in *Fluidization Technology*, ed. D. L. Keairns, vol. 2, pp. 95–109, Hemisphere, Washington, D.C.

Kettenring, K. N., Manderfield, E. L., & Smith, J. M. 1950 Heat and Mass Transfer in Fluidized Systems, *Chem. Eng. Prog.* 46(3):139–145.

Khan, A. R., Richardson, J. F., & Shakiri, K. J. 1978 Heat Transfer between a Fluidized Bed and a Small Immersed Surface, in *Fluidization*, eds. J. F. Davidson & D. L. Keairns, pp. 351–356, Cambridge Univ. Press, Cambridge, England.

Kim, S. D., Baker, C. G. J., & Bergougnou, M. A. 1977 Bubble Characteristics in Three-Phase Fluidized Beds, *Chem. Eng. Sci.* 32:1299–1306.

Kmiec, A. 1975 Simultaneous Heat and Mass Transfer in Spouted Beds, *Can. J. Chem. Eng.* 53:18–24.

Kobayashi, H. & Arai, F. 1965 Effects of Several Factors on Catalytic Reaction in a Fluidized Bed Reactor, *Kagaku Kogaku,* 29:885.

Kobayashi, H. & Arai, F. 1967 Determination of Gas Cross-Flow Coefficient between the Bubble and Emulsion Phases by Measuring Residence-Time Distribution of Fluid in a Fluidized Bed, *Kagaku Kogaku* 31:239–243.

Kobayashi, H., Arai, F., & Chiba, T. 1965 Behavior of Bubbles in a Gas-Solid Fluidized Bed, *Kagaku Kogaku* 29:858.

Kobayashi, H., Arai, F., Chiba, T., & Tanaka Y. 1969 Estimation of Catalytic Conversion in Gas-fluidized Beds by Means of a Two-Phase Model. Effect of Bed Diameter, *Kagaku Kogaku* 33:274–280.

Kolodney, M., Yerushalmi, J., Squires, A. M., & Harvey, R. D. 1976 The Behavior of Mineral Matter in a Fluidized Bed Gasifying Coal—The Godel Process, *Br. Ceram. Soc.* 75:85–91.

Kroll, K. K. 1978 Fluidat-Trockner in *Trockner und Trocknungsverfahren*, vol. 2, pp. 221, Springer-Verlag, Berlin.

Kubie, J. 1976 Bubble Induced Heat Transfer in Gas Fluidized Beds, *Int. J. Heat Mass Transfer,* 19:1441–1453.

Kunii, D. & Levenspiel, O. 1968 Bubbling Bed Model for Kinetic Processes in Fluidized Beds, *Ind. Eng. Chem. Process Des. Dev.* 7:481–492.

Kunii, D. & Levenspiel, O. 1969 *Fluidization Engineering*, Wiley, New York.

LaNauze, R. D. 1976 Circulating Fluidized Bed, *Powder Technol.* 15:117–127.

Large, J. F. Martinie, Y., & Bergougnou, M. A. 1976 Interpretative Model for Entrainment in a Large Gas Fluidized Bed, *Int. Powder Bulk Handling Process. Conf.,* Chicago.

Lee, J. C., Sherrard, A. J., & Buckley, P. S. 1974 Optimum Particle Size in Three-Phase Fluidized Bed Reactors, in *La Fluidisation et ses Applications,* pp. 407–416, Société Chimie Industrielle, Toulouse.

Lese, H. K. & Kermode, R. I. 1972 Heat Transfer from a Horizontal Tube to a Fluidized Bed in the Presence of Unheated Tubes, *Can. J. Chem. Eng.* 50:44–48.

Leung, L. S. & Jones, P. J. 1978 Flow of Gas-Solid Mixtures in Standpipes: A Review, *Powder Technol.* 20:145–160.

Leva, M. & Wen, C. Y. 1971 Elutriation, in *Fluidization,* eds. J. F. Davidson & D. C. Harrison, p. 627, Academic, New York.

Levenspiel, O. 1962 *Chemical Reaction Engineering,* Wiley, New York.

Levy, E., Martin, N., & Chen, J. 1978 Minimum Fluidization and Startup of a Centrifugal Fluidized Bed, in *Fluidization,* eds. J. F. Davidson & D. L. Keairns, pp. 71–75, Cambridge Univ. Press, Cambridge, England.

Lewis, W. K., Gilliland, E. R., & Glass, W. 1959 Solid-catalyzed Reaction in a Fluidized Bed, *AIChE J.* 5:419–426.

Lewis, W. K., Gilliland, E. R., & Lang, P. M. 1962 Entrainment from Fluidized Beds, *Chem. Eng. Prog. Symp. Ser.* 58(38):65–78.

Lim, C. J. 1975 Gas Residence Time Distribution and Related Flow Patterns in Spouted Beds, Ph.D. thesis, Univ. of British Columbia.

Lim, C. J. & Mathur, K. B. 1976 Flow Model for Gas Movement in Spouted Beds, *AIChE J.* 22:674–680.

Lim, C. J. & Mathur, K. B. 1978 Modelling of Particle Movement in Spouted Beds, in *Fluidization,* eds. J. F. Davidson & D. L. Keairns, pp. 104–109, Cambridge Univ. Press, Cambridge, England.

Littman, H., Morgan, M. H., Vukovic, D. V., Zdanski, F. K., & Grbavcic, Z. B. 1978 A Method for Predicting the Relationship between the Spout and Inlet Tube Radii in a Spouted Bed at Its Maximum Spoutable Height, in *Fluidization,* eds. J. F. Davidson & D. L. Keairns, pp. 381–386, Cambridge Univ. Press, Cambridge, England.

Locke, H. B., Lunn, H. G., Hoy, H. R., & Roberts, A. G. 1976 Fluidized Combustion in Great Britain–Environmentally Clean Steam and Power Generation from Coal, Heavy Oil and Dirty Fuels, *Proc. 4th Int. Conf. Fluidized-Bed Combustion,* pp. 69–92, Mitre Corp., McLean, Va.

Lockett, M. J. & Harrison, D. 1967 The Distribution of Voidage Fraction near Bubbles Rising in Gas-Fluidized Beds, *Proc. Int. Symp. Fluidization,* ed. A. A. H. Drinkenburg, pp. 257–267, Netherlands Univ. Press, Amsterdam.

Malek, M. A. & Lu, B. C. Y. 1964 Heat Transfer in Spouted Beds, *Can. J. Chem. Eng.* 42:14–20.

Mamuro, T. & Hattori, H. 1968 Flow Pattern of Fluid in Spouted Beds, *J. Chem. Eng. Jpn.* 1:1–5.

Mamuro, T. & Muchi, I. 1965 Mathematical Model for Fluidized Bed Catalytic Reactor, *Kogyo Kagaku Zasshi* 68:126.

Maskaev, V. K. & Baskakov, A. P. 1974 Features of External Heat Transfer in a Fluidized Bed of Coarse Particles, *Int. Chem. Eng.* 14:80–83.

Massimilla, L. 1971 Flow Properties of the Fluidized Dense Phase, in *Fluidization,* eds. J. F. Davidson & D. Harrison, pp. 651–676, Academic, New York.

Massimilla, L. & Johnstone, H. F. 1961 Reaction Kinetics in Fluidized Beds, *Chem. Eng. Sci.* 16:105–112.

Mathur, K. B. & Epstein, N. 1974 *Spouted Beds,* Academic, New York.

Mathur, K. B. & Gishler, P. E. 1955 A Technique for Contacting Gases with Coarse Solid Particles, *AIChE J.* 1:157–164.

Matsen, J. M. 1973 Evidence of Maximum Stable Bubble Size in a Fluidized Bed, *AIChE Symp. Ser.* 69(128):30–33.

May, W. G. 1959 Fluidized-Bed Reactor Studies, *Chem. Eng. Prog.* 55(12):49–56.

Meisen, A. & Mathur, K. B. 1978 Sulphur Coating of Fertilizer in a Spouted Bed, *CHISA '78,* paper C4.8, Prague.

Merrick, D. & Highley, J. 1972 Particle Size Reduction and Elutriation in a Fluidized Bed Process, *AIChE Symp. Ser.* 70(137):366–378.

Merry, J. M. D. 1971 Penetration of a Horizontal Gas Jet into a Fluidized Bed, *Trans. Inst. Chem. Eng.* 49:189–195.

Merry, J. M. D. 1975 Penetration of Vertical Jets into Fluidized Beds, *AIChE J.* 21:507–510.

Metcalfe, C. I. & Howard, J. R. 1978 Towards Higher Intensity Combustion-Rotating Fluidized Beds, in *Fluidization,* eds. J. F. Davidson & D. L. Keairns, pp. 276–279, Cambridge Univ. Press, Cambridge, England.

Mickley, H. S. & Fairbanks, D. F. 1955 Mechanism of Heat Transfer to Fluidized Beds, *AIChE J.* 1:374–384.

Mickley, H. S., Fairbanks, D. S., & Hawthorn, R. D. 1961 The Relation between the Transfer Coefficient and Thermal Fluctuations in Fluidized-Bed Heat Transfer, *Chem. Eng. Prog. Symp. Ser.* 57(32):51–60.

Miwa, K., Mori, S., Kato, T., & Muchi, I. 1972 Behaviour of Bubbles in Gaseous Fluidized Beds, *Int. Chem. Eng.* 12:187–194.

Mori, S. & Muchi, I. 1972 Theoretical Analysis of Catalytic Reaction in a Fluidized Bed, *J. Chem. Eng. Jpn.* 5:251–257.

Mori, S. & Wen, C. Y. 1975 Estimation of Bubble Diameter in Gaseous Fluidized Beds, *AIChE J.* 21:109–115.

Mori, S. & Wen, C. Y. 1976 Simulation of Fluidized Bed Reactor Performance by Modified Bubble Assemblage Model, in *Fluidization Technology,* ed. D. L. Keairns, vol. 1, pp. 179–203, Hemisphere, Washington, D.C.

Moss, G. 1976 The Chemically Active Fluidized Bed Gasifier, in *Fluidization Technology,* ed. D. L. Keairns, vol. 2, pp. 379–393, Hemisphere, Washington, D.C.

Muchi, I. 1965 Inclusive Two-Phase Model for Fluidized-Bed Reactors, *Mem. Fac. Eng. Nagoya Univ.* 17:79–89.

Murray, J. D. 1965 On the Mathematics of Fluidization: Steady Motion of Fully Developed Bubbles, *J. Fluid Mech.* 21:465–493.

Mutsers, S. M. P. & Rietema, K. 1977 The effect of Interparticle Forces on the Expansion of a Homogeneous Gas-Fluidized Bed, *Powder Technol.* 18:239–248.

Nack, H., Kiang, K. D., Liu, K. T., Murthy, K. S., Smithson, G. R., Jr., & Oxley, J. H. 1976 Fluidized-Bed Combustion Review, in *Fluidization Technology,* ed. D. L. Keairns, vol. 2, pp. 339–378, Hemisphere, Washington, D.C.

Nack, H., Weller, A. E., & Liu, K. T. 1977 Battelle's Multi-Solids Fluidized-Bed Combustion Process, *Proc. Fluidized Bed Combustion Technol. Exchange Workshop* 1:221–235.

Nakles, D. V., Massey, M. J., Forney, A. J., & Haynes, W. P. 1975 Influence of Synthane Gasifier Conditions on Effluent and Product Gas Production, *Pittsburgh Energy Research Center Rept.* PERC/RI-75/6.

Nelson, P. A. & Galloway, T. R. 1975 Particle to Fluid Heat and Mass Transfer in Dense Systems of Fine Particles, *Chem. Eng. Sci.* 30:1–6.

Newby, R. A. & Keairns, D. L. 1978 Fluidized Bed Heat Transport between Parallel, Horizontal Tube Bundles, in *Fluidization,* eds. J. F. Davidson & D. L. Keairns, pp. 320–326, Cambridge Univ. Press, Cambridge, England.

Nguyen, H. V. & Potter, O. E. 1974 Gas Mixing in Fluidized Beds as a Function of the Adsorbency of the Solids for the Gas, *Adv. Chem. Ser.* 133:290–300.

Nguyen, H. V. & Potter, O. E. 1976 Adsorption Effects in Fluidized Beds, in *Fluidization Technology,* ed. D. L. Keairns, vol. 2, pp. 193–200, Hemisphere, Washington, D.C.

Nguyen, T. H. & Grace, J. R. 1978 Forces on Objects Immersed in Fluidized Beds, *Powder Technol.* 19:255–264.

Nguyen, T. H., Johnsson, J. E., Clift, R., & Grace, J. R. 1976 Prediction of Bubble Distributions in Freely Bubbling Three-dimensional Fluidized Beds, in *Fluidization Technology,* ed. D. L. Keairns, vol. 1, pp. 205–214, Hemisphere, Washington, D.C.

Nicklin, D. J., Wilkes, J. O., & Davidson, J. F. 1962 Two-Phase Flow in Vertical Tubes, *Trans. Inst. Chem. Eng.* 40:61–68.

Noack, R. 1970 Lokaler Wärmeübergang an horizontalen Rohren in Wirbelschichten, *Chem. Ing. Tech.* 42:371–376.

O'Neill, B. K., Nicklin, D. J., Morgan, N. J., & Leung, L. S. 1972 The Hydrodynamics of Gas-Liquid Contacting in Towers with Fluidized Packings, *Can. J. Chem. Eng.* 50:595–601.

O'Neill, B. K., Nicklin, D. J., & Leung, L. S. 1974 Design Equations for the Fluidized Packing Contactor, in *La Fluidisation et ses Applications*, pp. 365–371, Société Chimie Industrielle, Toulouse.

O'Neill, E. P. & Keairns, D. L. 1977 Design Alternatives for Improved Sorbent Utilization (SO_2 Removal), in *Atmospheric Fluidized-Bed Combustion*, p. 1-1, Electric Power Research Institute, Palo Alto, Calif.

Orcutt, J. C., Davidson, J. F., & Pigford, R. L. 1962 Reaction Time Distributions in Fluidized Catalytic Reactors, *Chem. Eng. Prog. Symp. Ser.* 58(38):1–15.

Ostergaard, K. 1966 On the Growth of Air Bubbles Formed at a Single Orifice in a Water Fluidized Bed, *Chem. Eng. Sci.* 21:470–472.

Ostergaard, K. 1971 Three-Phase Fluidization, in *Fluidization*, eds. J. F. Davidson & D. Harrison, pp. 751–780, Academic, New York.

Page, R. E. & Harrison, D. 1972 The Size Distribution of Gas Bubbles Leaving a Three-Phase Fluidized Bed, *Powder Technol.* 6:245–249.

Page, R. E. & Harrison, D. 1973 Particle Entrainment from a Three-Phase Fluidized Bed, in *La Fluidisation et ses Applications*, pp. 393–406, Société Chimie Industrielle, Toulouse.

Partridge, B. A. & Rowe, P. N. 1966 Analysis of Gas Flow in a Bubbling Fluidized Bed when Cloud Formation Occurs, *Trans. Inst. Chem. Eng.* 44:349–358.

Partridge, B. A., Lyall, E., & Crooks, H. E. 1969 Particle Slip Surfaces in Bubbling Gas-fluidized Beds, *Powder Technol.* 2:301–305.

Patel, R. D. & Simpson, J. M. 1977 Heat Transfer in Aggregative and Particulate Liquid-fluidized Beds, *Chem. Eng. Sci.* 32:67–74.

Patterson, G. K. 1977 Studies of the Effects of Internals on the Fluidization Quality of Low-Density Solids, *AIChE Symp. Ser.* 73:59–63.

Petrie, S. J., Freeby, W. A., & Buckham, J. A. 1968 In-Bed Heat Exchangers, *Chem. Eng. Prog.* 64(7):45–51.

Pettigrew, C. K. 1966 Fluidized Bed Coating—Part 2 *Mod. Plast.* 44:111–156.

Piccinini, N. 1975 Coated Nuclear Fuel Particles, *Adv. Nucl. Sci. Technol.* 8:255–341.

Piccinini, N., Bernhard, A., Campagna, P., & Vallana, F. 1977 Segregation Phenomenon in Spouted Beds, *Can. J. Chem. Eng.* 55:122–125.

Piccinini, N., Grace, J. R., & Mathur, K. B. 1979 Vapour Phase Chemical Reaction in Spouted Beds: Verification of Theory, *Chem. Eng. Sci.* 34:1257–1263.

Potter, O. E. 1971 Mixing in *Fluidization*, eds. J. F. Davidson & D. Harrison, pp. 293–381, Academic, New York.

Priebe, S. J. & Genetti, W. E. 1977 Heat Transfer from a Horizontal Bundle of Extended Surface Tubes to an Air Fluidized Bed, *AIChE Symp. Ser.* 73(161):38–43.

Pyle, D. L. 1972 Fluidized Bed Reactors: A Review, *Adv. Chem. Ser.* 109:106–130.

Pyle, D. L. & Rose, P. L. 1965 Chemical Reaction in Bubbling Fluidized Beds, *Chem. Eng. Sci.* 20:25–31.

Raghuraman, J. & Varma, Y. B. G. 1972 Multistage Fluidization, *Chem. Process. Eng. (Bombay)* 53(7):48–50.

Ranz, W. E. 1952 Friction and Transfer Coefficients for Single Particles and Packed Beds, *Chem. Eng. Prog.* 48:247–253.

Ray, T. B. & Sarkar, S. 1976 Kinetics of Coal Pyrolysis in Spouted-Bed, *Indian Chem. Eng.* 18(2):11–19.

Rayner, J. W. R. 1952 Gasification by the Moving-Burden Technique, *J. Inst. Fuel* 25:50–59.

Reay, D. 1978 Particle Residence Time Distributions in Plug Flow Fluid Bed Dryers, *Proc. 1st Intern. Symp. Drying*, ed. A. S. Mujumdar, pp. 136–144, Science Press, Princeton.

Reh, L. 1971 Fluid Bed Processing, *Chem. Eng. Prog.* 67:58–63.

Reh, L., Schmidt, H. W., Ernst, J., & Rosenthal, K. H. 1974 Experience with the Calcination of Aluminum Trihydrate in a Circulating Fluid Bed, *AIME Meet.*, New York, TMS paper A71-14.

Rengarajan, R. 1978 Simulation of Fluidized Bed Coal Combustors, Ph.D. thesis, West Virginia Univ., Morgantown.

Riba, J. P., Routie, R., & Couderc, J. P. 1978 Mass Transfer from a Fixed Sphere to a Liquid in a Fluidized Bed, in *Fluidization,* eds. J. F. Davidson & D. L. Keairns, pp. 157–161, Cambridge Univ. Press, Cambridge, England.

Richardson, J. F. 1971 Incipient Fluidization and Particulate Systems, in *Fluidization,* eds. J. F. Davidson & D. Harrison, pp. 26–64, Academic, New York.

Richardson, J. F. & Meikle, R. A. 1961 Sedimentation and Fluidization: The Sedimentation of Uniform Fine Particles and of Two-Component Mixtures of Solids, *Trans. Inst. Chem. Eng.* 39:348–356.

Richardson, J. F. & Zaki, W. N. 1954 Sedimentation and Fluidization: Part I, *Trans. Inst. Chem. Eng.* 32:35–52.

Rietema, K. & Hoebink, J. 1976 Mass Transfer from Single Rising Bubble to the Dense Phase in Three Dimensional Fluidized Beds, in *Fluidization Technology,* ed D. L. Keairns, vol. 1, pp. 279–287, Hemisphere, Washington, D.C.

Rigby, G. R. & Capes, C. E. 1970 Bed Expansion and Bubble Wakes in Three-Phase Fluidization, *Can. J. Chem. Eng.,* 48:343–348.

Robinson, T., & Waldie, B. 1978 Particle Cycle Times in a Spouted Bed of Polydisperse Particles, *Can. J. Chem. Eng.* 56:632–635.

Robison, E. B. 1972 Study of the Characterization and Control of Air Pollutants from a Fluidized-Bed Combustion Unit, the Carbon Burnup Cell, *Pope, Evans and Robbins Rept.* PB 210-828, New York.

Romankov, P. G. 1971 Drying, in *Fluidization,* eds. J. F. Davidson & D. Harrison, p. 569, Academic, New York.

Romero, J. B. & Johanson, L. N. 1962 Factors Affecting Fluidized Bed Quality, *Chem. Eng. Prog. Symp. Ser.* 58(38):28–37.

Rosenweig, R. E. 1979 Fluidization: Hydrodynamic Stabilization with a Magnetic Field, *Science* 204:57–59.

Rowe, P. N. 1962 The Effect of Bubbles on Gas-Solids Contacting in Fluidized Beds, *Chem. Eng. Prog. Symp. Ser.* 58:42–56.

Rowe, P. N. 1964 A Note on the Motion of a Bubble Rising through a Fluidized Bed, *Chem. Eng. Sci.* 19:75–77.

Rowe, P. N. 1967 A Personal View of Fluidization in 1967, *Proc. Int. Symp. Fluidization,* ed. A. A. H. Drinkenburg, pp. 11–20, Netherlands Univ. Press, Amsterdam.

Rowe, P. N. 1971 Experimental Properties of Bubbles, in *Fluidization,* eds. J. F. Davidson & D. Harrison, pp. 121–192, Academic, New York.

Rowe, P. N. 1972 Fluidized Bed Reactors, *Proc. 2d Int. Symp. Chem. Reaction Eng.,* p. A9, Elsevier, Amsterdam.

Rowe, P. N. 1973 Estimation of Solids Circulation Rate in a Bubbling Fluidized Bed, *Chem. Eng. Sci.* 28:979–980.

Rowe, P. N. 1975 Particle to Liquid Mass Transfer in Fluidized Beds, *Chem. Eng. Sci.* 30:7–9.

Rowe, P. N. & Everett, D. J. 1972 Fluidized Bed Bubbles Viewed by X-rays, *Trans. Inst. Chem. Eng.* 50:42–48.

Rowe, P. N. & Nienow, A. W. 1975 Minimum Fluidization Velocity of Multicomponent Particle Mixtures, *Chem. Eng. Sci.* 30:1365–1369.

Rowe, P. N. & Nienow, A. W. 1976 Particle Mixing and Segregation in Gas Fluidized Beds: A Review, *Powder Technol.* 15:141–147.

Rowe, P. N. & Partridge, B. A. 1965 An X-ray Study of Bubbles in Fluidized Beds, *Trans. Inst. Chem. Eng.* 43:157–175.

Rowe, P. N., Partridge, B. A., & Lyall, E. 1964 Cloud Formation around Bubbles in Fluidized Beds, *Chem. Eng. Sci.* 19:973–985.

Rowe, P. N., Nienow, A. W., & Agbim, A. J. 1972 A Preliminary Quantitative Study of Particle Segregation in Gas Fluidized Beds—Binary Systems of Near Spherical Particles, *Trans. Inst. Chem. Eng.* 50:324–333.

Ruth, L. A. 1976 Regeneration of $CaSO_4$ in Fluid Bed Combustion, *Proc. 4th Int. Conf. Fluidized-Bed Combustion,* pp. 425–438, Mitre Corp., McLean, Va.

Sandstrom, W. A., Rehmat, A. G., & Bair, W. G. 1977 *Coal Processing Technology,* vol. 3, p. 180, American Institute of Chemical Engineers, New York.

Saxena, S. C., Grewal, N. S., Gabor, J. D., Zabrodsky, S. S., & Galershtein, D. M. 1978 Heat Transfer between a Gas Fluidized Bed and Immersed Tubes, *Adv. Heat Transfer* 14:149–247.

Schiller, L. & Naumann, A. 1935 A Drag Coefficient Correlation, *Z. Ver. Dtsch. Ing.* 77:318–320.

Schlünder, E. U. 1971 Wärmeübergang an bewegte Kugelschüttungen bei kurzfristigem Kontalet, *Chem. Ing. Tech.* 43:651–654.

Schugerl, K., Merz, M., & Fetting, F. 1961 Rheologische Eigenschaften von gasdurchströmten Fliessbettsystemen, *Chem. Eng. Sci.* 5:1–38.

Selzer, V. W. & Thomson, W. J. 1977 Fluidized Bed Heat Transfer–The Packet Theory Revisited, *AIChE Symp. Ser.* 73(161):29–37.

Shaw, I. D., Hoffman, T. W., & Reilly, P. M. 1974 Experimental Evaluation of Two-Phase Models Describing Catalytic Fluidized-Bed Reactors, *AIChE Symp. Ser.* 70:41–52.

Shen, C. Y. & Johnstone, H. F. 1955 Gas-Solid Contact in Fluidized Beds, *AIChE J.* 1:349–354.

Shine, N. B. 1971 Fluohmic Process of Hydrogen Cyanide, *Chem. Eng. Prog.* 67(2):52–57.

Smiley, S. H. 1961 Gas-Solids Reactors in Uranium Processing: A Critical Review, *Prog. Nucl. Energy Ser. 4* 4:191–278.

Squires, A. M. 1974 Clean Fuels from Coal Gasification, *Science* 184:340–346.

Staffin, H. K. & Choongnam, K. 1972 Calibration of Temperature Sensors Between 538°C and 1092°C in Air Fluidized Solids, in *Temperature: Its Measurement and Control in Science and Industry,* ed. H. H. Plumb, vol. 4, pt. 2, pp. 1359–1368, Instrument Society of America.

Staub, F. W. & Canada, G. S. 1978 Effect of Tube Bank and Gas Density on Flow Behaviour and Heat Transfer in Fluidized Beds, in *Fluidization,* eds. J. F. Davidson & D. L. Keairns, pp. 339–344, Cambridge Univ. Press, Cambridge, England.

Stern, K. H. & Weise, E. L. 1966 *High Temperature Properties and Deposition of Inorganic Salts, pt. 1, Sulfates,* Standard Reference Data Series, National Bureau of Standards, Washington, D.C.

Stewart, P. S. B. 1968 Isolated Bubbles in Fluidized Beds–Theory and Experiment, *Trans. Inst. Chem. Eng.* 46:60–66.

Stewart, P. S. B. & Davidson, J. F. 1964 Three-Phase Fluidization: Water, Particles and Air, *Chem. Eng. Sci.* 19:319–321.

Stewart, P. S. B. & Davidson, J. F. 1967 Slug Flow in Fluidized Beds, *Powder Technol.* 1:61–80.

Streeter, R. C. 1977 Recent Development in Fluidized-Bed Methanation Research, *Proc. 9th Synthetic Pipeline Gas Symp.,* pp. 151–166, American Gas Association, Chicago, Ill.

Sunkoori, N. R. & Kaparthi, R. 1960 Heat Transfer Studies Between Particles and Liquid Medium in a Fluidized Bed, *Chem. Eng. Sci.* 12:166–174.

Sutherland, J. P., Vassilatos, G., Kubota, H., & Osberg, G. L. 1963 The Effect of Packing on a Fluidized Bed, *AIChE J.* 9:437–441.

Syromyatnikov, N. I. 1974 The Theory of External Heat Transfer in a Fluidized Bed, *Int. Chem. Eng.* 14:483–485.

Szekely, J. & Fisher, R. J. 1969 Bed to Wall Radiation Heat Transfer in a Gas-Solid Fluidized Bed, *Chem. Eng. Sci.* 24:833–849.

Theys, L. F. & Lee, L. V. 1958 Union Miniere Successfully Solubilizes Copper-Cobalt Sulfide Concentrates by Sulfate Roasting, *J. Met.* 10:134–136.

Thiel, W. J. & Potter, O. E. 1977 Slugging in Fluidized Beds, *Ind. Eng. Chem. Fundam.* 16:242–247.

Thiel, W. J. & Potter, O. E. 1978 The Mixing of Solids in Slugging Gas Fluidized Beds, *AIChE J.* 24:561–569.

Thoumesm, F. J. & Coussement, R. 1964 Fluid Bed Roasting Reactions of Copper and Cobalt Sulfide Concentrates, *J. Met.* 10:831–834.

Toei, R., Matsuno, R., Miyagawa, H., Nishitani, K., & Komagawa, Y. 1969 Gas Transfer between a Bubble and the Continuous Phase in a Gas-Solid Fluidized Bed, *Ind. Chem. Eng.* 9:358–364.

Toor, F. D. & Calderbank, P. H. 1967 Reaction Kinetics in Gas-fluidized Catalyst Beds, Part II, Mathematical Models, *Proc. Int. Symp. Fluidization,* ed. A. A. H. Drinkenburg, p. 373, Netherlands Univ. Press, Amsterdam.

Tuot, J. & Clift, R. 1973 Heat Transfer around Single Bubbles in a Two-dimensional Fluidized Bed, *AIChE Symp. Ser.* 69:78–84.

Uemaki, O. & Mathur, K. B. 1976 Granulation of Ammonium Sulfate Fertilizer in a Spouted Bed, *Ind. Eng. Chem. Process Des. Dev.* 15:504–508.

Uemaki, O., Fujikawa, M., & Kugo, M. 1977 Cracking of Residual Oil by Use of a Dual Spouted Bed Reactor with Three Chambers, *Sekiyu Gakkai Shi* 20(5):410–415.

Uysal, B. Z. 1978 Hydrodynamics and Particulate Recovery Studies in Mobile Bed Contacting, Ph.D. thesis, McGill Univ., Montreal.

Van Deemter, J. J. 1961 Mixing and Contacting in Gas-Solid Fluidized Beds, *Chem. Eng. Sci.* 13:143–154.

Vanecek, V., Markvart, M., & Drbotilav, R. 1966 *Fluidized Bed Drying,* Hill, London.

Van Swaaij, W. P. M. 1978 The Design of Gas-Solids Fluid Bed and Related Reactors, in *Chemical Reaction Engineering Review,* eds. D. Luss & V. W. Weekman, Jr., p. 193–222, American Chemical Society, Washington, D.C.

Van Swaaij, W. P. M. & Zuiderweg, F. J. 1973 The Design of Gas-Solid Fluidized Beds—Prediction of Chemical Conversion, *Proc. Int. Symp. Fluidization,* p. 454, Société Chimie Industrielle, Toulouse.

Varma, Y. B. G. 1975 Pressure Drop of the Fluid and the Flow Patterns of the Phases in Multistage Fluidization, *Powder Technol.* 12:167–174.

Vaux, W. G. & Newby, R. A. 1978 Wear on Tubes by Jet Impingement in a Fluidized Bed, *Powder Technol.* 19:79–88.

Verloop, J. & Heertjes, P. M. 1974 On the Origin of Bubbles in Gas-fluidized Beds, *Chem. Eng. Sci.* 29:1101–1107.

Virr, M. J. 1976 Commercialization of Small Scale Fluidized Combustion Techniques, *Proc. 4th Int. Conf. Fluidized-Bed Combustion,* pp. 631–648, Mitre Corp., McLean, Va.

Voice, E. H. 1974 Coatings of Pyrocarbon and Silicon Carbide by Chemical Vapour Deposition, *Chem. Eng. (London),* December, pp. 785–792.

Volk, W., Johnson, C. A., & Stotler, H. H. 1962 Effect of Reactor Internals on Quality of Fluidization, *Chem. Eng. Prog.* 58(3):44–47.

Vreedenburg, H. A. 1952 Heat Transfer between Fluidized Beds and Vertically Inserted Tubes, *J. Appl. Chem.* 2:S26–S33.

Vreedenburg, H. A. 1958 Heat Transfer between a Fluidized Bed and a Horizontal Tube, *Chem. Eng. Sci.* 9:52–60.

Vreedenburg, H. A. 1960 Heat Transfer between a Fluidized Bed and a Vertical Tube, *Chem. Eng. Sci.* 11:274–285.

Vucović, D. V., Zdanski, F. K., & Littman, H. 1975 Present Status of the Theory and Application of Spouted Bed Technique, *CHISA '75,* paper D2.20, Prague.

Wall, C. J. & Ash, W. J. 1949 Fluid Solid Air Sizer and Dryer, *Ind. Eng. Chem.* 41:1247–1249.

Wallis, G. B. 1969 *One-dimensional Two-Phase Flow,* McGraw-Hill, New York.

Wen, C. Y. 1968 Noncatalytic Heterogeneous Solid-Fluid Reaction Models, *Ind. Eng. Chem.* 60(9):34–54.

Wen, C. Y. & Chang, T. M. 1967 Particle-to-Particle Heat Transfer in Air-fluidized Beds, *Proc. Int. Symp. Fluidization,* ed. A. A. H. Drinkenburg, pp. 491–506, Netherlands Univ. Press, Amsterdam.

Wen, C. Y. & Fan, L. T. 1975 *Models for Flow Systems and Chemical Reactors,* pp. 150–167, Dekker, New York.

Wen, C. Y. & Hashinger, R. F. 1960 Elutriation of Solid Particles from a Dense Phase Fluidized Bed, *AIChE J.* 6:220–226.

Wen, C. Y. & Leva, M. 1956 Fluidized Bed Heat Transfer: A Generalized Dense-Phase Correlation, *AIChE J.* 2:482–488.

Wen, C. Y. & Yu, Y. H. 1966a Mechanics of Fluidization, *Chem. Eng. Prog. Symp. Ser.* 62(62):100–111.

Wen, C. Y. & Yu, Y. H. 1966b a Generalized Method for Predicting the Minimum Fluidization Velocity, *AIChE J.* 12:610–612.

Wen, C. Y., Krishnan, R., Khosravi, R., & Dutta, S. 1978 Dead Zone Heights near the Grid of

Fluidized Beds, in *Fluidization,* eds. J. F. Davidson & D. L. Keairns, pp. 32–37, Cambridge Univ. Press, Cambridge, England.

Wender, L. & Cooper, G. T. 1958 Heat Transfer between Fluidized-Solids Beds and Boundary Surfaces–Correlation of Data, *AIChE J.* 4:15–23.

Werther, J. 1974 The Influence of the Bed Diameter on the Hydrodynamics of Fluidized Beds, *AIChE Symp. Ser.* 70(141):53–62.

Whitehead, A. B. 1971 Some Problems in Large-Scale Fluidized Beds, in *Fluidization,* eds. J. F. Davidson & D. Harrison, pp. 781–814, Academic, New York.

Whitehead, A. B., Gartside, G., & Dent, D. C. 1976 Fluidization Studies in Large Gas-Solid Systems: The Effect of Bed Depth and Fluidizing Velocity on Solids Circulation Patterns, *Powder Technol.* 14:61–70.

Wilhelm, R. H. & Kwauk, M. 1948 Fluidization of Solid Particles, *Chem. Eng. Prog.* 44:201–217.

Wilkins, G. S. & Thodos, G. 1969 Mass Transfer Driving Forces in Packed and Fluidized Beds, *AIChE J.* 15:47–50.

Wilson, J., Bailey, R., & Cunningham, A. J. 1976 Residence Times of Solids in a 3.3 m Fluidized-Bed Carbonizer, *J. Inst. Fuel* 49(401):171–183.

Wittman, T. J., McCabe, D. J., & Eifert, M. C. 1975 A Technical, Environmental and Economic Evaluation of the "Wet Processing System for the Recovery and Disposal of Municipal Solid Waste," *Systems Technology Corp. Rept.,* Xenia, Ohio, under EPA contract 68-01-2211.

Xavier, A. M. & Davidson, J. A. 1978 Heat Transfer to Surfaces Immersed in Fluidized Beds, Particularly Tube Arrays, in *Fluidization,* eds. J. F. Davidson & D. L. Keairns, pp. 333–338, Cambridge Univ. Press, Cambridge, England.

Yagi, S. & Kunii, D. 1961 Fluidized-Solids Reactors with Continuous Solids Feed. I. Residence Time of Particles in Fluidized Beds, *Chem. Eng. Sci.* 16:364–371.

Yang, W. C. & Keairns, D. L. 1976 Comparison of Recirculating Fluidized Bed Performance in Two-dimensional and Three-dimensional Beds, in *Fluidization Technology,* ed. D. L. Keairns, vol. 2, pp. 51–64, Hemisphere, Washington, D.C.

Yates, J. G. & Rowe, P. N. 1977 A Model for Chemical Reaction in the Freeboard Region above a Fluidized Bed, *Trans. Inst. Chem. Eng.* 55:137–142.

Yerushalmi, J. 1977 Fluid Bed Processing of Agglomerating Coals, in *Coal Processing,* vol. 3, pp. 156–165, American Institute of Chemical Engineers, New York.

Yerushalmi, J. & Cankurt, N. T. 1978 High Velocity Fluid Beds, *Chem. Technol.* 8:564–572.

Yerushalmi, J. & Cankurt, N. T. 1979 Further Studies of the Regimes of Fluidization, *Powder Technol.* 24:187–205.

Yerushalmi, J., Kolodney, M., Graff, R. A., Squires, A. M., & Harvey, R. D. 1975 Agglomeration of Ash in Fluidized Beds Gasifying Coal: The Godel Phenomenon, *Science* 187:646–650.

Yerushalmi, J., Turner, D. H., & Squires, A. M. 1976 The Fast Fluidized Bed, *Ind. Eng. Chem. Process Des. Dev.* 15:47–53.

Yerushalmi, J., Cankurt, N. T., Geldart, D., & Liss, B. 1978a Flow Regimes in Vertical Gas-Solid Contact Systems, *AIChE Symp. Ser.* 74(176):1–13.

Yerushalmi, J., Ehrlich, S., Maaghoul, M., & Lund, T. E. 1978b Apparatus and Method for Combusting Carbonaceous Fuels Employing in Tandem a Fast Bed Boiler and a Slow Boiler, U.S. Patent 4,103,646.

Yoon, P. & Thodos, G. 1973 Gas-Solid Fluidized Systems: Average Mass Transfer Potentials of Shallow Beds, *AIChE J.* 19:625–628.

Yoshida, K. & Kunii, D. 1968 Stimulus and Response of Gas Concentration in Bubbling Fluidized Beds, *J. Chem. Eng. Jpn.* 1:11–16.

Yoshida, K. & Wen, C. Y. 1970 Noncatalytic Solid-Gas Reaction in a Fluidized Bed Reactor, *Chem. Eng. Sci.* 25:1395–1404.

Yoshida, K. & Wen, C. Y. 1971 Behavior of Fluidized Beds Based on the Bubble Assemblage Model, *AIChE Symp. Ser.* 67:151–158.

Yoshida, K., Kunii, D., & Levenspiel, O. 1969 Heat Transfer Mechanisms between Wall Surface and Fluidized Bed, *Int. J. Heat Mass Transfer* 12:529–536.

Yoshida, K., Ueno, T., & Kunii, D. 1974 Mechanism of Bed-Wall Heat Transfer in a Fluidized Bed at High Temperatures, *Chem. Eng. Sci.* 29:77–82.

Young, D. T. 1977 Fluidized Combustion of Beds of Large Dense Particles in Reprocessing HTGR Fuel, *AIChE 70th Annu. Meet.,* paper 80c.

Zabrodsky, S. S. 1966 *Hydrodynamics and Heat Transfer in Fluidized Beds,* M.I.T. Press, Cambridge, Mass.

Zabrodsky, S. S. & Mikhailik, V. D. 1967 The Heat Exchange of the Spouted Bed with a Submerged Heating Surface, cited in Mathur & Epstein (1974).

Zabrodsky, S. S., Borodulya, V. A., & Dikalenko, V. I. 1972 Noncatalytic Reaction Gas-Phase Reaction in a Fluidized Bed, *Proc. Int. Symp. Fluidization,* pp. 488–500, Société Chimie Industrielle, Toulouse.

Zabrodsky, S. S., Antonishin, N. V., & Parnas, A. L. 1976 On Fluidized Bed-to-Surface Heat Transfer, *Can. J. Chem. Eng.* 54:52–58.

Zabrodsky, S. S., Epanov, Y. G., & Galershtein, D. M. 1978 On the Dependence of Fluidized Bed-Wall Heat Transfer Coefficients on the Thermal Conductivity and Volumetric Heat Capacity of the Particles, in *Fluidization,* eds. J. F. Davidson & D. L. Keairns, pp. 362–370, Cambridge Univ. Press, Cambridge, England.

Zenz, F. A. 1968 Bubble Formation and Grid Design, *Tripartite Chem. Eng. Conf. Symp. Fluidization,* session 1, p. 136, Institution of Chemical Engineers, London.

Zenz, F. A. 1977 How Flow Phenomena Affect Design of Fluidized Beds, *Chem. Eng. (N.Y.)* 84(27):81–91.

Zenz, F. A. & Othmer, D. F. 1960 *Fluidization and Fluid-Particle Systems,* Reinhold, New York.

Zenz, F. A. & Weil, N. A. 1958 A Theoretical-Empirical Approach to Mechanism of Particle Entrainment from Fluidized Beds, *AIChE J.* 4:472–479.

Zubrzycki, B. J. 1963 Application of Fluidization to Production of Alumina, in *Extractive Metallurgy of Aluminum,* eds. I. G. Gerard & P. T. Stroup, pp. 272–284, Interscience, New York.

9 SEPARATION

Subject coordinators: *Douglas W. Cooper and Mark P. Freeman*

9.1 Introduction

Mark P. Freeman and Douglas W. Cooper

This chapter is meant to be an introduction in depth to the principles and theoretical bases of separation of multiphase systems. It defines the vocabulary and concepts for the interested nonspecialist while, at the same time, many facets are explored in sufficient depth to serve as a handy reference for those skilled in the art.

9.1.1 DEFINITION

A separation unit operation is an assemblage of equipment that splits a feed material into two or more fractions that differ in the relative amounts of the constituents. This ubiquitous problem is present in almost every phase of industrial material processing, from upgrading and concentrating the source minerals to cleaning up gases and water that are to be reused or discharged into the environment. It is just as important in the laboratory, but there one can work with small volumes and take whatever time is necessary, so that it is much less apt to appear as a major problem.

It would be pointless to attempt to enumerate all the different physical separation schemes employed. Indeed, we shall ignore the whole important field of the dry separation of two or more solid materials, and concentrate on suspensions of solids and liquids (but not gases) in a carrier fluid. This still leaves us with a plethora of unit operations.

9.1.2 GAS VERSUS LIQUID

There seems to be little purpose in preserving generality, and so the chapter is divided into two parts according to whether the carrier is a gas (section 9.2) or a liquid (section 9.3 and 9.4). However, before we split them apart it will be instructive to say a little about the practical differences that, for all intents and purposes, make these two fields "immiscible."

The first difference is volumetric flow rate. The engineer designing a sewage solids separation for a municipality of, say, 100,000 people is designing a large-scale process accommodating 50,000 m^3/day or about 35 m^3/min. The engineer harvesting solids from a gas in material process recovery is frequently confronted with flows of 3000 m^3/min, two orders of magnitude larger. Whatever is to be done must thus be done in a small fraction of the time.

Related to this flow rate problem is the fact that, because of time constraints, the person cleaning a gas stream must remove the material as it exists. Thus the process must be tailored to accommodate particles of all sizes, and particle size distributions are of paramount importance. Common practice in liquid-solid separations, on the other hand, involve "flocculation" and "coagulation," where the material is agglomerated to facilitate its response to the separation forces. Primary particle size distributions of the feed for liquid-solid separations, although they may one day be important to people designing flocculents, for example, have thus far proved to be of only academic interest (except, of course, for classification).

A final though less clear-cut distinction is that in solid-liquid or liquid-liquid mixtures, separation may be the last thing one wants. Thus a whole science of making "stable" suspensions has developed that is clearly related to the separation problem, but which is not at all paralleled by developments in gas-phase technology.

9.2 Gas-Particle Separation

9.2.1 INTRODUCTION

Douglas W. Cooper

9.2.1.1 Scope

The removal of fine particles from a gas stream is important in air pollution control, in certain industrial processes, and in particulate sampling from a gas stream. In general, the value of a system for gas-particle separation depends on its effectiveness and cost. In this section the major emphasis is on air pollution control, although much of the information is applicable to process material recovery and gas sampling.

9.2.1.2 Gas Flow

Consider gas flow through channels or around obstacles. The primary determinants of gas behavior are the geometry of the system and the Reynolds number:

$$\text{Re} = \frac{\rho_G U_G D}{\mu_G} \qquad [9.2.1]$$

where ρ_G is the gas density, U_G is the gas superficial velocity, D is the diameter of the duct, and μ_G is the dynamic viscosity of the gas. For flow through a straight, smooth tube, it is well-known that the flow goes from laminar to sinuous to turbulent as the Reynolds number increases, with the transition to turbulence occurring approximately for $\text{Re} > 2 \times 10^3$. For flow past objects, formation of an eddying wake and finally a turbulent wake is the result of increasing Re, with the onset of turbulence occurring generally at $\text{Re} \ll 10^3$ (D becomes the obstacle diameter).

The power consumed by a control device has as one of its elements the product of the volume rate of flow through the device $\dot{V}_G$ and the (static) pressure drop across the device Δp. For the same geometry, increasing the Reynolds number (by increasing the flow rate) produces a transition from laminar to turbulent flow, for which the pressure drop becomes proportional to the square of the mean gas velocity rather than being proportional to the mean gas velocity. For virtually all industrial air pollution control devices, one is dealing with turbulent flow in the ducting and plenums.

9.2.1.3 Collection Efficiency

The total mass collection efficiency (often called *total efficiency*) is the difference between the inlet mass flux $\dot{M}_1$ and the outlet mass flux $\dot{M}$, divided by the inlet mass flux:

$$E = \frac{\dot{M}_1 - \dot{M}}{\dot{M}_1} \qquad [9.2.2]$$

The total penetration is just $\dot{M}/\dot{M}_1$; it is the fraction of the mass that penetrates the device, often more important than the efficiency for comparing devices. The efficiency for a particular particle size i (or narrow size range) is called the *fractional efficiency* and is

$$E_i = \frac{(\dot{M}_1 - \dot{M})_i}{(\dot{M}_1)_i} \qquad [9.2.3]$$

To compare gas-particle separation devices, one generally needs their fractional efficiencies over the particle size range of interest. If the fractions of aerosol mass in each size interval are denoted by F_i, then

$$E = \sum_i E_i F_i \qquad [9.2.4]$$

Elsewhere in this chapter equations are given for calculating collection efficiencies for various devices and collection mechanisms. Table 9.2.1 gives calculated values of some of the most important aerosol quantities. (The particles are assumed to be spheres of the density of water. The bases for calculating the values are given in the table). The sedimentation velocities, terminal-settling-velocity Reynolds numbers, mobilities, and relaxation times are given with and without the slip corrections appropriate to air at 20°C and pressure of 1 bar.

One of the uncertainties in the design and analysis of a gas-particle separation system is the degree of mixing to be expected. Assume that one has a collection surface area A in a long duct and can apply a force to the particles which makes them migrate toward this area at velocity U_p^* perpendicular to the mean gas velocity. For no mixing (laminar flow), the penetration is

$$\text{Pt} = 1 - \frac{U_p^* A}{\dot{V}_G} \qquad [9.2.5]$$

If there is mixing only perpendicular to the mean gas flow (the usual assumption for analyzing such devices), the penetration is

$$\text{Pt} = e^{-U_p^* A / \dot{V}_G} \qquad [9.2.6]$$

Table 9.2.1 Tabulated Values for Use in Aerosol Physics for Unit Density Spheres[a,b,c]

Particle diameter (μm)	Slip correction factor	Sedimentation velocity (cm/s)	Corrected sedimentation velocity (cm/s)	Reynolds number, terminal velocity	Diffusion coefficient (cm²/s)	Corrected diffusion coefficient (cm²/s)	Mobility (s/g)	Corrected mobility (s/g)	Relaxation time (s)	Corrected relaxation time (s)
0.001	2.1697 + 02	3.0110 − 09	6.5330 − 07	2.0046 − 15	2.3545 − 04	5.1084 − 02	5.8620 + 09	1.2719 + 12	3.0694 − 12	6.6595 − 10
0.002	1.0877 + 02	1.2044 − 08	1.3100 − 06	1.6037 − 14	1.1772 − 04	1.2804 − 02	2.9310 + 09	3.1880 + 11	1.2277 − 11	1.3354 − 09
0.003	7.2700 + 01	2.7099 − 08	1.9701 − 06	5.4124 − 14	7.8482 − 05	5.7057 − 03	1.9540 + 09	1.4206 + 11	2.7624 − 11	2.0083 − 09
0.004	5.4668 + 01	4.8177 − 08	2.6337 − 06	1.2829 − 13	5.8861 − 05	3.2179 − 03	1.4655 + 09	8.0117 + 10	4.9110 − 11	2.6848 − 09
0.005	4.3850 + 01	7.5276 − 08	3.3009 − 06	2.5057 − 13	4.7089 − 05	2.0649 − 03	1.1724 + 09	5.1410 + 10	7.6734 − 11	3.3648 − 09
0.006	3.6638 + 01	1.0840 − 07	3.9715 − 06	4.3299 − 13	3.9241 − 05	1.4377 − 03	9.7701 + 08	3.5796 + 10	1.1050 − 10	4.0484 − 09
0.007	3.1488 + 01	1.4754 − 07	4.6457 − 06	6.8758 − 13	3.3635 − 05	1.0591 − 03	8.3744 + 08	2.6369 + 10	1.5040 − 10	4.7357 − 09
0.008	2.7625 + 01	1.9271 − 07	5.3235 − 06	1.0264 − 12	2.9431 − 05	8.1302 − 04	7.3276 + 08	2.0242 + 10	1.9644 − 10	5.4266 − 09
0.009	2.4621 + 01	2.4390 − 07	6.0050 − 06	1.4513 − 12	2.6161 − 05	6.4411 − 04	6.5134 + 08	1.6037 + 10	2.4862 − 10	6.1213 − 09
0.01	2.2218 + 01	3.0110 − 07	6.6901 − 06	2.0346 − 12	2.3545 − 05	5.2312 − 04	5.8620 + 08	1.3025 + 10	3.0694 − 10	6.8197 − 09
0.02	1.1415 + 01	1.2044 − 06	1.3749 − 05	1.6037 − 11	1.1772 − 05	1.3438 − 04	2.9310 + 08	3.3458 + 09	1.2277 − 09	1.4015 − 08
0.03	7.8247 + 00	2.7099 − 06	2.1204 − 05	5.4124 − 11	7.8482 − 06	6.1409 − 05	1.9540 + 08	1.5290 + 09	2.7624 − 09	2.1615 − 08
0.04	6.0366 + 00	4.8177 − 06	2.9082 − 05	1.2829 − 10	5.8861 − 06	3.5532 − 05	1.4655 + 08	8.8466 + 08	4.9110 − 09	2.9645 − 08
0.05	4.9690 + 00	7.5276 − 06	3.7405 − 05	2.5057 − 10	4.7089 − 06	2.3399 − 05	1.1724 + 08	5.8257 + 08	7.6734 − 09	3.8129 − 08
0.06	4.2613 + 00	1.0840 − 05	4.6192 − 05	4.3299 − 10	3.9241 − 06	1.6722 − 05	9.7701 + 07	4.1634 + 08	1.1050 − 08	4.7087 − 08
0.07	3.7591 + 00	1.4754 − 05	5.5462 − 05	6.8758 − 10	3.3635 − 06	1.2644 − 05	8.3744 + 07	3.1480 + 08	1.5040 − 08	5.6536 − 08
0.08	3.3849 + 00	1.9271 − 05	6.5230 − 05	1.0264 − 09	2.9431 − 06	9.9621 − 06	7.3276 + 07	2.4803 + 08	1.9644 − 08	6.6493 − 08
0.09	3.0960 + 00	2.4390 − 05	7.5511 − 05	1.4613 − 09	2.6161 − 06	8.0994 − 06	6.5134 + 07	2.0166 + 08	2.4862 − 08	7.6973 − 08
0.1	2.8667 + 00	3.0110 − 05	8.6316 − 05	2.0046 − 09	2.3545 − 06	6.7494 − 06	5.8620 + 07	1.6804 + 08	3.0694 − 08	8.7988 − 08
0.2	1.8693 + 00	1.2044 − 04	2.2514 − 04	1.6037 − 08	1.1772 − 06	2.2006 − 06	2.9310 + 07	5.4789 + 07	1.2277 − 07	2.2950 − 07
0.3	1.5611 + 00	2.7099 − 04	4.2306 − 04	5.4124 − 08	7.8482 − 07	1.2252 − 06	1.9540 + 07	3.0505 + 07	2.7624 − 07	4.3125 − 07
0.4	1.4149 + 00	4.8177 − 04	6.8166 − 04	1.2829 − 07	5.8861 − 07	8.3283 − 07	1.4655 + 07	2.0736 + 07	4.9110 − 07	6.9486 − 07
0.5	1.3299 + 00	7.5276 − 04	1.0011 − 03	2.5057 − 07	4.7089 − 07	6.2623 − 07	1.1724 + 07	1.5592 + 07	7.6734 − 07	1.0205 − 06
0.6	1.2742 + 00	1.0840 − 03	1.3812 − 03	4.3299 − 07	3.9241 − 07	4.9999 − 07	9.7701 + 06	1.2449 + 07	1.1050 − 06	1.4079 − 06
0.7	1.2347 + 00	1.4754 − 03	1.8217 − 03	6.8758 − 07	3.3635 − 07	4.1530 − 07	8.3744 + 06	1.0340 + 07	1.5040 − 06	1.8570 − 06
0.8	1.2053 + 00	1.9271 − 03	2.3227 − 03	1.0264 − 06	2.9431 − 07	3.5472 − 07	7.3276 + 06	8.8318 + 06	1.9644 − 06	2.3677 − 06
0.9	1.1824 + 00	2.4390 − 03	2.8839 − 03	1.4613 − 06	2.6161 − 07	3.0933 − 07	6.5134 + 06	7.7017 + 06	2.4862 − 06	2.9398 − 06

(See footnotes on page 9–10.)

Table 9.2.1 Tabulated Values for Use in Aerosol Physics for Unit Density Spheres[a,b,c] (Continued)

Particle diameter (μm)	Slip correction factor	Sedimentation velocity (cm/s)	Corrected sedimentation velocity (cm/s)	Reynolds number, terminal velocity	Diffusion coefficient (cm²/s)	Corrected diffusion coefficient (cm²/s)	Mobility (s/g)	Corrected mobility (s/g)	Relaxation time (s)	Corrected relaxation time (s)
1	1.1642 + 00	3.0110 − 03	3.5054 − 03	2.0046 − 06	2.3545 − 07	2.7410 − 07	5.8620 + 06	6.8245 + 06	3.0694 − 06	3.5733 − 06
2	1.0821 + 00	1.2044 − 02	1.3033 − 02	1.6037 − 05	1.1772 − 07	1.2739 − 07	2.9310 + 06	3.1716 + 06	1.2277 − 05	1.3285 − 05
3	1.0547 + 00	2.7099 − 02	2.8582 − 02	5.4124 − 05	7.8482 − 08	8.2777 − 08	1.9540 + 06	2.0609 + 06	2.7624 − 05	2.9136 − 05
4	1.0410 + 00	4.8177 − 02	5.0154 − 02	1.2829 − 04	5.8861 − 08	6.1277 − 08	1.4655 + 06	1.5257 + 06	4.9110 − 05	5.1125 − 05
5	1.0328 + 00	7.5276 − 02	7.7748 − 02	2.5057 − 04	4.7089 − 08	4.8635 − 08	1.1724 + 06	1.2109 + 06	7.6734 − 05	7.9254 − 05
6	1.0274 + 00	1.0840 − 01	1.1136 − 01	4.3299 − 04	3.9241 − 08	4.0315 − 08	9.7701 + 05	1.0037 + 06	1.1050 − 04	1.1352 − 04
7	1.0235 + 00	1.4754 − 01	1.5100 − 01	6.8758 − 04	3.3635 − 08	3.4424 − 08	8.3744 + 05	8.5707 + 05	1.5040 − 04	1.5393 − 04
8	1.0205 + 00	1.9271 − 01	1.9666 − 01	1.0264 − 03	2.9431 − 08	3.0035 − 08	7.3276 + 05	7.4779 + 05	1.9644 − 04	2.0047 − 04
9	1.0182 + 00	2.4390 − 01	2.4834 − 01	1.4613 − 03	2.6161 − 08	2.6638 − 08	6.5134 + 05	6.6322 + 05	2.4862 − 04	2.5315 − 04
10	1.0164 + 00	3.0110 − 01	3.0605 − 01	2.0046 − 03	2.3545 − 08	2.3931 − 08	5.8620 + 05	5.9583 + 05	3.0694 − 04	3.1198 − 04
20	1.0082 + 00	1.2018 + 00	1.2117 + 00	1.6002 − 02	1.1772 − 08	1.1869 − 08	2.9310 + 05	2.9551 + 05	1.2277 − 03	1.2378 − 03
30	1.0055 + 00	2.6904 + 00	2.7051 + 00	5.3734 − 02	7.8482 − 09	7.8911 − 09	1.9540 + 05	1.9647 + 05	2.7624 − 03	2.7775 − 03
40	1.0041 + 00	4.7367 + 00	4.7561 + 00	1.2614 − 01	5.8861 − 09	5.9103 − 09	1.4655 + 05	1.4715 + 05	4.9110 − 03	4.9311 − 03
50	1.0033 + 00	7.2867 + 00	7.3106 + 00	2.4255 − 01	4.7089 − 09	4.7244 − 09	1.1724 + 05	1.1763 + 05	7.6734 − 03	7.6986 − 03
60	1.0027 + 00	1.0263 + 01	1.0291 + 01	4.0994 − 01	3.9241 − 09	3.9348 − 09	9.7701 + 04	9.7968 + 04	1.1050 − 02	1.1080 − 02
70	1.0023 + 00	1.3572 + 01	1.3604 + 01	6.3250 − 01	3.3635 − 09	3.3714 − 09	8.3744 + 04	8.3940 + 04	1.5040 − 02	1.5075 − 02
80	1.0021 + 00	1.7127 + 01	1.7162 + 01	9.1217 − 01	2.9431 − 09	2.9491 − 09	7.3276 + 04	7.3426 + 04	1.9644 − 02	1.9684 − 02
90	1.0018 + 00	2.0870 + 01	2.0908 + 01	1.2505 + 00	2.6161 − 09	2.6208 − 09	6.5134 + 04	6.5253 + 04	2.4862 − 02	2.4907 − 02
100	1.0016 + 00	2.4803 + 01	2.4844 + 01	1.6512 + 00	2.3545 − 09	2.3583 − 09	5.8620 + 04	5.8717 + 04	3.0694 − 02	3.0744 − 02

[a]Courtesy of BGI Inc., Waltham, Mass.; compiled by R. A. Gussman; copyright 1971.

[b]Exponents are presented in computer format. Thus, $1.0291 + 01 = 1.0291 \times 10^1 = 10.291$ and $1.6002 − 02 = 1.6002 \times 10^{-2} = 0.016002$.

[c]Physical constants used in the preparation of the table: $\lambda = 6.53 \times 10^{-6}$ cm = mean free path of gas molecules in air; $\eta = 1.810 \times 10^{-4}$ p = viscosity of air; $k = 1.3708 \times 10^{-16}$ erg/°C = Boltzmann's constant; $T = 293$ K = absolute temperature (20°C); $\rho = 1$ g/cm³ = particle density; $\rho' = 1.205 \times 10^{-3}$ g/cm³ = density of air; $g = 981$ cm/s² = acceleration due to gravity; C_D = drag coefficient. Slip correction factor (Davies 1945): $SC = 1 + 2A\lambda/d$; $A = 1.257 + 0.400 \exp(-1.10 \, d/2\lambda)$. Mobility (Green & Lane 1964): $B = (3\pi\eta d)^{-1}$. Diffusion coefficient (Green & Lane 1964): $D = kBT$. Relaxation time (Davies 1966): $\tau = d^2\rho/18\eta$. Reynolds number (terminal velocity) (Green & Lane 1964): $\text{Re} = C_D \, \text{Re}^2/24 = \rho\rho' g d^3/18\eta^2$. Sedimentation velocity (Green & Lane 1964): (1) for values of Re up to 0.05: $v = (\rho - \rho')g d^2/18\eta$; (2) for values of Re from 0.05 to 4: $v = [C_D \, \text{Re}^2/24 - 2.3363 \times 10^{-4} \, (C_D \, \text{Re}^2)^2 + 2.0154 \times 10^{-6} \, (C_D \, \text{Re}^2)^3 - 6.9105 \times 10^{-9} \, (C_D \, \text{Re}^2)^4]\eta/\rho'd$.

Finally, if there is complete mixing (back mixing),

$$Pt = \frac{1}{1 + U_p^* A / \dot{V}_G} \qquad [9.2.7]$$

9.2.1.4 Large-Scale Systems

Large-scale systems are needed for both process recovery and air pollution control. We focus on the latter.

Figure 9.2.1 is a flow chart for the selection of gas-cleaning equipment. Once the necessary collection efficiency has been determined, the control equipment alternatives are evaluated on the basis of the characteristics of the equipment, the

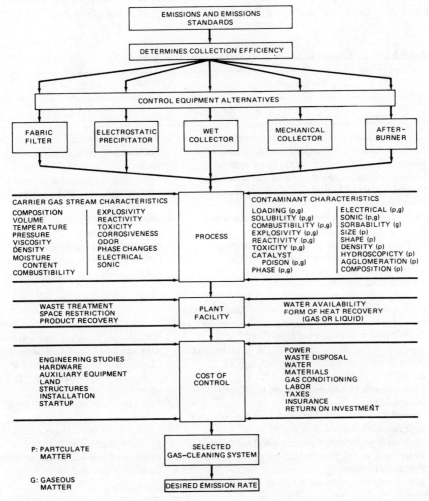

Figure 9.2.1   Flow chart for selection of gas-cleaning equipment (Vandergrift et al. 1971).

gas stream, and the particles. The candidates technically feasible are then compared with respect to cost, as discussed below.

Collection equipment can be subdivided into that which captures material dry (most filters, electrostatic precipitators, and cyclones) and that which uses a liquid, usually water (scrubbers). Table 9.2.2 gives the major advantages and disadvantages of both types. Generally, solid particles can be collected with either type, and liquid particles with wet collectors. Table 9.2.3 gives some useful information comparing various control options (Stern et al. 1973). More detailed cost information is given next.

9.2.1.5 Costs

Figure 9.2.2 is a generalized cost evaluation scheme, showing the major determinants of cost. The source and its operating characteristics influence control-type choice and the costs of control. Handling the collected materials is costly, but there

Table 9.2.2 Advantages and Disadvantages of Wet and Dry Collectors[a]

Wet collectors	Dry collectors
Advantages	
1. Can collect gases and particles at the same time.	1. Recovery of dry material may give final product without further treatment.
2. Recovers soluble material, and the material can be pumped to another plant for further treatment.	2. Freedom from corrosion in most cases.
3. High-temperature gases are cooled and washed.	3. Less storage capacity is required for product.
4. Corrosive gases and mists can be recovered and neutralized.	4. Combustible filters may be used for radioactive wastes.
5. No fire or explosion hazard if suitable scrubbing liquor is used (usually water).	5. Particles greater than 0.05 μm may be collected with long equipment life and high collection efficiency.
6. Plant is generally small in size compared to dry collectors such as baghouses or electrostatic precipitators.	
Disadvantages	
1. Soluble materials must be recrystallized.	1. Hygroscopic materials may form solid cake and be difficult to shake off.
2. Insoluble materials require settling in filtration plant.	2. Maintenance of plant and disposal of dry dust may be dangerous to operators.
3. Waste liquids require disposal, which may be difficult.	3. High temperatures may limit means of collection.
4. Mists and vapors may be entrained in effluent gas streams.	4. Limitation of use for corrosive mists for some plants (e.g., baghouses).
5. Washed air will be saturated with liquid vapor, have high humidity and low dew point.	5. Creation of secondary dust problem during disposal of dust.
6. Very small particles (submicron sizes) are difficult to wet, and so will pass through plant.	
7. Corrosion problems.	
8. Liquid may freeze in cold weather.	

[a]From Strauss (1966).

Type of collector	Particle size range (μm)	Removal efficiency	Space required	Maximum temperature (°C)	Pressure drop (cm, H_2O)	Annual cost ($ per year/m³)[b]
Baghouse (cotton bags)	0.1–1.0	Fair	Large	80	10	7.00
	1.0–10.0	Good	Large	80	10	7.00
	10.0–50.0	Excellent	Large	80	10	7.00
Baghouse (Dacron, nylon, orlon)	0.1–1.0	Fair	Large	120	12	8.50
	1.0–10.0	Good	Large	120	12	8.50
	10.0–50.0	Excellent	Large	120	12	8.50
Baghouse (glass fiber)	0.1–1.0	Fair	Large	290	10	10.50
	1.0–10.0	Good	Large	290	10	10.50
	10.0–50.0	Good	Large	290	10	10.50
Baghouse (Teflon)	0.1–1.0	Fair	Large	260	20	11.50
	1.0–10.0	Good	Large	260	20	11.50
	10.0–50.0	Excellent	Large	260	20	11.50
Electrostatic precipitator	0.1–1.0	Excellent	Large	400	1	10.50
	1.0–10.0	Excellent	Large	400	1	10.50
	10.0–50.0	Good	Large	400	1	10.50
Standard cyclone	0.1–1.0	Poor	Large	400	5	3.50
	1.0–10.0	Poor	Large	400	5	3.50
	10.0–50.0	Good	Large	400	5	3.50
High-efficiency cyclone	0.1–1.0	Poor	Moderate	400	12	5.50
	1.0–10.0	Fair	Moderate	400	12	5.50
	10.0–50.0	Good	Moderate	400	12	5.50
Spray tower	0.1–1.0	Fair	Large	540	5	12.50
	1.0–10.0	Good	Large	540	5	12.50
	10.0–50.0	Good	Large	540	5	12.50
Impingement scrubber	0.1–1.0	Fair	Moderate	540	10	11.50
	1.0–10.0	Good	Moderate	540	10	11.50
	10.0–50.0	Good	Moderate	540	10	11.50
Venturi scrubber	0.1–1.0	Good	Small	540	88	28.00
	1.0–10.0	Excellent	Small	540	88	28.00
	10.0–50.0	Excellent	Small	540	88	28.00

[a]From Stern et al. (1973).
[b]Includes water and power cost, maintenance cost, operating cost, capital and insurance costs, at unspecified date.

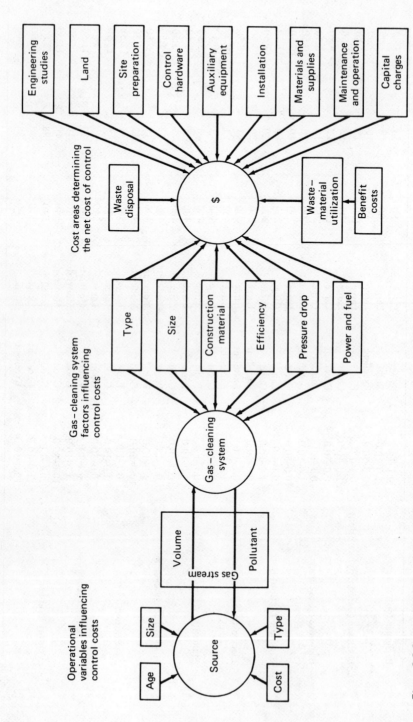

Figure 9.2.2 Diagram of cost evaluation scheme for a pollutant control system (Vandergrift et al. 1971).

may be salvage value. Finally, note that the cost of the control hardware is only a part of the total cost.

An approach to cost comparisons for various particulate control options was developed by Edmisten & Bunyard (1970). In brief, the goal is to develop a single cost parameter, the *total annualized cost,* by which different air pollution control devices can be compared with respect to cost. This is quite useful because, for example, electrostatic precipitators have relatively high initial costs and relatively low operating costs in comparison to scrubbers of comparable collection efficiency.

Edmisten & Bunyard (1970) divided the costs into three categories:

Capital investment cost. This includes the control hardware cost, the cost of auxiliary equipment, and the cost of installation, including initial studies.
Maintenance and operating costs. These are taken on a yearly basis, averaged over the life of the equipment.
Capital charges. These are the opportunity costs of capital investment, plus taxes and insurance.

To convert these various costs into a single number, the total annualized cost, one sums the annual capital investment costs, the operating and maintenance costs, and the capital charges.

In such contexts one usually assumes straight-line depreciation. One estimates the life of the equipment (Edmisten & Bunyard suggested 15 years) and calculates the yearly depreciation as the capital investment divided by the life expectancy. Thus, the total annualized cost TAC, in dollars per year, is given by

$$TAC = \frac{CI}{L} + MO + CC \qquad [9.2.8]$$

It is the sum of capital investment CI, in dollars, per lifetime L, in years, yearly maintenance and operating costs MO, in dollars per year, and capital charges CC, in dollars per year. Generally MO and CC are nearly proportional to CI.

For more details on conventional control device costs, see the article by Edmisten & Bunyard (1970) and the articles by Hanf & MacDonald (1975) and Fraser & Eaton (1975). Neveril et al. (1978) presented curves and equations for estimating the prices of electrostatic precipitators, venturi scrubbers, fabric filters, incinerators, and absorbers, in the first of a series of articles on control equipment costs. Subsequent articles by the same authors covered the costs of auxiliary equipment, ductwork and dampers, and such costs as operating, maintenance, and installation costs.

Although much of the necessary information on costs is obtained from manufacturers for a specific application, one can readily estimate power costs. Power-consumption figures are often given in terms of kilowatts per cubic meter per second flow rate. When the power is given as hydraulic power (pressure drop times volume flow rate), a pump-fan-motor efficiency factor must be used (as a divisor) to convert to actual electrical power; this efficiency factor is generally about 0.6, whether fans are moving gas or pumps are moving liquid. The power cost is given by the product of volume rate of gas flow, power consumption per unit flow of gas, cost per unit of energy, and operating time. Certain forms of power may be nearly free: The recovery of waste heat is free with regard to operating costs, although it will add to the capital investment and thus to the costs associated with capital investment. As with other costs, the power costs will vary considerably from situation to situation.

Specific circumstances greatly affect waste-disposal costs. Scrubbers produce wastewater that must be handled properly; wastewater treatment produces solid wastes that must be used or disposed. For more information about wastewater treatment, consult a text such as that by Eckenfelder (1966).

9.2.2 SCRUBBERS FOR GAS–PARTICLE SEPARATION

Douglas W. Cooper

9.2.2.1 Introduction

A scrubber is a device that uses liquid (usually water) to collect particles or gases or both from a gas stream. We limit our discussion to scrubbers having as their primary role the removal of particulate matter (solid or liquid) entrained in a gas.

The considerations for selection among the types of air pollution control equipment are summarized in figure 9.2.1. Table 9.2.2 gives the advantages and disadvantages of wet collectors (scrubbers) and dry collectors for air pollution control. Scrubbers are used not only for air pollution control, however, but also to recover valuable materials, to cool gas streams, and to add liquid or vapor to gas streams.

Most scrubbers conform to the schematic diagram shown in figure 9.2.3. A process produces emissions that are transferred partly to a liquid phase by the scrubber. A demister (or entrainment separator or mist eliminator) removes some of the droplets generated by scrubbing, and a water-treatment step prepares the scrubbing water for discharge. Each step requires the expenditure of energy. The mass throughput of particulate material is ultimately transferred from the process outlet into material emitted by the scrubber or the clarifier or as solid waste. In this section, our focus is the scrubber, with some attention given to the demister (see also the separation of solids and liquids from gases in this chapter) but none to the clarifier.

9.2.2.2 Scrubber Types

Scrubbers capture particles on droplets or liquid surfaces or liquid-coated surfaces. The droplets may be formed independently of the gas flow or they may be atomized by the flow. Scrubbers using preformed sprays include spray towers, cyclone spray scrubbers, water-jet scrubbers, and mechanical scrubbers. Venturi scrubbers and orifice scrubbers usually are designed to produce a spray by gas atomization of the scrubbing liquid. Impingement scrubbers and sieve plates involve

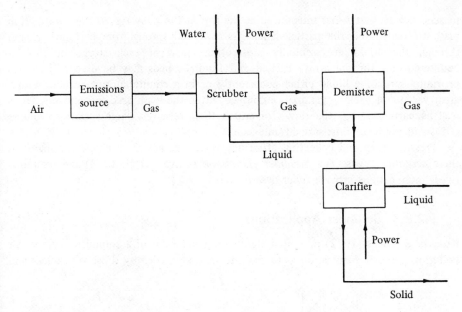

Figure 9.2.3 Generalized description of a scrubber system.

flow into or through a volume of liquid. Some scrubber types are shown in figures 9.2.4 and 9.2.5. Particles are captured primarily on liquid-coated surfaces and packed-bed scrubbers, fluidized-bed scrubbers, and fibrous-bed scrubbers. As is discussed more fully later, many of these different scrubber types use roughly the same power to achieve the same degree of particle collection efficiency, so that the choice among scrubber types often is dictated by space constraints, the availability of certain kinds of power (e.g., waste heat) and equipment (such as pumps, fans, ducting, piping), and the characteristics of the dust-scrubber combinations, which affect plugging, corrosion, and the handling of liquid and solid wastes.

In a spray tower, the particle-laden gas stream is directed upward through a spray falling downward. In a spray chamber, the gas flow is generally horizontal, and the spray may have any crosscurrent orientation. In a cyclone spray scrubber, a spray is introduced near the entrance of the cyclone, and the relative motion of spray and particles induced by the cyclone fosters collection of the particles and of the drops containing the captured particulate material. Mechanical scrubbers use sprays combined with moving baffling (fans, etc.) to induce particle capture. A venturi scrubber accelerates the gas in a converging channel, introduces a spray at the throat section at the end of this channel, and then lowers the gas velocity through a very gradually tapered diverging section. Orifice scrubbers operate in a similar fashion, except that the orifice is an abrupt change in duct cross-sectional area, of negligible length, followed by an abrupt expansion back to the original duct cross-sectional area.

Impingement scrubbers direct a jet or jets of gas at the surface of a liquid, causing intimate liquid-particle mixing, using a variety of geometries. Tray towers (sieve plates) are built from a series of multiply perforated plates arranged vertically in such a way that water introduced at the top of the array travels downward from plate to plate, and the particle-laden gas is passed through the perforations and through the liquid in essentially crosscurrent flow at each stage; the flow is countercurrent for the array. Packed and fluidized beds may be used with sprays providing scrubbing liquid either cocurrently or in a countercurrent fashion, with a great variety of packing materials employed; often these are used to remove gases as well as particles from the flow, for which their relatively large surface-to-volume ratios and residence times are advantageous.

Pressure drop and collection efficiency equations are given below for many of these scrubber types. The *Scrubber Handbook* (Calvert et al. 1972) and manufacturers' publications provide fuller descriptions.

9.2.2.3 Scrubber Applications

Krockta & Lucas (1972) presented the recommendations of a committee of the Air Pollution Control Association as to the information needed by those who select and

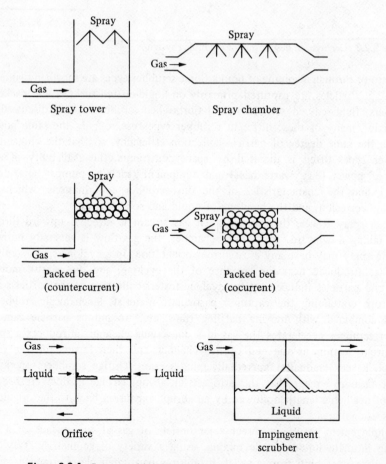

Figure 9.2.4 Some scrubber geometries.

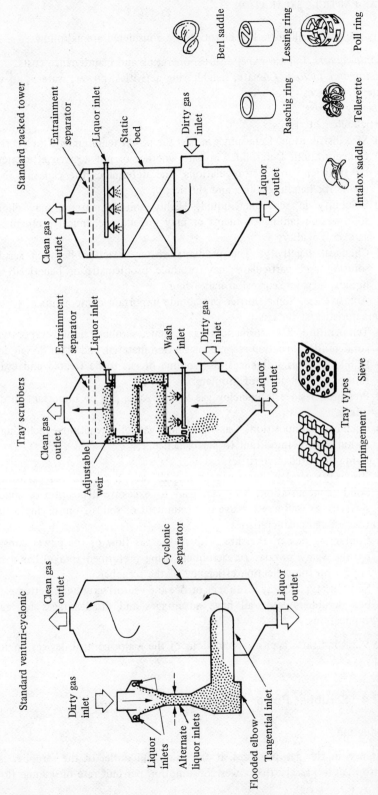

Figure 9.2.5 Scrubber examples. (Courtesy of Industrial Gas Cleaning Institute, Alexandria, Virginia.)

evaluate particulate scrubbers. The factors to be considered are as follows:

1. *Economic factors.* Capital expenditures, operating and maintenance costs.
2. *Environmental factors.* Climate, neighboring activities, power, water, and waste-treatment resources.
3. *Engineering factors.*
    a. Particle characteristics.
        (1) Size distribution. Determines in part the power requirements for a scrubber.
        (2) Concentration. Determines in part whether or not a given efficiency will be sufficient to meet regulations, and determines the capacity requirements for handling solids and slurries.
        (3) Solubility in scrubbing liquid. Highly soluble material may eliminate solid-waste-handling problems or may introduce chemical problems, such as excess acidity.
        (4) Chemical reactivity. The products of any reaction between scrubbing solution and particulate may produce problematic or beneficial solids, liquids, or gases; corrosion may occur.
        (5) Abrasiveness. Some slurries can abrade important components.
    b. Characteristics of the gas.
        (1) Temperature. This influences gas volume, scrubber liquid evaporation or condensation, reaction rates, construction material, and other design details.
        (2) Humidity. This influences the volume of gas to be treated and evaporation or condensation of droplets.
        (3) Pressure. Besides influencing gas volume, this can be important in design safety.
        (4) Chemical composition. Gas-liquid and gas-solid reactions, including corrosion, can be important to performance.
    c. Scrubbing liquid characteristics.
        (1) Viscosity, density, surface tension. All can affect scrubber performance.
        (2) Solids concentration. This can lead to excessive deposition of solids on surfaces, as well as excessive reentrainment of solids from drying droplets.
    d. Scrubber design characteristics.
        (1) Contacting power. Pressure drop in the gas flow or the power consumed by the spray nozzles (in scrubbers using preformed sprays) has a major impact on the collection efficiency of the scrubber.
        (2) Scrubber type. Spray scrubbers, orifice and venturi scrubbers, wetted packed-bed scrubbers, etc., all have advantages and disadvantages for certain applications.

Table 9.2.4 indicates typical applications of the major control devices, including scrubbers.

9.2.2.4 Scrubber Power Consumption

Introduction

The difference in the gas pressures at the inlet and outlet of the scrubber is the pressure drop Δp in pascals, the power consumption per unit rate of volume flow of

Table 9.2.4 Industrial Process and Control Summary[a]

Industry or process	Source of emissions	Particulate matter	Method of control
Iron and steel mills	Blast furnaces, steel-making furnaces, sintering machines	Iron oxide, dust, smoke	Cyclones, baghouses, electrostatic precipitators, wet collectors
Gray-iron foundries	Cupolas, shake-out systems, core making	Iron oxide, dust, smoke, oil, grease, metal fumes	Scrubbers, dry centrifugal collectors
Metallurgical (nonferrous)	Smelters and furnaces	Smoke, metal fumes, oil, grease	Electrostatic precipitators, fabric filters
Petroleum refineries	Catalyst regenerators, sludge incinerators	Catalyst dust, ash from sludge	High-efficiency cyclones, electrostatic precipitators, scrubbing towers, bag-houses
Portland cement	Kilns, dryers, materials-handling systems	Alkali and process dusts	Fabric filters, electrostatic precipitators, mechanical collectors
Kraft paper mills	Chemical recovery furnaces	Chemical dusts	Electrostatic precipitators, venturi scrubbers
Acid-manufacture—phosphoric, sulfuric	Thermal processes, phosphate rock acidulating, grinding and handling systems	Acid mist, dust	Electrostatic precipitators, mesh mist eliminators
Coke manufacturing	Charging and discharging oven cells, quenching, materials handling	Coal and coke dusts, coal tars	Meticulous design, operation, and maintenance
Glass and glass fiber	Raw-materials handling, glass furnaces, fiberglass forming and curing	Sulfuric acid mist, raw-materials dusts, alkaline oxides, resin aerosols	Glass-fabric filters, afterburners
Coffee processing	Roasters, spray dryers, waste-heat boilers, coolers, conveying equipment	Chaff, oil aerosols, ash from chaff burning, dehydrated coffee dusts	Cyclones, afterburners, fabric filters

[a]From U.S. Department of Health, Education and Welfare (1969).

air. For scrubbers having appreciable collection efficiency for submicron particulates, energy costs can outweigh all other costs, so that it is important to minimize the pressure drop while maintaining adequate collection efficiency.

Contacting-Power Theory

There are several ways in which power is supplied to produce a relative motion between gas and collector in a scrubber: from blowers producing gas flow, from pumps producing liquid flow, and from the movement of baffles (such as a mechanically driven rotor). There may be substantial inefficiencies in supplying power to the fans, pumps, rotors, etc., so the *contacting power* has been defined as that portion of the power consumption that is dissipated in the gas-liquid contacting process. Semrau & Witham (1974) continued the work of Semrau, Lapple, and others in relating the collection efficiency of several different types of scrubbers to the contacting power. They concluded that in the absence of condensation or evaporation effects, the scrubber efficiency is dependent only upon effective friction loss (contacting power), with no independent influences of gas velocity, liquid-to-gas ratio, or contactor orifice size, except possibly in the range of very low gas velocities, liquid-to-gas ratios, and pressure drops. Contacting-power theory is the hypothesis that scrubbers of any type that collect particles primarily due to impaction should have the same efficiency at the same value of contacting power.

Semrau et al. (1977) tested an orifice scrubber, a multiple-orifice contactor, a variety of spray-scrubber configurations, and the combination of a spray nozzle with an orifice. They cited earlier data that supported the contacting-power theory for all three types of power input (gas, liquid, mechanical rotor). Their experimental work was done with particles having mass median diameters smaller than about 1 μm. For these fine particles, the results were:

1. The various spray scrubbers gave the same collection efficiency at the same contacting power.
2. The orifice scrubber gave better collection efficiency at a given contacting power than did those sprays for which much of the contacting power was derived from the spray liquid.

These results are consistent with the analyses presented by Calvert (1974): At the high pressure drops appropriate to scrubbing particles of 1 μm aerodynamic diameter and less, the differences among various scrubber types become significant, in terms of the particle size for which they achieve 50% collection efficiency.

Muir et al. (1978) compared the collection efficiency of a venturi scrubber with that of a wetted-fiber (rotary-drum) scrubber and found excellent agreement between the collection efficiencies, at various pressure drops, up to the limit of their pressure drop testing range, about 6.2×10^3 Pa. For these quite different scrubbers, the contacting power is supplied by the gas streams.

Thus, power consumption is clearly an important determinant in scrubber efficiency, as well as a major contributor to operating costs. The relations governing power consumption in five scrubber types are presented next.

Venturi Scrubbers

Yung et al. (1977a) presented the following equation for the pressure loss in a venturi scrubber:

$$\Delta p = - 2\rho_L U_G^2 \frac{\dot{V}_L}{\dot{V}_G} [1 - X^2 + (X^4 - X^2)^{0.5}] \qquad [9.2.9]$$

where ρ_L is the scrubber liquid density, in kilograms per cubic meter; U_G is the gas velocity at venturi throat, in meters per second; $\dot{V}_L$ is the liquid flow rate, in cubic meters per second; $\dot{V}_G$ is the gas flow rate, in cubic meters per second; and X is the dimensionless scrubber throat length. The dimensionless throat length is

$$X = 1 + \frac{3hC_{D1}\rho_G}{16d_d\rho_L} \qquad [9.2.10]$$

where h is the throat length, in meters; C_{D1} is the drag coefficient for droplets at the throat inlet (see [9.2.38]); and d_d is the droplet diameter, in meters. This equation compares well with the more complicated equation offered by Boll (1973) and with his data and those of others, for dimensionless liquid-to-gas ratios of 10^{-4}-10^{-3}. It was assumed in deriving the equation that all the drops are accelerated in the venturi throat and that none of the momentum thus imparted is recovered as pressure gain when the drops decelerate in the diffuser; that there is no initial axial component of velocity for the droplets; that the flow is one-dimensional, incompressible, and adiabatic; that at any cross section the liquid fraction is small; that neither drop evaporation nor loss of drops to the walls occurs; and that the net pressure difference of wall friction minus pressure recovery in the diffuser is negligible. If the throat is long enough to accelerate the droplets to the velocity of the gas, the term in brackets in [9.2.9] becomes unity and [9.2.9] reduces to the equation given by Calvert (1968), which is simpler but somewhat overpredicts pressure drop for high-energy venturis (Yung et al. 1977b).

Spray Scrubbers

In a spray chamber or tower, the energy that goes into the relative motion of droplets and particles comes primarily from the spray nozzle ($\dot{V}_L \Delta p_L$) and/or gravity, but not from the gas flow. Energy is used in forming the droplets, however. The droplet initial velocity, upon exiting the spray nozzle, is proportional to the square root of the pressure on the nozzle (assuming potential flow): $U_d = (2\Delta p_L/\rho_L)^{0.5}$. Collection efficiency depends not only on particle aerodynamic diameter, but also on droplet concentration, size, velocity, and the distance the droplets travel with respect to the gas. Strauss (1966) (citing work by Stairmand and by Johnstone & Roberts) presented the optimal droplet diameter for collecting different particle diameters at droplet accelerations equal to gravity and 100 times gravity. For collection by impaction and interception, increased droplet velocity (before droplets reach their terminal velocity) increases collection, but whether or not it is worth the increased power consumption depends on the specific use. The pressure drop in the gas flow depends on the gas volume flow rate and the scrubber geometry, but at flow Reynolds numbers above about 10^3, losses in expansions, contractions, and bends usually predominate, and these are proportional to the gas velocity head, which is $0.5\,\rho_G U_G^2$.

Packed Beds

Packed beds have been studied extensively by chemical engineers for the separation of one gaseous constituent from another and, to a lesser extent, for the separation of particulates from gases. For a collector having packing with a mean surface-to-volume diameter D_{sv} (equal to six times the total solid volume of the packing material divided by total surface area), the following equation holds for the pressure drop when operated dry (Bird et al. 1960):

$$\Delta p = \frac{150\mu U_G L}{D_{sv}^2}\,\frac{(1-\alpha)^2}{\alpha^3} + \frac{1.75\rho_G U_G^2(1-\alpha)L}{D_{sv}\alpha^3} \qquad [9.2.11]$$

where L is the bed length, in meters; D_{sv} is the collector surface-volume mean diameter, in meters; and α is the volume void fraction, dimensionless. This equation, the Ergun equation, is just the sum of the Blake-Kozeny equation for laminar flow and the Burke-Plummer equation for turbulent flow (Bird et al. 1960). For $\mathrm{Re} = \rho_G U_G D_{sv}/\mu_G > 10^3$, the first term is negligible.

Perry & Chilton (1973) gave tabulated values for C_2 and C_3 for the following equation, which accounts for the effects of the addition of the scrubbing liquid:

$$\Delta p = C_2 10^{C_3 U'_L}\rho_G U_G^2 L \qquad [9.2.12]$$

(Here, U'_L is the liquid-phase superficial velocity.) An abridged from of their table is presented as table 9.2.5.

Sieve Plates

A perforated plate with liquid flowing across it from one downcomer region to another is sometimes called a sieve plate, a common type of plate scrubber adapted from gas-liquid contacting uses. Normally, several such plates are arranged vertically

Table 9.2.5 Values of C_2 and C_3 in [9.2.12][a]

Packing	Nominal size (cm)	C_2 (10^3 m^{-1})	C_3 (s/m)
Raschig rings	1.3	1.9	0.189
	2.5	0.44	0.114
	5.1	0.15	0.077
Berl saddles	1.3	0.83	0.089
	2.5	0.22	0.077
Intalox saddles	2.5	0.17	0.073

[a] Adapted from Perry & Chilton (1973).

in series, with the aerosol introduced at the bottom and the liquid introduced at the top. At liquid or gas flow rates that are too high for the design, flooding occurs, marked by a sharp decrease in liquid throughput and an increase in pressure drop. Avoiding this condition is one important goal of the design. If the gas flow becomes too low, liquid can seep through the perforations, decreasing contacting efficacy. The maximum gas flow rate that can be obtained without flooding depends upon the liquid density and surface tension, the gas density, and the liquid-to-gas flow ratio, as well as on the spacing between the plates and the ratio of the area of the perforations A_h to the active area A_a, if A_h/A_a is not greater than 0.1. (The active area is the total plate area minus the downcomer area.) Summarizing the wealth of detailed design material available (Perry & Chilton 1973), one notes that for air-water systems and plate spacings of about 0.2–1 m and liquid-to-gas volume flow ratios of 0.3×10^{-3} to 3×10^{-3}, the gas velocity through the holes (Q_G/A_h) at which flooding occurs is within a factor of two of 3 m/s, for nonfoaming systems using weirs that have heights 15% or less of the plate spacing and seive plate perforations of 0.6 cm diameter or less.

The pressure drop across the plates is due to the resistance to gas flow due to the geometric arrangement itself, as when dry, and the added resistance of the flow through the scrubbing liquid. For the dry plates, the gas flow can be apportioned among the holes, stage by stage, and one may use the equation for pressure drop across an orifice:

$$\Delta p = \frac{\rho_G U_G^2/2}{C_v^2} \qquad [9.2.13]$$

C_v depends on the ratio of the thickness of the orifice to its diameter as well as on the fraction of the orifice plate that is open area. The ratio of tray thickness to hole diameter is typically 0.4–0.7; for a ratio of 0.6 where $A_h/A_a = 0.1$, C_v is 0.65; in the range of thickness-to-diameter ratios of 0.2–0.8 and for A_h/A_a from 0.5 to 0.2, C_v ranges from 0.68 to 0.85, the higher values being for the larger thickness-to-diameter ratios and greater hole-area percentages (Perry & Chilton 1973). The pressure drop through the plates is approximately the pressure drop across the orifices when operated dry plus the height of clear liquid above the orifices, determined by the weir height and the degree of foaming.

9.2.2.5 Scrubber Collection Efficiency

Total Collection Efficiency

The analysis of collection on droplets (see Calvert et al. 1972 and Knettig & Beeckmans 1974) begins with a volume dV_G of particle-laden gas in relative motion with respect to droplets having a number concentration n_d and individual droplet cross-sectional areas A_d (figure 9.2.6). Gas and droplets are in a small volume $dx\,dy\,dz$, where dx is measured parallel to the gas mean flow. If the particles were point masses and if the droplets swept clean a volume equal to their single-droplet collection efficiency η times their cross-sectional area times the distance traveled relative to the gas, then the volume scrubbed per unit time dt would be

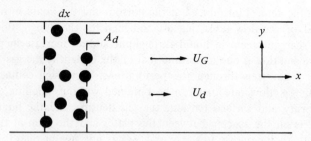

Figure 9.2.6 Infinitesimal scrubbing volume.

$$dV = \eta A_d \, n_d dx \, dy \, dz \, |U_G - U_d| \, dt \qquad [9.2.14]$$

The number of particles collected per unit time in the volume $dx \, dy \, dz$ would be the change in number concentration dn_p times the infinitesimal volume:

$$dn_p \, dx \, dy \, dz = -\eta n_p A_d \, n_d \, dx \, dy \, dz \, |U_G - U_d| \, dt$$

The change in the average concentration in time dt in the volume $A \, dx$ would be

$$\frac{1}{A \, dx} \int_y \int_z \eta n_p A_d |U_G - U_d| n_d \, dx \, dy \, dz \, dt \qquad [9.2.15]$$

Simple formulation Let the particle number concentration n_p and A_d, n_d, U_G, and U_d be uniform across the flow from x to $x + dx$; then (using $dt = dx/U_G$),

$$\frac{dn_p}{n_p} = -\eta \, \frac{|U_G - U_d|}{U_G} n_d A_d \, dx \qquad [9.2.16]$$

(e.g., Knettig & Beeckmans 1974).

From this point, the derivation can be performed with various degrees of sophistication:

1. The calculation of the single-droplet efficiency η can include some or all of the following mechanisms: impaction, interception, diffusion, electrostatic interactions, diffusiophoresis, thermophoresis.
2. The velocities U_G and U_d can be calculated in detail, including their dependence on position.
3. The spatial variation of n_d can be taken into account.
4. Various averages of droplet areas A_d can be used, or a functional form for their distribution employed.
5. Simultaneous equations for heat and mass transfer can be used to predict droplet size distribution changes.
6. Losses of droplets in the scrubber can be modeled.

If the various quantities on the right-hand side of [9.2.16] are independent of position, then

$$\frac{c}{c_0} = \exp\left(-\eta\,\frac{|U_G - U_d|}{U_G}\,n_d A_d L\right) \qquad [9.2.17]$$

where c_0 is the concentration at $x = 0$ and c is the concentration at $x = L$.

Droplet concentration One model for the concentration of the droplets n_d is just the volume of droplets supplied per unit time $\dot{V}_L$, divided by the average volume per droplet V_d, and divided by the volume rate of gas flow $\dot{V}_G$:

$$n_d = \frac{\dot{V}_L/\dot{V}_G}{V_d} \qquad [9.2.18]$$

(For packed beds, $\dot{V}_L/\dot{V}_G$ is replaced by the solids fraction.) For spherical droplets of mean squared diameter $\overline{d_d^2}$ and mean cubed diameter $\overline{d_d^3}$, $n_d A_d$ becomes

$$n_d A_d = \frac{\dot{V}_L}{(\pi/6)\,\overline{d_d^3}\,\dot{V}_G}\,\frac{\pi}{4}\,\overline{d_d^2} = \frac{3}{2}\,\frac{\dot{V}_L}{\dot{V}_G}\,\frac{\overline{d_d^2}}{\overline{d_d^3}} \qquad [9.2.19]$$

If this is combined with an empirically obtained factor f for $(U_G - U_d)/U_G$, one has

$$\frac{c}{c_0} = \exp\left(-\frac{3}{2}\,\eta f\,\frac{\dot{V}_L}{\dot{V}_G}\,\frac{\overline{d_d^2}L}{\overline{d_d^3}}\right) \qquad [9.2.20]$$

The concentration of collectors in a bed or a filter is fairly uniform, but this is often not true in a spray scrubber. In the steady state, the volume flow of droplets through the cross-sectional area of the duct A^* is equal to the injected spray volume flow $\dot{V}_L$, which is

$$\dot{V}_L = A^*\bar{U}_d \bar{n}_d V_d \qquad [9.2.21]$$

or the product of the area, the average droplet velocity, the average number concentration, and the average single-droplet volume. This means that the average concentration at A^* is

$$\bar{n}_d = \frac{(\dot{V}_L/\dot{V}_G)(U_G/U_d)}{V_d} \qquad [9.2.22]$$

and *not* $(\dot{V}_L/\dot{V}_G)/V_d$.

Thus, where the droplets are moving faster than the gas, their concentration is less than where they are moving slower than the gas with respect to the scrubber wall. Other things being equal, scrubbing becomes more intense when the gas is accelerating, and less intense where the gas is decelerating.

The incorporation of [9.2.22] into [9.2.17] yields

$$\frac{c}{c_0} = \exp\left(-\eta\,\frac{|U_G - U_d|}{U_d}\,\frac{\dot{V}_L}{\dot{V}_G}\,\frac{A_d L}{V_d}\right) \qquad [9.2.23]$$

It can be shown that, in calculating penetration, when one uses an average value for the argument of the exponent in [9.2.23], the ratio c/c_0 thus calculated is less than when c/c_0 values are calculated from each value of the argument and then averaged (which is much closer to the actual physical situation); the greater the dispersion of the values appropriate for the argument of [9.2.23], the greater the difference between the value calculated by using an average and the value appropriate to the situation (Cooper 1976a). For a scrubber, this means that for droplet distributions having an optimal average cross-sectional area, the distribution having the smallest standard deviation of size is most efficient, if the aerosol is monodisperse. It is generally advantageous to ensure flow and droplet concentration uniformity.

Single-Droplet Efficiency

The formulas for total collection efficiency require the single-droplet efficiency η, which involves a number of physical mechanisms. It is defined as

$$\eta = \frac{\text{flow area cleaned per collector}}{\text{collector cross-sectional area}} = \frac{A_c}{A_d} \qquad [9.2.24]$$

The calculation of the single-particle efficiency η depends in part on the flow past the collector. Two flow models are commonly in use: viscous flow and potential flow. Viscous flow is an appropriate model when the obstacle Reynolds number is small, that is, when

$$\mathrm{Re}_d = \frac{\rho_G |U_G - U_d| d_d}{\mu_G} \ll 1 \qquad [9.2.25]$$

Although the motion of the dust particles in the gas stream often meets this criterion, the flow around the collectors usually does not. A flow of 0.1 m/s past a fiber or droplet 100 μm in diameter gives $\mathrm{Re}_d \approx 1$. The potential-flow model is derived for $\mathrm{Re}_d \gg 1$, but even in this regime it is appropriate only up to near the point on the collector surface where the flow separates and forms a wake that trails behind the obstacle.

The single-droplet efficiency can be calculated for various collection mechanisms separately and then combined as though the mechanisms acted independently (Knettig & Beeckmans 1974), but this is not generally correct. The correct approach, although more difficult, is to solve the particle trajectory equations in the appropriate flow field, including the collection forces and mechanisms, as is done by Sparks (1971) and George & Poehlein (1974), among others. The disadvantage of the second approach is that it requires a great many calculations, one for every specific situation of interest.

When a dust particle strikes the collection surface because of its inertia, the collection is said to be due to *impaction*. The impaction process can be characterized by the impaction parameter ψ, which is defined as

$$\psi = \frac{C \rho_p U_p d_p^2}{18 \mu_G d_d} \qquad [9.2.26]$$

where ρ_p is the particle density, in kilograms per cubic meter, and C is the Cunningham correction factor, defined empirically as

$$C = 1 + 2.492 \frac{\lambda}{d_p} + 0.84 \frac{\lambda}{d_p} \exp\left(\frac{-0.435\, d_p}{\lambda}\right)$$

where λ is the molecular mean free path (0.063 μm for air at standard conditions). The following expression has been found empirically to approximate the single-droplet efficiency for impaction (Calvert et al. 1972):

$$\eta_I = \frac{\psi^2}{(\psi + 0.35)^2} \qquad [9.2.27]$$

Impaction is usually the most important collection mechanism for scrubbers, for particles larger than 0.1 μm.

   Interception occurs when a particle strikes a collector even though the particle center would not have. Incorporating it correctly with other collection mechanisms really means altering the boundary conditions for the problem in each case, which is sometimes quite difficult. Denote by N_R the ratio of (spherical) particle radius to (spherical or cylindrical) collector radius. Then the incremental efficiency due to interception (above that of impaction, if operative) is between $2N_R$ and $3N_R$ for potential flow around a spherical collector, and between N_R and $2N_R$ for potential flow around a cylinder, for intertialess and highly massive particles, respectively (Fuchs 1964).

   Capture by *diffusion* occurs because of the Brownian motion of the particles. It becomes appreciable only as the Peclet number (the gas velocity times the collector diameter divided by the particle diffusivity) becomes much less than one.

   Electrostatic forces (see also section 9.2.5) have been employed to augment the collection efficiency of scrubbers. The case in which the particles and the collectors are charged (Coulombic interaction) typically produces a much greater effect than those cases (image-force interactions) in which either the collectors or the particles are charged, but not both. The *migration velocity* is defined as the terminal velocity of a particle due to the electrical forces, at the surface of the collector. For electrostatic interaction to be important, the migration velocity should not be very much smaller than the product of the collection efficiency due to all other mechanisms and the relative velocity, $\eta(U_G - U_d)$. Figure 9.2.7 gives the migration velocities at normal temperature and pressure for particles charged to saturation in a field of 10 kV/cm, if charged, and collectors producing fields of 10 kV/cm at their surfaces, if electrified at all; the collectors are assumed to be 100-μm spheres. Electrostatic collection is intrinsically energy efficient because the collection force can be applied directly to the particles. (The power expended should not be used in contacting-power correlations.)

Summary of Collection Efficiency Relations

Here we briefly indicate how to use the foregoing to predict the collection efficiency of a scrubber design. In general, it is much safer, however, to scale up from a pilot scrubber or replicate a scrubber known to be adequate than to rely heavily on such predictions.

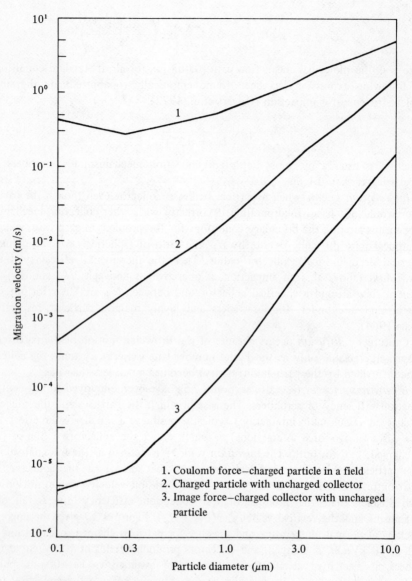

Figure 9.2.7 Theoretical migration velocities for three electrostatic mechanisms at particle diameters 0.1–10 μm (Cooper 1975).

Preformed spray scrubbers For spray towers and chambers, cyclone scrubbers, and jet ejector scrubbers, the penetration can be predicted using the varieties of the Kleinschmidt equation

$$Pt = \exp\left(-\eta A_d^* L_d\right) \qquad\qquad [9.2.28]$$

where A_d^* is the total droplet cross-sectional area presented to flow per unit volume, in square meters per cubic meter, and L_d is the distance of travel of droplet with respect to gas, in meters. The calculation of L_d and η may be difficult for some configurations.

Venturi and orifice scrubbers The design of the venturi scrubber is discussed in detail below. An orifice scrubber is approximately a venturi with a near-zero throat length.

Packed scrubbers Scrubbers with fibrous packings can also be modeled fairly successfully with the Kleinschmidt equation, if one takes into account the slightly different relationship between cross-sectional area and volume for a cylinder than for a sphere (Brady et al. 1977). Scrubbers with roughly isometric packings are often insufficiently porous to justify the use of collection efficiency equations obtained for isolated structures in a flow; thus, variants of the Kleinschmidt equation do not seem appropriate, but the equations for packed beds should be (see the section on depth filtration).

Foam scrubbers If the liquid in a sieve-plate scrubber is treated so as to produce a foam, the "foam scrubber" so created has collection characteristics somewhat different from those of the sieve-plate scrubber of the same geometry. The prediction of collection efficiency is rather different from the prediction of that for a spray scrubber. The following equation was developed and tested by Taheri & Calvert (1968) for the penetration through a foam scrubber as a function of particle size:

$$\mathrm{Pt} = \exp\left(-80 \, F_L^2 \psi\right) \qquad [9.2.29]$$

where F_L is the volume of clear liquid per volume of foam, and ψ is an impaction parameter (see [9.2.26]), based on the hole diameter and the velocity of the gas through the hole. Taheri & Calvert found that hydrophobic aerosols were collected less effectively than hydrophilic, which presumably grew by absorbing moisture, and the addition of wetting agents to the foam lessened collection efficiency by creating a less dense foam.

9.2.2.6 Some Design Considerations

Condensation

In particle collection by wet scrubbers, the role of condensation effects associated with the presence of vapor in the gas stream has been the subject of intensive investigation. When vapor condenses onto a scrubber droplet, a diffusiophoretic force is exerted on particles in the direction toward the droplet surface. This force has two sources: the net flow of water molecules to the droplet, a "wind" of sorts called *Stefan flow,* and a subtle component due to the gradient of the water vapor and the difference between its molecular weight and the molecular weight of air. When vapor condenses onto the particles, there is another important effect: the particles become larger and therefore are more easily captured by settling or by inertial impaction. These effects can be important for submicron particles.

The adsorption or absorption of water vapor by particles increases their aerodynamic diameters, thus enhancing their capture due to impaction, interception, and sedimentation. This is one reason why the addition of a second stage to a scrubber can be advantageous (Calvert et al. 1973). As the particle number concentration decreases, the growth of individual particles increases. Calvert et al. (1973) found the effects on collection to be independent of original particle size. A useful approximation is that the same amount of water vapor condenses on each particle larger than about 0.1 μm in diameter and that about one-quarter of the total vapor condenses on the particles rather than on the walls of the scrubber (Calvert & Parker 1978).

Regarding diffusiophoresis, if one assumes that thermophoresis (due to latent heat) is negligible, then condensation will enhance collection, and evaporation will impede collection. This has been shown theoretically (Sparks & Pilat 1970; Goldsmith & May 1966) and experimentally (Lapple & Kamack 1955; Semrau et al. 1958; Fuchs & Kirsch 1965; Calvert & Jhaveri 1974), contradicting the predictions of Slinn & Hales (1971). Whitmore (1976) discovered that the fraction of particles removed by diffusion of the condensing vapor is approximately equal to the fraction of the gas that condenses (Calvert & Parker 1978). This is quite plausible, although Lancaster and Strauss (1971) did not measure appreciable collection due to diffusiophoresis and concluded it was not important in conventional scrubbers to which steam is added.

Particle growth due to condensation certainly helps to increase scrubber efficiency. There is evidence that condensation of water vapor on scrubber surfaces and on collecting droplets helps as well.

Wettability

The addition of surface-active agents to scrubbing water sometimes improves the performance of scrubbers such as venturis that capture the particles on spray droplets. Hygroscopic particles, which are quite wettable, can be caught more readily than nonhygroscopic particles of the same aerodynamic diameter. These observations have led some to believe that wetting plays a major role in particle collection. Others disagree (Perry & Chilton, 1973). Surface-active agents may decrease average spray-droplet diameter and thus increase collection efficiency in some cases; hygroscopic particles can grow in humid atmospheres, also increasing the collection efficiency. Weber (1968) reported that when particles of 30 different dusts were shot at individual water droplets, regardless of particle type and velocity, a dust particle that hit a water droplet was always retained by the droplet, either on the droplet surface (if not wettable) or within. In another experiment (Fuchs et al. 1973) the impingement of particles of quartz, corundum, and coal was studied visually and photographically as they were directed toward a stationary water droplet in a jet at from 1 to 6 m/s. Rebound from the surface was not observed; the captured particles either remained on the surface of the drop or penetrated it, depending on whether pure water or water plus a surfactant was used. In some instances, nonwetting particles may coat the surface of the droplets and then cause rebound by particles striking them, but otherwise wetting is probably not an important factor in particle collection.

Single-Stage versus Multiple-Stage Scrubbers

Scrubbers have penetrations that can be approximated by one or more straight-line segments when plotted against pressure drop on log-log paper; if the logarithm of the penetration for particles of a given diameter equals $a(\Delta p)^b$, then multiple scrubbers should divide the pressure drop evenly among the stages for maximum collection efficiency (Cooper 1976b). A packed bed does divide the pressure drop evenly among its stages, and it is thus optimal in that respect. If, as is true for pressure drop at less than about 2.5 kPa (Semrau & Witham 1974), the relationship between the logarithm of the penetration and the pressure drop is stronger than linear ($b > 1$), then single-stage scrubbing is preferable to multiple-state scrubbing (Cooper 1976b).

Scale-up

It is unclear from first principles how well a small-scale model of a scrubber can be used to predict successfully the behavior of a full-scale model. As flow rate and geometric dimensions are increased, the Reynolds number for fluid flow increases, favoring turbulence; other dimensionless groups important to the determination of gas and particle behavior also change. From data presented on the performance of a 0.04-m^3/s Dust Difficulty Determinator (DDD) in comparison with full-scale Ventri-Rod Scrubbers (Balakrishnan and Cheng 1978), we calculated a regression equation for the emissions $\dot{M}_{VR}$ from the full-scale device as a linear function of the emissions $\dot{M}_{DDD}$ (under the same pressure drop) from the small device:

$$\dot{M}_{VR} = 0.877 \, \dot{M}_{DDD} + 0.000 \qquad [9.2.30]$$

(The exact zero intercept is puzzling.) This equation comes from data from measurements made at 13 different pressure drops of from 1.25 to 30 kPa, with volume flow rate scale-up factors of 180–3000. The coefficient of determination is $r^2 = 0.73$ (indicating the relationship postulated accounts for 73% of the variance in the correlation data). This supports the finding of Taheri et al. (1973) that increasing size and flow rate tend to improve the performance of scrubbers for the same pressure drop, which they attributed to the increased turbulence due to increased flow Reynolds number.

Behie & Beeckmans (1974) reviewed the work of many previous investigations and concluded that there was no appreciable effect of scaling up a scrubber. McIlvaine (1977) wrote that his experience with pilot-size and even miniature scrubbers (5×10^{-4} m^3/s) indicated that at low pressure drops (less than 2.5 kPa) large particles may not be captured in the same fashion in large and small scrubbers, but that for higher pressure drops only particles of less than about 10 μm aerodynamic diameter tend to penetrate, and these are less sensitive to details of flow geometry and scale. He noted the importance of using a small-scale scrubber for preliminary tests and that a manufacturer of scrubbers with full-size installations on more than 60 foundry cupolas finds it necessary to pilot each new installation.

9.2.2.7 Design Example—Venturi Scrubber

In general, designing a scrubber involves first determining the collection efficiency required and then developing a design to achieve that collection efficiency economically, considering investment costs as well as operating costs. Often the cost of power consumption (proportional to pressure drop times volume flow rate) and the costs of water use, treatment, and disposal will be greater than the annualized investment costs.

Venturi scrubbers are used widely (Calvert 1977a), being resistant to plugging and relatively efficient in collecting particles for a given cost. The venturi is generally mounted vertically; the gas flows downward through a converging section and a spray to the venturi throat, and from there to the diverging section and to a mist eliminator such as a cyclone.

As noted, a venturi scrubber is designed to produce a spray (generally by gas atomization) near its throat. Run without the liquid, a well-designed venturi can produce more than a 10-fold acceleration of the gas in the throat without producing a pressure drop of greater than 10–20% of the velocity head ($\frac{1}{2} \rho_G U_G^2$) of the gas in the throat; the angles of convergence and divergence for venturi scrubbers are about 20–25° and 5–7°, the gradual expansion being used to reduce energy losses. The pressure drop in a venturi scrubber depends on viscous losses and expansion and contraction losses, but predominantly on the power consumed in accelerating the droplets that scrub the gas (Yung et al. 1977a).

The factors to be decided on in the design of the scrubber include angles of convergence and divergence, throat cross-sectional area and length, and liquid-to-gas ratio. The angles of convergence and divergence are not critical within the range of the conventional designs. The cross-sectional area is determined by the gas volume flow rate and the desired throat velocity. The throat length criterion is given below; it represents a compromise between increased particle collection and increased frictional flow resistance as throat length is increased. The liquid-to-gas ratio affects both the pressure drop and the collection efficiency; in general, changing the ratio $\dot{V}_L/\dot{V}_G$ may improve collection efficiency at a given pressure drop, but it also changes the amount of water to be handled for recirculation and disposal.

Fairly complex design optimization procedures have been presented by Goel & Hollands (1977) and by Yung et al. (1977b). The method presented below is a hybrid of earlier work by Calvert (1974) and more recent work of Calvert and coworkers (Yung et al. 1977b).

The first step is to determine the design penetration $\overline{Pt}$, the fraction of the inlet mass concentration to be emitted from the outlet. The particle size distribution is approximated by a log-normal distribution of known mass median diameter d_{pg} and geometric standard deviation σ_g. The mass median aerodynamic diameter d_{pga} is determined either directly from the measurements made to obtain the size distribution (impactors classify by aerodynamic diameter, for example) or by using the mass median diameter corrected for density (for $d_p \gtrsim 1\ \mu m$):

$$d_{pga} \doteq \rho_p^{1/2} d_{pg} \qquad [9.2.31]$$

or corrected still further for both particle density and Cunningham slip correction by solving

$$\left(1 + 2.5 \frac{\lambda}{d_{pga}}\right) \rho_0 d_{pga}^2 = \left(1 + 2.5 \frac{\lambda}{d_{pga}}\right) \rho_p d_{pg}^2 \qquad [9.2.32]$$

The aerosol size distribution parameters and the required penetration can be used to determine the necessary cut diameter, using figure 9.2.8, which comes from Calvert et al. (1972a), who derived it by integrating an expression of the form

$$Pt = \exp - Ad_p^2 \qquad [9.2.33]$$

(approximately correct for a venturi) and log-normal aerosol distributions having various mass median diameters and geometric standard deviations. Figure 9.2.8 gives the total penetration $\overline{Pt}$ for various σ_g as a function of the ratio of the mass median aerodynamic diameter d_{pg} to the scrubber cut diameter d_{pac}, the diameter for which $\overline{Pt} = 0.5$. By using $\overline{Pt}$ and the aerosol size parameters, the necessary cut diameter can be found.

From a figure presented by Calvert (1974) showing the results of many measurements on venturi scrubbers, it can be determined that the relationship between particle cut diameter and scrubber pressure drop (in the ranges of gas velocities and liquid-to-gas ratios that are common) is

$$d_{pac} = (2.2 \ \mu\text{m}) \left(\frac{\Delta p}{0.25 \ \text{kPa}}\right)^{1/2} \qquad [9.2.34]$$

for Δp between 0.25 and 25 kPa, from which the required pressure drop can be

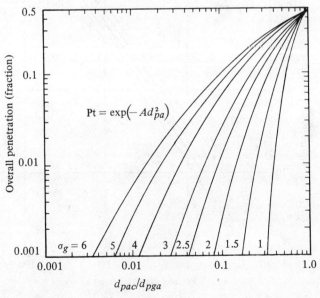

Figure 9.2.8 Overall penetration versus cut to mass median particle diameter ratio for log-normally distributed particles (Calvert et al. 1972).

calculated. The pressure drop is due almost entirely to the gain in momentum of the water spray. For air and water at dimensionless throat lengths of about 2, the pressure drop in pascals is (Sparks 1978)

$$\Delta p = 807 \; U_G^2 \; \frac{\dot{V}_L}{\dot{V}_G} \qquad\qquad [9.2.35]$$

The pressure drop required for adequate collection efficiency determines the product of the throat velocity squared and the liquid-to-gas ratio. Generally, $\dot{V}_L/\dot{V}_G$ should be on the order of 10^{-3}.

Another consideration is the size of the droplets formed by atomization, if the spray is not preformed. The characteristic drop diameter d_d predicted from the correlations developed by Nukiyama and Tanasawa (Green & Lane 1964) for a water-and-air system becomes (Yung et al. 1977b)

$$d_d = \frac{0.0050}{U_G} + 0.92 \left(\frac{\dot{V}_L}{\dot{V}_G}\right)^{1.5} \qquad\qquad [9.2.36]$$

To aid in the choice of the throat velocity and the liquid-to-gas ratio, figure 9.2.9 presents the optimally efficient drop diameter for the collection of particles of the

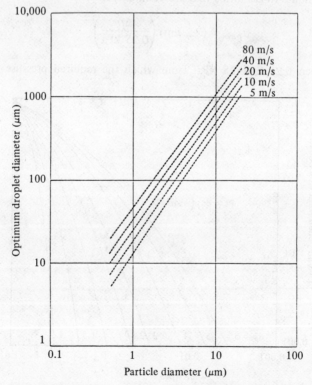

Figure 9.2.9 Scrubber droplet size for maximum collection efficiency, based on the Yung et al. (1977b) model (Wolffinden et al. 1978).

indicated aerodynamic diameter at various throat velocities. The finer the particles to be collected, the smaller the optimum droplet size.

The throat length criterion presented by Yung et al. (1977b) is that penetration at constant pressure drop is optimized for

$$2 \leqslant \frac{3}{2} \frac{C_{D1} L \rho_G}{d_d \rho_L} \leqslant 3 \qquad [9.2.37]$$

where L is the throat length, in meters, and C_{D1} is the drop drag coefficient at the throat inlet:

$$C_{D1} = 0.22 + \frac{24}{Re} (1 + 0.15 \, Re^{0.6}) \qquad [9.2.38]$$

where Re is the droplet Reynolds number at the throat inlet:

$$Re = \frac{\rho_C U_G d_d}{\mu_G} \qquad [9.2.39]$$

To sum up, the venturi-scrubber design method is as follows:

1. Determine the required cut diameter from the required penetration for the aerosol mass median aerodynamic diameter and geometric standard deviation.
2. Determine the pressure drop required to obtain the required cut diameter from [9.2.34].
3. Choose $\dot{V}_L / \dot{V}_G$ to be within a factor of two of 1×10^{-3}, constrained by the equation relating this ratio and the throat velocity to the pressure drop, taking into account the optimal drop diameter for collecting an aerosol particle somewhat smaller than d_{pga}, and taking into account that the throat length parameter includes not only the throat length but also the droplet diameter and the throat drag coefficient. A certain amount of trial and error is needed. The design can be checked against the predictions of one model (Calvert et al. 1972a) by a programmable calculator program, described next.

Sparks (1978) prepared a programmable calculator program for the determination of penetration of an aerosol with a log-normal size distribution through a venturi scrubber. From the gas velocity in the venturi throat U_G and the liquid-to-gas ratio $\dot{V}_L / \dot{V}_G$, the pressure drop and the droplet diameter are determined. The aerosol is specified by its mass median diameter and its geometric standard deviation. The integration of the equation for penetration (as a function of particle size) is performed by trapezoidal-rule numerical integration, the user specifying the lower and upper bounds of the integral

$$\overline{Pt} = \int_{d_{pi}}^{d_{pf}} Pt(d_p) \, f(d_p) \, dd_p \qquad [9.2.40]$$

as well as the increments for integration Δd_p. The user specifies temperature T, particle diameter and density, and gas viscosity, from which is calculated the inertial parameter. Specifying the scrubber liquid density and an empirical factor ($f = 0.5$, generally), the user obtains the integrated penetration $\overline{Pt}$ for the aerosol of fractional mass size distribution $f(d_p)$.

9.2.2.8 Mist Eliminators (Entrainment Separators, Demisters)

Introduction

Scrubbers use liquid droplets or wetted surfaces to clean the gas stream of particles. In either case, droplets containing solid and dissolved material must be captured before the gas is emitted to the atmosphere. (Wetted surfaces produce droplets due to atomization or due to liquid flow patterns that cause droplets to fall from the surfaces.) As liquid usage is increased, so is entrainment; as energy input to the scrubber is increased, through increased pressure drop in the gas or increased spray-nozzle pressure, the entrained liquid droplets can be expected to become smaller, and their mass concentration greater. To prevent emission of material due to droplet reentrainment, which can lead to concentrations of particles in the outlet that in some particle size ranges are greater than the inlet concentrations, the scrubber should be followed by a mist eliminator (also called an entrainment separator).

Types of Mist Eliminators

Mists formed by atomization from scrubber surfaces have number mean diameters of about 10^2–10^3 μm. Generally, the higher the gas velocity, the smaller the droplets. Mists from spray scrubbers have the size distributions characteristic of the spray. In cases where the mist forms from condensation of water vapor, the droplet size is usually less than 1 μm; these are much more difficult to collect and are not discussed further here. For the larger droplets, the collection mechanisms that come into use are gravity settling, centrifugal collection, and impaction (Calvert 1978).

Although sedimentation does occur, sedimentation chambers (having residence times long in comparison to the time it takes a droplet to fall a length equal to the chamber height) are rarely used as mist eliminators.

Centrifugal collection and inertial impaction are really the same collection mechanism: The gas stream has its direction (and sometimes speed) changed, and the droplet's inertia gives it a velocity component perpendicular to the mean gas flow. Devices operating on this principle include cyclones, baffled chambers (using chevrons, corrugated sheets, etc.) and packed beds (with packing material of many geometries, such as spheres, saddles, rings, fibers, and a range of characteristic collector dimensions and volume void fractions).

Design Goals

In general, mist eliminators should have the following characteristics: no clogging, low cost, ease of manufacture and installation, low pressure drop, and high efficiency over a wide range of superficial gas velocities and mist loadings. The units should be self-draining and self-cleaning, with low operating and maintenance charges, and able to operate for long periods without attention (Bell & Strauss 1973). Many of these factors will be considered in what follows.

Pressure drop The pressure drop across the mist eliminator represents the energy expended per unit volume of gas flowing through the device. The contributions to the pressure drop can be identified as friction drag and form drag, proportional to velocity and velocity squared, respectively. The pressure drop as a function of superficial velocity (gas volume flow divided by scrubber cross-sectional area before any baffles or obstacles are introduced) is of the form

$$p = aU_G + bU_G^2 \qquad\qquad [9.2.41]$$

As the surface-to-volume ratio in the scrubber decreases, for flows that are turbulent, the U_G^2 term predominates (e.g., Bell & Strauss 1973). Packed-bed pressure drop can be estimated using the Ergun equation (see section 9.2.4.2), and predictive correlations are available for cyclones (Leith & Mehta 1973). The pressure drop required will be determined by the collection efficiency needed, so the relationship between pressure drop and efficiency is discussed next.

Collection efficiency Primary collection efficiency is the fraction of the droplets that is caught on collection surfaces. Total collection efficiency is the fraction of droplets that is retained by the mist eliminator. The difference is due to reentrainment of the captured droplets.

Inertial collection of a droplet is correlated with the impaction parameter. Thus, demister collection efficiency can be expected to change as a function of droplet size. Droplet size is a function of scrubber type, geometry, power consumption, and flow velocity; for example, for a packed-bed cross-flow scrubber, Bell & Strauss (1973) found the number mean droplet size to decrease from 400 to 100 μm as superficial velocity in the scrubber increased from 3 to 5 m/s. Calculation of the total efficiency would require integrating the collection efficiency as a function of droplet size. By using the droplet cut diameter, Calvert (1974) described convenient methods for obtaining the total collection efficiency for droplets (or aerosols) assumed to be log-normally distributed in droplet size with known mass median diameter and geometric standard deviation. Figure 9.2.10 shows the droplet cut diameter as a function of entrainment-separator pressure drop for several types of separators. The power advantage of the wire mesh is apparent, although this may be offset by cleaning and plugging problems.

As noted, the pressure drop increases as volume throughput (superficial velocity) increases. At first this may lead to increased collection efficiency. Beyond some velocity, however, the flooding of the separator or the reentrainment of droplets from the separator surfaces will produce an increase in emissions, and thus an apparent decrease in efficiency. Approximate values of superficial velocity at which entrainment begins are given in table 9.2.6. As Calvert (1977) concluded, liquid drainage is best when the gas flow is horizontal and collection surfaces are near vertical; also, with this configuration, reentrainment occurs at higher flow rates than for horizontal elements.

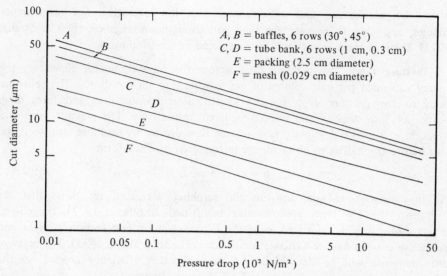

Figure 9.2.10 Entrainment-separator performance cut diameters (Calvert & Parker 1978).

Plugging Captured solids and dissolved material that precipitates from solution can build up on scrubber and entrainment-separator surfaces, leading to increased flow resistance. Recirculation of the scrubbing liquid aggravates this condition. Some actions that may help reduce this problem are:

1. Reduce slurry concentrations.
2. Design collection elements to have nearly vertical surfaces.
3. Provide for washing of the collection surfaces.
4. Avoid drying of the surfaces; if the scrubber is shut off, clean before reusing.
5. Design using geometries having larger, rather than smaller, minimum flow-path dimensions (i.e., choose a chevron over a knitted mesh, other things being equal).

9.2.2.9 Corrosion

Corrosion problems are often very specific to the source type under control. Here we focus on two important areas of application: the metallurgical and power production industries.

Table 9.2.6 Superficial Velocity at which Entrainment Begins[a]

Separator	Gas velocity (m/s)
Zigzag with upward gas flow and horizontal baffles	3.7–4.6
Zigzag with horizontal gas flow and vertical baffles	4.6–6.1
Cyclone (gas inlet velocity)	30.5–39.6
Knitted mesh with vertical gas flow	3.1–4.6
Knitted mesh with horizontal gas flow	4.6–7.0
Tube bank with vertical gas flow	3.7–4.9
Tube bank with horizontal gas flow	5.5–7.0

[a]From Calvert (1977a).

Some case histories of scrubber applications and problems in the metallurgical industry were presented by Steiner & Thompson (1977). For a variable-orifice venturi used by Armco Steel to control gaseous and particulate emissions on one of the company's boilers, abrasion of the mild-steel piping carrying the scrubber slurry for recycle was found to be a problem. Steiner & Thompson (1977) reported that the problem was cured by using rubber-lined piping and valving. Operation of a Steam-Hydro scrubber (a spray ejector type using waste heat) proved quite satisfactory for control of sinter-plant emissions, but corrosion (believed due to inadequate pH control) was substantial for the carbon steel in the water supply lines; no corrosion was noted for the 304 stainless steel used in the air flow part of the system. In a scrubber system used on an open hearth furnace, designed for operation without pH control, the same company experienced severe corrosion problems with mistakenly installed non-stainless-steel components. Changing to lime neutralization (pH of 8–8.5) gave widespread scaling due to calcium sulfate, later somewhat mitigated by switching to caustic neutralization (pH of 5.5–6). Steiner & Thompson (1977) emphasized that as water quality restrictions become more stringent, the problems of high recirculation rates, sophisticated chemical treatment modes, and solids removal and handling all make successful scrubber operation more difficult; water treatment problems coupled with energy considerations make scrubbers less attractive to the steel industry than previously.

The results of 59 corrosion tests in nine flue-gas desulfurization (FGD) processes at 14 plant locations were presented by Hoxie & Tuffnell (1976). They summarized their conclusions as follows: "Corrosion tests in a number of flue-gas desulfurization units have shown that carbon steel, low alloy steels, and Type 304L stainless steel are inadequate in the wet portions of the scrubbers. Type 316L stainless steel is sometimes subject to localized corrosive attack in scrubber environments with certain combinations of pH and chloride content. A corollary is that corrosion of Type 316L stainless steel might be controlled by control of scrubbing media pH and chloride content." They found molybdenum and nickel useful alloying elements in conferring resistance to localized corrosion; they presented rather complete corrosion and composition information for more than a dozen steels.

Busch et al. (1973) pointed out three options in providing corrosion protection: liners, different construction materials, and thicker materials. Listed below are their cost estimates (December 1970) for venturis with capacities of 23.6 m^3/s:

Construction material	Cost (December 1970)
0.64-cm carbon steel	$19,600
0.80-cm carbon steel	30,100
0.64-cm Type 304 stainless	36,000
0.64-cm Type 316 stainless	51,500
0.64-cm carbon steel with 0.48-cm rubber liner	22,200

These cost estimates can be updated readily, using the Marshall and Stevens index.

9.2.3 BAG FILTRATION

James H. Turner

9.2.3.1 Introduction

Baghouse design and operation are very much a matter of art. Equations used to describe other particle removal processes are not applicable to the complex processes taking place in a baghouse. It is only recently that modeling, by Dennis et al. (1977), has become effective for the design and operation of these installations.

9.2.3.2 Description of Fabric Filtration

Bag filtration makes use of fabric bags to trap dust particles from air pumped through the filter system (figure 9.2.11). In industrial applications the systems are called fabric filters or baghouses. Capacity may vary from a few cubic meters per minute up to several hundred thousand cubic meters per minute. The bags are most

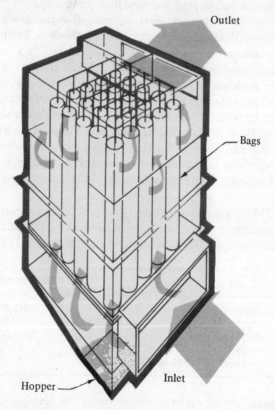

Figure 9.2.11 Baghouse.

commonly tube-shaped, and they may range from 10 cm to 1 m in diameter, and from about 1 to 10 m in length. It is essential to clean the bags periodically, to prevent excessive resistance to flow by accumulated dust cake (Leith et al. 1977, 1978).

9.2.3.3 Types of Baghouses

The fabric type and cleaning method may be used to categorize baghouses. Pore type, yarn count, fabric weight, nap, and finish are important in choosing woven fabrics for various bag applications. Nonwovens such as felts and spun-bonded fabrics are also used (Miller et al. 1977). Gas stream temperature and resistance to corrosion and abrasion are important factors in choosing which fabric to use for a particular application (McKenna et al. 1975). The fabric should trap dust particles, but must also release the dust during cleaning. Various treatments may enhance the performance of a particular fabric. A rough rule of thumb is that the effective pore diameter of the fabric should not be more than about 10 times the effective particle size of the dust to be trapped. Table 9.2.7 shows the compositional qualities of various filter fabrics.

The seam areas of bags can cause problems: (1) the seam area is a barrier to flow; (2) the seam area is susceptible to mechanical or chemical attack; (3) sewing thread may not match the bag fabric's characteristics; and (4) puckering of the seam induces stress.

The accumulated dust must be removed from operating bags, usually as clumps of particles that can fall into a waiting dust hopper. Both overcleaning and undercleaning can lead to serious problems—excess emissions, reduced bag life, excess energy consumption, shortened life of mechanical parts, and excessive pressure drops that may even lead to explosions from back pressure. Mechanical energy (shaking) or gas motion (pulse jet, reverse air or jet) is usually used to clean the bags. Shaking is typically carried out for one compartment at a time, and is preceded by a settling period of 1–2 min. A frame holding the bags is oscillated to impart a wave motion to the bags for up to a minute. Figure 9.2.12 shows a typical shaker bag attachment.

Pressure drop is used as an indicator of the need to clean the bags. Shake frequency and amplitude (half-stroke) are important factors in efficiency. A typical frequency is 4 Hz, with an amplitude of 5–8 cm. Too high an amplitude may result in reduced bag life and/or metal fatigue; increased frequencies can shake the whole structure to the point of collapse.

Pulse-jet cleaning involves a sharp blast of compressed air blown down the bag to expand the fabric and carry the dust cake away, as shown in figure 9.2.13. This method is not suited to woven fabrics, which would be overcleaned; felts are the normal choice. Mechanical complexity and compartmentalization are also avoided. Support cages are needed for these bags, owing to the inward gas flow.

Typical cages are made of 3-mm-diameter wire with cage wire spacings of about 5 by 20 cm. It is important not to allow the metal structure to become rusted or corroded, which can lead to fabric damage. Economic factors may suggest discarding bag and cage as a unit when bags must be replaced, especially when corrosion is present. Designs allowing outside access, to change bags and to find leaking bags, have been developed.

Table 9.2.7 Some Properties of Filter Fabrics[a]

Fiber	Operating exposure Long term (°C)	Short term (°C)	Supports combustion	Frazier permeability (m³/h)[b]	Resistance[c] to Abrasion	Mineral acids	Organic acids	Alkali	Remarks
Cotton	80	105	Yes	22–45	G	P	G	G	
Wool	95	120	No	45–135	G	F	F	P	Bags may last 20 yr in some applications.
Nylon	95	120	Yes	34–67	E	P	F	G	
Acrylic	130	135	Yes	45–101	G	G	G	F	Avoid strong alkalis and humid heat; inexpensive.
Polyester	135	165	Yes	22–135	E	G	G	G	
Polypropylene	95	120	Yes	16–67	E	E	E	E	Slick surface for good cake release; strong, inexpensive.
Nomex	195	230	No	56–123	E	F	E	G	Avoid hot, humid, acid conditions.
Glass	260	315	Yes	22–157	P–F	E	E	P	Once finishing agent degrades, fibers abrade and are destroyed.
Teflon	235	260	No	34–146	F	E	E	E	Dewpoint excursions and condensation of corrosives may be a problem. Good dust release; may shrink and/or stretch.
Gore-Tex									Laminate of microporous polytetrafluoroethylene layer and woven or felted fabric; provides exceptional filtration, release, and pressure-drop characteristics in difficult applications.
Stainless steel	500	650							Heavy and expensive; corrosion may be a problem; recent development, with not much data available.

[a] Adapted from Control Techniques for Particulate Air Pollutants.
[b] ASTM D 737; amount of air (ft³/min) flowing through 1 ft² of fabric under a differential pressure of 0.5 in H₂O (converted to SI units). Actual correlation with efficiency may be poor.

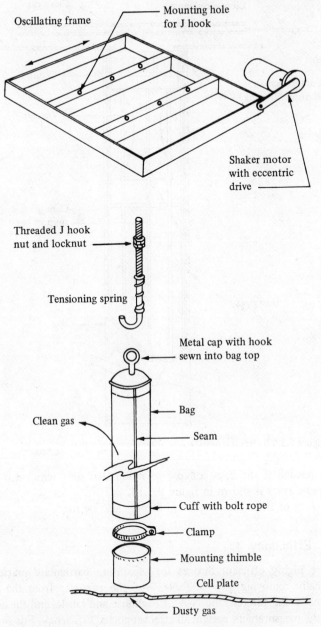

Figure 9.2.12 Representation of shaker bag attachment.

Reverse air cleaning is a gentle cleaning method used to extend the life of fragile fabrics such as glass. After a settling period of 30–90 s, fan-driven gas, usually from the baghouse exit duct, is blown through the filter bags in the direction opposite forward flow. The flexing of the fabric and the airflow remove a portion of the dust cake. A second or third cleaning cycle may be needed. Spreader

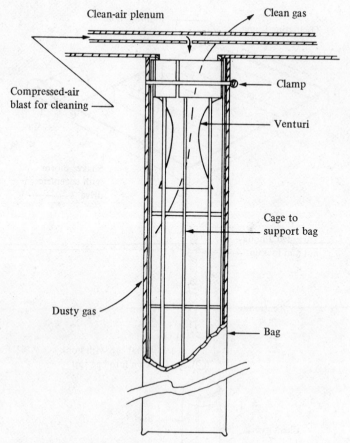

Figure 9.2.13 Representation of pulse-jet arrangement.

rings may be needed if the bags collapse so much that dust removal is impeded. A bag with spreader rings is shown in figure 9.2.14.

Combinations of these cleaning methods may also be used.

9.2.3.4 Efficiency

Bag filters are highly efficient devices for separating particulate matter from gas streams, typically removing 99.9–99.999+% of the particles from the gas (Dennis 1952). The dust being filtered, the type of baghouse and fabric, and the accuracy and sensitivity of the measurement system all affect reported efficiency. For small particles (0.003–0.5 μm), efficiency may be in the 97% range (Cass & Bradway 1976).

Fiber filters (e.g. furnace filters) are typically used only for comparatively light dust loadings and are discarded while dust accumulations are relatively low. Large amounts of void space (very open, porous structure) are typically present. Fiber filters are thus used primarily for light-duty applications.

In contrast, fabric filters can handle high dust loadings, accumulate considerable amounts of dust between cleanings, and have much less void space. Residual dust retained within the fabric and accumulated dust cake contribute largely to the efficiency after break-in of the bags. Most particles that penetrate leak through comparatively large openings in the fabric or seams. Penetration may increase by a factor of three for a tenfold increase in velocity. Overcleaning of the bags or the wrong fabric can also result in poor efficiency.

Pressure drop is the pressure difference in the gas stream between the baghouse inlet and outlet. With a cleaned bag, there is little resistance to flow at first, but pressure drop through the bags increases (e.g. 5-10 cm H_2O) until the bags are cleaned. Figure 9.2.15 shows changes in pressure drop during a typical filtration cycle.

9.2.3.5 Advantages and Disadvantages of Fabric Filtration

In relation to other particulate collection devices—cyclones (section 9.2.6), electrostatic precipitators (section 9.2.5), and scrubbers (section 9.2.2)—bag filters are used where there is a need for very high efficiency in removing particles in the micrometer or submicrometer range. Cyclones are comparatively inexpensive, but generally are not very efficient for particles smaller than about 5 μm. Scrubbers are smaller than baghouses or electrostatic precipitators (ESPs), but require more energy at high efficiencies, produce a liquid effluent, and have an exit gas stream that is

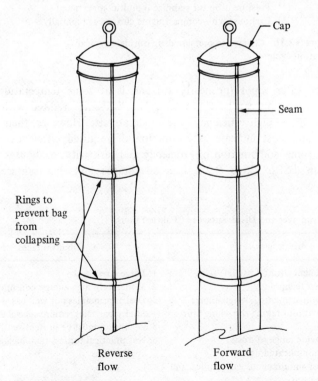

Figure 9.2.14   Bag with spreader rings to prevent collapse.

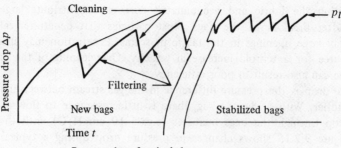

Pressure drop for single bag or compartment

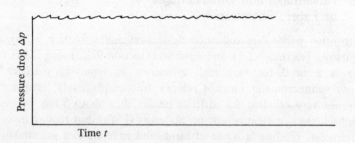

Pressure drop for stabilized, multicompartment
baghouse with compartments cleaned sequentially

Figure 9.2.15   Changes in pressure drop during a typical
filtration cycle.

saturated with water vapor (or nearly so) and is at some temperature below the
boiling point. Corrosion can be a problem. The ESPs are credited with having low
energy consumption, high efficiency, and moderate size. However, their size, energy
consumption, and cost increase as a function of required efficiency and particle
resistivity. At some combination of efficiency and resistivity, baghouses become less
expensive than ESPs. Table 9.2.8 lists advantages and disadvantages of fabric
filters.

Table 9.2.8   Advantages and Disadvantages of Fabric Filters

Advantages	Disadvantages
1. Very high efficiency for all particle sizes	1. Large size
2. Old, established technology	2. Moderately high energy consumption
3. Modular or compartmented design allows maintenance without taking the whole unit out of service	3. Design principles not well based in theory
	4. Sticky particles require special designs
	5. Operation must be protective of bags
4. Can handle a wide range of dusts	6. Not practical for less than high-efficiency applications
5. Relatively uncomplicated device	
6. Can be used for simultaneous gas sorption and particulate removal	

9.2.3.6 Applications

Baghouses are ubiquitous. The range of dusts they can handle is quite broad, and their physical size may be small enough to cover less than 1 m^2, or as large as hundreds of square meters. They can be used for any service in which the dust or gas properties do not destroy bags in an uneconomically short time. In some applications bag life may be a few months, and in others it may be 20 years.

Table 9.2.9 is a listing of baghouse applications. The table shows dusts for which design information exists. Designing for applications that have not previously been attempted can be a frustrating experience because of the lack of understanding of the fabric filtration process.

9.2.3.7 Design

The size of a baghouse depends on the gas volume to be treated, the cleaning method used, and the characteristics of the particles to be removed. The amount of fabric needed to clean the gas must be determined—pressure drop, limiting particle penetration, and past experience may be used as design criteria. The relationship between the gas flow and the amount of fabric needed to clean it is expressed as the air-to-cloth ratio (A/C). As high an A/C as possible would reduce size, capital cost, and number of bags. An allowance should be made for bag cuffs and seams and for the need to have compartments out of service for cleaning or maintenance. Too high an A/C leads to problems: excessive pressure drop, excessive penetration, reduced bag life, and difficulties in meeting legal emission standards. Gross A/C may be calculated as the total amount of fabric in the baghouse (bag circumference times length times number of bags) divided into the design gas volume flow.

The pressure drop Δp, in newtons per square meter, is directly related to the velocity of the gas flow through the fabric and its associated dust layer. One relationship, developed from Williams et al. (1940) is

$$\Delta p = S_E \langle U \rangle + K_2 G \langle U \rangle^2 t \qquad [9.2.42]$$

where S_E is the effective residual drag of cleaned, stabilized fabric, in newton-minutes per cubic meter; $\langle U \rangle$ is the average (superficial) velocity through filter, in meters per minute; K_2 is the dust specific resistance coefficient, in newton-minutes per gram-meter; G is the dust concentration in gas stream, in grams per cubic meter; and t is the filtration time, in minutes. Experimentally derived values of K_2 should be used, but with caution; Dennis et al. (1975, 1977) have shown that cleaning cycles often allow insufficient time for a true determination of K_2. If measured values of S_E are not available, see [9.2.48].

A mathematical model and machine computation method are available to improve the calculation of the pressure drop (Dennis et al. 1979a, b, c). The pressure drop across the individual compartments at any time in the filtration and cleaning cycle can be determined. Though the model was developed for coal fly ash collected on woven-glass fabrics, it should be applicable to other more or less spherical particles and woven fabrics. The model is based on findings that, during cleaning, dust came off the fabric in slabs or patches, leaving some parts of the bag clean to

Table 9.2.9 Baghouse applications[a]

Application	Fabric	Cleaning[b]	Air-to-cloth ratio (m/min)	K_2[c] (N min/g m)
Abrasives	Polyester	S	0.92	0.033
Alumina	Polyester	S	0.58	
			0.67	0.033
Aluminum	Cotton, nylon	S		
Aluminum oxide	Cotton	S	0.61	
Asphalt plant drier	Glass, Nomex, cotton, wool	P, R, S	0.76–2.23	0.284
Asbestos	Cotton, nylon	S	0.84	0.364
Baking powder			0.76	
Bauxite	Cotton		0.76	
Beryllium sinter	Polypropylene, acrylic	P, S	1.83–6.1	
Bismuth and cadmium	Cotton		1.83–2.44	0.451
B.O.F.	Cotton	R, S	0.55–1.37	20.04–38.91
Bronze powder			0.61	
Buffing operation			0.92–0.99	
Calcimine			0.79	
Carbon	Acrylic		0.61	
Carbon black	Glass, Nomex, Teflon, acrylic	R, S	0.34–0.49	3.67–9.35
Cement	Cotton, glass, acrylic, polyester	R, S	0.46–0.64	2.00–11.69
Ceramics		S	0.76	
Charcoal		S	0.69	
Chocolate		S	0.69	
Chrome ore		S	0.76	
Chrome salts	Wool		0.73	2.51
Clay	Cotton	S	0.69	
Cleanser		S	0.69	
Cocoa		S	0.69	
Coke		S	0.69	
Copper	Glass, acrylic	S	0.18–0.82	2.51–10.86
Corn				0.10–1.47
Cork		S	0.92	
Cosmetic		S	0.92	
Cotton		S	1.07	
Dolomite	Polyester	R	0.21	112.0
Electric furnace	Glass, acrylic	R, S	0.46–1.22	7.5–119.0
Feldspar		S	0.76	1.05–4.56
Fertilizer		S	0.61–0.73	
Flint		S	0.76	
Flour	Cotton		0.76	
Fly ash (coal)	Glass, Teflon	P, S, R	0.58–1.8	1.17–2.51
Fly ash (oil)	Glass	R	1.98–2.35	0.79
Fly ash (incinerator)	Glass, Teflon	P, R, S	0.61–1.83	
Foundry	Glass, polyester, polypropylene, nylon	S	0.64	0.10–20.0
Glass	Polyester	S	0.76	
Grain	Cotton	S	0.99	
Granite		S	0.76	

Table 9.2.9 Baghouse applications (*Continued*)

Application	Fabric	Cleaning[b]	Air-to-cloth ratio (m/min)	K_2[c] (N min/g m)
Graphite		S	0.61	
Grinding dust		S	0.69	
Gypsum	Cotton, acrylic	S	0.76	1.05–3.16
Hypochlorite mfg.	Acrylic	P	1.0	2.51
Iron ore		S	0.61	
Iron oxide		S	0.61	
Lampblack		S	0.61	7.88
Lead blast furnace	Polyester	R, S	0.31	9.52
Lead dust	Acrylic		0.73–10.7	
Lead oxide	Acrylic	S	0.69	
Leather dust		S	1.07	
Lime kiln	Glass	R	0.70–1.50	
Limestone		S	0.84	
Magnesium trisilicate			~0.15	
Manganese		S	0.69	
Marble		S	0.92	
Mica	Cotton	S	0.69	
Milk powder				0.75
Molybdenum	Wool			
Oats				0.26–1.84
Oyster shell		S	0.92	
Paper		S	1.07	
Perlite	Polyester, glass, Nomex	S, P	0.92–2.1	
Pigments	Cotton	S	0.61	0.38–0.48
PVA	Wool	R	3.05	4.18
PVC	Wool, polyester			
Plastics		S	0.76	
Quartz		S	0.84	
Resin	Cotton	S	0.82	0.10–4.21
Rock dust		S	0.99	
Sanding machine		S	0.99	
Silica	Nomex	S	0.84	
Soap	Polyester, acrylic	S	0.69	0.27–0.52
Soapstone		S	0.69	
Starch	Cotton, wool	S	0.69	
Stucco	Cotton, polyester	R, S	1.04	1.50
Sugar		S	0.69	
Talc		S	0.69	
Titanium dioxide	Cotton, acrylic			15.7–34.4
Tobacco	Cotton, polyester	S	1.07	6.01
Wood	Cotton	S	1.07	0.47–1.05
Zinc	Acrylic, cotton, Nomex	R, S	0.55–0.92	1.17–8.35
Zinc oxide				2.62

[a]Table compiled from various sources. For a given application, other fabrics, cleaning methods, and air-to-cloth ratio may be used. Many other sources use baghouses. Many cotton applications have been replaced by polyester.

[b]S = shake; P = pulse jet; R = reverse air.

[c]K_2 is the dust specific resistance coefficient; see [9.2.42].

the surface and others virtually uncleaned. The fraction of fabric cleaned can be estimated and used to calculate the pressure drop (see [9.2.45]). Little change in the size distribution of dust passing through the fabric was found, because penetration was primarily by leakage through large pores in the fabric that failed to seal over during filtration.

Drag may be calculated as follows:

$$S = \frac{\Delta p}{\langle U \rangle} = S_E + K_2 W \qquad [9.2.43]$$

where S is the drag, in newton-minutes per cubic meter and W is the dust loading on fabric, in grams per square meter. This relationship is shown graphically in figure 9.2.16.

The limiting pressure drop (the point at which the bags are to be cleaned owing to design factors) may be calculated with

$$\Delta p_l = S_E \langle U \rangle + K_2 \langle U \rangle (W_p - W_R) \qquad [9.2.44]$$

where Δp_l is the limiting pressure drop, in newtons per square meter; W_p is the fabric loading at Δp_l, in grams per square meter; and W_R is the residual fabric loading for cleaned areas, in grams per square meter.

The drag or pressure drop may be calculated by using the cleaning characteristics of the bags:

$$S = \frac{\Delta p}{\langle U \rangle} = \sum_{i=1}^{n} \left(\frac{A_c}{s_c} + \frac{A_{u1}}{s_{u1}} + \dots + \frac{A_{ui}}{s_{ui}} \right)^{-1} A \qquad [9.2.45]$$

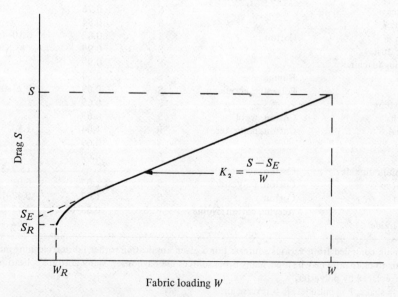

Figure 9.2.16 Plot of drag versus fabric loading (cake mass).

where A_c is the cleaned area of fabric, fraction; s_c is the drag of cleaned area (set $= S_E$), in newton-minutes per cubic meter; A_{ui} is the uncleaned area element of fabric, fraction; s_{ui} is the drag of uncleaned area element, in newton-minutes per cubic meter; A is the total surface fraction $= 1$; and n is the total number of fabric elements ($\leqslant 10 \times$ number of compartments). The term A_c is different for different kinds of cleaning. An example of the calculation for pressure-controlled intermittent cleaning by reverse-flow/bag-collapse is

$$W_p' = \frac{p_l - S_E\langle U\rangle}{K_2\langle U\rangle} + W_R + \frac{c_1\langle U\rangle\Sigma t}{2} \qquad [9.2.46]$$

where W_p' is a corrected dust loading, in grams per square meter; c_1 is the inlet dust concentration, in grams per cubic meter; and Σt is the time to clean all compartments, in minutes.

$$A_c = 1.51 \times 10^{-8}(W_p')^{2.52} \qquad [9.2.47]$$

Other cases that may be calculated via the model include reverse-flow/bag-collapse intermittent cleaning by timer, reverse-flow/bag-collapse continuous cleaning (first compartment cleaned in sequence immediately after last compartment), shake intermittent cleaning by pressure control, and continuous shake cleaning.

The computer model supplies default values for variables not experimentally determined, but predictive accuracy may suffer. For example,

$$S_E = 350 \text{ N min/m}^3 \text{ at } 25°C \qquad W_R = 50 \text{ g/m}^2 \qquad [9.2.48]$$

Although Dennis and Klemm (1979a) stress the importance of having experimental values of K_2 they provide an equation for adjusting K_2 as a function of velocity for coal fly ash with a mass median diameter (MMD) of 9 μm and a geometric standard deviation σ_g of 3 (at $25°C$):

$$K_2 = 1.8\,\langle U\rangle^{1/2} \qquad [9.2.49]$$

They also provide an equation for calculating K_2 for a dust of known specific surface parameter when K_2 is known for the same dust at another value of the specific surface parameter:

$$K_{2,\text{new}} = K_{2,\text{old}}\left(\frac{s_{0,\text{new}}}{s_{0,\text{old}}}\right)^2 \qquad [9.2.50]$$

where s_0 is the specific surface parameter, in centimeters^{-1}:

$$s_0 = \frac{6d_s^2}{d_v^3} = 6\,\frac{10^{1.151\log^2 \sigma_g}}{\text{MMD}} \qquad [9.2.51]$$

where d_s is the surface mean diameter, in micrometers and d_v is the volume mean diameter, in micrometers. Equation [9.2.51] includes the assumption of a log-normal particle size distribution. To predict K_2 when only the particle size distribution, discrete particle density, and bulk particle density of the cake are known, one may use

$$K_2 = \frac{\mu_G s_0^2}{6\rho_p C} \frac{3 + 2\,\beta_a^{5/3}}{3 - 4.5\,\beta_a^{1/3} + 4.5\,\beta_a^{5/3} - 3\,\beta_a^2} \qquad [9.2.52]$$

where μ_G is the gas viscosity, in poise; ρ_p is the density, in grams per cubic centimeter; C is the Cunningham correction factor, which approaches 1 for large (fly ash) particles, dimensionless; β_a equals $\bar{\rho}/\rho_p$; and $\bar{\rho}$ is the bulk particle density for cake, in grams per cubic centimeter.

Experiments by Penney (1978), Frederick (1978), and Miller et al. (1978) have shown that pressure drop (and efficiency) can be strongly influenced by electrostatic effects or electric fields. The charging of dust, either by impingement on metal surfaces or by corona charging, has provided altered cake structure formation and reduced pressure drop. Reductions in pressure drop of 80% across the fabric have been seen by placing fields near the fabric surface and perpendicular to the gas flow. Field strengths on the order of several thousand volts per centimeter were used.

Baghouse design may also be based on controlling the amount of penetration (material passing through the baghouse). In the EPA-Dennis fabric filtration model the following equation was derived from work with coal fly ash and glass fabrics:

$$c_2 = \text{Pn}_s + (0.1 - \text{Pn}_s)e^{-aW}c_1 + C_R \qquad [9.2.53]$$

where c_2 is the outlet concentration, in grams per cubic centimeter; Pn_s is the fractional penetration constant; a equals $3.6 \times 10^{-3}\,\langle U \rangle^{-4} + 0.094$, in square meters per gram; C_R is the rear face sloughoff $= 0.5$ mg/m^3; and

$$\text{Pn}_s = 1.5 \times 10^{-7} \exp\left[12.7\,(1 - e^{-1.03\langle U \rangle})\right] \qquad [9.2.54]$$

System penetration at any time may be calculated as

$$\text{Pn}_t = \frac{1}{\langle U \rangle_t IJ} \sum_{i=1}^{I} \sum_{j=1}^{J} \text{Pn}_{ij_t} \langle U \rangle_{ij_t} \qquad [9.2.55]$$

for I compartments, each subdivided into J areas.

Equation [9.2.55] is used in the computer model to give the system penetration at any time, for face velocities and fabric loadings that change with respect to both time and place within the baghouse.

9.2.3.8 Other Design Considerations

Precollectors such as cyclones are often used upstream of a baghouse. Since cyclones preferentially collect large particles, the size distribution of dust entering the baghouse is shifted to smaller particles, with a consequent increase in the pressure drop across the baghouse. For polydisperse dusts there is an economic balance between cyclone pressure drop and resulting baghouse pressure drop. As the cyclone is made more efficient, its pressure drop rises, but so does the pressure drop for the baghouse. Capital and operating cost considerations usually can determine if a cyclone should be used, and how efficient it should be.

Baghouses use force-draft (pushthrough) fans or induced-draft (pullthrough) fans. Forced-draft fans handle dusty gas and can suffer from erosion, imbalance, and high temperature. Induced-draft fans handle clean gas (until bags break or the house is bypassed) and may see significant amounts of in-leaking air that can raise the effective A/C, cool the incoming gas below the dew point, and cause maldistribution and stagnation in the gas flow. If there is a considerable temperature difference between the points where forced-draft or induced-draft fans would be placed, an induced-draft fan may be significantly smaller and use less heat-resistant materials and lubricants.

Fan selection is an important consideration. The fan must resist abrasion and dust buildup, even on the clean side of the baghouse. Corrosion, especially at high temperatures or near saturation, must be considered. Fan capacity must be sufficient to meet any anticipated loads or overloads. Fan power must be high enough to carry dust as well as gas loads, and to handle the almost inevitable pressure-drop excursions. Fan outages may lead to costly process interruptions. The impeller type depends upon the application. Backward-blade impellers with steep blade angles and fan efficiencies of the order of 85% are often a reasonable choice (McFarland 1979). Standard designs are available to about 200,000 m^3/h and 16,000 N/m^2. Casing wear may be accelerated by bends near the fan inlet or by improper use of vane controls.

Baghouses can be very large structures. They must be designed to withstand wind loads, fan loads, expansion and contraction stresses, and snow loads.

Dew-point excursions resulting in condensation of potentially corrosive compounds or leaching of salts from the dust cake, causing stiffness and brittleness of the fabric, are an ever-present danger. Especially in high-temperature applications, consideration must be given to air preheaters, hopper heaters, insulation, and a design that prevents cold spots or edges from coming in contact with process gas, to prevent dew-point problems.

Ash must be handled; ordinarily, the dust falls into a hopper below the baghouse. Screw conveyers are frequently used to move the ash, despite the cost and clogging or bearing-wear problems. Dump valves can stick or clog. Bang plates should be installed on hopper surfaces; they can be hit with sledge hammers when dust fails to empty from the hopper. Hopper capacity before emptying must be sufficient to prevent incoming gas from lifting hopper dust back up into the bags and causing them to wear or blind. The estimation of the true hopper dust bulk density is important in determining hopper capacity.

Fire and explosion must be guarded against when collecting flammable dusts. High electrostatic voltages and resultant sparks can be generated throughout a baghouse. Cleaning mechanisms and other friction points may inadvertently become hot enough to initiate fire or explosion. Spark arresters may be required to prevent the burning of holes in the bags (regardless of bag composition). Incipient explosion detectors with quench or inert-gas systems are used, as are explosion panels or vents. Overtemperature sensors may be used to cause bypass of the baghouse, start cooling sprays, or admit dilution air. (When water is used, corrosion or clogging may result.)

Valves and dampers of various designs have their advocates; poppet valves are perhaps more popular than leaf dampers of guillotine dampers. Operating mechanisms must be accessible for maintenance, and not located in high-temperature areas such as roof peaks.

As with any mechanical device, maintenance is required. Maintainability should be designed into the fabric filter system. If the system is used as a pollution control device, maintainability and reliability are of paramount importance in preventing process shutdown because emission standards are exceeded.

Instrumentation must be available to monitor and record the pressure drop across each compartment and the entire baghouse. Compartment opacity monitors may be desired for leak detection, although some systems allow detection by visual inspection and location of dust piles. Some states require opacity monitors on dust collection system outlets.

Control systems vary from none to complex. For systems with little variation in operating conditions, timer-actuated cleaning may be sufficient. If conditions may vary, pressure drop-initiated cleaning would be preferable. Automatic bypasses, cooling systems, stack-cap openers, vents, and alarms may be required.

For caged-bag designs, there should be a means of preventing swinging of the cages caused by turbulent gas flow in the baghouse. Locating rods, grids, and hooks are used to prevent bag-to-bag abrasion. For baghouses requiring bag changing from inside, bags must be within the reach of maintenance personnel. In any design, the bags should not be spaced so closely as to touch, during either filtering or cleaning.

For long bottom-entry bags, some elutriation may take place. Smaller particles reaching the upper part of the bag may tend to penetrate the bag more or, conversely, blind the bag. (The term *blinding* is used to indicate an unpreventable increase in pressure drop across the fabric without the use of extraordinary cleaning methods.) The pressure drop may be higher than expected.

For very-high-temperature filtration, one may wish to investigate the use of metal-fabric bags or ceramic-fiber bags. Ceramic fibers have the potential for use up to 1200°C; suitable filtration and cleaning methods are under study. Alternative designs include granular-bed and ceramic-fiber-bed filters.

Acknowledging the state of the art, one should strive for flexibility in the operating parameters of a bag-filter design.

9.2.3.9 Operation

The normal operation of a well-designed baghouse ordinarily produces a clear discharge (if no condensible gases appear) and cyclical pressure drop traces that vary only with changes in process conditions. Abnormal operation may result from faulty design, abnormal process conditions, or mechanical failures. Symptoms of problems in operations include excess emissions, high pressure drop, blinded bags, and rapid fabric deterioration. Especially for new applications and new fabrics, there is a tendency to design for too high an A/C. The fabric cannot accommodate the increased rate of dust accumulation; cleaning suffers, the bags begin to blind, the pressure drop goes up, and cleaning is accelerated (if possible) to lower the pressure drop. The accelerated cleaning, high velocity, and excess pressure tend to destroy the bags. The same sequence may be initiated by other causes. A dust of smaller size than anticipated, or stickier, or less amenable to being cleaned from the fabric because of electrostatic or other effects, can cause blinding.

Attempts to clear blinded bags may include repeated normal cleaning of bags in place, vacuum cleaning, water lancing or steam cleaning in place, or removal and washing. There is the possibility of permanent alteration of the fabric's dust collection properties, for either better or worse. Faulty design that produces too high a pressure drop may sometimes be corrected by increasing the bag tension, by using more intensive cleaning, by changing fabrics, by using a bag-in-bag method to increase the fabric area, or by adding more baghouse. Sometimes, the problems are electrostatic in nature and can be solved by recognizing which dust-fabric combination can ameliorate the problem (Frederick 1978; Koscianowski et al. 1979).

Walsh & Spaite (1960) list methods for determining the causes of operational difficulties by maintaining and analyzing records of residual filter drag, terminal filter drag (drag just prior to cleaning), and residual velocity (face velocity in a compartment just returned to service after cleaning). The causes of high pressure drop, excessive bag wear, and poor efficiency can be determined when these problems result from various forms of improper cleaning, aged fabric, dust abrasion of fabric, or the wrong choice of fabric. The method is of utility only when approximately normal values are known for the drags and residual velocity. See also Stephan & Walsh (1960).

Pulse-jet units can develop problems from the condensation (or freezing) of compressed cleaning air, especially in outdoor installations during cold weather. Blow-pipe misalignment or blockage can occur.

Excess penetration may be caused by improper fabric selection, aged bags, bags with holes, too frequent or too energetic cleaning, too high an A/C, or too high a pressure drop. Unless a baghouse is large, one leaking bag can cause visible emissions from a stack. For installations with roof monitors or with inside-out filtering and no enclosure, the effects of a broken bag are harder to see.

The location of a broken bag can be determined in several ways. Visual examination of the clean side of a baghouse may show piles of dust near broken bags. Tapping a bag may cause a spurt of dust through a bag tear. A flashlight beam parallel to the bag surface often aids in detecting the spurt. A transmissometer or other optical device on the baghouse outlet shows a decrease in dust count when a compartment with a broken bag is taken off line for cleaning. Fluorescent powder may be injected into the baghouse inlet just prior to shutting the baghouse (or a compartment) off; ultraviolet-light inspection of the clean side of the baghouse should then show where the powder has leaked through. If leaking bags are not found quickly in some inside-out filtering baghouses, the spurt from a leaking bag may cause leaks in adjacent bags.

Although penetration changes with A/C, baghouses are not particularly sensitive to changes in dust concentration. Conservative design allows a moderate variation in gas load without causing visible emissions.

9.2.3.10   Costs

Order-of-magnitude capital costs for baghouses (in 1979) range from about $70 to $700 for each cubic meter per minute capacity, depending on whether the cost is based on components only or on turnkey construction, on shop construction or field erection, on low- or high-energy cleaning, on polyester or Teflon bags, on ambient- or high-temperature service, and on mild steel or stainless. Kinkley & Neveril (1976) give cost equations for several types of baghouses as follows:

Pulse-jet baghouse
Structure (no bags):

$$\text{Cost} = 4660 + 71.01 \times \text{fabric area} \qquad [9.2.56]$$

For stainless-steel construction, add

$$\text{Cost} = 1290 + 41.96 \times \text{fabric area} \qquad [9.2.57]$$

For insulation, add

$$\text{Cost} = 4150 + 21.52 \times \text{fabric area} \qquad [9.2.58]$$

Costs are in December 1975 U.S. dollars. The fabric area is in square meters, and is the net area.

Mechanical shake baghouse
Structure (no bags):

$$\text{Cost} = 5780 + 32.28 \times \text{fabric area} \qquad [9.2.59]$$

For stainless-steel construction, add

$$\text{Cost} = 5780 + 16.14 \times \text{fabric area} \qquad [9.2.60]$$

For insulation, add

$$\text{Cost} = 1930 + 16.14 \times \text{fabric area} \qquad [9.2.61]$$

For induced-draft baghouse, add

$$\text{Cost} = 1960 + 2.37 \times \text{fabric area} \qquad [9.2.62]$$

Reverse-air baghouse
Structure (no bags):

$$\text{Cost} = 22,300 + 27.97 \times \text{fabric area} \qquad [9.2.63]$$

For stainless-steel construction, add

$$\text{Cost} = 9090 + 15.06 \times \text{fabric area} \qquad [9.2.64]$$

For insulation, add

$$\text{Cost} = 9470 + 15.06 \times \text{fabric area} \qquad [9.2.65]$$

For induced-draft baghouse, add

$$\text{Cost} = 1470 + 3.01 \times \text{fabric area} \qquad [9.2.66]$$

Custom baghouse (assumed larger than about 5000 m^2 of fabric area, and field-erected)

$$\text{Cost} = 101,600 + 29.05 \times \text{fabric area} \qquad [9.2.67]$$

For stainless-steel construction, add

$$\text{Cost} = 50{,}000 + 15.06 \times \text{fabric area} \qquad [9.2.68]$$

For insulation, add

$$\text{Cost} = 38{,}000 + 15.06 \times \text{fabric area} \qquad [9.2.69]$$

The costs of fabrics, relative to each other, vary with market conditions. The relative costs in table 9.2.10 are approximate. Polyester bag prices in 1975 were approximately \$5.92, \$3.34, and \$2.15 per square meter for pulse-jet, shake and reverse air, and custom baghouses, respectively.

Turner (1980) projected 1980 capital costs of \$549.78–772.09 per cubic meter (\$46.73–69.47 per kilowatt) for utility boilers in the size range 1000–2000 MW. Projected annualized costs were 1.58–2.30 mills/kWh. Reported costs for existing units were generally lower.

Billings & Wilder (1970) gave the following annual cost distribution for bag filters:

Installed equipment:		15%
Fabric filter:	5%	
Fan and ducts:	6%	
Other:	4%	
Cost of capital:		11%
Plant overhead:		24%
Space:	5%	
Heat:	15%	
Insurance, etc.:	4%	
Replacement bag purchases:		10%
Labor:		29%
Fabric replacement:	11%	
General maintenance:	11%	
Dust disposal:	7%	
Electric power:		11%

Table 9.2.10 Relative Costs of Filter Fabrics

	Relative cost		
Fabric type	Pulse-jet	Shake and reverse air	Custom baghouse
Polyester	1	1	1
Acrylic	1.6	1.8	1.5
Nylon		2.2	2.0
Nomex	2.3	3.3	3.0
Glass (woven)		1.3	1.3
Polypropylene	1.2	1.7	1.5
Teflon	10–12	10–12	10–12
Gore-tex (depending on substrate)	4–12	6–11	6–11

The distribution does not account for the dramatic increases in the costs of energy and capital since 1970.

9.2.4 NONFABRIC FILTERS

Douglas W. Cooper

9.2.4.1 Introduction

For industrial air pollution control, the use of woven or felted fabrics for filtration is more common than the use of other types of filtration media. Even so, nonfabric filters are in use, often as beds packed with fibrous or roughly isometric collectors. For sampling particles from a gas stream for subsequent analysis, however, the use of fabric filters is rare in comparison to the use of various nonfabric filter media.

We shall distinguish between those filters that capture particulate material at their front surfaces and those that capture particles throughout their depth. Fabric filters, sieves, Nuclepore filters, and (usually) membrane filters are used to capture particles predominantly at their surfaces. Packed beds, meshes, fluidized beds, and (generally) glass-fiber filters are used to capture particles throughout their depths. This section on nonfabric filters is subdivided into sections on depth filters and surface filters. This subdivision is somewhat arbitrary, depending essentially on particle size: A surface filter has a high efficiency, for the particles of interest, in its first layer; a depth filter has a lower efficiency.

9.2.4.2 Depth Filters

Depth filters, such as packed beds and highly porous fibrous structures, generally have lower flow resistance than surface filters for the same collection efficiency and have higher dust-holding capacity, both advantages being due to the relatively open structure. Packed beds can also be made from a wider variety of materials than can fabric filters or other surface filters. The more open structure of depth filters has the disadvantages, however, of inherently larger space requirements and greater difficulty in removing the captured materials.

Applications

Beds packed with granular materials have found use in the control of emissions from cement and lime kilns and foundry and glass furnaces, as well as in the control of oxides of sulfur in fluidized-bed combustors. Depth filters made from fibrous materials are used in applications ranging from the high-efficiency collection of radioactive or biologically active particulates to the relatively low-efficiency filters for air conditioners. Fibrous filters such as the cleanable high-efficiency air filter (CHEAF, Anderson 2000, Inc.) and various fibrous and packed-bed mist eliminators have also found widespread application in industry.

The use of high-efficiency sand filters in the radiochemical and nuclear industries was described in detail by Burchsted et al. (1976). The sand-bed filter is generally installed in the ground, with the gas to be cleaned entering from the bottom and moving upward through about 10 layers of gravel and sand. The coarsest gravel (5 cm in diameter) is at the bottom; the material becomes progressively finer in succeeding layers, about 30 cm thick each, up to the last layer, which is composed of moderately coarse material (2 cm in diameter). The total depth is roughly 3 m, and the pressure drop is about 2.5 kPa. The superficial velocity is typically 2.5 cm/s, the porosity is 0.4, and the collection efficiency can be greater than 99% on aerosols of 0.7-μm count median diameter. The advantages of sand filters include low maintenance, high chemical and heat resistance, and ruggedness. They are relatively expensive (about \$74,000/m^3/s installed, in 1976), have relatively high power requirements, need a large area, and are awkward to dispose of, often being sealed and abandoned.

A very different filter used in the same industry is the high-efficiency particulate air (HEPA) filter. The requirements for being classified as a HEPA filter are a filtration efficiency of greater than 99.97% on 0.3-μm-diameter particles, a pressure drop of less than 250 Pa at the rated flow, and full-depth rigid casing. Generally these filters are made of fibrous papers of fiberglass, having a mixture of fibers ranging from a few micrometers to a few tenths of a micrometer in diameter (Burchsted et al. 1976).

Depth filters are important in air sampling (section 10.5). An example of the filter types available for particle sampling are those sold by Gelman Instrument Co. Gelman's Type A glass fiber filters have collection efficiencies said to be 99.97% or greater for 0.3-μm particles. The company also sells Type A/E filters, similar to the Type A but having particularly low levels of zinc and lead and having much less reactivity with sulfur dioxide, at some cost in mechanical strength. Glass fibers of even higher chemical purity are available.

Another important application of depth filters is mist elimination (see section 9.2.2).

Pressure Drop—Fibrous Beds

The pressure drop across a fibrous filter depends on the gas superficial velocity U_0 and viscosity μ, the surface-to-volume ratio of the fibers S ($S = 4/D$ for cylinders of diameter D), and their depth L, as well as the void fraction or porosity ϵ and the orientation of the fibers. The traditional Kozeny-Carman equation for pressure drop is (Happel & Brenner 1965)

$$\Delta p = k'S^2\mu U_0 L \frac{(1-\epsilon)^2}{\epsilon^3} \qquad [9.2.70]$$

which, for circular cyclinders, becomes

$$\Delta p = 16k'\mu U_0 L \frac{(1-\epsilon)^2}{D^2\epsilon^3} \qquad [9.2.71]$$

where k' is the Kozeny constant, equal to about 5 for porosities between 0.2 and 0.8. For fibers oriented transverse to the flow, k' is 6.0, and for fibers parallel to the flow, k' is 3.1 (Strauss 1966).

Pressure drop depends strongly on porosity, as can be seen from figure 9.2.17, for which the term $(1 - \epsilon)^2/\epsilon^3$ has been calculated for $\epsilon = 0.2, 0.3, \ldots, 0.8$. Over that range of porosities, the pressure drop changes 1000fold.

The Kozeny-Carman equation is thought to be satisfactory for $\epsilon < 0.8$. Davies (1973) cited his prior research with filter pads of different materials, having porosities from 0.7 to 0.994, as support for the equation

$$\Delta p = 64 \mu U_0 L (1 - \epsilon)^{1.5} \frac{1 + 56(1 - \epsilon)^3}{D^2} \qquad [9.2.72]$$

in which D is the mean fiber diameter. Davies noted that generally the pressure drop across a homogeneous multicomponent filter is less than the pressure drop across a filter composed of layers of the same weight of each component in series (Davies 1973).

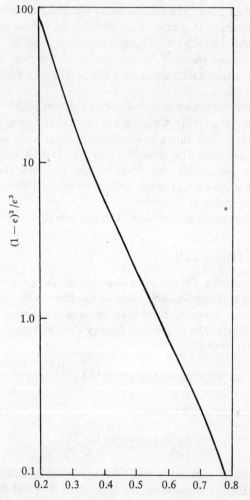

Figure 9.2.17 Values of $(1 - \epsilon)^2/\epsilon^3$ for $0.2 \leqslant \epsilon \leqslant 0.8$.

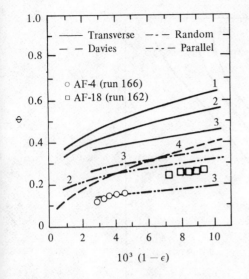

Figure 9.2.18 Comparison of (1) Kuwabara, (2) Happel, (3) Spielman and Goren, and (4) Davies empirical flow theories with experimental data for filters AF-4 and AF-18 at flow rates of 12.3–65.4 cm/s. The normalized pressure drop Φ is plotted as a function of fiber volume fraction $1 - \epsilon$ (Lawrence Livermore Laboratory 1978).

Other approaches to the prediction of the pressure drop include the cell models of Kuwabara and of Happel (Happel & Brenner 1965) and the model of Spielman & Goren (1968), which takes into account the damping effect of the presence of neighboring fibers. By expressing the pressure drop as

$$\Delta p = \mu U_0 L \Phi \frac{1 - \epsilon}{D^2} \qquad [9.2.73]$$

the function Φ of porosity was compared for these theories (and the equation of Davies) and for experiments, as shown in figure 9.2.18. The filters used were Johns-Manville AF-4 and AF-18 filters having diameters of approximately log-normal size distribution. The AF-4 had a number median fiber diameter of 0.73 μm and a geometric standard deviation of 2.0; the corresponding values for the AF-18 were 3.5 μm and 1.7. One reason why the experimental values are lower than most of the theoretical values is that any inhomogeneity in the packing of the fibers produces lower pressure drops than the homogenous packing assumed in the theories. For heterodisperse fiber diameters, it was recommended that Davies's equation be modified by using an effective fiber diameter

$$D_{ef}^2 = \frac{(\overline{D^2})^{3/2}}{\overline{D}} \qquad [9.2.74]$$

instead of D (Lawrence Livermore Laboratory 1978). Here, $\overline{D^2}$ is the fiber mean squared diameter.

A fibrous filter can be viewed as an array of fibers or as an array of pores. Figure 9.2.19 shows the results of calculations by Benarie (1969) for the percentage of flow through the upper 1, 5, and 10% of the pores (by size) versus the geometric standard deviation of the pore size distribution. When lines proportional to the mean fiber length are drawn at random to the required density, the areas of the resulting polygons (pores) are distributed log-normally, as had been noted by Benarie (1969) for the pores in a filter; the hydraulic radius distribution is also log-normal (Davies 1973).

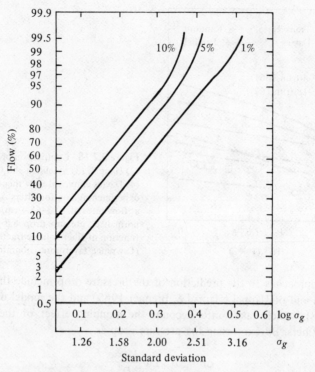

Figure 9.2.19 Percentage of the flow going through the largest 10, 5, and 1% of the pores in a filter, assuming laminar flow and a lognormal pore size distribution (Benarie 1969). The abscissa shows both the geometric standard deviation σ_g and its logarithm.

Pressure Drop–Granular Beds

For spherical collectors packed in a bed, a simple and useful equation for pressure drop, analogous to the Kozeny-Carman equation, is (Bird et al. 1960)

$$\Delta p = 150 \; \mu U_0 L \; \frac{(1 - \epsilon)^2 / \epsilon^3}{D^2} \qquad [9.2.75]$$

which is equal to [9.2.70] if one sets $S = 6/D$ and $k' = 25/6$. This is appropriate for

$$\mathrm{Re}_c = \frac{\rho U_0 D}{(1 - \epsilon) \mu} < 10$$

For higher collector Reynolds numbers, a second term should be added to give (Bird et al. 1960)

$$\Delta p = \frac{150 \mu U_0 L}{D^2} \frac{(1 - \epsilon)^2}{\epsilon^3} + 1.75 \frac{L}{D} \rho U_0^2 \frac{1 - \epsilon}{\epsilon^3} \qquad [9.2.76]$$

sometimes called the Ergun equation. For collectors of several different diameters, $D' = 6/S$ has been used instead of D, although Rudnick (1978) derived $D' = \overline{D^3}/\overline{D^2}$.

It has been noted that the solidity $1 - \epsilon$ for spheres ranges from 0.74 for closest packing (rhombohedral) to 0.524 for cubic packing, with 0.57–0.62 being typical (Lee et al. 1978); much more open structures are also possible if strong forces on collectors (such as adhesion) are present to counteract gravity.

Pressure Drop—Fluidized Beds

A fluidized bed is made of roughly isometric collectors resting on a perforated gas distributor plate and having free space above the surface they form when at rest (see chapter 8). Gas is introduced so as to flow upward through the distributor plate and through the collectors. As the gas velocity increases, the pressure drop across the bed increases, in accordance with the equations for packed beds, until the pressure drop is equal to the weight per unit area of the bed $[\rho_c(1 - \epsilon)gL]$. This velocity is the fluidization velocity. Above the fluidization velocity, the pressure drop across the bed does not increase with increasing velocity. The collector particles move freely, as though they were part of a fluid, and bubbling takes place as though the "fluid" were boiling. As the velocity is increased, the porosity and the height of the bed increase. The collectors become entrained in the gas as the gas velocity approaches their terminal settling velocities, setting a practical upper limit on the rate of flow.

Efficiency—Fibrous Beds

In principle, the problem of predicting fibrous-filter collection efficiency is straight-forward: Solve the Navier-Stokes equations for the flow of the gas, determine the forces acting on the particles, and integrate the particle equations of motion numerically to determine the particle trajectories and the fraction of those trajectories that result in capture. To make the problem tractable, however, various simplifications need to be made. For example, Yeh & Liu (1974a) performed such calculations using a modified Kuwabara-Happel flow field allowing for slip (non-continuum flow) effects. They found good agreement between their predictions and the results of their experiments and those of others (Yeh & Liu 1974b). Generally, one would not want to go to such lengths to predict collection efficiency, so various approximations are used.

The collection efficiency E_0 of a clean fibrous bed is approximately (e.g., Iinoya & Orr 1977)

$$E_0 = 1 - \exp\left[\frac{-4(1 - \epsilon)LE_c'}{\pi\epsilon D}\right] \qquad [9.2.77]$$

where E_c is the collection efficiency of a single fiber transverse to the flow, and E_c' is the collection efficiency of that fiber as part of an assemblage of fibers. If the collection is due to impaction, then it has been found that

$$E_c' = E_c \left[1 + a(1 - \epsilon)\right] \qquad [9.2.78]$$

where a is about 5–20 (Chen 1955). For impaction, the collection efficiency of a single fiber is approximately (from fitting data presented by May & Clifford 1967)

$$E_{cI} = \frac{\psi^2}{\psi^2 + 0.64}$$ [9.2.79]

where ψ is the impaction parameter:

$$\psi = \frac{U_0\tau}{D} = \frac{C\rho_p d_p^2 U_0}{18\mu D}$$

where τ is the particle relaxation time, D is the fiber diameter, U_0 is the gas velocity, C is the Cunningham correction factor, ρ_p is the particle density, d_p is the particle diameter, and μ is the gas viscosity. For collection by interception in viscous flow ($\text{Re}_D \ll 1$) (Fuchs 1964),

$$E_{cR} = \frac{(d_p/D)^2}{2.002 - \ln \text{Re}_D}$$

$$\text{Re}_D = \frac{\rho U_0 D}{\mu}$$ [9.2.80]

and in potential flow ($\text{Re}_D \gg 1$) (Fuchs 1964),

$$E_{cR} \cong 2 \frac{d_p}{D}$$ [9.2.81]

For most air pollution applications of fibrous filters, these two mechanisms dominate. Occasionally, gravitational settling is significant; the collection efficiency for a single fiber due to gravitation is approximately

$$E_{cg} \cong \frac{U_s}{U_0} = \frac{g\tau}{U_0}$$ [9.2.82]

Where gravitation is estimated to be the most important mechanism, then it may be worthwhile to use more exact equations for its effect (Iinoya & Orr 1977). Finally, for some situations involving submicron aerosols, diffusional collection can be dominant; it can be predicted with an equation by Friedlander (1958):

$$E_{cD} = 6 \, \text{Re}_D^{1/6} \left(\frac{U_0 D}{\mathfrak{D}}\right)^{-2/3}$$ [9.2.83]

Various methods have been proposed for estimating the effect of more than one collection mechanism. Only to a very rough approximation are they additive. For some collection-mechanism combinations, correlations available in the literature are quite successful in predicting collection efficiency (Davies 1973).

Electrical effects can occur or be induced. Particles may repel each other because they carry charges of the same polarity; they may be attracted or repelled by the fibers, depending on the electrical polarities; charged particles are attracted by their images in uncharged collectors. Uncharged particles are attracted by the inhomogeneous electric field from a charged collector (or from the divergence in field caused by the presence of dielectric collectors in an applied electric field).

Tables 9.2.11 and 9.2.12 (based on literature reviews by Cooper 1978 and Nielsen 1978) give the single-collector collection efficiency of an isolated collector, for a charged collector and a charged particle (F_{Qq}), a charged particle and an uncharged collector (F_{0q}), and a charged collector and an uncharged particle (F_{Q0}), for collection elements that are cylindrical or spherical, with electric force-parameter definitions. (K is the ratio of the migration velocity to U_0.) Note that the influence of neighboring fibers is not included in the table.

The collection efficiency is related to the total area of the collectors, the particle (migration) velocity induced toward the surface of these collectors, the volume flow rate, and the concentration profile. For collection to be appreciable, the product of the surface area and the migration velocity divided by the volume flow rate must be greater than 1. In figure 9.2.7 are presented the results of calculations of migration velocity for the electrostatic mechanisms.

The possible use of electrostatic augmentation with fibrous prefilters (for HEPA installations at nuclear plants) was studied by Nelson et al. (1978). They assumed that the penetration is the negative exponential of the product of the total migration velocity and the collection area divided by the flow rate, and that the total migration velocity could be set equal to the sum of the electrical migration

Table 9.2.11   Electrostatic Collection Efficiencies for Single Collectors
(Cooper 1978; Nielsen 1978)

Collector	Force	r dependence[a]	Parameter range	Efficiencies	Flow
Sphere	F_{Qq}	r^{-2}	All	$4K$	Incompressible
	F_{Q0}	r^{-5}	$K \gg 1$	$\left(\dfrac{15\pi}{8}K\right)^{2/5}$	Uniform
			$K \ll 1$	$4K$	All
	F_{0q}	$\dfrac{r}{(r^2-1)^2} - \dfrac{1}{r^3}$	$K \gg 1$	$\left(\dfrac{15\pi}{4}K\right)^{2/5}$	Uniform
			$K \ll 1$	$\left(\dfrac{72}{5}K\right)^{1/3}$	Potential
			$K \ll 1$	$(2K)^{1/2}$	Viscous
Cylinder	F_{Qq}	r^{-1}	All	πK	Incompressible
	F_{Q0}	r^{-3}	$K \gg 1$	$\left(\dfrac{3\pi}{2}K\right)^{1/3}$	Uniform
			$K \ll 1$	πK	All
	F_{0q}	$(r-1)^{-2}$	$K \gg 1$	$(4K)^{1/2}$	Uniform
			$K \ll 1$	$\left(\dfrac{4K}{2-\ln \mathrm{Re}}\right)^{1/2}$	Viscous
			$K \ll 1$	$(6\pi K)^{1/3}$	Potential

[a] r is made dimensionless by using the collector radius.

Table 9.2.12 Electric Force Parameter (K) Definitions (Nielsen 1978)

Sphere	Cylinder
Coulombic force F_{Qq} [a]	
$\dfrac{CQ_cQ_p}{24\pi^2\,\epsilon_0 R_p R_c^2 \mu U_0}$	$\dfrac{C\rho_c Q_p}{12\pi^2\,\epsilon_0 R_p R_c \mu U_0}$
Charged-collector image force F_{Q_0} [b]	
$\dfrac{\epsilon_p-\epsilon_0}{\epsilon_p+2\epsilon_0}\dfrac{CQ_c^2 R_p^2}{12\pi^2\,\epsilon_0 R_c^5 \mu U_0}$	$\dfrac{\epsilon_p-\epsilon_0}{\epsilon_p+2\epsilon_0}\dfrac{C\rho_c^2 R_p^2}{6\pi^2\,\epsilon_0 R_c^3 \mu U_0}$
Charged-particle image force $F_{0\,q}$	
$\dfrac{\epsilon_c-\epsilon_0}{\epsilon_c+2\epsilon_0}\dfrac{CQ_p^2}{24\pi^2\,\epsilon_0 R_p R_c^2 \mu U_0}$	$\dfrac{\epsilon_c-\epsilon_0}{\epsilon_c+\epsilon_0}\dfrac{CQ_p^2}{96\pi^2\,\epsilon_0 R_p R_c^2 \mu U_0}$

Definitions

Q_c = collector charge	C = Cunningham-Millikan slip correction factor
Q_p = particle charge	R_c = collector radius
ρ_c = collector charge per unit length	R_p = particle radius
ϵ_0 = fluid dielectric constant	U_0 = free-stream velocity
ϵ_p = particle dielectric constant	μ = viscosity
ϵ_c = collector dielectric constant	E_0 = uniform external electric field intensity

[a]For collectors of different geometry R_c is an arbitrary collector reference length (an equivalent radius, for instance) on which the definition of collection efficiency depends.
[b]For cylinders multiply by 2 to get Kraemer & Johnstone's (1955) definition.

velocities (U_{pc}, due to Coulombic forces, and U_{pp}, due to polarization forces) and the particle velocity due to all other collection mechanisms. Using a formula derived by Zebel (1966), they obtained the following expression for the negative logarithm of the ratio of the penetrations with (Pt) and without (Pt$_0$) electrical effects:

$$-\ln\frac{\text{Pt}}{\text{Pt}_0}=\frac{\alpha L}{\pi DV}\left[\frac{\epsilon_p-1}{\epsilon_p+2}\frac{\epsilon_f-1}{\epsilon_f+1}\frac{d^2E^2C}{12\,\pi\mu D}+\frac{nqEC}{3\pi\mu d}\frac{1+(\epsilon_f-1)/(\epsilon_f+1)}{1+nqEC/3\pi\mu U_a d_p}\right]$$

$$[9.2.84]$$

where L is filter thickness, α is its solidity, E is the imposed electric field, and U_a is the air velocity inside the filter (nearly U_0). If the electrical polarizabilities are much larger than one, which would be true for conductive materials and for time scales long in comparison to the time for charge to migrate in an insulator and generally short in comparison to the time the particles are in the vicinity of a collector (Cooper & Rei 1976), this expression simplifies to

$$-\ln\frac{\text{Pt}}{\text{Pt}_0}=\frac{\alpha L}{\pi DV}\left(\frac{d^2E^2C}{12\,\pi\mu D}+\frac{nqEC/3\,\pi\mu d_p}{1+nqEC/3\,\pi\mu d_p U_a}\right)\qquad[9.2.85]$$

Nelson et al. (1978) calculated the enhancement, $-\ln (Pt/Pt_0)$, for various field strengths, particle sizes, face velocities, fiber sizes, and packing densities. For particles of 0.29 μm diameter with five electronic charges passing through a filter of thickness 1.27 cm, fiber diameter 9 μm, and packing fraction 0.086, they predicted, for example, $-\ln (Pt/Pt_0) = 4.5$ at a filtration velocity of 0.325 m/s, assuming a fiber dielectric constant of 3.81 and a particle dielectric constant of 6.12. This represents nearly a 100-fold enhancement. In agreement with theory, their preliminary experiments showed particle penetration decreasing as electric field, packing density, and (generally) particle size were increased, and as face velocity and fiber diameter were decreased.

Besides these collection mechanisms, other effects can be important in determining the collection efficiency of fibrous beds. For example, sieving occurs when the particles are larger than the voids between the collectors. Sieving and other mechanisms can lead to the plugging of some flow channels, increasing the flow and changing the collection efficiency in the other channels.

A particle may rebound when it strikes a collector; it may continue to rebound throughout the bed or may come to rest as its kinetic energy is dissipated. One particle may strike another and dislodge it, or a particle may be reentrained in the gas flow. In general, rebound and reentrainment are more likely as particle size and gas velocity are increased.

The forces of adhesion depend on many factors (Davies 1973): Particle adhesion to fibers begins to fail when velocities increase past 4 m/s for 0.5-μm-diameter particles and is nearly complete below 1 m/s for 10-μm-diameter particles; aggregate chains of particles can be disrupted at lower velocities. Higher impact velocities increase adhesion. Particles may make several collisions with fibers before coming to rest in a filter. Liquid droplets adhere well, even when they do not wet the fiber, and liquid droplets may draw fine fibers together via capillarity, lowering filtration efficiency. Charged particles adhere better than uncharged particles.

Collection Efficiency—Granular Beds

A very extensive review of granular-bed filtration theory was presented by Tardos et al. (1978). They tabulated the flow fields studied by previous investigators, as well as the theoretical and experimental efficiencies. They concluded that the unit cell and statistical models provide reasonably good descriptions of the flow in loosely packed granular beds, but that the problem of filtration in a dense granular bed of solid granules is far from being solved. Lee & Gieseke (1979) achieved good agreement between experiment and theory by using the Kuwabara flow field for a packed bed and predicting collection efficiencies due to interception and diffusion.

Schmidt et al. (1978) reviewed and extended work on the prediction of efficiency and pressure drop in granular beds. They presented the following equation for the collection efficiency of a clean granular bed:

$$E_0 = 1 - \exp\left(-2kE_cL \, \frac{1-\epsilon}{D}\right) \qquad [9.2.86]$$

where the symbols mean for spheres what they meant for fibers in [9.2.77]. The value of k was determined empirically to be 3.75. For the single-sphere efficiencies they recommended the following [see Schmidt et al. (1978) for the original sources]:

$$E_{cD} = 8 \left(\frac{U_0 D}{\mathfrak{D}}\right)^{-1} + 2.308 \, \text{Re}_D^{1/8} \left(\frac{U_0 D}{\mathfrak{D}}\right)^{-5/8} \qquad [9.2.87]$$

$$E_{cR} = 1.45 \left(\frac{d}{D}\right)^2$$

$$E_{cI} = \frac{4.2 \, \psi}{\epsilon}$$

$$E_{cg} = \frac{U_s}{U_0}$$

They recommended that the single-sphere collection efficiencies be added to form the total single-sphere collection efficiency to be used in [9.2.87]:

$$E_c = E_{cD} + E_{cR} + E_{cI} + E_{cg} \qquad [9.2.88]$$

To minimize the ratio of penetration to pressure drop, one can use the design correlations they presented. These are

$$\frac{-\ln(1-E)}{\Delta p} \propto U_0^{-0.9} D^{-0.75} L^{0.0} (1-\epsilon)^{1.0} \qquad [9.2.89]$$

for particles having diameters larger than those for which efficiency is a minimum $(d_p > d_{\min})$, and

$$\frac{-\ln(1-E)}{\Delta p} \propto U_0^{-2.5} D^{-0.39} L^{0.0} (1-\epsilon)^{1.0} \qquad [9.2.90]$$

for particles smaller than $d_{\min}$. (This distinguishes between collection that is predominantly inertial and collection that is predominantly due to diffusion.) Note that this means low velocities, small collector diameters, and low porosities are generally favorable for reducing penetration per unit of power consumed. Factors such as rebound and reentrainment are much the same as they are for fibrous beds. For predicting electrostatic behavior, the electrostatic collection efficiency factors given in table 9.2.11 are useful first approximations, giving approximate single-collector efficiencies for spheres.

Collection Efficiency—Fluidized Beds

At velocities below the fluidization velocity, the bed acts as would any packed bed of similar geometry. Above the fluidization velocity, the motion of the bed particles generally enhances gas-particle-collector interaction, improving diffusion and mixing and facilitating the use of recirculating collectors. However, the channeling and bubbling that occur seriously degrade the collection efficiency. Figure 9.2.20 shows bed collection efficiency versus the ratio of the superficial velocity to the

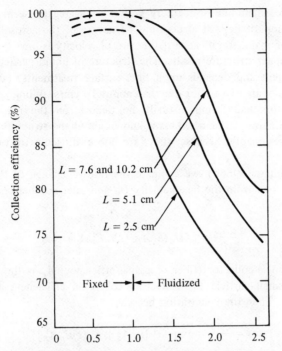

Figure 9.2.20 Collection of 0.67-μm DOP aerosol by beds of 175-μm alumina granules (Jackson 1974).

fluidization velocity for 0.67-μm-diameter dioctyl phthalate (DOP) droplets being collected on 175-μm alumina granules. The collection efficiency decreases markedly from above 95% as the velocity ratio exceeds 1.0.

Electrostatic forces can be used to enhance collection efficiency in fluidized beds (Zahedi & Melcher 1976). Zieve et al. (1978) reported collection efficiencies greater than 90% by mass on submicron particulates from an asphalt recycling operation. They found good agreement between the results and a theory that accounts for bubbling in the bed. The electric field was applied parallel to the flow, by use of screens that also helped to disrupt bubbling and channeling. Performance degraded somewhat as the bed became loaded, a condition identifiable by a decrease in pressure drop due to channeling, but the cycling rates for the collector particles (sand) can be adjusted to correct that problem.

Effects of Particle Accumulation— Fibrous and Granular Beds

Generally, a depth filter is designed to give the required collection efficiency at an acceptable pressure drop for the design flow rate. As captured particles accumulate within the filter, they present additional surface area for resisting the flow and capturing particles, often forming multiparticle chains.

"The dendritic, chain-like or feathery growth of aggregates seems to be a fairly common observation of deposit structure. The nature of the aerosol material does not seem to be of major significance if the aerosol velocity is low. If the velocity is high, a more compact structure results. The structure of liquid particle deposition is substantially different and depends upon fiber surface treatments" (Billings 1966a). "High" velocities apparently are greater than about 10 cm/s. Billings also noted that previous investigators had found virtually no deposit on the rear of fibers for velocities less than about 10^3 cm/s. Less is known about the structure of deposits in granular beds, presumably because they are more difficult to view under the microscope.

Following Billings (1966b), we estimate the rate of change of the number N_p of particles in the bed from the face velocity U_0 and inlet number concentration c_0 as

$$\frac{dNp}{dt} = c_0 U_0 (E_c' A_c + N_p E_p' A_p') \qquad [9.2.91]$$

where E_c' is the single-collector (fiber or grain) efficiency, A_c is the total collector area, E_p' is the single-particle (as collector) collection efficiency, and A_p' is the single-particle area. Then the penetration becomes

$$Pt(t) = \frac{c(t)}{c_0} = \exp \{- [E_c' A_c + N_p(t) E_p' A_p']\} \qquad [9.2.92]$$

or

$$\frac{Pt(t)}{Pt(0)} = \exp [- N_p(t) E_p' A_p']$$

If $N_p(t)$ is proportional to $c_0 U_0 t$, the penetration should decrease exponentially with time. [Davies (1970) presented an analysis that extended this kind of approach.]

In experiments he performed with monodisperse 1.3-μm-diameter aerosols, Billings (1966b) did find an exponential decrease in penetration versus loading for measurements using 10-μm-diameter fibrous mats having solidities $1 - \epsilon$ of 0.0087–0.027. Typically, penetrations were followed until they had decreased by a factor of two.

The pressure drop across the filter should increase linearly with time for very light loadings (collected mass per unit area). Because loading is the product of concentration, velocity, efficiency, and time, and since the resistance increment from each particle is proportional to velocity (assuming viscous flow around the particle), the rate at which the pressure drop increases due to collected particles should be proportional to the square of the filtration velocity.

The foregoing formulas for pressure drop in granular and fibrous beds indicate the effects of added particulate material: The bed porosity diminishes, and the mean square collector diameter changes; overall, the pressure drop increases (at a given flow rate). If the particles are added uniformly and singly throughout a very porous medium, the resistance increases linearly with the amount collected, each particle adding its unit of resistance. If the particles are not added uniformly, if they raise the collection efficiency, or if they result in a nonnegligible change in the porosity, they tend to make the pressure drop increase more than linearly with the amount deposited.

Davies (1970) found that filter resistance increased (for constant flow rate and inlet concentration) by e^{at}, where a depends on the structure of the filter and the nature of the aerosol and is smaller for filters of open structure. Davies noted, further, that filter papers show nonconstant values of a; they have large values initially, which become smaller as the paper pores are clogged and a cake forms with resistance that is characteristic of the particles, not the paper. Figure 9.2.21 shows that the increase in resistance with particle loading occurs at increasing rates for increasing velocities, as expected; that the data seem linear suggests $at \ll 1$ for these experiments.

For sand beds, Miyamoto & Bohn (1975) found that the ratio of initial penetration to final penetration was proportional to the mass of material collected per unit area, raised to a power between 0.57 and 1.0. They found that the pressure drops across the beds increased nonlinearly at higher loadings, with the onset of the nonlinear dependence being at heavier loadings for coarser sands.

Cleaning

The buildup of particulate matter in the bed can degrade performance by raising the pressure drop and, in some cases, by increasing the effective penetration as captured material dislodges from the bed.

The major alternatives for handling the particle buildup are:

1. *Disposal.* HEPA filters, some sand beds, and the high efficiency air filter (HEAF, formerly a product of Johns-Manville, now sold by Anderson 2000, Inc.) are simply disposed of when they are too dirty to use.

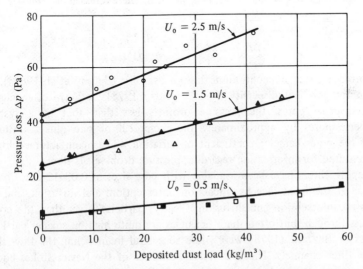

Figure 9.2.21 Pressure drop of fibrous filters with dust loading (Iinoya & Orr 1977).

2. *In-place washing.* Many packed-bed devices act as scrubbers, being constantly sprayed with water to remove captured material; the cleanable high efficiency air filter (CHEAF) (Brady et al. 1977) is cleaned in this way.
3. *In-place dust dislodging.* Some gravel beds and the panel-bed sand filter (Squires & Pfeffer 1971) are cleaned by reverse airflow while in place.
4. *Recirculation.* Fluidized beds as well as cocurrent, cross-current, and counter-current moving-bed collectors can be cleaned by continuous removal of dirty collectors and addition of clean ones. Cross-current operation produces inherently uneven flow, however. To prevent clogging and because collectors covered with fine particles are often more efficient than clean collectors (excluding reentrainment conditions), it is advantageous to run moving beds cocurrent with the flow, rather than countercurrent (which is preferable for gas heat and mass transfer processes).

9.2.4.3 Surface Filters

Nuclepore and Membrane Filters

Nuclepore (Nuclepore Corp., Pleasanton, Calif.) filters are made from thin ($\sim$10 μm) polycarbonate sheets that are exposed to neutrons from ^{235}U and etched in a bath to produce nearly cylindrical holes approximately perpendicular to the filter face (Spurny et al. 1969a; Fleischer et al. 1964). They are used for collecting aerosol samples for optical or electron microscopy. They have been proposed for use as a size-discriminating sampler (Spurny et al. 1969b), one that could be used to separate particles into respirable and nonrespirable fractions (Parker et al. 1977), the fractions smaller than and larger than about 3.5 μm.

Spurny et al. (1969a) found that the pressure drop for a clean Nuclepore filter followed the Hagen-Poiseuille law. This law can be expressed as (Fan & Gentry 1978)

$$\Delta p = 2.28 \times 10^{-2} \frac{\mu L\ U_0/\epsilon}{D^2} \qquad [9.2.93]$$

A slip correction (for noncontinuum flow) is available (Spurny et al. 1969a), as is a correction for pore polydispersity (Fan & Gentry 1978); both are often negligible. (For polydisperse pores, the pressure drop is less than that of a system of monodisperse pores by approximately the reciprocal of one plus six times the square of the pore diameter coefficient of variation.) The manufacturer's literature can be consulted for information regarding pressure drop versus flow.

Nuclepore filters have been available with pore sizes of 0.03–12 μm. Collection takes place at the front face by impaction, interception, and diffusion, and within the pores by interception and diffusion. Clearly, particles larger than the pore size do not pass through, but often the efficiencies are quite high on smaller particles.

Parker & Buzzard (1978) were quite successful in modeling the flow through Nuclepore filter channels. Their numerical solutions of the Navier-Stokes equations closely matched the behavior found using flow visualization techniques in a scaled-up glycerol-plastic system. The collection efficiencies they measured for particles from 2 to 8 μm in diameter were within 10% of the predicted efficiencies (ranging from 22 to 92%), based on incorporating impaction and interception in their mathematical model.

Spurny et al. (1969a) presented equations for collection by diffusion in the pores, as well as equations for collection by impaction and interception. They showed the implications of these equations for changes in particle size, pore diameter and length, gas flow rate, temperature, and pressure. Their measurements were made with particles for which diffusion (and occasionally interception) would have dominated, and these measurements matched their predictions very well. Manton (1978; 1979) presented an analysis for diffusion to the face of the filter, pointed out shortcomings of the flow fields and efficiency equations of Spurny and coworkers, and presented his own analysis of the collection efficiency due to impaction and interception. Zebel (1974) modeled the collection due to electrostatic effects. Collection efficiency for these filters was also studied analytically and experimentally by Kanaoka et al. (1979), who presented an extensive set of charts for its determination. Those wishing to predict collection efficiency as a function of particle size should see the works cited above.

Spurny et al. (1969a) presented a theory for the increase of pressure drop with amount of material collected by such filters. The results of their experiments did not match the theory for heavy deposits of solids but were deemed in good qualitative agreement for liquid aerosols and for the collection of light deposits of solid aerosols. Spurny et al. (1974) presented further experimental results for the clogging of the filters and pointed out three regimes: (1) relatively slow pressure increase as particles decrease the open cross section of individual pores, followed by (2) accelerated pressure drop increase as captured particles help capture more particles and tend to produce closed pores, and ending ultimately in (3) slower increases in pressure drop as a cake is formed over the pores and the particles add resistance by building up the thickness of the cake.

Membrane filters, highly porous structures formed from various materials, have been available in pore sizes of 0.45, 0.8, and 5 μm. Collection efficiencies for membrane filters have been measured by Liu & Lee (1976) and studied theoretically by Kanaoka et al. (1979).

Paper Filters

Filter papers can be viewed as depth or surface filters, depending on the particle size under consideration. Iinoya & Orr (1977) noted that conventional laboratory filter papers have collection efficiencies below 90% for 0.3-μm particles, in contrast to high-efficiency glass-fiber filters (such as the HEPA filters discussed above). The pressure drop is about 100 N/m^2 at 1 cm/s of superficial filtering velocity at no dust load, and is proportional to the velocity either with or without a dust deposit. In these filters, the fiber diameter is about 20 μm, and the volume fraction of fibers is about 0.25–0.30. The thickness of these filters is usually 0.2–0.3 mm (Iinoya & Orr 1977).

Collection efficiency as a function of particle size and of superficial velocity was measured by Stafford & Ettinger (1972). The filters used were Whatman 41

Table 9.2.13   Pertinent Filter Parameters (Liu & Lee 1976)

Filter	Mfr code	Nominal pore diameter (μm)	Pore density (pores/cm^2)	Porosity (%)	Thickness (μm)
Nuclepore	N060	0.6	3×10^7	8.4	10
	N100	1	2×10^7	15.6	10
	N300	3	2×10^6	14.1	10
	N500	5	4×10^5	7.8	10
	N800	8	1×10^5	5	10
Fluoropore	FH	0.5	–	85	125–150
	FA	1	–	85	125–150
Mitex	LS	5	–	60	125–150
	LC	10	–	68	125–150

filter paper and IPC 1478, a particularly loosely woven fiber mat paper. A minimum efficiency was shown to exist at a particular particle size that depended on filtration velocity. Similarly, a minimum efficiency was found at a particular velocity that depended on particle size. This was in qualitative agreement with theoretical predictions assuming only diffusion and impaction.

Table 9.2.13, based on manufacturers' information, comes from the work of Liu & Lee (1976). The membrane filters are manufactured by the Millipore Corp. (Bedford, Mass.); Mitex is the company's name for its 5- and 10-μm pore filters; Fluoropore is the company's name for its 0.5- and 1.0-μm pore filters. At the lowest flow rates studied, Liu & Lee found collection efficiency minima at particle diameters of a few tenths of a micrometer for 0.6- and 1.0-μm Nuclepore filters. For particles smaller than the minimum-efficiency particle size, diffusion predominated; for larger particles, impaction and interception predominated. For the other filters, collection efficiency increased as particle size increased. The Nuclepore filters were found to be less efficient for a given particle size (in the submicron range) than were membrane filters having similar pore sizes. For particles between 0.03 and 1.0 μm in diameter, the membrane filters had minimum efficiencies that ranged from 62% (for the 10-μm pore size) to 99.99+% (0.5- and 1.0-μm pores). The Nuclepore filters had efficiency minima that ranged from effectively zero to 80% (for the 0.6-μm pore filter).

The Nuclepore filters are preferable to the membrane filters in those applications (such as microscopy) where surface uniformity is important. A much greater resistance to flow, in comparison to membrane filters of the same pore size and face area and in comparison to glass-fiber filters of the same face area, is one of the disadvantages of such filters, however. Glass-fiber filters are typically employed where it is essential to have greater than 99% collection efficiency on the aerosol being sampled, although membrane filters are also this efficient for particle sizes equal to or greater than the pore size.

Summary—Surface Filters

The choice of which surface filters to use for sampling depends on the particle-analysis method chosen. Glass-fiber filters capture virtually all the particles drawn through them; membrane and paper filters are somewhat less efficient; Nuclepore filter collection efficiencies depend strongly on pore size and particle size. The pressure drop for the clean filters can be obtained from the literature, but it increases as particulate matter is collected; Nuclepore filters are particularly susceptible to abrupt increases in pressure drop as particle loading increases.

9.2.5 ELECTROSTATIC PRECIPITATION

Heinz L. Engelbrecht

9.2.5.1 Introduction

The continuing performance of electrostatic precipitators at high collection efficiency levels requires adequate sizing, suitable design, and good operation and maintenance procedures. Precipitator operation is always influenced by, restricted by, and dependent on the process equipment it serves. Thus, this equipment must be operated within given parameters and under specific conditions.

To understand the operation of an electrostatic precipitator, it is essential to know some basic facts about precipitator theory, such as the effects on the collection efficiency of changes in process conditions, fuels, etc. Each precipitator consists of certain components necessary to perform the tasks of charging, precipitating, and removing the collected particulates. Various designs are in use. Although specific maintenance program requirements may vary from process to process and from plant to plant, some basic steps and procedures are common to all. Normal precipitator operation includes proper procedures for startup and shutdown, as well as guidelines for troubleshooting. Electrostatic precipitators represent a major portion of the investment in an industrial plant. Equipment life and performance are essential to the operation of the plant.

The cost of an electrostatic precipitator depends on the (1) gas volume to be treated, (2) collection efficiency to be achieved, and (3) precipitability of the particulates to be collected. The latter characteristic is often referred to as the *precipitation-rate parameter* and is decisive for the specific size of the electrostatic precipitator, the collecting-surface plate area per unit gas volume.

Unit costs for electrostatic precipitators for various collection efficiency levels under easy or difficult precipitation conditions can be calculated. Such cost (circa 1979) can range from $70 to $175/m^3/min of gas at a collection efficiency of 99%,

Figures 9.2.22–9.2.27 are published courtesy of Wheelabrator-Frye Inc., Air Pollution Control Division.

and from \$100 to \$200 per m³/min of gas at a collection efficiency of 99.7%, typical for fly-ash precipitators in the power industry under the revised "New Source Performance Standards."

There are several reasons for proper precipitator operation and maintenance. The most important are (1) continuously meeting present emission control codes, (2) prolonging precipitator life, (3) maintaining the productivity of the process unit served by the precipitator, (4) reduction of operating expenses, and (5) maintaining good public relations.

9.2.5.2 Electrostatic Precipitation Process

Electrostatic precipitators are applied to separate particulate matter from waste or process gases in a variety of industrial processes. The fundamentals of their operation have been extensively described in the literature. Two of the many publications in this field are those by White (1963) and Oglesby (1970).

The electrostatic precipitation of particulate matter suspended in a gas flow requires that the particles, solids, or liquid droplets be electrically charged, transported toward a collecting surface, precipitated on this surface, discharged and removed from this surface into a hopper, and from there moved into an external dust-handling system for reuse or disposal. The gaseous components of the carrier gas are virtually unaffected by this process.

Electrostatic precipitation, a term that is commonly used, is really a misnomer, since the process is not "static" at all. An electric current flows between the discharge electrode (usually negatively charged) of a small cross-sectional area (such as wire) and the collecting electrode (usually at ground potential) of a large surface area (such as plate or tube). In operation, a unidirectional (dc) voltage of the order of 10,000–100,00 V is applied across the electrodes. The gas stream passes through the space between the electrodes.

At a certain voltage level, ionization of the gas molecules takes place at or near the surface of the discharge electrode and is evidenced by a corona without sparking. The ionized gas molecules migrate toward the collecting surface and charge passing particulates by field and diffusion mechanisms. Most of the particulates pick up negative charges and move to the grounded (positive) collecting-surface plates. The charging and collecting of the particulates continues through the electrostatic precipitator. The rate of migration of the particulates toward the collecting-surface plates depends on the charge acquired by the particulates and the electric field between the electrodes and can be described as a migration velocity:

$$U_p = \frac{QE_pC}{3\,\pi\mu d_p}$$ [9.2.94]

where U_p is the migration velocity, near collecting surface, of particle of diameter d_p, in meters per second; Q is the charge on particle, in coulombs; E_p is the electric field near the collecting electrode, in volts per meter; d_p is the particle diameter, in meters; μ is the gas viscosity, in kilograms per meter-second; and C is the Cunningham correction factor.

Several mathematical models are available that describe the collection efficiency of an electrostatic precipitator. The modified Deutsch-Anderson equation is an example:

$$E = 1 - \exp - \left[\left(\frac{U_k A}{V} \right)^k \right]$$

[9.2.95]

where E is the collection efficiency, fraction; U_k is the migration velocity, near collecting surface, of particles in monodisperse aerosol, in meters per second; A is the collecting surface area, in square meters; V is the gas volume, in cubic meters per second; and k is a nondimensional exponent. The residual dust content downstream of the precipitator is called the *penetration:*

$$Pt = 1 - E$$

[9.2.96]

where Pt is the fractional penetration. The ratio between collecting-surface area and gas volume is called the *specific collecting-surface area* (SCA):

$$SCA = U_k^{-1} (\ln Pt)^{1/k}$$

[9.2.97]

where SCA is the specific collecting-surface area, in seconds per meter. A commonly used expression for SCA is

$$SCA = 5.08 \ U_k^{-1} (\ln Pt)^{1/k}$$

[9.2.98]

where SCA is the specific collecting-surface area, in square feet per 1000 cubic feet per minute.

For a given application (for example, flue gas from a power boiler), the collection efficiency can be plotted as a function of the SCA with the precipitation rate as a parameter (Engelbrecht 1976a). Relative precipitator sizes as a function of collection efficiency for two different migration velocities U_k are shown in figure 9.2.22.

The design factors that should be considered in estimating U_k or SCA include (1) particle size, (2) specific dust resistivity, (3) gas velocity distribution through the precipitator, (4) gas analysis, (5) gas moisture content, (6) electrical sectionalization, (7) electrode design, (8) field height, (9) field length, (10) the number of fields and bus sections, and (11) electric power supply. A range of basic precipitator design parameters used in fly-ash applications was published by White (1977). Relative precipitator costs as a function of collection efficiency are shown in figure 9.2.23.

9.2.5.3 Advantages and Disadvantages

The operation and performance of an electrostatic precipitator, its capacity to achieve and maintain a required collection efficiency and/or dust emission level, depends on a number of factors closely related to the specific advantages and disadvantages of the electrostatic precipitation process. The main advantages of this process are (1) high collection efficiency, even for small particle sizes, (2) low pressure drop, (3) low energy requirements, (4) adaptability to various types of effluents (wet, dry, corrosive), and (5) fully automatic operation.

There are also inherent disadvantages that, when present, can cause a severe

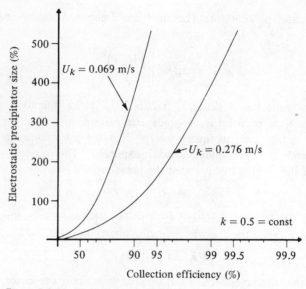

Figure 9.2.22   Electrostatic precipitator size as a function of collection efficiency.

reduction in the performance of the precipitator. Process-related disadvantages include (1) sensitivity to process changes in gas temperature, gas flow rate, gas analysis, dust load, dust particle size, and dust analysis; (2) problems caused by dust buildup; (3) extensive arcing, (4) back corona, and (5) corrosion. Design- and/or equipment-related problems include (1) dependency on good electrode alignment, (2) dependency on adequate power levels, (3) problems caused by dust buildup, (4) problems caused by uneven gas velocity distribution, dust distribution, and

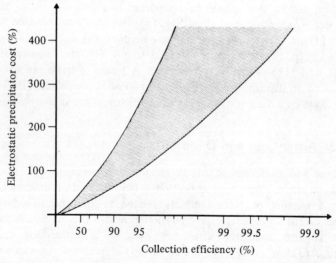

Figure 9.2.23   Electrostatic precipitator cost as a function of collection efficiency.

temperature gradients, (5) reentrainment (hopper, rapper, saltation), (6) sneakage (gases bypassing the electrode system, (7) breakage of electrodes, (8) failure of mechanical equipment, such as rappers and drives, (9) failure of electrical equipment, such as high-voltage transformer-rectifiers, automatic voltage controls, and rapper/heater controls, (10) failure or breakdown of insulators, (11) air inleakage through hoppers, precipitator shell, doors, etc., (12) hopper plugging, (13) inadequate rapping intensity and/or frequency, and (14) corrosion.

Each of these problems eventually manifests itself through a specific malfunction that can be analyzed and corrected. A summary of problems associated with electrostatic precipitators was published by Szabo et al. (1977).

Many of these problems become apparent at startup. Others may become apparent only after weeks, months, or even years of operation. Quite often, the situation is further complicated by the simultaneous occurrence of several of these problems. One must first determine whether they are process (P), design (D), or equipment (E) related, as in the following list, and treat them accordingly:

Excessive arcing (P)
Excessive dust buildup (P, D, E)
Back Corona (P)
Erosion (P, D, E)
Corrosion (P, D, E)
Equipment failure (D, E)
Misalignment (D, E)
Gas sneakage (D)
Air inleakage (D)
Hopper plugging (D, E)
Gas velocity distribution (D, E)
Gas temperature gradients (D, E)
Dust distribution (D, E)

The advantages and disadvantages of electrostatic precipitators, as compared with those of other particulate control devices of equal collection efficiency, are highly site-specific and defy generalizations.

9.2.5.4 Designs and Components

Single-stage electrostatic precipitators are used almost exclusively in industrial applications. They are characterized by the combining of the charging and collecting of particulates into a single electrical stage. Two-stage precipitators with separate charging and collecting stages are restricted to air-cleaning systems with extremely low dust loads and have not found widespread use in industrial gas-cleaning systems.

Single-stage electrostatic precipitators are available in various designs—for example, with horizontal or vertical gas flow, dry or wet process operation and/or dust removal, plate- or tube-type collecting surfaces, traverse plate configurations, and plate-needle discharge systems. Added to these are the new, more exotic designs, such as electrically charged droplet scrubbers, preionizers (particle chargers), and electrified cyclones and fabric filters. Probably over 95% of all precipitators in use are of the dry-process, plate-type, horizontal-gas-flow variety (figure 9.2.24).

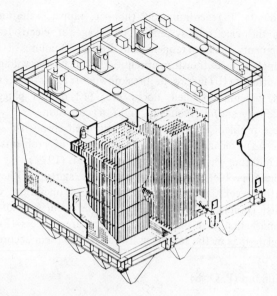

Figure 9.2.24 Electrostatic precipitator.

An electrostatic precipitator consists of a discharge system, collecting surface, rapping systems, high-voltage energizing system, precipitator casing, and ancillary equipment such as dust-handling systems. There are numerous differences in the designs of the dry-process, plate-type precipitators produced by different manufacturers.

In general, the discharge system consists of small-diameter wires spaced equally between the grounded collecting-surface plates. It is normally connected to the negative pole of the high voltage of the transformer-rectifier. The collecting surfaces consist of vertical plates with ribs and/or stiffeners. They are supported from the top and mounted in parallel rows up to 13.5 m high. The spacing between plates is normally 225–350 mm (figure 9.2.25).

Rapping systems are provided for each electrode system to keep their surfaces free of accumulated dust and to remove the precipitated dust into the dust hopper. Rapping systems act on one or more rows of plates at a time; they are normally single- or multiple-impact rappers or hammers, impacting at the top or bottom of the collecting surfaces. The discharge system is normally rapped by single-impact hammers, or rappers, or multiple-impact vibrators at the top or center. Electrical timers are provided to adjust the rapping frequency to the requirements of the specific application. Provisions are also made for adjusting the rapping intensity.

Electrical energizing systems for electrostatic precipitators have now developed into systems that include protective equipment, thyristors for ac voltage control, reactors, a transformer–silicone-rectifier combination immersed in an oil-filled tank, and electronic circuitry to control the thyristors so as to react to actual conditions inside the precipitator (Crynack 1978). A schematic of a typical electrical system is shown in figure 9.2.26.

The precipitator casing provides the enclosure and the support for all the

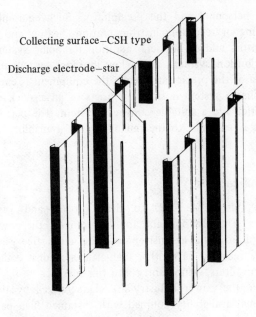

Collecting surface—CSH type

Discharge electrode—star

Figure 9.2.25 Typical gas passage.

internal parts. It is designed for particular gas temperature, operating pressure, and wind, snow, or seismic loads. Adequate openings for inspection and maintenance are provided for each electric field, for each hopper, and for each support insulator housing.

Depending on the application and requirements of a specific precipitator installation, ancillary equipment is added either to enhance performance or to

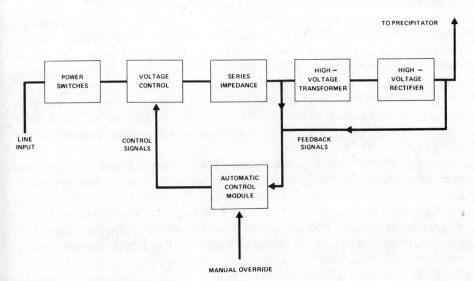

Figure 9.2.26 Electrical system.

protect operating personnel and the precipitator. Such equipment may consist of additional indicating or recording instrumentation, heating and ventilating systems for support insulators and/or hoppers, additional rapping systems for the hopper walls or gas distribution systems, and a key interlock system to prevent access to any hazardous area of the precipitator while the equipment is energized.

The dust discharge system normally consists of an air-lock–dust-discharge valve at the hopper outlet and a suitable conveyor system. The performance of each of these components is essential to the reliability and availability of the electrostatic precipitator.

9.2.5.5 Applications

Electrostatic precipitators are used to clean process and waste gases in many different industries. The predominant application is in the power industry, where electrostatic precipitators are extensively used to clean flue gases from fossil-fuel-fired boilers. Only recently have other high-efficiency dust collectors, such as wet scrubbers and fabric filters, gained entry into this market.

Precipitators in the power industry are characterized by the need for a high degree of operational availability coupled with sustained high particulate collection efficiencies, even under severe operating conditions. The increased use of low-sulfur, high-ash coals has led to even greater demands on this equipment. This application is also characterized by a wide range of gas volumes, up to 2400 m^3/s for a large pulverized-coal-fired, single-generator unit. Flue-gas precipitators with collection efficiencies of 99.9+% are in operation.

Electrostatic precipitators are used in the iron and steel industry for iron-ore sinter machines, basic oxygen furnaces, open-hearth furnaces, scarfing machines, and, in some instances, cupolas, electric-arc furnaces, and blast furnaces. They are also used as tar collectors for coke ovens and for similar applications.

In the nonferrous metallurgical industry, electrostatic precipitators are used for waste gases from sinter machines, reverberatory furnaces, blast furnaces, roasters, converters, and refining and electric-arc furnaces. Recovery of sulfur from SO_x in waste gases requires the use of high-efficiency wet-process precipitators in special designs, constructed of noncorrosive materials.

Electrostatic precipitators are used in the rock-products industry for kiln waste gases, for both dry- and wet-process kilns, and for raw-material and finish mills. Some of these require gas cooling and conditioning systems upstream of the precipitator.

In the chemical industry, electrostatic precipitators are used to clean waste gases from driers, kilns, ovens, and similar gas producers. Some of these require the use of special materials to provide protection against corrosion.

The main application for electrostatic precipitators in the pulp and paper industry is for salt-cake recovery boilers. Emphasis on the recovery of energy from waste materials had led to the design of boilers fired with bark and wood wastes and, thus, to a new application for electrostatic precipitators.

Waste gases from refuse incineration, with or without heat-recovery systems, are also cleaned in electrostatic precipitators.

Common to all these so-called industrial precipitator applications are the requirements of adequate collection efficiency, operational reliability, serviceability, and low capital and operating costs.

9.2.5.6 Sizing

The collection efficiency of an electrostatic precipitator follows an exponential function (see [9.2.95]). The collection efficiency is calculated from the expected inlet and required outlet dust loads,

$$E = \frac{\text{inlet dust} - \text{outlet dust}}{\text{inlet dust}} \qquad [9.2.99]$$

using consistent dimensions.

A precipitator rate parameter and exponent are selected from experience. This leads to the calculation of a required specific collecting-surface area and, thus, to the actual collecting-surface area:

$$\text{SCA} = k^{-1}(\ln \epsilon)^{1/k} \qquad [9.2.100]$$

$$A = \text{SCA} \times V \qquad [9.2.101]$$

A precipitator field height H (in meters) is selected, and the width W (in meters) of the precipitator is calculated using an average gas velocity U_G (in meters per second):

$$W = \frac{V}{U_G H} \qquad [9.2.102]$$

The number of parallel gas passages N_G is calculated from the width of the precipitator

$$N_G = \frac{W}{2B} \qquad [9.2.103]$$

where B (in meters) is the distance between the centerline of the discharge wire and the collecting-surface plate.

The total length L (in meters) of the electric fields in the precipitator is

$$L = \text{SCA} \times BU_G \qquad [9.2.104]$$

This length is then divided by the desired number of electric fields N_f, and the collecting-surface area for each field is calculated. If required, the electric fields can be subdivided into parallel bus sections N_b.

The electric current requirement I (in milliamperes) for the precipitator is calculated by multiplying the collecting-surface area in each bus section by the specific current i, in milliamperes per square meter, in this section:

$$I = Ai \qquad [9.2.105]$$

The transformer-rectifiers are sized to provide this current at the operating voltage of the electric field or bus section.

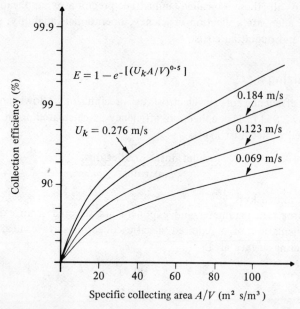

Figure 9.2.27   Collection efficiency as a function of specific collecting area.

A general relationship between the collection efficiency and the collecting-surface area of an electrostatic precipitator for different migration velocities U_k is shown in figure 9.2.27.

9.2.5.7 Selection and Installation

The installation of an electrostatic precipitator requires a careful review of its future operating conditions; together with other criteria, such as structural, mechanical, electrical, and operational requirements, they form the basis for the specification of the electrostatic precipitator. A specification includes instructions to bidders, technical specifications, contract terms and conditions, and evaluation sheets.

The instructions to bidders identify the bidding procedure, schedule, require information and data, etc.

The technical specifications include definitions and data to be used by all bidders; technical design data for structural, mechanical, and electrical equipment; operating data concerning the source of gas and the precipitator; descriptions of ancillary and safety equipment; and required code compliances for design, fabrication, erection, and operation.

The contract terms and conditions deal with shipments, billings and payments, taxes, benefits and insurance, installation and startup services to be supplied by the vendor, patent rights, warranties and tests, indemnity insurance, delays, cancellation or postponement of delivery, storage, and compliance with the law.

Evaluation sheets are provided to allow each vendor to describe its equipment and to allow the buyer to compare the equipment of various manufacturers bidding for the contract. A summary of design factors that should be included in precipitator design specifications and evaluations is given by White (1977).

The bid selection process is often complicated by differences in the design and size of the precipitators offered by the vendors, variations in technical and commercial terms and conditions, and differences in the general design philosophy. After the precipitator purchase contract has been awarded, the vendor designs, fabricates, and ships the precipitator components for assembly in the field. Component fabrication and precipitator construction are as critical to the performance of the electrostatic precipitator as is proper sizing.

Most precipitator manufacturers use an in-house standard precipitator design, which is based on their experience. Components are often fabricated by subcontractors, and careful planning and quality control are required to ensure that these parts are made to their specifications and drawings. The second important phase of quality control starts with the field construction of the precipitator and continues through the final inspection. During the construction of the electrostatic precipitator, one item is of prime importance. This is the alignment between the collecting-surface plates and discharge wires. Many problems can result from misalignment of the electrodes. After the construction of the precipitator is complete, a thorough checkout phase for all components is recommended.

9.2.5.8 Normal Operation

Each electrostatic precipitator installation is different from others, not only in application but also in design. Therefore, it is difficult to establish general checklists for startup, operation (troubleshooting), and shutdown. Some steps to be taken during these phases of precipitator operation have been reported (Engelbrecht 1976b). Deviations from these steps may be required due to the design of the precipitator, the user's preference, or air pollution control requirements. The latter become a major concern if the stack opacity requirements do not allow for specific startup conditions—periods of noncompliance with maximum emission-opacity levels.

Changes in process conditions need to be evaluated to observe any influences they could have on precipitator performance. Cunningham (1976) published voltage-current characteristics and information on changes in voltage and current readings at a specific precipitator installation. Routine surveillance of the electrostatic precipitator, its connecting ductwork, and ancillary equipment can provide additional input concerning the general performance level and the elimination of problem areas (for example, dust hoppers must be emptied continuously or periodically to prevent overfilling).

9.2.5.9 Improving Precipitator Operation

Improving precipitator operation means upgrading its performance, increasing its lifetime, and/or reducing its operating costs. Improvements in precipitator operation can possibly be achieved by (1) addition of pretreatment systems, (2) improving particulate collection, and (3) addition of ancillary equipment. The possible additions or changes include:

Pretreatment
  Gas conditioning
  Dust conditioning
  Particle agglomeration
  Precharging
  Gas distribution
  Dust distribution
  Temperature distribution
Particulate collection
  Pulse charging
  Trielectrode charging
  Wide plate spacing
  Improving components:
    Collecting plates
    Discharge wires
    Rapping systems

    High-voltage systems
  Adding components:
    Collecting surface
    Rapping systems
    High-voltage systems
  Fine tuning:
    Rapping intensity
    Rapping duration
    Rapping frequency
    High-voltage control
    Current, voltage, spark rate
    Monitoring/feedback control
Ancillary equipment
  Ash handling
  Heating systems
  Ventilating systems

The results of changes in each of these three categories cannot be predicted entirely, but useful estimates can be given, based on prior performance. Changes in the process served by the precipitator could result in more favorable gas volume, temperature, moisture, dust load, or particle size. Adding new equipment and/or replacing obsolete equipment can very definitely improve the performance of the electrostatic precipitator. Obviously, the most effective addition would be to increase the installed collecting-surface area by adding a precipitator section in series or in parallel; adding surface area in series will generally increase the collection efficiency, whereas adding it in parallel allows one to handle a larger gas volume at the same collection efficiency.

The fine tuning of an electrostatic precipitator requires the use of real-time instrumentation such as transmissometers and oscilloscopes to observe changes in precipitator operation. By using a transmissometer to measure the optical density or opacity of the gas leaving the precipitator, one can immediately recognize changes in precipitator performance caused by fine tuning of the precipitator through changes in such variables as rapping frequency, rapping intensity, electric power input, spark rate, flue-gas conditioning, gas velocity, and gas and dust distribution. These and other parameters affect the precipitator performance in different ways. The use of the transmissometer allows one to minimize the outlet dust concentration and to achieve the highest possible collection efficiency (Frenkel 1978).

An oscilloscope is another valuable tool for fine tuning. One can record the voltage and current immediately before and after sparking, and obtain a real-time indication of the voltage and current levels of an electrical section of the precipitator.

It is obvious that, in addition to these indicators of the performance of the precipitator, process-related data (for example, fuel rate and gas temperature) must also be scrutinized when the performance of the electrostatic precipitator is evaluated over a longer operating period.

9.2.6 CYCLONES

David Leith

9.2.6.1 Introduction

Cyclones separate particles from a gas stream by centrifugal force. They find wide use in the chemical and material process industries, both for separation of materials from process streams, and for gas-stream cleanup prior to release to the atmosphere. Cyclones are compact and rugged and can be designed to withstand operating conditions as extreme as 10,000 kPa or 1000°C (Stern et al. 1955). They can be made in many sizes, or connected in parallel to handle any gas flow rate. The collection efficiency increases and the pressure drop decreases as the dust load to a cyclone increases; dust loadings as high as several kilograms per cubic meter have been handled.

The collection efficiency of a properly designed cyclone approaches 100% for particles larger than about 50 μm in diameter, but decreases with particle size and may be less than 50% for particles smaller than several micrometers. Cyclones, therefore, are used to collect coarse dusts or liquid mists that have few small particles. Sometimes they are used as precleaners to reduce the dust load to a more efficient collector downstream. Cyclones should not be used to collect sticky particles or hygroscopic dusts, as these adhere to the cyclone walls, prevent proper discharge of collected dust, and cause collection efficiency to decrease markedly. The pressure drop across a cyclone is about 1 kPa.

Processes that use cyclones include doal driers, grain elevators, grain driers and grain mills, sawmills and woodworking shops, rock driers, detergent manufacturing processes, and catalytic cracking units at oil refineries.

9.2.6.2 Geometry

The cyclone geometry most often used is shown in figure 9.2.28; it is called a *reverse-flow* cyclone. The symbols used to represent each of the eight cyclone dimensions are shown in this figure. The aerosol inlet shown is tangential; the outside inlet wall is tangential to the cyclone cylinder body. Although inlets of this kind are used most often, other tangential inlets are also found. In the scroll-tangential inlet, sometimes used in cyclones designed for high gas throughput, the inner inlet wall is tangential to the cyclone cylinder. The outer inlet wall, displaced a distance W from the cyclone diameter at the point at which the aerosol enters the cyclone, spirals inward to join the cylinder body after making one-half to one full revolution. Some small-diameter cyclones do not have a tangential inlet, but introduce aerosol through the cyclone top, parallel to the cyclone axis, through the annulus formed by the cyclone cyclinder body and the gas outlet. In this design, stationary swirl vanes are located in the annulus to cause gas-stream rotation.

Cyclone dimensions are often expressed in dimensionless form by dividing by

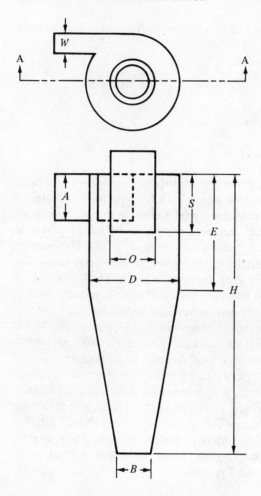

Figure 9.2.28 Dimensions of reverse-flow cyclone.

the cyclone diameter D. For example, the dimensionless aerosol inlet width is W/D. Table 9.2.14 lists several sets of cyclone dimension ratios, each of which comprises one recommended cyclone dimension pattern or "standard design." Also listed in this table for each standard design is a constant, $\dot{V}/D^2$. If this constant is divided into the gas flow rate $\dot{V}$, and the square root taken, the required cyclone diameter D is determined. All the other actual dimensions can then be found by multiplying this diameter by each dimension ratio. The other constants in the table, C and ΔH, reflect the collection efficiency and pressure drop characteristics of each design, as will be discussed.

Comparison of the standard designs shows that those recommended for "high-efficiency" applications are generally larger than other designs for the same gas flow rate. High-efficiency designs generally have proportionally smaller inlets and outlets than do other designs. It is apparent that no single cyclone design is appropriate for all applications; rather, cyclone proportions must reflect the requirements for collection efficiency, pressure drop, and cyclone size that are to be met. The standard designs listed in table 9.2.14 have been used with success for

Table 9.2.14 Standard Designs for Reverse-Flow Cyclones

Source	Recommended duty	D	A_i/D	W/D	O/D	S/D	E/D	H/D	B/D	C	ΔH	$\dot{V}/D^2$ (m/s)
Stairmand (1951)	High efficiency	1	0.5	0.2	0.5	0.5	1.5	4.0	0.375	55.1	5.4	1.53
Swift (1969)	High efficiency	1	0.44	0.21	0.4	0.5	1.4	3.9	0.4	64.6	9.2	1.37
Lapple (1951)	General purpose	1	0.5	0.25	0.5	0.625	2.0	4.0	0.25	50.4	8.0	1.91
Swift (1969)	General purpose	1	0.5	0.25	0.5	0.6	1.75	3.75	0.4	47.7	7.6	1.86
Stairmand (1951)	High throughput[a]	1	0.75	0.375	0.75	0.875	1.5	4.0	0.375	na[b]	7.2	4.58
Swift (1969)	High throughput[a]	1	0.8	0.35	0.75	0.85	1.7	3.7	0.4	na[b]	7.0	3.47

[a]Scroll-type gas entry used.
[b]Not applicable.

many processes. However, it is also possible to design a cyclone to meet specific dust collection requirements, as discussed below.

9.2.6.3 Gas Flow Pattern

The purpose of the aerosol inlet is to cause the aerosol to rotate and form a vortex. The tangential gas velocity achieved in the vortex causes a centrifugal force up to several thousand times that of gravity to act on particles and push them toward the cyclone wall. The tangential velocity U_t in a vortex depends on radial distance r from the vortex axis and on the degree to which the vortex approaches ideality as expressed by the vortex exponent n:

$$U_t r^n = \text{const} \qquad [9.2.106]$$

For an ideal fluid, $n = 1$; for rotation as a solid body, $n = -1$. Measurement of the gas tangential velocity within experimental cyclones has shown that n ranges from 0.5 to 0.7 (Shepherd & Lapple 1939; ter Linden 1949; First 1950). Alexander (1949) presents a relationship among n, gas temperature T (in Kelvins), and cyclone diameter D (in meters):

$$n = 1 - (1 - 0.67\, D^{0.14})\left(\frac{T}{283}\right)^{0.3} \qquad [9.2.107]$$

While rotating, the gas along the cyclone walls moves slowly downward, whereas the rotating gas near the cyclone axis moves slowly upward into the gas exit duct and out of the cyclone. At the same time, the gas along the cyclone walls slowly flows inward toward the cyclone axis. The tangential component of gas velocity is about 10 times higher than the radial or vertical; the dominant gas flow is rotational.

The downward component of gas velocity along the cyclone wall helps convey dust separated from the gas stream toward the dust outlet at the bottom of the cyclone cone. Downward gas velocity is more important than gravity for conveying dust to the dust outlet, as cyclones installed horizontally or even upside down still discharge dust.

Alexander (1949) determined that all the gas in a cyclone migrates to the axis and discharges within a certain distance below the bottom of the gas outlet, which he called the cyclone's "natural length." He found that the dimensionless natural length Z/D depends on the dimensions of the cyclone inlet and outlet, but not on inlet gas velocity or on cyclone height:

$$\frac{Z}{D} = 2.3\,\frac{O}{D}\left(\frac{D^2}{AW}\right)^{1/3} \qquad [9.2.108]$$

While it is advisable for the body of a cyclone to be at least as long as the cyclone natural length to realize the full separation potential of the vortex, there is no reason to extend the cyclone beyond the natural length, as this space will be wasted.

9.2.6.4 Collection Efficiency

Cyclone collection efficiency increases with

1. An increase in particle diameter or density
2. A decrease in cyclone diameter
3. The drawing of some of the gas through the dust outlet
4. Wetting of the cyclone walls

In addition, cyclone proportion affects efficiency, as some cyclones are more efficient than others. Efficiency increases with increasing gas flow rate, but only to the point at which increased reentrainment offsets the increase in separation due to centrifugal force (Kalen & Zenz 1974; Koch & Licht 1977). Wetting the cyclone walls may help prevent reentrainment (Stairmand 1951).

Several theories have been suggested to help predict collection efficiency. One approach, used by Lapple (1951) and others, allows prediction of the cut particle size d_{cut}, the size that is collected with 50% efficiency. Assumptions made in this approach are:

1. Flow in the cyclone is laminar.
2. The vortex exponent n is 0; the tangential gas velocity is constant at all radial positions.
3. Centrifugal force is independent of radial position.
4. Aerosol residence time within the cyclone can be expressed in terms of the number of turns N made by the gas stream.
5. The cyclone diameter is constant.
6. There is no particle acceleration in the radial direction.
7. There is no reentrainment of collected dust.

Some of these assumptions are wrong; others are questionable. However, they allow a simple solution to the otherwise complex equations that describe particle motion in a vortex. The Lapple (1951) equation illustrates the utility and simplicity of the relationship derived using this approach:

$$d_{cut} = \sqrt{\frac{9\,\mu W}{2\,\pi \rho_p U_1 N}} \qquad [9.2.109]$$

Here, the cut particle diameter is shown to depend on gas viscosity μ, particle density ρ_p, and inlet gas velocity U_1. The number of turns N that the gas stream makes within the cyclone is generally taken to be 5, although values from 0.2 to 10 have been reported. The only cyclone dimension affecting efficiency, according to this approach, is the inlet width W.

The Lapple equation is useful as a simple indicator of cyclone efficiency, to compare the effect of alternative operating conditions or alternative cyclone designs (inlet width). However, to characterize collection efficiency fully, it is necessary to have the relationship between efficiency and particle diameter for particles of all sizes. The Lapple equation gives only one point on this curve, the size collected with 50% efficiency.

Leith & Licht (1972) suggest an alternative method for characterizing cyclone efficiency, more complex than the Lapple approach, but one that gives efficiency for particles of any size and agrees reasonably well with data. The assumptions made in this derivation are

1. Flow in the cyclone is turbulent.
2. The vortex exponent n can be any value; the value defined by [9.2.107] is suggested.
3. Centrifugal force is inversely proportional to radial position: $F \propto U_t^2/r$.
4. Aerosol residence time within the cyclone is defined in terms of cyclone volume and gas flow rate.

The Lapple assumptions 5–7 remain as before. Although some of the Leith & Licht assumptions are still questionable, they are better approximations to actual conditions within the cyclone. The resulting relationship is

$$\eta = 1 - \exp\left[-2(C\Psi)^{1/(2n+2)}\right] \qquad [9.2.110]$$

in which Ψ, a constant times the Stokes number, describes the importance of cyclone operating conditions:

$$\Psi = \frac{d_p^2 \rho_p U_1}{18\mu D}(n+1) \qquad [9.2.111]$$

C is a dimensionless number that depends only on cyclone dimension ratios, and hence on the shape but not the size of the cyclone:

$$C = \frac{\pi D^2}{A W}\left\{2\left[1 - \left(\frac{O}{D}\right)^2\right]\left(\frac{S}{D} - \frac{A}{2D}\right) + \frac{1}{3}\frac{S+Z-E}{D}\left(1 + \frac{d}{D} + \frac{d}{D}\right)^2\right.$$

$$\left. + \frac{E}{D} - \left(\frac{O}{D}\right)^2\frac{Z}{D} - \frac{S}{D}\right\} \qquad [9.2.112]$$

$$\frac{d}{D} = \frac{D - (D-B)(S+Z-E)/(H-E)}{D} \qquad [9.2.113]$$

Here, d/D is the dimensionless diameter of the cyclone cone at the bottom of the vortex it contains, that is, at its "natural length." Because this effect of cyclone design on collection efficiency is contained in one dimensionless term C, the efficiency capabilities of any two cyclones can be compared easily by comparing their values of C; the cyclone with higher C has higher efficiency for particles of all sizes. Table 9.2.14 lists values of C for standard-design cyclones.

Equation [9.2.110] can be used to determine the fractional efficiency curve for any cyclone with a standard tangential inlet. However, measurement of a fractional efficiency curve, although time-consuming, results in data that are clearly superior to those given by the equation. The application of the fractional efficiency curve to determine the overall mass collection efficiency on a dust with a size distribution is discussed in the introduction to this chapter.

9.2.6.5 Pressure Drop

According to Shepherd & Lapple (1939), the factors that affect pressure drop are

1. The expansion of gas as it enters the cyclone
2. The energy necessary to cause vortex formation
3. Wall friction within the cyclone
4. Additional wall friction in the downstream ductwork due to gas rotation, in addition to friction associated with straight flow
5. The regaining of rotational kinetic energy as pressure energy downstream of the cyclone

The second and third factors are generally considered to be most important. Vortex-finder vanes and other devices are sometimes placed inside a cyclone to reduce pressure drop. These devices work by reducing the intensity of the vortex. However, because tangential gas velocity created by the vortex causes particles to be separated from the gas stream, devices that reduce pressure drop by disturbing the vortex reduce collection efficiency as well.

Pressure drop in a cyclone can be expressed in terms of the number of inlet velocity heads lost ΔH as gas passes through the cyclone. This dimensionless number depends on the cyclone's dimension ratios and hence the cyclone shape, but not on its size. Table 9.2.14 lists values of ΔH determined experimentally for standard-design cyclones. Values of ΔH can be converted to static pressure loss Δp across the cyclone by

$$\Delta p = U_i^2 \rho_G \frac{\Delta H}{2} \qquad [9.2.114]$$

where ρ_G is the gas density. Reviews of theories for predicting ΔH conducted by Strauss (1966) and by Leith & Mehta (1973) concluded that the approach taken by Shepherd & Lapple (1939, 1940) works about as well as any and is simpler than most:

$$\Delta H = 16 \frac{AW}{O^2} \qquad [9.2.115]$$

where O is the cyclone outlet diameter. This expression indicates that the only dimensions that affect pressure drop are cyclone outlet and inlet size. These dimensions affect the nature of the vortex formed, but do not reflect interior surface area. The fact that this approach works well suggests that vortex formation affects pressure drop in a cyclone considerably more than wall friction loss.

Values of ΔH determined from experiments on geometrically similar cyclones are much preferred over theoretical values obtained from equations such as that above, which are often in error by 50% or more.

9.2.6.6 Cyclone Design

The objective in cyclone design is to select cyclone dimensions to meet a specified efficiency requirement. The gas flow rate and properties must be known, along with the density and size distribution of the dust. Although pressure drop should be minimized, this requirement is not usually as important as achieving the required collection efficiency. The efficiency objective for design purposes should be somewhat higher than that actually required, to allow for uncertainties in the design procedure.

Because smaller-diameter cyclones operate at the same pressure drop with higher efficiency, it is sometimes advantageous to divide the gas stream and operate several cyclones in parallel to increase collection efficiency. Of course it is not possible to meet some efficiency requirements using a cyclone, and in this case a collector with higher inherent efficiency characteristics, such as a fabric filter (see section 9.2.3), electrostatic precipitator (see section 9.2.5), or high-efficiency scrubber, must be used.

One approach is to select a standard design from table 9.2.14, guided by the description given to each—high efficiency, high throughput, etc. First, determine the cyclone diameter for the selected design using the $\dot{V}/D^2$ constant listed in table 9.2.14. The dimensions of the cyclone can then be determined by multiplying the diameter by the appropriate dimension ratio from table 9.2.14. The cyclone size and shape are then fixed, and the design completed.

Next, it is necessary to determine whether the selected cyclone provides the required collection efficiency. This is done using the dust size distribution, the fractional efficiency curve for the designed cyclone, and the procedure outlined above. The fractional efficiency curve is established using the geometry factor C listed in table 9.2.14 for the selected design, in conjunction with cyclone diameter, particle density, and [9.2.110]. If the overall efficiency calculated using this procedure is greater than the design objective, the selected cyclone suffices. However, if the calculated efficiency is less than that required, it is necessary to select a standard-design cyclone with higher efficiency (higher value of C) and repeat the procedure. Pressure drop is found by using the value of ΔH listed in table 9.2.14 for the selected standard design, and [9.2.114].

Alternatively, a cyclone can be custom-designed to minimize pressure drop and penetration simultaneously. The design that results is superior, in theory, to the standard designs listed in table 9.2.14. Leith & Mehta (1973) developed a procedure for determining a cyclone design that is "optimized" for any gas flowrate, pressure drop, cyclone diameter, and collection efficiency requirements; that procedure is described below. An alternative approach is given by Koch & Licht (1977).

First, it is necessary to determine cyclone diameter from the following equation, which gives a diameter consistent with reasonable engineering practice:

$$\frac{\dot{V}}{D^2} = 1.8 \text{ m/s} \qquad\qquad [9.2.116]$$

Next, determine the efficiency required of this cyclone; that is, determine the required geometry factor C. This is done by trial and error, as in the selection among alternative standard designs discussed above. A value for C should be chosen arbitrarily and used to determine the cyclone's fractional efficiency curve using [9.2.110]. This curve can be used in conjunction with the dust size distribution to determine overall collection efficiency.

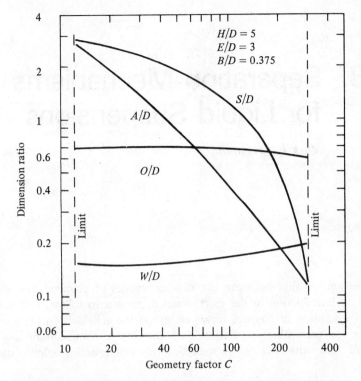

Figure 9.2.29 Dimension ratios versus geometry factor for optimized cyclones (Leith & Mehta 1973).

If the calculated overall efficiency is greater than the design objective, the selected value for C suffices. If the calculated overall efficiency is in excess of that required, a lower value for C can be selected and the procedure repeated. If the calculated efficiency is less than that required, a larger value of C can be selected and the procedure repeated.

When the required value for cyclone geometry factor has been determined, the dimension ratios for the "optimized" cyclone can be found from figure 9.2.29, in which dimension ratios are plotted against geometry factor. Cyclone dimensions are found by multiplying dimension ratios by cyclone diameter. The optimized cyclone design is now complete. Pressure drop can be found using [9.2.114] and [9.2.115].

It may be advisable to repeat this procedure using cyclone diameters 25% or so larger and smaller than that found from [9.2.115]. The cyclone with the largest diameter has the lowest pressure drop; the smallest cyclone has the highest pressure drop. The designer can exercise economic judgment and balance the relatively high initial cost and low operating costs of the large-diameter cyclone against the converse economic conditions for the small-diameter cyclone.

9.3 Separation Mechanisms for Liquid Suspensions

Mark P. Freeman

In this section we first delineate the various regimes of practical interest (figure 9.3.1), as an introduction to the more detailed sections to follow. This is followed by a brief discussion of physical forces acting on the individual particles important in causing (or preventing) separation, and then by a discussion of interparticle forces. We end with a brief introduction to sedimentation, flocculation, and dispersion.

9.3.1 REGIMES OF INTEREST

The separation process varies quite a lot, depending on the end objectives. We may think of the unit operation as a black box with one inlet slurry line and two (or more) output lines (figure 9.3.2). If the object is to separate the suspended particles according to size (and/or sometimes density), then it is called a classification device. If the objective is to provide a concentrated stream, the stream with least practical dilution, then we have a thickening device. Finally, if a clear slurry-free stream of carrier fluid is the desired objective, then we have a clarification device. It is useful to consider these categories separately.

The separation of two or more liquids, as in emulsion breaking, depends on the principles and forces enumerated below but is complicated by the phenomenon of coalescence. This subject is introduced in section 9.4.

9.3.1.1 Classification

Classification is done on a well-dispersed (or, rarely, selectively flocced) slurry. What is meant by dispersed is that the elementary particles in the slurry repel each other and the original size distribution is retained throughout. The easiest process to visualize is wet screening, in which the slurry is run across a screen (usually with washing) so that the fines can pass through (e.g., for a 325-mesh screen the -325 fraction passes, and the $+325$ fraction is retained). As a rough rule of thumb, the

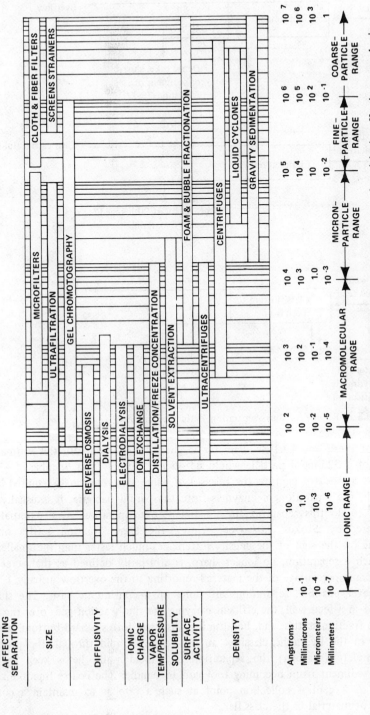

Figure 9.3.1 Some of the equipment used in liquid-liquid and liquid-solid separations, classed by range of particle-size effectiveness and primary factor affecting separation (Copyright © 1969 Dorr-Oliver Inc.).

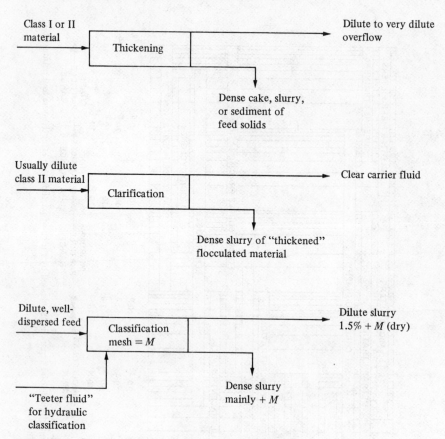

Figure 9.3.2 Regimes of slurry separation, defined by end use.

product of mesh and particle diameter is about 15,000 μm. By this estimate the diameter of a 325-mesh particle would be 46 μm (actual Tyler opening of 43 μm).

Unless a positive capture (or release) of some size fraction is required, as for example in the separation of enzymes from the parent bacteria, it is usually more profitable to do this separation in a sedimentation operation in an external force field where, by Stokes' law (see below), the larger fraction settles or rises (depending on the sign of the density difference) much faster than the smaller. The cut of such a separation, no longer sharp, is arbitrarily defined as that screen size retaining some percentage of the material reporting to the overflow, usually 1.5%.

Whenever possible, separations are done on a continuous basis. The slurry is introduced in a feed well, the effluent carrying the fine fraction goes over the weirs, the coarse fraction settles, and, because it is disperse, forms a hard bottom in a pool classifier. In the hydraulic classifier an up flow of liquid through the underflow helps complete (sharpen) the separation and incidentally helps keep the well-dispersed sediment from becoming too hard to handle. The coarse fraction is raked or flows to a central collection point at such a rate as to maintain a constant inventory of material in the classifier.

9.3.1.2 Zone Settling and Compression

Sedimentation of dispersed particles is called class I sedimentation; particles that agglomerate to ever bigger particles while the operation proceeds define class II sedimentation.

Well-mixed slurries of either class in large cylinders at several different concentrations have a critical concentration, characteristic of the suspension, at which a line of concentration discontinuity appears at the top and slowly settles. This is the onset of the regime called zone settling (Fitch 1962).

The reason for this unobvious phenomenon is that the particles as they settle are necessarily displacing an equal volume of liquid, which must flow in the reverse direction. The more concentrated the slurry, the lower the volume fraction of the liquid and so the higher must be its reverse flow velocity in stationary coordinates. But the relative velocities of the settling particles and the surrounding liquid are determined by external forces. These are the same whether the suspension is concentrated or dilute. Thus, again in stationary coordinates, any isolated particles in the dilute zone above the concentrated suspension will travel much faster than those in concentrated suspension, so that they soon catch up and join the others. The result is the sharp upper boundary of the zone. Just at the transition to zone settling, an excellent classification occurs because the coarser particles settle en masse, leaving the fine fraction behind. However, when the slurry is firmly into zone settling, everything appears to settle more or less together with a sharp upper bound. Whatever else is true, this zone settling is essential for any successful sedimentation operation. The zone seen in batch settling becomes the top of the sludge blanket in a continuous operation.

The more concentrated the slurry, the slower is the mass settling rate. The most rapid transfer rate is just at the onset of zone settling, where the first thin line occurs. This is called the bulk settling rate (Oliver 1964) and represents the maximum space rate (mass rate) at which the feed material will settle (figure 9.3.3). The transition to zone settling occurs at lower and lower concentration as the material is made more flocculant. Hence the first thing a professional does when given a sample is shake it up in a cylinder with some standard conditioning and qualitatively observe its settling behavior. If the line denoting zone settling appears, the professional will size the separator according to thickening requirements (see below), and the up-flow rate determined by overflow rate per unit area will control (Oliver 1964). Only the cross section of the settling basin counts, not its depth. If, with the same conditioning, no line appears, then the designer has to deal with the so-called clarification limited regime where superior conditioning and/or increased tank residence time must be provided. In this case the tank volume per unit of feed rate is important. The depth matters.

It is clear that, in the zone settling regime, the progressively decreasing flux with concentration may be thought of as due to the increasing hydraulic forces as the velocity of the displaced liquid increases. The mass of the particulates is supported by these hydraulic forces. However, at some point, interparticle forces become important. In the case of a well-dispersed material such as we use in classification, this effect is purely repulsive and is absorbed in the velocity versus

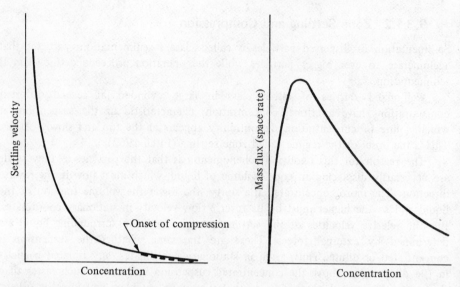

Figure 9.3.3 Typical settling velocity versus concentration curve (left), and the corresponding space rate versus concentration curve (right) showing the onset of compression.

concentration curve so that no explicit account need be taken of it, at least until settling stops completely as is sometimes the case. However, if the settling material is in the form of deformable flocs, then part and eventually all of the mass of the particles is supported by mechanical contact forces, which should cause the soft flocs to deform; thus, there is an explicit time dependence in the settling not related to the zone settling analysis above. No satisfactory way has yet been determined to take this effect into account, except by designing a large safety factor into thickeners. Between the free settling zone and the compression zone is a transition region where, in a batch operation, we see spouts of clear liquid erupting to the batch surface, much as bubbles erupt in a fluid bed. This related phenomenon has been explained by Kynch (1952).

9.3.1.3 Thickening

Thickening is the process of concentrating a component of a slurry in one of the output streams. It is done in a number of unit operations, usually on as concentrated a feed as possible. It is useful to divide thickening unit operations into two subclasses, filtration and sedimentation.

Filtration is either of the cake type, in which case the cake must be reslurried for continued fluid processing (e.g., spray drying), or cross-flow filtration, where the cake is continually removed by turbulent hydraulic, viscous, or mechanical forces so that liquid is removed from the already thickened (or, in a batch operation, thickening) product.

Sedimentation thickening is a class II process. For a continuous process the rate of removal of the underflow determines, for a particular material, the maximum solids throughput and hence the feed rate per unit area of thickener. Less obviously, it determines the concentration of the underflow. Consider the function of sedimentation space rate versus concentration in figure 9.3.3. Superimposed on this for a particular pumping rate is a linear downward velocity that gives an additional solids space rate proportional to concentration. The sum of these is a complex curve, as shown in figure 9.3.4. The minimum in the curve is the steady-state value, and it thus defines the permissible loading on the thickener as well as the concentration of the underflow. For a given sludge, say, this finally determines the height of sludge blanket needed to give the required concentration for a specified solids loading (figure 9.3.5). Because the sludge is supported by hydraulic forces, there is little dependence of underflow concentration on depth over 1 m, say, and so we have the corresponding curve of solids loading versus concentration of underflow shown in figure 9.3.5.

9.3.1.4 Clarification

Clarification is usually performed on fairly dilute streams. Again it may be done either by filtration or sedimentation. Clarifying filters are usually depth filters such as sand or mixed-media beds or sometimes matted materials. They can involve capture of the solid by magnetic forces, electric forces, surface forces, or (most often) entrapment. They can sometimes be back-washed and are sometimes discarded after use. For special purposes, clarification is also accomplished with ultrafiltration and other cross-flow filtration schemes.

Clarification as accomplished by sedimentation is exactly the same operation as thickening. The only difference is that to get into zone settling with the

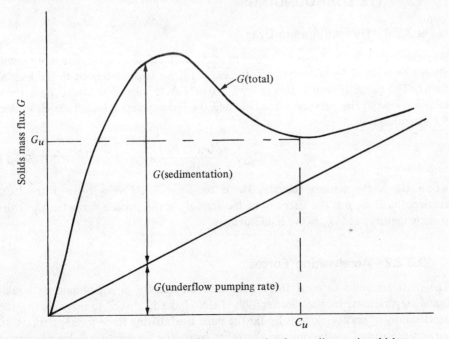

Figure 9.3.4 Solids loading and underflow concentration for a sedimentation thickener.

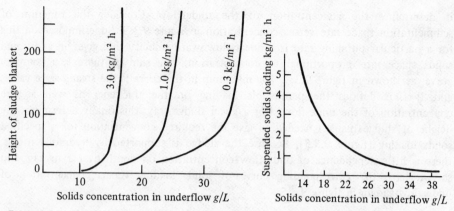

Figure 9.3.5 Underflow concentration of a particular activated sludge as a function of blanket height and pumping rate (left) and maximum suspended solids loading versus concentration of underflow (right) (Kos 1977).

characteristically dilute feeds, longer detention times and/or superior conditioning are required. As stated above, the residence-time adjustment is usually made by altering the depth, although because of varying efficiencies the area is also adjusted (Oliver 1964).

9.3.2 INTERACTION OF THE ISOLATED SUSPENDED PARTICLE WITH ITS SURROUNDINGS

9.3.2.1 Hydrodynamic Drag

Whatever other forces cause a particle to move in liquid suspension, the motion will always be resisted by fluid-dynamic forces, which are large compared to the inertial forces. The particles nearly always have a steady-state migration caused by a force balance between the external force field and the fluid-dynamic drag. Thus, in section 9.4 attention is focused on Stokes' law:

$$\mathbf{U}_p - \mathbf{U}_L = \frac{d_p^2(\rho_p - \rho_L)}{18\mu}\,\mathbf{a} \qquad [9.3.1]$$

where $\mathbf{U}_p$ is the settling velocity, $\mathbf{U}_L$ is the local liquid velocity, $\mathbf{a}$ is the local acceleration field, μ is the viscosity of medium, d_p is the particle diameter, ρ_p is the particle density, and ρ_L is the liquid density.

9.3.2.2 Acceleration Forces

The most common external force field used industrially in solid-liquid or liquid-liquid separations is the acceleration field. Indeed, on a tonnage basis, the acceleration of gravity alone is by far the most used driving force for separations. In various centrifugal operations, on the other hand, the acceleration fields due to the rotation are typically 5000 times the acceleration of gravity, as compared with 1000 g for the standard laboratory centrifuge with which most people are familiar. These g factors actually range from a few hundred up to a million for very specialized equipment. Stokes' law still works. Settling velocities are given as multiples of the velocity of gravitational settling (the constant of proportionality being the g factor), and equivalent areas are computed that equate the clarification of the centrifuge or hydrocyclone to that of a gravitational pond of equivalent capacity (Trawinski 1980).

In an acceleration field it appears deceptively easy to separate solid materials of different densities by having an up flow that causes the lighter material to flow against the acceleration field while the heavier material settles. Although this can be done in special cases, it generally does not work because the particles are almost never monodisperse. The diameter appears in Stokes' law to the second power, while the difference in density between particulate and liquid appears to the first power. Very little separation is realized in practice, with the exception of those instances in which one of the materials can be flocculated. Thus, finely ground nonmagnetic taconite iron ores are beneficiated by selectively flocculating the iron so it sinks while the slime is floated off in a deslime thickener (Frommer 1969). As mentioned above, classification of particulates by size in an acceleration field is accomplished in many different unit operations. Separation by density alone is usually accomplished by a heavy-medium sink-float operation [such as is practiced for the beneficiation of coal (Taggart 1967)].

9.3.2.3 Coriolis Force

Rotating systems, although subject to the same natural laws as other objects, generally appear to exhibit strange behavior. Centrifugal separations are no exception. The apparent acceleration field in a centrifuge or hydrocyclone can easily be resolved into its components by differentiation of the radius vector in a rotating coordinate system:

$$\mathbf{r} = r \exp i\omega t \qquad [9.3.2]$$

where ω is the angular velocity, and t is the time. Differentiation gives

$$\dot{\mathbf{r}} = (\dot{r} + ir\omega) \exp i\omega t \qquad [9.3.3]$$

$$\ddot{\mathbf{r}} = (\ddot{r} - r\omega^2 + 2i\dot{r}\omega) \exp i\omega t \qquad [9.3.4]$$

The term $-r\omega^2$ is the magnitude of the centripetal acceleration, while $\ddot{r}$ is the magnitude of the d'Alembertian acceleration. The term $i\dot{r}\omega$ merits discussion; it is the magnitude of the so-called Coriolis force, an apparent tangential force whose magnitude may be predicted from the product of radial velocity and angular velocity. It never helps separation. It causes vortical flow and short-circuiting in centrifugal devices, but it is mentioned here because it is important in a negative sense for centrifugal separations.

9.3.2.4 Magnetic Force

A magnetized particle (one with a permanent magnetic dipole) will orient its poles in a uniform field but does not move. However, in a magnetic field gradient it is attracted in the direction of converging lines of force. If the particle is not magnetized but is ferromagnetic, then it will develop an induced magnetic dipole in the field and again will migrate in any coincident field gradient. This is how magnetite, often suspended in water to make the heavy medium used in coal beneficiation, is recovered by capture on an array of permanent magnets formed into a rotating drum (Watts 1967). Indeed this is the traditional way of beneficiating magnetic taconite ores. Similarly, paramagnetic materials can be captured, but much higher fields and field gradients are required (Oberteuffer & Kelland 1973). In this case, microareas of high gradient are created by filling the gap of a powerful electromagnet with stainless-steel wool or, more commonly, expanded stainless-steel sheet (Oberteuffer 1973). The one dominating use for this at present is for the removal of ferrotitanates and other coloring matter from china clay (Oderr 1973). Whatever the magnetic separation, the material is held securely once it migrates to the pole or matrix element, but migration itself is slow. Thus, the transport of the material to the capturing surface is actually by hydrodynamic forces.

9.3.2.5 Brownian Motion

Brownian motion becomes important for smaller particles (below 10 μm, say); this coincides with the range in which separations become a problem, so that Brownian motion becomes a force to be reckoned with. Examining suspended fine particles under a microscope, the observer is struck with the ceaseless motion, random in both direction and magnitude, at first appearing to be caused by purposeful motion of animalculae; it is caused, of course, by participation of these relatively massive particles in the random motion of the molecules in the fluid.

This phenomenon was studied in great detail around the turn of the century (Einstein 1906), and it was experimentally shown with impressive precision that the mean kinetic energy of these suspended particles is $\frac{3}{2} kT$ (k is Boltzmann's constant) just as it is for the molecules of the suspending fluid, whether liquid or gas. Bypassing the lengthy but straightforward derivation, one can write for $\bar{x}$, the mean displacement in a given direction per unit time Δt (valid down to times of approximately 10^{-5} s)

$$\bar{x} = \frac{2 RT \Delta t}{3 N_{av} \pi^2 \mu d_p} \qquad [9.3.5]$$

where R is the universal gas constant, 8.314 J/K/g mol; N_{av} is Avogadro's number (6.023×10^{23}), and T is the absolute temperature. At 27°C in water, in 1 s, a 1-μm particle (or bacterium) will move, on the average, about $\frac{1}{2}$ μm as the result of hundreds of collisions with interim velocities two to three orders of magnitude higher. The net result is that suspended fine particles are continually colliding with each other at high speed; were it not for stabilizing interparticle repulsive forces, this would ensure immediate agglomeration even in the absence of stirring. With repulsive forces, on the other hand, Brownian motion helps to keep the suspension dispersed. Like the kinetic energy of molecules in a gas, Brownian motion is important in determining the behavior of a fine-particle suspension but is seldom used explicitly in calculations.

9.3.2.6 Coulombic Force

Because of the electric double layer (section 9.3.3.1), fine particles, especially those not wetted by the liquid, are said to be electrically charged. In actual fact, of course, all matter in chemically significant quantities is electrically neutral; fine particles in suspension are no exception. However, for reasons described in the next section, the charge does separate so that there is a preponderance of charge of one kind within the hydrodynamic boundary layer surrounding the particle, and an equal and opposite charge in the fluid region without. Thus, when a suspended particle is subjected to an electric field, a force couple acts on the particle and the surrounding fluid to push them in opposite directions. An isolated particle thus becomes an electric dipole and migrates only in the direction of convergence of an electric field gradient.

However, if there are enough other particles in the suspension so that the counterions (sometimes called the gegenion atmosphere) of neighboring particles overlap, then nothing keeps the suspended particles from moving one way and the fluid the other. The relative velocity is limited by the Stokes'-law viscous drag coefficient

$$\xi = 6\pi\mu d_p \qquad [9.3.6]$$

which, when multiplied by the relative velocity, gives the hydrodynamic drag force opposing the electric couple. The electric force on the particle with charge Q is $Q\mathbf{E}$. If this equals the viscous drag, then

$$\mathbf{U} = \eta Q\mathbf{E} = \frac{Q\mathbf{E}}{\xi} \qquad [9.3.7]$$

This defines the mobility η, which is often defined so as to include the charge Q, a practice of lesser flexibility and utility when colloidal separations are being considered. Note that liquid and solid are not free to move independently. If neither constituent is being drawn from the system, the volumetric flux $\mathbf{G}_L$ of liquid one way must equal the volumetric flux $\mathbf{G}_p$ of suspensoid the other way. If the volume fraction and velocity of the suspensoid and the velocity of the liquid are given by α, $\mathbf{U}_p$, and $\mathbf{U}_L$, respectively, then the relationship is

$$-\mathbf{G}_p = \mathbf{G}_L \qquad \mathbf{U}_p = \mathbf{G}_p \qquad \mathbf{U}_L = \frac{\mathbf{G}_L}{1-\alpha}$$

$$\mathbf{U}_p - \mathbf{U}_L = \frac{\mathbf{G}_p}{\alpha} - \frac{\mathbf{G}_L}{1-\alpha} = \mathbf{G}_p\left(\frac{1}{\alpha} + \frac{1}{1-\alpha}\right) = \eta Q\mathbf{E} \qquad [9.3.8]$$

Thus the volumetric flux of suspensoid (and hence liquid) in laboratory coordinates is

$$\mathbf{G}_p = \alpha(1 - \alpha) \, \eta Q \mathbf{E} \qquad\qquad [9.3.9]$$

The "charge" distribution surrounding the particle results in a potential distribution vis-a-vis that at infinite separation. From the integrated form of Poisson's equation, the potential at distance r_0 from the center of a spherical particle is

$$\psi_{r_0} = \frac{1}{2\kappa_\epsilon \epsilon_0} \int_\infty^{r_0} \rho_q \, dr \qquad\qquad [9.3.10]$$

where κ_ϵ, the dielectric constant, is 78.54 for ambient water (compared to 2.27 for benzine, say), ϵ_0 is the electric permittivity of vacuum (8.854×10^{-12} F/m), and ρ_q is the pointwise charge density. In particular, if we determine ψ_{r_0} at the hydrodynamic boundary layer, it is called the zeta potential, which lies usually between ±0.1 V. At first it would appear to be simply a measure of charge outside the hydrodynamic boundary layer, but experience has shown that the zeta potential has greater significance in that it can be directly related to the easily measurable mobility, regardless of the shape of the particle. This surprising result has been at least partially justified theoretically (Henry 1931).

Especially in aqueous suspensions, the problem is to apply an electric field to provide this force couple. This cannot be applied by an external voltage per se, because a static field can persist only over a distance of the order of a Debye length, the distance over which redistribution of ions in solution reduces a potential to $1/e$ of its effective value. A simplified expression for this distance in aqueous solution is (Fowler & Guggenheim 1952)

$$r_D = 0.308 \, I^{-1/2} \qquad\qquad [9.3.11]$$

where r_D is in nanometers, the ionic strength I is given by

$$I = 0.5 \sum_i N_i Z_i^2 \qquad\qquad [9.3.12]$$

and N_i is the molarity of each charged moiety with charge Z_i elementary charges. For a 10^{-4} M solution of a 1:1 electrolyte (characteristic of stable colloidal solutions), this distance is only 30 nm. Thus, any field present must be generated *in situ* by the action of a current density I passing through the conductivity Γ of the suspension:

$$E = \frac{I}{\Gamma} \qquad\qquad [9.3.13]$$

Thus a current density of 200 A/m² in a bath of conductivity 0.2 s/m will produce a field of 500 V/m. This is somewhat complicated by the charge transport of the suspensoid and its gegenions, which usually provide a major portion of the suspension conductivity. It follows that using this direct handle on the particles for physical separations involves the use of high current densities (at least in aqueous suspensions) and chronic electrode problems. In spite of this, a considerable number of industrially practical ad hoc separations have been based on this principle (Freeman et al. 1980) though as yet general-purpose equipment for doing this is not available.

9.3.3 COLLECTIONS OF SUSPENDED PARTICLES AND COLLOID STABILITY

A solid-liquid or liquid-liquid suspension with particle size above, say, 10 μm behaves much as described in section 9.3.1. Hydrodynamic drag may be high, and required settling areas large. And below about 100 μm, filter-cake drainage is impeded by viscous forces and by surface forces that resist attempts to drain the capillaries resulting from the close stacking of the fine particles. Typically, for aqueous suspensions, these viscous forces are dealt with by raising the temperature of the cake [e.g., steam application (Simons & Dahlstrom 1966)], which also reduces surface tension. Surface-tension effects are often diminished by the addition of anionic detergents or other surface-active agents (Silverblatt & Dahlstrom 1954). But by and large, separations are straightforward above 10 μm, and taking proper cognizance of the factors alluded to in section 9.3.1 generally permits a separation to be designed—from test results if not from first principles.

Below this size range, special measures must be employed to separate the suspensoid from what is approaching a colloidal solution. By far the most common step is to flocculate and coagulate these particles into particles in the larger size range (section 9.3.4), where again separation is straightforward. Alternatively, at considerably increased cost, one can effect a separation on the still dispersed colloid, e.g., by making use of the interaction of the electric double layer with an electric field, by use of hyperstrong magnetic fields and gradients, or by thickening hyperfiltration through a medium with pores so small that the smallest dispersed particle is excluded (Klinkowski 1978). Note that for the latter case considerable energy must be expended to prevent a cake from forming on the filtration medium, for any cake made of such fine solids would have effective pores too fine to pass water without a prohibitive pressure drop.

Whatever approach is taken to separating a colloidal suspension, knowledge of the various interparticle forces is in order. We consider two-body interactions only.

9.3.3.1 Electric Double Layer*

The electric double layer was mentioned above because of its importance in the interaction of colloidal particles with electric fields. Here we discuss it in more detail in relation to interparticle repulsion, which becomes effective (dominant in a stable hydrophobic suspension) whenever two particles get close enough so that their gegenion atmospheres overlap.

---

*For a remarkable complete discussion and compendium of references old and new, see Eaglund (1975).

Structure of the Boundary Layer

Helmholtz (1879) proposed the first model of the electric double layer. He proposed that the surface of the particle constitutes a distribution of charge of one kind, while the countercharge is confined to a second surface parallel to that surface but out in the fluid. This permits simple and useful calculations based on the model of a parallel-plate capacitor. For many applications this is still the most convenient model to use.

Other models that have subsequently been proposed appear a little closer to reality. The first was the Chapman (1913) model, which treated the charge distribution of the surface as before but with the free positive and negative charges in the solution distributed according to a barometric formula. Thus, for a spherical particle, the Poisson-Boltzmann equation (resulting from their derivation) is

$$\nabla^2 \psi = -\frac{e}{\epsilon}\left[nz_+ \exp\left(-\frac{z_+ e\,\psi}{kT} \; - nz_- \exp\; \frac{z_- e\,\psi}{kT} \right] \right. \qquad [9.3.14]$$

where ψ is the pointwise potential, r is the radial coordinate, e is the elementary charge, ϵ is the dielectric constant, n is the number density of solute molecules, z_+ and z_- are the charge number of the positive and negative moities, respectively, and kT has its usual significance.

Although a big step toward reality, [9.3.14] leads to a completely unrealistic concentration of gegenions at the particle surface. This problem was dealt with by the more recent theories of Stern (1924) and of Grahame (1947), who allow for the finite size of the ions and propose a firmly held layer of adsorbed ions at the surface of finite thickness known as the Stern layer and a diffuse charge region as before. The Stern model of the diffuse double layer is that most often referred to in the literature, although, in the final analysis, mathematics more involved than that represented in [9.3.14] is seldom justified.

The Grahame improvement on the Stern layer made it possible to explain ionic specificity in colloidal destabilization. It divides the layer in two parts, an inner adsorbed anion region and an outer Helmholtz region, the outer boundary of which corresponds with the thickness δ of the Stern layer. The inner layer is limited to anions, regardless of the net charge on the particle, because the hydration layer is disrupted by the adsorption, and anions are much more easily dehydrated. Potential changes across these various regions are shown in figure 9.3.6 relative to the hydrodynamic boundary layer (often called the shear plane). Note that the hydrodynamic boundary that defines the zeta potential, and which is a measure of the equal and opposite net charges within and without that surface, actually occurs somewhere out in the diffuse region.

Electric Repulsive Force
between Colloidal Particles

At large separations, colloidal particles do not affect each other. However, when they come within distances of the order of one Debye length, they become

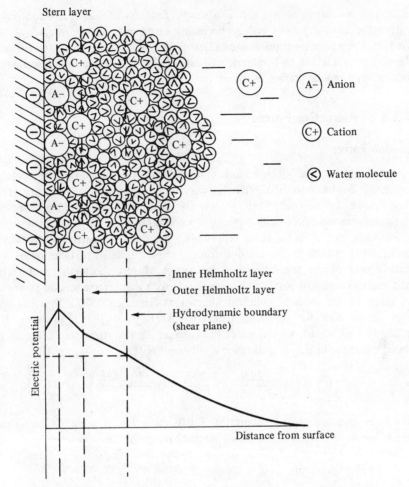

Figure 9.3.6 Pictorial representation of the full Grahame model of the electric double layer juxtaposed with an electric potential diagram.

repulsive. The closer they get, the less the mitigating effect of the intervening gegenions and the greater the repulsion force. The problem of calculating this force (and repulsive energy) is straightforward but rather sophisticated (Sanfeld et al. 1970) and subject to numerous degrees of supercilious refinement. The result [valid for uniunivalent electrolyte and due to Verwey & Overbeek (1948)] for the repulsive energy per unit area V_R between two parallel plates a distance d apart is

$$V_R = 64\, r_D nkT \exp \frac{-d}{r_D} \frac{\exp (ze\psi_0/2kT) - 1}{\exp (ze\psi_0/2kT) + 1} \qquad [9.3.15]$$

where ψ_0 is the (assumed constant) zeta potential; n, the number of ions per unit volume, and z, the number of elementary charges per moiety, refer to the molecules per cubic centimeter of the 1:1 electrolyte. Note that the repulsive energy decreases exponentially as the Debye length r_D, the thickness of the diffuse double layer, decreases. But, as shown above, this is a simple function of the square root of the ionic strength. Thus repulsive energy decreases very rapidly as more electrolyte is dissolved in the suspension, polyvalent electrolyte being much more effective than univalent. The result for hydrophobic colloids is always flocculation, revealing the presence of very general attractive forces.

9.3.3.2 Attractive Forces

London Forces

One must look beyond electric forces to explain the ubiquitous flocculation phenomenon. To be sure, the only known force of sufficient generality is the complex known as van der Waals forces. Of these, only the London dispersion forces (instantaneous-dipole–instantaneous-dipole interaction) should be of significance for bulk matter such as is represented by colloidal particles (Verwey & Overbeek 1948). Although the London forces between isolated particles decay with the sixth power of the separation and are hence of very short range, integration over the massive colloidal particle changes the decay to an inverse second-power law with a range of the order of colloidal dimensions (Hamaker 1937). This has again been an active area for academic theoreticians (Eaglund 1975); however, it is instructive to look at the original result of Hamaker for the attractive energy of two spheres of mean radius d_{12} at a distance r between centers:

$$V_A = \frac{A}{6}\left(\frac{2d_{12}^2}{r^2 - 4d_{12}^2} + \frac{2d_{12}^2}{r^2} + \ln\frac{r^2 - 4d_{12}^2}{r^2}\right) \qquad [9.3.16]$$

The Hamaker constant A has theoretical justification but is generally empirically evaluated; for mixed systems the two constants merge as the geometric mean. For close approach, where $r = d_{12} + \delta$ ($\delta \ll d_{12}$), the above equation reduces to the slowly decaying expression:

$$V_A = \frac{-Ad_{12}}{12\delta} \qquad [9.3.17]$$

9.3.3.3 Entropy Forces

It has been established by computer modeling (Medalia 1971) that when polymer molecules, often of colloidal dimensions, are dissolved, a new apparent repulsive force, an entropy force, emerges. This force is called apparent because it arises not from a potential, but from configurational considerations (Domb et al. 1965). This phenomenon may be important when polymer molecules are attached to the surfaces of colloidal particles. The associated configurational free energy increases inversely as the square of the eqilibrium polymer length (Clayfield & Lumb 1966) so that it is as though there were a spring repelling the colloidal particles. This becomes important when we attempt to understand the stabilization of a colloidal suspension by a nonionic polymer (section 9.3.4.2).

9.3.3.4 The Complete Potential Energy Function

The DLVO Theory

When the total potential energy function is considered, we find an interesting function, unique to colloidal suspensions. This *DLVO* (Derjaguin, Landau, Verwey, and Overbeek) function, shown in figure 9.3.7, consists of a steep overlap repulsion—perhaps softened by "entropy forces"—with London-force attraction dominating at small separations. At somewhat greater separations the electric repulsion becomes dominant. In between, there is a repulsive maximum in the potential energy curve that can be quite high for high zeta potentials in solutions of low ionic strength, or quite small if the zeta potential is small or the solution has high ionic strength (Sonntag & Strenge 1972).

The practical implications of this unusual potential energy function are directly reflected in the puzzling behavior of a drum of well-dispersed kaolin clay (zeta potential, 50 mV; background salt concentration, 10^{-4} *M*) at, say, 55% solids by weight. This suspension is tightly in compression. It can sit overnight and there will be no line settling—indeed, no detectable difference in concentration between the

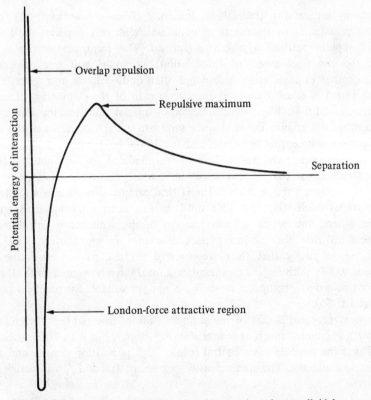

Figure 9.3.7 Complete potential energy of interaction of two colloidal particles as a function of the separation of the particles; the DLVO theory. The repulsive maximum occurs at about one Debye length.

bottom of the drum and the top. All the nearest-neighbor pairs of colloidal clay particles are well up the repulsive part of their interaction potentials. And yet, paradoxically, clay gradually disappears from the suspension, and a hard bottom grows in the drum. Within a week there is significant transfer.

At any one time a certain proportion of the colloidal particles—which have Maxwellian velocity distributions reflected in their Brownian motion—approach each other with enough velocity to overcome the potential energy maximum and thus become solidly entrapped in the deep London-force potential energy well. These heavier particles now slowly settle to the bottom where, because there is still a very small, elementary floc, a closely packed sediment forms. The rate of crossing the potential energy barrier can presumably be calculated using elementary second-order reaction rate theory, with the "activated complex" consisting of a pair of particles at the distance of maximum repulsion. It is unlikely that quantum-mechanical tunneling would make any appreciable contribution for such massive particles.

9.3.4 FLOCCULATION, COAGULATION, AGGREGATION, SEDIMENTATION, AND DISPERSION

For problem separations (i.e., those involving colloidal solutions) the principle separation practice is to flocculate or combine elementary particles until a significant and rapidly settling aggregate is formed. The term coagulation is usually reserved for the final stages of flocculation, when the still small floccules are brought together in large, easily visible and often quite delicate aggregates. Flocculation (the term) is usually reserved for the growth of the elementary floccules by single-particle addition. When uncomplicated by special additives, the way a floccule packs together determines the void space (and hence water content) of the floccule, the subsequent sedimenting aggregate, and finally the sediment.

These processes have successfully been modeled on computers. The first problem attacked was that of sedimentation in which discrete particles were allowed to drop randomly on the sediment. The critical parameter is stickiness (Vold 1960). If the particles don't stick, but slide until each is securely mechanically supported on three others, the solids volume fraction of the sediment is calculated to be comparable to that for randomly packed spheres (approximately 0.64). If the particles are so sticky that they are arrested at first contact, then the volume fraction is 0.13. Although experiment has qualitatively agreed with theoretical predictions in general, computer modeling is not yet suitable for practical prediction (Sutherland 1966).

The next problem is that of the sedimentation of material that flocculates first. Floc growth is handled much as sedimentation is above, but with 100% stickiness. It is found that the floccule has a central core of high population density and an outer region of low density. The mean density or volume fraction $\bar{f}_c$ of particles in the core is given by

$$\bar{f}_c = 0.693\,n \qquad [9.3.18]$$

where n is the number of elementary particles in the floccule.

If the floccules are now considered to be sticky spheres, we can use the sedimentation results (volume fraction = 0.13) to relate the average volume fraction of an aggregate or sediment (often less than one volume percent) to the number of elementary particles in a floccule:

$$\bar{f}_{sed} = 0.09n^{-0.287} \qquad [9.3.19]$$

Again, the results are good enough to demonstrate that the physical principles are understood, but not good enough for prediction.

9.3.4.1 Flocculation

If the process discussed in the preceding paragraph were being used to clean a municipal water supply, it would be standard practice to remove most of the aggregates by sedimentation and the remainder by deep-bed filtration. The colloidally suspended material (often quite stable) is induced to flocculate by the addition of polymers. In fact, for municipal water supplies the polymers are usually hydroxometal complexes of Al(III) or Fe(III) formed *in situ* by addition of lime and the metal sulfate (O'Melia 1972). (Some metal hydroxide must also be precipitated to enhance flocculation kinetics for the dilute suspension of this example.) Alternatively, a polymer solution (e.g., a polyacrylamid solution) could be added to accomplish the same thing (Ruehrwein & Ward 1952). These polymers act in two ways. Most important, they (1) adsorb to the colloid, sequestering its charges and thus lowering the zeta potential, and (2) bridge between two or more colloidal particles, facilitating the flocculation process (LaMer & Healy 1963). Mixing is of prime importance, because whatever these polymeric materials do is usually found to be finished within 1-5 s (O'Melia 1972).

9.3.4.2 Dispersion and Stabilization

If too much polymer is added, particularly if it is of high molecular weight, the suspension is found to be stabilized instead of flocculated. For an ionic polymer it is clear that if coverage on the surface of the colloid gets too high by primary adsorption, bridging contacts will be rare. Also, high reverse zeta potential is the result. For nonionic polymers it is less obvious that redispersion would take place, but some of the best dispersants are in fact nonionic polymers. This is because of the entropic repulsion. Sufficient adsorbed polymer can extend the primary repulsive part of the DLVO potential until the London-force dip is nonexistent or very shallow. Then the colloidal particles are purely repulsive. Many industries are switching to organic dispersants, but most of the dispersants sold prior to the organics were in fact not polymers in this sense but rather complex polybasic polysilicates and polyphosphates; the latter sequester positive charges on a clay or dirt particle and thus increase the magnitude of the zeta potential more than it is lowered by the additional cations thereby put into solution.

9.4   Liquid-Liquid Separation

Rajan A. Jaisinghani

9.4.1 INTRODUCTION

Liquid-liquid separation is an important operation in liquid-liquid extraction, oil pollution control, engine fuel filtration, and product clarification and recovery processes. The nature of the problem can be affected by the presence of other components (e.g., solids and surfactants), and it is rarely possible to use one type of approach for satisfactory phase separation in all applications. The logical classification of the various applications is on the basis of drop size and the stability and concentration of the dispersed phase. In most applications the drop-size distribution is dependent on dispersed-phase concentration and stability. Hence, a simpler classification may be based on dispersed-phase drop size alone (figure 9.3.1).

It is important to note that in most commercial equipment more than one physical principle plays an important role in liquid-liquid separation. Table 9.4.1 illustrates the potential of various liquid-liquid separation techniques with respect to the size of the dispersed phase. The dispersed phase may be classified according to size as free, dispersed, or dissolved (section 9.3). The free state is the dispersed phase that separates out in a short time period when the mixture is left undisturbed. The dispersed or emulsion state may be further classified (on the basis of decreasing size) as primary, secondary, and microemulsion. The drop-size range of these emulsions is not clearly defined. Drop size does not necessarily provide an estimate of emulsion stability, and hence emulsions are often classified in terms of stability. In many applications, emulsions account for a small volume fraction of the dispersed phase, of the order of 50–1000 ppm (Osamor & Ahlert 1978). The dissolved state can account for volume fractions of the order of hundreds of parts per million. Oil and water have limited solubility in each other; this solubility can be enhanced by the presence of other dissolved components. For example, the solubility of oil generally increases in the presence of dissolved organic matter in seawater (Boehm 1973; Boehm & Quinn 1974).

The author appreciates the timely help of Mr. Jacob Murkes of Alfa-Laval AB in sending appropriate literature and references on centrifugal separation. The author is also thankful to Nelson Industries, Inc. for supporting this endeavor.

Table 9.4.1 Effectiveness of Common Liquid-Liquid
Separation Techniques

| | Effectiveness with dispersed phase as | | |
Separation technique	Free	Primary emulsion[a]	Secondary emulsion[a]
1. Gravity separation			
API	XXX[b]	X	NA
Enhanced or plate types	XXX	XX	NA
2. Centrifugal separation			
Centrifuge	XXX	XXX	X or NA
Hydrocyclones	XXX	X	NA
3. Coalescence/Filtration			
Granular media (unconsolidated)	XXX	XXX	XX
Fibrous media	XXX	XXX	XXX
4. Other			
Ultrafiltration	XXX	XXX	XXX
Dissolved-air flotation	XXX	XXX	XX
Dispersed-air flotation	XXX	XX	X or NA

[a]It is assumed that some chemical treatment may be required.

[b]XXX = excellent separation; XX = average separation; X = poor separation;
NA = not applicable.

Emulsion stability is of fundamental importance in the separation of emulsions and selection of deemulsifiers. The principal interfacial properties affecting emulsion stability are interfacial viscosity, electric charge on drops, and interfacial tension. These properties reflect the chemical nature of the interfacial region. In addition, the continuous phase viscosity, dispersed-phase drop size, and concentration also affect emulsion stability. The stability of many oil-surfactant-water systems has been attributed to the presence of rigid interfacial films (Wasan & Mohan 1977; Mohan et al. 1977). Suspended solids at the interface can, in a similar manner, cause highly stable emulsions (Adamson 1967). Qualitatively, an interfacial viscosity of 10^{-5} kg/s seems to be high enough to prevent coalescence (Davies & Rideal 1963). The stabilizing films are less likely to be displaced from smaller drops than from larger drops (Davies & Rideal 1963). The interfacial tension thus tends to affect the interfacial geometry for film drainage.

In general, emulsion stability cannot be predicted from interfacial tension alone (e.g., Wasan & Mohan 1977). Mutual repulsion due to the presence of an electric double layer (section 9.3.3) on charged drops also plays an important part in emulsion stability (Davies & Rideal 1963). If the charge phenomenon is controlling, then qualitatively stable emulsions can be formed at zeta potentials higher than about 20-25 mV. Luthy et al. (1977) have studied in detail the surface properties of refinery oil-in-water emulsions. Charge reversal for oil in distilled water occurred at a pH of about 5, while in typical wastewater streams this occurred at much lower pH values. This was attributed to the presence of anionic surfactants. This illustrates the problem of specifying deemulsifiers and dosages. On the basis of their experimental work, Luthy et al. recommend the use of high-charge-density cationic surfactants of high molecular weight as effective waste-oil coagulants. In general, deemulsifiers are selected on the basis of jar and pilot-plant tests.

In the remainder of this section adequate chemical treatment is assumed to be necessary in the treatment of stable emulsions. More detailed discussion on emulsion stability is given by Davies & Rideal (1963) and Kitchener & Musselwhite (1968).

The estimation of drop size (see also section 4.2) can be useful in determining separation techniques, scaling equipment, and pipe sizing. For engineering calculations, Karabelas (1978) recommends the following form of the Rosin-Ramler equation for drop-size estimation in turbulent pipe flow:

$$V_d^+ = \exp\left[-2.996\left(\frac{D}{D_{95}}\right)^{2.5}\right] \qquad [9.4.1]$$

where V_d^+ is the cumulative volume fraction of dispersed phase with diameter greater than D. D_{95} is the drop diameter such that 95% of the volume of drops are smaller than D_{95}; it may be estimated from

$$\frac{D_{95}}{L} = 4.0 \ \text{We}^{-0.6} \qquad [9.4.2]$$

where We is based on the inside pipe diameter L and is defined by [4.2.6]. Equations [9.4.1] and [9.4.2] should be used only for dilute dispersions (i.e., discontinuous-phase concentrations less than about 1% by volume). The Rosin-Ramler equation is satisfactory at the large-diameter end of the spectrum (Karabelas 1978). It may be erroneous to assume this form of drop-size distribution for fine emulsions.

Treybal (1968) gives a method for the estimation of drop size for flow through orifices and nozzles. In most applications the fluid driver (pump) is an important component affecting the drop size. The most important variable, apart from pump type or principle of pumping operation, is the speed of the pump. Higher pump speeds result in smaller drop-size distributions, all other factors being equal. The relative oil-in-water dispersing characteristics of some common pumps have been studied by Shackleton et al. (1960) and Watanabe et al. (1978). The dispersing effectiveness of various pump types at "practical" speeds and low pressures may be rated as follows (in order of decreasing dispersion): flexible vane, centrifugal, gear, progressing cavity, reciprocating diaphragm. This rating is a crude guide and by no means absolute.

In the remainder of this section we shall focus on commonly used physical separation techniques, viz., gravity and centrifugal separation and separation via flow-induced coalescence in porous media. Other separation techniques (e.g., dissolved and dispersed air flotation, ultrafiltration, electrical coalescence) will not be discussed. Brief reviews of other methods, with reference to oil-water separation, are given by Osamor & Ahlert (1978).

9.4.2 GRAVITY SEPARATION

9.4.2.1 Theory

A rigid particle falling (or rising) due to gravitational force accelerates until the drag force balances the gravitational force (section 1.3). The constant velocity attained is the terminal or free settling velocity **U**. For free-falling spherical particles, in the absence of wall and hindered settling effects,

$$U = \sqrt{\frac{4(\rho_p - \rho_L)\, gD}{3\rho_L\, \xi}}$$
[9.4.3]

where ρ_p and ρ_L are the densities of particle and continuous liquid phase, D is the particle diameter, and ξ is the dimensionless drag coefficient. The value of ξ is dependent on the shape of the particle and Re based on particle size. Figure 9.4.1 illustrates the dependence of the drag coefficient ξ on Re for rigid spheres, disks, and cylinders. The terminal settling velocity in the Stokes' law region (Re < 0.3) is given by

$$U = \frac{gD^2(\rho_p - \rho_L)}{18\mu_L}$$
[9.4.4]

The above expression is based on $\xi = 24/\text{Re}$. In the Newton's law region ($1000 < \text{Re} < 200{,}000$), ξ is approximately constant (figure 9.4.1) and is approximately equal to 0.44 for rigid spheres (cf., Boucher & Alves 1973). The terminal velocity is then given by

$$U = 1.74\sqrt{\frac{gD(\rho_p - \rho_L)}{\rho_L}}$$
[9.4.5]

In the intermediate region ($0.3 < \text{Re} < 1000$), an expression for the value of ξ is

$$\xi = \frac{18.5}{\text{Re}^{0.6}}$$
[9.4.6]

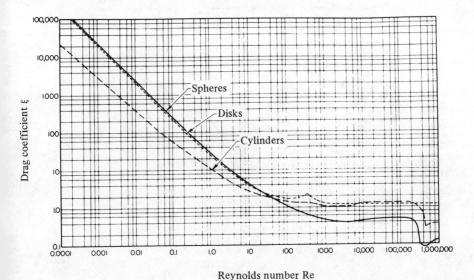

Reynolds number Re

Figure 9.4.1 Drag coefficients for spheres, disks, and cylinders (Lapple & Shepherd 1940). From *Chemical Engineers' Handbook*, by R. H. Perry & C. H. Chilton. Copyright © 1973 by McGraw-Hill Book Company. Used with permission of McGraw-Hill Book Company.

Liquid drops in motion can deviate from the spherical shape (section 1.3.9). Further, their terminal velocities are somewhat higher than predicted by the drag-coefficient curves for solids. This is due to the surface velocity on the drops not being zero as a result of internal circulation within the drops (Treybal 1968). On the other hand, surfactants can retard the terminal settling velocities of liquid drops (Thorsen et al. 1968; Levan & Newman 1976). Generally, small viscous drops can be assumed to be rigid spheres, and [9.4.3]–[9.4.6] are useful. According to Warshay et al. (1959), drop terminal velocities can be calculated from the rigid-sphere drag coefficients for Re up to 10. As the drop size increases, there occurs a transition from the spherical shape, and the drop oscillates and distorts (Klee & Treybal 1956). The terminal velocity is a maximum at this transition drop size and falls slowly for larger sizes.

Dimensionless analysis shows that the drag coefficient for liquid drops is dependent on both Re and We. For pure liquids (i.e. interfacial tension $> 2.5 \times 10^{-2}$ N/m) with low continuous-phase viscosity (about 0.005 Pa s), the Hu & Kintner (1955) correlation (figure 9.4.2) provides a method for calculating terminal velocity. The dimensionless parameter $\xi\, We\, P^{0.15}$ is correlated with the dimensionless parameter $Re/P^{0.15}$. Here P is given by

$$P = \frac{4\, Re^4}{3\, \xi\, We^3} = \frac{\rho_L^2 \gamma^3}{g\mu_L^4 (\rho_p - \rho_L)} \qquad [9.4.7]$$

and both the Re and We are calculated on the basis of drop diameter and terminal velocity. The transition maximum velocity occurs at an ordinate value of approxi-

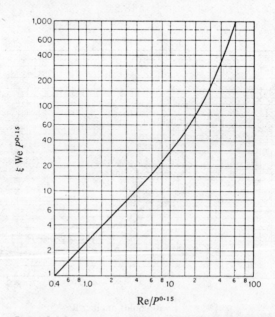

Figure 9.4.2 Hu-Kintner (1955) correlation. From *Mass Transfer Operations* by R. E. Treybal. Copyright © 1968 by McGraw-Hill Book Company. Used with permission of McGraw-Hill Book Company.

mately 70 (figure 9.4.2). A trial-and-error procedure is used to calculate the drop terminal velocity. The procedure is as follows:

1. Assume a value of ξ and calculate U with [9.4.3]. Then calculate P, Re, and We.
2. Using P, Re, We, and figure 9.4.2, calculate ξ.
3. If the calculated and assumed values of ξ are not within the required accuracy, repeat the procedure.

For larger continuous-phase viscosities (but less than 0.03 Pa s), the ordinate of figure 9.4.2 should be multiplied by $(\mu_{H_2O}/\mu_L)^{0.14}$, according to Johnson & Braida (1957). Figure 9.4.2 should not be extrapolated to an ordinate value below 1.0. For ordinate values below 1.0, the equation of Klee & Treybal (1956) is more accurate for low continuous-phase viscosities (< 0.002 Pa s):

$$U = \frac{0.8364(\rho_p - \rho_L)^{0.574} D^{0.704} g^{0.574}}{\rho_L^{0.445} \gamma^{0.019} \mu_L^{0.111}}$$ [9.4.8]

According to Thorsen et al. (1968), highly purified liquids have higher terminal velocities than predicted by the Hu & Kintner (1955) correlation. Slight additions of surfactants result in terminal velocities closer to the Hu & Kintner correlation.

The above discussion is relevant only to the free fall (or rise) of particles in Newtonian liquids. There are other limitations to the use of these expressions:

1. Drop size considerations. When the drop size is very small (about 0.1 μm), Brownian motion is distinctly more pronounced than the motion due to gravity (section 9.3.2).
2. Wall effects. When the drop size becomes appreciable with respect to the diameter of the container, the terminal velocities are usually lower than predicted by the above expressions (section 1.3.2). In most commercial liquid-liquid separation equipment, this effect is not important.
3. Hindered settling. At appreciable dispersed-phase concentration, the terminal velocity is reduced. This is due to the increase in the apparent viscosity and density of the suspension. This effect results in less than 1% reduction in the terminal velocity for particle volumetric concentrations below 0.1% (cf., Boucher & Alves 1973). For a spherical-shape suspension, the terminal settling velocity can be calculated as (Maude & Whitmore 1958)

$$U_s = U (1 - V_d^+)^n$$ [9.4.9]

where U_s is the spherical monosized suspension terminal settling velocity, and V_d^+ is the particle volume fraction. The index n is a function of Re (based on the terminal velocity of a free-falling single sphere) and is given by figure 9.4.3. In the Stoke's law region, $n = 4.65$; in the Newton's law region, $n = 2.33$.

9.4.2.2 Types and Applications of Gravity Settlers

Gravity settling (section 4.1.2.1) should always be the first principle considered for the separation of immiscible liquids, owing to the low energy requirements, low initial cost, and operational simplicity. Gravity separation is not cost-effective when

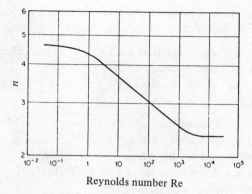

Figure 9.4.3 Values of the exponent n for use in [9.4.9] (Maude & Whitmore 1958).

the density difference (between the liquid phases) is small, the continuous-phase viscosity is high, or the dispersed-phase drop size is small. All these factors tend to increase residence time and vessel size. Hence, gravity settlers are typically used to separate immiscible liquids in the free state. Obviously, the system pump becomes a critical component in the system. Centrifugal pumps at high speeds should be avoided, if possible. Progressing-cavity pumps at 300–700 rpm are best suited for such applications.

Gravity separators are used mainly for land-based and shipboard oil-water separation and liquid-liquid extraction applications. Gravity separators may be batch or continuous in operation. Batch systems are advantageous in dealing with low and intermittent flows. A variety of continuous-flow gravity separators are available. Most of them are able to separate free dispersed phase and some amount of suspended solids. Some of the commercial continuous-flow gravity-type settlers are the American Petroleum Institute (API) separator (see figure 9.4.4), circular separators (see figure 9.4.6), and plate separators (see figure 9.4.7).

9.4.2.3 Design

Batch systems require adequate residence time to achieve a desired separation. By use of sections 9.4.2.1 and 1.3.9.1, the settling velocity of the smallest drop to be separated is first calculated. The vertical height of the batch separator is then divided by this velocity to obtain the residence time.

Rectangular vessels designed according to the API (1969) design method for the continuous separation of free oil from water are referred to as API separators. The API design is based on the separation of a 0.015-cm drop diameter as a lower limit. Generally, about 65–99% of free oil separation can be expected with API separators. A typical API oil-water separator is shown in figure 9.4.4. The flow is horizontal, entering the separator through trash screens and then moving into a sludge-removal section with an oil baffle, sludge hopper, and flow diffuser. A driven surface scraper moves in the flow direction, and an oil skimmer at the downstream end of the channel collects the separated oil.

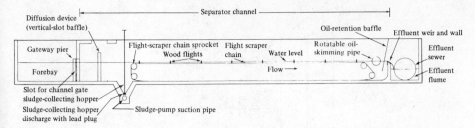

Figure 9.4.4 API oil-water separator. Reprinted from API (1969), *Manual on Disposal of Refinery Wastes, Volume on Liquid Wastes,* First Edition, p. 6-4, by courtesy of the American Petroleum Institute.

The API design method takes into account scale length and turbulence effects. The method is based on the Stokes' law terminal velocity [9.4.4], ignoring the internal drop circulation and deformation. The overall flow dimensions of the separator are determined by placing constraints on the horizontal sectioned area, horizontal average flow velocity, and depth-to-width ratio. The horizontal area (or surface area A_h) is such that the ratio of the depth D to the product of the residence time t and the turbulence and short-circuiting correction factor F is less than or equal to the terminal velocity [9.4.4] of the smallest drop to be separated:

$$\mathbf{U} \geqslant \frac{D}{Ft} = \frac{\dot{V}}{FA_h} \qquad [9.4.10]$$

For oil dispersed in water flows, the factor F is given in figure 9.4.5a as a function of $\mathbf{U}_h/\mathbf{U}$, where $\mathbf{U}_h$ is the average horizontal flow velocity. Table 9.4.2 gives the minimum recommended surface area for oils of various specific gravities in

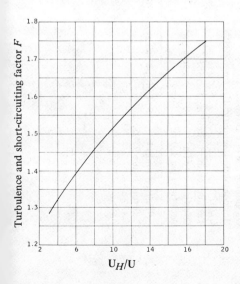

Figure 9.4.5(a) Recommended values of F for various values of $\mathbf{U}_H/\mathbf{U}$. Reprinted from API (1969), *Manual on Disposal of Refinery Wastes, Volume on Liquid Wastes,* First Edition, p. 5-5, by courtesy of the American Petroleum Institute.

Table 9.4.2 Minimum Surface Areas for Rectangular Separators (Fresh Water) (API 1969)

	Influent temperature								
	10° C			21° C			40.5° C		
Influent oil gravity, deg API	19.70	26.00	31.00	19.70	26.00	31.00	19.70	26.00	31.00
Specific gravity	0.94	0.90	0.87	0.94	0.90	0.87	0.94	0.90	0.87
Oil globule rise rate U (m/s × 10⁻⁴)	5.58	9.14	11.7	8.13	12.7	16.2	14.2	20.8	25.4
Horizontal flow velocity^a U_H (m/s × 10⁻³)	8.63	13.7	15.2	12.2	15.2	15.2	15.2	15.2	15.2
U_H/U	15.47	15.00	13.00	15.00	11.96	9.40	10.50	7.30	6.00
Turbulence-short-circuiting factor F^b	1.64	1.64	1.59	1.64	1.56	1.50	1.52	1.44	1.38
Overflow rate (m³/s × 10⁻⁴) per area (m²)	3.4	5.4	7.3	5.0	8.2	10.9	9.4	14.6	18.7
Area (m²) per 1.0 m³/s flow	2923	1835	1375	2006	1213	919	1060	685	536

^{a}Fifteen times U or 0.914 m/s, whichever is smaller.
^{b}From figure 9.4.5.

fresh water (API 1969). A minimum cross-sectional (vertical) area is to be used such that

$$U_h \leqslant 0.914 \text{ m/s}$$

and $$U_h \leqslant 15 \text{ U}$$

[9.4.11]

Further, a minimum depth-to-width ratio of 0.3 is recommended. The length of the separator can then be calculated:

$$L = F \frac{U_h}{U} D$$

[9.4.12]

These constraints are based on experimental studies and do not have a theoretical basis. In applying these constraints, two or more parallel flow channels may be required to satisfy practical limitations. Mechanical considerations usually limit the channel to 6 m in width, 36.5 m in length, and 2.5 m in depth, with flow capacities to 7 m^3/s.

Figure 9.4.5b–e (API 1969) contains nomographs that, in conjunction with table 9.4.2, are used to facilitate design calculations. It should be noted that many types of commercial horizontal flow separators are available. Most physical deviations from the API-design separators relate to inlet and outlet flow distribution methods, additional baffles, and oil-removal methods.

Circular separators (figure 9.4.6) have also found use in refinery wastewater treatment. These separators resemble circular clarifiers and have a central influent and peripheral effluent discharge via an oil-skimmer pipe. A rational design procedure for circular separators has not been developed (API 1969).

Plate separators utilize parallel (or corrugated) plates to enhance separator throughput and reduce residence time by increasing the surface area and reducing the separation distance. Coalescence at the plate surface plays a significant part in the separation process, and hence the nature of the surface is important. Generally, dispersed-phase preferentially wetted plates are beneficial. Plate separators can have horizontal or inclined plates, and collected dispersed phase may be removed by runners or by inclining the plates transverse to the flow direction. Figure 9.4.7 shows some of the common configurations used when the dispersed phase is the lighter. Plate separators occupy one-fifth to one-half the space required by API separators for equal performance characteristics (Osamor & Ahlert 1978). Owing to their smaller size, dispersed-phase removal without expensive skimmers is possible with plate separators. The main problem with plate separators is that they are susceptible to plugging by solids, biological growth, and viscous dispersed phase (Osamor & Ahlert 1978).

In oily-water applications, plates plugged by low-interfacial-tension viscous oils can form dense water-in-oil dispersions (that tend not to settle), resulting in a drastic drop in performance (Jaisinghani & Sprenger 1979).

The design of parallel-plate separators (Miranda 1977) is similar to the API method. Basically, the settling velocity must be greater than or equal to the overflow rate (or surface loading = $\dot{V}/A_n$). This can also be expressed as

$$U \geqslant \frac{H}{t \cos \alpha}$$

[9.4.13]

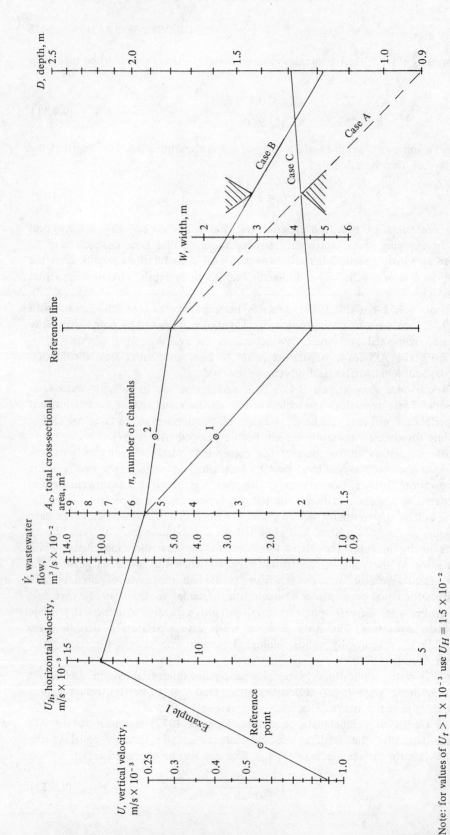

Figure 9.4.5b Design of API oil-water separator for flows between 8.5×10^{-3} and 1.4×10^{-1} m/s. *Example:* Assume $Q_m = 0.076$ m³/s and $U_t = 9 \times 10^{-4}$ m/s. Broken line shows calculation. All flows in this range can be handled by a separator of one channel; however, good practice requires the use of at least two channels. The depth and width are computed from figure 9.4.5e. If only one channel is used, the dimensions are +

Note: for values of $U_t > 1 \times 10^{-3}$ use $U_H = 1.5 \times 10^{-2}$

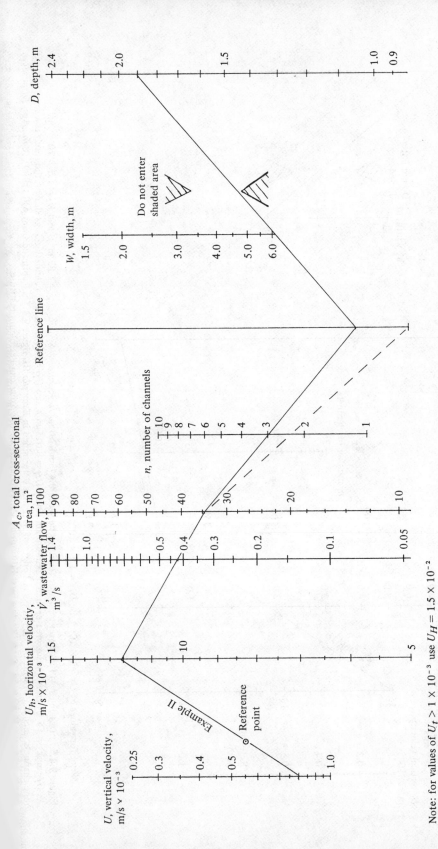

Figure 9.4.5c Design of API oil-water separator for flows between 0.05 and 1.4 m³/s. *Example:* Assume $Q_m = 0.43$ m³/s and $U_t = 8 \times 10^{-4}$ m/s. Extend lines as shown. Line to largest practical cross section of a channel, 14.8 m², gives a fractional number of channels; use next whole number of 3. Dimensions for the cross section of each of three channels are 6.1 m wide by 1.9 m deep. Length of 46.9 m is determined in *Example* II, figure 9.4.5e. Reprinted from API (1969), *Manual on Disposal of Refinery Wastes, Volume on Liquid Wastes*, First Edition, p. 5-8, by courtesy of the American Petroleum Institute.

Note: for values of $U_t > 1 \times 10^{-3}$ use $U_H = 1.5 \times 10^{-2}$

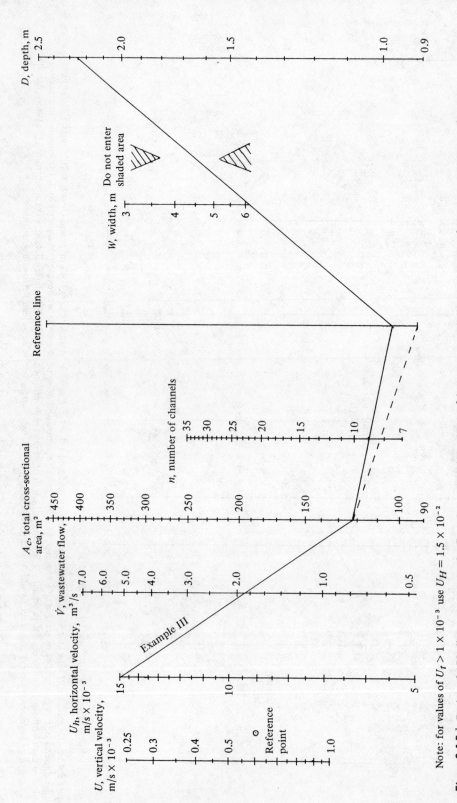

Figure 9.4.5d Design of API oil-water separator for flows between 0.47 and 7.0 m³/s. *Example:* Assume $Q_m = 1.89$ m³/s and $U_t = 1.5 \times 10^{-3}$ m/s. As $U_H(max) = 15\ U_t$ gives a value greater than maximum allowable $U_H = 0.015$ m/s, use $U_H = 0.015$ m/s. The calculation is as shown; the result is a separator with nine channels, each 6.1 m wide by 2.25 m deep. Length of 34.1 m is determined in *Example* III, figure 9.4.5e. Reprinted from API (1969), *Manual on Disposal of Refinery Wastes, Volume on Liquid Wastes*, First Edition, p. 5-9, by courtesy of the American Petroleum Institute.

Note: for values of $U_t > 1 \times 10^{-3}$ use $U_H = 1.5 \times 10^{-2}$

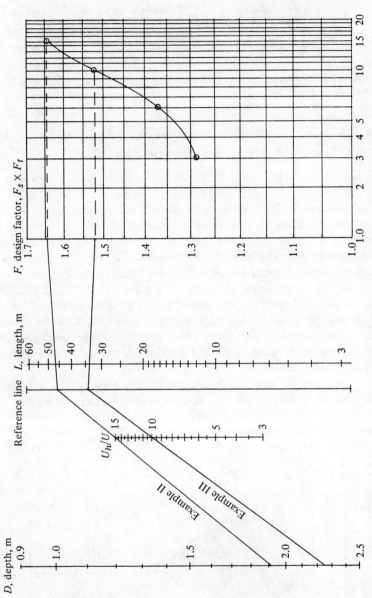

Figure 9.4.5e Design of API oil-water separator—length of chamber required for any flow. *Example:* The depth and U_H per U_t ratio are determined from figure 9.4.5b, c, or d. *Examples* II and III from figures 9.4.5c and d, respectively, are shown. The design factor F is determined from the U_H per U_t ratio, and the point on the *reference line* from the depth and U_H per U_t ratio. These points are connected to determine the length. Reprinted from API (1969), *Manual on Disposal of Refinery Wastes, Volume on Liquid Wastes,* First Edition, p. 5-10, by courtesy of the American Petroleum Institute.

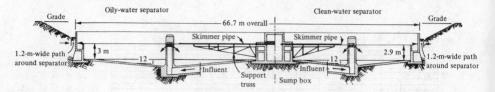

Figure 9.4.6   Circular separator (elevation). Reprinted from API (1969), *Manual on Disposal of Refinery Wastes, Volume on Liquid Wastes,* First Edition, p. 5-11, by courtesy of the American Petroleum Institute.

where $\dot{V}$ is the flow rate, $A_h = LW$ is the surface area of the plate, and L, W, H, and α are defined in figure 9.4.8. The residence time t is calculated as

$$t = \frac{LWH}{\dot{V}/N} \qquad [9.4.14]$$

Typically $\dot{V}$ is known, and W, H, N (number of plates), and α are assumed. W, H, and N are fixed on the basis of mechanical considerations, and α is typically assumed to be about 45°. The choice of these variables should be such that the flow between plates is laminar and that H is not so small that plate "blocking" can occur. Separators are designed for H to range from 0.635 cm to about 10 cm. The terminal settling velocity is calculated typically on the basis of a 0.015–0.005-cm drop size, using the appropriate equations (section 9.4.2.1). Equations [9.4.13] and [9.4.14] are then used to calculate t and L. Using these equations, it can be shown that, theoretically, the use of N horizontal plates in a rectangular configuration increases the throughput by a factor of N. Plates are inclined to aid in the removal of the separated dispersed phase.

Plate design may also be analyzed by means of trajectory calculations. For example, Jaisinghani & Sprenger (1979) have studied oil-water separation in

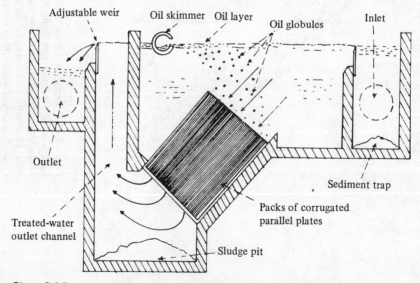

Figure 9.4.7a   Shell corrugated-plate interceptor (Osamor & Ahlert 1978).

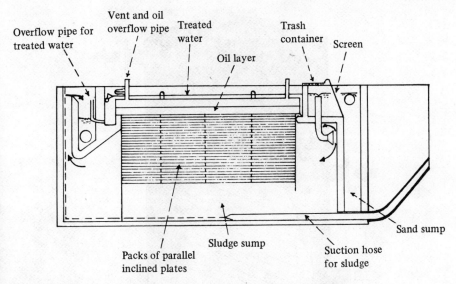

Figure 9.4.7*b*   Shell parallel-plate interceptor (Osamor & Ahlert 1978).

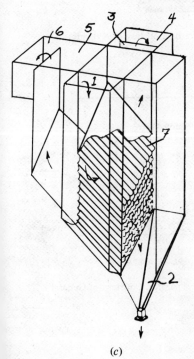

(*c*)

Figure 9.4.7*c*   Inclined corrugated-plate oily-water plate separator: (1) influent; (2) solids hopper; (3) effluent (water); (4) effluent wier; (5) oil wier; (6) oil effluent; (7) corrugated plates (from U.S. patent 3,837,501, 1974).

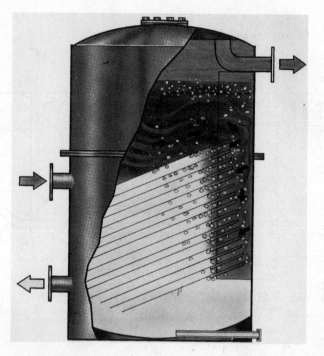

Figure 9.4.7d Parallel-plate oil-water separator. Courtesy of Nylands Verksted.

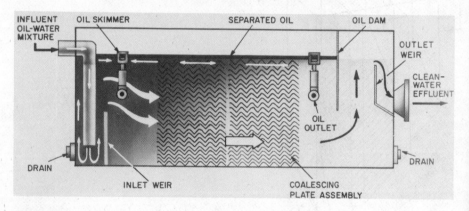

Figure 9.4.7e Horizontal-flow corrugated-plate oily-water separator. Courtesy of General Electric Co.

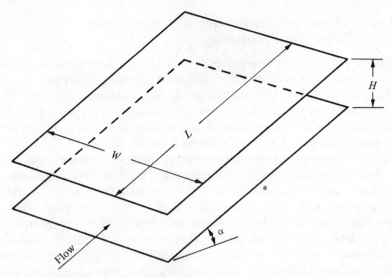

Figure 9.4.8   Parallel-plate design parameters.

corrugated plates experimentally and by using simplified trajectory calculations. Trajectory calculations balance the gravitational and drag forces on drops and require knowledge of the continuous-phase flow field.

9.4.3   CENTRIFUGAL SEPARATION

9.4.3.1   Theory

In section 9.4.2.1, the settling of particles under the gravitational field was described. Particles can similarly be accelerated if they are subjected to a centrifugal force, e.g., rotation of the containing vessel. The centrifugal acceleration is then (section 9.3.2)

$$a = r\omega^2 \qquad [9.4.15]$$

This may then be used in the appropriate expression (section 9.4.2.1) in place of g to describe the settling characteristics of the particle. Note that since a is acting in the direction of r and is a function of r, the particle never achieves a true terminal velocity. However, for sufficiently small particles, the particle velocity is close to the value of the local terminal velocity. Typically, commercial centrifuges develop centrifugal accelerations of about 5000–15,000 times the gravitational acceleration.

If the Stokes' law equation can be used to describe the steady-state motion of the particle, then

$$\frac{U_c}{U_g} = \frac{r\omega^2}{g} = G^+ \qquad [9.4.16]$$

where U_c and U_g are the Stokes terminal velocities under the effect of the centrifugal and gravitational accelerations, respectively. G^+ is the well-known G value or centrifugal coefficient.

9.4.3.2 Types and Applications of Liquid-Liquid Centrifugal Separators

The centrifugal force may be imparted to particles by flow-induced or mechanically induced rotation. Flow-induced centrifugal force occurs in devices such as cyclones. The major problem with such devices is that high turbulence is created. This can disperse liquid drops (section 4.2.1). Tepe & Woods (1943) report poor separation of isobutanol-water dispersions in such devices. This section is, therefore, restricted to mechanically induced centrifugal separators—centrifuges.

Figure 9.4.9 illustrates the different applications of common types of centrifuges. Basically, sedimenting-type centrifuges are used for liquid-liquid separation. Sedimentation centrifuges separate particles by causing the particles to travel to a collecting surface. Lighter particles travel toward the axis of rotation, while denser particles travel away from the axis of rotation. Most industrial applications utilize continuous flow, although intermittent-flow operation is possible. Further, the separated phases may be removed continuously or intermittently. Sedimenting centrifuges commonly used for liquid-liquid separation may be classified according to bowl design and the method of solid removal from the bowl. Some of the common types are as follows:

Tubular-bowl centrifuges are widely used in the purification of lubricating and other oils and in the food, biochemical, and pharmaceutical industries. Typically, the bowls are 10–13 cm in diameter and rotate at speeds of about 15,000 rpm, with G^+ factors of about 16,000 (Perry & Chilton 1973). The feed enters under pressure through a nozzle at the bottom of the tubular bowl (figure 9.4.10) and forms a jet. This serves to distribute the flow along the tube axis. The lighter liquid is discharged closer to the axis of rotation, and the heavier liquid is discharged near the wall of the tube. An appropriate baffle or dam, separating the two outlets, is often provided (figure 9.4.10). This also serves to set the position of the interface by adjusting the heavy-phase outflow. Some of the solids escape with the two liquids, depending on their size and density. A significant amount of solids is usually retained, and hence this centrifuge may be classified as a solids-retaining type. The centrifuge usually requires periodic cleaning, which can be accomplished manually in about 15 min.

	Filtering centrifuges			Sedimenting centrifuges			
Type of separation	Pusher	Peeler	Pendulum	Decanter	Nozzle	Solids-ejecting	Solids-retaining
Liquid/liquid							•
Liquid/liquid/solids					•	•	•
Liquid/solids	•	•	•	•	•	•	•

Figure 9.4.9 Common centrifuges and their applications. Courtesy of Alfa-Laval, A.B.

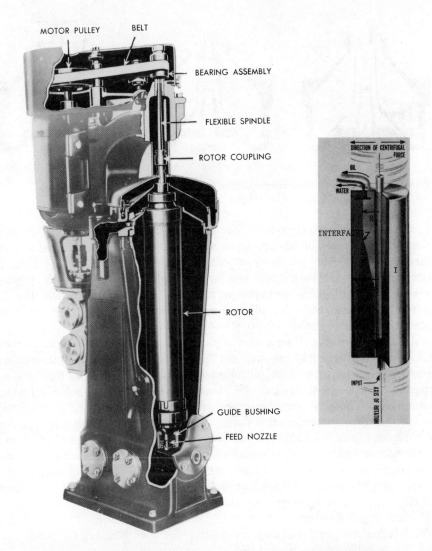

Figure 9.4.10 Oil-purifying tubular-bowl centrifuge. Courtesy of Sharples-Stokes Division of Pennwalt Corp.

Disk-stack centrifuges for solid-liquid separation are shown in figure 9.4.11. The purpose of the figure is only to illustrate the bowl designs used for various feed and discharge methods. In the open design (figure 9.4.11a) the feed enters through an open inlet, and the separated liquids overflow into collecting covers at atmospheric pressure. The liquids may also be discharged under pressure by utilizing one or two paring disks or centripetal pumps (figure 9.4.11b). This is known as the paring-disk design. In the hermetic design (figure 9.4.11c) the feed enters through a hollow spindle under pressure and leaves the bowl, still under pressure, through hermetic outlets. Since the bowl is completely filled with liquid (and the inlet and outlet seals prevent any air from entering), this design is ideal for liquids that tend to froth.

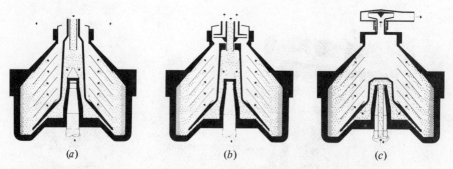

Figure 9.4.11   Feed and discharge methods in disk-stack centrifuges. (*a*) Open design. (*b*) Paring-disk design. (*c*) Hermetic design. Courtesy of Alfa-Laval, A.B.

Figure 9.4.12 shows typical liquid-liquid (and solid) separating disk-stack centrifuges. For liquid-liquid separation, a special top plate is used so that an outlet channel is provided for the heavier liquid. The bowl contains a stack of disks. The disks reduce the settling distance and increase the surface area. Further, the disks serve to reduce turbulence—an important factor in liquid-liquid separation. The disks are truncated cones with the half-cone angle typically of 35–50°. The stack may contain 100 or more disks spaced 0.04–0.4 cm apart.

In many liquid-liquid separation applications, solids removal is also necessary. Disk-type centrifuges may or may not have means for discharging solids during operation. Centrifuges without solid-discharge means are known as solids-retaining types (e.g., figure 9.4.12*a* and the tubular-bowl centrifuge). Solids removal is accomplished manually after centrifuge operation. Solids-ejecting-type centrifuges can intermittently discharge solids during operation via hydraulically operated valves or plungers (figure 9.4.12*b*). The use of this type of discharge is limited to solids having enough fluidity to flow out of the peripheral opening. In some applications it is possible to discharge the solids continuously. Such centrifuges utilize nozzles spaced along the bowl periphery and are called nozzle-discharge centrifuges (figure 9.4.12*c*). The nozzle openings are about twice the size of the largest solids particle and range typically from 0.06 to 0.32 cm (Perry & Chilton 1973). For both solids-ejecting and nozzle-discharge centrifuges, the bowl is sloped (or bulged) so as to facilitate sedimentation toward the discharge opening.

Disk centrifuge bowl diameters typically range from 10 to 80 cm, and G^+ factors from 4000 to 14,000 are developed at speeds ranging from 5000 to 10,000 rpm (Perry & Chilton 1973). Typically, disk centrifuges are capable of separating particles coarser than 0.5–1.0 μm. They are widely used in liquid-liquid separation applications, especially for the concentration of emulsions. One of the major applications of centrifuges is for cream separation or the concentration of butterfat in milk. Owing to the lower limit of particle-size separation, secondary dispersions usually cannot be separated to the high separation requirements of, say, oil pollution control. Further, the separation of unstable dispersions can be difficult. As the speed of the centrifuge increases, the G^+ factor increases, and consequently improved separation is expected. However, mechanically unstable dispersions may exhibit a maximum separation, due to drop dispersion at higher speeds. This is illustrated in figure 9.4.13. In such cases the use of the hermetic-design centrifuge is recommended.

9.4.3.3 Design and Scale-up

For disk-stack separators, if one assumes Stokes' law settling and other simplifications, the theoretical flow rate $\dot{V}$ required to separate particles of critical size D_c is given by (cf., Murkes 1966, 1967)

$$\dot{V} = \frac{D_c^2\,(\rho_L - \rho_d)}{18\mu}\left[\frac{2\pi}{3}\,\omega^2 N \cot \alpha\,(r_1^3 - r_2^3)\right] \qquad [9.4.17]$$

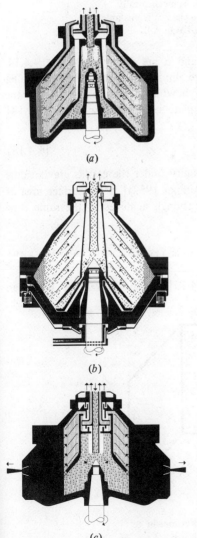

(a)

(b)

(c)

Figure 9.4.12 Solids-removal methods in disk-stack centrifuges. (a) Solids-retaining type. (b) Solids-ejecting type. (c) Nozzle-discharge type. Courtesy of Alfa-Laval, A.B.

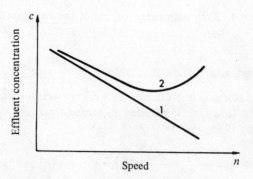

Figure 9.4.13 Effect of centrifuge speed on separation of unstable dispersed phase: curve 1, mechanically stable dispersed phase; curve 2, mechanically unstable dispersed phase. Courtesy of Alfa-Laval, A.B.

where N is the number of disks, and r_1, r_2, and α are defined in figure 9.4.14. Theoretically, all particles of size D_c or larger are eliminated. Some particles smaller than D_c are also separated, if they enter the bowl at a position such that the separation distance is considerably less than the plate separation. Equation [9.4.17] can be written as

$$\dot{V} = \mathbf{U} A_e \qquad [9.4.18]$$

where $\mathbf{U}$ is the Stokes' law terminal settling velocity under the earth's gravitational field, and A_e [also known as the sigma value (Ambler 1952)] is the surface area of a sedimentation tank such that equivalent separation is achieved at the same flow rate:

$$A_e = \frac{2\pi}{3g}\, \omega^2 N \cot \alpha \,(r_1^3 - r_2^3) = \Sigma \qquad [9.4.19]$$

The bracketed term in [9.4.17] or A_e in [9.4.19] can be considered to be an

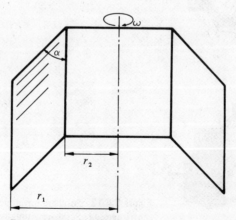

Figure 9.4.14 Definition of expressions in [9.4.17]. Courtesy of Alfa-Laval, A.B.

expression for the centrifugal separator size. The accuracy of this "size" or sigma value is improved by introducing empirical constants. Different empirical expressions are used by various manufacturers of commercial centrifuges.

For tubular-bowl centrifuges, the corresponding equivalent area or sigma value is given by

$$\Sigma = \frac{\pi}{2g} L\omega^2 \, (3r_1^2 + r_2^2) \qquad\qquad [9.4.20]$$

L, r_1, and r_2 for a tubular-bowl centrifuge are defined in figure 9.4.10. The size factor may be related to separation efficiency with due caution (Murkes 1967). For example, for the same suspension characteristics, flows, and bowl design, higher sigma values generally result in higher separation efficiency.

Equation [9.4.17] was developed with many simplifying assumptions, and hence it must be used only as a comparative tool for scale-up or design (Murkes 1967, 1969). Typically, a laboratory-scale centrifuge (of the same type) is used at varying flow rates with the suspension to be separated. From this test, a flow rate $\dot{V}_1$ is picked to give the desired separation. Scale-up is then conducted according to the equation

$$\frac{\dot{V}_1}{\dot{V}_2} = \frac{\Sigma_1}{\Sigma_2} \qquad\qquad [9.4.21]$$

In liquid-liquid centrifugal separation, the position of the interface (in the bowl) between the heavier and lighter liquids is important. If the lighter liquid occupies the disk stack (i.e., interface toward edge of disk stack) then the lighter liquid is purified and the heavier liquid typically contains some of the lighter phase. On the other hand, if the interface is located closer to the axis of rotation, the heavier liquid is better purified. The feed is usually introduced near the interface by means of distribution holes in the disk stack. The position of the interface is established by means of a so-called gravity disk of radius r_H (figure 9.4.15). The position of the interface r_S can be calculated as (cf., Alfa-Laval 1972)

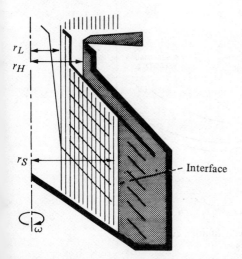

Figure 9.4.15 Liquid-liquid interface in a disk-stack centrifuge. Courtesy of Alfa-Laval, A.B.

$$\rho L \,(r_S^2 - r_L^2) = \rho_H \,(r_S^2 - r_H^2) \qquad\qquad [9.4.22]$$

where r_S is defined in figure 9.4.15. ρ_L and ρ_H are the densities of the lighter and heavier liquid phases, respectively. The position is established during startup by filling the bowl first with the heavier liquid. This prevents the lighter liquid from flowing to the heavy-liquid outlet. In some cases a sealing liquid is used, such that it is immiscible with one of the phases and its density is between those of the light and heavy phases.

9.4.4 COALESCENCE IN POROUS MEDIA

9.4.4.1 Theory

There are two different types of theoretical models for coalescence in porous media. The first type (Spielman & Goren 1972) is best described as a capillary conduction model. This model postulates three main steps in the coalescence process: (1) transport and attachment of small drops on fibers (and on other dispersed-phase surfaces already existing within the solid matrix), (2) drop size growth, and (3) formation of a continuum and, thus, capillary flow out of the bed. Consequently, for a solid matrix, preferentially wetted by the dispersed phase, the oil concentration must increase to a maximum at the effluent side of the matrix. Such a distribution has been measured by Richardson et al. (1952). However, measurements of Bitten & Fochtman (1971) (figure 9.4.16), and later X-ray absorption measurements in a

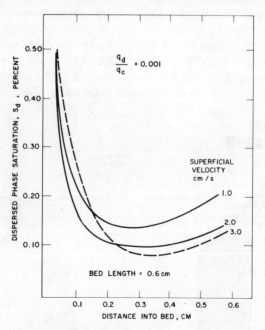

Figure 9.4.16 Saturation distribution curves (Bitten & Fochtman 1971).

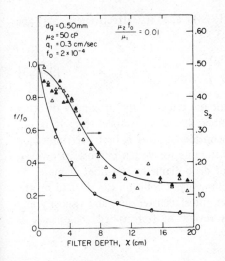

Figure 9.4.17 Typical results showing the total volume fraction of suspended oil (left ordinate) and total fraction saturation of held-up oil (right ordinate) as simultaneous functions of filter depth at steady state. The volume fraction of suspended oil is normalized with respect to the incoming volume fraction. Open and dark symbols respectively correspond to duplicated experiments under similar conditions. Reprinted with permission from Spielman & Su (1977). Copyright by the American Chemical Society.

glass-bead column by Spielman & Su (1977) (figure 9.4.17), show higher dispersed-phase concentrations at the influent section. This led Spielman & Su to include, in their material balance, dispersed-phase globules not in continuum with the capillary-conducted phase.

The second model (Sherony & Kintner 1971; Rosenfeld & Wasan 1974) is not in agreement with the first. In this model, the formation of a continuum phase due to dispersed-phase coalescence is discounted, owing to microscopic evidence (Sherony 1967; Bitten 1969) showing that drops attached to fibers tend not to coalesce with one another. Collisions between drops attached to the solid matrix and drops in the stream can result in coalescence and an increase in drop size. After a certain amount of growth, according to this model, the drops detach from the solid matrix, owing to hydrodynamic forces, and are transported out of the bed. Based on this model, higher dispersed-phase concentrations at the influent side of the bed are to be expected; the measurements of Bitten & Fochtman (1971) (figure 9.4.16) and Spielman & Su (1977) (figure 9.4.17) are in qualitative agreement. A basic criticism of this hypothesis is that the interfiber spacings in fibrous beds can be an order of magnitude smaller than the size of effluent drops.

Because of these basic disagreements, related to porous-media coalescence, it is premature to utilize these models for design purposes. Further, most of the available models involve parameters that are, at best, extremely difficult to measure. On the other hand, these models serve to provide two plausible concepts of coalescence and two-phase flow in fibrous beds. In deep beds (e.g., sand beds) the Spielman & Goren (1972b) and Spielman & Su (1977) model concepts are more plausible, while the Sherony & Kintner (1971) model concepts seem to be more applicable to thin fibrous beds.

Both concepts involve transport and attachment to the fibers. Theoretical work related to aerosol filtration is useful in estimating the importance of the various mechanisms (e.g., diffusion, interception-impaction) in this important step in the coalescence process (see section 1.3.9). Aerosol filtration has been well reviewed by Pich (1966). In fibrous beds, interception-impaction is generally the dominant mechanism of transport (Sherony et al. 1978), and its effectiveness may be estimated by use of the collector efficiency

$$\eta = 2A\left(\frac{D_d}{D_f}\right)^2 \qquad [9.4.23]$$

where A is a parameter that takes into account the effect of the proximity of other fibers, and D_d and D_f are the drop and fiber diameters, respectively. It is not possible to predict the value of A with any confidence; this is best determined by experiment. Equation [9.4.23] is therefore unsuitable for design purposes. However, it is useful for estimating the relative effect of drop diameter and fiber diameter on the capture efficiency. The efficiency of attachment per collision can depend on the drop size, impact velocity, electrostatic charges, interfacial tension, and viscosity and viscosity ratio (cf., Sherony et al. 1978). A review of fibrous-bed coalescence is given by Sherony et al. (1978).

Two-Phase Flow

As emulsion flow is started, in the absence of solid contaminants, the pressure drop across a coalescer bed increases to a quasisteady value. A typical pressure drop-time curve is shown in figure 9.4.18. The relative permeability of the continuous phase under steady-state two-phase flow conditions is given by

$$K^+ = \frac{\Delta p_i}{\Delta p_e} \qquad [9.4.24]$$

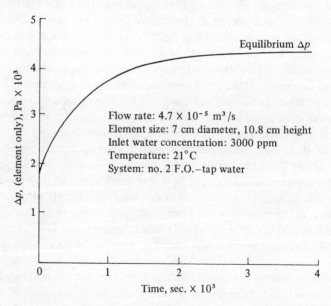

Flow rate: 4.7×10^{-5} m^3/s
Element size: 7 cm diameter, 10.8 cm height
Inlet water concentration: 3000 ppm
Temperature: 21°C
System: no. 2 F.O.–tap water

Figure 9.4.18 Typical pressure drop vs. time curve, for a fuel-water separator (Jaisinghani 1977).

where Δp_i is the single-phase pressure drop, and Δp_e is the two-phase steady-state pressure drop. The relative permeability is important, since it affects the life of a coalescer cartridge. It has been shown that the relative permeability increases as the velocity increases or bed porosity decreases, and that it is fairly insensitive to the drop size distribution (Jaisinghani et al. 1977). Spielman & Goren (1972b) found no dependence of relative permeability on dispersed-phase viscosity. Relative permeability is also affected by dispersed-phase-solid wettability. Preferentially wetting the dispersed phase generally results in higher continuous-phase relative permeabilities (Spielman & Goren 1972b; Jaisinghani et al. 1977).

9.4.4.2 Types and Applications of Filter-Separators (Coalescers)

Coalescers have found use in a variety of liquid-liquid separation applications, including gasoline, aircraft and diesel fuels, hydraulic and transformer oil purification, and bilge, ballast, and other wastewater treatment applications. Filter-separators, or coalescers, are used to separate low concentrations of liquid-liquid dispersions. Typically, the upper concentration limit is about 1–5%, although in some cases higher concentrations may be separated. Usually, with high concentrations the dispersed phase is mainly present in the free state or as a primary dispersion, and, hence, in such cases gravity separation is often utilized for preliminary separation. The coalescer is inherently a highly efficient filter, capable of separating fine solids; hence, coalescers are usually known as filter-separators. While this feature can be advantageous in some applications, it can also be a drawback since the solids tend to plug the coalescer. In most applications, prefilters are used upstream of the filter-separator and downstream of the gravity separator (if needed). The prefilter and coalescer must be optimized or matched for particle removal to minimize operating costs. In engine fuel applications, without prefiltration the *total* operating costs (including element replacement and labor costs) for fibrous coalescers are about \$0.2–0.5/m^3 (Jaisinghani et al. 1977) depending on the contaminant level. With proper prefiltration, the cost figure improves considerably.

Filter-separators may be regenerative (e.g., sand beds) or may consist of disposable fibrous or other consolidated-media cartridges. Separation efficiencies are usually higher for fibrous media than for sand beds. In typical wastewater applications, sand-bed filters can have oil removal efficiencies of about 90% (Nebolsine 1970). On the other hand, coalescers typically have efficiencies above 95–99% (Osamor & Ahlert 1978). Unless specifically designed, sand beds retain and coalesce the dispersed phase until breakthrough occurs.

Other devices such as coalescing tubes and screens may also be used. These devices are not very effective with fine emulsions.

Figure 9.4.19 shows a cross section of a typical multiple-cartridge (element) fuel-water filter-separator. The fuel with dispersed water enters the bottom distributor plate and flows from the inside out through a built-in prefilter stage, coalescer element, and concentric separator stage. Most of the coalesced water drips off the element, while some of the smaller drops travel to a porous (typically resin-coated,

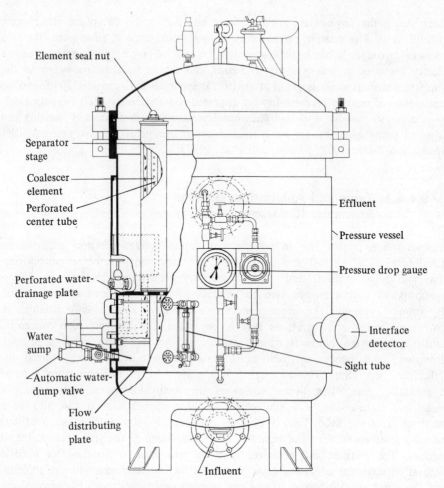

Figure 9.4.19   Multiple-element fuel-water filter-separator. Courtesy of Nelson Industries, Inc.

convoluted paper or screen) separating stage. The nonwetting separator retains the drops so that they can slide down to the openings in the water collection zone or sump. The purified fuel flows into a standpipe, with the outlet higher than the elements, and leaves the vessel. Often the separator stage is not concentric about the coalescer stage but is mounted independently. The cylindrical shape of the elements increases the available face area.

Often coalescer failure is related to low interfacial tensions. Hazlett & Carhart (1972) and Bitten (1969) have stressed the importance of interfacial tension as a parameter that strongly affects coalescer performance. However, they report many instances in which good coalescer performance is achieved at low interfacial tensions. Jaisinghani (1977) has shown that in general coalescer performance cannot be predicted from interfacial-tension data alone, and that excellent fuel-water separation is possible in the presence of surface-active fuel additives.

9.4.4.3 Element (or Bed) Design

Flow through an element is usually from the inside out. A typical element is shown in figure 9.4.20. Currently, element design is conducted via small-scale experiments simulating the fluid and interfacial conditions to be encountered in the field. The philosophy should be always to subject the coalescer to more difficult than anticipated field conditions. Scale-up is typically accomplished by maintaining superficial bed areas and velocities. The housing or container scale-up and design are accomplished by using the concepts of section 9.4.2. This aspect is very important, since the free space (around the elements) in the housing determines the sedimentation characteristics.

Element design guidelines are reviewed by Jaisinghani et al. (1977) and may be summarized as follows:

1. Superficial velocities of about 0.125–0.5 cm/s are typical for most applications.
2. Fiber diameters of 1–25 μm are typically used.
3. Fibrous mats must have a resinous binder or coating of low surface free energy so as to minimize surfactant adsorption and improve structural integrity.
4. The last layer of a coalescer (the release layer) should be highly porous (Hazlett & Carhart 1972). A highly porous release layer results in larger released drop sizes, owing to the larger pore size.

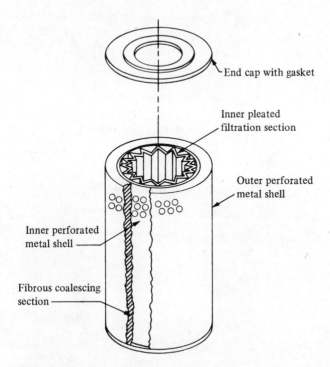

Figure 9.4.20 Typical coalescer element. Courtesy of Nelson Industries, Inc.

5. The surface characteristics of the materials should be such that they are preferentially wetted by the dispersed phase. This results in lower steady-state pressure drops.
6. The separator stage must be spaced at least about 1 cm away from the coalescer element. Further, the separator stage should be preferentially nonwetted by the dispersed phase.
7. Solids removal in the prefilter stage (typically built into the element, figure 9.4.20) is optimized by trial and error so that the solids-holding capacity is maximized (to a practical pressure drop limit and such that the separation efficiency is not significantly reduced).
8. Typically, fibrous coalescer-element bed depths vary from about 0.635 to 4 cm.

9.5 Nomenclature for Chapter 9

ROMAN LETTERS

a	acceleration, m/s^2
A	area, m^2
A	cyclone inlet height, m
A	Hamaker constant
A/C	air-to-cloth ratio
B	cyclone dust outlet diameter, m
c	concentration, m^{-3}
C	Cunningham correction factor
C	cyclone geometry factor
C_D	drag coefficient
C_R	rear face sloughoff, mg/m^3
d	diameter, μm
D	diameter, m
$\mathfrak{D}$	diffusivity, m^2/s
e	elementary charge
E	cyclone cylinder height, m
E	efficiency
E	electric field, coul/m
F	force, N
g	gravitational acceleration, m/s^2
G	dust concentration, g/m^3
G	solids mass flux, kg/s
G^+	centrifugal coefficient
h	throat length, m
H	height, m
H	velocity head
i	current, A
I	current, A
I	ionic strength

I	current density, A/m^2
k	Boltzmann's constant
k'	Kozeny constant
K_2	dust specific resistance coefficient, N min/g m
K^+	relative permeability
L	length, m
$\dot{M}$	mass flux, kg/s
n	vortex exponent
n	number concentration, m^{-3}
n	number
N	number of plates
N	number of turns
N_{av}	Avogadro's number
O	cyclone outlet diameter, m
p	pressure, N/m^2
$\overline{Pt}$	design penetration
Pt	penetration
Q	charge, coul
r	radius, m
r_D	Debye length, m
R	universal gas constant
s_0	specific surface parameter, cm^{-1}
S	drag, N min/m^3
S	surface-to-volume ratio, m^{-1}
S	cyclone outlet length, m
S_E	effective residual drag, N min/n^3
SCA	specific collecting-surface area
t	time, s
T	temperature, °K
U	velocity, m/s
$\langle U \rangle$	velocity, m/s
U_k	migration velocity, m/s
$\mathbf{U}$	vector velocity, m/s
$\dot{V}$	flow rate, m^3/s
V	volume
V_R	repulsive energy per unit area
W	dust loading, g/m^2
W	width, m
x	displacement, m
X	dimensionless scrubber throat length
z	charge number
Z	natural length

DIMENSIONLESS GROUPS

Re	Reynolds number
We	Weber number

GREEK LETTERS

α	solidity
α	angle
α	volume fraction
Δ	change
Γ	conductivity
γ	interfacial tension
ϵ	dielectric constant
ϵ	porosity
ϵ_0	electric permittivity
η	viscosity
η	efficiency
η	mobility
κ	dielectric constant
λ	mean free path
μ	dynamic viscosity, N s/m^2
ξ	viscous drag coefficient
ρ	density, kg/m^3
σ	standard deviation
τ	relaxation time, s
ψ	electric potential
ψ	impaction parameter
ω	angular velocity, s^{-1}

SUBSCRIPTS

a	aerodynamic
c	cleaned
c	collector
c	cross-sectional
d	droplet
g	geometric
G	gas
H	heavier
h	horizontal
i	index
I	impaction
l	limiting
L	liquid
L	lighter
p	particle
q	particle charge
Q	collector charge
R	residual
s	surface
s	interface

sv	surface to volume
t	tangential
u	uncleaned
v	volume
1	inlet
2	outlet

9.6 References for Chapter 9

Adamson, A. W. 1967 *Physical Chemistry of Surfaces,* 2d ed., pp. 514–515, Wiley-Interscience, New York.

Alexander, R. M. 1949 Fundamentals of Cyclone Design and Operation, *Proc. Australas. Inst. Min. Met.* (New Series) **152**:203–228.

Ambler, C. M. 1952 The Evaluation of Centrifuge Performance, *Chem. Eng. Prog.* **48**:150–158.

Alfa Laval 1972 *Laboratory Separation LAPX202 Users Guide,* pp. 18–20, Alfa Laval, Sweden.

API 1969 *Manual on Disposal of Refinery Wastes, Volume on Liquid Wastes,* chap. 5, American Petroleum Inst., New York.

Ariman, T. (ed.) 1978 Novel Concepts, Methods and Advanced Technology in Particulate-Gas Separation, proceedings of a workshop held at the Univ. of Notre Dame, Notre Dame, Ind., Apr. 20–22, 1977, *Rept.* EPA-600/7-78-120, U.S. Environmental Protection Agency.

Balakrishnan, N. S. & Cheng, G. H. S. 1978 Scale-up Effect of Venturi Scrubber, *71st Annu. Meet. Air Pollution Control Assoc., Houston, June 1978,.* paper 78-17.3.

Behie, S. W. & Beeckmans, J. M. 1974 Effects of Water Injection Arrangement on the Performance of a Venturi Scrubber, *J. Air Pollut. Control Assoc.,* **24**:943–945.

Bell, C. G. & Strauss, W. 1973 Effectiveness of Vertical Mist Eliminators in a Cross Flow Scrubber, *J. Air Pollut. Control Assoc.* **23**:967–969.

Benarie, M. 1969 Einfluss der Porenstruktur auf den Abscheidegrad in Faserfiltern, *Staub* **29**(2):74–78.

Billings, C. E. 1966a Effects of Particle Accumulation in Aerosol Filtration, Ph.D. thesis, California Inst. of Technology, Pasadena.

Billings, C. E. 1966b Effects of Particle Accumulation on Aerosol Filter Life, *Proc. 9th AEC Air Cleaning Conf., Boston, Sept.* 1966. pp. 656–677.

Billings, C. E. & Wilder, J. 1970 *Handbook of Fabric Filter Technology,* NTIS PB 200-648, Natl. Technical Information Service, Springfield, Va.

Bird, R. B., Stewart, W. E., & Lightfoot, E. N. 1960 *Transport Phenomena,* Wiley, New York.

Bitten, J. F. 1969 Study of Aviation-Fuel Filter/Separators, *Rept.* IITRI-C6088-12, Illinois Inst. of Technology Research Institute, Chicago, Ill.

Bitten, J. F. & Fochtman, E. G. 1971 Water Distribution in Fiberbed Coalescers, *J. Colloid Interface Sci.* **37**:312–317.

Boehm, P. D. 1973 Solubilization of Hydrocarbons by Dissolved Organic Matter in Seawater, M.S. thesis, University of Rhode Island, Kingston.

Boehm, P. D. & Quinn, J. G. 1974 The Solubility Behaviour of No. 2 Fuel Oil in Seawater, *Mar. Pollut. Bull.* **5**:101–105.

Boll, R. H. 1973 Particle Collection and Pressure Drop in Venturi Scrubbers, *Ind. Eng. Chem. Fundam.* **12**:40–50.

Boucher, D. F. & Alves, G. E. 1973 Fluid and Particle Mechanics, in *Chemical Engineers' Handbook*, eds. R. H. Perry & C. H. Chilton, sec. 5, McGraw-Hill, New York.

Brady, J. D., Cooper, D. W., & Rei, M. T. 1977 A Wet Collector of Fine Particles, *Chem. Eng. Prog.* 73(8):45–53.

Burschsted, C. A., Kahn, J. G., & Fuller, A. B. 1976 Nuclear Air Cleaning Handbook, ERDA-76-21, Oak Ridge Natl. Lab., Oak Ridge, Tenn.

Busch, J. S., MacMath, W. E., & Lin, M. S. 1973 Design and Cost of High Energy Scrubbers. I: The Basic Scrubber, *Pollut. Eng.* January 1973, pp. 28–32.

Calvert, S. 1968 Source Control by Liquid Scrubbing, in *Air Pollution*, ed. A. C. Stern, Academic, New York.

Calvert, S. 1974 Engineering Design of Wet Scrubbers, *J. Air Pollut. Control Assoc.* 24:929–934.

Calvert, S. 1977a Upgrading Existing Particulate Scrubbers, *Chem. Eng.* October 24, 1977, pp. 133–140.

Calvert, S. 1977b How to Choose a Particulate Scrubber, *Chem. Eng.* August 29, 1977, pp. 54–68.

Calvert, S. 1978 Guidelines for Selecting Mist Eliminators, *Chem. Eng.* February 27, 1978, pp. 109–112.

Calvert, S. & Jhaveri, N. C. 1974 Flux Force/Condensation Scrubbing, *J. Air Pollut. Control Assoc.* 24(10):947–952.

Calvert, S. & Parker, R. 1978 Particulate Control Highlights: Fine Particle Scrubber Research, *Rept.* EPA-600/8-78-005-a, U.S. Environmental Protection Agency.

Calvert, S., Goldschmid, J., Leith, D., & Mehta, D. 1972 *Scrubber Handbook*, U.S. Environmental Protection Agency.

Calvert, S., Goldschmid, J., Leith, D., & Jhaveri, N. C. 1973 Feasibility of Flux Force/Condensation Scrubbing for Fine Particulate Collection, APT, Inc., Riverside, Calif., *Rept.* EPA-650/2-73-036, U.S. Environmental Protection Agency.

Calvert, S., Jashnani, I. L., Yung, S., & Stalberg, S. 1974 Entrainment Separators for Scrubbers—Initial Report, *Rept.* EPA-650/2-74-119-a, U.S. Environmental Protection Agency.

Calvert, S., Lundgren, D., & Mehta, D. S. 1972 Venturi Scrubber Performance, *J. Air Pollut. Control Assoc.* 22:529–532.

Cass, R. W. & Bradway, R. M. 1976 Fractional Efficiency of a Utility Boiler Baghouse, Sunbury Steam Electric Station, NTIS PB 253-943/AS, Natl. Technical Information Service, Springfield, Va.

Chapman, D. L. 1913 Contributions to the Theory of Electrocapillarity, *Philos. Mag.* 25:475–481.

Chen, C. Y. 1955 Filtration of Aerosols by Fibrous Media *Chem. Rev.* 55:595–623.

Chmielewski, R. D. & Goren, S. L. 1972 Aerosol Filtration with Slip Flow, *Environ. Sci. Technol.* 6:1101–1105.

Clarenburg, L. A. & Werner, R. M. 1965 Aerosol Filters: Pressure Drop across Multicomponent Glass Fiber Filters, *Ind. Eng. Chem. Proc. Des. Dev.* 4:293–299.

Clayfield, E. J. & Lumb, E. C. 1966 A Theoretical Approach for Polymeric Dispersant Action, I: Calculation of Entropic Repulsion Exerted by Random Polymer Chains Terminally Adsorbed on Plane Surfaces and Spherical Particles, *J. Colloid Interface Sci.* 22:269.

Cooper, D. W. 1969 Control Techniques for Particulate Air Pollutants, AP-51, Dept. of Health, Education, and Welfare, National Air Pollution Control Administration, Washington, D.C.

Cooper, D. W. 1975 Fine Particle Control by Electrostatic Augmentation of Existing Methods, *68th Annu. Meet. Air Pollution Control Assoc., Boston, June 1975,* paper 75-02.1.

Cooper, D. W. 1976a Significant Relationships Concerning Exponential Transmission or Penetration, *J. Air Pollut. Control Assoc.* 26:366–367.

Cooper, D. W. 1976b Theoretical Comparison of Efficiency and Power for Single-Stage and Multiple-Stage Particulate Scrubbing, *Atmos. Environ.* 19:1001–1004.

Cooper, D. W. 1978 Approximate Equations for Predicting Electrostatic Particle Collection, in Ariman, T. (ed.) 1978 Novel Concepts, Methods and Advanced Technology in Particulate-Gas Separation, proceedings of a workshop held at the Univ. of Notre Dame, Ind., Apr. 20–22, 1977, *Rept.* EPA-600/7/78-120, U.S. Environmental Protection Agency.

Cooper, D. W. & Rei, M. T. 1976 Evaluation of Electrostatic Augmentation for Fine Particle Control, *Rept.* EPA-600/2-76-055, Environmental Protection Agency, Research Triangle Park, N.C.

Crynack, R. R. 1978 A Review of the Electrical Energization Equipment for Electrostatic Precipitators, *71st Annu. Meet.,* Paper 78-74.9, *Air Pollution Control Assoc. Houston, June 1978.*

Cunningham, R. L. 1976 Operational Monitoring and Maintenance of Industrial Electrostatic Precipitators for Optimum Performance, *IEEE-I.A.S. Annu. Meet.* Chicago.

Davies, C. N. 1945 Definitive Equations for the Fluid Resistance of Spheres, *Proc. Phys. Soc.* 57(322):259.

Davies, C. N. (ed.) 1960 *Aerosol Science,* Academic, London.

Davies, C. N. 1970 The Clogging of Fibrous Aerosol Filters, *J. Aerosol Sci.* 1:35–39.

Davies, C. N. 1973 *Air Filtration,* Academic, New York.

Davies, J. T. & Rideal, E. K. 1963 *Interfacial Phenomena,* pp. 359–386, Academic, New York.

Dennis, R. & Klemm, H. A. 1979a *Fabric Filter Model Format Change,* vol. I, Detailed Technical Report, NTIS PB 293 551/AS, Natl. Technical Information Service, Springfield, Va.

Dennis, R. & Klemm, H. A. 1979b *Fabric Filter Model Format Change,* vol. II, User's Guide, EPA-600/7-79-043b, NTIS PB 294 042/AS, Natl. Technical Information Service, Springfield, Va.

Dennis, R. & Wilder, J. 1975 Fabric Filter Cleaning Studies, NTIS PB 240-372/AS, Natl. Technical Information Service, Springfield, Va.

Dennis, R., Klemm, H. A., & Battye, W. H. 1979c Fabric Filter Model Sensitivity Analysis, NTIS PB 297 755/AS, Natl Technical Information Service, Springfield, Va.

Dennis, R., Johnson, G. A., First, M. W., & Silverman, L. 1952 How Dust Collectors Perform, *Chem. Eng.* 59:196–198.

Dennis, R. et al. 1977 Filtration Model for Coal Fly Ash with Glass Fabrics, NTIS PB 276-489/AS, Natl. Technical Information Service, Springfield, Va.

Domb, C., Gillis, J., & Wilmers, G. 1965 On the Shape and Configuration of Polymer Molecules, *Proc. Phys. Soc.* 85:625–645.

Eaglund, D. 1975 The Influence of Hydration on the Stability of Hydrophobic Colloidal Systems, *Water, a Comprehensive Treatment,* vol. 5, *Water in Disperse Systems,* ed. Felix Franks, pp. 1–74, Plenum, New York.

Eckenfelder, W. W., Jr. 1966 *Industrial Water Pollution Control,* McGraw-Hill, New York.

Edmiston, N. G. & Bunyard, F. L. 1970 A Systematic Procedure for Determining the Cost of Controlling Particulate Emissions from Industrial Sources, *J. Air Pollut. Control Assoc.* 20:446–452.

Einstein, A. 1906 Zur Theorie der Brownschen Bewegung, *Ann. Phys.* 19:371–381.

Engelbrecht, H. L. 1976a Hot or Cold Electrostatic Precipitators for Fly Ash from Coal-fired Boilers, *Air Pollution Control Assoc. Western Pennsylvania Technical Meet. Coal Utilization, Pittsburgh, Apr. 1976,* pp. 106–122.

Engelbrecht, H. L. 1976b Plant Engineer's Guide to Electrostatic Precipitator Inspection and Maintenance, *Plant Eng.,* Apr., pp. 193–196.

Fan, K. C. & Gentry, J. W. 1978 Clogging in Nuclepore Filters, *Environ. Sci. Technol.* 12:1289–1294.

First, M. W. 1950 Fundamental Factors in the Design of Cyclone Dust Collectors, Sc.D. thesis, Harvard Univ., Cambridge, Mass.

Fitch, B. 1962 Sedimentation Process Fundamentals, *Trans. Soc. Min. Eng.* June, pp. 129–137.

Fleischer, R. L., Price, P. B., & Symes, E. M. 1964 Novel Filter for Biological Materials, *Science,* 143:249–250.

Fowler, R. & Guggenheim, E. A. 1952 *Statistical Thermodynamics,* Cambridge Univ. Press, New York.

Fraser, M. D. & Eaton, D. R. 1975 Cost Models for Venturi Scrubber System, *68th Annu. Meet. Air Pollution Control Assoc., Boston, 1975,* paper 75-30, 4.

Frederick, E. R. 1978 *Electrostatic Effects in Fabric Filtration,* vol. II, Triboelectric Measurements and Bag Performance (annotated data), NTIS PB 287 207/AS, Natl. Technical Information Service, Springfield, Va.

Freeman, M. P., Talcott, R. M., & Willus, C. A. 1980 Filtration, in *Kirk-Othmer Encyclopedia of Chemical Technology,* 3d ed., Vol. 10, Academic Press, New York.

Frenkel, D. I. 1978 Tuning Electrostatic Precipitators, *Chem. Eng.* **85**:105–110.

Friedlander, S. K. 1958 Theory of Aerosol Filtration, *Ind. Eng. Chem.* **50**:1161–1164.

Frommer, D. W. 1969 A New Way to Handle Nonmagnetic Taconite, *Eng. Min. J.* August pp. 92–97.

Fuchs, N. A. 1964 *The Mechanics of Aerosols,* Macmillan, New York.

Fuchs, N. A. & Kirsch, A. A. 1965 The Effect of Condensation of a Vapor on the Grains and of Evaporation from Their Surface on the Deposition of Aerosols in Granular Beds, *Chem. Eng. Sci.* **20**:181–185.

Fuchs, N. A., Murashkevich, F. I., & Raikin, A. D. 1973 Preliminary Report on the Efficiency of Collisions between Dust Particles and Water Droplets, *Staub* **33**(4):182–183.

George, H. F. & Poehlein, G. W. 1974 Capture of Aerosol Particles by Spherical Collectors: Electrostatic, Inertial, Interception, and Viscous Effects, *Environ. Sci. Technol.* **8**:46–49.

Goel, K. C. & Hollands, K. G. T. 1977 Optimum Design of Venturi Scrubbers, *Atmos. Environ.* **11**:837–845.

Goldsmith, P. & May, F. G. 1966 Diffusiophoresis and Thermophoresis in Water Vapor Systems, in *Aerosol Science,* ed. C. N. Davies, pp. 163–194, Academic, New York.

Grahame, D. C. 1947 The Electrical Double Layer and the Theory of Electrocapillarity, *Chem. Rev.* **41**:441–501.

Green, H. L. & Lane, W. R. 1964 *Particulate Clouds: Dusts, Smokes, and Mists,* Spon, London.

Hamaker, H. C. 1937 The London-van der Waals Attraction between Spherical Particles, *Physica* **4**:1058–1072.

Hanf, E. M. & MacDonald, J. W. 1975 Economic Evaluation of Wet Scrubbers, *Chem. Eng. Prog.* **71**:48–52.

Happel, J. & Brenner, H. 1965 *Low Reynolds Number Hydrodynamics,* Prentice-Hall, Englewood Cliffs, N.J.

Hazlett, R. N. & Carhart, H. W. 1972 Removal of Water from Fuel Using a Fibrous Bed, *Filtr. Sep.* **9**:456–460.

Helmholtz, H. 1879 Studien über electrische Grenzschichten, *Ann. Phys. Chem.* **7**:337–382.

Henry, D. C. 1931 The Cataphoresis of Suspended Particles, I: The Equation of Cataphoresis, *Proc. R. Soc. London* **A133**:106–129.

Hoxie, E. C. & Tuffnell, G. W. 1976 A Summary of INCO Corrosion Tests in Power Plant Flue Gas Scrubbing Processes, in *Resolving Corrosion Problems in Air Pollution Equipment,* pp. 65–71, National Association of Corrosion Engineers, Houston.

Hu, S. & Kintner, R. C. 1955 The Fall of Single Liquid Drops through Water, *AIChE J.* **1**:42–48.

Iinoya, K. & Orr, C., Jr. 1977 Filtration, *Air Pollution,* ed. A. C. Stern, chap. 4, Academic, New York.

Jackson, M. 1974 Fluidized Beds for Submicron Particle Collection, *AIChE Symp. Ser.* **70**(141):82–87.

Jaisinghani, R. A. 1977 Effect of Commercial Fuel Oil Additives on Coalescer Performance, *Filtr. Sep.* **14**:367–373.

Jaisinghani, R. A. & Sprenger, G. S. 1979 A Study of Oil/Water Separation in Corrugated Plate Separators, *Trans. ASME, J. Eng. Ind.* **101**:441–448.

Jaisinghani, R. A., Wilkie, C., Roberts, R., Sprenger, G., & Deeley, G. 1977 Design Aspects of Fibrous Bed Coalescers, *Conf. Theory Practice and Process Principles Physical Separations,* Pacific Grove, Calif.

Johnson, A. I. & Braida, L. 1957 The Velocity of Fall of Circulating and Oscillating Liquid Drops through Quiescent Liquid Phases, *Can. J. Chem. Eng.* **35**:165–172.

Kalen, B. & Zenz, F. A. 1974 Theoretical-Empirical Approach to Solfation Velocity in Cyclone Design, *AIChE Symp. Ser.* **70**:388–396.

Kanaoka, C., Emi, H., & Aikura, T. 1979 Collection Efficiency of Aerosols by Micro-perforated Plates, *J. Aerosol Sci.* **10**:29–41.

Karabelas, A. J. 1978 Droplet Size Spectra Generated in Turbulent Pipe Flow of Dilute Liquid/Liquid Dispersions, *AIChE J.* **24**:170–180.

Kinkley, M. L. & Neveril, R. B. 1976 Capital and Operating Costs of Selected Air Pollution Control Systems, NTIS PB 258 484, Natl. Technical Information Service, Springfield, Va.

Kitchener, J. A. & Musselwhite, P. R. 1968 The Theory of Stability of Emulsions in *Emulsion Science*, ed., P. Sherman, chap. 2, Academic, New York.

Klee, A. J. & Treybal, R. E. 1956 Rate of Rise or Fall of Liquid Drops, *AIChE J.* 2:444–447.

Klinkowski, P. R. 1978 Ultrafiltration: An Emerging Unit-Operation, *Chem. Eng.* May 8, pp. 165–173.

Knettig, P. & Beeckmans, J. M. 1974 Inertial Capture of Aerosol Particles by Swarms of Accelerating Spheres, *J. Aerosol Sci.* 5:225–233.

Koch, W. H. & Licht, W. 1977 New Design Approach Boosts Cyclone Efficiency, *Chem. Eng.* 84:80–88.

Kos, P. 1977 Fundamentals of Gravity Thickening, *Chem. Eng. Prog.* 73(11):99–105.

Koscianowski, J. R., Koscianowska, L., & Szablewicz, M. 1979 Test of Fabric Filtration Materials, EPA-600/7-79-087, NTIS PB 297 500/AS, Natl. Technical Information Service; also Filtration Parameters for Dust Cleaning Fabrics, EPA-600/7-79-031, NTIS PB 292 381/AS, Natl. Technical Information Service, Springfield, Va.

Kraemer, H. F., & Johnstone, H. F. 1955 Collection of Aerosol Particles in Presence of Electrostatic Fields, *Indus. Eng. Chem.* 47:2426.

Krockta, H. & Lucas, R. L. 1972 Information Required for the Selection and Performance Evaluation of Wet Scrubbers, *J. Air Pollut. Control Assoc.* 22:459–462.

Kynch, G. V. 1952 A Theory of Sedimentation, *Trans. Faraday Soc.* 48:166–176.

LaMer, V. K. & Healy, T. W. 1963 Adsorption-Flocculation Reactions of Macromolecules at the Solid-Liquid Interface, *Rev. Pure Appl. Chem.* 13:112–132.

Lancaster, B. W. & Strauss, W. 1971 A Study of Steam Injection into Wet Scrubbers, *Ind. Eng. Chem. Fundam.* 10:362–369.

Lapple, C. E. 1951 Processes Use Many Collector Types. *Chem. Eng.* 58:144–151.

Lapple, C. E. & Kamack, H. J. 1955 Performance of Wet Dust Scrubbers, *Chem. Eng. Prog.* 51:110–121.

Lapple, C. E. & Shepherd, C. B. 1940 Calculation of Particle Trajectories, *Ind. Eng. Chem.* 32:605–617.

Lawrence Livermore Laboratory 1978 Hazards Control Progress Report 55, Lawrence Livermore Laboratory, Livermore, Calif.

Lee, K. W. & Gieseke, J. A. 1979 Collection of Aerosol Particles by Packed Beds, *Environ. Sci. Technol.* 13:466–470.

Lee, K. W., Reed, L. D., & Gieseke, J. A. 1978 Pressure Drop Across Packed Beds in the Low Knudsen Number Regime, *J. Aerosol Sci.* 9:557–565.

Leith, D. & First, M. W. 1977 Filter Cake Redeposition in a Pulse-Jet Filter, NTIS PB 266 233, Natl. Technical Information Service, Springfield, Va.

Leith, D. & Licht, W. 1972 Collection Efficiency of Cyclone Type Particle Collectors, A New Theoretical Approach, *AIChE. Symp. Ser.* 68(126):196–206.

Leith, D. & Mehta, D. 1973 Cyclone Performance and Design, *Atmos. Environ.* 7:527–549.

Leith, D., First, M. W., & Gibson, D. D. 1978 Performance of a High Velocity Pulse-Jet Filter, NTIS PB 284 332, Natl. Technical Information Service, Springfield, Va.

Levan, D. M. & Newman, J. 1976 The Effect of Surfactant on the Terminal and Interfacial Velocities of a Bubble or Drop, *AIChE J.* 22:695–701.

Liu, B. Y. H. & Lee, K. W. 1976 Efficiency of Membrane and Nuclepore Filters for Submicrometer Aerosols, *Environ. Sci. Technol.* 10:345–350.

Luthy, R. G., Selleck, R. E., & Galloway, T. R. 1977 Surface Properties of Petroleum Refinery Waste Oil Emulsions, *Environ. Sci. Technol.* 1:1211–1217.

Manton, M. J. 1978 The Impaction of Aerosols on a Nuclepore Filter, *Atmos. Environ.* 12:1669–1675.

Manton, M. J. 1979 Brownian Diffusion of Aerosols to the Face of a Nuclepore Filter, *Atmos. Environ.* 13:525–531.

Maude, A. D. & Whitmore, R. L. 1958 A Generalized Theory of Sedimentation, *Br. J. Appl. Phys.* 9:477–482.

May, K. R. & Clifford, R. 1967 The Impaction of Aerosol Particles on Cylinders, Spheres, Ribbons, and Discs, *Ann. Occup. Hyg.* 10:83–95.

McFarland, J. 1979 Fans for Filtration, *Fil. Sep.* March:pp. 144–149.

McIlvaine, R. W. 1977 When to Pilot and When to Use Theoretical Predictions of Required Venturi Pressure Drop, *70th Annu. Meet. Air Pollution Control Assoc., Toronto,* paper 77-17.1.

McKenna, J. D., Mycock, J. C., & Lipscomb, W. O. 1975 Applying Fabric Filtration to Coal Fired Industrial Boilers, NTIS PB 186/AS, Natl. Technical Information Service, Springfield, Va.

Medalia, A. I. 1971 Computer Simulation of Colloidal Systems, *Surf. Colloid Sci.* 4:1–92.

Miller, B. et al. 1978 Studies of Dust Cake Formation and Structure in Fabric Filtration, NTIS PB 283 179/AS, Natl. Technical Information Service, Springfield, Va.

Miller, B., Lamb, G., Costanze, P., & Craig, J. 1977 Non-Woven Fabric Filters for Particulate Removal in Respirable Dust Range, NTIS PB 273 359/AS, Natl. Technical Information Service, Springfield, Va.

Miranda, J. G. 1977 Designing Parallel-Plate Separators, *Chem. Eng.* 84:105–107.

Miyamoto, S. & Bohm, H. 1975 Filtration of Airborne Particulates by Gravel Filters, II: Collection Efficiency and Pressure Drop in Filtering Fume, *J. Air Pollut. Control Assoc.* 25:40–43.

Mohan, V., Shah, S. M., Patel, P. S., & Wasan, D. T. 1977 Interfacial Rheological Properties and Emulsion Stability, *83d AIChE Natl. Meet., Houston,* paper 50E.

Muir, D. M., Grant, C. D., & Miheisi, Y. 1978 Relationship between Collection Efficiency and Energy Consumption of Wet Dust Collectors, *Filtr. Sep.* 15:332–340.

Murkes, J. 1966 Outline of the Theory of Separation Processes in Centrifugal Separators, *Filtr. Sep.* 3:112–114.

Murkes, J. 1967 The Influence of Difference Factors on the Result Obtained by Centrifugal Separation of Mineral Oils, *Gas Oil Power* 63:115–119.

Murkes, J. 1969 The Effect of Suspension Characteristics in Centrifugal Separation, *Br. Chem. Eng.* 14:636–641.

Nebolsine, R. 1970 New Methods for the Treatment of Oily Wastewater Streams, *Proc. 25th Industrial Waste Conf., Purdue Univ.,* pp. 885–891.

Nelson, G. O., Bergman, W., Miller, H. H., Taylor, R. D., Richards, C. P., & Biermann, A. H. 1978 Enhancement of Air Filtration Using Electric Fields, *Am. Ind. Hyg. Assoc. J.* 39:472–479.

Neveril, R. B., Price, J. U., & Engdahl, K. L. 1978 Capital and Operating Costs of Selected Air Pollution Control Systems, I–V, *J. Air Pollut. Control Assoc.* 28:829–836, 963–968, 1069–1072, 1171–1174, 1253–1256.

Nielsen, K. A. 1978 Written discussion, in Ariman, T. (ed.) 1978 Novel Concepts, Methods and Advanced Technology in Particulate-Gas Separation, proceedings of a workshop held at the Univ. of Notre Dame, Ind., Apr. 20–22, 1977, *Rept.* EPA-600/7-78-120, U.S. Environmental Protection Agency.

Oberteuffer, J. A. 1973 Characteristics of HGMS Devices, in *Proceedings of the High Gradient Magnetic Separation Symposium,* eds. J. A. Oberteuffer & D. R. Kelland, pp. 86–101, M.I.T. Press, Cambridge, Mass.

Oberteuffer, J. A. & Kelland, D. R. (eds.) 1973 *Proceedings of the High Gradient Magnetic Separation Symposium,* M.I.T. Press, Cambridge, Mass.

Oderr, R. R. 1973 Magnetic Separation Technology in the Kaolin Industry, in *Proceedings of the High Gradient Magnetic Separation Symposium,* eds. J. A. Oberteuffer & D. R. Kelland, pp. 55–70, M.I.T. Press, Cambridge, Mass.

Oglesby, Sabert, Jr. 1970 *A Manual of Electrostatic Precipitator Technology,* Southern Research Institute, Birmingham, Ala.

Oliver, R. H. 1964 Specifying Clarifier Size Based on Batch Laboratory Tests in Unit Processes in Hydrometallurgy, in *Metallurgical Society Conferences,* ed. M. E. Wadsworth, & F. T. Davis, vol. 124, pp. 416–422, Gordon & Breach, New York.

O'Melia, C. R. 1972 Coagulation and Flocculation, in *Physicochemical Processes for Water Quality Control,* ed. W. J. Weber, Jr., chap. 2, Wiley-Interscience, New York.

Osamor, F. A. & Ahlert, R. C. 1978 Oil/Water Separation: State of the Art, *Rept.* EPA-600/78-069, pp. 10–31., U.S. Environmental Protection Agency.

Paretsky, L., Theodore, L., Pfeffer, R., & Squires, A. M. 1971 Panel Bed Filters for Simultaneous Removal of Fly Ash and Sulfur Dioxide, II: Filtration of Dilute Aerosols by Sand Beds, *J. Air Pollut. Control Assoc.* 21:204–209.

Parker, R. D. & Buzzard, G. H. 1978 A Filtration Model for Large Pore Nuclepore Filters, *J. Aerosol Sci.* 9:7–16.

Parker, R. D., Buzzard, G. H., Dzubay, T. G., & Bell, J. P. 1977 A Two Stage Respirable Aerosol Sampler Using Nuclepore Filters in Series, *Atmos. Environ.* 11:617–621.

Penney, G. W. 1978 *Electrostatic Effects in Fabric Filtration,* vol. 1, Fields, Fabrics, and Particles (annotated data), NTIS PB 288 576/AS, Natl. Technical Information Service, Springfield, Va.

Perry, R. H. & Chilton, C. H. 1973 *Chemical Engineers' Handbook,* 5th ed., McGraw-Hill, New York.

Pich, J. 1966 Theory of Aerosol Filtration by Fibrous and Membrane Filters, in *Aerosol Science,* ed. C. N. Davis, Academic, New York.

Pilat, M. J. & Prem, A. 1977 Effect of Diffusiophoresis and Thermophoresis on the Overall Particle Collection Efficiency of Spray Droplet Scrubbers, *J. Air Pollut. Control Assoc.* 27:982–988.

Richardson, J. E., Kerver, J. L., Hafford, J. A., & Osaba, J. S. 1952 Laboratory Determination of Relative Permeability, *Trans. AIME* 195:187.

Rosenfeld, J. I. & Wasan, D. T. 1974 Coalescence of Drops in a Liquid-Liquid Dispersion by Passage through a Fibrous Bed, *Can. J. Chem. Eng.* 52:3–10.

Rudnick, S. N. 1978 Fundamental Factors Governing Specific Resistance of Filter Dust Cakes, Sc.D. thesis, Harvard School of Public Health, Boston.

Ruehrwein, R. A. & Ward, D. W. 1952 Mechanism of Clay Aggregation by Polyelectrolytes, *Soil Sci.* 73:485–492.

Sanfeld, A., Devillez, C., & Terlinck, P. 1970 A Local Thermodynamical Approach of the Repulsive Energy between Colloidal Articles, *J. Colloid Interface Sci.* 32:33–40.

Schmidt, E. W., Gieseke, J. A., Gelfand, P., Lugar, T. W., & Furlong, D. A. 1978 Filtration Theory for Granular Beds, *J. Air Pollut. Control Assoc.* 28:143–146.

Semrau, K. T. 1977 Practical Process Design of Particulate Scrubbers, *Chem. Eng.* Sept. 26, pp. 87–91.

Semrau, K. & Witham, C. L. 1974 Wet Scrubber Liquid Utilization, Stanford Research Inst., Menlo Park, Calif., *Rept.* EPA-650/2-74-108, U.S. Environmental Protection Agency.

Semrau, K. T., Marynowski, C. W., Lunde, K. E., & Lapple, C. E. 1958 Influence of Power Input on Efficiency of Dust Scrubber, *Ind. Eng. Chem.* 50:1615–1620.

Semrau, K. T., Witham, C. L., & Kerlin, W. W. 1977 Relationships of Collection Efficiency and Energy Dissipation in Particulate Scrubbers, *2d Fine Particle Scrubber Symp., New Orleans, May 1977.*

Shackleton, L. R. B., Douglas, E., & Walsh, T. 1960 Pollution of the Sea by Oil, II: Disintegration Effects of Pumps on Mixture of Oil and Water, *Inst. Mar. Eng. Trans.* 72:415–422.

Shepherd, C. B. & Lapple, C. E. 1939 Flow Pattern and Pressure Drop in Cyclone Dust Collectors, *Ind. Eng. Chem.* 31:972–984.

Shepherd, C. B. & Lapple, C. E. 1940 Flow Pattern and Pressure Drop in Cyclone Dust Collectors, *Ind. Eng. Chem.* 32:1246–1248.

Sheppard, S. V. 1972 Particulate Collection with Packed Crossflow Scrubbers, *J. Air Pollut. Control Assoc.* 27:278–281.

Sherony, D. F. 1967 *The Coagulation of a Dispersion in a Fibrous Bed Coalescer,* Ph.D. thesis, Illinois Inst. of Technology, Chicago.

Sherony, D. F. & Kintner, R. C. 1971 Coalescence of an Emulsion in a Fibrous Bed, I: Theory, *Can. J. Chem. Eng.* 49:314–319.

Sherony, D. F., Kintner, R. C., & Wasan, D. T. 1978 Coalescence of Secondary Emulsions in Fibrous Beds, in *Surface and Colloid Science,* ed. E. Matijevic, pp. 99–159, Plenum, New York.

Silverblatt, C. E. & Dahlstrom, D. A. 1954 Moisture Content of a Fine-Coal Filter Cake, *Ind. Eng. Chem.* **46**:1201–1207.

Simons, C. S. & Dahlstrom, D. A. 1966 Steam Dewatering of Filter Cakes, *Chem. Eng. Prog.* **62**(1):75–81.

Slinn, W. G. N. & Hales, J. M. 1971 A Re-evaluation of the Role of Thermophoresis as a Mechanism of In- and Below-Cloud Scavenging, *J. Atmos. Sci.* **28**:1465–1471.

Sonntag, H. & Strenge, K. 1972 *Coagulation and Stability of Disperse Systems,* Wiley, New York.

Sparks, L. E. 1971 The Effect of Scrubber Operating and Design Parameters on the Collection of Particulate Air Pollutants, Ph.D. thesis, University of Washington, Seattle.

Sparks, L. E. 1978 SR-52 Programmable Calculator Programs for Venturi Scrubbers and Electrostatic Precipitators, *Rept.* EPA-600/7-78-026, U.S. Environmental Protection Agency.

Sparks, L. E. & Pilat, M. J. 1970 Effect of Diffusiophoresis on Particle Collection by Wet Scrubbers, *Atmos. Environ.* **4**:651–660.

Spielman, L. & Goren, S. L. 1968 Model for Predicting Pressure Drop and Filtration Efficiency in Fibrous Media, *Environ. Sci. Technol.* **4**:279–287.

Spielman, L. A. & Goren, S. L. 1972a An Experiment in Coalescence by Flow through Fibrous Mats, *Ind. Eng. Chem. Fund.* **11**(1):73–83.

Spielman, L. A. & Goren, S. L. 1972b Theory of Coalescence by Flow through Porous Media, *Ind. Eng. Chem. Fund.* **11**:66–72.

Spielman, L. A. & Su, Y. P. 1977 Coalescence of Oil-in-Water Suspensions by Flow through Porous Media, *Ind. Eng. Chem. Fund.* **16**(2):272–283.

Spurny, K. R., Havlova, J., Lodge, J. P., Ackerman, E. R., Sheesley, D. C., & Wilder, B. 1974 Aerosol Filtration by Means of Nuclepore Filters: Filter Pore Clogging, *Environ. Sci. Technol.* **8**:758–761.

Spurny, K. R., Lodge, J. P., Frank, E. R., & Sheesley, D. C. 1969a Aerosol Filtration by Means of Nuclepore Filters: Structural and Filtration Properties, *Environ. Sci. Technol.* **3**:453–464.

Spurny, K. R., Lodge, J. P., Frank, E. R., & Sheesley, D. C. 1969b Aerosol Filtration by Means of Nuclepore Filters: Aerosol Sampling and Measurement, *Environ. Sci. Technol.* **3**:464–468.

Squires, A. M. & Pfeffer, R. 1970 Panel Bed Filters for Simultaneous Removal of Fly Ash and Sulfur Dioxide, I: Introduction, *J. Air Pollut. Control Assoc.* **20**:534–538.

Stafford, R. G. & Ettinger, H. J. 1972 Filter Efficiency as a Function of Particle Size and Velocity, *Atmos. Environ.* **6**:353–362.

Stairmand, C. J. 1951 The Design and Performance of Cyclone Separators, *Trans. Inst. Chem. Eng.* **29**:356–383.

Steiner, B. A. & Thompson, R. J. 1977 Wet Scrubbing Experience for Steel Mill Applications, *J. Air Pollut. Control Assoc.* **27**:1069–1075.

Stephan, D. G. & Walsh, G. W. 1960 Residual Dust Profile in Air Filtration, *Ind. Eng. Chem.* **52**:999–1002.

Stern, A. C. (ed.) 1977 *Air Pollution,* 3d ed., Academic, New York.

Stern, A. C., Caplan, K. J., & Bush, P. D. 1955 *Cyclone Dust Collectors,* American Petroleum Institute, New York.

Stern, A. C., Wohlers, H. C., Boubel, R. W., & Lowry, W. P. 1973 *Fundamentals of Air Pollution,* Academic, New York.

Stern, O. 1924 Zur Theorie der Elektrolytischen Doppelschicht, *Z. Elektrochem.* **30**:508–516.

Strauss, W. 1966 *Industrial Gas Cleaning,* Pergamon, New York.

Strauss, W. 1977 Mist Elimination, in *Air Pollution,* 3d ed., ed. A. C. Stern, chap. 7, Academic, New York.

Stulov, L. D., Murashkevich, F. I., & Fuchs, N. A. 1978 The Efficiency of Collision of Solid Aerosol Particles with Water Surfaces, *J. Aerosol Sci.* **9**:1–6.

Sutherland, D. N. 1966 Comments on Vold's Simulation of Floc Formation, *J. Colloid Interface Sci.* **22**:300–302.

Swift, P. 1969 Dust Control in Industry, 2, *Steam Heat Engineer* **38**:453–456.

Szabo, M. R., Szabo, M. F., & Gerstle, R. W. 1977 Electrostatic Precipitator Malfunction in the Electric Utility Industry, PEDCO Environmental, Inc., Cincinnati, Ohio.

Taggart, A. F. 1967 Sink-Float Separation, in *Handbook of Mineral Dressing,* Wiley, New York, 11-125.

Taheri, M. & Calvert, S. 1968 Removal of Small Particles from Air by Foam in a Sieve-Plate Column, *J. Air Pollut. Control Assoc.* **18**:240–245.

Taheri, M. & Haines, G. F. 1969 Optimization of Factors Affecting Scrubber Performance, *J. Air Pollut. Control Assoc.* **19**:427–431.

Taheri, M., Beg, S. A., & Beizie, M. 1972 Gas Cleaning in a Wetted Butterfly Valve, *J. Air Pollut. Control Assoc.* **22**:794–798.

Taheri, M., Beg, S. A., & Beizie, M. 1973 The Effect of Scale-up on the Performance of High Energy Scrubbers, *J. Air Pollut. Control Assoc.* **23**:963–966.

Tardos, G. I., Abuaf, N., & Gutfinger, C. 1978 Dust Deposition in Granular Bed Filters, *J. Air Pollut. Control Assoc.* **28**:354–363.

Tepe, J. B. & Woods, W. K. 1943 Design of Ether-Water Contacting System, *U.S. Atomic Energy Commission Rept.* AECD-2864.

ter Linden, A. J. 1949 Investigations into Cyclone Dust Collectors, *Proc. Inst. Mech. Eng. London* **160**:233–240.

Thorsen, G., Stordalen, R. M., & Terjesen, S. G. 1968 On the Terminal Velocity of Circulating and Oscillating Liquid Drops, *Chem. Eng. Sci.* **23**:413–426.

Tompa, H. 1956 *Polymer Solutions,* Butterworth, London.

Trawinski, H. 1981 Centrifugals: Highly Effective Solid-Liquid Separators, *Theory Practice Process Principles Physical Separations, Pacific Grove, Calif., Nov. 1977,* in press.

Treybal, R. E. 1968 *Mass Transfer Operations,* pp. 420–424, McGraw-Hill, New York.

Turner, J. H. 1980 Application of Fabric Filtration to Combustion Sources, *AIChE Symp. Ser.* **76**, 196:369–379.

U.S. Department of Health, Education and Welfare 1969 Control Techniques for Particulate Air Pollutants, *Rept.* AP-42, U.S. Dept. of Health, Education, and Welfare, Washington, D.C.

Vandergrift, A. E., Shannon, L. J., Lawless, E. W., Gorman, P. G., Sallee, E. E., & Reichel, M. 1971 *Particulate Pollutant Systems Study,* vol. III: *Handbook of Emission Properties, Rept.* APTD-0745, U.S. Environmental Protection Agency (NTIS PB 203-522).

Verwey, E. J. W. & Overbeek, J. T. G. 1948 *Theory of the Stability of Lyophobic Colloids,* Elsevier, Amsterdam.

Vold, M. J. 1960 The Sediment Volume in Dilute Dispersions of Spherical Particles, *J. Phys. Chem.* **64**:1616–1619.

Waldmann, L. & Schmitt, K. H. 1966 Thermophoresis and Diffusiophoresis of Aerosols, in *Aerosol Science,* ed. C. N. Davies, pp. 139–161, Academic, New York.

Walsh, G. W. & Spaite, P. W. 1960 Characterization of Industrial Fabric Filters, ASME Winter Meeting 60-WA-336, New York.

Warshay, M., Bogusz, E., Johnson, M., & Kintner, R. C. 1959 Ultimate Velocity of Drops in Stationary Liquid Media, *Can. J. Chem. Eng.* **37**:29–36.

Wasan, D. T. & Mohan, V. 1977 Interfacial Rheological Properties of Fluid Interfaces Containing Surfactants, in *Improved Oil Recovery by Surfactants and Polymer Flooding,* eds. D. O. Shah & R. S. Schechter, pp. 161–203, Academic, New York.

Watanabe, K., Kutoh, H., & Ueta, Y. 1978 Oil Drop Size Distribution in Inflow of Oily Water Separator, *Bull. MESJ Jpn.* **13**:273–282.

Watts, R. L. 1967 Recent Developments in Magnetic Separation Equipment, preprint, Dings Magnetic Separator Co., Milwaukee, Wis.

Weber, E. 1968 The Influence of Dust Wettability on Wet Scrubbing, *Staub* **28**(11):37–43.

Werner, R. M. & Clarenburg, L. A. 1965 Aerosol Filters: Pressure Drop Across Single-Component Glass Fiber Filters, *Ind. Eng. Chem. Proc. Des. Dev.* **4**:288–293.

White, H. J. 1963 *Industrial Electrostatic Precipitation,* Addison-Wesley, Reading, Mass.

White, H. J. 1977 Electrostatic Precipitation of Fly Ash, *Air Pollut. Control Assoc.* **27**(3):206–217.

Whitmore, P. J. 1976 Diffusiophoretic Particle Collection under Turbulent Conditions, Ph.D. thesis, Univ. of British Columbia, Canada.

Williams, C. E., Hatch, T., & Greenburg, L. 1940 Determination of Cloth Area for Industrial Air Filters, *Heat. Pipe Air Cond.* 5:259–263.

Wolffinden, G. J., Markowski, G. R., & Ensor, D. S. 1978 Effects of Interfacial Properties on Collection of Fine Particles by Wet Scrubbers, *Rept.* EPA-600/7-78-097, U.S. Environmental Protection Agency, Washington, D.C.

Yeh, H.-C. & Liu, B. Y. H. 1974a Aerosol Filtration by Fibrous Filters, I: Theoretical, *J. Aerosol Sci.* 5:191–204.

Yeh, H.-C. & Liu, B. Y. H. 1974b Aerosol Filtration by Fibrous Filters, II: Experimental, *J. Aerosol Sci.* 5:205–217.

Yung, S.-C., Barbarika, H. F., & Calvert, S. 1977a Pressure Loss in Venturi Scrubbers, *J. Air Pollut. Control Assoc.* 27:348–351.

Yung, S.-C., Calvert, S., & Barbarika, H. F. 1977b Venturi Scrubber Performance Model, *Rept.* EPA-600/2-77-172, U.S. Environmental Protection Agency, Washington, D.C.

Zahedi, K. & Melcher, J. R. 1976 Electrofluidized Beds in the Filtration of a Submicron Aerosol, *J. Air Pollut. Control Assoc.* 26:345–352.

Zebel, G. 1966 Improving the Separation Efficiency of Fiber Filters by Electrical Fields, *Staub.* 26:18–22.

Zebel, G. 1974 A Simple Model for the Calculation of Particle Trajectories Approaching Nuclepore Filters with Allowance for Electrical Forces, *J. Aerosol Sci.* 5:473–482.

Zieve, P. B., Zahedi, K., Melcher, J. R., & Denton, J. F. 1978 Electrofluidized Bed in Filtration of Smoke Emissions from Asphaltic Pavement Recycling Process, *Environ. Sci. Technol.* 12:96–99.

10 MEASUREMENT TECHNIQUES

10.1   Introduction

10.1.1   CLASSIFICATION OF QUANTITIES

G. F. Hewitt

Many thousands of reports have been written on two-phase flow measurements. To systematize and present this vast amount of information, it is necessary to devise a classification scheme. The two most obvious forms of classification are

1. Classification by parameter (e.g., consider all the methods applied to the measurement of a particular quantity, such as void fraction)
2. Classification in terms of the "type" of measurement method employed (optical methods, electrical methods, etc.)

Alternative classification schemes might include

1. Classification by time response and/or localization of the measurements (e.g., fast response, average, overall, and local)
2. Classification by flow pattern (bubble flow, annular flow, etc.)
3. Classification by the extent of interference with flow and heat transfer (intrusive, nonintrusive)

It is often best to take the pragmatic approach of using a mixed classification scheme, as is done in this chapter. The scheme we shall use is detailed in the last part of this section. First, however, it will be worthwhile to discuss the classification of two-phase measurements by parameter and by method.

10.1.1.1   Classification by Parameter

Classification by parameter is obviously a useful approach. However, rather than simply produce a list of two-phase flow parameters and their associated measurement methods, it is helpful to group the parameters according to their ultimate application. An example of such a grouping is the classification of Hewitt (1972, 1978):

1. *First-order parameters.* These are parameters that are of direct relevance to design. Hewitt (1978) subdivides first-order parameters into three categories as follows:
   a. Primary design parameters (steady state). These include pressure drop, heat transfer coefficient, mass transfer coefficient, mean phase content (void fraction), and critical heat flux.
   b. Primary design parameters (fault conditions). Modern design practice is increasingly concerned with the behavior of systems under fault conditions. Parameters that must be studied (in the particular context of nuclear reactors) include system discharge (blowdown), bubble growth and collapse, dryout under fault conditions, and rewetting.
   c. Secondary design parameters. These are parameters that need to be investigated as part of the overall design but that would not necessarily be the *first* consideration of the designer. They include vibration, flow distribution, stability, quality and mass flow measurement, and liquid-level detection.
2. *Second-order parameters.* Here, one is concerned with parameters that are of interest in research aimed at obtaining better system design. The designer would not normally calculate these parameters, but would use only the correlations for first-order parameters that have been derived as a result of studies on second-order parameters. The second-order parameters defined by Hewitt include flow pattern, time-averaged film thickness, wave amplitude distribution, mass flow distribution, local phase concentration (void fraction), velocity and momentum flux distribution, concentration distribution, mixing characteristics, drop or bubble size distribution, wall shear stress, temperature distribution, entrainment (film flow rate), and contact angle.
3. *Third-order parameters.* Two-phase flows are characterized as being fundamentally unsteady. An understanding of the fluctuations of such quantities as velocity, phase content, temperature, pressure, and wall shear stress can aid in the development of improved design methods and, hence, better systems. Such fluctuating parameters are referred to by Hewitt as third order. The designer is unlikely to use this information directly, but it still may be of interest. Hewitt included in this area the use of high-speed photographic techniques for the observation of fluctuating local phenomena.

10.1.1.2 Classification by Method

The types of methods employed in two-phase flow measurements include

1. Optical methods
2. Radiation absorption and scattering methods
3. Electrical capacitance and conductance methods
4. Tracer methods
5. Heat and mass transfer methods
6. Methods employing the Seebeck (thermocouple) effect

7. Differential pressure and momentum methods
8. Flow separation methods

Although this list covers most of the available techniques, it is by no means exhaustive. To further illustrate this classification scheme, each type of method is now considered briefly.

Optical Methods

With the advent of lasers, a range of new optical techniques has evolved to supplement the many useful techniques already available. Optical techniques can be further classified in terms of the light modulation process (absorption, scattering, interference, refraction, excitation, and complex) and by the method of recording the signal (electronic or photographic). Examples of optical techniques are shown in table 10.1.1.

Further details on the various techniques listed in table 10.1.1 are given by Hewitt (1978), and a review on advanced laser instrumentation in two-phase flow is given by Hewitt & Whalley (1979).

Radiation, Absorption, and Scattering

Radiation absorption techniques have been used very widely, and for many years. Absorption of gamma rays is the most ubiquitous technique for the measurement of void fraction, and gamma and X-ray absorption can be used for the determination of flow pattern from void fraction fluctuation data and for the determination of film thickness in annular flow. Absorption of β rays and neutron beams has also been used quite extensively.

Radiation can also be scattered in two-phase mixtures, the scattered radiation usually being of a different energy and/or form from that of the incident radiation. Scattering techniques have the advantage that, with collimation of the source beam

Table 10.1.1 Classification of Optical Techniques

Light modulation process	Method of recording	
	Electronic	Photographic
Absorption	Film thickness, by light absorption	X-radiography for flow pattern
Scattering	Drop size, by laser scattering	Drop size (holography), axial view (laser)
Interference	Velocity (laser Doppler anemometer)	Concentration, temperature (laser holographic interferometry)
Refraction	Void fraction (optical phase sensors)	Heat transfer visualization by Schlieren photography, shadowgraph
Excitation	Film thickness, fluorescence method, Raman spectroscopy for temperature and concentration	Phosphorescence (velocity profile)
Complex	Two-phase velocity (correlation)	Visual photography, axial view (ordinary)

and the scattered beam, a local measurement can, in principle, be made. However, the sensitivity of scattering techniques is usually low, since the scattered beam is often of rather low intensity. Again, further details concerning these techniques are given by Hewitt (1978).

Electrical Capacitance and Conductance Methods

The difference in conductance and/or capacitance between the liquid and gas phase can often be used to advantage in measuring two-phase flow parameters. The following are examples of the application of electrical techniques:

1. Determination of film thickness in annular flow by measurement of the conductance between two electrodes placed flush with the surface (Hewitt et al. 1962)
2. Needle-contact devices for the measurement of local void fraction in bubbly flow (Serizawa et al. 1975) and for the determination of film thickness distribution in annular flow (Hewitt et al. 1962)
3. Overall void fraction measurement using concentric ring electrodes spaced over the full flow (Olsen 1967)
4. Double needle-contact device for drop size measurement in annular flow (Wicks & Dukler 1966)

Tracer Methods

In these methods, a tracer is added to one or the other of the phases, and, by downstream sampling or detection of the tracer, information can be obtained on mixing, on stream velocities, etc. Examples of the application of this technique are studies of mixing in models simulating reactor fuel bundle subchannels (Mayinger et al. 1977) and studies of droplet mass transfer in two-phase annular flow (Cousins & Hewitt 1968). Major difficulties in the application of tracer techniques are (1) ensuring good initial mixing of the tracer with the flow and (2) obtaining representative samples of the flow downstream. A method that appears to be very promising in this respect is the pulsed neutron activation technique (Kehler 1978). Here, a pulse of neutrons is passed through the flow within the channel, and this generates ^{16}N (half life, 7.24 s) by the reaction ^{16}O (n, p) ^{16}N. The ^{16}N can be detected downstream by means of a gamma detector.

Heat and Mass Transfer Methods

Methods depending on the determination of highly localized heat and mass transfer as a means of characterizing the adjacent fluid flows are classic in fluid mechanics. Examples of the application of these techniques in two-phase flow are the use of hot-wire anemometry for local velocity and void fraction measurement (Hsu et al. 1963), the hot-film technique for wall shear stress measurement (Shiralkar 1970), and the use of the diffusion-controlled electrolysis technique for shear stress fluctuation studies (Kutateladze et al. 1972).

Techniques Using the Seebeck (Thermocouple) Effect

Thermocouples are used widely in two-phase flow systems. Their applications include:

1. Wall temperature measurement in the determination of heat transfer coefficients.
2. Fluid temperature measurements. There are difficulties here, owing to the effect of the temperature sensor on the local fluid state.
3. Microthermocouples for studies of locally fluctuating temperature fields in boiling (e.g., Siboul 1976).
4. Use of the reverse-current cooling effect (Peltier effect) of thermocouples to determine local dew point (Doe 1967).

Differential Pressure and Momentum Flux Methods

Differential pressure is obviously important as a design parameter, but differential pressure measurements are also used in both global and local determinations of two-phase flow rates. The differential pressure across orifice meters and venturi meters is used as a basis for quality measurement (e.g., Chisholm 1972). Local measurements of impact pressure on Pitot probes have also been widely used in two-phase flow studies (e.g., Banerjee et al. 1978).

Measurements of total momentum flux have been used frequently as one component of a dual system for measuring mass flux and quality (e.g., Arave et al. 1977). Local momentum flux measurements have been made using special momentum probes (Ryley & Kirkman 1967) and deceleration probes (Dussourd & Shapiro 1955).

Flow Separation Methods

In this class of technique, the flow is physically separated and measured. Examples of this approach are as follows:

1. The use of isokinetic probes for local flow measurement (e.g., Alia et al. 1968). Here, flow is withdrawn through a probe in such a way that there is no impact pressure at the mouth. This means (ideally) that the flow into the probe is identical to the flow that existed in the channel at that point before insertion of the probe.
2. Suction methods for film flow rate (e.g., Cousins et al. 1965). Here, the liquid film is withdrawn from the channel through a porous section of the wall.
3. Quick-closing-valve method for void fraction (e.g., Agostini & Premoli 1971). A section of the channel is isolated by simultaneously closing two valves at the entrance and exit of the section. The liquid is drained from the section, and its volume measured, thus allowing the void fraction to be calculated.

Flow separation methods do, of course, generally alter the flow downstream of the separation point and are, therefore, particularly intrusive.

10.1.1.3 Organization of the Chapter

Section 10.2, on overall measurements for gas-liquid flows, is divided into discussions of

1. Parameters of design significance. These include pressure drop, space void fractions, heat transfer coefficients, critical heat flux, and mass flow and/or quality measurement.
2. Parameters of scientific interest. These include film flow rate and entrainment measurement in annular flow, film thickness measurement, wall shear stress measurement, phase mass transfer rate measurement, local velocity measurement, and drop bubble and particle size measurement.

In section 10.3, on local measurement techniques for statistical analysis, specific reference is made to the use of local probes of various types. These include electrical probes, optical probes, thermal anemometers, and microthermocouples. Aerosol measurement and analysis is dealt with in section 10.4.

Throughout the chapter, specific methods are recommended, and these methods are described in detail. However, the methods described are not necessarily the only ones available. A vast number of alternative techniques have been proposed in the literature on two-phase flow. References to alternative techniques are given, for example, in the book by Hewitt (1978).

10.1.2 FUNDAMENTAL QUANTITIES DESCRIBING TWO-PHASE PIPE FLOWS

J. M. Delhaye

Given the fluctuating character of two-phase flows, averaging operators have to be introduced. These operators, which act in space or time domains, are discussed in detail in section 1.2.

10.1.2.1 Phase Density Function

The presence or absence of phase k ($k = 1, 2$) at a given point $\mathbf{r}$ and a given time t is characterized by the unit value (or zero value) of a *phase density function* $X_k(\mathbf{r}, t)$, defined as follows:

$$X_k(\mathbf{r}, t) \triangleq \begin{cases} 1 & \text{if point } \mathbf{r} \text{ pertains to phase } k \\ 0 & \text{if point } \mathbf{r} \text{ does not pertain to phase } k \end{cases} \qquad [10.1.1]$$

The phase density function is a binary function analogous to the intermittency function used in single-phase flow.

10.1.2.2 Instantaneous Space-averaging Operators

Instantaneous field variables may be averaged over a line, an area, or a volume, i.e., over an n-dimensional domain ($n = 1, 2, 3$ for a segment, area, or volume). For instance, in pipe flow, the field variables can be averaged over a diameter, a chord, a plane cross section, or a finite control volume. At a given time, this n-dimensional domain $\mathfrak{D}_n$ can be divided into two subdomains $\mathfrak{D}_{kn}$ pertaining to each phase ($k = 1, 2$):

$$X_k(\mathbf{r}, t) = 1 \quad \text{for any } \mathbf{r} \text{ pertaining to } \mathfrak{D}_{kn}$$

Consequently two different *instantaneous space-averaging operators,*

$$\ll \gg_n \overset{\Delta}{=} \frac{1}{\mathfrak{D}_n} \int_{\mathfrak{D}_n} d\mathfrak{D}_n \qquad\qquad [10.1.2]$$

and

$$\ll \gg_n \overset{\Delta}{=} \frac{1}{\mathfrak{D}_{kn}} \int_{\mathfrak{D}_{kn}} d\mathfrak{D}_n \qquad\qquad [10.1.3]$$

are introduced. The *instantaneous space fraction* R_{kn} is defined as the average over $\mathfrak{D}_n$ of the phase density function $X_k(\mathbf{r}, t)$:

$$R_{kn} \overset{\Delta}{=} \ll X_k \gg_n = \frac{\mathfrak{D}_{kn}}{\mathfrak{D}_n} \qquad\qquad [10.1.4]$$

This definition leads directly to the usual instantaneous space fraction,

$$R_{k1} = \frac{L_k}{\Sigma_{k=1,2} \, L_k} \quad \text{over a segment} \qquad [10.1.5]$$

where L_k is the cumulated length of the segments occupied by phase k;

$$R_{k2} = \frac{A_k}{\Sigma_{k=1,2} \, A_k} \quad \text{over a surface} \qquad [10.1.6]$$

where A_k is the cumulated area occupied by phase k; and

$$R_{k3} = \frac{V_k}{\Sigma_{k=1,2} \, V_k} \quad \text{over a volume} \qquad [10.1.7]$$

where V_k is the volume occupied by phase k.

The *instantaneous volumetric flow rate* Q_k through a pipe cross section of area A is defined by

$$Q_k \overset{\Delta}{=} \int_{A_k} U_{kz} \, dA = A R_{k2} \, \langle U_{kz} \rangle_2 \qquad [10.1.8]$$

where U_{kz} is the axial component of the velocity of phase k.

The *instantaneous mass flow rate* $\dot{M}_k$ is given by

$$\dot{M}_k \triangleq \int_{A_k} \rho_k U_{kz} \, dA = AR_{k2}\langle \rho_k U_{kz}\rangle_2 \qquad [10.1.9]$$

where ρ_k is the density of phase k.

10.1.2.3 Local Time-averaging Operators

Local field variables can be averaged over a time interval $[t - T/2, t + T/2]$. As for single-phase turbulent flow, this time interval of magnitude T must be chosen large enough compared with the turbulence fluctuations, and small enough compared with the overall flow fluctuations. This is not always possible, and a thorough discussion of this delicate question can be found in Delhaye & Achard (1977, 1978).

Consider a given point $\mathbf{r}$ in a two-phase flow; phase k passes this point intermittently, and a field variable $f_k(\mathbf{r}, t)$ associated with phase k is a piecewise-continuous function. Denoting by $T_k(\mathbf{r}, t)$ the cumulated residence time of phase k within the interval T, one may define two different *local time-averaging operators,*

$$\overline{} \triangleq \frac{1}{T} \int_{[T]} dt \qquad [10.1.10]$$

and

$$\overline{}^X \triangleq \frac{1}{T_k} \int_{[T_k]} dt \qquad [10.1.11]$$

The *local time fraction* α_k is defined as the average over T of the phase density function X_k:

$$\alpha_k(\mathbf{r}, t) \triangleq \overline{X_k(\mathbf{r}, t)} = \frac{T_k(\mathbf{r}, t)}{T} \qquad [10.1.12]$$

10.1.2.4 Commutativity of Averaging Operators

Considering all the definitions given previously, one can easily derive the identity

$$\overline{R_{kn}\langle f_k\rangle_n} \equiv \langle\!\langle \alpha_k \overline{f_k}^X \rangle\!\rangle_n \qquad [10.1.13]$$

A particular case for [10.1.13] is obtained by taking $f_k \equiv 1$, which leads to

$$\overline{R_{kn}} \equiv \langle\!\langle \alpha_k \rangle\!\rangle_n \qquad [10.1.14]$$

Note that identities [10.1.13] and [10.1.14] are valid for segments ($n = 1$), areas ($n = 2$), or volumes ($n = 3$). As a consequence, the time-averaged volumetric and mass flow rates can be expressed in the following ways:

$$\overline{Q_k} = A\overline{R_{k2}\langle U_{kz}\rangle_2} \equiv A\langle\!\langle \alpha_k \overline{U_{kz}}^X \rangle\!\rangle_2 \qquad [10.1.15]$$

$$\overline{\dot{M}_k} = A\overline{R_{k2}\langle \rho_k U_{kz}\rangle_2} \equiv A\langle\!\langle \alpha_k \rho_k \overline{U_{kz}}^X \rangle\!\rangle_2 \qquad [10.1.16]$$

10.1.2.5 Qualities

The *mass velocity* is defined as

$$\overline{\dot{m}} \triangleq \frac{\overline{\dot{M}}}{A} \qquad [10.1.17]$$

where $\overline{\dot{M}}$ is the time-averaged total mass flow rate. The (true) *quality* x is defined as the ratio of the gas mass flow rate to the total mass flow rate:

$$x \triangleq \frac{\overline{\dot{M}_G}}{\overline{\dot{M}_G} + \overline{\dot{M}_L}} = \frac{\overline{\dot{M}_G}}{\overline{\dot{M}}} \qquad [10.1.18]$$

It is currently impossible to measure or calculate with high precision the quality of a liquid-vapor mixture flowing in a heated channel and withstanding a phase change. Nevertheless, a fictitious quality, the so-called equilibrium or thermodynamic quality, can be calculated by assuming that both phases are flowing under saturation conditions, i.e., that their temperatures are equal to the saturation temperature corresponding to their common pressure.

10.1.2.6 Volumetric Quantities

The *volumetric quality* β is defined as the ratio of the gas volumetric flow rate to the total volumetric flow rate:

$$\beta \triangleq \frac{\overline{Q_G}}{\overline{Q_G} + \overline{Q_L}} \qquad [10.1.19]$$

The *local volumetric flux* j_k is a local time-averaged quantity defined as

$$j_k \triangleq \overline{X_k U_{kz}} = \alpha_k \overline{U_{kz}}^X \qquad [10.1.20]$$

Its area average J_k over the total cross-sectional area A is a space/time-averaged quantity called the *superficial velocity*. This quantity is defined by

$$J_k \triangleq \langle\!\langle \overline{X_k U_{kz}} \rangle\!\rangle_2 = \langle\!\langle j_k \rangle\!\rangle_2 \qquad [10.1.21]$$

This quantity is directly related to the volumetric flow rate. In fact, taking identity [10.1.13] into account gives

$$J_k = \langle\!\langle \alpha_k \overline{U_{kz}}^X \rangle\!\rangle_2 = R_{k2}\langle U_{kz}\rangle_2 = \frac{\overline{Q_k}}{A} \qquad [10.1.22]$$

If the density of phase k is constant, the superficial velocity J_k can be expressed in terms of the quality x_k and the mass velocity $\overline{\dot{m}}$ as follows:

$$J_k = \frac{\overline{\dot{m}_k}}{\rho_k A} = \frac{x_k \overline{\dot{m}}}{\rho_k} \qquad [10.1.23]$$

The *mixture superficial velocity* J is defined as the sum of the superficial velocities of the phases:

$$J \overset{\Delta}{=} J_1 + J_2 \qquad [10.1.24]$$

One can show that J is the velocity of a cross-sectional plane though which the total volumetric flow rate is equal to zero.

10.2 Overall Measurements

10.2.1 PARAMETERS OF DESIGN SIGNIFICANCE

10.2.1.1 Measurement of Pressure Drop

G. F. Hewitt

Background

Pressure drop is a key design parameter since it governs the pumping power required to circulate two-phase fluids through a system or, in the case of natural circulation systems, the circulation rate. Pressure drop measurement is also important in a variety of flow-metering applications (e.g., in measuring the pressure drop across orifice meters or venturi meters).

In two-phase flow, measurement of pressure drop presents special difficulties (as is discussed below) because of possible ambiguities of the content of the lines joining the tapping points to the measuring device. Another problem is that of pressure drop fluctuations, which tend to be quite large in two-phase systems. A further area of difficulty is that of making pressure drop measurements in heated systems, particularly systems that are Joule-heated.

Selection of Method for Pressure Drop Measurement

Among the most important techniques available for measuring pressure drop are

The author acknowledges permission from the United Kingdom Atomic Energy Authority (UKAEA) to reproduce figures 10.2.1, 10.2.2, 10.2.3, 10.2.4, 10.2.5, 10.2.6, 10.2.7, 10.2.8, 10.2.9, 10.2.11, 10.2.18, 10.2.19, 10.2.20, 10.2.21, 10.2.22, 10.2.24, 10.2.25, 10.2.26, 10.2.28, 10.2.34, 10.2.35, 10.2.36, 10.2.37, 10.2.38, 10.2.40, 10.2.41, 10.2.42, 10.2.43, 10.2.44, 10.2.47, 10.2.48, 10.2.49, 10.2.51, 10.2.53, 10.2.54, 10.2.55, 10.2.56, 10.2.57, 10.2.58, 10.2.59, 10.2.60, 10.2.61, 10.2.66, 10.2.67, 10.2.69, 10.2.71, 10.2.72, 10.2.73, and 10.2.74, which remain UKAEA copyright material.

1. Fluid-fluid manometers
2. Subtraction of signals from two locally mounted pressure transducers
3. Differential pressure transducers of the reluctance or strain-gauge type

Each of these techniques encompasses a number of alternative configurations; to help in the selection of a device and configuration, a selection chart is given in figure 10.2.1. The main questions raised in this chart are

1. Is a rapid time response needed, as, for example, in the study of pressure drop fluctuations? If so, then the use of locally mounted pressure transducers is almost mandatory. If fluctuating measurements are to be made, then the choice of response time and temperature dictates the choice of transducer type and whether direct access of the fluid to the transducer is feasible. This question is discussed further below.

2. Is electrical (automatically recordable) output required? If so, then it is necessary to use some form of differential pressure-transducer system, as shown in figure 10.2.1. If not, then fluid-fluid manometers may be used.

3. Are the tapping lines to be kept full of liquid or gas? (The problems of tapping-line content are discussed in detail shortly.) Usually, it is preferable to fill the tapping lines with liquid and, even better, to have a liquid purging system. In principle, more accurate pressure drop measurements could be made with gas-filled lines, provided the line content was completely unambiguous. In practice, this is usually unachievable, and highly accurate measurements are not possible. However, there may be a few special cases in which gas-filled lines are possible.

4. Is the channel fluid condensable or evaporable? Ambiguities in the tapping-line content give rise to ambiguities in the interpretation of the measurement. However, there are some circumstances in which the tapping-line fluid can be made single-phase by either condensation or evaporation near the pressure tapping. Thus, if a steam-water mixture is flowing along the channel, then a condenser around the tapping line can condense any steam bubbles that enter the line. This condenser can take the form of a concentric tube around the tapping line. Conversely, if pressure drop measurements are being made for a two-phase flow of a cryogenic fluid, then a small evaporator placed on the tapping line near the pressure tapping can evaporate the cryogenic liquid and ensure that the lines are gas-filled.

5. Is high accuracy required? Although there are fundamental difficulties in obtaining high accuracy in two-phase pressure drop measurement, improved accuracy can be obtained by using a variety of systems. For example, if liquid-filled tapping lines are used, an inverted liquid-gas manometer gives higher accuracy than a liquid-mercury manometer. In those special cases in which gas-filled pressure lines can be employed, inclined manometers or micromanometers could be used. Furthermore, in the case of differential pressure transducers, it is possible to overcome range problems and increase accuracy by using compensating manometers.

Of course, it may not be possible to satisfy competing requirements for a specific application, so that a solution that is less than ideal must be employed.

Pressure Drop Measurement Using Fluid/Fluid Manometers

Principle of operation The principle of operation of a manometer used for the measurement of two-phase pressure drop is illustrated in figure 10.2.2. The

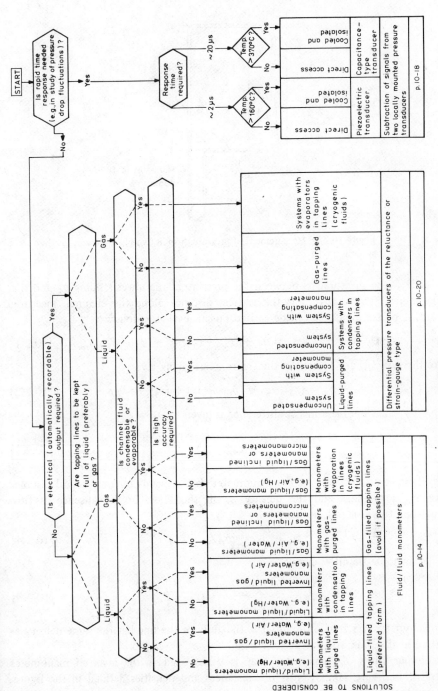

Figure 10.2.1 Selection chart for pressure drop measurement methods.

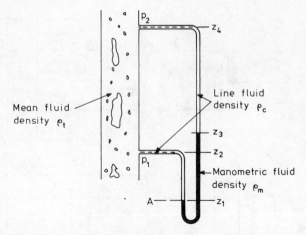

Figure 10.2.2   Measurement of pressure drop in two-phase flow systems.

difference to be measured is between the pressure at the lower tapping p_1 and that at the upper tapping p_2; z is the vertical distance along the channel, measured upward. A pressure balance can be carried out at level A as follows:

$$p_1 + (z_2 - z_1)g\rho_c = p_2 + (z_4 - z_3)g\rho_c + (z_3 - z_1)g\rho_m \qquad [10.2.1]$$

where the symbols are defined in the figure; rearranging gives

$$p_1 - p_2 = (z_3 - z_1)g\,(\rho_m - \rho_c) + (z_4 - z_2)g\rho_c \qquad [10.2.2]$$

If $p_1 = p_2$, then the manometric difference is given by

$$z_3 - z_1 = -(z_4 - z_2)\frac{\rho_c}{\rho_m - \rho_c} \qquad [10.2.3]$$

Thus, there is an "offset" on the manometer that depends on the vertical distance between the tappings and the density ρ_c in the lines. In the absence of flow through the tubes, it follows that

$$p_1 - p_2 = g\rho_t(z_4 - z_2) \qquad [10.2.4]$$

and the manometric difference is

$$z_3 - z_1 = \frac{\rho_t - \rho_c}{\rho_m - \rho_c}(z_4 - z_2) \qquad [10.2.5]$$

The manometer has zero differential if the fluid in the line has the same density as the fluid in the tube, for this no-flow case.

Another form of manometer that is often used is the inverted manometer illustrated in figure 10.2.3; with the distances and densities defined in the figure, the equation for this manometer is

$$p_1 - p_2 = g(z_4 - z_3)\,(\rho_c - \rho_m) + g\rho_c(z_2 - z_1) \qquad [10.2.6]$$

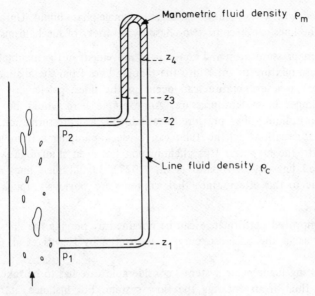

Figure 10.2.3 Inverted manometer system.

To increase sensitivity, inclined manometers are often used (figure 10.2.4); these can be obtained in the normal and inverted modes, as illustrated, and the equation relating manometric difference d and pressure difference is as follows:

$$p_1 - p_2 = g\rho_c(z_2 - z_1) + gd\,(\rho_c - \rho_m)\sin\theta \qquad [10.2.7]$$

where θ is the angle of inclination of the manometer tubes.

Problems in applications As can be seen from the above equations, to determine the pressure difference from the manometer difference, the density of the fluid in the tapping lines has to be known. In practice, this means that the lines

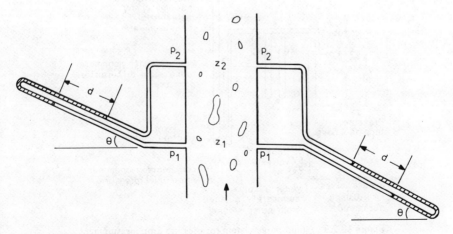

Figure 10.2.4 Inclined manometer systems.

must be filled with either single-phase gas or single-phase liquid. Unfortunately, the content of the lines can become two-phase by a variety of mechanisms:

1. Changes in pressure drop and consequent movement in the manometer can cause a two-phase mixture to enter into the tapping lines from the channel.
2. Condensation or evaporation can occur in the lines, particularly as a result of rapid changes in system pressure. An example here would be vapor bubble generation in liquid-filled pressure lines following a depressurization.
3. Pressure fluctuations in the tube can cause a pumping action, leading to gas ingress into the tappings. This phenomenon has been studied in some detail for liquid-filled lines by Azzopardi et al. (1977). Liquid-filled lines are much less susceptible to this effect, since their contents are, obviously, much less compressible.

Generally, improved performance can be obtained by purging the lines continuously with liquid, as in the balanced purge system used by Hewitt et al. (1962) (figure 10.2.5).

In operating manometer systems, considerable care has to be taken to keep the manometric fluid from entering the flow system. For instance, if mercury from manometers enters a metal flow system, the results can be disastrous! To avoid this difficulty, large-diameter catch pots should be introduced into the tapping lines.

Pressure Drop Measurement Using Subtraction of Signals from Two Locally Mounted Pressure Transducers

Principle of operation If a very rapid response is required, then the only feasible method of measuring pressure drop is to use subtraction of the signals from two pressure transducers mounted locally at the points between which the pressure drop is to be measured. The principle is illustrated schematically in figure 10.2.6.

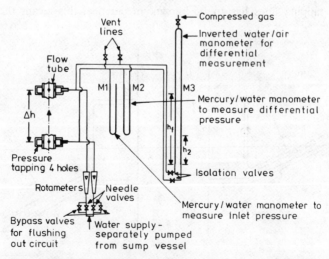

Figure 10.2.5 Liquid purge system for pressure drop measurement in two-phase flow (Hewitt et al. 1962).

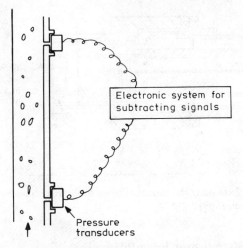

Figure 10.2.6 Mounting for pressure transducers
subtracted for measuring two-phase pressure drop.

The pressure transducer operates by detection of the flexing of a diaphragm (to which the system fluid has access through the tapping hole, as illustrated in figure 10.2.6). A variety of methods are available for detecting the movement of the diaphragm; types of pressure transducers that are particularly suitable for measurements using signal subtraction are as follows:

1. Capacitance-type transducers. These are very stable and accurate (sensitivity of 0.01% full scale) and have a response time of the order of 20 μs with a maximum operating temperature of about 370°C.
2. Piezoelectric-type transducers. These transducers have a very fast response time (typically 2 μs) and are highly sensitive (0.001% full scale). However, they have a relatively low maximum operating temperature (160°C) and are much less stable than the capacitance type.

Problems in applications The most obvious problem is that signals from two separate instruments are being measured and subtracted, and this obviously increases error. However, this is unavoidable if rapidly fluctuating pressure drops are to be determined. Special care has to be taken in calibrating the transducers and in ensuring that the outputs are properly converted to the required pressure drop.

Although the amount of fluid between the channel and the transducer is rather small in this system, the volume of the tapping line and the fluid adjacent to the diaphragm should be kept as small as possible to avoid reductions in frequency response. Also, both capacitance and piezoelectric transducers are limited as to operating temperature and, for higher operating temperatures, should usually be cooled. A system used by Borgartz et al. (1969) to overcome these difficulties is illustrated in figure 10.2.7. Here, a silicone rubber plug was cast into the channel wall and was in direct contact with the diaphragm. The transducer was cooled by a cooling-water system as illustrated. Reasonably rapid response was possible using this system, notwithstanding the high system pressure and temperature.

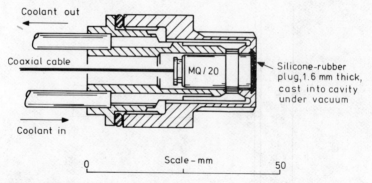

Figure 10.2.7 Cooling and isolating system for pressure transducers (Borgartz et al. 1969).

Pressure Drop Measurement Using Differential Pressure Transducers

Principle of operation The problem of subtracting signals from two separate instruments can be overcome by using a differential pressure transducer. Here, the tapping lines are connected respectively to each side of the diaphragm, and the diaphragm movement is proportional to the difference in pressure. Capacitance and piezoelectric transducers are unsuitable for differential pressure operation; instead, the following types are most often used:

1. Reluctance-type transducers. These have a sensitivity of the order of 0.1% full scale, a maximum operating temperature of about 320°C, and a response time of around 200 μs. They are fairly stable.
2. Strain-gauge-type transducers. These have a sensitivity of about 0.3% full scale, a maximum operating temperature of around 320°C, and a response time of 10–100 μs. They have good stability.

Problems in applications Since differential pressure transducers are operated with tapping lines, all the problems associated with tapping lines (as described in the context of manometers) also apply in this case. Again, it is very desirable to keep the lines full of liquid. One advantage that differential pressure transducers do have over manometers in this respect is that the diaphragm movement is quite small, and hence the amount of channel fluid passing into the lines following a change in pressure drop is minimized.

Differential pressure transducers can be used for fluctuating-pressure measurement, although the influence of the lines on the frequency response is critical, as discussed by Ybarrondo (1975). However, for high-frequency response, the subtraction of the signals from directly mounted transducers is preferable, as described in the preceding section.

The "offset" corresponding to zero pressure difference can sometimes present serious problems. If one is measuring pressure differentials that are small compared to the offset, then the accuracy is necessarily limited, since a differential pressure transducer must be chosen with a range at least equal to the offset value. A solution to this problem utilized by Webb (1970a) is to use a compensating (for example, CCl_4-water) manometer, as illustrated in figure 10.2.8.

10.2.1.2 Measurement of Void Fraction

G. F. Hewitt

Background

Void fraction measurements are of considerable technical importance in two-phase systems. A knowledge of void fraction is important in the calculation of pressure gradients and is relevant to the calculation of the amount of liquid and gas present in a system during, say, a transient. Furthermore, the overall holdup of liquid within the system is related to void fraction, and this can be significant from the point of view of calculating the inventory of materials within, say, a chemical plant. In nuclear reactors, the void fraction is significant because the absorption and moderation of neutrons is related to the density of the vapor-liquid mixture in the system, which, in turn, is related to the void fraction.

A vast range of methods have been proposed for the measurement of void fractions, but in this section only those methods that have been widely applied, or that have special advantages, are referred to. A more extensive listing of methods and appropriate references is given by Hewitt (1978a).

Selection of Method

As an aid in the selection of methods for void fraction measurement, a selection chart is given in figure 10.2.9. The following main questions are raised in making the selection:

1. What void measurement is required? The various methods of averaging

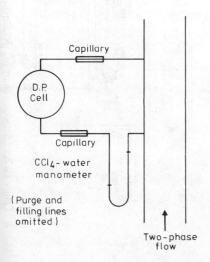

Capillary

D.P. Cell

Capillary

CCl_4- water manometer

(Purge and filling lines omitted)

Two-phase flow

Figure 10.2.8 Offset compensation using a compensating manometer (Webb 1970a). Purge and filling lines have been omitted.

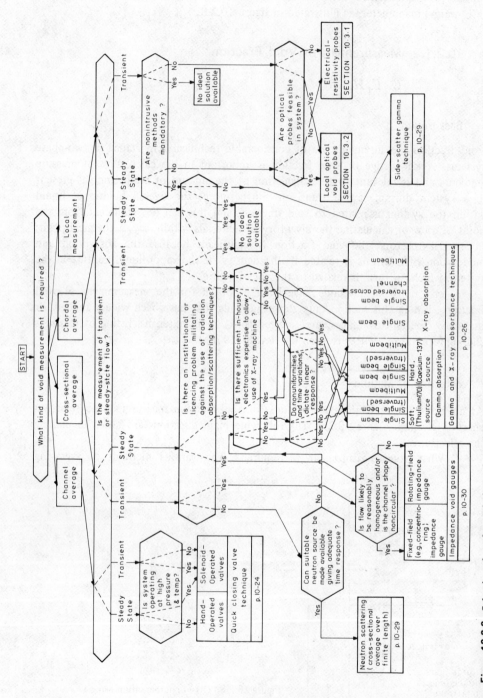

Figure 10.2.9 Selection chart for techniques for void fraction measurement.

quantities were discussed in section 10.1.2. For practical purposes, there are four main types of void fraction measurement:

a. Channel-average measurements. Here the average void fraction is required over a full section of channel. In principle, this can be obtained by integrating many of the more localized measurements, although this is tedious and expensive, particularly in the case of transient measurements. A convenient and generally satisfactory method for obtaining channel-average measurements is the use of quick-closing valves, and only this method is shown in the selection chart.
b. Cross-sectional average. The average void fraction is sought over a given channel cross section. This can be obtained by integrating chordal-average measurements over the cross section (for instance, by using traversable single-beam radiation absorption methods or, particularly for transients, using multibeam radiation absorption techniques) or by using the so-called one-shot technique. However, by using neutron-scattering techniques, a direct measurement of cross-sectional-average void fraction is feasible. Alternatively, if radiation methods are unacceptable, cross-sectional-average measurements can be made (although with less accuracy) by using impedance void gauges.
c. Chordal-average void fraction. Measurement is made of the average void fraction across, say, the diameter of a channel of circular cross section. This kind of measurement is achieved naturally by means of radiation absorption methods; if such methods are unacceptable, then there is no convenient alternative method of getting this particular average.
d. Local void measurements. Void fraction is measured at a particular position within the channel. Usually, this void fraction is a time average at a point. Here, local optical or electrical void probes are normally employed (see section 10.3), although side-scatter gamma techniques can be used for steady-state measurements.

2. Is the measurement of a transient or a steady-state flow? Many techniques are infeasible for application in transient measurements. For instance, the side-scatter gamma technique requires very long counting times and cannot be used for transient measurement.

3. Is the system operating at high pressure and temperature? In the selection chart, this question is shown as including the choice of valves in the quick-closing-valve technique. For high temperature and pressure, solenoid-operated valves must normally be used. As will be realized, the pressure and temperature levels are an important factor in the design of all void fraction measurement systems.

4. Are nonintrusive methods mandatory? This question applies to local void fraction measurement techniques in particular. If the insertion of void probes is unacceptable, then the best available technique is the side-scatter gamma method, but this is unsuitable for transient measurements. Thus, there is no ideal solution available if transient nonintrusive local void measurements are required.

5. Do institutional or licensing problems militate against the use of radiation absorption and scattering techniques? Many laboratories face considerable difficulties in installing any form of radiation method. Such methods are relatively straightforward to apply in laboratories that have adequate health-physics support,

etc., but are less easy where such an infrastructure does not exist. The difficulties in applying radiation methods may sometimes dictate the use of alternative methods. Usually, this will mean that chordal-average measurements are infeasible (as shown in the selection chart), and intrusive techniques such as quick-closing valves, impedance-void gauges, or local optical or electrical probes have to be employed.

6. Is there sufficient in-house electronics expertise to allow use of an X-ray machine? By using X-ray absorption, as distinct from gamma-ray absorption, it is possible to obtain considerable technical advantages. The main advantage is that orders-of-magnitude higher photon fluxes are possible with X-ray machines than are feasible with gamma sources. This gives great improvement in the counting statistics. However, to operate an X-ray machine requires fairly substantial in-house electronics expertise, and, for many applications, this may simply not be feasible. Another consideration for this (and other) methods is that of expense. The choice of system can sometimes depend on the availability of a suitable machine within the laboratory.

7. Are optical probes feasible in the system? This question is applied in particular to the use of local probes in local void measurement. Optical probes appear to give better response and performance than do resistivity probes and should be used where feasible. Optical probes are the subject of continuous development, and probes now coming onto the market operate with high pressure and temperature systems.

8. Do nonuniformities and time variations dictate linear response? This question applies specifically to gamma-absorption techniques. The absorption of a gamma beam is exponential, and the averaging process depends on the geometry and on time fluctuations. This problem can be avoided by using hard gamma beams, which are weakly absorbed and for which the absorption approximates a linear form.

9. Can a suitable neutron source giving adequate time response be made available? If a suitable neutron source is available, and if cross-sectional-average void fraction is required in transient conditions, then the neutron-scattering method can sometimes be the optimum technique. However, there may be some difficulty in obtaining a sufficiently strong source to make the counting statistics adequate for transient measurements, and, for the steady state, it may be simpler and cheaper to use a traversing or multibeam X-ray or gamma-ray absorption method.

10. Is flow likely to be reasonably homogeneous and/or is the channel shape noncircular? This question applies specifically to the impedance-void-gauge method, which is particularly subject to ambiguities due to the distribution of voids. This can be overcome to some extent (in circular pipes) by using a rotating-field gauge, but fixed-field (concentric-ring) impedance gauges have to be used for other channel geometries and may be used fairly effectively if the flow is reasonably homogeneous.

Each of the recommended methods is described in the subsections shown in figure 10.2.9.

Void Fraction Measurement Using the Quick-Closing Valve Technique

Principle of operation In this method, valves (which can be quickly and simultaneously operated) are placed at the beginning and end of the section of channel over which the void fraction is to be determined. At the appropriate moment, the valves are actuated and the liquid phase trapped in the channel is drained and its volume measured. Since the channel volume is known (or can be estimated), the channel-average void fraction can be found. Usually, it is desirable to use a specially designed valve. In a typical air-water experiment, for instance, the valves can have the same cross section as the channel when open, thus offering no perturbation to the flow. The valves can be linked mechanically and can be operated by hand. A remarkable degree of reproducibility in the measurements is often obtained. Typical of the many applications to air-water systems are the studies of Johnson & Abou-Sabe (1952) and Serizawa (1974).

For high-pressure systems, solenoid-operated valves may be used. The accuracy and flexibility of the technique have been demonstrated in a series of experiments at the CISE Laboratories in Italy (e.g., Agostini & Premoli 1971). Figure 10.2.10 shows results obtained for a heated channel using this technique. For transient tests, the CISE work has demonstrated that the method is applicable to blowdown tests. A section of the channel is isolated at a particular time; typically, 15 or more individual measurements are taken in the first 2 or 3 s of a blowdown transient. The solenoid valves developed in this work have diameters up to 6.35 cm and can operate at up to 10 MN/m^2 and 350°C with closure times of 10–15 ms. In fluctuating flows (e.g., slug flow), several samples must be taken to obtain an average.

Problems in applications The main problems in applying the quick-closing-valve technique are as follows:

1. A finite time is required to close the valves, and this must, in principle, lead to an inaccuracy in the method since, during the valve closure time, the flow pattern within the channel must be changing. In practice, the measured void

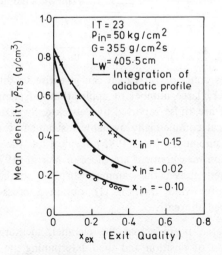

Figure 10.2.10 Mean density data obtained by quick-closing-valve technique for heated tubes (Agostini et al. 1969).

fraction is surprisingly insensitive to the closure time, provided the valve closing is relatively brisk. Synchronization between the two valves is important.

2. For each measurement, the flow system has to be closed down. In fact, care must be exercised to arrange simultaneous diversion of the flow; otherwise harmful pressure transients can occur within the system. Once the measurement is made, the system must be brought back to the steady state. Typically, reinstatement of the conditions for each new test might take about 15 min.

Void Fraction Measurement Using Gamma and X-Ray Absorption Techniques

Principle of operation Beams of gamma rays or X-rays are attenuated by the materials through which they pass, by a combination of photoelectric, pair-production, and Comptom scattering effects. The relative importance of each of these scattering mechanisms depends on the substance and on the energy of the incident photon beam. The absorption of a collimated beam of initial intensity I_0 (photons per square meter per second) is described by an exponential absorption law as follows:

$$I = I_0 \exp(-\mu z) \qquad [10.2.8]$$

where μ is the linear absorption coefficient, and z the distance traveled through a homogeneous absorbing medium. In applying this technique to the measurement of void fraction, a collimated beam of X-rays or gamma rays is passed through the channel wall, through the two-phase mixture, and through the opposite channel wall before it passes into a detector (typically a plastic scintillator coupled to a photomultiplier). The received intensities I_G and I_L with the channel full of gas and liquid, respectively, are first measured. The void fraction is then related to the intensity I measured during the two-phase flow in the channel and to I_G and I_L as follows:

$$R_{G1} = \frac{\ln I - \ln I_L}{\ln I_G - \ln I_L} \qquad [10.2.9]$$

This equation assumes constant I_0, which can give rise to difficulty in some cases.

Typical of the very large number of applications of gamma absorption to void fraction measurement are those reported by Petrick & Swanson (1958) and Thomas et al. (1977). A typical commercially available instrument for gamma densitometry is described by Measurements Inc. (1975); typical of the many applications of X-rays for void fraction measurement are those of Martin (1972) and Lahey (1977).

As was mentioned above, the gamma-absorption method essentially gives a chordal mean value for void fraction. To obtain a cross-sectional-average void fraction, there are three alternatives:

1. Traverse a collimated beam across the channel, measuring the chordal mean values as a function of position and then determining the cross-sectional average by means of a suitable mathematical manipulation of the chordal mean values. This is, of course, inapplicable in the case of transients.

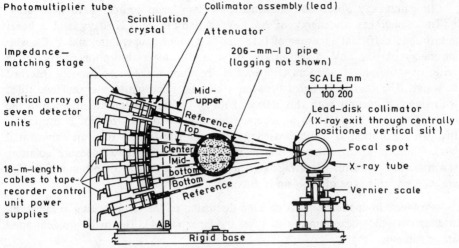

Outline A represents rigid detector support plate
Outline B represents lead shielding box (cut away for beam entry)

Figure 10.2.11 Multibeam X-ray system for determination of multiple cordal-mean void fractions (and hence general average void fraction) during a blowdown from a horizontal tube (Smith 1975).

2. Use multibeam gamma or X-ray densitometers. Here, multibeams are taken from a single X-ray or gamma source, as illustrated in figures 10.2.11 and 10.2.12, respectively. Note that for the X-ray system (Smith 1975) a reference beam is also used with a fixed attenuator. This allows compensation for fluctuations in the X-ray source strength. Multibeam systems are particularly useful for transient tests and have been used widely in blowdown studies in nuclear reactor safety work.

3. Use a broad radiation beam (as wide as this channel) with special collimators to adjust for the different path lengths and wall adsorption. This "one-shot" method is described by Lottes (1967).

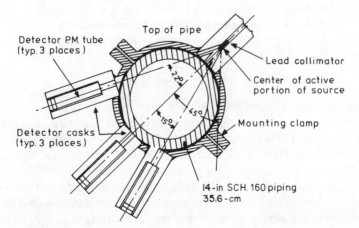

Figure 10.2.12 Three-beam gamma densitometer in LOFT tests (Wesley 1977).

In gamma-ray absorption measurements, two main sources have been used: ^{170}Tm, which has an energy of 84 keV, a half-life of 127 days, and a linear absorption coefficient in water of 0.18 cm^{-1} at room temperature, and ^{137}Cs, with an energy of 662 keV, a half-life of 30 yr, and a linear absorption coefficient in water of 0.086 cm^{-1} at room temperature. Thulium is the more strongly absorbed in water. The change in signal between a channel filled with water and one filled with steam is greatest with this source. With ^{137}Cs, there is less attentuation of the beam. This gives a reduction in accuracy for a given source size, but it also means that the absorption is approximated by a linear law (rather than an exponential law). Thus, if a large enough source strength is used to give adequate counting statistics, the problems of averaging errors due to spatial and time nonuniformities are reduced: this type of problem is discussed further below.

Problems in applications   A detailed discussion of the errors arising in radiation-attenuation void measurements is given by Piper (1974). The main problem areas are as follows:

1. There are obvious safety problems associated with the handling of radiation. These should be carefully considered before an attempt to use these techniques. A useful general source on the safety problems is the book by Clark (1963).

2. Owing to the random nature of the creation of photons, there is a fundamental statistical error in all radiation measurements. The standard deviation σ on the count rate is given by

$$\sigma = \sqrt{\frac{R}{\tau}} \qquad [10.2.10]$$

where τ is the counting time over which the count rate R is determined. Clearly, the standard deviation decreases (as a fraction of R) as R increases and as τ increases.

3. There are certain effects of void orientation and of fluctuations in void fraction with time. The calculation of void fraction from [10.2.9] is valid only if the phases are homogeneously mixed or if they exist in successive layers perpendicular to the beam. If the liquid in vapor exists in layers *parallel* to the beam, then the measured intensity I is given by $I_G R_{G1} + I_L(1 - R_{G1})$ and thus the void fraction is

$$R_{G1} = \frac{I - I_L}{I_G - I_L} \qquad [10.2.11]$$

Obviously, this case is somewhat unlikely, but in most real systems there is a definite effect of void orientation. These effects are discussed, for instance, by Petrick & Swanson (1958). An analogous effect is that of time fluctuations. An extreme example of these latter fluctuations is that of slug flow, where the void fraction fluctuates periodically from nearly zero to nearly unity. This case, again, should be calculated from [10.2.11] rather than from [10.2.9]. The difficulty is that, a priori, there is no implicit knowledge of the flow pattern within the tube. A solution to both the void orientation and time-fluctuating effects is to use a hard (i.e., ^{137}Cs) source for which the absorption is weak and can be approximated by a linear law. High source strength is required to obtain the required accuracy in this case.

Local Void Fraction Measurement Using the Side-Scatter Gamma Technique

Principle of operation Part of the process of attenuation of a gamma beam is due to Compton scattering. Here, the gamma photon interacts with an atomic electron, gives some energy to it, and proceeds with a lower energy and altered course. The energy E' of the scattered photon is related to the initial energy E and the scattering angle θ by

$$E' = \frac{E}{1 + 1.96E(1 - \cos \theta)} \qquad [10.2.12]$$

The scattered photons can also be detected, and by collimating both the beam and the detection, so that only photons scattered from a particular point are detected, it is possible to obtain the local void fraction. Allowance has to be made, of course, for the attenuation of the scattered photons between the point of generation and the point of detection. The side-scatter gamma technique has the unique advantage of being able to detect local voids in a nonintrusive way. Applications of the technique are described by Kondic & Hahn (1970), Zielke et al. (1975) and Kondic & Lassahn (1978).

Problems in applications The overriding problem in applying the side-scatter gamma technique is that the intensity of the photon beam scattered in a narrow solid angle from a given point in the fluid is very small. Thus, to obtain any reasonable accuracy, very long counting times are required; for instance, counting times of the order of an hour may be required, even with primary-source strengths of 25 Ci. This clearly makes the techniques impossible for transient measurements, and it is difficult to maintain absolutely steady conditions during the whole period over which the counts are being taken.

Another problem with this method is that allowance has to be made for self-absorption of the scattered beam; this depends, in turn, on a knowledge of the distribution of voids in the system. Thus, calculation of local void fraction distribution tends to be iterative and complicated, with consequential uncertainties. Since the technique is linked to gamma absorption, the inaccuracies associated with gamma absorption are also relevant, particularly those associated wtih spatial and temporal inhomogeneities.

Void Fraction Measurement Using Neutron Scattering

Principle of method In this method, the section in which the void fraction is to be measured is placed in a fast epithermal neutron beam (from an accelerator target, say), and the scattered and transmitted fluxes are measured by counting. The arrangement is illustrated in figure 10.2.13. If the incident beam is at a relatively uniform intensity, then the scattered thermal flux depends on the amount of hydrogenous material in the cross section, and not on its distribution. The method is, therefore, ideally suited for measuring cross-sectional-average void fractions. Applications and investigations of the technique are described, for instance, by Rousseau & Riegel (1978) and by Banerjee et al. (1978b).

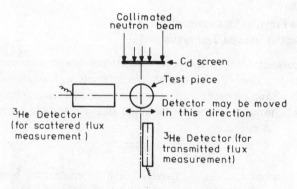

Figure 10.2.13   Neutron-scattering method for void fraction (Rousseau & Riegel 1978; Banerjee et al. 1978b).

Problems in applications   The most obvious problem in the application of this technique is the availability of a suitable neutron source. If such a source can be easily made available, then the technique has many advantages and is well worth considering. However, the construction of a special source would normally be considered to be unacceptably expensive.

Void Fraction Measurement Using Impedance Gauges

Principle of operation   The electrical impedance of a two-phase flow depends on the concentration and distribution of the phases, and the use of impedance measurement is attractive because it gives a virtually instantaneous response. Depending on the system, the impedance will be governed by conductance or capacitance or both. It is usually best to operate so that either one or the other is dominant. Generally, it is better to operate at a high enough frequency to ensure domination by capacitance, since there are often changes in liquid conductivity (e.g., as a function of temperature), whereas the dielectric constant varies less.

The relationship between void fraction R_{G3} and admittance (the reciprocal of impedance) A is often calculated from the Maxwell (1881) equations; for a homogeneous dispersion of gas bubbles in the liquid, we have

$$R_{G3} = \left[\frac{A - A_c}{A + 2A_c}\right]\left[\frac{C_G + 2C_L}{C_G - C_L}\right] \qquad [10.2.13]$$

where A_c is the admittance of the gauge when immersed in the liquid phase alone, and C_G and C_L are the gas and liquid phase conductivities if the conductivity is dominating, and the dielectric constants of the gas and liquid if the capacity is dominating. For liquid droplets dispersed in a gas, the Maxwell equations give

$$R_{G3} = 1 - \left[\frac{AC_L - A_cC_G}{AC_L + 2A_cC_G}\right]\left[\frac{C_L + 2C_G}{C_L - C_G}\right] \qquad [10.2.14]$$

Equations can also be derived for other flow configurations (slug flow and annular flow). A comparison of the variation of admittance with void fraction for the various regimes is shown in figure 10.2.14.

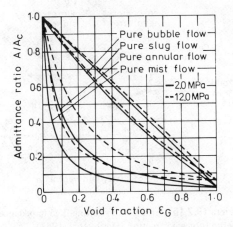

Figure 10.2.14 Effect of flow pattern on
conductivity in the conductance method for
void fraction. Curves calculated by Bouman
et al. (1974).

The impedance method has been quite widely used [see, e.g., Spigt (1966) and
van Vonderen & van Vlaardingen (1970)], and a variety of electrode geometries
have been investigated. A thorough study of the impedance method is that of Olsen
(1967), who stresses the importance of designing electrodes that have a homogeneous electric field between them, have several bubble diameters between sources of
current, and have a relatively uninterrupted channel cross section. Typical designs
investigated by Olsen are illustrated in figure 10.2.15. The concentric-ring type of
electrode appears to be the best for fixed-field application. However, an alternative
electrode system is described by Merilo et al. (1977) and is illustrated in figure
10.2.16. Six electrodes are mounted flush with the channel wall, and respective
pairs of these are energized by oscillators such that the electric-field vector rotates

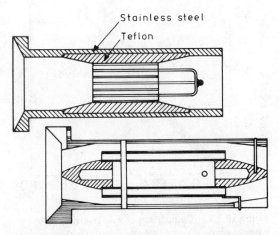

Figure 10.2.15 Electrode types for impedance void
fraction studies (Olsen 1967).

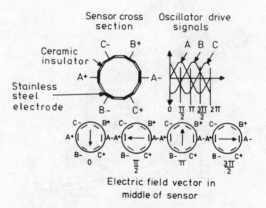

Figure 10.2.16 Principle of rotating-field impedance method for void fraction (Merilo et al. 1977).

as illustrated. By taking an average of the three pairs, a more valid mean void fraction can, it is suggested, be obtained. A comparison between this method and the quick-closing-valve method is shown in figure 10.2.17.

Problems in applications The principal difficulty with the impedance technique is potential sensitivity to flow pattern. Depending on the flow configuration, a wide range of impedance values might be expected for a given void fraction (figure

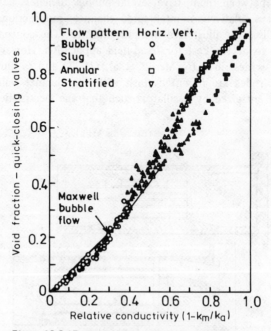

Figure 10.2.17 Comparison of void fraction, using quick-closing-valve and rotating-electric-field methods (Merilo et al. 1977).

10.2.14); in practice, however, agreement between this method and other methods is better than might be expected. This is exemplified by the results shown in figure 10.2.17. However, it will be noted that, at high qualities, where stratified or annular flow is prevalent, there are considerable differences between horizontal and vertical flows, indicative of the sensitivity of the technique to flow configuration. The rotating-field impedance-gauge device appears to offer some advantage in reducing configuration sensitivity, but if the flow is reasonably homogeneous there is probably little to be gained by using this device.

In general, one could say that the impedance method offers very rapid response, but that uncertainties in data interpretation make its accuracy somewhat doubtful. Nevertheless, as is shown in figure 10.2.9, there are circumstances in which alternative techniques are not available.

10.2.1.3 Measurement of Heat Transfer Coefficient

G. F. Hewitt

Background

The heat transfer coefficient (defined as the ratio of the heat flux from a surface to the difference between the surface temperature and a suitably defined temperature for the bulk fluid) is of great technical importance in various contexts. Thus, in the sizing of heat exchangers involving two-phase flow (including boilers and condensers), a knowledge of heat transfer coefficients is important in determining the system size. A knowledge of the two-phase heat transfer coefficient is also important in safety considerations, particularly in the postburnout region.

In condensation, and in evaporation under preburnout conditions, heat transfer coefficients are often very large (see chapter 5). This means that the difference between the surface and bulk temperatures is correspondingly small and thus difficult to determine accurately. Fortunately, the boiling or condensation coefficients are often not the controlling ones in a given system, and great accuracy is often unnecessary, but unfortunately this is not universally true. An example in which more accurate values of the coefficients are required is that of process plant boilers that are heated with a condensing fluid.

At the burnout transition, a large excursion of temperature occurs in heat flux-controlled situations, such as that found in experiments using electrical heating. However, in the practical systems (e.g., boilers heated by condensing vapor or by a hot fluid) there may be restriction on the extent to which the wall temperature can increase. This results in a rather different postburnout situation than is found in the case of electrical heating. Experimental representation of the real system, therefore, may necessitate a close simulation of the heating method or the use of special techniques such as transient heating.

Selection of Method

A schematic basis for the selection of a technique for the measurement of the heat transfer coefficient is illustrated in figure 10.2.18. The following major questions should be asked in proceeding to the selected method:

1. Is electrical heating, fluid heating or cooling, or transient heating to be used? Most studies of boiling heat transfer have been carried out using electrical heating of one form or another. In the case of cooling (for example, in condensation experiments), it is obviously necessary to use a fluid as the heat sink. Fluid heating is often used in experiments where electrical heating is impractical (e.g., in the determination of the overall performance of large heat exchangers) or in cases where the mode of heating has an effect on the system performance (for example, in the case of postburnout heat transfer described above). Fluid heating is, however, relatively inconvenient, and it is sometimes possible to use transient techniques for the study of the postburnout region. These transient techniques combine the advantages of electrical heating with the possibility of a controlled rate of change of surface temperature. A further discussion of these techniques is given below.

2. Is direct electrical heating acceptable? In "direct" electrical heating, a current is passed through the channel wall, leading to the Joule heating of the wall, with this heat being transmitted to the fluid. By measuring the current through, and the voltage drop along, the wall, an accurate estimate of the heat release rate can be obtained. Clearly, this method is sometimes impractical (e.g., with conducting fluids passing through the channel), and often the electrical supply requirements, particularly the large currents required for thick-walled, low-resistance channels, render the method infeasible. However, it is often practical to employ indirect heating methods; here, the heat generation is in elements that are separated from the channel wall by some form of electrical insulating layer. In the direct heating method, wall temperature measurement is relatively straightforward (although there are still problems if the temperature differences are small), whereas in the indirect heating methods, temperature measurement is generally more difficult.

3. Are the flows internal or external? A large proportion of the experiments on boiling heat transfer have been carried out with internal flows (e.g., flow inside a round tube), and here direct electrical heating with externally mounted thermocouples is particularly convenient. Indirect heating by wound-on coils or by using electrically heated radiant heaters is feasible, but more difficult for the internal flow case. External flows (e.g., flows over bundles of heated rods in either the longitudinal or cross-flow direction) are often more conveniently dealt with using indirect electrical heating employing heaters embedded in an insulating matrix that fills the inside of the rod (see below). Direct electrical heating (discussed below) can also be used for external flows, and the difficulties of wall temperature measurement for this case may be overcome (where appropriate) by using radiation equilibrium thermocouples.

4. If fluid heating or cooling is to be used, are local or average coefficients required? Predictions of two-phase flow heat transfer system are often carried out by integrating relationships for local coefficients throughout the system. Thus, local measurements are required in the development of correlation methods, and

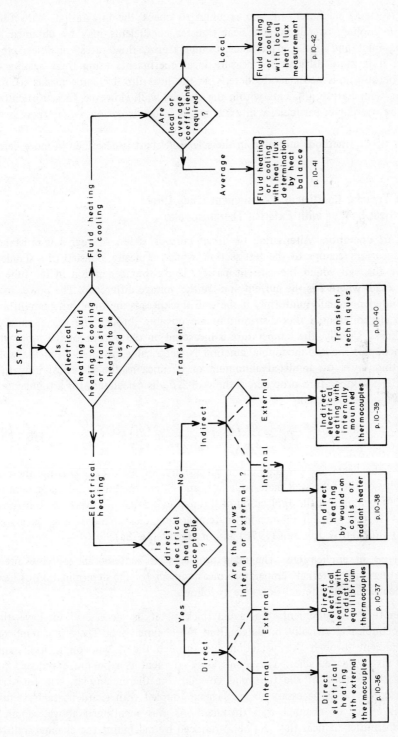

Figure 10.2.18 Selection chart for heat transfer coefficient measurement methods.

integral (system) measurements are required to check the integration. With fluid heating or cooling, overall average heat transfer coefficients may be obtained by measuring inlet and outlet parameters (temperatures, flow rates, qualities, etc.). However, it is more difficult to measure local coefficients using fluid heating or cooling, because it is necessary to determine the heat flux by some means such as measuring temperature gradients within the channel wall. However, these difficulties have to be overcome, particularly in experiments in condensation, where there is no alternative.

Each of the methods indicated in the selection chart is described in more detail below.

Heat Transfer Coefficient Measurement Using Direct Electrical Heating with External Thermocouples

Principle of operation Alternating or direct current is fed through low-resistance leads and current clamps to the test section, which, typically, consists of a stainless steel tube through which the current passes. The power generation in the tube is given by $I \, \Delta v$, where I is the current and Δv the voltage difference. The power may be distributed nominally uniformly if the wall thickness is uniform, but nonuniform axial and circumferential flux distributions are possible through the use of variable wall thickness. Usually, the temperature is measured on the outside of the tube with a thermocouple; the thermocouple junction is electrically insulated from the wall, using a thin layer of anodized aluminum or of mica as the electrical insulating material. The temperature drop across the wall ΔT_W is calculated, for a tubular test section, from the expression

$$\Delta T_W = \frac{\dot{q} r_i}{k_W} \left(\frac{1}{2} - \frac{r_i^2}{r_o^2 - r_i^2} \ln \frac{r_o}{r_i} \right) \qquad [10.2.15]$$

where $\dot{q}$ is the heat flux per unit inside surface area of the tube, k_W is the thermal conductivity of the tube wall material, and r_i and r_o are the inner and outer radii of the tube. An example of the application of this method is that of Laverty & Rohsenow (1967). A further general discussion on temperature measurements is given in the reviews of Brockett & Johnson (1976) and of Hewitt (1978a).

Problems in applications The main problems encountered in applying direct Joule heating with external temperature measurement for the determination of heat transfer coefficient in internal flows are as follows:

1. Temperature measurement. To avoid pickup, it is necessary to have the thermocouples electrically insulated from the channel wall. There is a temperature gradient through the insulation and through the thermocouple itself, and this leads to inaccuracies. The temperature gradient can be much reduced by lagging the outside of the tube and covering the thermocouples, but, for very high accuracy, it is necessary to use lagging coupled with guard heater systems.
2. Nonuniformity of channel wall thickness. As was mentioned above, required nonuniformities in heat flux can be introduced by machining the channel wall to

give variable thickness and, thus, variable rates of heat generation. The converse of this is that commercial tubes tend to have significant variations in wall thickness, both axially and circumferentially. This gives rise to heat flux variations and consequential errors.

3. Accuracy of thermal conductivity data. The wall temperature difference is inversely proportional to the wall thermal conductivity. If the wall temperature difference is a significant part of the overall temperature difference between the outside wall and the bulk fluid temperature (the latter often being defined as the local saturation temperature), then errors in thermal conductivity values cause errors in heat transfer coefficient. In fact, wall thermal conductivity is often not known accurately, particularly for alloys. One way to overcome this is to use material of high thermal conductivity, such as copper, but this tends to have a low electrical resistivity and thus demands very high current flows to achieve a given heat flux.

4. Power-supply requirements. To produce a sufficiently high heat flux, large current flows are often required. The current is typically several hundred amperes in the case of steel tubes, and several thousand amperes for copper tubes. Thus, the provision of suitable power supplies is expensive, particularly if dc heating is required. Alternating-current heating is often acceptable, but then, with thin-wall tubes, heat flux fluctuations of significant amplitude can occur.

Heat Transfer Coefficient Measurement for External Flows Using Direct Electrical Heating

Principle of operation The principle of operation for direct heating with external flows is similar to that for internal flows. If $\dot{q}$ is the heat flux related to the outer surface of a tube, then the wall temperature difference is given by

$$\Delta T_W = \frac{\dot{q} r_o}{k_W} \left(\frac{1}{2} - \frac{r_i^2}{r_o^2 - r_i^2} \ln \frac{r_o}{r_i} \right) \qquad [10.2.16]$$

The main problem for external flows is the measurement of the inside wall temperature. The thermocouples must be in good thermal contact with the wall, and there are obvious difficulties in ensuring that this is so when the measurement has to be made inside a tube, particularly if the tube is long. A method that is convenient for measuring average wall temperature, and that is recommended to be used wherever possible, is the radiation-equilibrium thermocouple system as described by Bennett et al. (1959) and illustrated in figure 10.2.19. The thermocouple is brazed to a short section of copper that is in radiation equilibrium with the tube wall. The thermocouple unit can be traversed along the channel, and the axial distribution of wall temperature determined. This method is obviously unsuitable for the measurement of rapid transients.

Problems in applications The problems listed above for direct heating with internal flows also apply to its use with external flows. Furthermore, there is the difficulty (mentioned above) of making temperature measurements inside tubes. With external flows, there are also often problems in making current connections.

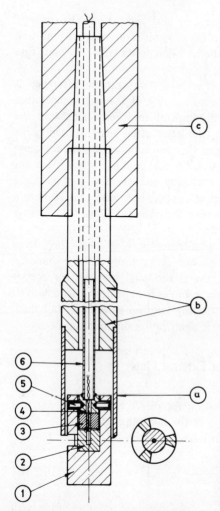

Figure 10.2.19 Radiation equilibrium thermocouple arrangement for inside wall temperature measurement in studies of boiling heat transfer (Bennett et al. 1959): 1 and 3, pyrophilite shields; 2, copper cylinder to which thermocouples are brazed; 4 and 6, stainless steel cylinders; 5, grub screws holding block to stainless steel cylinder; a, heated tube; b, copper connecting tube; c, electrode connection.

Often, this is done by connecting rods or tubes of low-resistivity material (copper or nickel) to each end of the test section and using these rods or tubes to carry the current into and out of the apparatus. However, though the heat generation rate in these end pieces is relatively small, there can still be a problem in successfully removing this small amount of heat, and great care has to be taken about this factor in design.

Heat Transfer Coefficient Measurement with Indirect Heating by Wound-on Coils or Radiant Heaters

Principle of operation Indirect heating is more difficult to apply in the case of internal flows than in the case of external flows (see below). However, it is possible to carry out heat transfer coefficient measurements by isolating the heating coils from the test section wall by, for instance,

1. Relying on radiant transfer through the gap between the coils and the test-section surface.
2. Using mineral-insulated heating cable and winding it onto the tube. In this case, better thermal contact can be obtained by brazing or soldering the outer sheath of the coils to the tube.

Such forms of heating are employed when, for instance, a conducting fluid (e.g., a liquid metal) is being heated, or where economics militates against the installation of high-current power supplies. In these systems, wall temperature measurement is normally achieved by inserting a thermocouple into the tube wall as near as possible to the inner surface.

An example of the use of wound-on coils of minerally insulated heating cable is the work of Penman & Tait (1965), and the use of radiant heating is cited, for instance, by Chojnowski & Wilson (1972b).

Problems in applications The main problem in using this method is that of obtaining very high heat fluxes. For radiant heating, the flux is limited by the maximum temperature of the heating coil; for wound-on coils, there are similar limitations. Also, temperature measurement is difficult with this system. Nevertheless, indirect heating with internal flows is necessary in some circumstances.

Heat Transfer Coefficient Measurement for External Flows Using Indirect Electrical Heating

Principle of operation Indirectly electrically heated rods are used widely in experiments simulating heat transfer from nuclear fuel elements. A typical design of rod is illustrated in figure 10.2.20. A heating tape is embedded in an insulator (typically boron nitride or magnesia), and the thermocouples are mounted inside the outer sheath. Other examples of this system are reported by Tschuke & Moller (1978) and Engler & von Holzer (1977). Single rods or arrays of rods are mounted in the fluid stream.

Problems in applications The main problems in heat transfer measurements using indirectly heated rods are as follows:

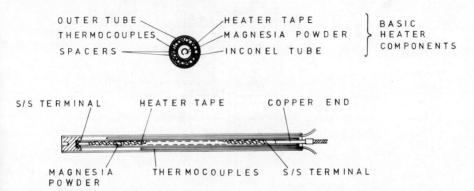

Figure 10.2.20 Heater rod assembly used in emergency core cooling studies (Hawes 1976).

1. The rods tend to be very expensive, particularly if high heat fluxes are used. Large investments are required if studies are to be made of multirod arrays.
2. There is a difficulty in relating the thermocouple readings to the outer wall temperature. Often, the conduction path is complex, and the accurate measurement of outer wall temperature infeasible. Certainly, it would be impossible to measure high heat transfer coefficients by these techniques; however, they are suitable for the postdryout regime, where the coefficients are much lower.

Transient Techniques

Principle of operation With electrical heating, at the burnout transition (see chapter 6) an excursion occurs, and the wall temperature rises rapidly to a high value corresponding to the wall temperature for the appropriate postburnout condition at the *full burnout heat flux*. Often, this temperature rise can be sufficient to melt the channel wall if the heat flux is not immediately reduced. However, postburnout conditions can be maintained at lower temperatures if the channel wall temperature rather than heat flux is controlled. This can be achieved by, for instance, heating with a condensing vapor, but often this is inconvenient at the rather high temperatures required in many experiments of this kind. A solution to this problem can be found, using transient techniques. These techniques are illustrated by the work of Ralph et al. (1977), whose test section is illustrated in figure 10.2.21. Here, the flow channel passes through a series of copper test blocks. The blocks are preheated to the required temperature, and flow is introduced into the channel. The

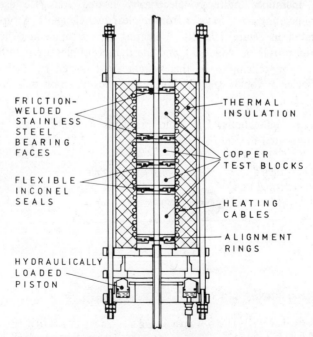

Figure 10.2.21 Multiple-block test section used in the film boiling studies of Ralph et al. (1977).

channel-side wall temperature of the blocks and the heat flux can be determined by using an array of thermocouples in the blocks. The heat flux is determined by using an inverse transient conduction calculation, and the wall temperature by extrapolation of the temperature profile through the blocks.

Problems in applications The obvious problem is that the heat transfer processes are not at the steady state, and this may, in itself, induce differences from the correct value. For instance, rewetting of a hot surface usually proceeds by a "rewetting front" passing up the surface. Thus, rewetting from upstream or downstream can occur before spontaneous rewetting of the surface happens locally via the gradual decrease of the surface temperature. This problem can be avoided (as it was in the experiment illustrated in figure 10.2.21) by slowing down the rewetting front propagation by having the uppermost and lowermost parts of the test section independently heated to a higher temperature. Transient techniques are unlikely to give high accuracy, owing to the inaccuracies of the inverse-conduction solutions, which are very sensitive to fluctuations in the measured temperature.

Heat Transfer Coefficient Measurement Using Fluid Heating or Cooling with Heat Flux Determination by Heat Balance

Principle of operation Here, the rate of heat transfer from the heating or cooling stream is determined by heat balance, and the overall heat transfer coefficient is calculated from the known inlet and outlet temperatures of the two fluids. Examples of this technique are as follows:

1. Overall heat transfer coefficient measurement in a shell-and-tube condenser in which the coolant fluid is a single-phase liquid (e.g., water) flowing either on the shell side or the tube side, with the condensation process occurring on the opposite side
2. Determination of boiling coefficients in a steam-heated evaporator, where the heat transfer rate is determined by measuring the condensate rate on the steam side

The overall heat transfer coefficient U is given by the expression

$$U = \frac{\dot{Q}}{A \, \Delta T_{LM}}$$
[10.2.17]

where $\dot{Q}$ is the rate of heat transfer (watts), A is the surface area, and ΔT_{LM} is the logarithmic mean temperature difference,

$$\Delta T_{LM} = \frac{\Delta T_1 - \Delta T_2}{\ln{(\Delta T_1/\Delta T_2)}}$$
[10.2.18]

where ΔT_1 and ΔT_2 are the temperature differences at the inlet and outlet ends of the system, respectively. The overall coefficient is related to the individual coefficients for the two sides of the experimental heat exchanger by the expression (assuming zero fouling resistances)

$$\frac{1}{U} = \frac{A}{\alpha_i A_i} + \frac{2xA}{k_W(A_i + A_o)} + \frac{A}{\alpha_o A_o} \qquad [10.2.19]$$

where α_i and α_o are the coefficients on the respective sides (e.g., on the inside and outside of a tube), A_i and A_o are the respective surface areas, x is the wall thickness, and k_W is the thermal conductivity of the wall.

To determine α_i or α_o, two methods are commonly used:

1. The coefficient on the other side is estimated from correlations or from previous experience. The inaccuracy in this procedure is lowest when the coefficient is highest. Thus, in an evaporator heated by condensing steam, the steam-side coefficient is often sufficiently high so that it has little relative contribution to the overall value of U.

2. In a system heated or cooled by a single-phase fluid, it is possible to vary the fluid velocity in such a way as to vary the heat transfer coefficient on the single-phase fluid side. For example, in studies of condensation on the outside of round tubes with cooling water on the inside, α_i is proportional to $v^{0.8}$, where v is the tube-side fluid velocity. A plot of $1/U$ versus $1/v^{0.8}$ is a straight line that can be extrapolated to $1/v^{0.8} = 0$, and α_o calculated from the intersect. This method of plotting is referred to as the *Wilson plot*.

Problems in applications   The most obvious and most serious difficulty with the overall averaging approach is that the coefficients in boiling and condensation vary as a function of heat flux and as a function of local flow conditions within the channel. Since boiling and condensation lead, respectively, to the removal and generation of vapor, the flow conditions are continuously changing. This means that the basic assumption implicit in treating the system in terms of an overall heat transfer coefficient (namely that the coefficients are constant along the experimental heat exchanger) is vitiated. In general, overall coefficient measurements in boiling and condensation are of value only in checking calculations that involve local coefficient prediction with subsequent integration. The Wilson plot method is likely to give large errors, since the two-phase coefficient varies with heat flux, and hence with the value of the single-phase coefficient.

Local Heat Transfer Coefficient Measurement with Fluid Heating or Cooling

Principle of operation   As was mentioned above, heat transfer coefficients in two-phase systems tend to vary with position along the channel, owing to changes in quality, etc. Local coefficient measurement is relatively straightforward, when electrical heating is used; then the main problem is in wall temperature measurement. However, to determine local heat transfer coefficients with fluid heating or cooling, it is necessary to make local measurements of both the flux and the wall temperature. There are two main methods of achieving this:

1. The change in temperature of the heating or cooling fluid can be determined along the test section, and the heat flux determined from this. Here, the wall temperature is measured using a thermocouple located as close as possible to the surface from which the heat transfer coefficient is being determined.

2. The heat flux can be determined by measuring the temperature gradient in the wall separating the two-phase stream and the heating (or cooling) fluid. The surface temperature is determined in this case by extrapolation.

The first method is subject to considerable inaccuracy, and the second technique is recommended wherever applicable. Two examples of this technique can be cited:

1. Experiments carried out by Butterworth et al. (1974) on in-tube condensation are illustrated in figure 10.2.22. Thermocouples were placed in a groove on the outer surface of the tube (which was then sealed using braze material) and in obliquely drilled holes leading to a position near the inner surface of the tube. The thermocouple pair could be calibrated using single-phase flow in both the tube and the outer annulus, to give heat flux as a function of temperature difference and wall temperature as a function of the individual temperature readings and the heat flux. The experiment was used to discriminate local variations in heat transfer coefficient around the circumference of a tube.

2. Rose and co-workers (LeFevre & Rose 1964, Aksan & Rose 1973; Niknejad 1979) have developed very precise techniques for the determination of condensing coefficients on vertical flat plates. The apparatus used by Niknejad, for example, is illustrated in figure 10.2.23. Here, a copper condenser block was used with water cooling on one side and condensing vapor on the other. A series of small holes were drilled in the block, and thermocouples inserted. The heat flux could be determined from the gradient of a plot of temperature versus position in the block, and the condensing-surface temperature determined by extrapolation of this plot. Very high accuracy was possible using this technique.

Problems in applications Clearly, local heat transfer coefficient measurement in systems with fluid heating or cooling is very difficult and requires attention to detail. Experiments of the type described by Butterworth et al. (1974) and Niknejad (1979) are extremely time-consuming, and great care has to be exercised if

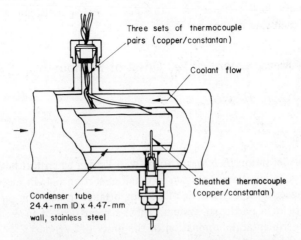

Figure 10.2.22 Measurement of wall heat flux and surface temperature in horizontal tube condensation (Butterworth et al. 1974).

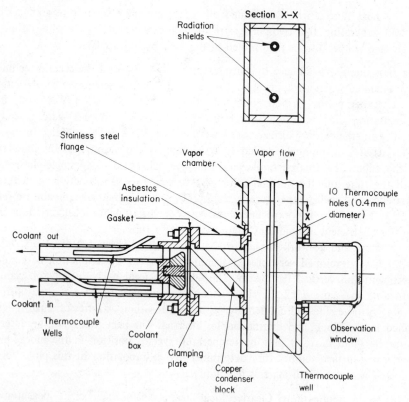

Figure 10.2.23 Heat transfer coefficient measurement in mercury condensation (Niknejad 1979).

reasonable accuracy is to be obtained. Clearly, it becomes difficult to model simultaneously the heat transfer on both sides of real systems, and attention has to be focused on each side in turn.

10.2.1.4 Measurement of the Onset of Burnout

G. F. Hewitt

Background

The nature and definition of *burnout* (otherwise known as critical heat flux, boiling crisis, DNB, dryout, etc.) are discussed in detail in section 6.4. In many applications of boiling, knowledge of burnout is of key importance in deciding on the operating limits and safety of a particular system. Thus, a great deal of investment has been made in the experimental determination of the onset of burnout.

In most experiments on burnout, electrical heating has been employed, and here it is necessary to determine the point at which an inordinate change in surface temperature occurs at some point along the test section, for a small increase in the imposed heat flux. Many practical systems have fluid heating, and a number of experiments have been carried out to simulate this. In this case, burnout may be defined as that condition in which a small increase in heating-fluid temperature gives rise to a decrease (rather than an increase) in the heat flux on some part of the surface. Experimental methods for the determination of the onset of burnout have to be designed for both these extreme cases, with the electrical-heating case presenting the least difficult problems.

Selection of Method

A selection chart for burnout detection methods is shown in figure 10.2.24. The principal questions to be answered as are follows:

1. Is electrical or fluid heating being used? If fluid heating is employed, the burnout has to be inferred from a plot of heat transfer coefficient versus fluid heating temperature and/or position.

2. If electrical heating is employed, is the heating direct or indirect? With direct heating, a current is passed through the test-section walls, giving rise to the generation of heat by the Joule effect. In indirect heating, the electrical heat generation is in heating elements isolated from the channel wall. (A more detailed discussion of these forms of heating is given in section 10.2.1.3.) With indirect heating, burnout usually has to be determined by using strategically placed thermocouples.

3. Do geometric or other factors dictate the use of thermocouples? Even with direct heating, it may be necessary to use thermocouples to detect the onset of burnout. For instance, it may not be possible to make suitable connections to the test section (e.g., on the inside of tubes) to allow detection by the bridge method, and, similarly, the view factor may not be sufficient to allow infrared burnout detection. In these cases, thermocouples have to be used.

4. Is the change in wall electrical resistivity with temperature sufficient to allow detection using the bridge method? The most rapid method of detection of burnout is the bridge method, but this depends on the detection of what are often quite small changes in resistivity due to temperature excursions at some point along the channel. If the resistivity does not change greatly with temperature, then the sensitivity of the method may be insufficient. This is the case, for example, with copper test sections. In these cases, it is sometimes possible to use infrared detection (see below).

Measurement of the Onset of Burnout
Using the Bridge Method

Principle of operation The detection of an inordinate temperature rise due to burnout is achieved by balancing the voltage drop across the test-section region where burnout is likely to occur against the voltage drop in the region immediately upstream. The principle is illustrated in figure 10.2.25. When overheating occurs, the bridge off-balance voltage is used to trigger a warning or, if necessary, to switch off the power input. The voltage drop across the zone of channel in which the critical phenomenon is likely to occur is v. In the precritical condition, resistances R_3 and R_4 are adjusted such that $R_1/R_2 = R_3/R_4$, leaving the off-balance voltage δv as

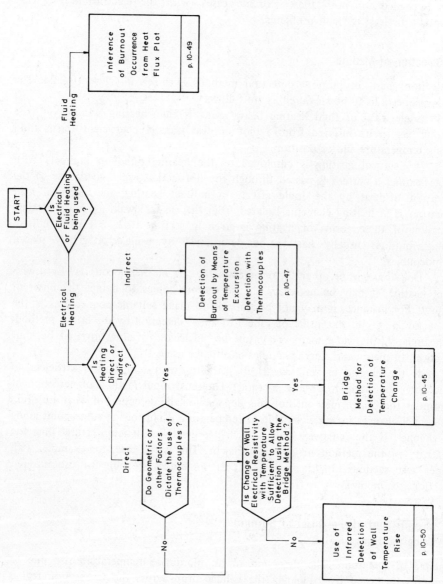

Figure 10.2.24 Selection chart for burnout detection methods.

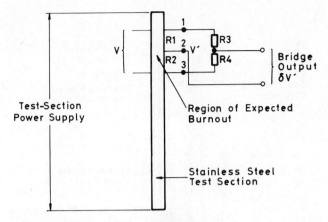

Figure 10.2.25 Bridge system for detection of the onset of burnout.

zero. If that part of the channel in the region corresponding to R_1 (for example) experiences a temperature excursion ΔT, the bridge becomes off balance by

$$\delta v = \frac{vR_1 \; \gamma \beta \; \Delta T}{R_1 + R_2}$$ [10.2.20]

where γ is the fraction of the surface in the region corresponding to R_1 that is overheated, and $1 + \beta \Delta T$ is the factor by which the electrical resistance of the overheated zone increases.

The design of bridge-type burnout detectors is discussed, for example, by Green (1967), Kichigin (1976), and Jackson (1976).

Problems in applications Even though the bridge balance method has the advantage of detecting burnout occurring in arbitrary positions in the regions over which the voltages are balanced, the sensitivity decreases as these regions are expanded. Thus, there is always a dichotomy between the requirements of sensitivity and the certainty of detecting the true point of onset of burnout. Fortunately, in many experiments, burnout is likely to occur in the downstream part of the test section, and, with uniform heating, it almost invariably occurs at the end of the test section.

Another difficulty in the bridge balance method is that the off-balance voltage changes slowly as the power is increased, even though burnout is not occurring. This is because there is a nonuniform distribution of two-phase heat transfer coefficient along the channel. Thus, for each change in power, a small adjustment has to be made to the bridge balance.

Measurement of Onset of Burnout
Using Thermocouples

Principle of operation Temperature excursions are detected using thermocouples. Examples of the application of this technique are given in the papers of Chojnowski & Wilson (1972a) and Bailey (1977) (in-tube studies—thermocouples attached to the

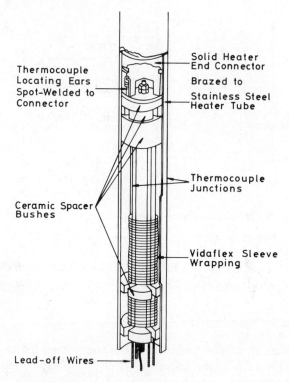

Figure 10.2.26 Radiant thermopile burnout detector (Adnams et al. 1972).

outside of the tube) and of Moeck et al. (1966) and Gustafsson & Kjellen (1971) (flow outside rods—thermocouples attached internally). In directly heated rod-bundle experiments, the sensitivity of burnout detection was increased by using a thermopile in the work reported by Adnams et al. (1972), whose system is illustrated in figure 10.2.26.

Problems in applications Problems concerning the proper installation of thermocouples for wall temperature measurement were discussed in detail in section 10.2.1.3. For the detection of burnout, where rapid transients are being observed, the problems are compounded. For instance, with thermocouples that are insulated from the electrically direct-heated tube wall by means of mica films, the response time can be as long as 280 ms, and this may be insufficient to prevent test-section damage by burnout in some circumstances. The need for insulation can be avoided by using three-wire thermocouples where responses from the respective pairs are balanced. This system has a much more rapid response [typically 7 ms (Mayinger et al. 1967)].

Perhaps the most difficult problem in the use of thermocouples for the detection of burnout is that burnout can often be localized, and there can be no certainty that a thermocouple is placed in the exactly proper locality. Thus, the occurrence of burnout can sometimes remain undetected when thermocouples are used. However, there is no alternative to the use of thermocouples in many instances. Care must be exercised to use enough of them to be reasonably certain that burnout will be properly detected.

Inference of Burnout Onset from Heat Flux Plots (Fluid Heating)

Principle of operation Here, the onset of burnout is detected (for fluid-heated systems) by simply plotting heat flux versus one of the system parameters and detecting the point at which the heat flux reaches a maximum. Two examples may be cited:

1. Determination of maximum heat flux in a chemical-plant kettle reboiler by measuring the heat input as a function of the heating-fluid (e.g., condensing vapor) temperature. The heat input rate passes through a maximum, the maximum point being designated as the burnout point.
2. Measurement of burnout in liquid-metal-heated evaporators. Here, the heat flux can be deduced from the axial rate of temperature change of the liquid-metal heating fluid. Results obtained by France (1974) using this technique are illustrated in figure 10.2.27. Clearly, the heat flux reaches a maximum at a given distance along the test section, which, in this case, consisted of a tube in which boiling took place, the tube being heated by liquid metal in a surrounding annulus flow channel.

   Problems in applications The determination of burnout conditions in fluid-heated systems is, obviously, very much more tedious and time-consuming than in the case of electrically heated experiments.

   It should be remembered that the heat flux profile in the system with fluid

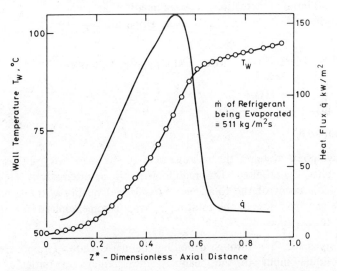

Figure 10.2.27 Heat flux-distance plots for a liquid-metal-heated evaporator tube, showing peak in heat flux equivalent to the onset of burnout (France 1974).

heating is a dependent variable. This has often led to confusion in making comparisons between electrical and fluid-heated systems. The two are only really comparable if the electrical-heating system is made to match exactly the flux profile resulting from the application of the fluid heating.

Great care has to be exercised in the interpretation of overall average-flux versus heating-fluid-temperature curves of the type obtained in the kettle reboiler experiment cited above. There may be onset of burnout in some parts of the bundle while heat flux continues to increase on the average, owing to the increases on the remaining tubes. Quite extensive regions of burnout may be necessary to give a *net* decrease with increasing heating-fluid temperature.

Burnout Detection Using an Infrared Technique

Principle of operation   Here, the test section is viewed by an infrared detector, and sudden changes in the output of the detector are amplified and made to trigger (if necessary) a switch cutting off the power supply to the test section. A detector of this form is described by Shock (1973) and Benn & Shock (1974). In their experiments a copper tube was used, and it was not feasible to use a bridge detector in this case. The infrared detector viewed a 30-cm length at the end of the (tubular) test section. To provide a view of the other side of the tube simultaneously, a half-cylindrical mirror was placed around it. It was possible to obtain rather rapid response, and successful operation was reported.

Problems in applications   Obviously, there are limitations in sensitivity to this device. It would be incapable of detecting small temperature rises, particularly if they occurred over small regions of the test section. However, as a safety device to prevent gross overheating of the test section, it is very satisfactory. In any application of infrared detection, it is axiomatic that a good view be obtained of the test-section wall where burnout is likely to occur.

10.2.1.5   Mass Flow and/or Quality Measurement

Y. Y. Hsu

Background

In many two-phase systems, the measurement of the mass rate of flow of the gas and liquid phases is required. This requirement can be alternatively expressed as a need for measurement of the total mass flow $\dot{M}$ and quality x, the latter being the ratio of the gas mass flow to the total mass flow. In some applications, only x or $\dot{M}$ is required; for instance:

1. If the total mass flow through a boiling channel is known (from a measurement of the liquid input to the channel), measurement of outlet quality x is sometimes required to determine the vapor generation rate in the channel.
2. In blowdown (i.e., pressurized-system evacuation) experiments, interest often

focuses on the rate at which mass is lost from the system. Here, it may not be important to know whether the mass loss is in the form of vapor or liquid, the only important thing being the overall mass loss. In this case, measurements of mass flow only are sufficient.

In these latter cases, a single measurement may be sufficient. On the other hand, if both $\dot{M}$ and x are required and both are unknown, then at least two measurements are needed.

The great interest in recent years in mass flow measurements, in the context of nuclear safety experiments, has led to the investigation and development of a large variety of techniques.

Selection of Method

A selection chart for mass-flow measuring techniques is given in figure 10.2.28. The main questions raised in the selection of a method are as follows:

1. Is the mass flow known, and quality only to be measured? As mentioned above, this situation occurs in practice where the vapor generation rate from the particular boiling channel is to be determined. In this case, it is often convenient to use a single measuring device of the differential-pressure type (e.g., a venturi meter or drag body); this method is discussed below. However, in most applications, the mass flow and/or quality are unknown.

2. Are transient flows to be measured? This is a very important question, since, at the present state of development, one of the most versatile and accurate techniques (pulsed neutron activation) is not suitable for transient applications.

3. Is measurement of only mass flow acceptable and, if so, is it feasible to use the true-mass flowmeter? The principle of the true-mass flowmeter is described below, but its use implies that information on the flow quality is essentially lost. At the current stage of development, the true-mass flowmeter is limited to flows of less than 5 kg/s.

4. Is the pulsed neutron activation (PNA) technique economically feasible? The PNA technique is the most accurate and versatile of the techniques (though it is not at the present time suitable for transient measurements). However, the neutron sources that are required are expensive to acquire, and there are difficulties in operation and detection systems. Often, this means that the only alternative is to use multiple-sensor (spool-piece) methods that are generally less satisfactory.

Mass Flow and/or Quality Measurement Using Multiple-Sensor (Spool-Piece) Methods

Principle of operation Suppose there are two instruments responding with readings S_1 and S_2 to phenomena in a two-phase flow stream with a mass flow rate $\dot{M}$ and a quality x. In general terms, S_1 and S_2 are given by

$$S_1 = f_1(\dot{M}, x) \qquad\qquad [10.2.21]$$

$$S_2 = f_2(\dot{M}, x) \qquad\qquad [10.2.22]$$

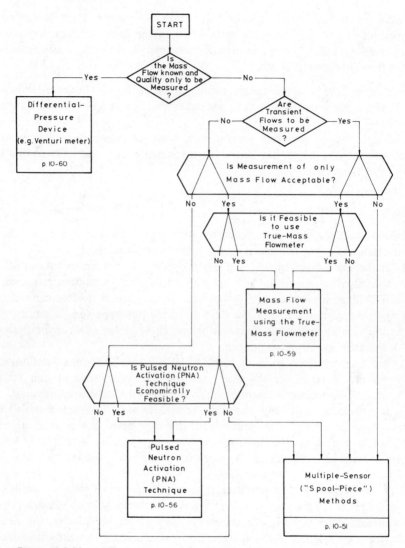

Figure 10.2.28 Selection chart for mass flow and quality measurement methods.

where f_1 and f_2 are functions determined either by calibration or by theoretical methods. $\dot{M}$ and x are determined from S_1 and S_2 by simultaneous inversion of [10.2.21] and [10.2.22]. Clearly, if more than two sensors are used, then a matrix of alternative values for $\dot{M}$ and x can be obtained (i.e., three values for three sensors, four values for four sensors, etc.). For reasons that are explained below, difficulties in establishing the response functions can lead to ambiguities, and it does not necessarily follow that the mass flows and qualities calculated from respective pairs of instruments will be identical.

Multiple-sensor determination of mass flow rate and quality has been applied widely in nuclear safety studies. Here, commonly, a number of devices are placed on a common mounting, and the combination is referred to as a *spool piece*. A spool piece usually consists of a gamma densitometer, a drag body, a turbine meter, and a thermocouple. A typical spool piece is shown in figure 10.2.29. The gamma densitometer gives information on the void fraction R_{G2} (see section 10.2.1.2), which is a function, in general, of $\dot{M}$ and x for the particular configuration used. For the "homogeneous" model (without relative velocity between the phases), R_{G2} is independent of $\dot{M}$ and depends only on x:

$$R_{G2} = \frac{\rho_L x}{\rho_G(1 - x) + \rho_L x} \qquad [10.2.23]$$

The drag body can be either a drag disk, a drag screen, or a drag plate (figure 10.2.30). It measures the momentum flux I_d of the flow, often calculated from the "separated flow model" as

$$I_d = \frac{C_{dG}\dot{M}^2 x^2}{A^2 \rho_G R_{G2}} + \frac{C_{dL}\dot{M}^2(1 - x)^2}{A^2 \rho_L(1 - R_{G2})} \qquad [10.2.24]$$

where ρ_G and ρ_L are the gas and liquid densities, C_{dG} and C_{dL} are the drag coefficients for the gas and liquid phases, respectively, and A is the channel cross-sectional area.

The turbine meter measures the velocity (volume flux) of the flow U_t as sensed by the turbine coil. The relationship between U_t and the true volume flux (the sum of the volume flows of the two phases divided by the cross-sectional area) is not clear. Three models are in existence:

1. Volumetric model (Silverman & Goodrich 1977):

$$U_t = \frac{\dot{M}x}{A\rho_G} + \frac{\dot{M}(1 - x)}{A\rho_L} \qquad [10.2.25]$$

2. Aya model (Aya 1975):

$$C_{L,t}\rho_L(1 - R_{G2})\left[U_t - \frac{\dot{M}(1 - x)}{A(1 - R_{G2})\rho_L}\right]^2 = C_{G,t}\rho_G(1 - R_{G2})\left(\frac{\dot{M}x}{R_{G2}\rho_G A} - U_t\right)^2$$

$$[10.2.26]$$

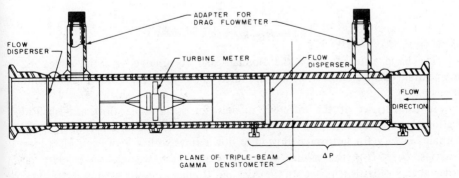

Figure 10.2.29 Typical spool-piece unit, shown disassembled (Turnage et al. 1979).

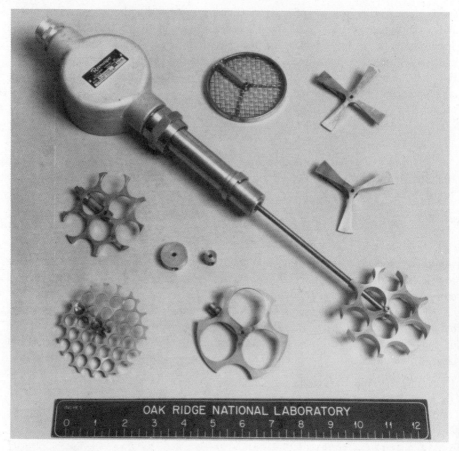

Figure 10.2.30 Typical drag body flowmeter and experimental drag targets (Turnage et al. 1979).

where $C_{L,t}$ and $C_{G,t}$ are coefficients. The Aya model is based upon the assumption that the force of the gas flow exerted upon the turbine blade (moving at U_t) is equal to the force exerted by the blade on the liquid flow.

3. Rouhani model (Rouhani 1964):

$$C_{L,t}(1-x)\left[U_t - \frac{\dot{M}(1-x)}{(1-R_{G2})\rho_L A}\right] = C_{G,t}\, x\left(\frac{\dot{M}x}{R_{G2}\rho_G A} - U_t\right) \quad [10.2.27]$$

The basic assumptions of the Rouhani and Aya models are the same, i.e., a momentum balance. However, they use different ways of expressing the momentum terms.

A comparison of the different models for steady-state flow at Oak Ridge National Laboratory showed that the Aya and Rouhani models accurately predict turbine velocity for horizontal flow. For down flow with velocity ratio less than 1 (that is, $U_G < U_L$), the volumetric model works best, whereas for velocity ratio larger than 1 (that is, $U_G > U_L$), the Aya and Rouhani models do better.

In general (since R_{G2}, I_d, and U_t are functions of $\dot{M}$ and x), three estimates of $\dot{M}$ and x could be obtained by using R_{G2} and I_d, U_t and I_d, and U_t and R_{G2}, respectively. This is feasible if the relationships between the measured quantities and $\dot{M}$ and x are obtained by calibration, but, in practice, recourse has to be made to theoretical relationships of the type exemplified by [10.2.23]-[10.2.25]. It is useful to cite two examples of this approach:

1. Estimate of $\dot{M}$ from I_d and U_t. Equation [10.2.27] may be rewritten as

$$U_t = \frac{C_{G,t}\dot{M}x/R_{G2}\rho_G A}{C_{L,t}(1-x)} + \frac{C_{L,t}\dot{M}(1-x)/(1-R_{G2})\rho_L A}{C_{G,t}x} \qquad [10.2.28]$$

If $C_{L,t} = C_{G,t} = 1$ and if $C_{dG} = C_{dL} = C_d$, then combination of [10.2.28] and [10.2.24] gives the simple result

$$\dot{M} = \frac{I_d A}{C_d U_t} \qquad [10.2.29]$$

Analysis of mass flux data using [10.2.29] indicates that C_d must be about 0.8 or 0.9. The error is in the range of 20%.

2. Estimate of $\dot{M}$ and x from R_{G2} and I_d. Steam-water data from transient blowdown experiments at Idaho National Laboratory show that calculating x from the R_{G2} values given by a gamma densitometer, using [10.2.23] without relative velocity between the phases, and inserting these values into [10.2.24] together with I_d measured by a drag disk gave the best results.

There are many variations in spool-piece setup. The gamma densitometer can be a multiple-beam device to give more accurate density measurements through profile determination. The drag body can be of many shapes; those consisting of perforated plates or screens are more desirable. Other measurement devices can be used in lieu of the drag body; these include pitot-tube rakes or any flow restrictions.

Spool pieces using full-flow measurements have been made for pipes with diameters up to 20 cm. For large pipes, it is difficult to use full-flow turbine meters, and even drag bodies. Here, rakes of turbine meters or pitot tubes have to be used. A combination of a full-flow multihole drag plate and a five-pitot-tube rake has been tested in 66-cm-diameter pipe for the blowdown condition and found to give an error of less than 10% (Fincke & Deason 1979).

Problems in applications The main difficulty in using multisensor measurements is that of obtaining the correct relationships between sensor reading and mass flow and quality. The relationships mentioned above are idealized. For instance, in using equations like [10.2.27] for turbine meters, there is an implicit assumption of a flat profile of density and velocity. For full-flow measurements, radially nonuniform profiles of density and velocity give a mean momentum flux distribution on the blade different from that based upon flat profiles, since the force acting upon blade tip has higher moment than the force acting on the root of the blade; thus, the velocity measurement is biased in favor of the flow condition near the blade tip.

For free-flow measurements, care must always be exercised to ensure correct spatial sampling through proper location of the sensors. Another problem with spool pieces is the flow disturbance caused by upstream sensing devices. The shadow effect is particularly strong if a turbine meter is upstream of a drag screen (or plate). Thus, for bidirectional flow, it is wise to have drag screens located on both sides of a turbine meter so that for either flow direction there is a drag body upstream of the turbine meter. An additional benefit of having two drag bodies is that additional information on flow velocity can be deduced from cross-correlation of signals from the two sensors, and used to check turbine meter velocity.

Mass Flow and Quality Measurement Using the PNA Technique

The PNA technique is one of several available tracer techniques. It is superior to any other tracer method in that the tracer is distributed effectively uniformly and instantaneously in the flow. This is because, if the fluid is water, the atom ^{16}O is present in every molecule and can be activated into ^{16}N by a neutron source. Thus ^{16}N tracer is more uniformly distributed in the activated volume of the fluid. The ^{16}N activity is then sensed by a detector (or several detectors) downstream of the activation station. The typical count-rate distribution is shown in figure 10.2.31.

Consider first the activation zone, which has a volume V. In this zone, at the time of activation, there are a number of elements of mass dm and the mean

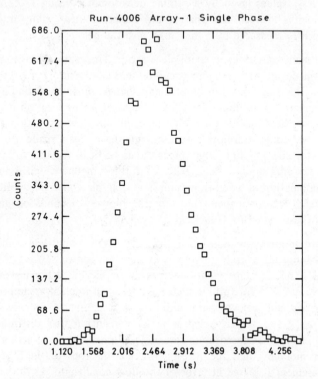

Figure 10.2.31 Count-rate distribution obtained using the PNA technique with single-phase liquid flow at a velocity of 0.49 m/s.

density in the zone is given by

$$\rho = \frac{\int dm}{V} \propto \int dm \qquad [10.2.30]$$

One may define a mass-averaged velocity U_m as

$$U_m = \frac{\int v\,dm}{\int dm} \qquad [10.2.31]$$

where v is the velocity of a mass element. It should be noted that

$$\dot{M} = A\rho U_m \qquad [10.2.32]$$

where $\dot{M}$ is the mass rate of flow and A is the channel cross-sectional area.

In the activation process, each element of mass dm is given an activity corresponding to da, which is proportional to dm. At the detector, a number of counts dc_r are received from the element of mass dm; this number is proportional to the *residual* activity in the element (taking account of radioactive decay) and proportional to the residence time of the mass element in the counting zone. This residence time is, in turn, inversely proportional to the velocity v of the mass element. Thus,

$$dc_r \propto \frac{da\ e^{-\lambda t}}{v} \qquad [10.2.33]$$

where λ is the decay constant for the activity and t is the time at which the mass element dm passes the detector. Thus,

$$dm \propto v\ dc_r e^{\lambda t} \qquad [10.2.34]$$

Since the time taken for the mass element to reach the detector is inversely proportional to v, we have

$$dm \propto \frac{dc_r e^{\lambda t}}{t} \qquad [10.2.35]$$

In practice, the number of counts received by the detector is determined as a function of time. Suppose that the number of counts received by the detector is determined in each of a sequence of time intervals Δt, starting from the time of activation. The number of counts received in the ith time interval is C_i, which represents the summation of the counts dc_r received from those elements of mass which pass through the counting zone in the interval Δt. It follows from [10.2.30] and [10.2.35] that

$$\rho = k \sum_{i=1}^{\infty} \frac{C_i e^{\lambda t}}{t_i} \qquad [10.2.36]$$

where t_i is the time at the midpoint of the ith time interval Δt. The mass average velocity (defined in [10.2.31]) is deducible from similar arguments and is given by

$$U_m = z_0 \sum_{i=1}^{\infty} \frac{C_i e^{\lambda t}}{t_i^2} \Bigg/ \sum_{i=1}^{\infty} \frac{C_i e^{\lambda t}}{t_i} \qquad [10.2.37]$$

where z_0 is the distance along the channel between the activation point and the detection point.

It will thus be seen that the PNA technique gives both the density and the mass rate of flow. It does not give specific information about the quality, although this may be deduced (for homogeneous flow) from the relationship

$$x = \frac{\rho_G \rho_L - \rho \rho_G}{\rho \rho_L - \rho \rho_G} \qquad [10.2.38]$$

The sources of error in PNA measurements are collimation error, error in the distance measurement between the source and detector and in time measurements, and statistical error. The PNA technique has been used to determine single-phase flow with less than 1% error. For two-phase flow, although the modeling does not involve any assumption of flow pattern, a count profile is obtained that is quite different from the normal distribution experienced in single-phase flow (cf. figures 10.2.32 and 10.2.31).

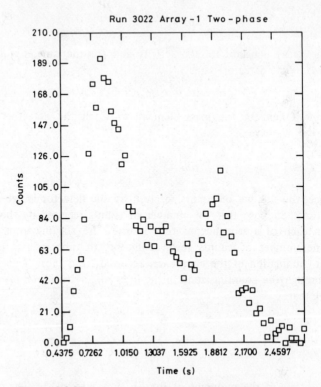

Figure 10.2.32 Count-rate distribution obtained for a two-phase flow with gas and liquid superficial velocities of 1.0 and 0.49 m/s.

Table 10.2.1   Estimated Accuracy of DNA Measurements for 10-cm Insulated Pipes (Kehler 1979)

Neutron source	No. of sources	Gamma detectors	No. of detectors	$K = \dfrac{CU}{\rho}$	Error of velocity reading (%)	Lower limit of density reading (g/cm³)
Old (10^9 n/pulse)	1	Flat	1	2,850	4	0.1
Old	1	Flat	1	2,300	4.5	0.1
Old	2	Flat	3	13,000	1.8	0.04
New (10^{10} n/pulse)	2	Flat	3	46,000	1.0	0.02
Old	2	Torus	1	27,600	1.3	0.03
New	2	Torus	1	92,000	1.0	0.02

Since the activity count is a statistical ensemble, the accuracy increases with the number of counts. Counts can be increased by using a longer pulse time and sampling time, by increasing the pulse strength, or by increasing the detector sensing area. Thus, PNA does best in the steady-state condition with repeated activation. For slow transients, PNA is still useful if pulse strength is increased or a ring detector is used. Table 10.2.1 gives a comparison of the accuracy of the PNA technique with various sources and detectors.

The PNA method was tested on two-phase flow in 7.5 and 12.5-cm-diameter pipe, using a neutron pulse generator giving 3×10^9 neutrons per pulse. Detectors were placed at 1.08 and 5.99 m downstream for the 7.5-cm pipe, and 1.08 and 4.58 m for the 12.5-cm pipe. The accuracy found for density measurements was ±0.04 g/cm³. Velocity uncertainty was about 4% for the 1.19-m case, and 0.5% for the longer distance. The larger error for the shorter distance station is due to the fact that collimation width is about 20% of station distance.

Further details of the PNA technique are given, for instance, by Kehler (1978).

Problems in applications   Although the PNA technique offers great advantages in flexibility and accuracy, the main problem in applying it is the acquisition of suitable neutron sources, detection equipment, and the necessary shielding. This can be rather expensive. With repeated activation pulses, a significant amount of residual activity is built up in the circuit, and this can be a problem under some circumstances.

Mass Flow Measurement Using the True-Mass Flowmeter

Principle of operation   This device, developed at Karlsruhe (Barschdorff et al. 1978), is illustrated in figure 10.2.33. The basic principle of the true-mass flowmeter (TMFM) is that the torque on the stator is the product of the mass flow rate and the centrifugal acceleration $r^2\omega$:

$$\text{Torque} = \dot{M}r^2\omega \qquad [10.2.39]$$

The concept is very simple; however, as the sketch shows, the design is fairly complex. So far, only TMFMs of small size (5 kg/s) have been built. Test results

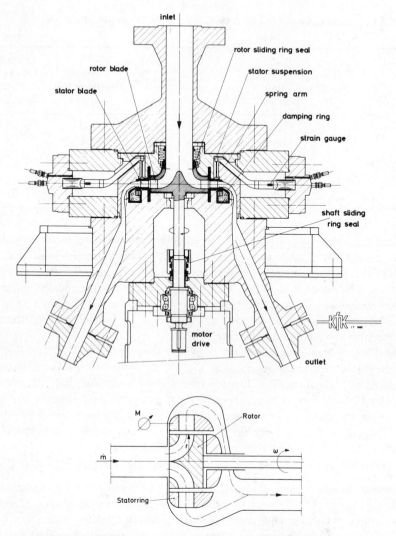

Figure 10.2.33   TMFM based on turbine principle (Class et al. 1979).

have been very encouraging, but tests with larger devices are needed to establish the credibility of the TMFM.

Problems in applications   Clearly, a TMFM strongly influences the nature of the two-phase flow passing through it. Thus, the device can only be used for exit-flow measurements (e.g., in blowdown experiments). Large-scale TMFMs are likely to be very expensive.

Quality Measurement Using Differential-Pressure Devices or Drag Bodies in Flows Where the Mass Flow Rate Is Known

Principle of operation   Here, the flow is passed through some device across which the differential pressure is measured, or the drag on a drag body is measured. For a given mass flow, the differential pressure or drag force can be related to the quality. Examples of the application of differential-pressure devices are discussed by Chisholm (1972) (orifices), Harris (1967) and Frank et al. (1977) (venturis), and Colombo & Premoli (1972) (pipe elbows). The case of drag bodies is discussed above. A number of forms of relationship have been proposed to estimate the pressure drop across such devices. For instance, Chisholm (1972) proposes the following type of expression for the two-phase pressure drop Δp_{TP} across the device:

$$\frac{\Delta p_{TP}}{\Delta p_L} = 1 + \frac{C}{X} + \frac{1}{X^2} \qquad [10.2.40]$$

where Δp_L is the pressure drop for the liquid phase flowing along through the device, and X is the Martinelli parameter [equal to $(\Delta p_L/\Delta p_G)^{1/2}$, where Δp_G is the pressure drop for the gas phase flowing alone]. The parameter C is given by Chisholm as

$$C = \frac{1}{S}\left(\frac{\rho_L}{\rho_G}\right)^{1/2} + S\left(\frac{\rho_G}{\rho_L}\right)^{1/2} \qquad [10.2.41]$$

where S is the velocity ratio; if (as is often done) homogeneous flow is assumed, then $S = 1$.

Problems in applications Because these devices depend on the measurement of pressure drop, the problems of pressure drop measurement referred to in section 10.2.1.1 pertain specifically to them. These difficulties are particularly severe in transient or heated conditions. There, the use of a drag body may be preferable. Very often, the pressure drop is fluctuating with time (Ishigai et al. 1965). Another major problem with differential-pressure devices is that their response depends critically on the upstream flow conditions. To obtain accurate results for quality, it is necessary to use careful calibration of the devices. This point is well demonstrated in the work of Harris (1967) on venturis.

10.2.2 PARAMETERS OF SCIENTIFIC INTEREST

10.2.2.1 Film Flow Rate and Entrainment

G. F. Hewitt

Background

In the usual situation in annular two-phase flow, part of the liquid phase is entrained as droplets in the gas core of the flow (see chapter 2). The extent of this liquid entrainment is important in governing the characteristics of the flow, and measurements of the amount entrained are of considerable interest in model-development studies for annular flow.

If the total liquid flow rate in the channel is known, then the extent of entrainment can be most conveniently measured by determining the flow rate in the liquid film, and then finding the entrained-liquid flow rate by difference. Direct measurement of the entrained liquid flow rate is feasible by measuring drop flow distribution using, say, isokinetic probes (Hewitt 1978a). Alternatively, the flow rates can be determined by the use of tracer measurements (see section 10.2.2.4). However, for both overall entrained flow measurement and local film flow distribution measurements, it is best either to extract the film or to determine its local flow rate by mixing, and these are the methods recommended here.

Selection of Method

A simple selection chart is given in figure 10.2.34. The main questions raised in selecting a method are as follows:

1. Are local measurements required? In many applications, an overall measurement of film flow rate on a given surface is sufficient. This is particularly so when the distribution film flow rate is uniform over the surface. However, there are a number of situations in annular flow in which the film flow rate distribution is nonuniform; these include flow in a horizontal channel, where the film flow rate at the bottom of the channel can often be an order of magnitude higher than that at the top. In these latter cases, local measurements are often required, since the *distribution* of film flow rate is of considerable technical interest in the modeling of these flows. If local measurements are not required, then the porous wall extraction technique is recommended as being widely used and well established (see below).

2. Where local film flow rate measurements are required, is the salt injection method acceptable? The salt injection method is described below. The method is clearly feasible only in the case of a polar liquid (e.g., water) in which the salt is

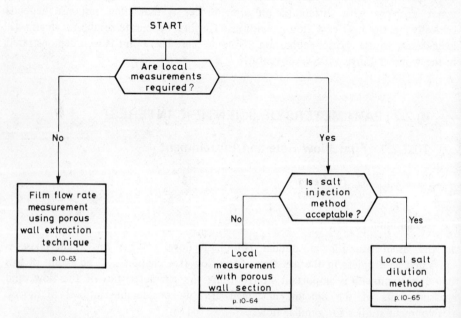

Figure 10.2.34 Selection chart for film flow and entrained flow measurement methods.

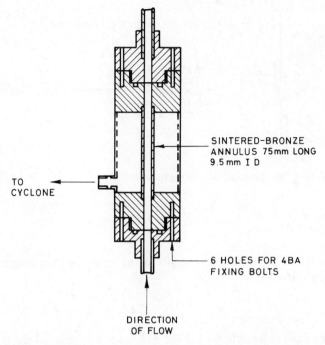

TO
CYCLONE

SINTERED-BRONZE
ANNULUS 75mm LONG
9.5 mm I D

6 HOLES FOR 4BA
FIXING BOLTS

DIRECTION
OF FLOW

Figure 10.2.35 Porous wall film extraction device (Cousins et al. 1965).

soluble and in which the conductivity can be measured locally. This method is clearly unsuitable for most organic fluids. Where it is feasible, the salt injection method is recommended for local film flow rate measurement as being slightly preferable to local measurement using restricted porous wall sections.

Film Flow Rate and Entrainment Measurement Using the Porous Wall Extraction Technique

Principle of operation Here, the film is removed through a section of the channel wall that is porous. Accurately produced porous tubing is available for this purpose; a typical porous wall extraction device is illustrated in figure 10.2.35. In general, the film flow is unsteady, and the upper part of the porous wall section is intermittently dry. This means that some of the gas phase is also extracted. The liquid droplets, however, are not readily diverted into the porous section and they overshoot it, contributing only negligibly to the rate of liquid extraction. Thus, a plot of liquid extraction rate versus gas extraction rate has, ideally, a plateau region corresponding to complete film extraction.

For single-component fluids, the pressure change in passing through the porous wall can lead to flashing, but the extraction rate can be determined by means of a heat balance as illustrated schematically in figure 10.2.36. The enthalpy h_{TP} of the extract stream can be determined by a heat balance (with symbols as defined in figure 10.2.36) as follows:

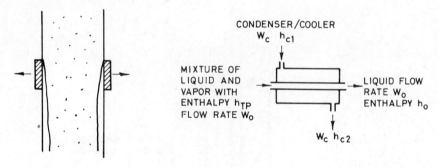

Figure 10.2.36   Film extraction method for single-component systems using a heat balance.

$$h_{TP} = h_0 + \frac{W_c}{W_0}(h_{c2} - h_{c1}) \qquad [10.2.42]$$

the quality of the stream leaving the channel can be estimated from the expression

$$x = \frac{h_{TP} - h_L}{h_G - h_L} \qquad [10.2.43]$$

where h_L and h_G are the saturated liquid and vapor enthalpies at the tube pressure. Since the quality is given by [10.2.43], the liquid-extract flow rate is given simply by $W_0(1 - x)$.

Applications of the technique are described by Cousins et al. (1965) (air-water systems), Hewitt et al. (1965) (low-pressure steam-water systems), Staniforth et al. (1965) (refrigerant vapor-liquid mixtures), and Keeys et al. (1970) and Subbotin et al. (1978) (high-pressure steam-water mixtures).

Problems in applications   Film flow (entrainment) measurements tend to be rather tedious and time-consuming, particularly in one-component, high-pressure flows. Another major problem is that, when the mass flux in the channel is very high, it is sometimes difficult to obtain a clear "plateau" in the plot of liquid-extract flow rate versus vapor-extract rate. When this happens, any measurement of the film flow rate must be subject to some doubt.

Most applications of the porous wall extraction method have been for upward flows. For downward flow, the liquid passing into the outer chamber of the extraction device (see figure 10.2.35) tends to leak back into the channel in some cases. This phenomenon was observed by Webb et al. (1970).

Local Film Flow Rate Measurement Using the Porous Wall Suction Technique

Principle of operation   The principle of operation of this technique is illustrated in figure 10.2.37. A segment of the film flow is separated by fins, between which is sited a porous wall section through which the separated film segment is removed. In the application illustrated in figure 10.2.37 (i.e., for measurement of the distribution of film flow rate in horizontal annular flow), the device is designed so that the position of measurement can be rotated around the circumference of the tube. The application of devices of the form illustrated in figure 10.2.37 is described by, for instance, Butterworth & Pulling (1973) and Maddock et al. (1974).

Problems in applications In addition to the problems encountered with full-film extraction devices (see above), the partial extraction devices have the difficulty that, once the film begins to be thinned in the extraction segment, splashing from adjacent films, not compensated by splashing from the extract segment, may occur. Obviously, the splashing can be minimized by making the separation fins higher, but then the fins themselves begin to collect liquid droplets from the gas core, and this adds to the total extraction rate. Butterworth & Pulling (1973) found small but significant differences between the high-fin and low-fin designs (illustrated in figure 10.2.37); some of their results for variation of peripheral film flow rate with angular position are illustrated in figure 10.2.38.

Measurement of Local Film Flow Rate Using the Salt Dilution Method

Principle of operation This method [described by Coney & Fisher (1976)] is illustrated in figure 10.2.39. Potassium chloride solution is pumped at a constant rate into the sector of liquid film, with which it mixes. The mixed concentration is measured with a miniature conductivity probe that is small enough so that its response depends only on the solution conductivity. The concentration of potassium chloride in the film can be determined from the conductivity, and the flow rate in the sector can be determined from a mass balance, since the flow rate and potassium chloride concentration of the injected stream are known. The effectiveness of mixing in the film is determined by using two successive conductivity probes, as illustrated. Since

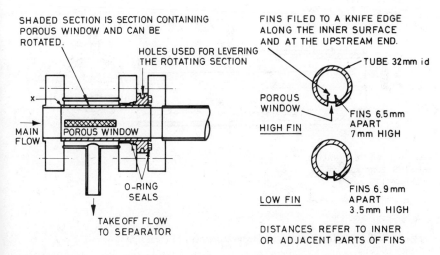

Figure 10.2.37 Local film flow rate measurement in horizontal annular flow (Butterworth & Pulling 1973).

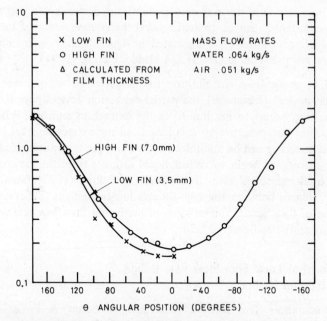

Figure 10.2.38 Results obtained by Butterworth & Pulling (1973) for variation of liquid-film flow rate around the periphery of the tube for air-water annular flow in a 32-mm-ID tube.

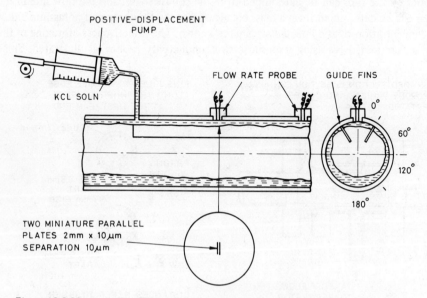

Figure 10.2.39 Salt dilution method for measurement of local film flow rate (Coney & Fisher 1976).

only a small flow of potassium chloride solution is injected, the film flow rate is changed only slightly, and splashover between the measured film segment and the adjacent film segments is possibly less severe than the porous wall extraction technique.

Problems in applications The method can be applied only to polar liquid systems, including water. The measurement system is somewhat more complicated than the porous wall extraction system, but this is offset by the fact that the method is probably more rapid in use. Although it is argued that the splashover problem is less severe with this method, more evidence is required to confirm this.

10.2.2.2 Measurement of Liquid-Film Thickness

G. F. Hewitt

Background

Liquid films occur in many situations. For instance, in annular two-phase flow, part of the liquid phase flows as a film on the channel wall. Measurement of the thickness of this film is important in developing models for annular flow. Film thickness measurements are also important in such applications as filmwise mass transfer equipment, engine manifolds, etc.

Although there are many circumstances in which average film thickness values or statistical information on amplitude distribution is sufficient, there is also considerable interest in the continuous measurement of the thickness of liquid films over which interfacial waves are traveling. The existence of these waves is the norm rather than the exception, and local film thickness measurements play an important part in determining the characteristics of these waves.

A large variety of techniques have been developed for the determination of film thickness; reviews of these are given by Collier & Hewitt (1964), Hewitt & Hall-Taylor (1970), Hewitt (1978a), and Solesio (1978).

Selection of Method

The suggested procedure for the selection of a film thickness measurement method is illustrated in figure 10.2.40. The questions raised are as follows:

1. Is a continuous record required? In nearly all practical systems, film thickness fluctuates with time, owing to the presence of interfacial waves. In studying these waves, there is often a requirement for continuous metering of the local film thickness (i.e., as a function of time). However, where this information is not required, and where time-average film thickness distribution and mean film thickness values are sufficient, the needle-contact method may be appropriate.

2. Is the needle-contact method feasible? The needle-contact method is described below; it depends on observing contacts between an accurately positioned needle tip and the surface of the film. The contacts are usually determined by a conductance method, and, obviously, the method is infeasible where the liquid is not electrically conducting. Furthermore, the application of this technique is often

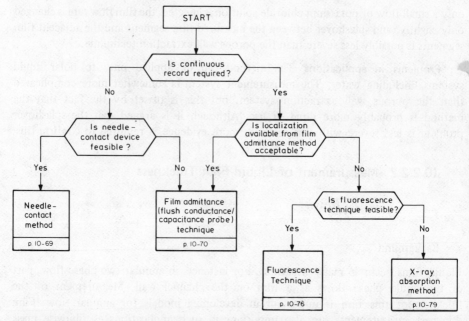

Figure 10.2.40 Selection chart for film thickness measurement techniques.

restricted by geometric considerations. However, where the method is feasible, it provides a very simple and (with care) accurate measurement of mean film thickness and distribution of film thickness, although there may be some problems concerning contact hysteresis.

3. Is the degree of localization available from the film admittance method acceptable? One of the most widely used, economical, and effective methods of measuring film thickness is to use flush conductance or capacitance probes placed in the surface over which the film is passing (see below). With such probes, the measured admittance (conductance or capacitance) increases linearly with film thickness at first, but, as the film gets thicker, the rate of change of admittance with increasing film thickness decreases. Ultimately, an asymptotic value of admittance is approached, and, in this range, the probes are insensitive to changes in film thickness. The linear range increases as the probe separation increases; however, the localization of the film thickness value decreases as the probe spacing is increased. There is, therefore, a dilemma in designing a system for the film admittance method. For accurate measurements of a film with a wavy surface, the wavelength must be large compared to the probe spacing, but this requirement is often inconsistent with the requirement for operating the probe in a sensitive range. This problem is discussed further below. In a number of experiments, where large-amplitude, short-wavelength waves are present, the localization achievable by the film admittance technique is unacceptable, and alternative methods have to be sought.

4. Is the fluorescence technique feasible? Highly localized measurements of film thickness are achievable using the fluorescence method (see below). However, application of this method demands the addition of a fluorescent dyestuff to the

liquid phase, and this may often be infeasible. In this case, it may sometimes be possible to achieve localized film thickness measurements by using the X-ray absorption method.

Film Thickness Measurement Using the Needle-Contact Method

Principle of operation The principle of this technique is very simple: A needle probe is brought up to the surface of the film. When it makes contact with the liquid, a conduction path is established between the probe tip and the tube wall, allowing the contact to be detected electrically. Since the film is usually wavy, the probe first makes contact with the wave tips. As the probe tip is brought closer to the channel surface, the time it spends in contact with the film increases until the contact is permanent, corresponding to the situation in which the distance between the wall and the probe tip is equal to the minimum (wave-trough) film thickness. By recording the fraction of time the probe spends in contact with the film, a film thickness probability distribution can be established.

Typical of the many exploitations of this technique is that reported by Hewitt et al. (1962); the probe assembly used by them is illustrated in figure 10.2.41. Usually, the films to be measured in annular flow are quite thin (typically 0.25 mm). To obtain accurate measurements, considerable care has to be taken in avoiding backlash in the probe and incorrectly recording the probe-tip position. Typical results obtained by the needle-contact method are illustrated in figure 10.2.42.

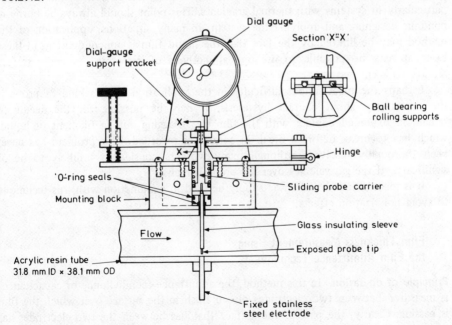

Figure 10.2.41 Needle-contact device for film thickness measurement in air-water annular flow (Hewitt et al. 1962).

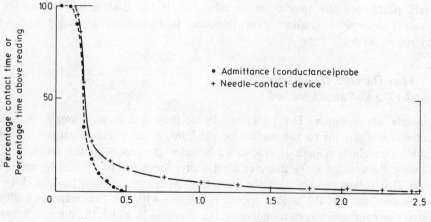

Figure 10.2.42 Results obtained by Hewitt et al. (1962) for needle-contact device and comparison with results for similar conditions obtained using the film admittance (conductance) method.

The needle-contact technique can be applied in a wide range of conditions including high-pressure steam-water flows (e.g., Kirillov et al. 1978).

Problems in applications Considerable care has to be taken to obtain accurate positioning of the needle tip, and there are often problems of dimensional stability, particularly in systems with thermal gradients. This point should always be borne in mind in designing and applying the system. In many situations, application of the method may be limited by the fact that the liquid film is nonconducting. In these cases, it may be possible to use optical methods of detecting the contacts (see section 10.3.2).

Perhaps the most serious difficulty in the application of this kind of probe is the uncertainty about contact hysteresis. It may be possible for the needle to remain in extended contact with the film by "dragging out" a filament of liquid, which has to break before a break in contact is recorded. This problem has never been thoroughly resolved, although many workers consider it unlikely to be of significance if the gas velocity over the probe is high.

It is recommended that an ac supply be used in conjunction with this technique to avoid polarization effects.

Film Thickness Measurement Using the Film Admittance Technique

Principle of operation In this method, the admittance (conductance or capacitance) is measured between two electrodes placed flush in the surface over which the film is passing. Clearly, the part of the surface that lies between the two electrodes has to be insulating, typically of acrylic or thermosetting resin or, for high temperatures, of ceramic. The response of admittance probes can be expressed in the general nondimensional form

$$G^* = \text{fn}\ (h) \qquad [10.2.44]$$

where G^* and h are the nondimensional admittance and nondimensional film thickness, respectively. For probes operating in the conductance mode, G^* is given by

$$G^* = \frac{C}{\gamma l_1} \qquad [10.2.45]$$

where C is the measured conductance across the probes (in siemens), γ is the specific conductivity of the liquid (siemens per meter), and l_1 is a characteristic length. For probes operating in the capacitance mode, G^* is given by

$$G^* = \frac{A}{\epsilon\epsilon_0 l_1} \qquad [10.2.46]$$

where A is the measured capacitance (in farads), ϵ the dielectric constant (relative permittivity) of the liquid, and ϵ_0 the electric constant of free space $[(\frac{1}{36}/\pi) \times 10^{-9}$ F/m].

The dimensionless film thickness h is given by

$$h = \frac{m}{l_2} \qquad [10.2.47]$$

where m is the film thickness, and l_2 a characteristic length that may be equal to or different from l_1, depending on the probe design.

A wide variety of probe geometries have been employed (Hewitt 1978a), Leskovar et al. 1979), but here three alternative designs are suggested that, it is believed, cover most applications. These designs are illustrated in figure 10.2.43 and are as follows:

1. *Two pin probes* (figure 10.2.43a) are probably the easiest to manufacture. Two holes are drilled in the (nonconducting) wall, and metal pins are inserted into

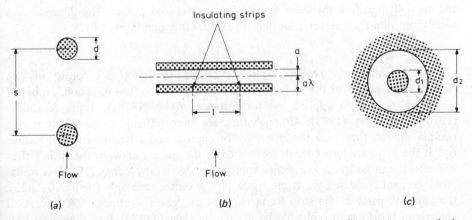

Figure 10.2.43 Recommended electrode configurations for use with the film admittance method. (a) Two-pin electrodes. (b) Parallel-strip electrodes. (c) Concentric electrodes.

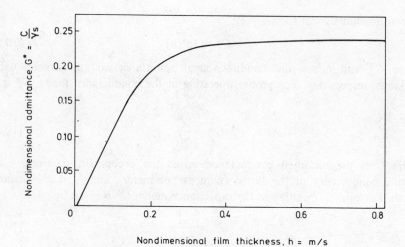

Figure 10.2.44 Nondimensional calibration curve for two-pin film admittance probes with $s/d = 4$. Derived from film conductance calibration data of Hewitt et al. (1962).

the holes, their ends being flush with the surface over which the liquid film is flowing. If the channel surface is curved, then it is usually necessary to shape the ends of the probes accordingly. Probes of this type have been used in the conductance mode by, for instance, Hewitt et al. (1962). In their experiments, the ratio of probe diameter to spacing (d/s in figure 10.2.43a) was 4, and probes of 12.7 and 3.18 mm spacing were employed. The calibration data of Hewitt et al. (1962) can be expressed in nondimensional form (by setting $l_1 = l_2 = s$, where s is the probe spacing), and the probe calibration expressed in this form is illustrated in figure 10.2.44. As will be seen, the response is initially linear, but the dimensionless admittance reaches an asymptotic value as the dimensionless film thickness increases. The linear range extends to a dimensionless film thickness of approximately 0.15, corresponding to films of 1.9 mm thickness for the 12.7-mm-spaced probes, and to 0.48 mm film thickness for the 3.18-mm-spaced probes. The dimensionless admittance/film thickness relationship for the linear region is given by

$$G^* = 1.15 \, h \qquad\qquad [10.2.48]$$

2. In *parallel-strip probes* (figure 10.2.43b), the electrodes consist of two parallel strips placed in the surface, usually normal to the flow direction. Probes of this form have been applied by, for instance, Webb (1970a), Telles & Dukler (1970), and Coney (1973). Although they are more difficult to manufacture than two-pin probes, they have the advantage of approaching a two-dimensional geometry. If the strips are long enough (compared to the spacing between the strips), then end effects can be ignored. Another approach, suggested by Coney (1973), is to use probes in which measurements are made on the center zone only (figure 10.2.43b), the adjacent parts of the strip being regarded as "guard electrodes." A theoretical analysis of this form of probe has been given by Coney (1973). Coney expressed his results in dimensionless form, defining $l_1 = l$ and $l_2 = a$, where l and a are the probe

active length and half-spacing, respectively (see figure 10.2.43b). Coney's result was as follows:

$$G^* = \frac{K(M)}{K(1-M)} \qquad [10.2.49]$$

where $K(M)$ is a complete elliptic integral of the first kind, defined by

$$K(M) = \int_0^{\pi/2} (1 - M \sin^2 \theta)^{-1/2} \, d\theta \qquad [10.2.50]$$

and where M is given by

$$M = \frac{\sinh^2 [\pi(\lambda - 1)/2h]}{\sinh^2 [\pi(\lambda + 1)/2h]} \qquad [10.2.51]$$

where λ is the ratio of the distances between the probe centerline and the outer and inner edges of the conducting strips (see figure 10.2.43b), and $h = m/a$. Values of G^* as a function of h, with λ as a parameter, were calculated by Coney and are shown in figure 10.2.45. At very low values of h, $G^* = 0.5 \, h$.

3. The *concentric probe* (figure 10.2.43c) is particularly convenient for application to metal-walled channels. Here the channel wall acts as one electrode, and a central pin as the other. Applications of this form of electrode are described by, for instance, Butterworth (1968), Brown (1978), and Leskovar et al. (1979). If d_1 is the diameter of the central electrode, and d_2 the diameter of the insulated zone, then we may define $l_1 = l_2 = d_2 - d_1$, and, for the linear region, we have

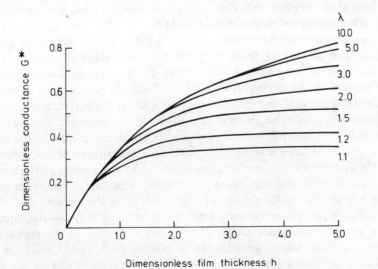

Figure 10.2.45 Nondimensional admittance versus film thickness curves calculated by Coney (1973) for parallel-strip electrodes used in the film admittance method.

$$G^* = \frac{2\pi h}{\ln{(d_2/d_1)}}$$ [10.2.52]

For the nonlinear region, Leskovar et al. (1979) point out that, for the condition where d_1 approaches d_2, the probe can be considered as a parallel-plate probe and analyzed as the two-dimensional strip probe described as item 2 above.

Although the theoretical calibrations given in the above equations and graphs are helpful in designing probe systems, it is often difficult to control the probe geometry precisely, and probe calibration (and, wherever possible *in situ* calibration) is recommended. With probes of tubular geometry, for instance, calibration can be achieved by machining plugs that can be passed into the tube, leaving zones with gaps between the plug surface and the tube wall. If these zones are filled with the system fluid, then the admittance can be measured for a known film thickness. Calibrations using devices of this kind are described by, for instance, Butterworth (1968) and Brown (1978).

It is often possible to design systems so that they operate only within the linear range. However, where this is not possible, the linear range can be artificially extended by linearizing the response curve using function generators. This procedure has been adopted, for instance, by Coney (1973) and Brown (1978). The probe circuit used by Coney (1973) is illustrated in figure 10.2.46.

Problems in applications The main problem in using admittance-probe devices is the insensitivity of the probes to changes in film thickness, when the film thickness becomes large. The larger the spacing of the probes, the larger the range of film thickness that can be measured. Conversely, the larger the spacing, the less the sensitivity to local variations. This represents a fundamental dilemma for this kind of device.

Comparisons between the film admittance method and the needle-contact method are reported by Hewitt et al. (1962) and are illustrated in figure 10.2.42. The response from the 3.18-mm-diameter, 12.7-mm-spaced admittance (conductance) probes is plotted in terms of percentage time above a particular reading, versus the value of that reading. This allows direct comparison with the needle-contact probes. As will be seen from figure 10.2.42, the two methods agree well on mean film thickness (i.e., the film thickness value where the percentage contact time is 50%), but the admittance method fails to record the larger-amplitude waves that are clearly seen by the needle-contact probe. This happens in spite of the fact that much of the larger-amplitude signal is within the linear range of the conductance probe; the discrepancy is, therefore, primarily due to the averaging effect over the probe zone. Notwithstanding these differences, admittance probes provide an effective way of tracking the passage of large waves along the surface.

Admittance probes are normally operated so as to be either in the capacitance mode or in the conductance mode. Thus, a major problem is the elimination of capacitance effects when operating in a conductance mode, and vice versa. Difficulties arise in this respect due to electric-double-layer effects on the surface, and these are discussed in detail by Coney (1973). To avoid these problems, it is recommended that:

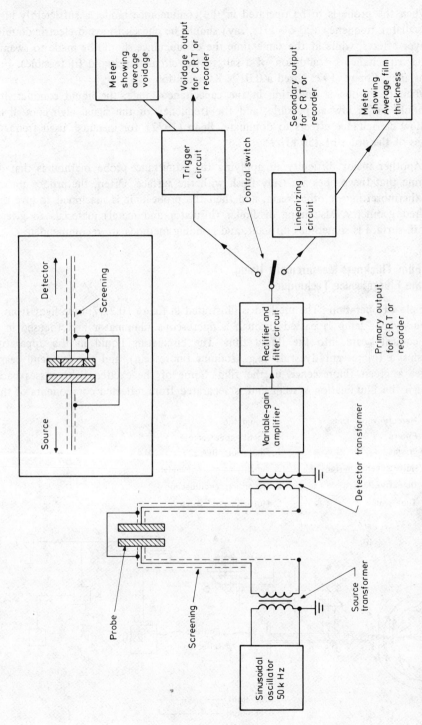

Figure 10.2.46 Electric circuit used by Coney (1973) for film thickness measurement in the conductance mode using parallel-strip probes.

1. When the probe is to be operated in the conductance mode, a sufficiently high oscillator frequency (20–50 kHz, say) should be chosen to avoid electric-double-layer effects, while at the same time the conductance should be made to swamp the capacitance by addition of a salt to the circulating liquid (if feasible). For instance, Coney (1973) used a 0.01 N KCl solution.
2. When the probe is operating in the capacitance mode, the liquid conductivity should be as low as possible, and the frequency of the signal high enough to allow capacitance effects to dominate. Benn (1972), for instance, used frequencies of the order of 450 kHz.

Another major difficulty in applying the admittance-probe method is that of ensuring that the probes are truly flush with the surface. Often, the probes are set in a thermosetting or other resin, and then the probe unit is machined to give the required geometry. Machining dissimilar (insulator and metal) materials to give a smooth surface is sometimes difficult, and grinding methods are recommended.

Film Thickness Measurement Using the Fluorescence Technique

Principle of operation The method is illustrated in figure 10.2.47; blue light from a mercury-vapor lamp is passed through a microscope illuminator and focused in a fine conical beam into the liquid film. The circulating liquid in the apparatus contains a fluorescent dyestuff (e.g., sodium fluorescein), and the incident beam excites a green fluorescence in the film. Some of the excited light passes back through the illumination system and is separated from reflected components of the

A. Mercury–vapor lamp   G. Liquid film

B. Filters   H. Barfitt spectrometer

C. Prisms   I. Photomultiplier

D. Half-silvered mirror   J. Amplifying microammeter

E. Objective lens   K. Recording oscilloscope

F. Tube wall   L. Multichannel switch

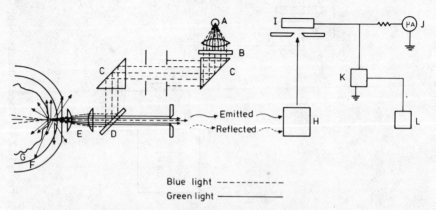

Blue light -----------
Green light ————

Figure 10.2.47 Fluorescence technique for film thickness measurement (Hewitt et al. 1964).

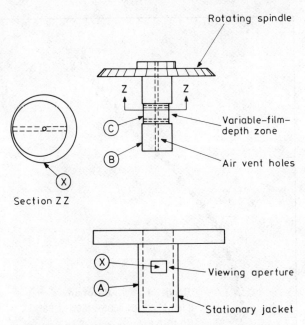

Figure 10.2.48 Calibration cell with rotatable plugs used for calibration in the fluorescence method (Hewitt et al. 1964).

incident light; its intensity is recorded by means of a photomultiplier. In the original exploitation of the technique by Hewitt et al. (1964) and Hewitt & Nicholls (1969), a spectrometer was used to separate out the excited and reflected incident components of the received light, but adequate separation can be achieved by using modern filter systems (Anderson & Hills 1974).

Hewitt et al. (1964) calibrated the instrument using the rotating calibration cell illustrated in figure 10.2.48. The cell consists of an acrylic-resin vessel A of the same internal and external diameter as the tube to be used in the experiments, with a zone of the outer wall flattened to make a viewing aperture up to which the fluorescence system is brought. Inner plugs B of various sizes were constructed so that they fit closely into the vessel A, except for the region C, which was machined eccentrically. As the plugs are rotated, the distance between the inner surface of the vessel and the surface of the plug varies in a known way; by using various plug sizes, it is possible to cover a range of film thickness. The calibration curve obtained by Hewitt et al. is illustrated in figure 10.2.49, and it will be seen that consistent and accurate calibrations can be obtained. A particularly noteworthy feature of this calibration curve is that the same response is obtained for a given film thickness, but with different plugs having different film thicknesses on the opposite side of the tube. This demonstrates that the focusing of the beam into the film, on the wall through which the beam enters, eliminates any response from the film on the opposite wall.

A theoretical expression for the response of the fluorescence device is given by Azzopardi (1978) as follows:

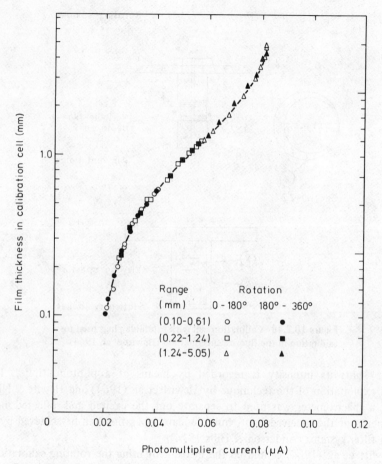

Figure 10.2.49 Calibration curve for film thickness measurement using the fluorescence method (Hewitt et al. 1964).

$$I = \int_0^m \frac{E a I_0 k_1 c y}{1 + k_2 c} \exp\left(-k_1 c y - k_3 \sqrt{cy} + k_4 c y\right) dy \qquad [10.2.53]$$

where I_0 is the incident intensity, E is the fluorescence efficiency, a is the fraction of fluorescence received by the detector, k_1 is the absorption coefficient for incident light, k_2 a self-quenching coefficient, k_3 and k_4 are self-absorption coefficients, y is the distance from the wall, m is the film thickness, and c is the concentration of the dyestuff. Solving [10.2.53] by numerical methods, Azzopardi was able to predict the calibration curve using physically reasonable values of the various constants. However, in any given situation, calibration (and preferably *in situ* calibration) is necessary.

The fluorescence method gives highly localized values and a virtually instantaneous time response. It is particularly suitable for studying situations in which high-amplitude, low-wavelength waves occur.

Problems in applications The fluorescence method is obviously limited to those situations in which a suitable fluorescent dyestuff can be introduced into the liquid phase, and where suitable optical access to the liquid film is feasible. In those situations where its application is possible, care has to be taken concerning the following aspects:

1. The method tends to be sensitive to the positioning of the illumination system, and care should be taken to ensure that this system is positionally stable.
2. The system should be run with clear liquid (i.e., without any fluorescent dyestuff in solution) and checked that there is negligible response in this situation. This gives a check on whether the separation of the excited light from the reflected incident light has been sufficient.
3. Frequent checks are recommended on the calibration of the instrument; preferably, *in situ* calibration should be attempted, but, if not, then arrangements to swing the illumination system directly from the flow channel to the calibration cell can be made (see Hewitt et al. 1964).

With these precautions, the technique can give excellent and accurate results; further development of the technique is continuing at a number of centers.

Film Thickness Measurement Using the X-Ray-Absorption Method

Principle of operation Figure 10.2.50 illustrates the method and shows some results obtained by Solesio (1978) for a falling film flow on an inclined plate. A thin beam of X-rays is passed through the wall and through the film, and the net intensity is recorded by a photomultiplier. The method is thus similar in principle to the radiation-absorption method for void fraction described in section 10.2.1.2. The photomultiplier output can be converted into an output representing film thickness by suitable signal processing. Figure 10.2.50 shows that a quite rapid time response is feasible with the method; it also demonstrates that the more localized response of this method allows the peaks and troughs of the waves to be recorded more accurately than does the film admittance (conductance) method that was used simultaneously in Solesio's experiments.

Problems in applications Clearly, the X-ray-absorption technique can be used only where there is a clear path for the beam, through the film and into the detector. In a tubular geometry, a beam passing through the tube would pass through two films. However, it would be possible to apply the method in this case by feeding the beam through the near-side wall through, say, a purged carrying tube.

In addition to these geometric limitations, there are also the many problems associated with radiation-absorption measurements and described in section 10.2.1.2. Notwithstanding these problems, the method does offer a number of advantages and could possibly be applied in situations where the alternative highly localized technique (fluorescence) is infeasible.

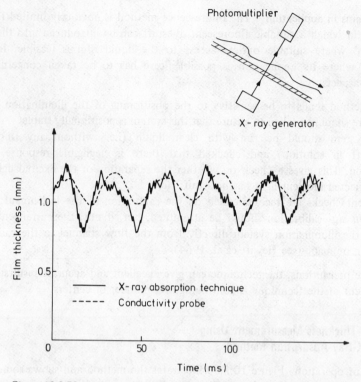

Figure 10.2.50 Results obtained by Solesio et al. (1978) for film thickness fluctuations in falling film flow on an inclined plate, using the X-ray-absorption method.

10.2.2.3 Measurement of Wall Shear Stress

G. F. Hewitt

Background

The wall shear stress (defined as the rate of transfer to the wall of the axial component of the fluid momentum) is an important parameter in the interpretation of two-phase flow systems. For instance, the measurement of wall shear stress allows one of the components of two-phase pressure gradient to be determined (see section 2.2).

Shear stress is a relatively difficult parameter to measure, and its determination is not always feasible. In that case, shear stress has to be deduced from other measurements, such as total pressure drop and void fraction.

Selection of Method

A simple selection chart is shown in figure 10.2.51. The main questions arising in selection are as follows:

1. Are highly localized or continuous (time-varying) values required? One of the most effective ways of measuring average wall shear stress is to use a balancing technique, specifically the so-called τ meter. However, this device is capable only of giving values that are time-averaged and zonal-averaged. It is not suitable for continuous (time-varying) measurements (which are of interest in understanding the fundamental nature of the flows) or in giving highly localized values (which are of interest, say, in studying variations of average shear stress along and around two-phase flow channels). For these latter cases, heat or mass transfer probes must be used.

2. Is the diffusion-controlled electrolysis method feasible? To apply the diffusion-controlled electrolysis technique, a suitable electrolyte must be added to the circulating liquid. This is often impossible, and then recourse must be had to the (less satisfactory) hot-film probe technique.

As was mentioned above, it is often not feasible to make wall shear stress measurements in practical systems, particularly when there is a net heat flux through the wall.

Wall Shear Stress Measurement Using the Balancing (τ-Meter) Method

Principle of operation In the balancing method, the force on a section of the channel wall of area A (that is, τA, where τ is the wall shear stress) is measured by a force-balancing technique. The most successful of the balancing methods is the

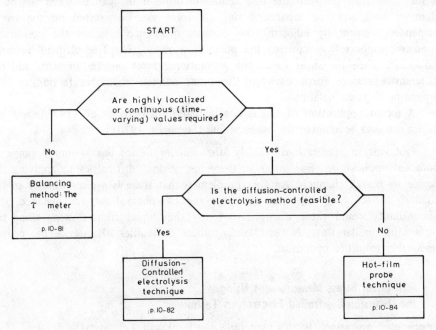

Figure 10.2.51 Selection chart for wall shear stress measurement methods.

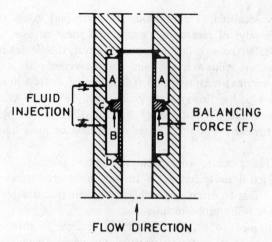

Figure 10.2.52 Schematic representation of balancing (τ-meter) method for wall shear stress measurement (Cravarolo et al. 1964).

so-called τ meter described by Cravarolo et al. (1964) and illustrated in figure 10.2.52. This device consists of a freely suspended element of tube contained in an outer annular space that is divided into two parts with a separating ring as shown. A liquid purge (whose flow rate is small compared to that of the channel flow) is fed into the two parts of the annular chamber as shown; this liquid may flow into the channel through the gaps between the suspended element and the channel walls, and it may also flow between the two chambers through the gap between the outer chamber wall and the separating ring. A force can be exerted on the freely suspended element by adjusting the pressure difference between the two outer annular chambers (by adjusting the purge flow rates). The free element becomes suspended when the shear force, the gravitational force on the element, and the differential-pressure force between the outer annular chambers (acting on the separating ring) are balanced.

A recent application of the device is that of Kirillov et al. (1978), and the device can also be adapted for use in annuli (Stephens, 1970).

Problems in applications Clearly, the τ-meter device has a limited range of potential applications. For instance, there are obvious difficulties in applying the device to heated channels. Another problem is that there is a discontinuity in the channel surface, and this may influence the two-phase flow; for instance, this discontinuity could cause disruption of any thin liquid films flowing along the surface in annular flow. Notwithstanding these difficulties, the device has proved reasonably robust in operation.

Wall Shear Stress Measurement Using the Diffusion-Controlled Electrolysis Technique

Principle of operation In this technique, the local wall shear stress is deduced from a mass transfer coefficient measured on a small element of surface. The mass transfer coefficient is determined electrolytically; the small surface element forms one electrode, and a much larger (and noncontrolling) electrode is placed elsewhere in the system. It is convenient to use a redox reaction; a suitable one is the ferricyanide-ferrocyanide reaction, which, at the cathode, is

$$Fe(CN_6)^{3-} + e \rightarrow Fe(CN_6)^{4-} \qquad [10.2.54]$$

and at the anode

$$Fe(CN_6)^{4-} \rightarrow Fe(CN_6)^{3-} + e \qquad [10.2.55]$$

As the voltage between the electrodes is increased, the concentration $\check{C}_W$ of ferricyanide ions at the cathode surface falls and ultimately reaches zero. At this condition, the current is governed by the diffusion of ferricyanide ions through the boundary layer adjacent to the cathode and is constant at a value I_{lim} over a wide range of voltage as illustrated in figure 10.2.53. In this limiting condition, one may define a mass transfer coefficient k_c for the transfer of ions across the boundary layer, and this is related to the limiting current by the expression

$$\frac{I_{lim}}{AF} = k_c(C_B - C_W) = k_c C_B \qquad [10.2.56]$$

where A is the cathode area, F the Faraday number, and C_B the concentration of ferricyanide ions in the bulk fluid.

In applying this electrochemical technique to the determination of wall shear stress, the cathode is usually in the form of a very short nickel section, as illustrated in figure 10.2.54, and a very much larger nickel anode is situated also in the surface downstream of the measuring cathode. For this situation, the Leveque solution can be used to relate the shear stress to the measured mass transfer coefficient:

$$k_c = 1.68 \, D_{AB} \left(\frac{\tau_0}{\mu_L D_{AB} x} \right)^{1/3} \qquad [10.2.57]$$

where D_{AB} is the diffusion coefficient of the ferricyanide ions, τ_0 is the wall shear stress, μ_L is the liquid viscosity, and x is the width of the cathode (see figure 10.2.54).

Typical of applications of the diffusion-controlled electrolysis method to the measurement of wall shear stress in two-phase flow are those of Sutey & Knudsen (1969) and Kutateladze et al. (1972). The latter authors use the technique for measuring shear stress fluctuations in two-phase flow and show how these fluctuations depend on the particular flow regime.

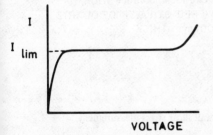

Figure 10.2.53 Current-voltage curve for diffusion-controlled electrolysis method.

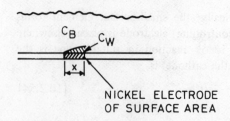

Figure 10.2.54 Application of diffusion-controlled electrolysis method to measurement of wall shear stress.

NICKEL ELECTRODE
OF SURFACE AREA

Problems in applications The most obvious problem in applying this technique is that the circulating liquid must contain a redox electrolyte, for instance, alkaline solutions of potassium ferricyanide-ferrocyanide mixtures. This restricts the applications to those in which liquid phases of this type are acceptable.

In contact with air, a ferricyanide-ferrocyanide solution oxidizes, and if, as usual, the experiments are conducted with air-fluid mixtures, then the solution deteriorates with time. The rate of deterioration can be minimized by presaturation of the solution with nitrogen. The time response of this method has not yet been definitively established.

Wall Shear Stress Measurement Using the Hot-Film Probe Technique

Principle of operation The method is illustrated schematically in figure 10.2.55. A small heated layer is set flush with the surface, and the heat flux $\dot{q}$ required to maintain it at a constant temperature T_0 is determined. It is convenient to use a commercially available hot-film probe for this purpose, and the dimensions indicated in figure 10.2.55 refer to such a probe.

Shiralkar (1970) derived the following expression for the response of the probe:

$$\frac{\dot{q}}{T_0 - T_\infty} = 0.538 \, k_L \left(\frac{\tau_0}{\mu_L \alpha_L x} \right)^{1/3} \qquad [10.2.58]$$

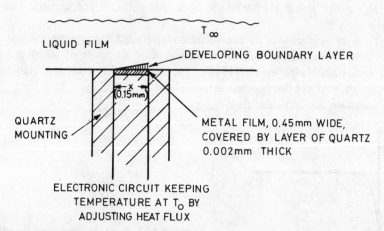

Figure 10.2.55 Hot-film probe method for wall shear stress measurement.

where T_∞ is the bulk fluid temperature (see figure 10.2.55), k_L is the thermal conductivity of the liquid, μ_L is the liquid viscosity, α_L is the liquid thermal diffusivity ($= k_L/\rho_L C_{pL}$, where C_{pL} is the liquid specific heat, and ρ_L the liquid density), τ_0 is the wall shear stress, and x is the heated-layer width. This equation is analogous to [10.2.57] for the diffusion-controlled electrolysis method.

Problems in applications The main problems in application are as follows:

1. Commercially available hot-film units have flat ends, and there is, therefore, the possibility of disturbing the film if such units are introduced into curved channels (e.g., tubes). In the work of Shiralkar et al. (1970) a rectangular channel was used, and this difficulty did not arise. The problem can be minimized by carefully grinding the area of surface immediately surrounding the probe to avoid sudden steps.
2. The fact that the probe is warm may give rise to degassing of the flowing liquid, causing bubbles to be formed on the surface of the probe and leading to ambiguity in its response. This effect can be minimized by using the lowest acceptable overheat ratio for the probe.

There are obvious difficulties in using the probe in systems with heat transfer where there is a heat transfer boundary layer and a preexisting temperature profile exists. Also, the time response of the system has not yet been thoroughly studied.

10.2.2.4 Liquid-Phase Mass Transfer Rate in Annular Flow

G. F. Hewitt

Background

In annular two-phase flow, the normal situation is a continuous entrainment of liquid droplets from the tips of disturbance waves on the interface. The entrained droplets flowing in the gas core may redeposit on the film, and, for "hydrodynamic equilibrium," the entrainment and deposition rates are equal and opposite (i.e., the film flow rate and/or the entrained-liquid flow rate are invariant along the channel). The situation of hydrodynamic equilibrium only achieved in very long channels, and, normally, the local rate of entrainment is not equal to the local rate of deposition. In modeling annular flow, therefore, it is necessary to have some means of predicting these liquid-phase mass transfer rates. This has led to an interest in the development of measurement techniques for the determination of rates of entrainment and deposition. A general review of liquid-phase mass transfer in annular flow is given by Hewitt (1978b).

Selection of Method

A selection chart for liquid-phase mass transfer methods is shown in figure 10.2.56; the questions raised in the selection chart are as follows:

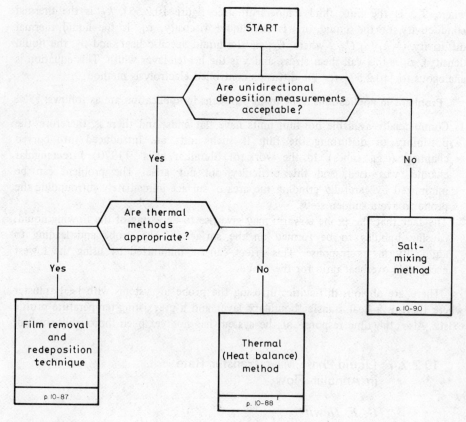

Figure 10.2.56 Selection chart for liquid-phase mass transfer measurement methods in annular flow.

1. Are unidirectional deposition measurements acceptable? Two reasonably well-established techniques are available (i.e., the film removal-redeposition technique and the thermal method) that depend on the removal of the liquid film and determination of the unidirectional rate of deposition under conditions under which reentrainment is avoided. The question obviously arises as to how representative such measurements are of the interchange rate in fully developed flow, where the deposition rate is equal and opposite to the entrainment rate. One could argue that interfacial waves would influence the deposition rate, in addition to being the source of entrainment. Furthermore, recent evidence (Hewitt & Whalley 1979) suggests that deposition occurs by means of a complex combination of droplet diffusion (for the smaller droplets) and droplet impaction resulting from initial release velocities (for the large droplets). In this case, unidirectional deposition experiments may give unrepresentative results. On the other hand, deposition rates under conditions for which the film flow is near zero are of direct interest in studying the occurrence of burnout, since a lower limit for the burnout flux can be considered to be that under which the deposition rate and evaporation rate are equal and opposite. Moreover, recent studies by Nigmatulin et al. (1978) show that

measurements of unidirectional deposition rate (following film removal) and measurements of the interchange rates in fully developed flows using the salt-mixing method (see below) are in reasonably good agreement. The conclusion is, therefore, that unidirectional deposition measurements may give useful information on liquid interchange rates in annular flow, but they should be interpreted with caution.

2. Are thermal methods appropriate? In the thermal methods, the film is dried out by evaporation and entrainment, and, from the point of dryout, the heat flux is decreased until it reaches a value that just balances the deposition rate and just keeps the downstream zone wet. This technique is relatively cheap to implement and has the advantage that deposition can be investigated in the presence of a heat flux, which is the condition to which deposition data are often applied. Clearly, this technique is inapplicable to air-water systems, but it can be very useful, for instance, in high-pressure steam-water studies.

Liquid Deposition Rate Measurement Using the Film Removal and Redeposition Technique

Principle of operation The basis of the technique is illustrated in figure 10.2.57. A fully developed annular flow is set up, and the film is then removed, using a porous-wall extraction device of the form described in section 10.2.2.1. The entrained droplets then begin to redeposit, forming a new film that is then extracted at a further extraction device, which is a distance z_D upstream as shown. The length of the redeposition zone is selected such that the film flow at the end of this zone is still below the minimum required to give rise to entrainment. The deposition is, therefore, "unidirectional" and is not offset by reentrainment.

The most common way of representing the droplet deposition rate D (kilograms per square meter per second) is in terms of the equation

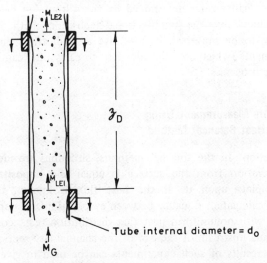

Figure 10.2.57 Film extraction and redeposition method for determining unidirectional droplet deposition rate in annular flow.

$$D = kC \qquad [10.2.59]$$

where C is the droplet concentration (kilograms per cubic meter) in the gas core (calculated by treating the gas core as a homogeneous mixture) and k is the droplet mass transfer coefficient (meters per second). For the experiment illustrated in figure 10.2.57, where the initial entrained-liquid flow rate is $\dot{M}_{LE1}$ and where the entrained-liquid flow rate after a deposition length z_D is $\dot{M}_{LE2}$, the deposition mass transfer coefficient can be calculated from the expression

$$k = \frac{\dot{M}_G \ln (\dot{M}_{LE1}/\dot{M}_{LE2})}{\pi d_0 z_D \rho_G} \qquad [10.2.60]$$

where $\dot{M}_G$ is the gas mass rate of flow, ρ_G is the gas density, and d_0 is the tube diameter.

Experiments using the system illustrated in figure 10.2.57 are described by Cousins et al. (1965) and Cousins & Hewitt (1968b). Other applications of the technique are described by Anderson & Russell (1970), Namie & Ueda (1972), and Ueda et al. (1978). Measurements of the rate of deposition of sprayed-in droplets (as distinct from droplets generated in an annular flow) are described by Alexander & Coldren (1951), Kirillov & Smogalev (1974), and Simpson & Brolls (1974).

Problems in applications Quite accurate measurements of film flow rate are necessary, and (for the reasons described in section 10.2.2.1) this may not be feasible, particularly at high mass flows. Care has to be taken to avoid reentrainment of the liquid in the redeposition section.

Perhaps the major difficulty with this technique is that the unidirectional deposition process may not be representative of the interchange rate in a fully developed flow, where there are interfacial waves that may affect the rate of deposition. However, Nigmatulin et al. (1978) have demonstrated reasonable agreement between interchange rates determined by the salt-mixing method and deposition rates determined by the unidirectional-deposition method. Although this finding is unlikely to be universal, it does give an indication that unidirectional-deposition experiments (which are relatively easy to carry out) can throw some light on the interchange processes.

Deposition Rate Measurement Using the Thermal (Heat Balance) Method

Principle of operation In the thermal methods, situations are identified in which the rate of evaporation from the surface is equal and opposite to the rate of deposition of droplets upon it. If the heat flux is known, then the rate of deposition can be calculated. Equality between evaporation and deposition rates can occur in channels with nonuniform heat flux distribution (e.g., cosine distribution) when burnout occurs upstream of the end of the channel (see section 6.4).

Although the results of such experiments can be used to give an approximate indication of the range of values of deposition rate, the position of burnout is difficult to identify precisely, and this gives large errors in the estimation of deposition mass flux. A much more accurate determination of mass flux is possible using a modified thermal method (Hewitt et al. 1969; Hewitt 1970), as illustrated in figure 10.2.58. Fluid (water in the experiments of Hewitt et al.) is evaporated in upward flow in a tube that is heated uniformly except for a small zone at the end of the tube, which has a lower heat flux (this can be achieved by passing some of the direct heating current through a water-cooled shunt, as shown in figure 10.2.58). By adjustment of the relative heat flux levels in the main part of the channel and in the end zone, and by varying other conditions within the channel (mass flux, inlet subcooling, etc.), it is possible to arrange to have simultaneous burnout at both z_1 and z_2 in figure 10.2.58. Under these conditions, in the end zone of the channel, the vapor generation rate is equally balanced by the deposition flux. The mass transfer coefficient (defined by [10.2.59]) is then given by

$$ k = \frac{\dot{q}_E [x\rho_L + (1 - x)\rho_G]}{\rho_G \rho_L h_{LG} (1 - x)} \qquad [10.2.61] $$

where $\dot{q}_E$ is the heat flux in the end zone, x is the mean quality in the zone, h_{LG} is the latent heat of vaporization, and ρ_G and ρ_L are the vapor and liquid densities.

Problems in applications Clearly, the method can be used only in one-component (evaporating) systems. This limits its range of application but, conversely, allows measurements to be made in situations representative of those encountered in burnout prediction (one of the main applications of annular flow modeling—see section 6.4). A vapor flux is generated from the surface, which might possibly inhibit deposition (although the evidence is generally against this).

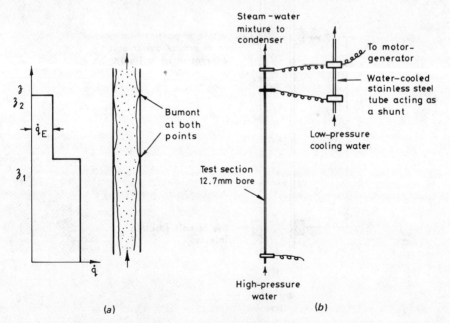

Figure 10.2.58 Thermal deposition flux measurement technique. (*a*) Principle of method. (*b*) Experimental arrangement used by Hewitt et al. (1969).

It is necessary to design electrode connections at z_1 that are small enough to avoid the production of a low-flux zone on which additional deposition can occur.

Measurement of Phase Interchange Rate Using the Salt-Mixing Method

Principle of operation The method is illustrated in figure 10.2.59. A fully developed annular flow is set up with equal and opposite deposition rate D and entrainment rate E. The rates D and E are expressed as mass flux per unit surface area of the tube, i.e., in kilograms per square meter. A dyestuff is added to the film at A, and the concentration of dyestuff in the film decays with distance z. By measuring the concentration of dyestuff in the film (i.e., by extraction at points B at distances z from the dyestuff injection point), it is possible to estimate the interchange rate. For an interchange rate I (where $I = E = D$), the following expression is defined for the variation of the concentration of dyestuff in the liquid film as a function of z:

$$\ln \frac{c_f - c_m}{c_m} = \ln \frac{F_E}{1 - F_E} - \frac{\pi d_0 I z}{F_E(1 - F_E)\dot{M}_L} \qquad [10.2.62]$$

where c_f is the local concentration in the film at distance z, c_m is the mean

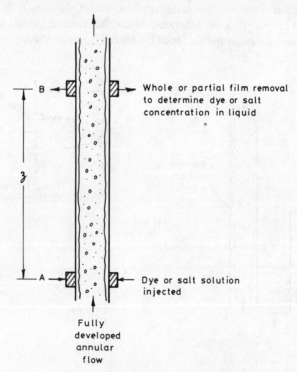

Figure 10.2.59 Salt-mixing method for determination of interchange rate in annular flow.

concentration of dyestuff in the liquid, d_0 is the tube diameter, F_E is the fraction of the liquid phase that is entrained as droplets, and $\dot{M}_L$ is the total liquid flow rate. Thus, a plot of $\ln\left[(c_f - c_m)/c_m\right]$ against z should be a straight line, I and F_E being determined from the slope and the intercept.

The injected material can be either a dyestuff solution [in which case the concentration in the film extract may be determined photometrically (Cousins et al. 1965)] or a salt solution [in which case the concentration determination may be done conductimetrically (Nigmatulin et al. 1978)].

Problems in applications In the original version of this technique (Quandt 1965) the film samples were extracted at a low flow rate—only a few percent of the film flow rate. By comparing such samples with the mean concentration in the film (obtained by extracting the whole film), Cousins et al. (1965) were able to show that the basic assumption of the method (i.e., that the tracer material is uniformly distributed through the film) was incorrect. On this basis, they were able to explain apparently inconsistent results for F_E that had been obtained by Quandt. Their observations appeared to vitiate the method, but a theoretical analysis by Andreussi & Zanelli (1976) indicates that the tracer is relatively well mixed within the film, apart from a very thin layer adjacent to the channel wall, from which the abnormally high-concentration samples taken in the earlier work presumably came. Thus, provided a substantial fraction of the liquid film is extracted for the purpose of determining the mean concentration in the film, reasonable results can be obtained. This is confirmed in the recent work of Nigmatulin et al. (1978).

Since the salt-mixing method depends on maintaining a constant interchange rate over the length downstream of the tracer addition point, care must be taken to ensure that equilibrium annular flow exists. This may require a very long upstream length (typically several hundred diameters).

10.2.2.5 Local Velocity Measurements

Y. Y. Hsu

Background

Measurements of time-averaged local velocity and of the statistics of local velocity fluctuations are important in supporting and developing models for two-phase flow. In general, at a given point within the channel, the phase present is instantaneously either gas or liquid; at that instant, the gas or liquid phase possesses a velocity normally considered to be composed of three components—one in the axial direction and two in the plane normal to the channel axis. Knowledge of the flow velocity (and, in particular, of the axial component of the velocity) is important in understanding two-phase flows.

Obviously, the fluctuations in local velocity, and the fact that the local phase present is changing with time, make local velocity measurement in two-phase flow exceedingly difficult in general. With modern methods such as laser anemometry, measurements are now beginning to appear and throw interesting light on the nature of the flows. However, useful information can also be obtained with less sophisticated techniques such as cross-correlation methods and Pitot probes.

A discussion of local measurement methods that are particularly suitable for obtaining statistical information on local velocity, etc., in two-phase flows is given in section 10.3. In this section, following a discussion of the procedure for selecting a method (including those methods described in section 10.3), the cross-correlation, Pitot probe, and laser-Doppler anemometry methods will be described.

Selection of Method

A selection chart is shown in figure 10.2.60. The main questions raised in the selection of a method for local velocity measurement are as follows:

1. What type of flow pattern exists in the channel? There is a close link between the method selected and the type of flow pattern existing within the channel. A general discussion of two-phase flow regimes is given in section 2.1. For the selection of local velocity measurement methods, three broad classifications are suggested in figure 10.2.60:

a. *Bubble-type flows.* These include bubble flow and plug flow and refer to cases in which relatively well-ordered dispersions of bubbles, or successions of single large bubbles, occur in the channel.

b. *Annular and dispersed flows.* These include annular flows (with or without liquid entrainment), stratified flow, and mist flows. The general characteristic is the existence of a region (which may occupy the whole channel) where the gas phase is continuous.

c. *Complex flows.* These include the regimes occurring at high mass fluxes (such as froth flow and wispy annular flow), where the flow structure is exceedingly complex and is not easily susceptible to local measurement methods. Usually, the best that can be done in these cases is to assume the flow to be locally homogeneous (i.e., with the gas and liquid velocities equal).

2. If the flow is of the bubble type, is the velocity of the continuous phase or of the bubbles required? If there is slip between the gas and the liquid, then the local continuous-phase and bubble velocities are different. In many investigations, both velocities are required.

3. If the flow is of the annular or dispersed type, are measurements required in the gas core or in the liquid layer? If the flow is a mist flow with no liquid layer, the answer is obvious. However, rather different techniques are required if measurements are to be made in liquid layers than are required for measurements in a droplet-laden gas stream. Again, some investigations will require that measurements in both streams be made.

4. Are laser anemometry methods feasible and economically acceptable? In recent years, there has been a vast increase in the number of studies of single- and two-phase flows using laser anemometry. For single-phase flows, the technique is now almost routine. However, in two-phase flows, the interpretation of signals from laser-Doppler anemometry devices is very much more difficult. The cost of the basic

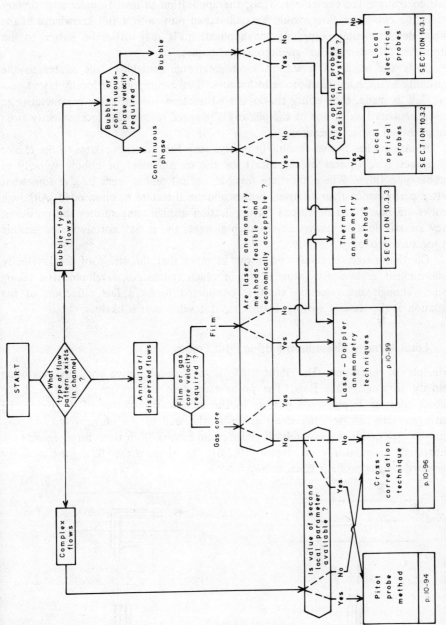

Figure 10.2.60 Selection chart for local velocity measurement techniques.

equipment and of the associated signal-processing equipment can be rather large, and (probably more important) it may take several years to develop suitably trained staff to operate the equipment. Thus, the application of laser-Doppler anemometry studies to two-phase flow should be undertaken only with a full knowledge of the likely developmental nature of the application. It may often be better to use alternative (but perhaps less glamorous) techniques.

5. Is the value of a second local parameter available? This relates to the feasibility of applying Pitot-probe techniques. If an assumption of locally homogeneous flow is made, then either the local void fraction or some other parameter (e.g., the local mass flux of one of the phases) is required to calculate local velocity from the measured impact pressure.

6. Are optical probes feasible in the system? This question relates to the choice of probes (i.e., optical or electrical) for the measurement of bubble velocity in bubble-type flows. Where they are feasible, optical probes seem to give somewhat better performance than electrical probes and are therefore recommended. Although probes are now being developed for application at high temperatures and pressures, they are still in a somewhat developmental stage, and it may not always be feasible to use such probes.

On the whole, it should be borne in mind that the study of local velocity measurement in two-phase flow is one in which continuous development is taking place. Though the selection chart is considered to be a fair reflection of the situation at the time of writing, further rapid development is likely.

Local Velocity Measurement Using Pitot Probes

Principle of operation The Pitot tube is a classical device used in measuring velocity in single-phase flow. The probe faces into the oncoming fluid, and the impact pressure is measured relative to the local static pressure of the fluid. The static pressure can be determined either at the wall of the channel (an ordinary Pitot probe) or on the probe itself (Pitot-static probe). Both these arrangements are illustrated schematically in figure 10.2.61. In single-phase flow, the velocity measured by the probe is given simply by

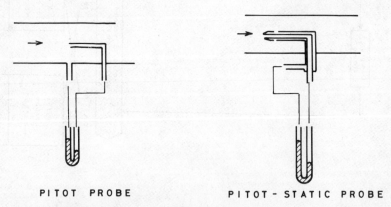

PITOT PROBE   PITOT-STATIC PROBE

Figure 10.2.61   Pitot and Pitot-static tubes for local velocity measurement.

$$U = \sqrt{\frac{2\,\Delta p}{\rho}} \qquad\qquad [10.2.63]$$

where Δp is the pressure difference recorded from the probe, and ρ is the single-phase fluid density.

The Pitot probe has been applied quite widely in two-phase flow studies, but the interpretation of the recorded impact pressure is somewhat difficult. One approach, which works quite well under some circumstances, is to assume that the two-phase flow behaves as a homogeneous mixture with no relative velocity between the phases. This is effective in considering high mass velocity flows or in considering drop or particle-laden flows in a gas continuum.

To estimate the velocity using [10.2.63], the mean homogeneous density $\bar{\rho}$ must be known. One approach is to deduce local density from a void fraction measurement:

$$\bar{\rho} = (1 - \epsilon_G)\rho_L + \epsilon_G\rho_G \qquad\qquad [10.2.64]$$

where ϵ_G is the void fraction, and ρ_L and ρ_G are the liquid and gas densities, respectively. This approach has been adopted, for instance, by Banerjee et al. (1978b), and by Gill et al. (1963, 1964), in making measurements in the gas core of annular dispersed flows. In above-referenced experiments, the local liquid mass flux $\dot{m}_L$ was measured by collecting the droplets via the probe. If $\dot{m}_L$ is known and the assumption of homogeneous flow is made, then U can be calculated. We have

$$\bar{\rho} = \frac{\dot{m}_L + \dot{m}_G}{\dot{m}_L/\rho_L + \dot{m}_G/\rho_G} \qquad\qquad [10.2.65]$$

and

$$U = \frac{\dot{m}_L}{\rho_L} + \frac{\dot{m}_G}{\rho_G} \qquad\qquad [10.2.66]$$

Combining [10.2.65] and [10.2.66] to eliminate the (unknown) gas mass flux $\dot{m}_G$ and substituting into [10.2.63] yield a quadratic equation in U whose solution is

$$U = \frac{-\dot{m}_L(1 - \rho_G/\rho_L) + \sqrt{\dot{m}_L^2(1 - \rho_G/\rho_L)^2 + 8\rho_G\,\Delta p}}{2\rho_G} \qquad\qquad [10.2.67]$$

Using this method to interpret Pitot-probe impact pressure, Gill et al. were able to show reasonable agreement between measured and known (i.e., input) gas flows.

Problems in applications Obviously, the main problem in the use of Pitot probes to measure local velocity is that they can be applied only where the flow is likely to be reasonably homogeneous, and the velocities of the two phases close to equal.

Since the Pitot-probe method depends on a differential-pressure measurement, all the difficulties associated with measuring differential pressures in two-phase flows (as described in section 10.2.1.1) are encountered. Gill et al. (1963, 1964) used a gas-purged probe coupled with a gas-liquid manometer. Banerjee et al. (1978b) used a differential-pressure transducer. The normal difficulties in measuring two-phase differential pressures are likely to limit the accuracy of the Pitot-tube method.

Local Velocity Measurement Using the Cross-Correlation Technique

Principle of operation When a probe is used to sense a local parameter such as void fraction or temperature, a time-varying, fluctuating curve results, such as that shown in figure 10.2.62. This particular curve shows the variation of electrical conductance with time at a given point; similar curves can be obtained for the variation of capacitance, temperature, thermal conductivity, etc. If another probe is located immediately downstream, a similar curve with a more or less constant time shift can be obtained. The time shift represents the time required for the fluctuation to travel from one location to the other. If the fluctuation travels with the flow at flow velocity, the fluctuation can be treated as a tracer.

In the cross-correlation method, a cross-correlation coefficient R_{12} is computed:

$$R_{12}(\tau) = \frac{\int_0^T f_1(t)f_2(t+\tau)\,dt}{\int_0^T f_1^2(t)\,dt} \qquad [10.2.68]$$

where $f_1(t)$ is the measured quantity at one point as a function of time, and $f_2(t+\tau)$ is the quantity measured at the downstream point at time $t+\tau$. The averaging is done over a sufficiently long time T such that $R_{12}(\tau)$ is constant with T.

The value of $R_{12}(\tau)$ reaches a maximum (see figure 10.2.63) at $\tau = \tau_{M'}$ where

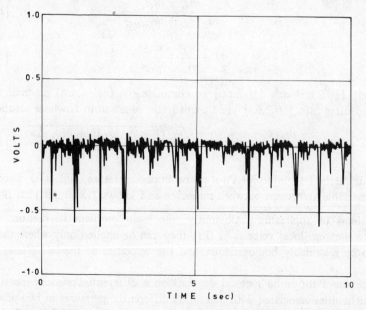

Figure 10.2.62 Voltage-time trace obtained from an X-string conductance probe in a two-phase flow with a void fraction of 0.03 (Leavell & Shahrokhi 1979).

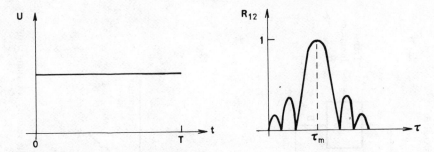

Figure 10.2.63   Schematic representation of results obtained for cross-correlation coefficient R_{12} for a system with constant velocity.

τ_M is the most likely transit time of the fluid between the measuring stations. The fluid velocity U is then given by

$$U = \frac{z_{12}}{\tau_M} \qquad [10.2.69]$$

where z_{12} is the distance between the measuring stations.

The conventional cross-correlation method is meant for steady-state flow, where transit time τ_M does not change much with time. For transient flow in which velocity (and thus transit time) varies rapidly, the normal cross-correlation method cannot be used. For such transient flow, a special form of cross correlation, called the *adaptive cross-correlation algorithm* (Leavell & Shahrokhi 1979) may be used. In this algorithm, the sampling rate and transit-time shift are constantly revised to anticipate the changing velocity. The principle is illustrated in figure 10.2.64*a*. The sampling time is progressively reduced $(T_1 \rightarrow T_2 \rightarrow T_3)$ until the variation of transit time τ_M is relatively small with further variation of sampling time. Since enough samples are needed to obtain a statistically meaningful ensemble, the sampling frequency has to be increased as the sampling time decreases. However, the increased frequency demands a large-capacity data-acquisition system and more data-processing time; both are very expensive, unless some built-in correlator is available for data processing. The latter uses the principle of frequency-domain correlation through Fourier transformation. The transit time can be obtained from the slope of the relatively smooth part of the phase plot (figure 10.2.64*b*).

Problems in applications   A major problem with the cross-correlation technique is that it measures only one velocity. This velocity is equal to the local velocity only if the assumption of homogeneous flow is valid. Where there is known relative velocity between the phases, it is difficult to interpret the results. Some transient data reported for these conditions are illustrated in figure 10.2.65; it will be seen that the measured velocity generally lies between the velocities of the phases (the latter being estimated from the known volume flows and the measured void fraction). It may be possible to interpret the signals in more detail, but this requires more development effort.

It should be noted that this discussion of cross correlation is based on the assumption that no other periodic fluctuation is superimposed. For example, if a

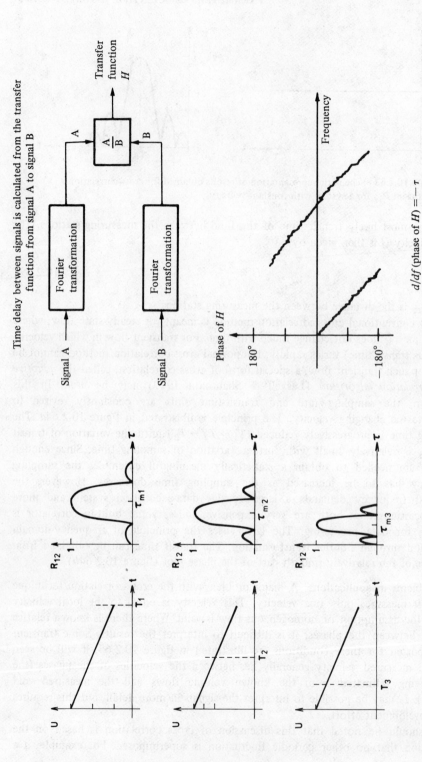

Figure 10.2.64 (a) Basis of adaptive algorithm for application of the cross-correlation technique to a system in which the velocity is varying with time (Leavell & Shahrokhi 1979). (b) Principle of frequency-domain correlation (Hylton 1979).

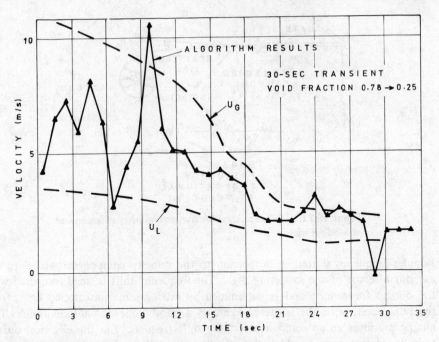

Figure 10.2.65 Comparison of phase velocities (determined from void fraction measurement) and transit velocity measured using the cross-correlation technique (Leavell & Shahrokhi 1979).

pressure wave is superimposed and causes its own periodic fluctuation in the signals, then the cross correlation may very well yield a transit velocity that is related to the wave velocity, so that totally misleading information is obtained.

Local Velocity Measurement Using Laser-Doppler-Anemometry

Principle of operation The two main variations of the laser-Doppler-anemometry technique are illustrated in figures 10.2.66 and 10.2.67. In the first variation (figure 10.2.66), light scattered from a laser beam by particles moving with the fluid is

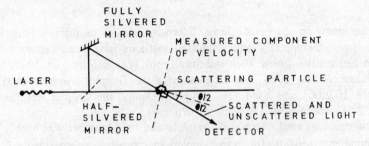

Figure 10.2.66 Doppler frequency-shift method for laser anemometry measurement of local velocity.

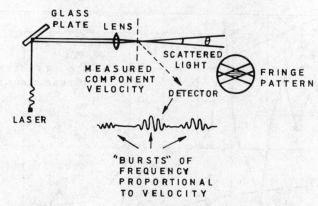

Figure 10.2.67   Fringe method for laser anemometry measurement of local velocity.

Doppler frequency-shifted in proportion to the velocity component parallel to the exterior bisector of the scattering angle. The frequency shift is small compared with the optical frequencies and is determined by mixing some unscattered light, from the same laser, with the scattered light, on a photodiode or photomultiplier. This mixing produces an ac component (at the shift frequency) in the electrical output from the detector, from which the velocity can be derived. In this variation of the technique, the component of velocity being measured, and its relationship to the frequency shift, are dependent on the positioning of the detector relative to the incident beam.

In the second variation of the laser anemometry technique (figure 10.2.67), two beams split from the same laser output are made to intersect to produce an interference fringe pattern. Light scattered by the particles moving through the fringes is intensity modulated, at a frequency in direct proportion to the velocity component normal to the fringes and in reverse proportion to their spacing. This modulation can be detected in light scattered in any direction from the fringes, and it produces an ac component (at the modulation frequency) in the output of a detector in any position relative to the beams.

A very wide variety of optical arrangements have been used in laser anemometry [see Hewitt (1978b) for a brief review]. For present purposes, it suffices to cite a few examples in which laser anemometry has been applied in two-phase flow systems:

1. Measurements in dispersed flows. Extensive studies of dispersed-droplet flows using laser anemometry and associated methods have been carried out at the State University of New York at Stony Brook (Lee & Srinivasan 1977, 1978a, b; Srinivasan & Lee 1978). An adaptation of the Doppler frequency-shift method (figure 10.2.66) was used. The droplet velocity and droplet size (see section 10.2.2.6) were measured in these experiments.
2. Measurement of continuous-phase velocity and bubble velocity in bubbly flows. A development program for laser-Doppler anemometry measurements in bubbly flow has been proceeding over the past few years at Osaka University, Japan

(Ohba et al. 1976, 1977a, 1977b; Ohba & Yuhara 1979a, 1979b). In the system illustrated in figure 10.2.68a, two beams are used (cf. figure 10.2.67); photo-multiplier PMT 1 receives signal bursts from scattering centers in the liquid phase, and its output therefore gives the liquid-phase velocity between bubbles. A second photomultiplier tube (PMT 2) receives reflected light from the bubble surfaces, and this light is modulated with a frequency proportional to the bubble velocity. Figure 10.2.68*b* illustrates how the two photomultiplier tubes respond as a function of time. Successful measurements were made of the distributions of gas and liquid velocity at void fractions up to 0.3.

3. Measurements in liquid films. The application of laser-Doppler anemometry to film velocity profile measurement is described, for instance, by Oldengarm et al. (1975). They used the two-beam (cf. figure 10.2.67) method coupled with a rotating grating that split the beams and gave a frequency shift. Normally, frequency shifting is used in laser-Doppler anemometry systems to allow discrimination between negative and positive velocities of the same magnitude. In the system used by Oldengarm et al., however, it was used to improve the accuracy of velocity measurement in the low-velocity region near the channel wall. Highly localized and accurate measurements were obtained in a film of only 240 μm thickness.

Development is continuing in this field, and one may expect to see an increase in the application of laser-Doppler anemometry techniques to two-phase flow.

Problems in applications   As was mentioned above, a new program of laser-Doppler anemometry measurements in two-phase flow almost certainly means the commitment of large amounts of money and effort. For many purposes, alternative (and cheaper) techniques are available.

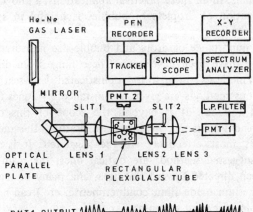

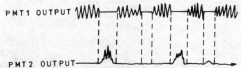

Figure 10.2.68 System used by Ohba & Yuhara (1979a, 1979b) for simultaneous measurement of bubble velocity and liquid velocity in bubbly flow.

The principal technical difficulty in applying laser-Doppler anemometry techniques to two-phase flow is that of interfacial refraction and scattering. It is important that the incident and scattered beams can intersect at the measurement point and can pass unimpeded to the detector. By definition, the beams must pass through interfaces for some of the time, and the interfaces cause them to be refracted. During the period of refraction, the signal is obscured. However, as Ohba and co-workers have shown, reasonable amounts of information can be obtained at void fractions up to 30% in bubbly flow. The situation can be improved by carrying the beams closer to the point of measurement through suitable light guide tubes.

10.2.2.6 Measurement of Drop and Bubble Size

G. F. Hewitt

Background

In many two-phase flows, isolated drops or bubbles exist in a gas or liquid continuum. The physical size of the drops or bubbles is often a critical factor in determining their behavior within the system. Thus, there is considerable scientific interest in knowing the mean value and the distribution of sizes of drops or bubbles, to satisfactorily model two-phase flow systems. Of course, drop-size measurement is of very wide interest in other contexts; these include spray-drying systems, paint-spraying systems, fuel spray-injection systems, meteorology, and internal-combustion engines. Knowledge of bubble size is of interest in many industrial systems including gas-liquid contacting devices, distillation towers, and sewage aeration systems. In all these practical applications, a knowledge of the mean size and size distribution of droplets or bubbles is helpful in system design and analysis.

Because of the importance of drop- and bubble-size measurement, a very wide variety of techniques have been developed. These range from direct measurement using photographic methods through to sophisticated laser-scattering techniques. Reviews of the various methods are given, for instance, by Jones (1977), Azzopardi (1977), and Hewitt (1978a). It is beyond the scope of this chapter to give a historical review of developments in this area. Rather, the methods that meet various requirements most effectively will be suggested. It is no accident that practically all the suggested methods are optical ones; the main thrust of recent development has been directed toward this area, and many of the older techniques (photographic, magnesium oxide film, conductimetric, etc.) can now be regarded as having been superceded for most purposes.

Selection of Method

A selection chart for drop- and bubble-size measurement methods is given in figure 10.2.69. The questions raised in making the selection are as follows:

1. Is the distribution of size required? For many purposes, it is sufficient to have information only on mean size. It should be borne in mind that there are a

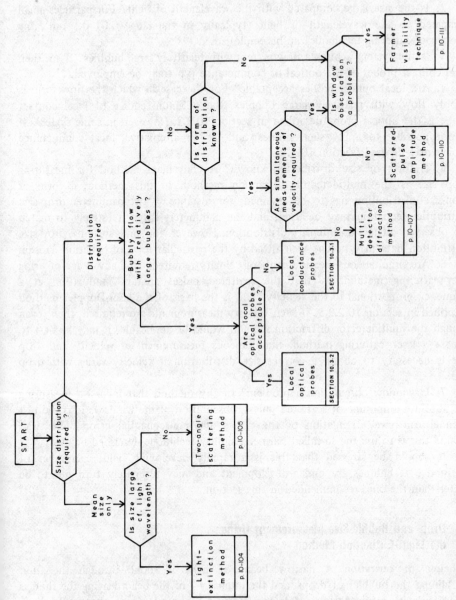

Figure 10.2.69 Selection chart for drop- and bubble-size measurement method.

number of ways of defining the mean size (surface-area mean, volumetric mean, arithmetic mean, etc.), and to convert from one form of mean to another implicitly requires a knowledge of the size distribution.

2. Is the size large compared with the wavelength of light? For particles small compared to the wavelength of light (typically in the range 0.01–0.1 μm), the two-angle scattering technique can be employed.

3. Is the system a bubble flow system with relatively large bubbles? If so, then local contact probes of the optical or conductance type may be employed.

4. Are local optical probes acceptable? For the case in which the flow form is bubbly flow with relatively large bubbles, the optimum choice of local contact probe is the optical probe described in section 10.3.2. However, in some systems it is not possible to apply such probes, and, as an alternative, local conductance probes may be used (section 10.3.1).

5. Is form of size distribution known? A convenient method for measuring drop size is the multidetector diffraction method. In this method, a form of drop-size distribution has to be assumed; for instance, a two-parameter drop-size distribution equation may be used, and the parameters fitted iteratively to match the observed diffraction intensity distribution. However, for some systems, drop-size distribution data may not be well fitted by the particular form of equation chosen.

6. Are simultaneous measurements of velocity required? One advantage of using laser-scattering methods is that the scattered pulses contain modulation at a frequency proportional to the velocity. This is the basis of the laser-Doppler method described in section 10.2.2.5. If such velocity measurements are required, then (even though the multidetector diffraction method would be applicable) it may be best to choose a laser-scattering method. Simultaneous measurement of velocity and drop size is necessary to obtain a correct size distribution if velocity varies with drop size.

7. Is window obscuration a problem? In any method that relies on measuring the absolute amplitude of scattered pulses, obscuration of the windows into the test channel can give attenuation of the pulses and consequential errors. One way around this is to use the so-called Farmer visibility technique described below.

It should be stressed that this is a rapidly developing field; a number of alternative techniques are under development and may ultimately turn out to be better than the ones recommended in this section.

Drop- and Bubble-Size Measurement Using the Light-Extinction Method

Principle of operation A narrow beam of light is shone through the fluid containing the bubbles or drops, and the intensity I of the beam leaving the fluid is measured with a photoelectric detector (such as a photodiode or photomultiplier). The access to the detector is carefully collimated to be in line with the original beam. When the beam passes through a droplet or bubble, it is scattered; and this gives rise to a reduction in the intensity received, as compared to the intensity I_0 received in the absence of the bubbles or drops. I is related to I_0 through the classical photo-extinction law

$$I = I_0 \exp\left(-\frac{3\epsilon z_0}{2\bar{d}_{32}}\right) \tag{10.2.70}$$

where ϵ is the concentration of bubbles or drops in the fluid (i.e., the void fraction for a bubbly flow), z_0 is the distance the beam travels through the fluid, and $\bar{d}_{32}$ is the Sauter mean diameter, defined by

$$\bar{d}_{32} = \frac{\bar{d}^3}{\bar{d}^2} \tag{10.2.71}$$

where $\bar{d}^3$ and $\bar{d}^2$ are the volumetric and surface-area mean diameters, respectively. To obtain the mean drop size in the extinction method, the concentration ϵ (volume of drops or bubbles per unit volume) has to be known. Alternatively, if $\bar{d}_{32}$ is known, then the method can be used to determine ϵ.

The technique has been widely applied, and examples of applications are the studies of Calderbank (1958) (bubble flows), Walters (1969, 1971) (mist flows), and Lockett & Safekourdi (1977) (liquid-liquid emulsions). A recent study of the light-extinction technique (in the context of void fraction measurement) has been conducted by Ohba and co-workers at Osaka University (Ohba & Itoh 1978a, 1978b; Ohba et al. 1978; Ohba 1979). These studies have provided detailed theoretical and experimental justification for the technique; for example, it was shown that (with a detector angle below $6°$) the bubble is optically equivalent to an opaque body of the same shape and dimensions.

Problems in applications The light-extinction method has the obvious disadvantage that, to measure the mean diameter, the concentration of drops or bubbles must be known, and that the particular mean diameter $\bar{d}_{32}$ may not be suitable for a particular application. Also, the method becomes inaccurate as the bubble or drop concentration increases. For instance, Ohba & Itoh (1978b) show a thousandfold attenuation in intensity for bubbly-flow void fractions of around 0.3. Clearly, this implies considerable inaccuracies in the measurement of mean bubble size at void fractions of this magnitude (and higher), although the method can be used effectively at lower void fractions (less than 0.15, say). Moreover, care has to be taken that additional attenuation is not occurring due to obscuration of windows, etc.

Droplet-Size Measurement Using the Two-Angle Scattering Method

Principle of operation The general theory of the scattering of light by transparent particles was originally developed by Mie (1908); a useful source of reference on the Mie theory and other aspects of light scattering is the book by Kerker (1969). It is possible to deduce drop size from the *distribution* of scattered intensity, rather than from the intensity of scattering (as in the scattered-pulse amplitude method below) or the nature of the pulse of light scattered by the droplets (Farmer visibility technique).

Although techniques based on scattered intensity distributions can, in principle,

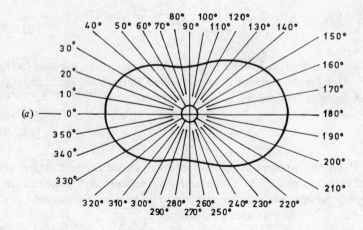

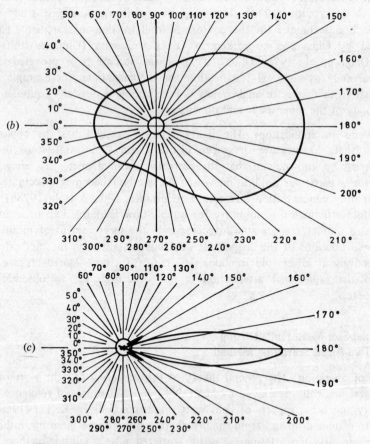

Figure 10.2.70 Distribution of scattered light intensity as a function of scattering angle (Engelhard & Friess 1937). Refractive index = 1.44, and $\alpha = 2\pi d/\lambda$ is (a) 0.4, (b) 1, and (c) 8, where d is the particle diameter and λ is the light wavelength.

be used for a wide range of particle sizes, the angular intensity distributions become exceedingly complex for larger particles. Typical distributions of intensity of scattering from a particle are illustrated in figure 10.2.70 for various values of the parameter $\alpha = 2\pi d/\lambda$, where d is the droplet diameter and λ is the wavelength of the light. The complex "spikes" that appear at the highest value of α are characteristic of the diffraction pattern obtained for larger particles and on whose existence the multidetector diffraction method (see below) depends.

For droplets whose size is small compared to the wavelength of light, one may use a two-angle method as described, for instance, by Deich et al. (1971, 1972). Their investigations were of wet-steam flows, where the droplets were very small. The method employed was to pass a neon-helium laser beam through the wet steam and to measure the intensity I_A of light scattered forward at an angle close to the direction of the incident beam, and the intensity I_B of light scattered backward at an angle close to 180° with respect to the incident beam. The drop size is a unique function of I_B/I_A, the form of this function being illustrated in figure 10.2.71.

Problems in applications Clearly, this particular manifestation of the method is suitable only for droplets that are small compared to the wavelength of light (i.e., for α values up to, say, about 1.5). However, very useful information was obtained by Deich and co-workers for the situation in which droplets were nucleating and growing in wet steam.

Multidetector Diffraction Method

Principle of operation Consider a dispersion of particles through which a plane parallel beam of light passes, as illustrated in figure 10.2.72. Beyond the particle

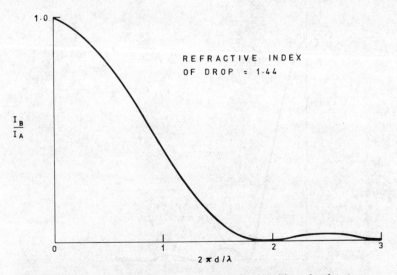

Figure 10.2.71 Ratio of the intensity I_B of light scattered by a droplet at an angle close to 180° with respect to the incident beam to the intensity I_A of light scattered in a direction close to that of the incident beam as a function of $2\pi d/\lambda$, where d is the particle diameter, and λ is the wavelength of the incident light. Calculated from data of Engelhard & Friess (1937).

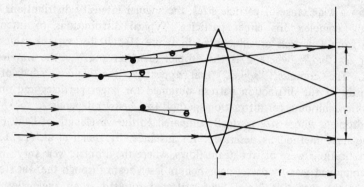

Figure 10.2.72   Diffraction of a plane parallel beam of light by a particle stream.

field, the light passes through a lens that focuses the original beam to a point at the focal plane, at distance f from the lens. If the beam is of monochromatic, coherent light, diffraction patterns are formed by each of the particles. Light diffracted at an angle θ from *any position* within the particle field passes through the lens and impinges on the focal plane at a distance $r = \theta f$ from the axis. If a cylindrical parallel beam, rather than a plane parallel beam, is used, then, if the particles are of uniform size, the intensity is distributed over the focal plane in the manner illustrated schematically in figure 10.2.73. A more detailed discussion of this functional dependence is given by Azzopardi (1977). The radial distribution of intensity can be determined by placing a series of annular-ringed detectors in the

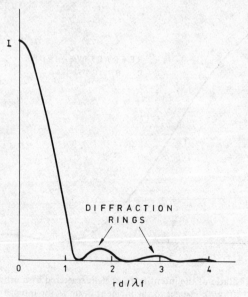

Figure 10.2.73   Schematic representation of the intensity distribution over the focal plane in the multidetector diffraction technique.

focal plane. As will be seen from figure 10.2.73, a wide range of intensities is encountered, and the advantage of annular rings of given width is that the further the distance from the axis, the larger the area over which light is collected.

Normally, there is a distribution of drop sizes; to interpret the intensity distribution, therefore, it is necessary to assume some functional form for the drop-size distribution. For instance, one may use the Rosin-Rammler distribution

$$R = \exp\left[-\left(\frac{d}{X}\right)^N\right] \qquad [10.2.72]$$

where R is the weight or volume fraction of particles larger than diameter d, and X and N are characterizing parameters. To obtain a drop-size distribution from the measured intensity distribution, an iterative process is employed in which X and N are optimized.

The multiple-detector diffraction technique as described above was due originally to Swithenbank et al. (1976). An instrument based on their technique is now available commercially (Malvern Instruments Ltd., England). Systematic tests of the technique are described by Negus & Azzopardi (1978), and the application of the technique to drop-size measurements in annular flow is reported by Azzopardi et al. (1978). The apparatus used in this latter work is illustrated schematically in figure 10.2.74. A parallel light beam arising from a helium-neon laser was passed through a droplet stream arising from an annular flow (the liquid film having been removed); the diffracted light fell onto a detector that was linked with a minicomputer, which interpreted the output to give the drop-size distribution.

Problems in applications Although the multidetector diffraction method has proved robust and effective, its basic weakness is that a particular form of droplet distribution must be assumed *ab initio*. Azzopardi et al. (1978) confirmed the applicability of the chosen distribution (Rosin-Rammler) to annular flow measurements, but this would not necessarily apply in all situations.

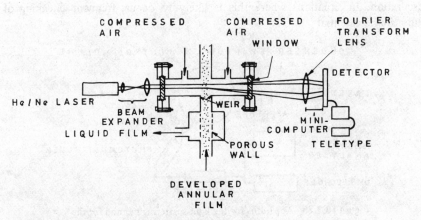

Figure 10.2.74 Application of the multidetector diffraction method for drop-size distribution in annular flow (Azzopardi et al. 1978).

Droplet- and Bubble-Size Measurement Using the Scattered-Pulse Amplitude Method

Principle of operation   In this method, the amplitude of pulses of light scattered by individual droplets or bubbles is measured, and the pulse amplitude is related to bubble size either by calibration or theoretically. An example of the application of this technique to bubble-size measurement is that of Keller (1972), whose apparatus is illustrated in figure 10.2.75. Bubbles passing through the control volume scattered a pulse of light into the photomultiplier, the amplitude of the pulse being characteristic of the bubble size. Keller calibrated the system using electrolytically generated bubbles. The minimum size that could be produced by this technique was about 10 μm; for smaller sizes, a theoretical estimate was made of the variation of scattering intensity with bubble radius.

The scattered-pulse amplitude method has been applied to drop-size measurement by, for instance, Lee and co-workers at the State University of New York at Stony Brook (Lee & Srinivasan 1977, 1978a, b; Srinivasan & Lee 1978). The relationship between pulsed amplitude and droplet diameter was established by calibration with droplets of known size; the calibration curve is illustrated in figure 10.2.76. Lee and co-workers also used the scattered pulse to deduce the velocity of the droplet (via laser-Doppler anemometry, section 10.2.2.5).

Problems in applications   A major difficulty is that of distinguishing between the pulses received from large droplets passing only partially through the scattering volume and smaller droplets passing totally through it. Lee and co-workers overcame this problem by using the simultaneous velocity data, coupled with the pulse-duration data, to provide an estimate of the track length of the centerpoint of the scattering volume through the droplet. Only those pulses for which the pulse amplitude indication of the drop size and the track length were in agreement were accepted for droplet-size measurement. That is, measurements were made only when the scattering volume tracked axially through the droplet.

Another problem in using absolute amplitude measurements is that of window obscuration. In situations where this is likely to occur, frequent checking of the calibration is essential.

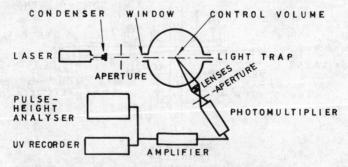

Figure 10.2.75   Apparatus for the light-scattering method for the determination of the size of cavitating bubbles (Keller 1972).

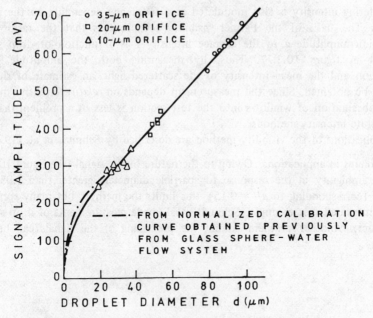

Figure 10.2.76   Calibration curve relating laser-Doppler anemometer burst amplitude and drop size (Lee & Srinivasan 1978b).

Droplet-Size Measurement Using the Farmer Visibility Technique

Principle of operation   The principle of the Farmer (1972) visibility technique is illustrated in figure 10.2.77. Droplets pass through a fringe pattern set up at the intersection of two laser beams (see figure 10.2.67). A droplet of small size compared with the width of the dark and light fringes generated at the beam-crossing point gives a scattering signal fluctuating between zero intensity and the maximum amplitude (figure 10.2.77). A larger droplet, on the other hand, always lies partly within one of the light fringes, and there is always scattering, although

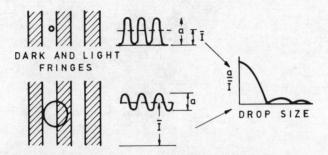

Figure 10.2.77   Principle of the Farmer (1972) visibility technique for drop-size measurement.

the scattering intensity is also modulated at a frequency depending on the droplet velocity. The basis of the Farmer visibility technique is that the ratio of the modulation amplitude a to the average intensity $\bar{I}$ is a function of drop size, as sketched in figure 10.2.77. Thus, by measuring both the amplitude of the modulation and the mean intensity of the scattered light, an estimate of the drop size can be obtained. Since the measurement depends on *relative* intensity measurements, obscuration of windows into the test section is less of a problem than with the absolute intensity methods.

Applications of the visibility method are described by Schmidt et al. (1976).

Problems in applications   Owing to the nature of the signal (see figure 10.2.77), there is ambiguity in the response for particle diameters greater than 1.05 fringe spacings (corresponding to $a/\bar{I} = 0.15$); this limits the method, but many sprays can still be measured (for example, Schmidt et al. made measurements of drop sizes up to 90 μm). Another problem is that the processing of the signals can be quite expensive.

10.3 Local Measurement Techniques for Statistical Analysis

J. M. Delhaye

Two-phase flow modeling efforts require, among other information, local instantaneous measurements of phase density functions, liquid and gas velocities, interfacial passage frequencies, and liquid and vapor temperatures and their statistical characteristics, such as probability density functions and spectral densities. The purpose of these measurements is to obtain data regarding interfacial area densities and correlation coefficients between void and velocity, void and energy, etc., and to verify hypotheses regarding the shape of void, velocity, and temperature profiles, their interrelations, and their statistical variations. A detailed review of transient and statistical measurement techniques for two-phase flows, including local techniques, can be found in the paper by Jones & Delhaye (1976).

10.3.1 ELECTRICAL PROBES

The first requirement to be met when using an electrical probe in two-phase flow is that one phase has a significantly different electrical conductivity from the other. Consequently, variations in conductance permit the measurement of the local void fraction and the arrival frequency of the bubbles at a given point in a continuous, conducting fluid. By using a double probe, a transit velocity can be measured, but one has to be very careful when giving a physical significance to this velocity (Galaup 1975; Delhaye & Achard 1977).

Figure 10.3.1 shows the classical electrical diagram of a resistive probe, while figure 10.3.2 displays a typical probe geometry. Impedance changes due to the passage of bubbles at the tip of the probe produce a fluctuation in the output signal. One of the principal features that differentiates electrical circuits of the type shown in figure 10.3.1 is the electrical supply. Direct-current supply requires low voltages to reduce electrochemical phenomena on the sensor. The resultant electronics may become troublesome, and sensors may still sustain alteration owing to electrochemical deposits at low flows. When an alternating-current supply is used, phase changes are detected by amplitude modulation of the alternating output signal. This technique has been used by several investigators to eliminate the

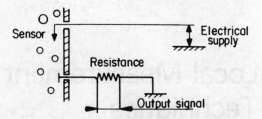

Figure 10.3.1 Electrical diagram of a resistive probe.

electrochemical phenomena on the sensor. When high-speed flows are investigated, the required supply frequency can be very high (for example, 1 MHz), and much trouble occurs with the electronics. Galaup (1975) used a supply frequency lower than the frequency of the physical phenomenon, eliminating electrochemical effects and providing pseudo-dc operation in each half wave.

According to the way in which the sensor is energized, the ideal output signal of a resistive probe is either a binary-wave sequence, or a sequence of bursts of constant-amplitude oscillations separated by zero-voltage zones. Actually, the output signal is mishapen with respect to the ideal signal because of the interface deformations. The true signal is generally transformed into a binary sequence with the help of a trigger level. Galaup (1975) used a level adjustment based upon a comparison between the integrated void profile and the line void fraction obtained with a gamma-ray-absorption method.

10.3.2 OPTICAL PROBES

An optical probe is sensitive to the change in the refractive index of the surrounding medium and is thus responsive to interfacial passages, enabling measurements of local void fraction and of interface passage frequencies to be obtained even in a nonconducting fluid. By using two sensors and a cross-correlation method, some information may be obtained on a transit velocity (Galaup 1975).

A tiny optical sensor was proposed by Danel & Delhaye (1971) and developed by Galaup (1975). This probe consists of a single optical fiber, 40 μm in diameter. The overall configuration is shown in figure 10.3.3. The active element of the probe

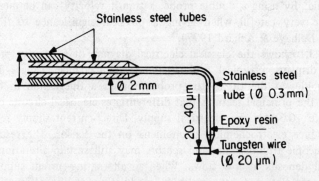

Figure 10.3.2 Miniature probe geometry (Lecroart & Porte 1971).

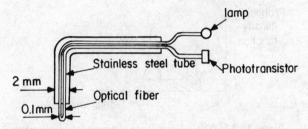

Figure 10.3.3 U-shaped fiber-optical sensor (Danel & Delhaye 1971).

is obtained by bending the fiber into a U shape. The entire fiber, except the U-shaped bend, is protected inside a stainless steel tube, 2 mm in diameter. The active part of the probe, shown in figure 10.3.4, has a characteristic size of 0.1 mm.

Signal analysis is accomplished through an adjustable threshold that enables the signal to be transformed into a binary signal. Consequently, the local void fraction is a function of this threshold, which is adjusted and then held fixed during a traverse to obtain agreement between the profile average and a gamma-ray measurement of the line void fraction. Experimental results for void profiles in Freon two-phase flow with phase change and in air-water flow are given by Galaup (1975).

10.3.3 THERMAL ANEMOMETERS

It has been found that hot-wire or hot-film anemometry can be used in two-component two-phase flow or in one-component two-phase flow with phase change. In the first case, e.g., an air-water flow, it is possible to measure the local void fraction, the instantaneous velocity, and the turbulence intensity of the liquid phase. In the second case, however, e.g., a steam-water flow, it has been so far impossible to obtain consistent results on liquid velocity measurements. Nevertheless, in both cases, the anemometer gives a signal that is characteristic of the flow pattern, although the signal is misshapen because of the interaction between the probe and the pierced interfaces (Bremhorst & Gilmore 1976; Remke 1978).

It is evident that if the gas and liquid signals could be separated, the turbulent

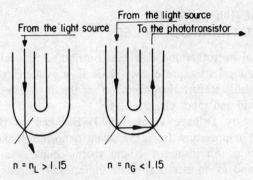

Figure 10.3.4 Active part of the U-shaped fiber-optical sensor (Danel & Delhaye 1971).

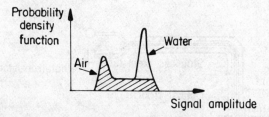

Figure 10.3.5   Typical amplitude histogram of anemometer signal (Delhaye 1969).

structure of the liquid phase could be obtained. To achieve this separation, Delhaye (1969) and Galaup (1975) used the amplitude probability density function of the output signal (figure 10.3.5). In a first approximation, the local void fractions were calculated as the ratio of the hatched area to the total area. The separation line was set to ensure the identity between the averaged value of the local void fraction and the line void fraction measured by means of a gamma-ray-absorption technique. The liquid time-averaged velocity and the liquid turbulent intensity were calculated from the nonhatched area of the amplitude histogram (figure 10.3.5) and the calibration curve of the probe immersed in the liquid. The same method was used by Serizawa et al. (1975), Herringe & Davis (1976), and Remke (1976) for measuring the turbulent characteristics of air-water two-phase flow in a pipe. A different signal processing was proposed by Resch and co-workers (1972, 1974, 1975) in a study of bubbly two-phase flow in a hydraulic jump. The analog signal from the anemometer is digitally analyzed according to a conditional sampling. Another technique was proposed by Jones (1973), who used a discriminator that had a cutoff level depending on the local velocity.

For steam-water flow, Hsu et al. (1963) noticed that the only reference temperature is the saturation temperature. If water velocity measurements are carried out, the probe temperature must not exceed saturation temperature by more than 5°C to avoid nucleate boiling on the sensor. Conversely, if only a high sensitivity to phase change is sought, then the superheat should range between 5 and 55°C, causing nucleate boiling to occur on the probe.

10.3.4   PHASE-INDICATING MICROTHERMOCOUPLES

Although the classical microthermocouple has contributed to a large extent to the understanding of the local structure of two-phase flow with change of phase, it has not provided any reliable statistical information on the distribution of the temperature between the liquid and vapor phases.

The work done by Delhaye et al. (1973) is based on the possibility of separating the liquid temperature from the steam temperature and of determining the local void fraction. An insulated 20-μm thermocouple was used both as a temperature sensor and as an electrical phase indicator by means of a Kohlrausch bridge that sensed the presence of conducting liquid between the noninsulated junction and the ground. The phase signal was used to route the thermocouple

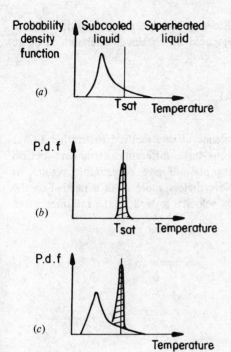

Figure 10.3.6 Subcooled boiling temperature histograms (Delhaye et al. 1973). (*a*) Liquid temperature. (*b*) Steam temperature. (*c*) Unseparated histogram.

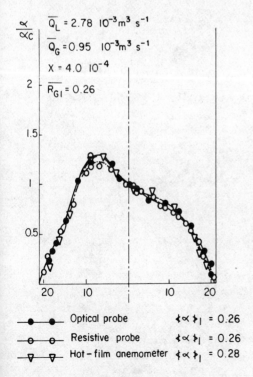

Figure 10.3.7 Comparison of results of optical, resistive, and thermal probe techniques in air-water flow (Galaup 1975). $\bar{Q}$ = volumetric flow rate; x = quality; $\overline{R_{G_1}}$ = time-averaged line void fraction measured with gamma rays; α = local void fraction; α_c = centerline local void fraction; $\langle\alpha\rangle_1$ = averaged void fraction measured on the profile.

signal to two separate subgroups of a multichannel analyzer. As a result, separate histograms of liquid and vapor temperatures could be obtained, as shown in figure 10.3.6, for subcooled boiling.

10.3.5 RELIABILITY OF LOCAL MEASUREMENTS

Questions on reproducibility and the equivalence of one method to another always arise. It is encouraging that the results from three different instruments—optical probe, thermal anemometer, and resistive probe—all give comparable results, as shown by Galaup (1975) in figure 10.3.7. Nevertheless, more work is needed on the cross-correlation technique to obtain the gas velocity as well as the interface speed of displacement.

10.4 Aerosol Measurement and Analysis

A. Lieberman

10.4.1 INTRODUCTION

Aerosols can be broadly defined as random dispersions of liquid, solid, or combined liquid-solid particles within a body of gas. Aerosols pervade every human activity. In some cases they are desired, as are the popular aerosol spray products and industrial cooling sprays and clouds. In other cases, the aerosols are undesirable adjuncts to normal life, in the form of particulate air pollution, smokes, or industrial process emissions.

The composition, shape, and size of the particular aerosol depends on its generation process and the environment that it may encounter. In common with many multiphase systems, the discontinuous particle phase is randomly distributed within the gas phase. The particles are in motion relative to one another because of external forces of gravity, electric or thermal energy gradients, or gas-molecule bombardment. Since the aerosol particles are present in a range of sizes depending on the nature of the formation process and the age of the aerosol, the number and concentration of particles varies from place to place within an air parcel and changes with time. The aerosol can be defined as being in a state of quasi-stability, mainly because the particles usually are large enough compared to gas molecules so that their reaction to external forces is related to their mass. At the same time, they are small enough so that aerodynamic effects (depending on surface and shape) are significant in comparison to inertial effects (see figure 10.4.1).

10.4.1.1 Measurement Objectives

To define hazards due to aerosol effects or to follow processes that can be traced by aerosol generation, it is often useful to characterize the aerosols in terms of their particle size and size distribution, particle concentration, or particle composition. Particle size is typically defined in terms of a linear, area, or volume dimension. The dimension is usually stated in terms of an equivalent sphere. Equivalency is based on the physical function that is being measured. Thus, diameters representing length, surface area, volume, specific surface, and settling rate of an equivalent

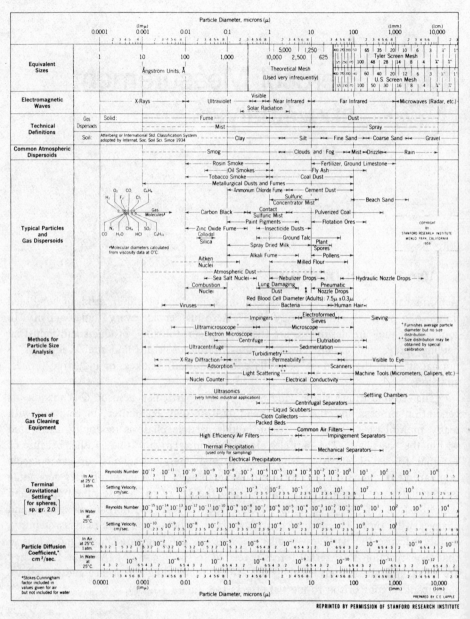

Figure 10.4.1   Characteristics of particles and particle dispersoids (Lapple 1961). Reprinted by permission of Stanford Research Institute.

sphere are determined. The choice of a specific diameter representation depends on the process variable that is under study. For example, a diameter based on equivalent area is of importance in defining paint or pigment materials, whereas deposition in the respiratory tract or other curved ducts is related to the mass and aerodynamic diameters of the particles. Reaction rates, droplet growth, etc., are related to particle surface area. Table 10.4.1 presents a number of useful size parameters.

Most aerosol systems contain particles with a distribution of sizes. In many cases, the distribution is monomodal and can be described by a logarithmic probability function, particularly if the diameter of concern is the arithmetic mean rather than a surface or volume mean diameter. Geometric standard deviations in urban aerosols range from 2 to 6.

Because of the phenomena leading to particle generation and removal in an aged aerosol, the concept of a self-preserving size distribution was developed by Friedlander (1965). The self-preserving size distribution is described as

$$\frac{dn}{dr} = Cr^{-a}$$

where n is the number of particles per unit volume, r is the particle radius, C is the concentration parameter of the particular aerosol distribution, and a is a constant ranging from 3 to 4 for most cases. If one observes an aerosol size distribution based on surface area or volume, then in most aerosols the increasing contribution as particle size increases indicates that a multimodal distribution is present. Typically, a trimodal aerosol distribution is found (Whitby 1978). One mode occurs at approximately 0.01 μm, due to generation of primary particles from vapor; a second mode occurs at approximately 0.3 μm due to coagulation and condensation growth of the primary particles; a third mode occurs at 5–15 μm, due to the presence of mechanically generated particles.

In characterizing an aerosol, one defines the composition of the aerosol particles. For the most part, this procedure involves collection of the particulate material on a suitable substrate to concentrate the particulate material to a level where conventional wet chemistry or absorption or emission spectroscopy can be used to define the particulate material.

In defining aerosols to ensure protection against hazard, two situations can be

Table 10.4.1 Mathematical Definitions of Average Diameters

Average diameter	Symbol	Mathematical definition	Description
Arithmetic mean	d_{av}	$\Sigma nd/\Sigma n$	Sum of all diameters divided by the total number of particles
Surface mean	d_s	$\sqrt{\Sigma nd^2/\Sigma n}$	Diameter of a hypothetical particle having average surface area
Volume mean	d_v	$\sqrt[3]{\Sigma nd^3/\Sigma n}$	Diameter of a hypothetical particle having average volume; the median value of this frequency distribution is often called the mass median diameter
Volume-surface mean	d_{vs}	$\Sigma nd^3/\Sigma nd^2$	Average size based on the specific surface per unit volume
Weight mean diameter	d_w	$\Sigma nd^4/\Sigma nd^3$	Average size based on the unit weight of the particles

described. In the first situation the aerosol particles may be toxic, and the concentration in the inhalable particle-size ranges must be limited to no more than a maximum concentration as specified by industrial hygiene or toxicological standards. The aerosols are described in terms of total mass of particulate material in the inhalable size, defined in terms of aerodynamic diameters. The second hazard situation is typified by an assembly area in an optical or microelectronic manufacturing plant. The aerosol concentration and size are limited to ensure that the number of particles that may be deposited on or ingested into mechanical systems is maintained below a predetermined maximum. In this case, the particle concentration is defined in terms of number of particles per unit volume of air, and particle size is defined by a surface mean diameter or other optically defined diameter.

Air pollution control regulations define either the total mass of particles in a given volume of air or the visibility loss due to the aerosol in a linear traverse of air. In industrial hygiene applications, the total mass of specific materials per unit volume of air is defined, with the exception of those environments where asbestos fibers may be present. In this case, a maximum number of fibers per unit volume of air is specified. Another requirement exists in defining the operation of aerosol-dispensing devices. A mass emission rate is specified; at the same time a mean particle diameter and upper and lower particle-size limits are usually indicated.

Some other aerosol measurement and control requirements exist in a number of isolated systems. For example, military and industrial marking smokes should contain a majority of particles within a fairly narrow size distribution, based on maximum visibility for particles whose diameter is close to the wavelength of visible light. Cloud seeding requires the generation of silver iodide particles whose sizes are slightly under 1 μm in diameter for optimum nucleation effectiveness. Diesel and jet engine fuel spray nozzles produce droplet aerosols whose size must be limited; if too large, they cause excessive smoke, while excessive energy requirements exist for production of overly small particles. The effective design of stack emission cleanup systems requires that the smoke particle diameter be known. Aerogenic vaccines can be most effective when the particles are small enough to be retained within the lower portions of the repiratory system but sufficiently large to transport an effective quantity of therapeutic material.

Thus it is seen that the measurement objective defines the size and concentration parameter that are selected, and it often defines the sample size measurement and sample collection procedure as well.

10.4.1.2 Measurement Protocol

The first step in carrying out an aerosol measurement or characterization is to specify the size, concentration, or composition parameter that is of concern. Next, one should attempt to indicate an overall range of variation that can be expected or is within the area of interest. Once these two broad levels are defined, it is possible to select optimum devices and protocols from the wide range of techniques that are available.

The next step is to select the measurement method that will provide maximum information on the parameter of concern. This method may produce information on mass concentration, area measurement, particle number, particle concentration, particle radioactivity, viable particle level, specific element or compound composition, etc. Then one chooses a method of collection or observation that will produce a sample that can be easily handled within the selected measurement method. As one obvious example of the basis for choice, compare the requirement of examination by scanning electron microscope for particle morphology with the requirement of determination of bacterial content. In the first case, one would deposit particles on an electron microscope screen; in the second case, one would deposit directly on the surface of the nutrient medium. If one is concerned with visibility through an aerosol cloud, then collection techniques would not be considered at all. A direct optical determination would be made within the cloud.

Following the measurement of the aerosol parameters of concern, best advantage must be taken of the data obtained. Often, a simple mathematical description of the particle-size distribution can be defined; in some cases mass concentrations are specified, and in other cases the fractional composition of various materials is defined. The levels of particular material components are specified. Many aerosol measurements are carried out to ensure that a maximum level of a particular component or parameter is never exceeded. In this case, it may be adequate to ensure that no data are produced until that level is exceeded.

The remainder of this section is a description of aerosol measurement techniques; first techniques involving collected samples are presented, and then *in situ* techniques. Included in the former are a discussion of sample-handling methods and some comments on the analysis of collected samples.

10.4.2 COLLECTION SYSTEM OPERATION

Successful aerosol collection requires (1) that a sample be acquired from the environment to be characterized and (2) that the sample be collected or deposited on a suitable surface in a suitable container. The sample must be representative of the environment and must be large enough to permit accurate and statistically valid characterization, but not so large as to disturb the environment from which it was removed. Moreover, it is necessary to remove a sample of particles and gas from the environment and transport it to a collecting system with due consideration for the fact that the aerosol particles are not stably embedded within the gas phase.

10.4.2.1 Sample-Acquisition Considerations

Aerosol sampling conditions can be considered as being of three general types. In the first, the aerosol exists within a reaction chamber, with the gas and aerosol flow fields being generated primarily as a result of nonuniform thermal effects. In this situation, the aerosol generation or the process that is being investigated is recent. In the second situation, the aerosol is well aged and exists in an open atmosphere with perhaps a prevailing horizontal wind component, but overall the air velocity changes randomly in the horizontal and vertical directions. In the third situation, the aerosol is transported in a duct at a fixed, definable velocity and aerosol distribution across the duct.

Since many aerosols have a log-normal particle-size distribution and a random spatial concentration distribution, geometric mean values are often used in describing size concentrations or composition distributions in aerosols. If the sample size is too small, then errors can be unacceptably high, as is shown by Michels (1977). Michels points out that as the geometric standard deviation of the distribution (the standard deviation of the distribution of ratios of values around the mean value) increases, the sample size must be increased accordingly to ensure that the statistical error is acceptably low.

Aerosol sampling in calm air requires that both the gas and the particles be sampled without changing the relative location of particles in the gas sample. However, in withdrawing the sample, it is necessary to accelerate the aerosol into the sampler inlet. The relaxation time for gas molecules is essentially zero; the relaxation time for aerosol particles increases with the particle size.

The *relaxation time* is the time for a particle initially at rest to acquire $1/e$ of the velocity of a suddenly applied airstream. It is defined as

$$\tau = \frac{2}{9} \frac{r^2 \rho}{\mu_G}$$

where τ is the relaxation time, ρ is the particle density, and μ_G is the gas viscosity.

The *stopping distance* of a particle is the distance that particles travel in zero-velocity air when they are injected with an initial velocity U. The stopping distance is defined as the product of relaxation time and initial velocity.

Since the gas, which is initially at rest, must accelerate as it approaches the sampling inlet, the aerosol particles tend to fall behind, owing to their inertia, which is related to the particle relaxation time. It has been suggested (Davies 1968) that the sampler inlet radius be specified in terms of the particle relaxation time (or stopping distance) and that, at the same time, the air-sample velocity into the sampler inlet be appreciably larger than the terminal sedimentation velocity of the largest particles to be sampled. Limitations on the range of sampler inlet radius and velocities have been discussed in some detail by Breslin & Stein (1975) and by Fuchs (1975). Although Davies recommends that the air velocity at the inlet be at least 25 times the sedimentation velocity of the largest particles and that the inlet radius be at least 5 times the particle stopping distance, Breslin & Stein indicate that Davies' conditions are overly restrictive and that good sampling can be accomplished with the ratio of inlet radius to stopping distance being 1.5 or more, rather than 5 or more. Observation of the performance of several commercial air samplers indicates that Davies' recommendations are too restrictive and that the smaller sampler inlets operate quite satisfactorily.

In free air sampling, where the aerosol is in a state of almost constant horizontal and vertical motion, good sampling over the maximum particle size range should be done isokinetically. This same requirement holds if the aerosol is flowing in a duct. Because of the difficulty of matching air velocity in free air, a vertical probe with an inlet directed upward is frequently used. For sample flow rates of 20–30 L/min, a tube with a 1-cm inside diameter is adequate. The inlet should be conical, with a 60° flare opening to approximately 3 cm. With this arrangement, particle losses of no more than 10% will occur for unit-density particles as large as

20 μm in diameter. The axis of the sampling probe, in either case, should be parallel to the flow lines in the gas stream, and the mean flow velocity in the probe should be equal to the flow velocity in the gas being sampled. If the duct velocity is less than the gas flow velocity, then the gas flow lines diverge at the entry to the sampling probe, and the particles drift across the flow lines owing to their inertia. The concentration in the sample becomes larger than that in the gas. If the sample probe velocity is greater than the gas flow velocity, the flow lines converge at the probe entry, and particle inertia causes the particles to miss the probe, resulting in an indication of lower-than-actual concentration.

Obviously, the controlling factor is the Stokes number, defined as the product of original gas velocity and relaxation time, divided by the diameter of the sampling probe. For particles with sufficiently small Stokes number (less than 10), the error due to anisokinetic sampling is negligible. For particles smaller than 1-2 μm in diameter, isokinetic sampling requirements can be ignored in most situations. Figure 10.4.2 shows some anticipated anisokinetic sampling errors.

In the open atmosphere, the wind speed varies markedly, and the wind direction fluctuates, both horizontally and vertically. In the horizontal plane, the wind can shift through a 360° range in a very short period of time. Thus, changes in both isokinetic and isoaxial sampling can occur quite rapidly. It is suggested,

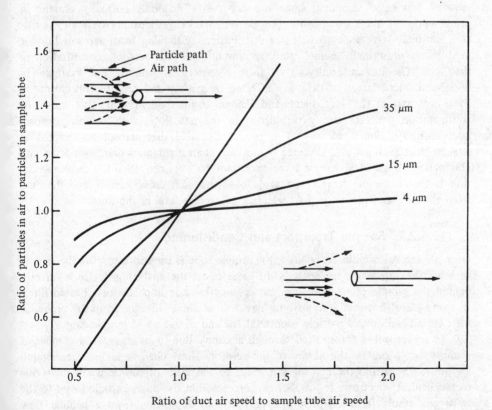

Figure 10.4.2 Anisokinetic sampling effects.

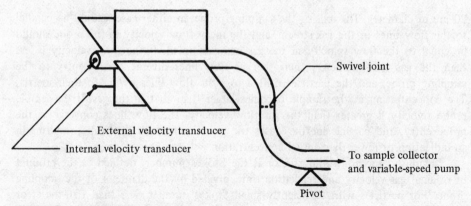

Figure 10.4.3 Automatic isokinetic sampler.

therefore, that the sampling probe be attached to a low-inertia vane that is mounted on a three-dimensional bearing, along with a means of maintaining isokinetic sampling in an automatic manner as described by Rosinski & Lieberman (1956). The operating principle of their device is shown in figure 10.4.3.

Aerosol sampling from ducts, whether they are horizontal or vertical, invariably requires isokinetic sampling, since the particulate materials normally present in process line gas ducts, combustion process vent stacks, gas cleaning system exhausts, etc., normally have wide particle-size distributions. Sampling from aerosols flowing in ducts is additionally complicated by nonuniformity of aerosol concentration in the duct. The nonuniformity arises from a variety of sources. For example, in horizontal ducts, larger particles are affected by gravity and tend to concentrate in the lower part of the duct; bends and changes in duct orientation, duct width, or configuration generate strong turbulence in the gas flow, with resulting aerosol nonuniformity. For these reasons, it is recommended that aerosol be sampled in straight duct sections at a distance of not less than eight duct diameters from any obstruction. If an ideal sample location cannot be obtained, then the recommendation is that a sample traverse be made over the duct cross section, and the data from all sample points be used to calculate an average level in the duct.

10.4.2.2 Sample Transport and Conditioning

Once an aerosol sample is acquired, the sample tube is used to transport the sample to a location or device for analysis. In some cases, the analyzing device is directly behind the sample probe inlet, e.g., an in-stack cascade impactor or a heated filter. In many cases, however, the analytic device is at some distance from the probe, as for example, an optical particle counter at the end of 2–5 m of sample tube.

As an aerosol is transported through a sample line to an analyzer, a number of changes can occur in the nature of the aerosol. These changes include accelerated agglomeration within the aerosol and losses to the walls of the transport duct, due to mechanical, electrostatic, or thermal forces within the duct. Particle losses to the walls can result from diffusive and gravitational deposition from a laminar flow stream, from turbulent deposition (at higher flow speeds), or from centrifugal effects in curved ducts due to the inertia of the particulate material. Wall losses in a duct of uniform cross section vary directly with the Reynolds number for fluid flow, the duct line length, the particle mass, and the aerosol space charge, and inversely with the radius of curvature in the sample duct. As found by Sehmel (1970), large losses can occur in a sample tube of relatively small radius of curvature. As particle size increases, losses reach a maximum and then begin to decrease again. The latter is due to reentrainment of particles that have been deposited on the duct walls as the deposit height exceeds the boundary layer. Significant losses can also occur in a straight section of duct, primarily due to turbulent diffusion, as found by Wasan et al. (1973). Note that this work is based on theoretical analysis and does not include the effect of reentrainment of solid particles. Thus, for solid particles, wall losses in tubing will be somewhat smaller than those indicated here. However, if liquid droplets are present, reentrainment does not occur, and particles lost to the duct walls remain entrapped. For these reasons, sample transport ducts should be as short as possible, and changes in direction should be avoided as much as possible. If curved sample ducts are required, then the radius of curvature should never be smaller than 15 cm. Smooth inner surfaces as recommended.

One additional point must be considered in sampling from ducts. In many cases, the gas phase in a duct is at an elevated temperature and contains condensable vapors. When the sample is withdrawn, it may be necessary to maintain the sample temperature above the dew point for the vapors within the duct. Otherwise, condensation will occur, and particularate material will be indicated as being much larger than it actually is, or the particles may be lost via solution within droplets formed by condensation.

10.4.2.3 Sample-Collection Mechanisms

Once the aerosol sample has been satisfactorily removed from the overall aerosol and has been transported to a point where it can be retained or deposited for analysis or observation, there is a choice of collection mechanisms. One can retain the aerosol sample in an enclosure where the only force affecting it is gravity. In this situation, the gas molecules remain suspended, but the particles settle under the influence of gravity. Practically speaking, sedimentation collectors are seldom used for particles smaller than 10 μm in diameter.

It is also possible to collect particles from an aerosol by causing the aerosol fluid trajectory to be curved. This can be done by using a gas centrifuge, where centrifugal forces result in deposition of the aerosol particles on the interior surfaces of the centrifuge while the gas continues in the curved trajectory; alternatively, the gas streamlines can be curved by passing the aerosol through a cyclone, where circular flow is obtained by using a tangential entry or suitable vanes. Cyclone collectors are used for particles larger than a few micrometers in diameter, while centrifuges are capable of collecting submicron particles. Figure 10.4.4 shows a typical tangential-entry cyclone configuration. Typical air-sampling cyclones with tangential entry are from 1 to 10 cm in diameter, with lengths 5–8 times the diameter. Airflows range from 2 L/min for the 1-cm cyclone (typically used to

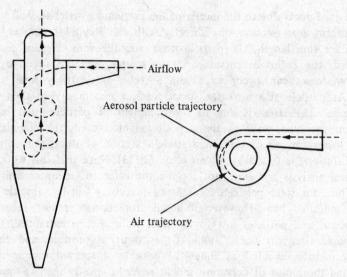

Figure 10.4.4   Tangential-entry cyclone.

classify the respirable fraction of dust in the atmosphere) to several hundred liters per minute for the larger cyclones. Most air-sampling cyclones use tangential entry.

An inertial collector can be used to collect particles significantly smaller than those removed only by gravity. The inertial collector makes use of the phenomenon that particles moving in an air streamline tend to continue in the original direction when the streamline is deflected by an obstacle. The particles impact on the obstacle and can be retained by a suitable adhesive coating for subsequent analysis. Most inertial collectors in use today accelerate the aerosol stream by passing it through a nozzle that faces an impaction plate. By careful design of the nozzle and selection of nozzle-to-plate distance and nozzle diameter, it is possible to collect particles equal to or larger than a preset size with a constant efficiency. Particles having sufficient inertia impact on the collection surface, and smaller particles remain suspended within the aerosol. If one then passes the aerosol through a following nozzle with higher air velocity, smaller particles are collected. As shown in figure 10.4.5, a series of nozzle-plate combinations can be arranged sequentially so as to fractionate the particles in a series of size ranges. The nozzle-plate combinations can be arranged as single nozzles with circular or rectangular cross sections or can be arranged as a number of parallel nozzles for larger total aerosol sample passage. An alternative procedure is to have a single-nozzle collection-plate system submerged below the surface of the liquid. Particles collected on the deposition plate will be washed into the liquid and retained for analysis within the liquid. Particles smaller than 1 μm can be collected at near-atmospheric pressure.

Filtration can also be used for collection from an aerosol sample. In the broadest sense, the filter can be considered as any coarse structure composed of granular or fibrous materials that possesses the ability to remove suspended material from a fluid passed through it. The filtration process can be reduced to a few universal considerations. These include fluid flow through a porous medium, deposition of particles on or within the medium, and knowledge of the total aerosol fluid that has passed through the medium. The filter medium used in any particular application is selected on the basis of the type of analysis to be performed on the selected particles. For example, visual observation indicates use of a surface collection medium. If analysis by weight is required, then high-flow, high-capacity systems of paper or glass-fiber medium retaining particles larger than a fraction of a micrometer are usually indicated. If chemical analysis is to be carried out, then the use of membranes that can be dissolved, ashed, or otherwise removed from the analytical field is indicated.

Note that the filter medium captures particles from the aerosol by the action of one or more of a number of forces. These include inertial, impaction, electrostatic, and diffusion forces. In addition to these collection mechanisms, mechanical sieving also occurs.

Filtration is one of the oldest and most reliable methods for the collection of dry, particulate materials. Filter systems are high-efficiency devices, are simple to operate and maintain, and can be selected to meet a variety of requirements. Filters can be used under high-temperature operations if suitable ceramic or metallic fibrous media are selected. A minor problem is the selection of a medium that will not adsorb reactive gases that can destroy the particulate sample as well.

Exposing particles to a high energy gradient causes them to move across the gas streamlines. The energy gradient may be electrostatic or thermal. Collection by electrostatic gradient requires first that the particle to be collected have an electric charge, and second that it be introduced into an electric field through which it is directed toward a collecting substrate maintained at a polarity opposite to that of the charged particle. An electrostatic precipitator for airborne particles is useful for collecting relatively large samples with a high collection efficiency for all practical

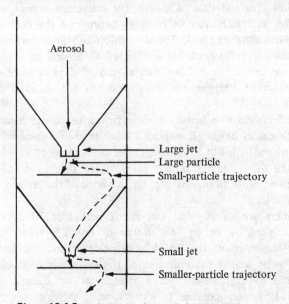

Figure 10.4.5 Schematic of cascade impactor.

sizes. Electrostatic precipitation can also be used for depositing small quantity samples directly onto an electron-microscope grid for examination. The sampling rate is not affected by mass loading or the total collected material in the sample, and the sample is in a readily recoverable form. Additional discussion is given in section 10.4.2.4.

Thermal precipitators deposit dust particles from a small volume of air onto a surface where they may be examined or counted. Deposition is accomplished by the thermophoretic force that airborne particles experience in a temperature gradient. This force causes the particles to be driven toward a cold substrate. A thermal precipitator collects particles from the smallest size that can be observed practically to those approximately 3-5 μm in diameter. Most thermal precipitators operate at a sampling rate of a few milliliters per minute. High-capacity precipitators that sample up to 30 L/min have been developed; however, these precipitators deposit the particulate material on a substrate that is several square centimeters in area. Further details are given in section 10.4.2.4.

10.4.2.4 Typical Device Operation

In this section, some representative commercially available sample-collection devices are discussed. The discussion is not designed to be all-inclusive, but rather to indicate typical operating system specifications.

Sedimentation Devices

Particulate air pollution levels are often characterized in terms of particle fallout, as well as atmospheric aerosol concentration. Results are reported in terms of mass collected per unit area and time. Although the collecting devices are quite simple, the interpretation of results may be complex because of the diverse nature of the deposition of particulate material. The deposition and precipitation of particles in collecting devices are influenced by a variety of factors, particularly changes in meteorological conditions. In addition, during the 30 days or so of exposure, many physical and chemical changes can take place in the material retained in the collection device.

The dust-fall collector is usually a glass, metal, or plastic container, 15 cm in diameter and 20 cm in height. It is placed in a stand at a level where reentrained dust from normal traffic is not lifted to its interior. A layer of liquid is often placed in the bottom of the container, with a fungicide or algicide included. Bird guards are used to prevent birds from perching on the edge of the jar and adding deposits to the fluid in the jar.

The containers are usually left out for a period of 30 days, and collected materials are analyzed by weight. An aliquot of liquid is taken after the settled material is well redispersed; the liquid is evaporated, and the settled material is analyzed in terms of weight per unit area of the collecting container. The result is then extrapolated to unit weight per square meter per month, as discussed by Paxton (1951). It is also possible to extract, with suitable solvents, the organic solubles and water-soluble components, to determine combustible materials and to report each component separately.

A variation on this technique is to use an adhesive sheet oriented with the adhesive surface upward and placed in a suitable location for a period of time ranging up to approximately 1 week, as described by Fletcher (1950). The sheet is examined visually for specific particulate contamination. Note that variations on this technique allow the use of nutrient media to replace the adhesive sheet, for analysis of viable materials.

In general, the measurement of settled particulate material is useful in determining trends in air pollution, but quantitative correlations between ambient air pollution levels in terms of mass per unit volume in the atmosphere and total number or mass of settled particles are difficult to achieve. The original basis for the use of these settling devices was that, at the time of their introduction, municipal pollution control agencies were concerned with the amount of dust that would settle or deposit on surfaces to cause soiling or corrosion. Settlement collectors were assumed to simulate the environment affected by settled dust. In addition, the costs of initial purchase and use were extremely low. Unfortunately, the data obtained by settlement collectors are grossly inadequate to define airborne materials; they are primarily used to determine long-term trends in the concentration of particles large enough to fall into or onto the devices. Perhaps their greatest value is in maintaining a historical record of information on air pollution levels.

A sedimentation device has been developed by Fleming Instruments, Ltd., in Stephenage, England, particularly for use in industrial environments. This device samples aerosol at 0.5–2 cm^3/min and introduces the stream along the axis of a horizontal settlement duct, forming part of a closed system through which clean air travels in a horizontal laminar stream. All particles are carried along the duct at the velocity of the airstream and settle on the surface at their individual falling speeds. Location and type of particle are observed on the collecting surface. Particles from 20 μm down to 1 μm can be collected from an airstream at 100 ml/min for microscopic observation of settled materials. The device is shown in figure 10.4.6.

For collecting larger samples of dust, the Hexhlet elutriator, whose operation is shown in figure 10.4.7, draws air through a large number of shallow horizontal ducts that will pass essentially all particles larger than 7 μm in diameter with a flow rate of 50 L/min, as defined by Wright (1954). Particles smaller than 7 μm in diameter are collected in a filter bag or thimble and weighed or solid-extracted to determine the total weight of "respirable" material that was in the air.

Sedimentation collectors should be used when the aerosol particles are too fragile for collection by inertial or centrifugal collectors without breakage or distortion of the particle structure. A device such as the Fleming Instruments collector is best used when information on particle morphology is desired. The Hexhlet elutriator is best suited for determination of particle mass loadings, particularly in areas where concentrations are less than 10 mg/m^3. The adhesive sheet is used where information on the morphology of depositing particles is desired. The dust-fall collector is used where one is following trends in long-term deposition rates of settleable particles.

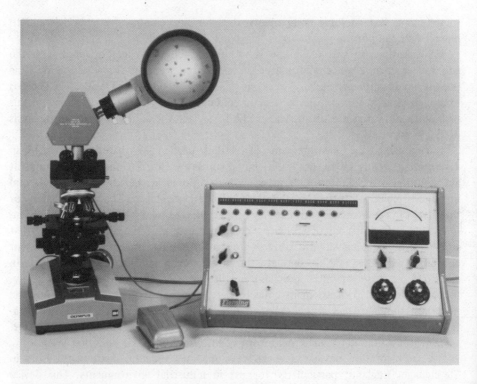

Figure 10.4.6 Fleming aerosol spectrometer.

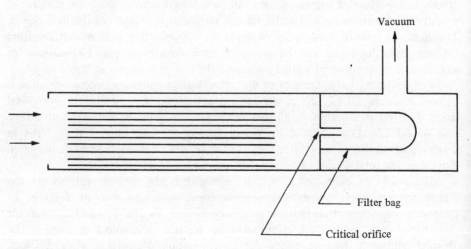

Figure 10.4.7 Hexhlet elutriator.

Cyclone Collectors

The cyclone collector is frequently used as the first stage of a personal air sampler, where information on respirable and nonrespirable aerosol concentrations is desired. A cyclone collector of 10 mm diameter at a flow rate of 2 L/min or so collects particles larger than 2–3 μm in diameter with 50% efficiency. As the flow rate increases, the retention of smaller particles also increases, as found by Chan & Lippmann (1977). Typically, the 10-mm cyclone is used in industrial environments where concentrations of up to several milligrams per cubic meter can be expected. Material collected within the cyclone is weighed for subsequent analysis of nonrespirable particles, while material that has penetrated the cyclone is collected on a backup filter and weighed to indicate the concentration of respirable particles. For the collection of large quantities of materials, cyclones of larger dimensions can be used, as was shown by Freudenthal (1971). For example, a cyclone of some 7.5 cm diameter has been operated at 2 m^3/min to remove 50% of 0.6-μm-diameter particles. Similar devices are used as first-stage collectors in stack-gas sampling at high temperatures for mass determination of combustion-product particles.

Impaction and Impingement Devices

For convenience, the term impaction is often reserved for deposition on dry or adhesive-coated surfaces, whereas deposition below the surface of a liquid is described as impingement. Impactors can have single or multiple nozzles and can be a single stage or series-operated in a cascade.

A number of single-stage impactors were developed during the period 1910–1930, particularly for use in mine atmospheres. A fixed volume of air is drawn through a conically shaped nozzle by means of a hand-operated pump. The stream of air issuing from the nozzle impacts directly upon a disk that is pretreated with adhesive. The disk is designed so that a number of target areas can be rotated under the jet for collection of several samples sequentially. The hand pump is operated so that a single-stroke sample of 5 cm^3 is obtained. Quite frequently, a prefocused microscope is incorporated in the design of the device. Samples containing up to several thousand particles larger than 1 μm can be examined. Collection efficiency is typically 60–80%.

Bacteria samples are frequently obtained by impaction of aerosol samples onto an agar or other nutrient surface. The impaction nozzle faces a disk that is rotated at a fixed rate over long periods of time, so that concentration-time data can be obtained by observing colony concentrations at specific locations on the deposit.

Several single-nozzle-per-stage cascade impactors are commercially available. Cascade impactors with single-nozzle operation can be used for the collection of particles in the size range from 200 μm down to 0.5 μm. Perhaps the first cascade impactor was designed by May (1945). This device draws 17.5 L/min of air through a series of four jets arranged at right angles to each other. Each jet orifice is smaller than the preceding one, causing the air velocity to increase as it passes from jet to jet. The size of the particles or droplets collected on microscope slides or cover glasses facing each jet decreases from the first to the fourth jet. The glass plates are generally coated with a nondrying adhesive film to cause the particles to adhere.

Single-jet impactors having up to seven stages have been produced with 50%-efficiency cutoff diameters of 0.5 μm or greater at atmospheric pressure. Note that the operation of an impactor at subatmospheric pressure results in the collection of smaller particles with equal efficiency, as found by Hering et al. (1978). For the most part, cascade impactors are operated at or near atmospheric pressure, with flow rates of 2–40 L/min, depending on the manufacturer. Collection at 50% efficiency ranges from approximately 0.5–30 μm from the last to the first stage. Concentrations of up to several grams per cubic meter can be handled, with the total dust sample load limited as the deposit on each stage builds up to the point where the jet-to-stage distance is decreased significantly. Suitable construction materials permit operation at temperatures up to several hundred degrees centigrade and in corrosive atmospheres. A typical single-jet cascade-impactor design is shown in figure 10.4.8.

The roto-rod sampler of Webster (1963)—an example of a single-stage impactor—reverses the usual process of aspirating air through the collector nozzle

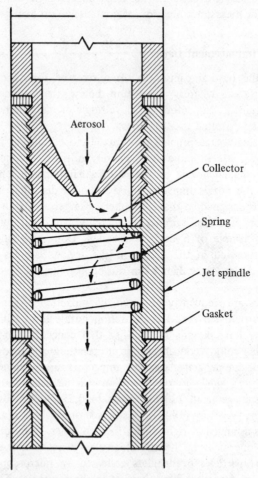

Figure 10.4.8   Single-jet cascade impactor.

and impacting on a stationary surface, by rotating a collecting rod through the relatively quiescent air. Particles are impacted on the collecting rod face for subsequent examination under a microscope; each collector rod assembly is individually calibrated to determine its sampling rate. It will effectively sample particles 10 μm in diameter and larger at an effective rate of 115 L/min; for particles 1-10 μm in diameter, a smaller rod diameter samples effectively at 40 L/min at essentially the same rotational rate.

The wet impinger is essentially a single-stage impactor. Its efficiency is kept constant by continuously washing off the collected substrate with the liquid in which the substrate is submerged. Thus, particles that have been collected are moistened and retained in the liquid. The wet impinger consists of a flat-bottom container for impaction, with a tube constricted to a jet facing the bottom of the container. Sufficient liquid is added to ensure that the bottom of the tube is covered. Air is then drawn through the tube at a rate sufficient to provide sonic or near-sonic velocity through the jet. The collection efficiency for 0.5-1-μm particles is near 90% at sample flow rates of 2-20 L/min, depending on the size of the impinger. Particles in the liquid are measured by microscopic analysis, by wet chemical or colorimetric analysis, or by depositing an aliquot of the sample on nutrient plates for bacteriological culture production.

A modification of the standard cascade impactor involves deposition of the particles from each stage on quartz crystals whose vibrational frequency is determined by the mass loading of particulate materials that have been collected on that stage. It is thus possible to monitor the mass concentration distributions of particles ranging in size from approximately 0.1 to 25 μm in up to 10 size ranges, for concentrations between 10 μg/m^3 and 65 mg/m^3.

In a standard impactor, the sampled particles are accelerated and impacted onto a plate or other collection surface. Some problems always exist in that large particles can bounce off the collection surface and become reentrained in the flow stream, or friable particles can be broken by the impaction process. A means of overcoming this difficulty was developed wherein particles impact into a void or air space rather than a solid surface and are then passed through a receiver tube to a filter medium, as described by Dzubay & Stephens (1975). The commercial version of this special-type cascade impactor samples and fractionates suspended particles into two size fractions with a cut at 3.5 μm diameter. The sampling flow rate is 49 L/min, and the concentration range is virtually without an upper limit. The device is used practically for ambient air sampling, and particles collected on the membrane filters following the virtual impaction "surface" are normally analyzed by gravimetric, radiometric, or fluorescence techniques. These and other analytic techniques are discussed in section 10.4.5.

The selection of an impactor or impinger for aerosol collection should take into account the need for sufficient material for analysis, collection requirements based on the aerodynamic size of the aerosol particles, and simplicity of operation. The choice of the number of stages is based on the objectives of the measurement and the extent to which size-concentration or size-composition information is required. Basically, the choice between a single-jet impactor and a multijet impactor depends on the cleanness of the desired cut point. The operating characteristics of single-jet systems have been studied in more detail than those of multistage devices. Cost considerations for these devices depend mainly on the number of stages and the anticipated operating environment.

Centrifugal Devices

Two general types of air centrifuges have been developed to collect particulate material from aerosols. The Goetz (1962) aerosol spectrometer is a high-rotational-speed separator in which airborne material is subjected to a constantly increasing centrifugal acceleration as it flows along two rotating helical channels. The aerosol is accelerated by a rotating cone, and deposition is achieved on a removable substrate of either filter paper or metal foil covering the inner surface of the stationary outer cone. Particles are deposited on the substrate according to size. The effective particle size that can be handled in this device is from 0.03 to 3 μm, with aerosol concentrations ranging up to approximately 1 mg/m^3. The deposit can be analyzed microscopically, by weighing, or by any microchemical procedure. This instrument is shown diagrammatically in figure 10.4.9.

To improve the resolution of aerosol centrifuge systems, the flow control can be modified somewhat. The modified flow control is designed to introduce the aerosol stream at a narrowly defined location within the centrifugal field and to minimize Coriolis forces. These effects are obtained by using air that has already passed through the centrifuge and has been stripped of particles as a sheath to contain the air sample at a specific location in the centrifugal field, as described by

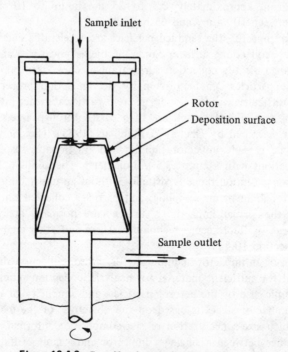

Sample inlet

Rotor

Deposition surface

Sample outlet

Figure 10.4.9 Centrifugal aerosol spectrometer.

Hochreiner (1971). This instrument is suitable for handling particles in the range 0.2–1.1 μm at a flow rate of approximately 7 cm^3/s. Concentrations are limited to a few micrograms per cubic meter to avoid multiple deposition, and analysis can be carried out by microscopic observation, weighing, or chemical analytic techniques.

Filtration Devices

Generally speaking, filtration devices involve a means of sealing a section of filter medium to a suitable support and drawing air at a known flow rate or of a fixed volume through a measured cross-sectional area of the filter medium. The filter medium can be chosen from a wide range of materials with a wide range of flow, retention, and surface characteristics. The holder for the filter medium is required primarily to provide a positive seal at the edge of the medium so that the area and flow are definitely known and uniform. Single-use, single-sample collecting filter media can be employed, or the filter medium can be arranged in a long tape so that a series of samples can be obtained at various locations on that tape.

Typical commercially available filter media include cellulose fiber papers that have the advantages of low ash content and good strength but tend to pick up water easily from the atmosphere; this last can result in difficulty in gravimetric aerosol measurements. Glass-fiber filters have been used widely for the collection of aerosol samples at high collection efficiency with low water-vapor pickup and ease of extraction for subsequent chemical analysis. Filter media consisting of porous membranes can be procured with a wide range of pore-size distributions, with the pores being extremely tortuous in cross section through the membrane; this gives an efficiency that is quite high. At the same time, the membrane materials are easily soluble and have a low ash content. Thus, analysis is made much easier. In addition, particle collection takes place at or near the surface of the membrane, which makes optical examination easy. These comments apply also to Nuclepore filters. While membranes are produced by formation of a gel containing pores, Nuclepore filters are made by placing thin polycarbonate sheets in a neutron flux that penetrates the plastic. Chemical etching subsequently penetrates and dissolves the neutron-damaged plastic in such a way that uniform pores with diameters of from 0.2 μm to approximately 10 μm can be provided. Because of their extremely smooth surface, Nuclepore filters are often used for collecting particles to be analyzed by visual or electron microscopy. For the collection of large quantities of material that will be subsequently analyzed by weight, fiber, sintered-glass, or alundum thimbles are often used.

Materials for microscopic observation or chemical analysis are often collected on a filter medium in a holder of 25–100 mm diameter. Flow rates of 0.1–50 L/min are used. If the aerosol is to be analyzed for mass concentration, then often a fibrous sheet is placed on a 20 × 25-cm open-face filter holder with flow rate of 1.5 m^3/min. For the most part, pressure drop through the filter holder is maintained at approximately $\frac{1}{3}$ bar. At higher pressures, flow control becomes prohibitively difficult, and volumetric measurement becomes uncertain in this so-called hi-vol filter.

A separate category of filtration devices is described by the term "tape sampler." This device is a sampler that passes aerosol through an area on a filter tape. The filter tape is normally of paper or a related material, 2.5 cm wide and up to several hundred meters long, and supplied in roll form. The tape is threaded from a supply spool through the sampling head onto a take-up spool. In the sampling head, the tape is supported so that an area is sealed within the sample line. Particles in the aerosol passing through the tape are collected on the medium during a fixed time period or for a fixed gas volume, on a series of spots that can be indexed for identification. In some of these devices, the quantity of aerosol collected can be identified in terms of the optical density or reflectance of the collected particulate material. In other tape samplers, the pressure differential across the filter is continuously measured to indicate the amount of particles deposited on the tape. In still others, the mass of particulate material is determined by measurement of beta-ray attenuation. (If radioactive particulate material is of interest, then the activity can be the subject of measurement rather than the means.) The tape spots can be evaluated by instrumentation contained within the tape sampler at or immediately after the time of aerosol collection; the reel of tape can be transported to the laboratory for later evaluation. For most of these devices, airflows range from 1 to 20 L/min, and concentrations up to 20 mg/m^3 can be handled. Tape samplers are typically enclosed in a weathertight container and can be operated in ambient air in almost any weather for periods up to 30 days without attention.

Analytic Electrostatic Precipitators

Electrostatic precipitators are used for aerosol collection because of a number of specific advantages. The electrostatic precipitator collects a large sample of aerosol particles with constant, relatively high efficiency over a very wide particle-size range; the sampling rate is not affected by the concentration of aerosol or the amount of material that has been collected; and the material can be deposited in a form convenient for recovery and/or examination by a number of means.

The basic design for most analytic precipitators used for the collection of material for gravimetric or chemical analysis was developed by Barnes & Penney (1938). This device is normally operated with negative corona, wherein negative high voltage is applied to a central electrode located within a grounded tube through which the aerosol passes. Typically, the grounded tube is 2.5–3.75 cm in diameter and 15–25 cm long, while the central corona wire is of the order of $\frac{1}{2}$ mm in diameter, with a sharp point, and 2.5–5 cm long. Good collection efficiency is obtained for particles ranging from 0.1 μm to approximately 100 μm in concentrations from a few micrograms per cubic meter to several hundred milligrams per cubic meter. Sampling flow rates up to 2 m^3/min can be obtained with very low pressure drop and precipitation voltages of 10–20 kV.

Some special air samplers, used for collecting particles from approximately 0.8 to 10 μm in low concentrations, have been developed for handling air sample rates up to 10,000 L/min. Air enters through a central nozzle and flows radially outward between a high-voltage plate containing a ring of corona discharge needles and a rotating collection disk maintained at ground potential; a liquid flowing slowly over the collection disk removes particles that are deposited on it. Analysis of collected materials is carried out on an aliquot of the liquid that is circulated over the collection disk.

To increase uniformity of deposition over the size range 0.02–10 μm, a two-stage sampler has been developed by Liu et al. (1967). The two-stage sampler consists of a charging section and a collection section. As aerosol passes through the charging section, the particles are subjected to alternating pulses of positive ions generated by corona discharge. When the aerosol containing the positively charged particles has filled the collecting section, a positive voltage gradient is applied, driving the charged particles to the plate which is maintained at a lower voltage. After a sufficient time to deposit all the charged particles, the voltage is shut off, allowing the collecting chamber to again fill with particles. By separating the charging section and the collecting section and using a pulsed precipitating voltage, the device is made capable of producing a uniform, representative sample that can be evaluated without bias due to particle characteristics.

The point-to-plane precipitator is not a commercially available device; however, its application is so convenient and its construction so simple that it is used in many laboratories. The design has been described by Morrow & Mercer (1964). Aerosol is passed through a tube of nonconducting material in which is located a needle maintained at a voltage of up to 20 kV. The needle is directed toward a plane that normally supports an electron microscope grid maintained at ground potential. For a cross-sectional area of air duct of approximately 0.8 cm^2 and a duct 8 cm long, airflow is typically 0.2 L/min. The separation between point and plane is approximately 1 cm. Under these conditions, a collection efficiency of 60–80% is obtained for all particles.

An electrical aerosol analyzer that operates by analyzing aerosol mobility has been developed for determination of particle-size distribution in the size range 0.01–5 μm, as described by Whitby & Clark (1966). The aerosol is passed through a unipolar electrical charger, causing each particle to acquire a charge that is simply related to its aerodynamic size. The charged aerosol flows concentrically in laminar flow to the analyzing-tube section. The aerosol flow configuration is that of an annular cylinder surrounding a core of clean air. An axially located metal rod, to which a variable negative voltage can be applied, is at the center of the analyzer tube. Small particles with high mobility are drawn to the collecting rod, and larger particles pass through the analyzer tube and are collected by a filter at the tube outlet. The electric charge on the particles on the filter is measured with an electrometer. Stepwise increases in rod voltage then cause particles of larger size to be collected by the rod. A series of stepwise increases permits measurement in, for example, 10 size ranges from 0.01 to 0.5 μm in diameter. Particle concentrations ranging from 6 to 600 μg/m^3 can be handled at a flow rate of 5 L/min. Direct readout of the mobility distribution can be obtained.

Thermal Precipitation Devices

A thermal precipitator removes particles from an aerosol by passing it through a channel in which a high temperature gradient exists. Gradients ranging upward from 750°C/cm are frequently used. To produce such high gradients, the aerosol passage is normally made quite small. Thus, aerosol sample flow rates are typically below 10 cm³/min. A thermal precipitator removes essentially all particles from below 0.01 μm in diameter upward. Because of the low precipitation velocity, shattering or breakup of agglomerated particles does not occur during sampling. On the other hand, poor adhesion of collected materials is often noted. Thermal precipitators should not be used where volatile or thermally unstable materials may be present. Much the same as in the point-to-plane electrostatic precipitator, an electron microscope grid can be placed within the thermal gradient on the cold surface and used as a convenient collection surface for particles that can be analyzed later by electron microscopy. Alternatively, a thin glass cover slip can be placed on the cold surface for visual microscope measurement.

Diffusion Batteries

The motion of particles smaller than about 0.1 μm in diameter is strongly affected by random collisions from gas molecules moving in Brownian motion. An aerosol particle in this size range travels in a random, irregular path. Its position at any given time depends on gas-molecule Brownian motion. Smaller particles with less momentum are more easily affected by gas-molecule bombardment than larger particles. Thus, when an aerosol is passed into a "diffusion battery" consisting of a number of long, narrow, parallel channels or a cluster of small parallel tubes, the probability of deposition on the tube wall becomes quite high as the particle mobility increases. From the fraction of particles deposited on the walls or, conversely, the fraction penetrating through the diffusion battery, the diffusion coefficient of the particles can be calculated. The diffusion coefficient is, of course, related to the particle size. The particle concentration penetrating the diffusion battery can be measured with a condensation nuclei counter or with an electrical aerosol analyzer, as described by Sinclair (1972). Note that the deposition on the walls of a diffusion battery is independent of the particle density and shape factor; however, aerosol charge, gas temperature, pressure, and humidity greatly influence the deposition rate.

10.4.2.5 Analytic Evaluation Techniques for Collected Aerosol Particles

Mass Determination by Weighing

Direct weight measurement of collected dust samples is carried out to provide mass concentration data in ambient air when large samples are taken or in highly polluted environments where high concentrations of particulate materials may be present. The procedure for mass determination by weighing filtered particles requires that a tare weight be determined after the filter sheet or filter thimble has been conditioned in an environment of known temperature and relative humidity. Following exposure to the aerosol cloud, the filter sheet or thimble is reconditioned with the same temperature and humidity routine as was used for the original tare determination and then weighed. A sensitive and accurate microbalance should be used, with the collected aerosol mass being no less than 10-20% of the tare weight. A great deal of care is required in handling the filter elements to ensure that particulate material is not shaken off during the handling or transport from the collection point to the area where the material is to be weighed. It is also necessary to be sure that no reactive gases that may affect the particle content are absorbed on or in the filter surface.

In some cases, the material to be weighed is collected in liquid that is evaporated before the weighing, as in the settled-dust measurement procedure. Care is required to ensure that the evaporation temperature is not so high as to volatilize low-boiling-point organic compounds, or so low as to leave undesired hydrates within the material to be weighed. Control of interferences for this process means simply that care must be taken to avoid artifact introduction.

Mass Determination by Beta-Radiation Absorption

The mass of aerosol particles can be determined by their attenuation of beta particles from radioactive sources. Typically, the procedure is applied to particles that have been collected on filter tape, as described by Nader & Allen (1960) or Dresia & Mucha (1974). The mass is determined by measuring the beta intensity transmitted through the substrate before and after particle collection. Note that with sufficient particulate material collected, it is possible to make a series of mass concentration determinations by sampling at a fixed or known flow rate and sequentially determining beta attenuation for a single deposition area. Several commercial instruments have been developed to carry out this procedure.

Beta-radiation sources such as ^{14}C, ^{147}Pm, and ^{85}Kr are typically used at levels of 50-250 μCi. Air-sampling flow rates in the range of 1-3 m^3/h are used for periods ranging from minutes to several hours. Particle mass concentrations can be determined in the range from less than 10 $\mu g/m^3$ to several hundred milligrams per cubic meter, depending on sample flow rate, sample interval, etc. Once the material has been collected, error sources involve only the possible addition or removal of collected material. The beta-absorption procedure is almost independent of interferences, since the mass absorption coefficient for low-energy beta emitters is nearly independent of the chemical composition of the material that is absorbing the beta radiation, as pointed out by Husar (1974). Thus, significant variations in the composition of collected material do not affect the accuracy of the weight measurement.

Most commercially available instruments collect atmospheric particulate material on a filter tape at a fixed flow rate. The mass concentration is reported at intervals or summarized over a long period of time. In one interesting modification, a two-stage system is described by Macias & Husar (1976) wherein particles above and within the respiratory size range can be measured independently. In this device, coarse particles larger than 3 μm in diameter are impacted on a glass-fiber filter tape; remaining particles that are smaller than the cut point of the impactor follow the airstream and are subsequently filtered through a second section of high-efficiency glass-fiber filter tape. Two independent beta-radiation absorption devices are used to indicate mass concentration in both size ranges.

Mass Determination by Quartz-Crystal Frequency Measurement

The resonant frequency of an oscillating piezoelectric quartz crystal decreases if mass is deposited on the surface of the crystal. An electronic oscillator circuit measures the resonant frequency shift of such a crystal, and by tracking the resonant frequency a deposited mass-frequency relationship can be defined. The frequency shifts downward linearly with deposited mass (Olin & Sem 1971). Particulate material is deposited directly on the face of the quartz crystal either by impaction or electrostatic precipitation, and the resonant frequency is measured continuously. Since sensitivities of the order of 5 Hz/μg can be obtained, with a sampler operating at 1 L/min, mass concentrations of atmospheric aerosols in the range 50–100 μg/m^3 can be measured in 1-min periods.

By using crystals as collection stages in a cascade impactor, particle-size distribution by weight can be determined. One commercial cascade impactor with 10 stages is available with a quartz-crystal microbalance as part of each stage. The 50% cut points for the stages range from 25 μm for the first stage to 0.05 μm for the tenth stage. In general, quartz-crystal microbalances can be used effectively for the measurement of particle concentrations from 2 μg/m^3 up to 300 mg/m^3. Sample flow rates of the order of 1 L/min are generally used.

Comparison of the readout from a quartz-crystal microbalance device with measurements made by manual filter-weight procedures indicates good correlation. Interferences in the operation of these devices include the need for cleaning of the crystals from time to time to ensure that precipitation or deposition is satisfactory and that material will adhere satisfactorily to the crystal surface. In addition, sample conditioning is required, to minimize the effect of vapor or gas adsorption and the inclusion of the mass of such adsorbed material on the readout for the collected aerosol particles.

Relative Mass by Light Transmission and Reflectance

The filter-tape sampler described briefly in section 10.4.2.4 provides an extremely convenient method of obtaining and storing samples of collected particulate material from the atmosphere. The deposits are relatively permanent, can be stored and examined at leisure, and represent a long time record of airborne-particle concentration. In most cases, the area of the filter tape used for collection is significantly darkened, particularly in an urban or industrial environment where large quantities of combustion and reaction products are in the air. The extent of darkening can be quantified by measuring the light transmitted through or reflected from the filter tape with and without deposit. The apparatus required to carry out the measurement is inexpensive and simple to operate. For this reason, fairly wide application has been made of this method for defining particulate material collection.

Although there is no direct relationship between optical measurements and particle mass, empirical relations can be calculated for specific cases if particle-size distribution, particle shape, particle composition, atmospheric relative humidity, and other factors are reasonably constant. Thus, with some calibration it is possible to determine the relative mass in terms of the light transmission or reflectance of the deposited materials. A rough relationship was obtained by Noll et al. (1968). This relationship was between visibility and the mass concentration of particles in urban air. It was concluded that low sample visibility values are associated with high mass concentrations, high turbidity, high light-scattering coefficients, and decreased visibility through the atmosphere. Thus, a conversion to direct mass measurement from transmitted light for particle deposits on a tape can be obtained for specific environments and situations.

For the most part, however, it is felt that light transmitted through deposits of collected material indicates the visibility of that quantity of material suspended in the air; light reflected from collected material indicates the degree of soiling that that material would produce if deposited on surfaces. In general, optical measurements on collected deposits of materials indicate changes over a period of time in a relative manner.

Viable-Particle Definition

For the most part, definitions of bacterial aerosols have been based on impingement on a nutrient surface and culture, followed by observation over a period of time. Since bacteria may exist in clusters or may be on the surface of otherwise inert dust particles, size discrimination may not be meaningful. For this reason, single-stage impactors depositing directly on a nutrient agar surface are used. The agar surface may be on the surface of a slowly rotating drum. At the end of a day or so of collection, bacterial colony growth is visually determined.

In a similar manner, particles can be collected on a membrane filter, and the entire filter transferred to a nutrient medium. However, collection on a membrane filter can introduce errors, since the bacteria can be dessicated by airflow through the filter, with resulting loss in bacterial colony count.

At high concentrations (either of bacteria solely or in combination with inert material) that would overload impaction devices or filters, the air can be sampled with an impinger in which the aerosol is collected below the level of a suitable liquid. The collected material can be diluted and subsequently cultured in suitable growth media to determine the concentration of viable materials. Note that the impinger inlet-tube design can provide some discrimination of particles larger than 10–50 μm in diameter.

These devices require collection and subsequent colony culture, which may take hours or days. More rapid evaluation methods have been developed. Primarily, such methods involve optical examination and image analysis of particulate materials. One example is described by Bond et al. (1972). For a specific material such as short, rodlike bacteria, visible light is scattered in such a way that peaks are encountered in the angular scattering diagram.

If suspensions such as those that might be collected in an all-glass impinger are subjected to either pulsed-dc or ac electric fields, then changes in the scattered light can be interpreted in terms of the particle size and electrical properties of the bacteria (Jennings & Morris 1974). Multiple-angle light scattering to define particle shape and structure has been used to indicate bacteria in samples. Salzman et al. (1975) have developed a flow-cell analysis instrument in which cells from a heterogeneous population are characterized by their light-scatter patterns alone. As the cells pass at high speed through a focused helium-neon laser beam, the scatter pattern from each cell is sampled simultaneously by a diode array at up to 32 angles from 0 to 30° to the laser beam axis, and the scatter pattern for each cell is transferred to a computer. If bacterial cells are in suspension, differential light scattering can be used to identify living bacterial cells (Wyatt 1968).

A somewhat unique bacterial analyzer has been described by Nelson et al. (1962). In this device, the standard microscopic analysis of stained materials has been automated. The automation requires a processing system to collect and stain bacteria and a scanner to recognize the stained organism against the background of unstained, inert particles. The instrument responds to color rather than particle size or total number of particles.

Direct Microscopic Examination

A light microscope or electron microscope can be used to provide magnified images of particle deposits on a suitable substrate. A great deal of information on particle size, morphology, shape, and composition can be obtained by such examination. The techniques, procedures, and equipment required to carry out such examinations are dealt with in great detail in the journal *Microscope* and in standard optical texts. Some general comments are given here.

The optical microscope is a convenient and useful instrument for characterizing collected materials. It has the advantage that it is visual, and both subjective and objective observation can be made quickly. Typically, a light microscope can be used up to magnifications of approximately 1000 times the numerical aperture of the objective lens. Thus, the smallest particles that are typically defined are approximately 0.5 μm in diameter. With the light microscope, one can define the refractive index of particulate materials by simple comparison techniques. To check the identity of unknown materials, dispersion staining can be used (Brown et al. 1963). Both light and electron microscopes are used for the determination of particle size and particle-size distribution. The use of an eyepiece reticle that has been calibrated against a stage micrometer is common. Eyepiece reticles can be calibrated in terms of linear dimensions or directly in area for whichever particle-size parameter is of concern. Further details on techniques for measuring particle size with a light microscope are given British Standard 3406 (1963).

For particles less than 1 μm in diameter, generally a transmission electron microscope or scanning electron microscope is used. Calibration of the electron microscope is typically based on comparison with monodisperse latex particles in sizes ranging from approximately 0.09 to 5 μm in diameter. For particles smaller than 0.1 μm in diameter, calibration is based on crystallographic determination of lattice parameters.

In general, measurements of microscopic images by manual techniques can be performed with reasonable accuracy for short periods of time. After an hour or so, operator error begins to enter into the measurements. Thus, automated systems involving sophisticated image analysis have been developed. The microscope is still used, but the image itself is analyzed by electronic means. Particles can be counted and measured at very high rates of speed with programming for any diameter parameter, areas, specific shape factors, etc. Thousands of particles can be counted and sized in seconds. A video camera is used to acquire the image through the microscope, and computer processing permits rapid measurement of a number of factors. Typically, up to eight basic dimensional measurements can be obtained directly, and a wide variety of algebraically derived additional measurements can be prepared. Results can be graphic, in terms of alphanumeric output; with statistical information, histograms can be presented; hard-copy outputs can be provided; and digital or analog information can be produced (Morton 1975).

Measurements in Liquid Suspension

Certain measurements can be conveniently carried out on particles suspended in liquids. In particular, direct measurement of particle volume by electrical resistance measurement is a useful technique. This procedure requires that particles collected by any of the methods discussed in section 10.4.2.4 be transferred to a conductive liquid that does not degrade the particles by solution, agglomeration, or chemical attack of any kind. The conductive liquid is then passed through a small orifice ranging in diameter from a few micrometers up to a millimeter or so, with an electrode on either side of the orifice. As a particle passes through, the electrode-to-electrode impedance varies in a manner dependent on the particle volume (Coulter 1956). The use of this technique for particle volume determinations is restricted to particles whose diameters vary within a range of 3:1 or so in any single sample. Concentration in the liquid must be limited to avoid coincidence errors. Great care must be taken to avoid modification of the physical form of the particles by suspension in the conductive liquid.

In a similar manner, it is possible to transfer collected particles into a liquid for passage through an optical particle-counting device. In this variation, the diameter range can be extended to approximately 60:1 with a much larger choice of suspension fluids, since the optical device does not require a conductive liquid. However, it is necessary that the refractive index of the particles and of the liquid be different.

Chemical Analysis

When information on the chemical composition of aerosols is required, it is normally necessary that the aerosol particles be collected before analytic techniques are used. With the exception of a scintillation spectrometer, there are essentially no instruments that can provide useful information on the chemical composition of aerosol particles *in situ*. One should consider that a typical aerosol particle of 1-10 μm diameter has a mass of approximately 10^{-10}-10^{-12} g and is very difficult to retain in place for a period of time long enough for most analytic beam-interpretation devices to operate satisfactorily. For this reason, particles are concentrated on suitable substrates for manipulation, handling, or insertion in a suitable analytic system.

A number of analytic procedures can be used for definition of aerosol composition. These range from classical wet-chemical analytic procedures through spectroscopic and electrochemical methods. It is beyond the scope of this discussion to describe all the methods in detail. Some of the more useful and appropriate techniques are discussed briefly.

Sampling for composition analysis is carried out primarily with filters. Once the material has been collected on the filter surface, the filter can be transported or stored, and the material remains stable. In addition, the filter surface can be subdivided to permit the use of a number of measurement techniques—some of which may be destructive—on a single sample. Some care, therefore, is required in selecting the filter medium for the particular analytic procedure and the material to be analyzed. When a particular compound or element is to be analyzed, a filter medium with a low background level of that material should be selected; if the analytic procedure is one that observes primarily surface structure, then the filter medium should be chosen so that particulate material is collected on the surface of the filter rather than within the interstices of that medium; for certain sulphur compounds, it is necessary to ensure that the filter medium does not sorb or retain reactive gases.

In general, water-soluble anions are analyzed by conventional wet-chemical, spectroscopic, and electrochemical methods, while water-soluble cations are analyzed by those methods along with X-ray-fluorescence and activation techniques. Mineral components are typically analyzed by emission spectroscopy and X-ray fluorescence, while metals are analyzed by a number of spectroscopic and fluorescence methods. Organic compounds are typically analyzed by gas chromatography, mass spectrometry, and infrared or ultraviolet methods. Note, however, that these are general guidelines, and not hard and fast rules. A number of variations and preferential exceptions always exist.

Traditional wet-chemistry techniques Frequently, in carrying out a chemical analysis, it is desirable that the material collected on the filter surface be concentrated even further. In this case, a fibrous-medium filter is used, and the material is concentrated while some elemental separation is carried out, by using the ring-oven technique as described by West (1966). In this device, a solvent is added to the sample on a filter paper, and the paper is placed in a ring oven. The solution migrates under the action of capillarity, and heat causes the solvent to evaporate. The material is then analyzed by standard spot-test techniques. Appel et al. (1976) used a technique of solvent extraction followed by carbon determination to identify elemental carbon primary and secondary organic materials.

A series of tests that can be applied to aerosol particles of masses down to 10^{-16} g are described by Bigg et al. (1974). Precoated electron microscope screens are used. The screens are coated with a thin film of reagent, and reaction is caused to proceed by exposure to the vapor of a suitable solvent. The reaction products are then examined in the electron microscope and compared with similar particles captured on a nonreactive surface.

A method using gas chromatography is suggested by De Maio & Corn (1966). In this device, a single benzene extraction of particles collected on filter paper is followed by use of a conventional packed column.

Dulka & Risby (1976) discuss general sampling techniques that are particularly applicable to the collection of material for microtrace analysis. They describe current methods of microanalysis, including detection limits and areas of applicability.

The application of an automatic technique for determining carbon, hydrogen, and nitrogen in size-fractionated ambient aerosol simultaneously is described by Lee & Hein (1974). In this technique a sample is burned in pure oxygen at high temperature, converting the elements to carbon dioxide, water, and nitrogen.

In the hands of a skilled operator, morphological analysis, preferably with the aid of an optical or electron microscope, is a valuable and useful tool. McCrone (1967) discusses procedures for morphological analysis of particulate samples. A number of procedures and laboratory systems are outlined, including techniques for morphological analysis based on refractive index. This identification technique is based on recognition of the difference in dispersion of the refractive index of a particulate solid and that of the liquid medium in which the solid is imbedded. Particle boundary color changes are the tool used to identify the specific materials. The particle atlas prepared by McCrone Associates is an extremely useful aid in describing specific materials.

Spectrometric, photometric, and other analytic techniques The X-ray-fluorescence analysis of aerosols is described by Adams & Van Grieken (1975). The use of the method is described, along with a procedure for correcting absorption by the filter medium.

The use of X-ray spectroscopy is described by Birks (1978). Birks applies the method to the analysis of airborne pollutants and indicates the cost effectiveness of the technique.

A novel multielectrode flame-ionization detector is described by Altpeter (1975). In this device, the individual particle appears to provide its own event marker as it is consumed in the flame. The marker pulse is followed by another current pulse, which may be due to the actual charge carriers delayed by their time of flight from the flame to the electrode.

A discussion of flameless atomic absorption spectrometry for metal analysis is given in Begnoche & Risby (1975). A complete description of the method for sampling particles from ambient air in volumes of 20–300 L is given, as are analytic procedures with reference to a number of metals.

An example of the use of neutron activation for the analysis of specific radionuclides is given by Benson & Gleit (1963).

The use of infrared spectroscopic analysis is described by Cunningham et al. (1974). They clearly show the variations in the chemistry of airborne particles as a function of particle size and time by use of the infrared technique.

A number of mass spectrometric devices are available. One is described by Davis (1977). In this device the particles impinge on a heated ribbon, and the resulting burst of ions produced by each particle is analyzed in a 7.6-cm-radius magnetic-sector mass spectrometer. Particles containing 1000 atoms of a particular element in concentrations of less than 1 particle/cm^3 can be detected.

Improved mass spectrometric techniques are described by Cronn et al. (1977). By use of computer-controlled, high-resolution mass spectrometric thermal analysis, sample handling was minimized since portions of the fiber filters could be inserted directly into the spectrometer, and molecular information was obtained simultaneously for organic and some inorganic pollutants in submicrogram quantities.

Proton-induced X-ray-emission analysis is useful in measuring changes in the particle-size distributions of a number of compounds (Desaedeleer et al. 1977). This technique has found very wide use in the measurement of the general composition of collected aerosols.

Gamma-ray emission induced by inelastic scattering of protons has been described by Macias et al. (1978) for simultaneous determination of carbon, nitrogen, and sulfur in collected samples.

Ion and electron microprobes are useful for analyzing individual particles or areas on specific particles as small as 1 μm in cross section. Applications and capabilities of ion and electron microprobe instruments in characterizing particulate matter are described by Gavrilovic & Majewski (1977). Resolution limits, sample-handling requirements, and some typical data are given.

An example of emission spectroscopic methods is given by Seeley & Skogerboe (1974). When a sample is heated by an arc or other suitable energy source, light in wavelengths specific to the elements in the sample is emitted, and the intensity gives quantitative information on concentration. Consideration has been given to the use of Raman spectroscopy for particulate analysis by Rosen & Novakov (1977). A detailed discussion of the spectroscopic analysis of surfaces, using low-energy electrons or ions, that is particularly suitable for particle analysis is given by Hercules (1978).

In some cases, surface analysis of collected particulate material is of particular interest, as indicated by Keyser et al. (1978). They point out a number of spectrometric techniques that are particularly applicable for surface analysis. These include electron microprobe analysis, X-ray-emission spectrometry, electron spectroscopy for chemical analysis, Auger electron spectrometry, and secondary-ion mass spectrometry. These techniques are often useful for the analysis of individual particles ranging in size down to 1 μm in diameter. In some of the techniques, ion bombardment to remove surface material permits analysis of the composition of several layers of the particulate material.

The summary of analytic methods in this section is not a complete discussion of the methodology; nor does it provide details as to exactly which elements and compounds can be analyzed by which methods. The discussion is designed primarily to give an overview of techniques that have been used in the analysis of aerosol particles and to indicate sources where additional information can be procured. Moreover, the listing of methods is not complete. Even as this discussion is being written, new methods are being disseminated.

10.4.3 *IN SITU* SYSTEMS FOR AEROSOL OBSERVATION

10.4.3.1 Optical Detectors

Airborne particles have dimensions that are within approximately one order of magnitude of the wavelength of visible light. When a particle or particles are illuminated by a beam of visible light or by a beam of laser light in the wavelength range 350–800 nm, the amount of light that is scattered by the particle or particles varies roughly with the projected area of that particle. By causing particles to pass in an airstream through a brightly illuminated volume sufficiently small so that only single particles are present at any time, it is possible to collect the light scattered by each particle over a specific range of angles as a pulse. The amount of light and the angular distribution of that light depend on the particle size, shape, and refractive index. The total light from each pulse can be analyzed, and particle-size-distribution and concentration data can be obtained once the flow rate of the airstream in which the particles are suspended is known. Single-particle counters now in use operate over a variety of scattering angles.

Alternatively, an aerosol photometer collects the light scattered from a volume of aerosol containing many particles and produces data that indicate the total projected area of all the particles in the illuminated volume.

Light-scattering single-particle counters detect particles of approximately 0.1-μm diameter and larger. Scattering angles in common use include near-forward angles, scattering about a $90°$ angle, and total angular scattering. The illumination sources are typically tungsten filaments producing white light. In some cases, helium-neon lasers are used as illumination sources. Photomultiplier or photodiode detectors are used to collect scattered light from the particles. A dynamic size range capability of approximately $1\frac{1}{2}$ orders of magnitude is typical. Sample flow rates vary from a few milliliters per minute to 30 L/min. Concentrations up to approximately 10,000 particles/ml of air can be measured. A counter handling 30 L/min is capable of observing concentrations of no more than 10–20 particles/ml of air; counters designed to measure several thousand particles per milliliter are limited to sample flow rates of a few milliliters per minute.

In use, the air sample is drawn through the sensor portion of the particle counter. Scattered light pulses produced by the aerosol particles are collected by the photodetector, and amplitude and frequency information is processed. Pulse count rate in each of several sizes can be stored, recorded, or transmitted as required with or without processing to provide secondary information on particle-size distribution as a function of projected diameter or area. A general discussion of the theory of optical behavior of aerosols and its application to analysis has been given by Hodkinson (1966).

Because optical instruments are so widely used for the measurement of aerosols, it is advisable to discuss the particle parameters, optical characteristics, and instrument parameters that affect the response of such devices. Basically, the operation of an optical particle-analyzing device involves the observation of particles suspended in a fluid that differs optically from those particles. The fluid suspension is passed through a finite viewing or sensing volume, and the amount of light flux emitted from that volume with and without particles is noted over a specific viewing-angle range. As the size of the particle or particles present in the sensing volume increases, the amount of light that is scattered for a given illumination light flux level varies in a complex manner. The variation is a function of the wavelength of the light, the convergence angle of the illuminating beam, the geometry of the collecting aperture, the scattering angles, the refractive index of the particles and the suspending fluid, and the particle size.

The response from a particle in the viewing volume of an optical particle counter is expressed as

$$i_0 = \iiint Rf(\lambda)\, F(\theta, \phi)\, d\lambda\, d\theta\, d\phi$$

where i_0 is the response for a particular system; R is the Rayleigh ratio, or the flux scattered in the direction θ per steradian, relative to the incident flux level; $f(\lambda)$ is the wavelength distribution function, combining the lamp emission level and photodetector sensitivity; $F(\theta, \phi)$ is the geometric factor for the system; and θ is the scattering angle with respect to the incident beam; and ϕ the angle between the incident beam and the illumination axis. Note that the value of R depends on θ, on the particle-size parameter, and on the particle refractive index. Figure 10.4.10 illustrates the effects of size, refractive index, and scattering-angle geometry on the response of optical particle counters.

Most practical instruments using light scattering for particle measurement operate with tungsten filaments at a color temperature of approximately 2800° and with a photomultiplier or photodetector that results in an operating wavelength close to the visible. In some cases a helium-neon laser emitting light at 633 nm is used, along with a photodiode that has reasonable response at this wavelength.

The scattering angles in use vary over an extremely wide range, but, in general, the tungsten-filament-illuminated systems are based on one of two optical geometries. In both, the converging illumination beam is focused at the point where the particles pass through. The direct beam is captured in a suitable light trap so that

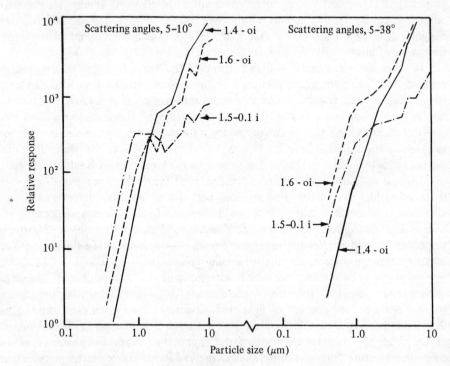

Figure 10.4.10 Relative scattering response.

minimum reflected light escapes. In one optical system, the scattered light from the particles is collected in an annular aperture that surrounds the central light beam but does not include the light beam. In the other system, the collecting aperture is offset at an angle to the direct beam and does not view that beam whatsoever. When converging light is used for illumination, the smallest angle at which scattered light can be measured without observing the direct beam is typically 8-10° offset from the light beam. The largest angle that might be considered is approximately 120°. If a laser is used for illumination, the coherent collimated telecentric beam permits collection of scattered light at angles of less than 5° without interference from the direct beam.

At any particular scattering angle, as particle size increases, the scattered light flux level is an oscillatory function so that a single measurement may yield an ambiguous value for particle size, particularly where the scattering function is shifting from Rayleigh scattering to Mie scattering—and especially for particles ranging from a few tenths of a micrometer to several micrometers in diameter. The use of white light with a relatively large range of collecting angles tends to damp out oscillations to some extent. Since the response curve for scattering also includes an effect of refractive index, the oscillatory nature of the response curve varies with both particle size and refractive index. A more complete discussion of the effects of scattering angles and refractive index on the response as a function of particle size for light-scattering aerosol particle counters is given by Cooke & Kerker (1975). The calculations on which this work was based include the assumption that the particles are isotropic, homogeneous spheres. In practice, however, this situation seldom occurs. Most airborne aerosol particles are irregular in surface, not spherical, and may be composed of mixtures of liquid and solid materials, along with sorbed gases. This irregularity tends to further remove oscillations from the response curve.

In addition to the theoretical response of optical instruments, it is necessary to consider also the effect of instrument construction limitations. These limitations are primarily due to variations in the manufacturing tolerances, from 0.1 to 5% in mechanical dimensions, lens focal length, electronic components, etc. As one example of the effect of tolerance variations, consider uniformity of response. When the viewing volume is illuminated by an incandescent filament, the dimensions of that viewing volume are defined by an aperture illuminated by a condensing lens. The aperture is imaged at the sample stream by a relay lens, and the light scattered by particles in the sample stream is collected and measured by a photodetector. With this type of illumination, light intensity across the sample stream varies by 1-2%, except at the edges where some 5% of the illuminated area is used to transit from full illumination intensity to zero light level. Further, the dimensions of a practical sample stream may result in a light intensity variation from front to back of about 5% when a relay lens with good depth of field is used. In addition, the fluid in which the particles are suspended will be moving in laminar flow at the point of observation. The resulting parabolic velocity profile results in the particle dwell time varying by a factor of two, since the maximum stream velocity at the central line of flow is twice the average velocity. The dwell-time variation requires that the electronic system bandwidth be adequate to minimize response changes as pulse rise and fall time varies. The increased bandwidth requirement may affect the electronic noise level. The result of the several variations in light level, flow, electronic components, etc., therefore can result in variations in response from particles of identical size. For a good commercial instrument, these variations may range from ±1% to ±3%, depending on instrument design parameters.

The normal concentration of aerosol particles in the measured samples should not exceed the maximum capability of the single-particle counting instrument. When the particles are randomly distributed in a sample of fluid, there is a finite probability that more than one particle will be present within the finite sensing volume at any time. Since these particle-counting devices are not imaging instruments, but measure only light level at the time of particle passage, the devices cannot differentiate between the light flux produced by several particles present in the sensing volume and that produced by a single particle of somewhat larger size. The effect of coincident particles in the sensing volume is an exponentially increasing error in indicated concentration as the actual concentration increases. Coincidence errors can be calculated for an assumed Poisson distribution in the cell and have been described by Jaenicke (1972).

Figure 10.4.11 illustrates the effect of coincidence error on the reported concentration data. Note that eventually the instrument will report zero concentration when the actual concentration is so high as to fill the sensing volume continuously.

One almost insoluble difficulty in defining the output of optical detectors for aerosol size measurement is the question of calibration. Typically, the optical detector is calibrated with spherical, monodisperse particles. The median pulse height produced by these particles is used as a reference level for sizing, and a reasonable correlation in counting is obtained between different particle counters

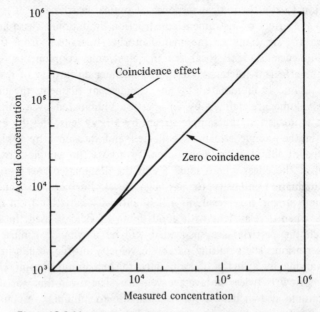

Figure 10.4.11   Effect of coincidence on measured concentration.

and different transparent spherical materials. However, most natural particulate material is irregular in shape, polydisperse, and has a refractive index different from that of the calibration materials. For this reason, particle size for optical system measurement often is defined in terms of equivalent optical diameter. One possible solution to this problem has been suggested by Marple & Rubow (1976). In their procedure, the optical particle counter is calibrated by using an impactor with known cut size based on aerodynamic sizing. Calibration points are obtained by using nozzles of different diameters to achieve different cut sizes for the impactor placed in the sensor inlet line and indicating the mean pulse height as the cut size is changed.

10.4.3.2 Optical Instruments

Multiple-Particle Photometric Analyzers

Two general classes of optical instruments are produced for the measurement of assemblages of particles. These instruments are *photometers,* for the determination of aerosols in the range of micrograms per milliliter to micrograms per cubic meter, and *visibility indicators* or *smoke densitometers,* for the indication of aerosol concentrations in the range of milligrams per liter. Photometers are generally used for the measurement of relatively clean environments, whereas densitometers (or transmissometers) are used for the measurement of stack-dust concentrations.

Forward-scattering-angle photometric instruments are optically similar to the dark-field microscope: A cone of light converges on the aerosol cloud, but dark stops are used to protect the photodetector from the direct beam. Only the light scattered from the particles in the near-forward direction is measured. The instruments usually read out in terms of mass or number concentration, based upon calibration with submicron particles. The typical forward-scattering photometer shown in figure 10.4.12 is a near-forward-scattering instrument that draws air at 28.3 L/min. The air sample passes through the light cone, and light scattered from particles over angles ranging from 4 to 36° in the forward direction falls on a photomultiplier whose current output indicates the aerosol particle concentration. The instrument operates over the range of 10^{-3}-100 μg/L. The design is essentially that given by Knudson and White (1945). (This device is still used for the testing of high-efficiency particulate air filters.)

For measurement in the open air, an integrating nephelometer can be used (Charlson et al. 1967). This instrument determines the scattering coefficient of haze and aerosol particles in the atmosphere and has been used to indicate roughly the mass concentration of submicron particles in the air. The device uses a xenon flash tube operated at 1-2 flashes/s. Light scattered from particles over the range 8-170° is collected by a phototube during the duration of the photo flash and is fed to a peak-reading voltmeter. Air is drawn through the nephelometer at a flow rate of about 100 L/min. The nephelometer is calibrated by measuring Rayleigh scatter from particle-free carbon dioxide and freon. By determining atmospheric scattering with an integrating nephelometer over a range of illumination wavelengths, one may also infer the exponent of the power-law distribution model, as was demonstrated by Ahlquist & Charlson (1969).

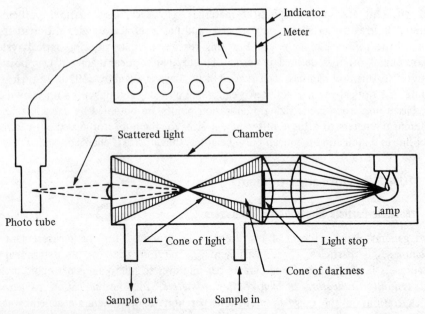

Figure 10.4.12 Photometer.

A perhaps simpler device normally used for measuring particle concentrations in stacks involves light attenuation across the stack. This device measures the extinction of light by an aerosol. The sensing volume may be quite large and must usually contain a large number of aerosol particles, typically around 10^6 particles/cm^2 of beam area, to produce a measurable reduction in light level. Using straightforward Beer's law calculations and ensuring that forward-scattered light is excluded, these devices can indicate aerosol number concentration with reasonable accuracy. Both single-beam and dual-beam instruments have been used in stacks over a wide range of operating temperatures and dust or smoke concentrations. Care is required to ensure that the optical system is not affected by deposition of dust particles during measurement. Calibration is usually carried out on these devices by means of neutral density attenuators that provide 0, 20, 40, 60, or 80% attenuation of the light beams.

Single-Particle Optical Counting and Sizing Devices

A variety of commercial and development-stage single-particle analyzing devices are available. They all have in common a capability for transporting an air sample through an illuminated section that is sufficiently small so that only individual particles are present at any time within the concentration limits of the device; as the particle passes through the illuminated volume, a pulse of light is scattered and collected over a range of scattering angles. Figures 10.4.13–10.4.15 illustrate the optical component layout and light paths for right-angle optical counters, near-forward-angle optical counters, and one version of a very large solid-angle optical counter. The scattered light flux for each pulse produced by particle passage is

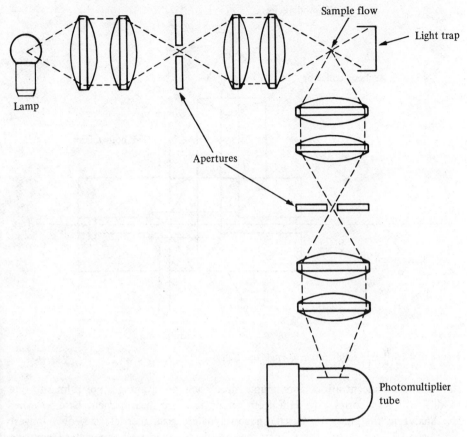

Figure 10.4.13 Right-angle-scattering optical system.

collected, and its amplitude measured. Pulse-amplitude and concentration data are reported in terms of the calibration for the particular device.

The great advantages of these devices are their convenience, their speed in determining aerosol concentration and size-distribution data, and their portability and capability for use in a wide variety of operating regimes in terms of particle

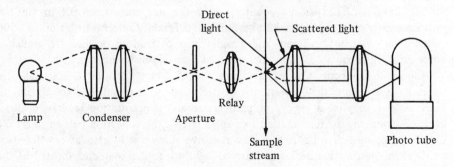

Figure 10.4.14 Near-forward-scattering-angle optical system.

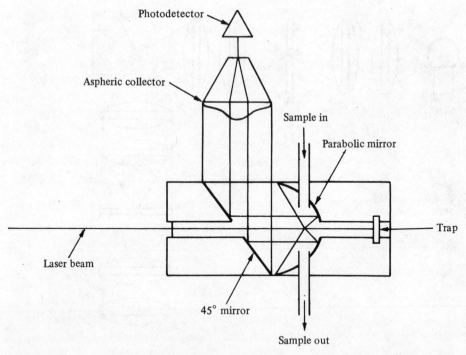

Figure 10.4.15 Large solid-scattering-angle optical system.

size, particle concentration, and sample size. Their disadvantages are primarily due to difficulties in correlating data from an optical size measurement base to other size analyzers that may be based on aerodynamic size, inertial size, or a longest dimension. In addition, there may be problems in correlating data from one instrument to another if optics differ between the two instruments. These difficulties are discussed in more detail by Lieberman (1976).

Some of the commercially available optical particle counters will now be described briefly, to indicate their operating ranges and capabilities.

Perhaps the most widely known manufacturer of optical aerosol particle counters is Royco Instruments, Inc., in Menlo Park, Calif. This company manufactures right-angle, near-forward-angle, and large-included-angle scattering single-particle counters. The particle counters cover the size range from 0.1 to 100 μm with flow rates that vary from 280 ml/min to 30 L/min. Concentrations up to 3500 particles/cm^3 can be measured, and a wide range of readout options are available. These capabilities are spread over the range of available instrument models.

Climet Instrument Co. of Redlands, Calif., manufactures a single-particle counting instrument that covers the particle-size range from 0.3 to 10 μm in diameter and supplies a variety of particle-size and concentration readout options. In this instrument, the illumination half-angle is 16°, the collection half-angle is 90°, and the trapping half-angle is 36°. The sensitive volume is located at one focus of an elliptical mirror that reflects scattered light to a photodetector located at the second focus. Maximum concentration for this instrument is stated as approximately 3×10^4 particles/m^3.

The Bausch and Lomb Co. of Rochester, N.Y., has manufactured a dust counter, model 40-1, for many years. This instrument is a forward-scattering device. The light beam is focused at the aerosol stream in the center of the sensitive volume and passes through the center of a parabolic mirror. Light scattered from 24–50° is reflected by the parabolic mirror, back to a photodetector located behind the light source. An air sample flow rate of 0.17 L/min permits measurement of particles in concentrations up to 35 particles/ml over the size range 0.3–10 μm. In the basic instrument, the several size ranges are sequentially selected, and concentration in each of the size ranges is shown in terms of the rate at which particles are being accumulated.

Coulter Electronics of Hialeah, Fla., markets an airborne-particle counter that uses near-forward optics, samples at the rate of 28.3 L/min, and sizes particles 0.5 μm and larger. The maximum concentration capability is indicated at approximately 3.5 particles/ml. Particle-size information is normally defined in up to four size ranges.

Met-One, of Grants Pass, Ore., manufactures a particle counter for clean area measurement. The sample flow rate is 28 L/min. Its size sensitivity is 0.5 μm and greater with a maximum concentration capability of 3.5 particles/ml.

Particle Measuring Systems, Inc., of Boulder, Colo., manufactures optical single-particle counters that use laser beam illumination systems. A number of devices are available from this company. In one device, the classical scattering aerosol spectrometer, the particle stream is illuminated by a focused laser beam approximately 60 μm in diameter at a power density in excess of 200 W/cm^2. A forward-scattering optical system permits measurement in the size range 0.3–3 μm, or 1–20 μm at a flow rate of 0.1 cm^3/s. A second system, the active scattering aerosol spectrometer, uses a hybrid helium-neon laser tube that is designed to permit the passing of the aerosol sample stream through the active-cavity portion of the laser. At the sample volume the laser beam is approximately 500μm in diameter, and the power density is in excess of 500 W/cm^2. Forward scattering from the particles in the cavity is collected to permit measurement of particles as small as 0.15 μm in diameter at a flow rate of 1 cm^3/s. The dynamic range for this instrument is 0.15–3 μm.

A third nonimaging scattering system is provided with laser illumination. In this system, the aerosol stream passes through the laser beam, which is focused to approximately 300 μm diameter with a power density in excess of 10 W/cm^2. Aerodynamic focusing of the aerosol stream permits the entire aerosol to pass within the central 60% of the beam for maximum resolution. Scattered light is collected on a parabolic mirror over scattering angles ranging from 35 to 120° and focused on a photodiode. The particle-size-range capability for this instrument is from 0.1 to 6 μm with a sample flow rate of 5 cm^3/s.

For the measurement of somewhat larger particles, an imaging particle-counting device has been developed that uses a photodiode array and photodetection electronics, along with a high-speed front-end memory enabling each photodetector element to encode sufficient bits of shadow information from each particle to develop a two-dimensional image. With this imaging optical system, particles in the size ranges 25–800 and 200–6400 μm can be analyzed and described. The use of fairly sophisticated electronic systems permits significant definition of shape, as well as particle size, within these ranges.

The Dan Science Co., Ltd., of Japan, manufactures an optical particle counter (right-angle optics) with an illumination half-angle of approximately 20°. Particles between 0.3 and 10 μm can be measured at a flow rate of 1 L/min in concentrations up to 70 particles/ml. Sequential readout in terms of the number of particles in each of the five size ranges between 0.3 and 10 μm is used in this device.

Hitachi Corp., near Tokyo, has also developed an optical particle counter. This instrument uses a hollow-cone illumination system and collects forward-scattered light from particles passing through the focal point of the illumination beam. Particles in the size range of 0.3–10 μm can be measured at a flow rate of 2.8 L/min. The maximum concentration capability is 350 particles/ml. In normal operation, eight threshold size measurements are chosen in the overall range, and particles per unit volume are selected sequentially.

The H. Gertsch Co. of Zurich, Switzerland, manufactures a model HC15 particle counter. A right-angle scattering system is used to image a preselected volume in the open atmosphere through which particles move as dictated by prevailing air currents. Particles can be measured in the size range 0.3–60 μm in gas velocities ranging from 0.2 to 15 m/s. Particles smaller than approximately 10 μm in diameter can be measured in concentrations up to 10^5 particles/cm^3. Somewhat larger particles, e.g., up to 22 μm, can be measured in concentrations up to 0.7 particles/cm^3. Particle-size distribution data are stored in up to 64 size fractions with a logarithmic distribution of equivalent particle diameters.

In addition to the commercially available single-particle-counting optical devices, a number of instruments have been fabricated in laboratories and have been described in the literature. Most of these devices are similar in operation to the commercial instruments described above; further information can be found by searching the files of the *Journal of Aerosol Science* or *Atmospheric Environment*. Some rather unique instruments have been developed, however, and five of these will be described briefly.

1. Gonia et al. (1978) have described a method for measuring optical extinction cross section for very small particles. The method is based on measurement of the complex amplitude, rather than the intensity, of the interacting optical beams of an interferometer.

2. Gravatt's (1973) instrument measures the intensity of light scattered by a single particle simultaneously at two small scattering angles. The ratio of the intensities is a direct measurement of size and is fairly independent of the refractive index of the particle. Scattering angles of 5 and 10° are used to indicate particles in the size ranges from 0.2 to 4 μm.

3. For more complete characterization of the scattering from individual particles, Gucker et al. (1973) developed an instrument in which an airstream containing aerosol particles intercepts a helium-neon laser beam at one focus of an elliptical mirror, which directs a 360° slice of scattered light to a photomultiplier at the

other focus. A nearly complete 360° scattering diagram is obtained by a 5° rotating aperture between the scattering plane and the photomultiplier.

4. In a variation of the use of laser-Doppler velocimetry, Chabay & Bright (1977) use a horizontally propagating laser beam to illuminate falling particles. Light that is scattered is collected at a single angle in the vertical scattering plane. Peak frequencies in the photocurrent of the detector due to the Doppler shift of the radiation scattered by the settling aerosol are analyzed to determine particle settling velocity. Data on Stokes' diameters are obtained for particles of known density, while the amplitude of the peak frequency component contains information on the number of particles of that size. Particles in the size range 1–100 μm can be measured, with number densities in the scattering-volume reading from single particles up to concentrations of 10^5 particles/cm^3.

5. Laser-Doppler velocimeters (LDV) have been used for many years to measure flow velocities. Yanta (1973) discusses the operation of an LDV for the measurement of aerosol size distribution. The LDV is used to measure the particle lag of individual aerosol particles as they are accelerated in a supersonic nozzle that is used to produce a known flow field. The measured velocity lag is then used in conjunction with numerical predictions to determine the particle size.

Fraunhofer Diffraction Analyzers

A helium-neon laser beam passing through an aerosol produces Fraunhofer diffraction patterns in a plane orthogonal to the laser beam direction. A diffraction pattern through a monodisperse aerosol would be essentially coaxial Airy rings, as shown in figure 10.4.16. The diffraction pattern through polydisperse material shows a monotonic intensity distribution. Smaller particles diffract the laser beam over a larger angle than do larger particles; the overall energy level at any point varies with the particle concentration. By placing a rotating spatial filter in the Fraunhofer diffraction plane of the collecting lens, light flux levels can be defined as a function of scattering angle. To obtain a volume response for the particles in the aerosol, the spatial filter is rotated to extract signals serially; since the transmission characteristics of the filter as a function of scattering angle are specially shaped, the transmitted light intensity can provide information on the fourth, third, and second moments of particle diameter. After the three signals have been collected, ratios are

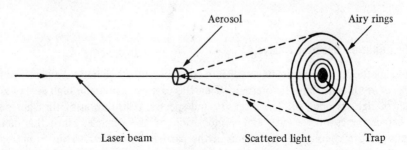

Figure 10.4.16   Fraunhofer plane diffraction from monodisperse aerosol.

computed to define volume mean diameter, area mean diameter, and variance for a particle-size distribution, as discussed by Wertheimer & Wilcock (1976). Northrup Co., North Wales, Pa., and Cilas, in France, make commercially available instruments designed on this principle.

Fraunhofer diffraction analyzers are used primarily for the determination of particle volume and areas for particles ranging from approximately 1 to 100 μm in diameter. Concentrations up to 0.5% by volume can be handled easily, and excellent correlation with data from other methods is reported on a wide variety of materials.

Holographic Particle-Sizing Analyzers

Thompson (1974) reviewed holographic particle-sizing technology as of 1974. Most work in this area involves forming an in-line Fraunhofer hologram—the interference pattern formed between the far-field diffraction pattern of the particles to be analyzed and an in-line background. This hologram is then used to form an image of the original three-dimensional sample. Visual observation of this image can be used to provide particle-size and concentration data *in situ*. Alternatively, a pulsing ultraviolet laser can be used to produce "instantaneous" images of aerosol droplets, which are observed by a video camera. The video signals are fed to an image analyzer that reduces the data immediately, as described by Hotham (1974).

Remote-Observation Devices

Remote observation of aerosol clouds by laser radar (lidar) is used for both cloud information and remote smoke-plume mapping. Since the original development of the procedure in the middle 1960s, much refinement has been carried out, as is described by Allen & Evans (1972).

Basically a lidar system uses a pulsed laser beam, with pulse widths under 30 ns, and a coaxial receiving optical system. By sequentially advancing the lidar system along an elevation or azimuth angle between each pair of lidar pulses, it is possible to scan over a preselected air volume. Examination of the return signal as a function of time permits definition of back-scattered energy from particulate material in the atmosphere. Particle concentration can be obtained from the data as received. One might also consider the possibility of using pulsed lidar systems at wavelengths other than that from the typical ruby laser used for this purpose, and examining the back-scattered light with Raman techniques for particle composition analysis.

Scintillation Spectral Analysis

In this method, aerosol is injected into the measuring chamber, where either a plasma or hydrogen flame is present. When the particles enter the high-energy zone, a flash of light is emitted. The intensity and spectral distribution of the light pulses are characteristics of the size and composition of the particle. Since this method depends on the chemical composition of the particles, some calibration is necessary. Note that mass concentration as well as number concentration can be described

(Binek & Dohnalova 1967). Sartorius, Inc., in Germany, manufactures a commercial version of this instrument. In that device, aerosol is sampled at a flow rate of 200 ml/min. For particle concentrations of from $10\mu g/m^3$ to 20 mg/m^3, the smallest measurable particle size is approximately 0.03 μm for sodium-containing aerosols. Data are read out in 10 size ranges.

10.4.3.3 Particle Detectors Other than Optical Instruments

Condensation-Nuclei Counters

Condensation-nuclei counters often use photometric or single-particle counting optics in their operation, which indicates the number of particles capable of initiating water condensation from vapor in the atmosphere. The method is particularly useful for determining number concentrations of such particles from approximately 0.005 to 2 μm in diameter. In operation, a sample of gas to be analyzed is saturated with water vapor and then placed in an environment where supersaturation will occur. Supersaturation is induced either by adiabatic expansion of the gas or by diffusion of water from a cold surface. Water then condenses on the particles so that a fog appears in the measurement chamber. Either the opacity of the fog is measured optically or the individual water droplets are measured by a single-particle counting device, as described by Hudson & Squires (1973).

Energy Transfer Devices

Goldschmidt (1965) studied the use of a hot-wire anemometer for detecting particles in an airstream. The device is particularly applicable to the detection of water droplets. When a droplet strikes the heated probe, the heat loss to the droplet reduces the probe temperature enough to drop the electrical resistance, so that a measurable electrical pulse is produced. A similar device has recently been marketed by KLD Associates, Inc., of Huntington, N.Y., for observing the size and concentration of water droplets in wet-scrubber gas streams. A hot-wire probe is used to generate pulses by including the probe as one leg of an electrical bridge. The manufacturers of this device claim measurement of droplets in the range of 1–600 μm diameter for any aqueous solutions. Counting rates up to 500 droplets/s are accomplished.

Momentum transfer has been used for the measurement of particles in gas streams in the past. One such device, described by Benarie (1965), is a particle-counting device that consists of a very thin cantilevered stainless steel plate attached to a microphone-type sensing element. On impact, particles as small as 5 μm in diameter are able to produce a signal that can be detected by conventional pulse-counting systems.

Indication of electric-charge transfer was first described by Keily & Miller (1960). In their instrument, each particle to be measured is removed from the airstream by impaction on a charged probe and is detected in number and size by the magnitude of the electric charge it accepts from the probe. The device is reported to be able to count and size droplets in the range of 2–60 μm at a rate of 10,000 droplets/s. A commercial version of this technique, produced by IKOR, Inc., of Burlington, Mass., is designed for use in emission stack-gas monitoring applications. The manufacturer's specifications indicate a capability for particulate emission mass measurements from 20 μg/m^3 to 200 g/m^3 over a particle size range of 0.1–100 μm.

When a particle traveling at near-sonic velocity passes through a restriction in a gas line, shock-wave formation occurs close to the restriction and causes the generation of an audible clicking sound. It is not possible to obtain a simple relationship between sound intensity and particle size; however, the presence of particles larger than about 10 μm is enough to initiate the sound generation. Thus, this simple technique can be used for the detection of a large number of materials (Langer 1972).

Other Devices

A surface ionization monitor has been developed by Extranuclear Laboratories, Inc., Pittsburgh, Pa. This device operates by causing airborne dust to strike a hot wire, where the dust particles decompose. The surface-ionizable constituents are ionized, and those atomic constituents that have low ionization potentials are reemitted from the surface of the hot wire as positively charged ions, in concentrations depending on the particle size and chemical composition of the particles. The ions are collected onto a nearby electrode, producing a voltage pulse that is processed to indicate the total ionizable material detected and the concentration of particles with sizes above a predetermined value. Depending on the chemical nature of the aerosol, this device can detect particles from less than 0.1 μm in diameter up to approximately 10 μm in diameter, in concentrations ranging from 10 to 10^5 particles/ml.

An electrostatic aerosol size analyzer was developed at the University of Minnesota by Whitby & Clark (1966). This device passes particles through a cloud of unipolar ions, where each particle acquires a quantity of charge simply related to its size. The charged aerosol flows concentrically with a sheath of clean air from the charger to the mobility-analyzer section, where the charged particles are removed if a sufficiently high voltage is applied. Particles not collected by the analyzer section are collected on a filter, and their charge is recorded on a sensitive electrometer. Mobility analysis is accomplished by stepwise changes of the analyzer-section voltage. Thermosystems, Inc., of St. Paul, Minn., distributes the commercial version of this device. Particles are measured in the diameter range 0.01–1 μm, with concentrations ranging from 6 to 600 μg/m^3 at a sample flow rate of 5 L/min. Data are recorded in 10 size classes with approximately 10 min required per size distribution measurement.

Another type of electric-charge transfer device was developed at the University of Albany by Mohnen (1971). In this device, the aerosol particles intercept ions produced by a ^{60}Co source. Ion transfer by aerosol particles produces a current that indicates the quantity of aerosol particles.

An example of a combination system is described by Bruce & Pinnick (1977).

In this device, the absorption of energy produced by a CO_2 laser is determined as a function of particle concentration and mean particle diameter.

10.4.4 SUMMARY COMMENTS

10.4.4.1 Standard Methods and Materials

In the preceding discussion, methods and devices for sampling and analyzing aerosols have been discussed. At several points it has been mentioned that the correlation of results from one instrument or method with those of another may be quite difficult. For this reason, work is in progress to develop standard methods for sampling and analyzing aerosols, as well as standard reference materials for use in calibrating devices and procedures. Examples of such standards are as follows:

1. The Joint AIHA-ACGIH* Aerosol Hazards Evaluation Committee has prepared recommended procedures for sampling and counting asbestos fibers and has presented these in the AIHA *Journal* 36:83–90, 1975. A standard for sampling and processing collected samples to evaluate occupational hazards and exposure to asbestos fibers is presented.
2. The ASTM[†] has prepared a document entitled, Continuous Counting and Sizing of Airborne Particles in Dust Controlled Areas by the Light-Scattering Principle, as procedure F50-65T, February 17, 1965. In this document, procedures for the measurement of concentration and size distribution of airborne particles in the 0.5–5.0-μm size range are given.
3. ASTM procedure D1739-70, October 15, 1970, is entitled Standard Method for Collection and Analysis of Dustfall. In this procedure, a method for the field collection of particles settling from the atmosphere and for preliminary characterization of the sample is described.
4. The U.S. Environmental Protection Agency has prepared a number of standard methods for stack-emission monitoring. These involve procedures for determining flow, for establishing isokinetic sample rates, for maintaining temperature to avoid condensation or evaporation of particulate material in the sample line, and for collecting particles to avoid interferences from gas-phase reactions.

With regard to standard reference materials at present and in the forseeable future, there is no procedure, material, or device that can be used to generate a standard aerosol suspension that is accepted by any reputable regulatory agency. Although a number of aerosol-generating devices are available, only one device has been developed that is capable of generating monodisperse aerosols in controllable, definable concentrations. This is the vibrating orifice monodisperse aerosol generator, described by Berglund & Liu (1973). A vibrating orifice is operated under controlled conditions with specific liquids; the concentration and size of droplets generated by this device are controllable. However, cost, operating complexity, and

---

*American Industrial Hygiene Association–American Council of Government Industrial Hygienists.
[†] American Society for Testing and Materials.

limitations to liquids or soluble materials prevent it from being a truly universal standard aerosol generator.

A variety of monodisperse particles are available for aerosol generation purposes. However, the particle concentration of the aerosols generated from these materials is not easily controllable. For the most part, they are generated by nebulizing a water suspension of the particles and allowing the water to evaporate. Materials are available from Coulter Electronics, Hialeah, Fla., from the Dow Chemical Co., Indianapolis, Ind., from Duke Scientific Corp., Palo Alto, Calif., and from Particle Information Service, Grants Pass, Ore. The particle size and standard deviation of the size are supplied by the manufacturer. At this time these data are not verified by any regulatory agency. In general, the measurement and control capabilities of the agencies are not better than those of the manufacturers. In the final analysis, the accuracy of sampling, of sizing, or of measuring any aerosol parameter depends on the experience and skill of the operator in adjusting the instrument, in carrying out the procedure being used, and in interpreting the data developed by the system.

10.4.4.2 Data Processing

In characterizing aerosol samples, particularly for concentration and/or size data, it must be remembered that a sample is procured from a much larger population. If the sample is too small, then variability from point to point, even within a single air parcel, will result in wide differences among measurements. Thus, if very small samples are obtained, then the variance may be unacceptably large. On the other hand, if the sample is too large or too concentrated, instrumental operation limits can introduce errors. Consider single-particle counting instruments as one example. Individual particles are examined within the finite sensing volume of the instrument. As a concentration of particles increases, even though randomly distributed within an air sample, there is a finite probability that more than one particle may occur within that sensing volume. This situation can be referred to as "coincidence," which is a statistically defined error that increases exponentially as actual concentration increases (Jaenicke 1972).

If one wishes to convert data from one instrument to another, it is necessary to convert, for example, particle-number data from one instrument to particle-volume data (with specific-gravity correction) for another instrument, or vice versa. In addition, the effect of the breadth of the particle distribution, as well as the more mundane problem of good operating and sampling protocol, must be included in the conversion process.

Once the particular problems have been defined and the objectives for sampling stated clearly, a protocol is selected in accordance with desired data presentation. Then, one should consider the objectives of data collection and select optimum procedures. Obviously, for the characterization of a specific aerosol sample, one procures the largest possible fraction of that sample and carries out necessary analyses on the material. On the other hand, to characterize the aerosol in a larger air parcel, one should select sample sizes, sample locations that are representative of the overall air sample, and determine a sampling schedule that will represent the typical operation within the area or the environmental factors that may affect the aerosol. That is, the sampling schedule should include some consideration of activities within the environment that is analyzed. If one is inspecting activities within a manufacturing plant, then sampling should be carried out during the manufacturing workday. If one is examining long-term atmospheric effects, then both day and night sampling must be carried out to include the effects of diurnal variations in natural and human activities.

On the other hand, sometimes only abnormal conditions may be of interest. In this case, the question of records, their disposition, and/or storage arises. One may consider the possibility of storing data for a fixed period of time and continuously cleaning out and discarding data that have been stored for a given time period. Alternatively, one may consider the possibility of acquiring and storing data only when an out-of-specification condition occurs, and ignoring the acquired particle-characterization data the rest of the time. Even with present computerized high-density data-storage systems, the quantity of data that can be acquired and recorded from particle-measuring systems can be enormous. It is possible to encode and store large quantities of data that describe routine conditions in great detail but do not justify more than the simple description "satisfactory." That type of information should be recorded and stored only if there is a requirement that the details of such data be maintained.

A variety of instruments, devices, and procedures for the sampling and analysis of aerosols have been described here. A question always asked when one begins such a program refers to the selection of the optimum system for the particular problem. Unfortunately, there is no simple answer. One must first define the problem in terms of the objectives of sampling and analysis, the accuracy of data required, the averaging time and sampling frequency (for transient and unstable systems), the type of data desired and the volume of data that can be handled, the allowable response time for data production, the scale of effort that can be applied, the skill level of available operators, the funding available for purchase or lease of equipment, the funding available for consumables, the service and maintenance requirements, the choice of laboratory versus field instrument types, the portability of samples and/or of instruments, the environmental constraints, and the system capabilities. In addition, it may be necessary to include some intangible factors, such as the possible necessity for correlation with historical data (witness the continuing use of the fallout collector) for coordination with participating organizations in a group study or because enforced inheritance defines available equipment. In selecting a system for aerosol sampling and analysis, one examines the details of the problem and chooses an instrument system, a sampling and analysis protocol, and data-processing procedures in accordance with those details. The device performance characteristics discussed in this chapter should be of assistance in making these choices.

10.5 Nomenclature for Chapter 10

ROMAN LETTERS

a	probe half spacing, m
a	fraction of fluorescence received by detector
a	constant
A	admittance, S
A	cross-sectional area, m^2
A	electrode surface area, m^2
A_c	admittance of gauge immersed in liquid phase, S
A_i	inside surface area, m^2
A_o	outside surface area, m^2
c	dyestuff concentration, kg/m^3
c_f	dyestuff concentration in film, kg/m^3
c_m	mixed mean dyestuff concentration, kg/m^3
dc_r	number of counts received from mass element dm
C	Chisholm parameter, [10.2.40] and [10.2.41]
C	conductance, S
C	droplet concentration, kg/m^3
C	concentration parameter
C_B	concentration of ferricyanide ions in bulk electrolyte, mol/m^3
C_{dG}	gas drag coefficient
C_{dL}	liquid drag coefficient
C_i	counts received in ith time interval
C_G	gas-phase conductance, S/cm
C_G	gas-phase dielectric constant
C_L	liquid-phase conductance, S/cm
C_L	liquid-phase dielectric constant
$C_{L,t}$	coefficient in [10.2.26] and [10.2.27]
$C_{G,t}$	coefficient in [10.2.26] and [10.2.27]
C_{pL}	liquid specific heat, J/kg K
C_W	concentration of ferricyanide ions at electrode, mol/m^3
d	drop, bubble, or particle diameter, m

d_1	diameter of center electrode, m
d_2	diameter of insulated zone, m
$\bar{d}_{32}$	Sauter mean diameter, [10.2.71], m
d_0	tube diameter, m
D	droplet deposition rate, kg/m^2 s
$\mathfrak{D}$	domain
D_{AB}	diffusion coefficient, m^2/s
E	energy of incident photon, MeV
E	fluorescence efficiency
E	entrainment rate, kg/m^2 s
E'	energy of scattered photons, MeV
f	function
F	Faraday number, C/mol
F_E	fraction of liquid phase entrained
g	acceleration due to gravity, m/s^2
G^*	nondimensional admittance, [10.2.45]
h	nondimensional film thickness, [10.2.47]
h_{c1}	cooling-water inlet enthalpy, J/kg
h_{c2}	cooling-water outlet enthalpy, J/kg
h_0	condensate enthalpy, J/kg
h_L	saturation enthalpy of liquid, J/kg
h_{LG}	latent heat of vaporization, J/kg
h_{TP}	two-phase enthalpy, J/kg
i_0	optical system response
I	measured photon beam intensity, photons/m^2 s
I	current, A
I	droplet interchange rate, kg/m^2 s
I_A	intensity scattered in direction close to that of incident beam, photons/m^2 s
I_B	intensity scattered backward at angle close to 180° with respect to incident beam, photons/m^2 s
I_d	momentum flux, kg m^3/s^2
I_G	photon beam intensity after passage through tube filled with vapor phase, photons/m^2 s
I_L	photon beam intensity after passage through tube full of liquid phase, photons/m^2 s
$I_{\lim}$	limiting current in electrochemical method for shear stress, [10.2.56], A
I_0	photon intensity of incident beam, photons/m^2 s
j	local volumetric flux, [10.1.20] m^3/m^2 s
J	superficial velocity, [10.1.24] m/s
k	droplet mass transfer coefficient, m/s
k_1-k_4	coefficients in [10.2.53]
k_c	mass transfer coefficient, m/s
k_L	liquid thermal conductivity, W/m K
k_W	thermal conductivity of wall material, W/m K
l_1	characteristic length, m
l_2	characteristic length, m

L	length, m
m	film thickness, m
$\dot{m}$	mass velocity, $kg/m^2 s$
$\dot{m}_G$	gas mass flux, kg/m^2 s
$\dot{m}_L$	liquid mass flux, kg/m^2 s
dm	mass element, kg
M	dimensionless group defined by [10.2.51]
$\dot{M}$	mass rate of flow, kg/s
$\dot{M}_G$	gas-phase mass rate of flow, kg/s
$\dot{M}_L$	liquid-phase mass rate of flow, kg/s
$\dot{M}_{LE1}$	entrained-liquid flow rate at $z = 0$, kg/s
$\dot{M}_{LE2}$	entrained-liquid flow rate at $z = z_D$, kg/s
n	number
N	exponent in [10.2.72]
p	pressure, N/m^2
Δp	pressure drop, N/m^2
Δp_G	pressure drop for gas phase flowing alone in system, N/m^2
Δp_L	pressure drop for liquid phase flowing alone in system, N/m^2
Δp_{TP}	two-phase pressure drop, N/m^2
$\dot{q}$	heat flux, W/m^2
$\dot{q}_E$	end-zone heat flux, W/m^2
Q	volumetric flow rate, m^3 s
$\dot{Q}$	heat transfer rate, W
r	radius, m
r_i	inside radius, m
r_o	outside radius, m
$\mathbf{r}$	position vector
R	count rate, s^{-1}
R	space fraction, [10.1.4]
R	resistance, Ω
R	Rayleigh ratio
R_{12}	cross-correlation coefficient, [10.2.68]
R_{G1}	line-averaged void fraction
R_{G2}	area-averaged void fraction
R_{G3}	volume-averaged void fraction
s_1	reading of sensor 1
s_2	reading of sensor 2
t	time, s
T	temperature, K
T	total time of measurement, s
T	time interval, s
T_0	hot-film-probe wall temperature, K
T_∞	bulk temperature, K
ΔT	extent of temperature rise following burnout, K
ΔT_1	temperature difference between streams at inlet of heat exchange system, K
ΔT_2	temperature difference between streams at outlet of heat exchange system, K

ΔT_{LM}	logarithmic mean temperature difference, [10.2.18], K
ΔT_W	temperature difference across electrically heated tube, K
U	overall heat transfer coefficient, W/m^2 K
U	flow velocity, m/s
U_m	mass-averaged velocity, m/s
U_t	volume flux past turbine coil, m^3/s
U_z	component of velocity vector, m/s
v	superficial velocity, m/s
V	volume, m^3
v	voltage change, **V**
v	velocity associated with mass element *dm*, m/s
Δv	voltage drop, V
W_c	cooling-water flow rate, kg/s
W_0	condensate flow rate, kg/s
x	wall thickness, m
x	quality
x	width of cathode, m
x	width of heated layer, m
X	phase density function, [10.1.1]
X	Martinelli parameter, [10.2.40]
X	characterizing factor, [10.2.72], m
y	distance from wall, m
z_{12}	distance between measuring stations, m
z_D	deposition length, m
z_0	distance light beam travels through dispersion, m
Z	axial distance, m

GREEK LETTERS

α	characterizing parameter in Mie theory ($= 2\pi d/\lambda$)
α	local time fraction [10.1.12]
α_i	heat transfer coefficient on the inside surface, W/m^2 K
α_L	liquid thermal diffusivity, m^2/s
α_0	heat transfer coefficient on the outside surface, W/m^2 K
β	volumetric quality
β	temperature coefficient of resistance, K^{-1}
γ	fraction of surface overheated by amount ΔT, [10.2.20]
γ	specific conductivity, S/m
ϵ	fraction of volume occupied by bubbles or drops
ϵ	dielectric constant
ϵ_0	electric constant of free space, F/m
ϵ_G	void fraction
θ	angle of inclination (inclined manometer)
θ	scattering angle
λ	ratio of distances between probe centerline and outer and inner edges of conducting strips

λ	decay coefficient, [10.2.33], s^{-1}
λ	wavelength, m
μ_G	gas viscosity, kg/ms
μ_L	liquid viscosity, kg/m s
ρ	density, kg/m^3
$\bar{\rho}$	homogeneous mean density, kg/m^3
ρ_c	line fluid density, kg/m^3
ρ_G	gas density, kg/m^3
ρ_L	liquid density, kg/m^3
ρ_m	manometric fluid density, kg/m^3
ρ_t	mean density of fluid in channel, kg/m^3
σ	standard deviation in counts
τ	counting time, s
τ	relaxation time
τ	time interval [10.2.68], s
τ_0	wall shear stress, N/m^2
τ_M	time interval at which R_{12} is a maximum, s
ϕ	angle of incident beam
ω	angular velocity, rad/s

SUBSCRIPTS

k	phase index
n	domain index

OPERATORS

$\langle\!\langle\ \rangle\!\rangle$	space-averaging operator over $\mathfrak{D}$, [10.1.2]
$\langle\ \rangle$	space-averaging operator over $\mathfrak{D}_k$, [10.1.3]
$\overline{}$	time-averaging operator over T, [10.1.10]
$\overline{}^X$	time-averaging operator over T_k [10.1.11]

10.6 References for Chapter 10

Adams, F. C. & Van Grieken, R. E. 1975 Absorption Correction for X-Ray Fluorescence Analysis of Aerosol Loaded Filters, *Anal. Chem.* 47:1167–1773.

Adnams, D. J., Salt, K. J., & Wintle, C. A. 1972 The Development of Instruments for the Detection of Dryout in Uniform and Non-Uniform Axially Heated Rod Clusters, *Rept.* AEEW-R574, UKAEA, Winfrith.

Agostini, G. & Premoli, A. 1971 Valvola di Intercettazione Rapida per Imprego a Aqua-Vapore, *Energ. Nucl. Milan* 18:295–310.

Agostini, G., Era, A., & Premoli, A. 1971 Density Measurements of Steam-Water Mixtures Flowing in a Tubular Channel under Adiabatic and Heat Conditions, *CISE Milan Rept.* CISE-R-291.

Ahlquist, N. C. & Charlson, R. J. 1969 Measurement of the Wavelength Dependence of Atmospheric Extension Due to Scatter, *Atmos. Environ.* 3:551–564.

Aksan, S. N. & Rose, J. W. 1973 Dropwise Condensation—The Effect of Thermal Properties of the Condenser Material, *Int. J. Heat Mass Transfer* 16:461–467.

Alexander, L. G. & Coldren, C. L. 1951 Droplet Transfer from Suspending Air to Duct Wall, *Ind. Eng. Chem.* 43:1325–1331.

Alia, P., Cravarolo, L., Hassid, A., & Pedrocchi, E. 1968 Phase and Velocity Distribution in Two Phase Adiabatic Annular Dispersed Flow, *Euratom rept.* EUR 3759E.

Allen, R. J. & Evans, W. E. 1972 Laser Radar (LIDAR) for Mapping Aerosol Structure, *Rev. Sci. Instrum.* 43:1422–1432.

Altpeter, L. L. 1975 New Analytical Prospects for an Old Detector, *Proc. Int. Conf. Environmental Sensing Analysis, Las Vegas.*

Anderson, G. H. & Hills, P. D. 1974 Two Phase Annular Flow in Tube Bends, *Inst. Chem. Eng. Symp. Ser.* 38:paper J1.

Anderson, R. J. & Russell, T. W. F. 1970 Film Formation in Two-Phase Annular Flow, *AIChE J.* 16:626–633.

Andreussi, P. & Zanelli, S. 1976 Liquid Phase Mass Transfer in Annular Two Phase Flow, *Ing. Chim. Ital.* 12:132–136.

Appel, B. R., Colodny, P., & Wesolowski, J. J. 1976 Analysis of Carbonaceous Materials in Southern California Atmospheric Aerosols, *Environ. Sci. Technol.* 10:359–363.

Arave, A. E., Colson, J. B., & Fincke, J. R. 1977 Full Flow Drag Screen, *Proc. Meet. Review Group Two-Phase Flow Instrumentation,* paper 1.5; *Rept.* NUREG-0375, U.S. Nuclear Regulatory Commission.

Aya, I. 1975 A Model to Calculate Mass Flow Rate and Other Quantities of Two-Phase Flow in a Pipe with a Densitometer, a Drag Disk and a Turbine Meter, *Rept.* ORNL-TM-47591, Oak Ridge Natl. Lab.

Azzopardi, B. J. 1977 Measurement of Drop Sizes, *Rept.* AERE-R8667, UKAEA, Harwell (see also *Int. J. Heat Mass Transfer* 22:1245–1279, 1979).

Azzopardi, B. J. 1978 Consideration of the Fluorescence Film Thickness Technique, *Oxford Univ. Engineering Lab. Rept.* 1229/78.

Azzopardi, B. J., Serizawa, A., & King, D. J. 1977 The Behaviour and Effect of Bubbles within Pressure Tapping Lines and Orifices, *Rept.* AERE-R8792, UKAEA, Harwell.

Azzopardi, B. J., Freeman, G., & Whalley, P. B. 1978 Drop Sizes in Annular Two-Phase Flow, *Rept.* AERE-R9074, UKAEA, Harwell.

Bailey, N. A. 1977 Dryout and Post-Dryout Heat Transfer at Low Flow in a Single Tube Test Section, *Rept.* AEEW-R1068, UKAEA, Winfrith.

Banerjee, S., Heidrick, T. R., & Rhodes, E. 1978a Development and Calibration of Instruments for Measurements in Transient Two Phase Flow, *2d OECD/NEA/CSNI Specialists Meet. Transient Two-Phase Flow, Paris,* paper I4.

Banerjee, S., Heidrick, T. R., Saltvold, J. R., & Flemons, R. S. 1978b Measurement of Void Fraction and Mass Velocity in Transient Two-Phase Flow, *Transient Two-Phase Flow,* eds. S. Banerjee & K. R. Weaver, pp. 789–834, Atomic Energy Canada Ltd., Toronto.

Barnes, E. C. & Penney, G. W. 1938 An Electrostatic Dust Weight Sampler, *J. Ind. Hyg. Toxicol.* **20**:259–265.

Barschdorff, D., Class, G., Loffel, R., & Reimann, J. 1978 Mass Flow Measuring Techniques in Transient Two Phase Flow, *Transient Two Phase Flow,* eds. S. Banerjee & K. R. Weaver, pp. 835–867, Atomic Energy of Canada Ltd., Toronto.

Begnoche, B. C. & Risby, T. H. 1975 Determination of Metals in Atmospheric Particulates Using Low Volume Sampling and Flameless Atomic Absorption Spectrometry, *Anal. Chem.* **47**:1041–1045.

Benarie, B. M. 1965 Microdynamometric Evidence of Dust Particles, *Proc. 4th Annual Conf. Aerosol Technology, Mainz.*

Benn, D. N. 1972 An Experimental Capacitance Liquid Film Thickness Monitor, Operating Instructions and Circuit Details, *Rept.* AERE-R7155, UKAEA, Harwell.

Benn, D. & Shock, R. A. W. 1974 An Infra-Red Burnout Detector, *Rept.* AERE-R7338, UKAEA, Harwell.

Bennett, J. A. R., Collier, J. G., Pratt, H. R. C., & Thornton, J. D. 1959 Heat Transfer to Two Phase Gas-Liquid Systems, I: Steam Water Mixtures in the Liquid Dispersed Region in an Annulus, *Rept.* AERE-R3159, UKAEA, Harwell.

Benson, P. A. & Gleit, C. E. 1963 Neutron Activation and Radio Chemical Determination of Molybdenum, Chromium and Iron Content of Individual Microspheres, *Anal. Chem.* **35**:1029–1032.

Berglund, R. N. & Liu, B. T. H. 1973 Generation of Monodisperse Aerosol Standards, *Environ. Sci. Technol.* **7**:147–153.

Bigg, E. K., Ono, A., & Williams, J. A. 1974 Chemical Tests for Individual Sub-Micron Aerosol Particles, *Atmos. Environ.* **8**:1–13.

Binek, B. & Dohnalova, B. 1967 Using the Scintillation Spectrometer for Aerosols and Research in Industry, *Staub* **27**:1–7.

Birchenough, A. & Mason, J. S. 1977 Particle Velocity and Axial Turbulence Intensity Measurements in a Dilute Gas-Side Suspension Flowing Vertically Upwards, *J. Powder Bulk Solids Technol.* **1**:6–12.

Birks, L. S. 1978 Pinpointing Airborne Pollutants, *Environ. Sci. Technol.* **12**:150–153.

Bond, C. P., Berry, D. J., & Crawley, J. A. 1972 The Quantimet 720P for Routine Biological Assay and Potency Calculation, *Microscope* **20**:165–174.

Borgartz, B. O., O'Brien, T. P., Rees, N. J. M., & Smith, A. V. 1969 Experimental Studies of Water Depressurization through Simple Pipe Systems. *Symp. on Depressurization Effects in Water Cooled Power Reactors,* Batelle Inst., Frankfurt.

Bouman, H., van Koppen, C. W. J., & Raas, L. J. 1974 Some Investigations of the Influence of the Heat Flux on the Flow Patterns in Vertical Boiler Tubes, *European Two-Phase Flow Group Meeting,* Harwell, June, paper A2.

Bremhorst, K. & Gilmore D. B. 1976 Response of Hot Wire Anemometer Probes to a Stream of Air Bubbles in a Water Flow, *J. Phys. E.* **9**:347–352.

Breslin, J. A. & Stein, R. L. 1975 Efficiency of Dust Sampling Inlets in Calm Air, *Am. Ind. Hyg. Assoc. J.* **36**:576–583.

British Standards House 1963 Methods for the Determination of Particle Size of Powders, British Standard 3406, part 4, London.

Brockett, G. F. & Johnson, R. T. 1976 Single-Phase and Two-Phase Flow Measurement Techniques for Reactor Safety Studies, *Rept.* EPRI-NP-195, Electric Power Research Inst., Palo Alto, Calif.

Brown, D. J. 1978 Disequilibrium in Annular Flows, Ph.D. thesis, Oxford Univ.

Bruce, C. W. & Pinnick, R. G. 1977 In Situ Measurements of Aerosol Absorption with a Resonant CW Laser Spectrophone, *Appl. Optics* 16:1762–1764.

Butterworth, D. 1968 Air-Water Climbing Film Flow in an Eccentric Annulus, *Rept.* AERE-R5787, UKAEA, Harwell.

Butterworth, D. & Pulling, D. J. 1973 Film Flow and Film Thickness Measurements in Horizontal Annular Air-Water Flow, *Rept.* AERE-R7576, UKAEA, Harwell.

Butterworth, D., Hazell, F. C., & Pulling, D. J. 1974 A Technique for Measuring Local Heat Transfer Coefficients in a Horizontal Tube, *I. Chem. Eng. Symp.* no. 38, paper D1.

Calderbank, B. H. 1958 Physical Rate Processes in Industrial Fermentation, I: The Interfacial Area in Gas-Liquid Contacting with Mechanical Agitation, *Trans. Inst. Chem. Eng.* 36:443–463.

Chabay, I. & Bright, D. S. 1977 Measurement of the Size Distribution of Liquid and Solid Aerosols by Doppler Shift Spectroscopy, *Proc. American Chemical Society Symp. Light Scattering, New Orleans.*

Chan, T. & Lippmann, M. 1977 Particle Collection Efficiencies of Air Sampling Cyclones: An Empirical Theory, *Environ. Sci. Technol.* 11:377–382.

Charlson, R. J., Horvath, H., & Pueschel, R. F. 1967 The Direct Measurement of Atmospheric Light Scattering Coefficient, *Atmos. Environ.* 1:469–478.

Chisholm, D. 1972 The Compressible Flow of Two-Phase Mixtures through Orifices, Nozzles and Venturi Meters, *NEL Rept.* 549, pp. 66–79, Natl. Engineering Lab., East Kilbride, Scotland.

Chojnowski, B. & Wilson, P. W. 1972a Critical Heat Flux for Large Wall Boiler Tubes, *Rept.* CEGB-R-M-M652, Central Electricity Generating Board, U.K.

Chojnowski, B. & Wilson, P. W. 1972b Critical Heat Flux for Steam Generating Tubes When Heated by Thermal Radiation from One Side, *European Two-Phase Flow Group Meet., Rome,* paper B5.

Clark, C. L. 1963 Encyclopedia of X-rays and Gamma Rays, Reinhold, New York.

Class, G., Hain, K. et al. 1979 True Mass Flow Meter, Entwicklung und Einsatz eines Massenstrom-Messgerätes für instationäre Zweiphasenströmungen, *KfK-Bericht* 2790.

Collier, J. G. & Hewitt, G. F. 1964 Film Thickness Measurements, *Rept.* AERE-R4684, UKAEA, Harwell.

Colombo, A. & Premoli, A. 1972 An Experimental Investigation on the Use of Elbows as Two-Phase Quality Meters, *European Two-Phase Flow Group Meet., Rome,* paper D9.

Coney, M. W. E. 1973 The Theory and Application of Conductance Probes for the Measurement of Liquid Film Thickness in Two-Phase Flow, *J. Phys.* 6:903–910.

Coney, M. W. E. & Fisher, S. A. 1976 Instrumentation for Two-Phase Flow in Use or Under Development at the Central Electricity Research Laboratories, European Two-Phase Flow Group Meeting, Erlangen, paper B2.

Cooke, D. D. & Kerker, M. 1975 Response Calculations for Light Scattering Aerosol Particle Counters, *Appl. Optics,* 14:734–739.

Coulter, W. H. 1956 High Speed Automatic Blood Cell Counter and Cell Size Analyzer, *Proc. National Electronics Conf., Chicago.*

Cousins, L. B. & Hewitt, G. F. 1968a Liquid Phase Mass Transfer in Annular Two-Phase Flow: Radial Liquid Mixing, *Rept.* AERE-R5693, UKAEA, Harwell.

Cousins, L. B. & Hewitt, G. F. 1968b Liquid Phase Mass Transfer in Annular Two Phase Flow: Droplet Deposition and Liquid Entrainment, *Rept.* AERE-R5657, UKAEA, Harwell.

Cousins, L. B., Denton, W. H., & Hewitt, G. F. 1965 Liquid Mass Transfer in Annular Two-Phase Flow, *Symp. Two Phase Flow, Exeter,* paper C4; *Rept.* AERE-R4926, UKAEA, Harwell.

Cravarolo, L., Georgina, A., Hassid, A., & Pedrocchi, E. 1964 A Device for the Measurement of Shear Stress on the Wall of a Conduit, Its Application in the Mean Density Determination in Two-Phase Flow, Shear Stress Data in Two-Phase Adiabatic Vertical Flow, *CISE Milan Rept.* CISE-R-82.

Cronn, D. R., Charlson, R. J., Knight, R. L., Crittenden, A. L., & Appel, B. R. 1977 A Survey of the Molecular Nature of Primary and Secondary Components of Particles in Urban Air by High Resolution Mass Spectrometry, *Atmos. Environ.* 11:929–937.

Cunningham, P. T., Johnson, S. A., & Yang, R. T. 1974 Variations in Chemistry of Airborne Particulate Material with Particle Size and Time, *Environ. Sci. Technol.* 8:131–135.

Danel, F. & Delhaye, J. M. 1971 Sonde Optique pour Mesure du Taux de Présence Local en Ecoulement Diphasique, *Mes. Regulation Autom.*, pp. 99–101.

Davies, C. N. 1968 The Entry of Aerosols into Sampling Tubes and Heads, *Br. J. Appl. Phys.*, 1:921–932.

Davis, W. D. 1977 Continuous Mass Spectrometric Analysis of Particulates by Use of Surface Ionization, *Environ. Sci. Technol.* 11:587–592.

Deich, M. E., Saltanov, G. A., & Kurshakov, A. V. 1971 Investigating the Kinetics of Phase Transitions in Shock Waves in Wet Steam Flow, *Thermal Eng.* 18:127–131.

Deich, M. E., Tsiklauri, G. W., & Shanin, V. K. 1972 Investigation of Flows of Wet Steam in Nozzles, *High Temp.* 10:102–107.

Delhaye, J. M. 1969 Hot-Film Anemometry, in *Two-Phase Flow Instrumentation,* eds. B. W. LeTourneau & A. E. Bergles, pp. 58–69, ASME, New York.

Delhaye, J. M. & Achard, J. L. 1977 On the Use of Averaging Operators in Two-Phase Flow Modeling, in *Thermal and Hydraulic Aspects of Nuclear Reactor Safety,* vol. 1, *Light Water Reactors,* eds. O. C. Jones & S. G. Bankoff, pp. 289–332, ASME, New York.

Delhaye, J. M. & Achard, J. L. 1978 On the Averaging Operators Introduced in Two-Phase Flow Modeling, in *Transient Two-Phase Flow,* eds. S. Banerjee, & K. R. Weaver, vol. 1, pp. 5–84, Atomic Energy of Canada Ltd., Toronto.

Delhaye, J. M., Semeria, R., & Flamand, J. C. 1973 Void Fraction, Vapor and Liquid Temperatures: Local Measurements in Two-Phase Flow Using a Micro-Thermocouple, *J. Heat Transfer* 95:365–370.

DeMaio, L. & Corn, M. 1966 Gas Chromatographic Analysis of Polynuclear Aeromatic Hydrocarbons with Packed Columns, *Anal. Chem.* 38:131–133.

Desaedeleer, G. G., Winchester, J. W., & Akselsson, K. R. 1977 Monitoring Aerosol Elemental Composition in Particle Size Fractions for Predicting Human Respiratory Uptake, *Nucl. Instrum. Methods* 142:97–99.

Doe, P. E. 1967 A New Method of Measuring Humidity in a Small Space, *Int. J. Heat Mass Transfer* 10:311–319.

Dresia, H. & Mucha, R. 1974 Registering Radiometric Measuring Instrument for Combined Measurement of the Immisions of Dust and Radioactivity in Air, *Staub* 34:103–106.

Dulka, J. J. & Risby, T. H. 1976 Ultra-trace Metals in Some Environmental and Biological Systems, *Anal. Chem.* 48:640A–653A.

Dussourd, J. L. & Shapiro, A. H. 1955 A Deceleration Probe for Measuring Stagnation Pressure and Velocity of a Particle-laden Gas Stream, *M.I.T. Rept. contract* N50 M-07878.

Dzubay, T. G. & Stephens, R. K. 1975 Ambient Air Analysis with Dichotomous Sampler and X-Ray Fluorescent Spectrometer, *Environ. Sci. Technol.* 9:663–668.

Engelhard, H. & Friess, H. 1937 Uber die Brauchbarkeit des Mieeffektes zur Teilchengrossenbestimmung weisser Aerosole, insbesondere grobdisperser weisser Aerosole, *Kolloid. Z.* 81:129–142.

Engler, C. & von Holzer, G. 1977 Fitting of Thermocouples into the Cladding Walls of Electrically Heated Experimental Fuel Pins, Proceedings of a Specialist Conference, Hannover, Experimental Techniques in the Field of Thermodynamics and Fluid Dynamics, II: Thermometry Techniques and Simulation of Thermodynamic Processes, 115, Interatom, Berg-Gladbach, West Germany.

Farmer, W. M. 1972 Measurement of Particle Size, Number Density, and Velocity Using a Laser Interferometer, *Appl. Opt.* 11:2603–2612.

Fincke, J. R. & Deason, V. A. 1979 The Measurement of Phase Velocities in Mist Flows Using Stagnation Probes, *Rept.* NUREG-CR-0648, TREE-1350, U.S. Nuclear Regulatory Commission.

Fletcher, A. H. 1950 Pollens: Sampling in Control Source, *Ind. Med. Surg. J.* 19:129–140.

France, D. M. 1974 Liquid Metal Heated DNB Experiments in High Pressure Forced Convection Boiling of Freon-12, *Inst. Chem. Eng. Symp. Ser.* 38:paper E4.

Frank, R., Mazars, J., & Ricque, R. 1977 Determination of Mass Flow Rate and Quality Using a Turbine Meter and a Venturi, *Proc. Conf. Heat Fluid Flow Water Reactor Safety, Manchester,* pp. 63–68.

Freudenthal, P. 1971 High Collection Efficiency of the Aerotec-3 Cyclone for Sub-Micron Particles, *Atmos. Environ.* 5:151–154.

Friedlander, S. K. 1965 The Similarity Theory of the Particle Size Distribution of the Atmospheric Aerosol, in *Aerosols,* ed. K. R. Spurny, pp. 115–130, Gordon and Breach, New York.

Fuchs, N. A. 1975 Review Papers–Sampling of Aerosols, *Atmos. Environ.* 9:697–707.

Galaup, J. P. 1975 Contribution à l'Etude des Méthodes de Mesure en Ecoulement Diphasique, thèse de docteur-ingénieur, Univ. Scientifique et Médicale de Grenoble, Inst. National Polytechnique de Grenoble.

Gavrilovic, J. & Majewski, E. 1977 Use of Ion and Electron Microprobes for Full Characterization of Particulate Matter, *Am. Lab.* 9:19–28.

Gill, L. E., Hewitt, G. F., Hitchon, J. W., & Lacey, P. M. C. 1963 Sampling Probe Studies of the Gas Core in Annular Two-Phase Flow, I: The Effect of Length on Phase and Velocity Distribution, *Chem. Eng. Sci.* 18:525–535.

Gill, L. E., Hewitt, G. F., & Lacey, P. M. C. 1964 Sampling Probe Studies of the Gas Core in Annular Two-Phase Flow, II: Studies of the Effect of Phase Flow Rate on Phase and Velocity Distribution, *Chem. Eng. Sci.* 19:665–682.

Goetz, A. 1962 Instrumentation for Determining Size and Mass Distribution of Sub-Micron Aerosols, *J. Air Pollut. Control Assoc.* 12:479–486.

Goldschmidt, V. W. 1965 Measurement of Aerosol Concentration with a Hot Wire Anemometer, *J. Colloid Sci.* 20:617–634.

Gonia, P. S., Mueller, R. K., & Collins, R. J. 1978 Interferometric Measurement of Optical Extinction Cross Section, *Proc. Powder Conf.,* Chicago.

Gravatt, C. C. 1973 Real Time Measurement of the Size Distribution of Particulate Matter in Air by Light Scattering Method, *J. Air Pollut. Control Assoc.* 23:1035–1038.

Green, S. J. 1967 Some Experimental Techniques Used in Reactor Heat Transfer and Fluid Flow Research, *Rept.* WAPD-TM-386, Westinghouse Electric Co.

Gucker, F. T., Tuma, J., Lin, H.-M., Huang, C.-M., Ems, S. C., & Marshall, T. R. 1973 Rapid Measurement of Light Scattering Diagrams from Single Particles in an Aerosol Stream and Determination of Latex Particle Size, *J. Aerosol. Sci.* 4:389–404.

Gustafsson, B. & Kjellen, B. 1971 Two Phase Flow in a Nine Rod Bundle with Inclined Power Distribution, *European Two-Phase Flow Group Meet., Riso, Denmark,* paper A5.

Hain, K., Brüderle, F., et al. 1980 Flüssigkeitsdämpfung der Statorschwingungen am True Mass Flow Meter 50 einem Massentrom-Messgerät Für instationäre Zweiphasenströmungen, *KFK-Bericht* 3031.

Harris, D. M. 1967 Calibration of a Steam Quality Meter for Channel Par Measurement in the Prototype SGHW Reactor, *European Two-Phase Flow Group Meet., Bournemouth.*

Hawes, R. I. 1976 Heater Pins for LOCA Simulation Studies, *European Two-Phase Flow Group Meet., Erlangen,* paper B6.

Hercules, D. M. 1978 Challenges in Surface Analysis, *Anal. Chem.* 50:734A–744A.

Hering, S. V., Flagan, R. C., & Friedlander, S. K. 1978 Design and Evaluation of New Low Pressure Impactors, *Environ. Sci. Technol.* 12:667–673.

Herringe, R. A. & Davis, M. R. 1976 Structural Development of Gas-Liquid Mixture Flows, *J. Fluid Mech.* 73:97–123.

Hewitt, G. F. 1970 Experimental Studies on the Mechanism of Burnout in Heat Transfer to Steam-Water Mixtures, *Proc. 4th Int. Heat Transfer Conf., Versailles,* paper B6.6.

Hewitt, G. F. 1972 The Role of Experiments in Two-Phase Systems with Particular Reference to Measurement Techniques, *Prog. Heat Mass Transfer* 6:295–343.

Hewitt, G. F. 1978a *Measurement of Two Phase Flow Parameters,* Academic, New York.

Hewitt, G. F. 1978b Liquid Mass Transport in Annular Two Phase Flow, invited lecture at the 1978 International Seminar of the International Centre for Heat and Mass Transfer, Dubrovnik.

Hewitt, G. F. & Hall-Taylor, N. S. 1970 *Annular Two Phase Flow,* Pergamon, Oxford.

Hewitt, G. F. & Nicholls, B. 1969 Film Thickness Measurement in Annular Two-Phase Flow Using a Fluorescence Spectrometer Technique, II: Studies of the Shape of Disturbance Waves, *Rept.* AERE-R4506, UKAEA, Harwell.

Hewitt, G. F. & Whalley, P. B. 1979 Advanced Optical Instrumentation Methods, invited lecture at the EPRI Workshop on Basic Two Phase Flow Modeling and Reactor Safety and Performance, Tampa.

Hewitt, G. F., King, R. D., & Lovegrove, P. C. 1962 Techniques for Liquid Film Pressure Drop Studies in Annular Two Phase Flow, *Rept.* AERE-R3921, UKAEA, Harwell.

Hewitt, G. F., Lovegrove, P. C., & Nicholls, B. 1964 Film Thickness Measurement Using a Fluorescence Technique, I: Description of the Method, *Rept.* AERE-R4478, UKAEA, Harwell.

Hewitt, G. F., Kearsey, H. A., Lacey, P. M. C., & Pulling, D. J. 1965 Burnout and Film Flow in the Evaporation of Water in Tubes, *Rept.* AERE-R4864, UKAEA, Harwell.

Hewitt, G. F., Kearsey, H. A., & Keeys, R. K. F. 1969 Determination of Rate of Droplet Deposition in a Heated Tube with Steam-Water Flow at 1000 psia, *Rept.* AERE-R6118, UKAEA, Harwell.

Hochreiner, D. 1971 A New Centrifuge to Measure the Aerodynamic Diameter of Aerosol Particles in the Sub-Micron Range, *J. Colloid Interface Sci.* 36:191–194.

Hodkinson, J. R. 1966 The Optical Measurement of Aerosols, in *Aerosol Science,* ed. C. N. Davies, chap. 10, Academic, London.

Hotham, G. A. 1974 Sizing Aerosols in Real Time by Pulsing UV Laser Machine, in *Aerosol Measurements,* eds. W. A. Cassatt & R. S. Maddock, N.B.S. special publication 412, U.S. National Bureau of Standards, Gaithersburg, Md.

Hsu, Y. Y., Simon, F. F., & Graham, R. W. 1963 Application of Hot-Wire Anemometry for Two-Phase Flow Measurements Such as Void Fraction and Slip-Velocity, in *Multiphase Flow Symposium,* ed. N. J. Lipstein, pp. 26–34, ASME, New York.

Hudson, J. G. & Squires, P. 1973 Evaluation of a Recording Continuous Cloud Nucleus Counter, *J. Appl. Meteorol.* 12:175–183.

Husar, R. B. 1974 Atmospheric Particulate Mass Monitoring with a Beta Radiation Detector, *Atmos. Environ.* 8:183–188.

Hylton, J. (Oak Ridge National Laboratory) 1979 Private communication.

Ishigai, S., Yamane, M., & Roko, K. 1965 Measurement of Component Flows in a Vertical Two Phase Flow by Making Use of the Pressure Fluctuations, *Bull. JSME* 8:375–390.

Jackson, C. 1976 A Wheatstone Bridge Burnout Detector, *Rept.* AERE-R8363, UKAEA, Harwell.

Jaenicke, R. 1972 The Optical Particle Counter: Cross Sensitivity and Coincidence, *J. Aerosol Sci.* 5:95–111.

Jennings, B. R. & Morris, V. J. 1974 Light Scattering by Bacteria No. 2, *J. Colloid Interface Sci.* 49:89–97.

Johnson, H. A. & Abou-Sabe, A. H. 1952 Heat Transfer and Pressure Drop for Turbulent Flow of Air-Water Mixtures in a Horizontal Tube, *Trans. ASME* 74:977–987.

Jones, A. P. 1977 A Review of Drop Size Measurement—The Application of Technique to Dense Fuel Sprays, *Prog. Energy Combust. Sci.* 3:225–234.

Jones, O. C. 1973 Statistical Considerations in Heterogeneous, Two-Phase Flowing Systems, Ph.D. thesis, Rensselaer Polytechnic Inst., Troy, N.Y.

Jones, O. C. & Delhaye, J. M. 1976 Transient and Statistical Measurement Techniques for Two-Phase Flows: A Critical Review, *Int. J. Multiphase Flow,* 3:89–116.

Keeys, R. K. F., Ralph, J. C., & Roberts, D. N. 1970 The Effect of Heat Flux on Liquid Entrainment in Steam-Water Flow in a Vertical Tube at 1000 lb/sq in (6.894 × 10⁶ N/m²), *Rept.* AERE-R6294, UKAEA, Harwell.

Kehler, P. 1978 Two Phase Flow Measurement by Pulsed Neutron Activation Technique, *Rept.* ANL-NUREG-CT-78-17, Argonne Natl. Lab.

Kehler, P. 1979 Pulse Neutron Activation Techniques for the Measurement of Two-phase Flow, *Meet. Review Group Adv. Instr. Reactor Safety Res.,* NUREG/CP-0007, p. III-9-13, U.S. Nuclear Regulatory Commission.

Keily, D. P. & Miller, S. G. 1960 An Airborne Cloud Drop Size Distribution Meter, *J. Meteorol.* 17:349–356.

Keller, A. 1972 The Influence of the Cavitation Nucleous Spectrum on Cavitation Inception Investigated with a Scattered-Light Counting Method, *J. Basic Eng.* 94:917–925.

Kerker, M. 1969 *The Scattering of Light and Other Electromagnetic Radiation*, Academic, New York.

Keyser, P. R., Natusch, D. F. S., Evans, C. A., & Linton, R. W. 1978 Characterizing the Surfaces of Environmental Particles, *Environ. Sci. Technol.* 12:768–773.

Kichigin, A. M. 1976 Sensitivity of the Bridge and the Thermocouple Methods for Detection of Boiling Heat Transfer Crisis, *Heat Transfer Sov. Res.* 8:32–36.

Kirillov, I. I. & Smogalev, I. P. 1974 Effect of Droplet Size on Mass Transfer in a Two-Phase Flow, *High Temp.* 11:1179–1180.

Kirillov, P. L., Smogalev, I. P., Suvorov, M. Y., Shumsky, R. V., & Stein, Y. Y. 1978 Investigation of Steam-Water Flow Characteristics at High Pressures, *Proc. 6th Int. Heat Transfer Conf., Toronto* 1:315–320.

Knudson, H. W. & White, L. 1945 Development of Smoke Penetration Meters, *Naval Research Lab. Rept.* P-2642.

Kondic, N. N. & Hahn, O. J. 1970 Theory and Application of the Parallel and Diverging Radiation Beam Method in Two-Phase Systems, *Proc. 4th Int. Heat Transfer Conf., Paris,* paper MT1.5.

Kondic, N. N. & Lassahn, G. D. 1978 Non-intrusive Density Distribution Measurement in Dynamic High Temperature Systems, *Proc. 24th Int. Instrumentation Symp.*

Kutateladze, S. S., Nakoryakov, V. E., & Burdokov, A. P. 1971 Spectral Density of Fluctuations of Friction in a Turbulent Wall Flow, *Sov. Phys. Dokl.* 16:87–89.

Kutateladze, S. S., Nakoryakov, V. E., & Burdukov, A. P. 1972 Spectral Characteristics of Vertical Two Phase Flow, *Sov. Phys. Dokl.* 16:718–719.

Lahey, R. T. 1977 USNRC Sponsored Instrumentation Research at Rensselaer Polytechnic Institute (RPI), Proc. Meet. Review Group Two-Phase Flow Instrumentation; Rept. NUREG-0375, U.S. Nuclear Regulatory Commission.

Langer, G. 1972 Further Evaluation of the Acoustical Particle Counter, *Powder Technol.* 6:5–8.

Lapple, C. E. 1961 *Stanford Res. Inst. J.* 5:94.

Laverty, W. F. & Rohsenow, W. M. 1967 Film Boiling of Saturated Nitrogen Flowing in a Vertical Tube, *Trans. ASME* 90–98.

Leavell, W. H. & Shahrokhi, F. 1979 Non-stationary Signal Correlation, *Rept.* NUREG-CP-0006, U.S. Nuclear Regulatory Commission.

Lecroart, H. & Porte, R. 1971 Electrical Probes for Study of Two-Phase Flow at High Velocity, *Int. Symposium on Two-Phase Systems, Haifa, Israel.*

Lee, R. E. & Hein, J. 1974 Method for the Determination of Carbon, Hydrogen and Nitrogen in Size Fractionated Atmospheric Particulate Matter, *Anal. Chem.* 46:931–933.

Lee, S. L. & Srinivasan, J. 1977 Development of Laser-Doppler Anemometer Technique to Study Droplet Hydrodynamics in LOCA Reflood, *NRC 5th Water Reactor Safety Research Information Meet., Gaithersburg, Md.*

Lee, S. L. & Srinivasan, J. 1978a An Experimental Investigation of Dilute Two-Phase Dispersed Flow Using LDA Technique, *Proc. 1978 Heat Transfer and Fluid Mechanics Inst.,* Stanford Univ. Press, Stanford, Calif., pp. 88–101.

Lee, S. L. & Srinivasan, J. 1978b Measurements of Local Size and Velocity Probability Density Distributions in Two-Phase Suspension Flows by Void Fraction Measurement in Two-Phase Bubbly Flow, III: Doppler Effect Technique, *J. Phys. E.* 8:203–205.

LeFevre, E. J. & Rose, J. W. 1964 Heat Transfer Measurements during Dropwise Condensation of Steam, *Int. J. Heat Mass Transfer* 7:272–278.

Leskovar, B., Sun, R. K., Colbe, W. F., & Turko, B. 1979 Measurement of the Thickness of Liquid Films by Means of a Capacitance Method, Special report on EPRI Research Project RP1379-1.

Lieberman, A. 1976 Variability Sources in Data from Airborne Particle Counters, *Proc. 3d Int. Symp. Contamination Control, Copenhagen,* pp. 144–162.

Liu, B. Y. H., Whitby, K. T., & Yu, H. H. S. 1967 Electrostatic Aerosol Sampler for Light and Electron Microscopy, *Rev. Sci. Instrum.* 38:100–102.

Lockett, M. J. & Safekourdi, A. A. 1977 Light Transmission through Bubble Swarms, *AIChE J.* 23(3):395–398.

Lottes, P. A. 1967 Shaped Collimator Improves One-Shot Void Detector, *PWR Reactor Technol.* 10:148–149.

Macias, E. S. & Husar, R. B. 1976 Atmospheric Particulate Mass Measurement with Beta Attenuation Mass Monitor, *Environ. Sci. Technol.* 10:904–907.

Macias, E. S., Radcliffe, C. D., Lewis, C. W., & Sawicki, C. R. 1978 Proton-induced Gamma Ray Analysis of Atmosphere Aerosols for Carbon, Nitrogen and Sulfur Compounds, *Anal. Chem.* 50:1120–1124.

Maddock, C., Lacey, P. M. C., & Patrick, M. A. 1974 The Structure of Two Phase Flow in a Curved Pipe, *Inst. Chem. Eng. Symp. Ser.* 38:paper J2.

Marple, V. A. & Rubow, K. L. 1976 Aerodynamic Particle Size Calibration of Optical Particle Counters, *J. Aerosol Sci.* 7:425–433.

Martin, R. 1972 Measurements of the Local Void Fraction at High Pressure in a Heating Channel, *Rept.* BT269-38, Centre d'Etudes Nucleaires de Grenoble, France.

Maxwell, J. 1881 *A Treatise on Electricity and Magnetism,* Clarendon, Oxford.

May, K. R. 1945 The Cascade Impactor—An Instrument for Sampling Coarse Aerosols, *J. Sci. Instrum.* 22:187–195.

Mayinger, F., Schad, O., & Weiss, O. 1967 Investigation into the Critical Heat Flux to Boiling Water, *Euratom Rept.* Eur 3347e1811, Brussels.

Mayinger, F., Langern, H., & Seiffert, V. 1977 Experimental and Theoretical Investigations in Reactor Fluid Behaviour, *European Two-Phase Flow Group Meet., Grenoble.*

McCrone, W. C. 1967 Particle Analysis, *Res. Dev.,* 9:30–31.

McCrone, W. C. 1968 Systematic Identification of Particles Using Dispersion Staining, *Powder Technol.* 2:366–367.

Measurements, Inc. 1975 *Gamma Densitometer* (brochure).

Merilo, M., Dechene, R. L., & Cichowlas, W. M. 1977 Void Fraction Measurement with a Rotating Electric Field Conductance Gauge, *J. Heat Transfer* 99:330–332.

Michels, D. E. 1977 Sample Size Effect on Geometric Average Concentrations for Log Normally Distributed Contaminants, *Environ. Sci. Technol.* 11:300–302.

Mie, G. 1908 Contributions to the Optics of Turbid Media—Especially Callaudal Metal Solutions, *Ann. Phys.* 25:377–445.

Moeck, E. O., Garg, S. C., & Wikhammer, G. A. 1966 Swift Dryout for a Nineteen-Rod, 3.25 in. Diameter Bundle, Cooled by Steam-Water Fog at 515 psia, *Rept.* AECL-2586, Atomic Energy of Canada Ltd.

Mohner, V. A. 1971 Ionometric Counters, *Atmos. Environ.* 5:137–145.

Morrow, P. E. & Mercer, T. T. 1964 A Point-to-Plane Electrostatic Precipitator for Particle Size Sampling, *Am. Ind. Hyg. Assoc. J.* 25:8–14.

Morton, R. R. A. 1975 Techniques for Particle Measuring Using Image Analysis, *Proc. 4th Int. Congress for Stereology, Gaithersburg, Md.,* pp. 483–486, N.B.S. special publication 431, U.S. National Bureau of Standards, Gaithersburg, Md.

Nader, J. S. & Allen, D. R. 1960 A Mass Loading and Radioactivity Analyzer for Atmospheric Particulates, *Am. Ind. Hyg. Assoc. J.* 21:300–307.

Namie, S. & Ueda, T. 1972 Droplet Transfer in Two-Phase Annular Mist Flow, *Bull. JSME* 15:1568–1580.

Negus, C. & Azzopardi, B. J. 1978 The Malvern Particle Size Distribution Analyser: Its Accuracy and Limitations, *Rept.* AERE-R9075, UKAEA, Harwell.

Nelson, S. S., Bolduan, O. A., & Shurcliff, W. A. 1962 The Partichrome Analyzer for the Detection and Enumeration of Bacteria, *Ann. N.Y. Acad. Sci.* 99:290–297.

Nigmatulin, B. I., Dolinin, I. V., Rachkov, V. I., & Semenov, V. P. 1978 Use of the Salt Method of Determining the Intensity of Moisture Exchange and Distribution of Liquid between the Core and Film in a Dispersed Annular Steam-Water Flow, *High Temp.* 18:711–716.

Niknejad, J. 1979 An Investigation of Heat Transfer during Filmwise and Dropwise Condensation of Mercury, Ph.D. thesis, Univ. of London.

Noll, K. E., Mueller, P. K., & Imoda, M. 1968 Visibility and Aerosol Concentration in Urban Air, *Atmos. Environ.* 2:467–475.

Ohba, K. 1979 Light Attenuation Technique for Void Fraction Measurement in Two-Phase

Bubbly Flow, IV: Derivation of I*-α Relationship Using Statistical Theory, *Technol. Rept. Osaka Univ.* **29**(1509):477–484.

Ohba, K. & Itoh, T. 1978a Light Attenuation Technique for Void Fraction Measurement in Two-Phase Bubbly Flow, I: Theory, *Technol. Rept. Osaka Univ.* **28**(1448):487–494.

Ohba, K. & Itoh, T. 1978b Light Attenuation Technique for Void Fraction Measurement in Two-Phase Bubbly Flow, II: Experiment, *Technol. Rept. Osaka Univ.* **28**(1449):495–506.

Ohba, K. & Yuhara, T. 1979a Study of Turbulence Structure in Vertical Square Duct Flow of Bubbly Mixture Using LDV, in *Multiphase Transport: Fundamentals, Reactor Safety, Applications,* ed. T. N. Veziroğlu, vol. 5, pp. 2633–2654, Hemisphere, Washington.

Ohba, K. & Yuhara, T. 1979b Velocity Measurements of Both Phases in Two-Phase Flow Using Laser Doppler Velocimeter, *IMEKO Tokyo Flow Symp., Tokyo.*

Ohba, K., Kishimoto, I., & Ogasawara, M. 1976 Simultaneous Measurement of Local Liquid Velocity and Void Fraction in Bubbly Flows Using a Gas Laser, I: Principle and Measuring Procedure, *Technol. Rept. Osaka Univ.* **26**(1328):547–556.

Ohba, K., Kishimoto, I., & Ogasawara, M. 1977a Simultaneous Measurement of Local Liquid Velocity and Void Fraction in Bubbly Flows Using a Gas Laser, II: Local Properties of Turbulent Bubbly Flow, *Technol. Rept. Osaka Univ.* **27**(1358):229–238.

Ohba, K., Kishimoto, I., & Ogasawara, M. 1977b Simultaneous Measurement of Local Liquid Velocity and Void Fraction in Bubbly Flows Using a Gas Laser, III: Accuracy of Measurement, *Technol. Rep. Osaka Univ.* **27**(1383):475–483.

Ohba, K., Itoh, T., & Yuhara, T. 1978 Light Attenuation Technique for Void Fraction Measurement in Two-Phase Bubbly Flow, III: Effect of Some Parameters on Accuracy of Measurement, *Technol. Rep. Osaka Univ.* **28**(1450):507–516.

Oldengarm, J., van Krieken, A. H., & van der Klooster, H. W. 1975 Velocity Profile Measurement in a Liquid Film Flow Using the Laser-Doppler Technique, *Int. J. Multiphase Flow* **4**:141–155.

Olin, J. G. & Sem, G. J. 1971 Piezo Electric Microbalance for Monitoring the Mass Concentration of Suspended Particles, *Atmos. Environ.* **5**:653–668.

Olsen, H. O. 1967 Theoretical and Experimental Investigation of Impedence Void Meters, Kjeller, Norway, *Rept.* 118.

Paxton, R. R. 1951 Measuring Rate of Dust Fall, *Rock Prod.* **54**:114–118.

Petrick, M. & Swanson, B. S. 1958 Radiation Attenuation Method of Measuring Density of a Two-Phase Fluid, *Rev. Sci. Inst.* **29**:1079–1085.

Piper, T. C. 1974 Final Report on the Semi-Scale Gamma Attenuation Two-Phase Water Density Measurement, Microfiche No IN-1487.

Quandt, E. R. 1965 Measurement of Some Basic Parameters in Two-Phase Annular Flow, *AIChE J.* **11**:311–318.

Ralph, J. C., Sanderson, S., & Ward, J. A. 1977 Experimental Studies of Post-Dryout Heat Transfer to Low Quality Steam-Water Mixtures at Low Pressures, *European Two-Phase Flow Group Meet., Grenoble,* paper C3.

Remke, K. 1976 Ein Beitrag zur Anwendung der Heissfilmanemometrie auf die Turbulenzmessung in Gas-Flüssigkeitsströmungen, *ZAMM,* **56**:480–483.

Remke, K. 1978 Some Remarks on the Response of Hot-Wire and Hot-Film Probes to Passage through an Air-Water Interface, *J. Phys. E.* **11**:94–96.

Resch, F. J. 1975 Phase Separation in Turbulent Two-Phase Flow, *Turbulence in Liquids, Proc. 3d Symp. Turbulence Liquids,* eds. G. K. Patterson & J. L. Zakin, pp. 243–249, Department of Chemical Engineering, University of Missouri-Rolla.

Resch, F. J. & Leutheusser, J. H. 1972 Le Ressaut Hydraulique: Mesures de Turbulence dans la Région Diphasique, *Houille Blanche* **4**:279–293.

Resch, F. J., Leutheusser, H. J., & Alemu, S. 1974 Bubbly Two-Phase Flow in Hydraulic Jump, *J. Hydraul. Div. ASCE* **100**:137–149.

Rosen, H. & Novakov, P. 1977 Raman Scattering and the Characterization of Atmospheric Aerosol Particles, *Nature* **266**:708–709.

Rosinski, J. & Lieberman, A. 1956 Automatic Isokinetic Sampling, *Appl. Sci. Res.* **A6**:92–96.

Rouhani, S. Z. 1964 Application of the Turbine-Type Flow Meters in the Measurement of Steam Quality and Void, *Symp. In-Core Instrumentation, Oslo.*

Rousseau, J. C. & Riegel, B. 1978 Super-CANON Experiments, *2d OECD/NEA/CNSI Specialists Meet. Transient Two-Phase Flow, Paris.*

Ryley, D. J. & Kirkman, G. A. 1967 The Concurrent Measurement of Momentum and Stagnation Enthalpy in a High-Quality Wet Steam Flow, *Proc. Inst. Mech. Eng.* **182**:250–257.

Salzman, G. C., Crowell, J. M., Goad, C. A., Hansen, K. M., Hiebert, R. D., Labause, P. M., Martin, J. C., Ingram, M. L., & Mullaney, P. F. 1975 A Flow System Multi-Angle Light Scattering Instrument for Cell Characterization, *Clin. Chem.* **21**:1297–1304.

Schmidt, E. W., Boiarski, A. A., & Gieseke, J. A. 1976 Applicability of Laser Interferometry Technique for Drop Size Determination, *Symp. American Chemical Society, San Francisco.*

Seeley, J. L. & Skogerboe, R. K. 1974 Combined Sampling Analysis Method for the Determination of Trace Elements in Atmospheric Particulates, *Anal. Chem.* **46**:415–421.

Sehmel, G. A. 1970 Particle Sampling Bias Introduced by Anisokinetic Sampling and Deposition within the Sampling Line, *Am. Ind. Hyg. Assoc. J.* **31**:758–771.

Serizawa, A. 1974 Fluid Dynamic Characteristics of Two-Phase Flow, Ph.D. thesis, Kyoto Univ., Japan.

Serizawa, A., Kataoka, I., & Michiyoski, I. 1975 Turbulence Structure of Air-Water Bubbly Flow, I: Measuring Techniques, *Int. J. Multiphase Flow* **2**(3):221–223.

Shiralkar, B. S. 1970 Two Phase Flow and Heat Transfer in Multi-Rod Geometries: A Study of the Liquid Film in Adiabatic Air-Water Flow with and without Obstacles, *Rept.* GEAP-10248, General Electric Co.

Shock, R. A. W. 1973 The Evaporation of Binary Mixtures in Forced Convection, Ph.D. thesis, Oxford Univ.

Siboul, R. 1976 Study of the Significant Output from Screened Thermocouples in the Flow of Water Vapour which Is Not at Equilibrium Conditions, *CENG Rept.* TT514, Centre d'Etudes Nucléaires de Grenoble, France.

Silverman, S. & Goodrich, L. D. 1977 Investigation of Vertical, Two Phase Steam Water Flow of Three Turbine Models, *Rept.* NUREG-0375, U.S. Nuclear Regulatory Commission.

Simpson, H. C. & Brolls, E. K. 1974 Droplet Deposition on a Flat Plate, from an Air-Water Mist in Turbulent Flow over the Plate, *Inst. Chem. Eng. Symp. set.* **38**:paper A3.

Sinclair, D. 1972 A Portable Diffusion Battery: Its Application to Measuring Aerosol Size Characteristics, *Am. Ind. Hyg. Assoc. J.* **33**:729–735.

Smith, A. V. 1975 Fast Response Multi-Beam X-Ray Absorption Technique for Identifying Phase Distributions during Steam-Water Blowdowns, *J. Br. Nucl. Energy Soc.* **14**:227–235.

Solésio, J. N. 1978 Mesure de l'Epaisseur Instantanée d'un Film Liquide Ruisselant sur une Paroi, *Rept.* CEA-R-4925, Centre d'Etudes Nucléaires de Grenoble, France.

Solésio, J. N., Flamand, J. C., & Delhaye, J. M. 1978 Liquid Film Thickness Film Measurement by Means of an X-Ray Absorption Technique, in *Topics in Two-Phase Transfer and Flow,* ed. S. G. Bankoff, pp. 193–198, ASME, New York.

Spigt, C. L. 1966 On the Hydraulic Characteristics of a Boiling Water Channel with Natural Circulation, *Technical Univ. of Eindhoven Rept.*

Srinivasan, J. & Lee, S. L. 1978 Measurement of Turbulent Dilute Two-Phase Dispersed Flow in a Vertical Rectangular Channel by Laser-Doppler Anemometry, *ASME Winter Annual Meet., San Francisco.*

Staniforth, R., Stevens, G. F., & Wood, R. W. 1965 An Experimental Investigation into the Relationship between Burn-out and Film Flow Rate in a Uniformly Heated Tube, *Rept.* AEEW-R430, UKAEA, Harwell.

Stephens, M. J. 1970 Investigation of Flow in a Concentric Annulus with a Smooth Outer Wall and Rough Inner Wall, I: Transverse Type Roughness, *CEGB Rept.* RD/BN1535.

Subbotin, V. I., Sorokin, D. N., Nigmatulin, B. I., Milashenko, V. I., & Nikolayev, V. E. 1978 Integrated Investigation into Hydrodynamic Characteristics of Annular-Disperse Steam-Liquid Flow, *Proc. 6th Int. Heat Transfer Conf., Toronto* **1**:327–332.

Sutey, A. M. & Knudsen, J. G. 1969 Comments of the Application of the Redox Method of Measuring Mass Transfer Coefficients in Two Phase (Air-Liquid) Systems, *Int. J. Heat Mass Transfer* **12**:373–374.

Swithenbank, J., Beer, J. N., Taylor, D. S., Abbot, D., & McCreath, C. G. 1976 A Laser Diagnostic for the Measurement of Droplet and Particle Size Distribution, *Rept.* AD-A021, AFOSRTR-76-0068, *Dept. of Chemical Engineering and Fuel Technol. Rept.* Univ. of Sheffield.

Telles, A. S. & Dukler, A. E. 1970 Statistical Characteristics of Thin, Vertical, Wavy, Liquid Films, *Ind. Eng. Chem. Fundam.* 9:412–421.

Thomas, D. G., Baucum, W. E., & Bohanan, 1977 Quarterly Progress Report on Blowdown Heat Transfer, Separate Effects.

Thompson, B. J. 1974 Holographic Particle Sizing Techniques, *J. Phys. E* 7:781–788.

Tschuke, H. & Moller, R. 1978 Experimental Determination of Cladding Temperature Fields in the Critical Regions of Rod Bundles with Turbulent Sodium Flow and Comparison with Calculations, *Proc. 6th Int. Heat Transfer Conf., Toronto* 5:29–34.

Turnage, K. G., Davis, C. E., & Thomas, D. G. 1979 Advanced Two-Phase Flow Instrumentation Program Quarterly Progress Report for July-September 1978, *Rept.* NUREG/CR-0686, ORNL/NUREG/TM-309, Oak Ridge Natl. Lab.

Ueda, T., Tanaka, H., & Kiozumi, Y. 1978 Dryout of Liquid Film in High Quality R-113 Upflow in a Heated Tube, *Proc. 6th Int. Heat Transfer Conf., Toronto* 1:423–428.

van Vonderen, A. C. M. & van Vlaardingen, H. F. 1970 Impedance Void Gauge for Cylindrical Channels (Inside Cooling), *European Two-Phase Flow Group Meet., Milan,* paper BN.

Walters, P. T. 1969 Optical Methods for Measuring Water Droplets in Wet-Steam Flows, *CEGB Rept.* CERL RD/L/N-107/69.

Walters, P. T. 1971 The Optical Measurement of Water Droplets in Wet-Steam Flows, *CEGB Rept.* CERL/RD/L/R1765.

Wasan, D. T., Sood, S. K., Davies, R., & Lieberman, A. 1973 Aerosol Transport: Particle Charge and Re-Entrainment Effects, *J. Colloid Interface Sci.* 43:144–149.

Webb, D. R. 1970a Studies of the Characteristics of Downward Annular Two-Phase Flow, parts 1-4, *Rept.* AERE R6426, UKAEA, Harwell.

Webb, D. R. 1970b Two-Phase Flow Phenomena, Ph.D. thesis, Cambridge Univ.

Webb, D. R., Dukler, A. E., & Hewitt, G. F. 1970 Downwards Annular Flow, *European Two-Phase Flow Group Meet., Milan,* paper C1.

Webster, F. X. 1963 Collection Efficiency of the Rotorod Sampler, *Technical Rept.* 98, Metronics Assoc., Palo Alto, Calif.

Wertheimer, A. L. & Wilcock, W. L. 1976 Light Scattering Measurements of Particle Distributions, *Appl. Optics* 15:1616–1620.

Wesley, R. D. 1977 Performance of Drag-Disc Turbine and Gamma Densitometer in LOFT, *Proc. Meet. Review Group Two-Phase Flow Instrumentation; Rept.* NUREG-0375, U.S. Nuclear Regulatory Commission.

West, P. W. 1966 The Identification and Determination of Airborne Particulates by Means of the Ring Oven Technique, *J. Air Pollution Control Assoc.* 16:601–603.

Whitby, K. T. 1978 Physical Characteristics of Sulphur Aerosol, *Atmos. Environ.* 12:135–159.

Whitby, K. T. & Clark, W. E. 1966 Electrical Aerosol Particle Counting and Size Distribution Measuring System for the 0.015 to 1 Micrometer Size Range, *Tellus* 18:573–586.

Wicks, M. & Dukler, A. E. 1966 In-situ Measurements of Dropsize Distribution in Two-Phase Flow—A New Method for Electrically Conducting Liquids, *AIChE Symp. Two-Phase Flow, Chicago.*

Wright, B. M. 1954 A Size Selecting Sampler for Airborn Dust, *Br. J. Ind. Med.* 11:284–288.

Wyatt, P. J. 1968 Differential Light Scattering: A Physical Method for Identifying Living Bacterial Cells, *Appl. Optics* 7:1879–1895.

Yanta, W. J. 1973 Measurements of Aerosol Size Distributions with a Laser Doppler Velocimeter, *A.I.A.A. 6th Fluid Plasma Dynamics Conf., Palm Springs, Calif.,* paper 73-705.

Ybarrondo, L. 1975 Pressure Measurement Investigation—Overview, *3d Water Reactor Safety Research Information Meeting, Washington, D.C.,* NRC.

Zielke, L. A., Morgan, C. D., Howard, C. G., & Currie, R. L. 1975 Rod Bundle Subchannel Void Fraction by Gamma Scattering, *Proc. ANS Meeting—Reactor Fluid Flow Heat Transfer,* pp. 412–413.

Index